RATTLESNAKES

A captive-bred adult hybrid rattlesnake (lower left) with its parents: father (upper) a southern Pacific rattlesnake (*Crotalus viridis helleri*), mother (center) a red diamond rattlesnake (*Crotalus ruber ruber*). Both parents from San Diego County, California.

RATTLESNAKES

Their Habits, Life Histories, and
Influence on Mankind

In Two Volumes ◆ *Volume II*

LAURENCE M. KLAUBER

PUBLISHED FOR THE ZOÖLOGICAL SOCIETY OF SAN DIEGO BY THE

UNIVERSITY OF CALIFORNIA PRESS

Berkeley and Los Angeles ◆ 1956

University of California Press
Berkeley and Los Angeles

Cambridge University Press
London, England

Copyright, 1956, by
The Regents of the University of California

Library of Congress Catalog Card Number: 56–5002

Printed in the United States of America
Designed by Rita Carroll

Contents

Tables

Illustrations

Chapter 12

Chapter 14

Chapter 15

Chapter 16

Chapter 17

Chapter 18

11.   Poison Apparatus

INTRODUCTION

To most persons the subject of rattlesnake bite, particularly its frequency and severity, is the most interesting and important phase of rattlesnake natural history. In the next three chapters, I shall discuss the relevant factors that affect the danger from rattlesnake bite, including the biting mechanism and venom, the effects of the bite, the cures that have been tried, together with the recommended treatment as of today, and the precautions that should be taken to avoid being bitten.

It may astonish the reader to learn that no really authentic statistics are available in the United States, either on the frequency of rattlesnake bite or on the resulting mortality. Not only are rattlesnakes not separated from other snakes in the United States Public Health Service reports, but snakes are not segregated from other venomous creatures. As will be shown in the discussion of such statistics as are available, snakes are not the sole, or even, in some areas, the principal, offenders that come within the venomous category; and so it is that only guesses can be made as to the gravity of the snake-bite hazard in our country. Probably fewer than 1,000 persons in the United States are bitten by rattlesnakes each year, and fewer than 30 or 35 die. Compared with other causes of accidental death in a population exceeding 160 million, these figures indicate an extremely minor risk; and it is this very insignificance of the danger that has to some extent retarded American medical research on rattlesnake venom, its effects and treatment. This situation cannot be criticized, in view of the many graver health problems awaiting solution. Researches on rattlesnake venoms, if they are to increase our present knowledge of the subject, will be difficult, time-consuming, and expensive, and will require the highest skill in medicine and biochemistry. The securing of adequate venom supplies will complicate the problems, for they will require the collection of many snakes, some of which are rare and occur only in relatively inaccessible places.

The gravity of a rattlesnake bite is something that cannot be closely defined or predicted, any more than one can predict the seriousness of a fall, without knowing the exact circumstances of the accident, such as the height of the fall, the character of the surface struck, the age of the victim, and similar pertinent details. And in a snake-bite case the conditions are even more obscure, since there are important factors that cannot be ascertained, even after the accident has occurred. So no one can give an offhand opinion as to the gravity of such a case. Those having the responsibility for its treatment can only presume the factors to be adverse, and take appropriate steps upon this supposition.

As one studies the reports of snake-bite cases, in an attempt to become informed upon the symptoms—for a knowledge of symptoms should be valuable in judging the gravity of a particular case and hence the treatment to be adopted—it is invariably found that the symptoms of the bite are partly masked, not only by the psychological impact on the victim, but by the effects of the treatment. This uncertainty begins with the moment when any initial first aid in the field may have been given, and continues with the remedial measures taken by the doctor. The gravity of the bite is thus obscured and confused, and there is a resulting difficulty in assessing the effectiveness of the cure. As treatment is always neces-sary, this confusion of malady and treatment is a difficulty that cannot be sur-mounted, except to whatever extent the symptoms may be determined by tests on experimental animals. And here another source of uncertainty arises, since different animals react differently to the venoms of the several kinds of snakes. This confusion of the effects of the snake bite itself with those of the remedies applied, has greatly reduced the value of studies of past cases, even of such as may have been competently reported in the medical literature.

The very fact that rattlesnake bite is an accident of infrequent occurrence means that few doctors become experienced in its treatment. Many cases reach the physician only after the patient's condition has been materially modified by field or home treatments. These may vary from the currently approved methods recommended by the public health agencies to folklore remedies, some of which may be as dangerous as the bite itself. For these reasons, although remedial meas-ures are fairly well standardized in recent medical texts, the treatment does not afford the physician that confidence which would accompany his handling of a more frequent and less variable malady.

VARIABLE FACTORS AFFECTING THE GRAVITY OF SNAKE BITE

The variability involved in rattlesnake bite makes accurate prognosis impossible and treatment difficult. The patient may presume he has been bitten by a venomous snake when actually he has been bitten by one completely innocuous. This is an occurrence not at all infrequent, for people are so badly frightened by snakes that the all-important factor of identification may be mistaken or neglected. Or, for a variety of reasons, even though the bite may have been that of a venomous snake, yet no venom may have been injected. Wall (1928, p. 69) refers to this uncertainty as the difference between snake *bite* and snake *poisoning*. Snake bite, even when a venomous snake has been the culprit, is not a simple affliction with uniform results; it varies from a condition involving no danger and little discom-fort to one of extreme gravity. It is this wide variability, including, particularly, the many cases that would recover without any treatment, that has appeared to validate one after another of the folklore remedies that have been used, and are still being used down to the present day. It has seemed to confirm the efficacy of the many other remedies, having at least some semblance of scientific justification, that physicians of the past employed with apparently beneficial effects, when in reality they were completely useless or even harmful. So important are these variable factors in the effects of snake bite, and in the history of its treatment, that I shall begin by listing the more important, although such a summary might be thought more appropriate at the conclusion of this discussion.

These, then, are some of the variable factors:

(1) The age, size, sex, vigor, and health of the victim, which are important in determining his absorptive power and systemic resistance to the venom.

(2) The allergy complex of the victim; his susceptibility to protein poisoning; the sensitization (anaphylaxis), or partial immunity imposed by previous bites or treatment.

(3) The emotional condition and nature of the victim; extreme fear and apprehension will affect his heart action and therefore the rapidity of venom absorption; and there may be more direct reactions from fear alone.

(4) The site of the bite, which will be less dangerous in the extremities, or in tissues where absorption will be less rapid (in fat, for example), as compared to a bite near the vital organs or penetrating a blood vessel.

(5) The nature of the bite, whether a direct stroke with both fangs fully imbedded, or a glancing blow or scratch. The movement of the victim (a jump backward, for instance) may cause a partially ineffective bite; or a bone may be struck, thus causing imperfect penetration. Only the point of the fang may penetrate the skin, in which case there will be no venom injection, for the discharge orifice of the fang is well above the tip. The snake may misjudge its distance and have the fangs only partially erected at contact, thus effecting only a slight penetration; or it may, for the same reason, eject and lose venom before the fangs are imbedded.

(6) The protection afforded by clothing, which, by interposing thickness, will permit less depth of fang penetration, and will cause the external and harmless absorption, in the cloth, of part or all of the venom.

(7) The number of bites; occasionally an accident involves two or more distinct bites.

(8) The length of time the snake holds on, for it may withdraw or be torn loose before injection takes place. This is likely to be more important with the elapid snakes, with their shorter and less specialized fangs, than with such long- and hook-fanged snakes as the rattlers.

(9) The extent of the anger or fear that motivates the snake. The muscles that wring the venom glands and thus eject venom are separately controlled from the biting mechanism. The snake's natural tendency is to withhold venom, since this is its means of securing prey; but if hurt or violently excited it is likely to inject a large part of the venom contained in the glands.

(10) The species and size of the snake, affecting the venom toxicity and physiological effects (there are extensive differences between kinds of rattlesnakes), the venom quantity, and, by reason of the length and strength of the fangs, the depth of injection. The age of the snake is likewise important; not only are young snakes less dangerous because of their smaller size (and therefore reduced quantity of venom and shorter fangs), but also the venom is less toxic. Snakes that have passed their prime also may secrete less venom and this of a reduced virulence.

(11) The condition of the venom glands, whether full or partially depleted or evacuated by reason of recent feeding, defense, ill-health, or captivity. The season of the year (proximity to hibernation) may also cause a variation, but this is not definitely known.

(12) The condition of the fangs, whether entire or broken, lately renewed or ready for shedding.

(13) The presence, in the mouth of the snake, of various microorganisms, some of which, gaining access to the wound, may, abetted by an antibactericidal action of the venom, entail serious sequelae.

(14) The nature of the instinctive first-aid treatment, if any, such as suction, or circulation stoppage by pressure.

These various factors, depending on both the snake and its victim, as well as many incidental conditions involved in the strike and bite, will be elaborated in subsequent discussions. Most of these uncertainties have long been known; they have been commented upon by such authors as Redi (1673, supp. p. 12), Mead (1702, p. 6; 1745, p. 9), Fontana (1787, vol. 1, p. 295; vol. 2, pp. 35, 44), Clavigero (1937, p. 392, but writing in 1789), Gibson (1825, vol. 1, p. 103), Mitchell (1861, p. 272), Richards (1885, p. 26), Willson (1908, p. 552), Houssay (1923, p. 449), Crimmins (1927a, p. 200; 1927b, p. 23), Klauber (1932a, p. 29; 1936c, p. 211), and King (1941, p. 49). Probably the particular variable effect, the great importance of which, as far as rattlesnakes are concerned, that has been least appreciated until recently, is the wide difference in the virulence of the venoms of the several kinds of rattlesnakes. Drop for drop, some of these have been shown to be 60 times as powerful as others. In the early days, even in scientific research, a rattlesnake was a rattlesnake, and it was generally assumed that the venoms of the several species were quite similar. Now it is known that they differ greatly both in strength and in the nature of their physiological effects.

To conclude: with variable factors of such importance in snake bite, it is to be expected that some cases will prove extremely grave, whereas others may cause little or no discomfort. It is the latter class, which really require no treatment, that have given an entirely fictitious reputation to some of the remedies that have been proposed, for the patient recovers in spite of the remedy, rather than through its use.

THE FANGS

Our knowledge of how a venomous snake bites, how the venom is injected, and how it affects the animal bitten, is not of great antiquity. For a long time it was almost universally believed that all snakes were venomous, although this had been denied by Nicander as early as 150 B.C. (translation of 1953, p. 61). The period from 1650 to 1790 was marked by the beginning of a series of truly scientific investigations of the biting mechanisms of poisonous snakes, and their venoms and antidotes. This was the period of the first adequate experiments and dissections, replacing to some extent the mass of folklore that had traditionally surrounded the subject. Most of the experiments were made on the European viper (*Vipera berus*) because of its availability, although several of the workers had access to a few rattlesnakes. However, much of the new information, particularly with respect to the biting mechanism, while based on vipers, is equally applicable to rattlesnakes. The most prominent workers during this period were Redi, Charas, Tyson, Ranby, Mead with his two collaborators Areskine and Nicholls, and, finally, Fontana, the most prolific of all in experiment, who made no less than 6,000 tests, in which he used more than 4,000 animals and over 3,000 vipers (1787, vol. 2, p. 73). Of course, not all of the findings of these scientists have stood the test of time—Charas, particularly, completely misunderstood the source of the destructive power of venom—but all contributed to our knowledge of how a snake bites, how the venom is injected, and its effect on the victim.

The biting mechanism of a venomous snake, such as a rattlesnake, comprises provisions for venom generation and storage, and means for injecting the venom into the victim, these means, in their highest development, consisting of hollow fangs having the mechanical perfection of dual hypodermic syringes. Snakes have their venom primarily to subdue, secure, and digest their prey; any value that it may have as a protection against larger enemies is incidental to these primary purposes.

It is impossible to draw a sharp line between venomous and nonvenomous snakes, or even between dangerous and nondangerous snakes. I hope that this statement will not lead to the indiscriminate destruction of the many useful and harmless snakes that far outnumber the dangerous snakes, both in kinds and in numbers of individuals almost everywhere. In the United States, for example, as a practical matter, a definite distinction can be drawn between dangerous and nondangerous snakes. The former include only the 30 subspecies of rattlesnakes, the 6 subspecies of moccasins and copperheads, and the 4 kinds of coral snakes. The moccasins and copperheads are often placed in separate categories, but they are more closely related to each other than are some of the rattlesnakes to other rattlesnakes. All of the other kinds of snakes in this country—there are about 240 subspecies—are harmless to man.

The reason I have drawn attention to the lack of sharp distinction between dangerous and nondangerous snakes (to human beings) is because of the varying degrees of perfection achieved in the venom-injecting mechanisms, and because of the wide range of venom toxicity in the different families and kinds of snakes.

VARIATIONS IN OPHIDIAN DENTITION AND VENOMS

Most kinds of snakes have solid, backwardly curved or slanting teeth, two rows on each side of the upper jaw, and one on each side of the lower. These teeth, which are slim and sharply pointed, are never used for masticating or dismembering prey; they serve to catch, hold, and aid in swallowing the prey, which is always swallowed whole.

The first modification in the tooth arrangement and character toward the development of a venom-injecting apparatus is the enlargement and grooving of two or more of the posterior teeth (on each side of the head) in the two outer (maxillary) rows of teeth in the upper jaw. To whatever extent the saliva of the snake is venomous, or more specialized venom glands are developed, these enlarged and grooved teeth may be used to introduce the venom into a wound by a sort of chewing action. With prey of small diameter—lizards, for example—this is a moderately effective method of introducing venom, but the prey must be worked into the back part of the mouth and held there while the venom is chewed in by repeated bites. Because of the necessity of getting and holding the part to be poisoned in the back of the mouth, only relatively large back-fanged snakes are at all dangerous to man.

A few small species of back-fanged snakes occur in the United States (p. 17). As far as is known, no one has ever been seriously injured by the bite of any of them; and it is difficult to see how a dangerous bite could be inflicted except by the deliberate permission of the victim. But in other countries, where the back-fanged snakes are larger and more numerous, there are records of a few serious human cases resulting from their bites. Such cases have been described by FitzSimons (1909, p. 271; 1912, pp. 141, 490), Corkill (1929b, p. 33), and Grasset and Schaafsma (1940, p. 23). For a chronology of early research on the back-fanged snakes, see Stejneger, 1895, p. 346; and, for a recent discussion of their evolution, Smith and Bellairs, 1947, p. 354.

The next group of snakes, in the order of the perfection of the biting mechanism, comprises the so-called elapids and their relatives—snakes, in which, on each side of the head, two of the anterior maxillary teeth are enlarged and hollow, with an upper venom inlet and a lower venom outlet, through which the contents of the venom glands are injected into the wound. Although it is stated that there are two fangs on each side of the head, actually, it would be somewhat more accurate to say that there are two fang positions or sockets on each side. The fangs are shed periodically, and just before one fang is lost its fellow becomes seated and functional in the adjacent socket. It is only during this brief overlap in the fang-shedding process that both sockets on a side contain active fangs.

The fangs of the elapids are fixed in an erect position. However, Marie Phisalix determined (1922, vol. 2, p. 358; see also Rose, 1950, p. 239) that some fang rotational movement is evident in the African mambas (*Dendraspis*); and Fairley (1929b, p. 315) has shown the same condition to be true of some Australian elapid snakes, particularly the death adder (*Ancanthophis antarcticus*). Bogert (1943, p. 318) has noted a limited rotation of the maxilla in certain cobras. This slight fang movement somewhat increases the effectiveness of the biting mechanism. All of these genera belong to the elapid group.

Although there is a wide difference in the gravity of the bite of the different kinds of elapid snakes, because of differences in venom quantity and toxicity, as well as the length of the fangs, this group does include the most dangerous snakes in the world, such as the king cobra of southeastern Asia, the mambas of Africa, and the giant brown snake or taipan (*Oxyuranus*) of Australia, as well as others almost equally dangerous. However deficient, compared with the vipers, the elapids may be in the perfection of their biting mechanisms—for their fangs are relatively short—the inefficiency is more than counterbalanced by the remarkable toxicity of the venoms of many of them.

The ultimate in the efficiency of the biting mechanism is achieved in the viperine snakes, the vipers of the Old World, and the pit vipers of eastern Europe, Asia, and the Americas. The pit-viper group includes the rattlesnakes, which are restricted to the Americas. In these viperine snakes, the maxillary bone, to which the fangs are attached, is shortened and is capable of being rotated so that the fangs, when not advanced into the biting position, may be folded back against the roof of the mouth. Thus fangs so long that they would otherwise protrude far below the lower jaw are accommodated, and by this means the viperine snakes are superior to all others in the perfection of their biting mechanisms—in the provision for the certain and deep injection of venom.

In addition to the group names that I have used, the following are frequently applied to the four classes of snakes differing in the character of their teeth: The solid-toothed snakes without fang differentiation are called aglyphs; the back-fanged snakes with enlarged and grooved posterior teeth are known as opistho-glyphs; the front-fanged snakes whose fangs are permanently erect are referred to as proteroglyphs; and the folding-fanged snakes as solenoglyphs. A further segregation that involves the separation of the snakes usually included in the opisthoglyphous group into two groups, the true opisthoglyphs and another with a somewhat different tooth conformation, has been proposed by Stickel (1943, p. 112), who called the newly segregated group pleuroglyphs. A similar division was independently proposed by Bogert and Oliver (1945, p. 375), who suggested the name pseudo-opisthoglyphs. *Sonora, Chionactis, Chilomeniscus,* and *Pseudoficimia* are some of the American genera that would be assigned to this new group. They are characterized by having lateral, shallow grooves in the enlarged posterior maxillary teeth, rather than deeper anterior or anterior-lateral grooves, as in the true opisthoglyphs. H. M. Smith (1952, p. 214) has suggested a still more elaborate nomenclature for the several groups of snakes, based on the characteristics of their maxillary teeth.

Venom classifications are not so categorical as those of the biting mechanism, for there is a great variability in the virulence and composition of the venoms of the species of snakes comprising each group, particularly the last two. Alcock and Rogers (1902, p. 446), Noguchi (1909, p. 51), Winton (1916, p. 477), and Marie Phisalix and Caius (1916, pp. 213, 343, 415; 1917, p. 37; 1918, p. 923), among others, have shown that the salivas of harmless snakes are toxic if introduced into the blood stream of a victim. West (1898, p. 524), Sarkar (1923, p. 295), and Smith and Bellairs (1947, p. 351) have pointed out the gradual transition between the salivary or venom glands of aglyphous, opisthoglyphous, proteroglyphous, and solenoglyphous snakes. What the harmless snakes lack is the means for inject-ing venom rather than the venom itself. Although some venoms are remarkable for their high degree of adaptation directed at the kinds of prey on which the particular snakes feed, and some are outstanding for concentrated venom virulence, by and large it can be said that dangerously venomous snakes are more remark-able for the specialization of their venom-injecting apparatus—the venom gland, venom duct, and hollow tooth—than they are for the development of the venom itself. Most protein substances—the white of an egg, for example—are toxic if introduced into the blood stream. Thus the ill effects of venom might well be expected (although certainly not the degree of toxicity that is evident in many of them), but the perfected efficiency of the snake's biting mechanism, especially that of the viperine snakes, cannot but be judged the most remarkable feature of this intricate prey-securing device.

West (1895, p. 812), Boulenger (1896, p. 615), and Sarkar (1923, p. 318) visualize the viperids as having evolved directly from the back-fanged snakes, rather than through the moderately specialized elapids. In this, some more recent authors do not concur; they believe that the proteroglyphs were ancestral to the solenoglyphs (Bogert, 1943, p. 315). However, Haas (1952, p. 591; see also Anthony, 1955, p. 48) has concluded, from studies of head musculature, that the viperids were evolved directly from primitive aglyphous ancestors, rather than from either opisthoglyphs or proteroglyphs.

THE FANG-TILTING MECHANISM

Although the head bones of the rattlesnake, like those of other snakes, are thin and delicate, yet they are beautifully formed to withstand the stresses of both biting and feeding, the latter, because of the relatively large size of the prey engulfed, being particularly important.

As has been stated, the biting mechanism is most highly developed in the viperine snakes, in that the fangs—the greatly elongated and caniculated maxillary teeth—can be rotated from a resting to an acting position. In the resting position, they are folded back against the upper jaw, with base and point at about the same level, and with the bulge of the fang-curve fitting into a hollow in the lower jaw, just outside of the mandibles. To assume their active—their striking or biting—position, the fangs are rotated downward, the points describing a forward arc of about 90 degrees, until the proximal part of the fang is substantially perpendicular to the upper jaw, or slightly farther advanced. It is this duality of position that allows the snake to have such long fangs, which, were they fixed in an erect position, would pose a serious handicap to the snake in all activities except that of biting. An enormous development of the lower jaw would be required to cover and shield them, or they would protrude, unprotected, below the jaw.

The bones of the rattlesnake head are illustrated and listed in figures 11:1 to 11:4, which show the fangs in both the resting and active positions. Photographic representations of a rattlesnake skull are shown in figures 11:5 and 11:6; and a rattlesnake head with fangs exposed in figures 11:7 to 11:9. Also, in figures 11:10 and 11:11 there are indicated, by means of a simplified analogy, the parts that the various bones play in rotating the fangs. This linkage and its operation were fully described in a previous publication (Klauber, 1939b, p. 16). The figures are here reprinted, but I shall not repeat the details of the interactions and methods of attachment of the several bones that cause the fang rotation. Suffice it to say that, from its normal resting position, the quadrate (11) rotates downward, pushing forward the pterygoid (9), reinforced anteriorly by the ectopterygoid (10), which in turn causes the maxilla (1) to rotate downward, carrying the fangs, which are rigidly attached to the maxilla. The connection between the pterygoid and the maxilla, via the palatine (8), is not so positive as that between the ectopterygoid and the maxilla, so it is the ectopterygoid that is most important in rotating the maxilla. The two maxillae on the opposite sides of the head can and do operate quite independently of each other, a feature particularly useful when the snake is employing the fangs to aid in engulfing prey.

The muscles that serve to advance or refold the fangs have been described by Mitchell (1860, p. 8), Kathariner (1900, p. 49), Willson (1908, p. 526), Aurich (1908, p. 6), Noguchi (1909, p. 66), Marie Phisalix (1922, vol. 2, p. 443), and Haas (1952, p. 591).

The fact that the fangs of viperine snakes could be either folded against the roof of the mouth, or rotated downward and forward, had been observed from the earliest times in the Old World vipers. That the same condition existed in the rattlesnakes was noted by many of the colonial writers (e.g., Marcgravius, 1642, p. 240; Tyson, 1683, p. 51; Beverly, 1722, p. 265; Carver, 1779, p. 481; and Loskiel, 1794, part 1, p. 87). Some likened the fang movement to the action of the claws of a cat, which is not an apt simile as the fangs are hinged and not retracted. Jeter (1854, p. 10) had the erroneous idea that a rattlesnake could erect its fangs only by first hooking them to something, and therefore a snake confined in a glass jar could not bite effectively. As a matter of fact, rattlers may occasionally be seen to erect their fangs when opening their mouths to yawn.

FANG SUCCESSION

The method whereby the fangs are periodically shed and replaced by new fangs is as intricate as the provision for rotation. On either side of the head, in each maxilla, there are two contiguous sockets (indicated by the two positions of the fangs in figures 11:12 and 11:13), and these are occupied alternately by active fangs, except that, for a brief time, both sockets are occupied—an overlap in the fang succession to avoid any interval wherein an active fang would be lacking on either side of the head. The delicacy and fragility of the fangs, especially in the smaller snakes, make such a provision for replacement imperative, as does also the necessity for providing larger fangs as a snake grows. Whether replacement is hastened if a functional fang is broken before the normal time of change is not known. Of the two sockets on each side of the head, one, the inner, is slightly forward of the outer. They are so close together that their edges touch.

At one time there were two conflicting theories respecting the functions of the paired sockets. One theory held that the inner sockets were only transitionary depots, to be occupied by the fangs only while on their way to a more extended seating and use in the outer sockets. The other, the correct theory, partly inferred by Nicholls (in Mead, 1745, p. 61) and Knox (1826, p. 415), was first described in detail by Tomes (1877, p. 377). It pictures the use of the inner and outer sockets alternately to hold the active fang. The future but as yet immature fangs are contained in a magazine in a staggered group behind the two sockets, the most mature of the reserve series being always behind the vacant socket, as shown diagrammatically in figure 11:15. When the time for a change arrives, this fang advances to the vacant socket anterior to it and becomes seated rigidly therein. The adjacent superseded fang drops out, leaving a vacant socket, to which, in due course, the next replacement advances. Thus the active fangs are alternately in the inside and the outside positions.

In every normal rattlesnake there will be found two fully formed fangs on each side of the head, in addition to the less mature members of the replacement series. When the protective sheath has been cut away to expose these two, one, the active or functional fang, will be found firmly fixed in its maxillary socket; the other is the first reserve fang and is nearly always loose, that is, with its base unanchored to any part of the skull. In representative series of snakes, these first reserves are found in all stages of development, from some still imbedded in their natal capsules, to others fully advanced but not yet affixed to the maxillary.

Key to Figures 11:1–11:4. The bones of the rattlesnake skull:

1. Premaxilla
2. Prefrontal (lachrymal of some authors)
3. Frontal
4. Parietal
5. Basisphenoid
6. Squamosal (supratemporal of some authors)
7. Maxilla (maxillary or supermaxillary)
8. Palatine (palatal)
9. Pterygoid (internal pterygoid)
10. Ectopterygoid (external pterygoid or transpalatine)
11. Quadrate
12. Mandible (mandibular)
    12A. Dentary
    12B. Articular
13. Pro-otic
14. Exoccipital (lateral occipital)
15. Poison fang
16. Mandibular teeth
17. Pterygoid teeth
18. Palatine teeth
19. Supraoccipital
20. Stapes (or columella auris)
21. Postfrontal
22. Basioccipital
23. Nasal
24. Turbinal
25. Vomer

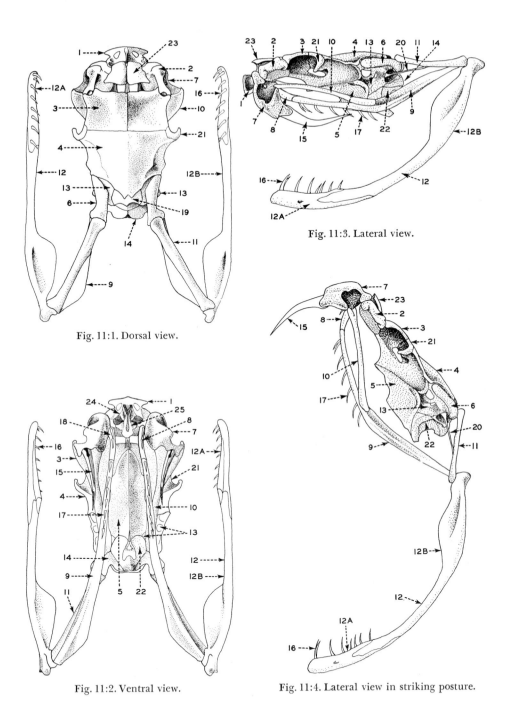

Fig. 11:1. Dorsal view.

Fig. 11:3. Lateral view.

Fig. 11:2. Ventral view.

Fig. 11:4. Lateral view in striking posture.

Figs. 11:1 to 11:4. Skull of *Crotalus ruber ruber*.

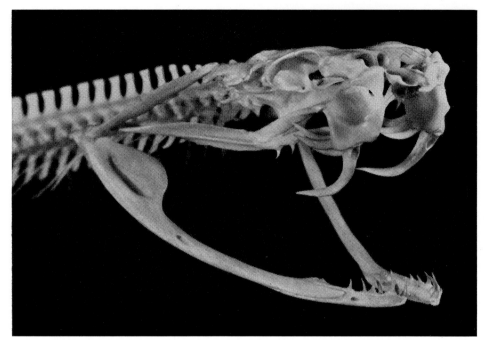

Fig. 11:5. Angular view of the skull of a rattlesnake.

Fig. 11:6. Lateral view of the skull of a rattlesnake. For clarity, the fangs, mandible, pterygoid, and other bones that would appear in the rear have been removed. The functional fang has been rotated downward from its normal position when not in use, in order to show the reserve fangs. The usual resting position of the fang is illustrated in fig. 11:3.

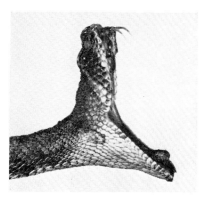

Figs. 11:7 to 11:9. Poses of a freshly killed specimen of *Crotalus atrox*, with mouth opened to show the fangs. In the fig. 11:7 (top) the fangs are folded against the roof of the mouth, and are covered by their sheaths. In fig. 11:8 (center) the fangs are slightly advanced, and the sheaths have been cut away. In fig. 11:9 (lower) the mouth has been widely opened and the fangs advanced, as at the end of the forward drive of a strike.

These two fangs, on a side, have been referred to as being fully formed or complete. This is true of the fangs proper, but not of their bases. One, the presently functional fang, is anchored solidly in its maxillary socket upon a bony base or pedestal. The other, the reserve that will shortly become functional, has a softened, immature base. The degree of hardening of this base corresponds to the closeness of the approach of the first reserve to its socket. Sometimes the first reserve is still grouped with the other, less mature reserves; or it may be found in a later stage of development, that is, advanced to the maxillary position, and

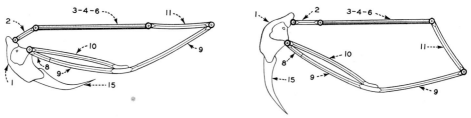

Figs. 11:10 and 11:11. Fang-tilting linkage. Fig. 11:10 (left) shows the fang folded out of use; fig. 11:11 (right) shows the fang advanced to the biting position. Key to names of bones: 1 maxillary, 2 prefrontal, 3 frontal, 4 parietal, 6 squamosal, 8 palatine, 9 pterygoid, 10 ectopterygoid, 11 quadrate, 15 fang.

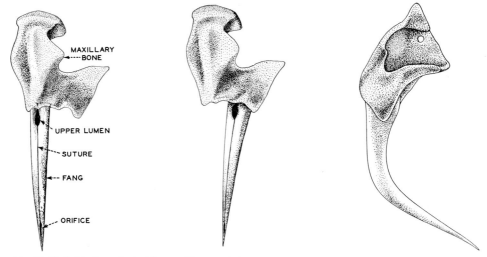

Fig. 11:12 (left). Fang in inside maxillary socket.

Fig. 11:13 (center). Fang in outside maxillary socket. (The discharge orifice appears foreshortened, because of the backward direction of the lower half of the fang.)

Fig. 11:14 (right) Side view of fang and maxillary bone.

with the base somewhat hardened, so that, as the maxillary is tilted, the reserve tends to rise also, just as does the fully functioning fang. When in this condition, the reserve can still be distinguished from the fang it is about to replace by a slight looseness at the base, evident if the fang be moved with a forceps.

Rarely, both of the fangs on a side are found to be firmly set in their respective maxillary sockets, that is, at the exact interval when the new fang is fully functioning but the older has not yet dropped out. This is observed so infrequently, however, that we know the period of overlap must be rather short, compared with the time between fang changes. On the other hand, so seldom is a functional fang missing and the first reserve not yet in place, that we know an overlap, i.e., an interval with two functional fangs on a side, though short, must be the normal sequence. The absence of a functional fang on one side can, no doubt, be attributed to some mishap incident to the capture of the snake; certainly this is not a condition representing a normal sequence of replacement.

In 1939, I (1939b, p. 5) made certain anatomical and statistical studies of fang positions. The alternate and independent use of the sockets was demonstrated, for there was no synchronism or symmetry in the use of the sockets on the opposite sides of the head. However, I erroneously stated that there was no symmetry in newly born snakes; this has since been disproved by Bogert (1943, p. 324), who showed that young rattlesnakes are born with functional fangs in the two inner sockets. The nonsynchronous use of the sockets on the opposite sides of the head is a development of later life, resulting from accidents and other conditions lead-

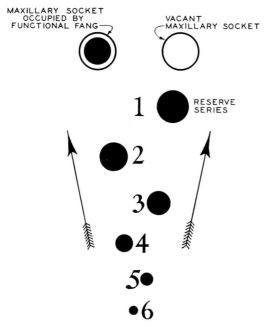

Fig. 11:15. Diagram of fang succession.

ing to a longer retention of the fang on one side than on the other, so that the natal synchronism is lost. Of 210 adult rattlesnakes whose fang positions I examined, 111 had an asymmetrical arrangement with one inside and one outside socket in use. In the other 99 cases, the symmetrical ones, both outside sockets were occupied in 52 specimens, and both insides in the other 47. These are completely random distributions which may be attributed to chance, rather than to any schedule. Bogert (1943, p. 323) found that symmetry in arrangement was maintained in cobras to a later adolescence than in rattlers. Nicholls should be given credit for noting, as early as 1745 (in Mead, p. 61), the lack of synchronism in the use of the fang sockets in the European viper.

The separation of the two sockets on each side of the head in the rattlesnake is just sufficient to provide an anchorage for each fang, and to prevent interference during the short interval when both sockets contain active fangs. The inner socket is a short distance anterior to the outer. In describing arcs, when erected, the two fangs on a side tend to swing toward the same point, so that the separation of the puncture points of a bite is not appreciably greater when inflicted by two outer than when made by two inner fangs. This is shown by the fact that when two active fangs are found on a side, the lateral clearance between the points is usually less than the center-to-center separation of the sockets. However, one point may be in advance of the other in a longitudinal plane.

In a large western diamondback (*Crotalus atrox*), with the head length taken as a basis equal to 100 per cent, the fang sockets were found to be situated posterior to the rostral by about 18 per cent. The separation of the outer sockets was about 42 per cent of the head length, and that of the inner sockets about 36 per cent. Thus the centers of two sockets on one side of the mouth were separated by about 3 per cent of the head length, and the head length was about 2½ times the fang separation. From data on head sizes (table 4:2), a rough approximation may be made of the size of a rattlesnake that has caused an injury, if the distance between the fang punctures and the species of snake be known. However, because the articulation of the erecting mechanism permits a considerable lateral play, there can be no great accuracy in this determination.

Even when still imbedded in the sac that holds the immature reserve fangs, the distal section of the first reserve fang, from the middle of the upper orifice to the point, is fully hardened on the exterior and is of full length; that is to say, the length will agree, to a fraction of a millimeter, with the length of the adjacent functional fang that it is shortly to replace. However, above the mid-point of the upper opening or lumen, the pedestal, which will later engage the socket, will be found to vary considerably in completeness, depending on the imminence of replacement. It is the solidification of this pedestal that anchors the fang in the socket.

From a study of the paired fangs on a side, in rattlers which are exactly at the time of fang change, that is, when both the new and old fangs are firmly anchored, it is observed that the solidification of the pedestal has a considerable effect on the direction in which the fang points. Sometimes the two fangs are parallel, with the points almost touching each other, but often one of the points is advanced somewhat ahead of the other. Occasionally one fang may be crossed over the other.

When the first reserve fangs are examined in a series of specimens in which all degrees of advancement are represented, it is found that if a long time is to intervene prior to replacement, the first reserve fang does not move if the maxillary is tilted. On the other hand, if replacement is imminent, the fang tends to rise as the maxillary is rotated, although it is not yet fixed. Finally, complete solidification in the socket takes place, and then, when the maxillary is rotated, both the new functional fang and the old fang about to be replaced rise as a unit. Examination indicates that the posterior part of the bony pedestal is the last to solidify.

Snakes change their fangs so frequently, compared with the growth of head or body, that measurements do not ordinarily indicate a larger size of the first reserve fang, as compared with the functional fang it is about to succeed. Only in adolescent rattlesnakes is the growth sufficiently rapid so that the first reserve fang is found to be longer than the active fang it will shortly supplant.

Little seems to be known concerning the normal frequency of fang change. It is to be presumed that the final loss of the obsolescent fangs usually occurs in feeding. Discarded fangs are frequently found in the digestive tract or feces. Dr. Charles A. Vorhies has shown in motion pictures that the western diamond rattler (*C. atrox*), in feeding on rabbits, uses the fangs alternately to pull the prey into the mouth, just as a colubrine snake uses its maxillary teeth. This use would no doubt break off a fang about to be lost, quite as certainly as would the striking of prey or an enemy.

The method of removal of the functional fangs is not known with certainty. To judge from an examination of obsolete and defecated fangs, and on observations when fangs are broken off in the venom-milking process, the fracture occurs near the outer or distal edge of the maxillary socket, which is at the proximal end of the dentine area of the fang. This leaves a considerable amount of the pedestal within the socket. Whether this drops out later, or is resorbed, is not known; at least it is not retained for use with the next fang, since a resting maxillary socket is completely empty.

The following fang-change schedules have been deduced from observations of captive rattlesnakes: Burnett (1854a, p. 313) found, by experiment, that fangs were replaced at intervals of six weeks. Yarrow (1888, p. 327) had a rattler in which the fangs were replaced twice after intervals of three weeks. Jones (1928, p. 5) reported that as many as 16 consecutive pairs of fangs had been removed from a rattler in as many weeks, and were regularly and duly replaced by a new set. Guthrie (1929, p. 351) had a timber rattler that shed 10 pairs of fangs in 15 months. Mrs. Grace Wiley (1929, p. 9) expressed the opinion that the western diamond sheds its fangs every 20 days; this she judged from her examination of her captive rattlesnakes' mouths and the removal of loose fangs. Bogert (1943, p. 326) observed that this statement left it doubtful whether this meant one fang for each maxilla every 40 days, or one fang from any one of four sockets every 20 days. Stimpson (1948, p. 461) expressed the opinion that rattler fangs are shed every six to eight weeks; Cochran (1929, p. 108) mentions an interval of three months; Lloyd (1925, p. 32) three times a year; Lueth (1941b, p. 15) every three to six weeks; and DeLys (1948, p. 77) infers a semiannual change. H. E. Evans told me of a captive western diamondback that shed seven fangs in nine months. This determination was made by sifting the sand in the cage and examining feces. The fangs that had passed through the intestinal tract were darkened.

There have been various guesses as to the time intervening between the loss of one fang and its replacement. Damiri (Jayakar, 1906–8, vol. 1, p. 57), the Arabian writer of the 14th century, expressed the opinion that if a viper loses a fang it will be restored in three days. Mitchell (1860, p. 16) stated that a fang lost naturally would be replaced in a few days, but one violently wrenched out would not be restored for several weeks. Stanley (1897, p. 28) thought replacement would occur in 36 hours. Actually a distinction should be drawn, as has been done by Mitchell, between a normal loss and one through violence. But we cannot agree with one of his conclusions, namely, that there is a fangless interval involved in a normal loss, for there is every evidence that in these circumstances there is no interval, since the new functional fang becomes active before the failing fang drops out. It is assumed that, by replacement, Mitchell and the others meant the availability of a functional fang in the adjacent socket on the same side of the head. We know, since most snakes have one occupied and one vacant socket on each side of the head, that this is the normal condition, and that, after a fang has been lost, its socket enters a resting period of considerable length equal to the active period of the adjacent fang less the overlap. Allen and Swindell (1948, p. 12) found the overlap in moccasins to be five days. Basing my estimate on all these data, I should assume (and this is only a guess) that the normal active life of each fang in an adult rattlesnake is from 6 to 10 weeks, and that each change involves a double-fang overlap of 4 or 5 days.

It has been suggested that fang changes are synchronous with skin-changing (Lucy Audubon, 1869, p. 81; Kunzé, 1879, p. 333). This is certainly not true, since the fang replacements on the opposite sides of the head are not synchronous with each other.

There is an idea as old as Pliny (1855–57, vol. 3, p. 58; book xi, chap. 62), and probably much older, that the fangs of a snake are barbed, and are lost when it bites. Bruce (1930, p. 93) asked, in Bevan's snake-lore column in *Outdoor Life,* whether it is true that a rattler leaves its fangs in any human being or animal it bites, and soon dies. The derivation of this myth from the bee and its sting is evident. Louise Pound (1946, p. 172) mentions a Nebraska folk myth to the effect that when a snake strikes, its fangs drop out and it cannot bite until they grow in again.

The fact that, during a transition period, viperine snakes, including rattlers, may have two fangs on one or both sides of the head, has led to various myths and misinterpretations. There was a theory dating back to 150 B.C. that male and female vipers differ in the number of fangs they have (Nicander, 1953, p. 43). Sometimes it was stated that male vipers have four fangs and females two, and sometimes the female was presumed to have more than the male (Topsell, 1608, p. 299). A similar sexual difference has been attributed to the rattlesnakes (Lanman, 1863, p. 231) but there is no foundation for this belief. Charas pointed out as early as 1673 (p. 25) that there was no sexual dimorphism in the number of fangs in vipers. Several early writers thought that all rattlesnakes have four fangs (Jonstonus, 1653, p. 26; Montanus, 1851, p. 79, first published 1671; Winterbotham, 1795, p. 405). An early explorer reported in 1658 that rattlers have two fangs in the upper jaw and two in the lower (Thwaites, 1896–1901, vol. 43, p. 153). Others have thought the finding of two fangs on a side to be remarkable enough to be worth recording (Knox, 1826, p. 416; Anon., 1899, p. 185; Murphy, 1917, p. 67). But, as has been stated, this is periodically quite normal.

FANG STRUCTURE

The shape of the functional fang is such as to preclude a simple description. It may be likened to a thin or gradually tapering cone, with a spreading or buttressed base, and with the central section bent into a circular curve describing an arc of from 60 to 70 degrees (fig. 11:14). The basal tangent section is short and is of irregular shape, because of spreading to form the entrance lumen, and with a reinforcing abutment at the anchorage. This abutment surrounds the pulp cavity, which is greatly enlarged at the base. The reinforcement is largely secured by material massed posteriorly around the pulp cavity, with some lateral increase as well. In this, the two fangs on a side are slightly asymmetrical, the inner fang spreading inwardly, and the outer in the contrary direction. However, most of the asymmetry required by the dissimilar shapes of the two sockets is not provided by the fangs proper, but by the supporting bone pedestals, whose difference from the fangs is evidenced by a discontinuity in the surface, the bony frustums having a duller and softer surface than the dentine-covered fangs. The bases are striated or corrugated for reinforcement; and, as some of the striations continue across the proximal parts of the dentine-covered surface, a partial continuity with the fang is indicated. The pedestals are irregularly shaped to engage the sides (rather than the bottoms) of the bony maxillary sockets; and, in this engagement, the asymmetry of the two sockets is compensated.

The tangent at the point of the fang is proportionately longer than the basal tangent. The former is produced, not only by the straightening of the axis of the cone, but by the elliptical opening of the discharge lumen as well. Often, espe-

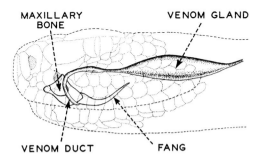

Fig. 11:16. Relative positions of venom gland, duct, and fang.

cially in the larger specimens, there is a slight reverse curve in evidence at this point; this serves to prevent the fang, when in its resting position against the roof of the mouth, from being directed against the tissue (especially of the venom gland) lying immediately above it (fig. 11:16).

Figure 11:17 shows the details of the conformation of a fang. The canal (f) within the fang tapers as does the outer section. Cross sections show the fang to be slightly eliptical, especially in the proximal section. The walls are thickened opposite the major axis, as would be desirable from a structural standpoint; for the forces exerted in biting, striking, or drawing in prey are likely to be in the plane of the curve.

At the base of the fang, the pulp cavity (c) lying behind the venom canal, with which it has no connection, is of considerable size. There is an aperture in the rear of the basal pedestal giving access to the pulp cavity. The cavity, which has the effect of dividing the fang into a pair of tubes, one within the other, decreases in size distally until it practically disappears at the central curve, at which place only a vestige usually remains.

However, in large fangs the pulp cavity can be traced into the very point of the fang. The extent and location of the pulp cavity can best be ascertained by the pinching off of successive pieces of a well-dried fang; the cavity can sometimes be followed by a discoloration between the interior and exterior tubes, which tend to shatter and separate along the pulp cavity surface. The inner tube is much thinner than the outer; its polish is not so high, and it is slightly softer. Often there is no space or color between the tubes, although they are still dis-

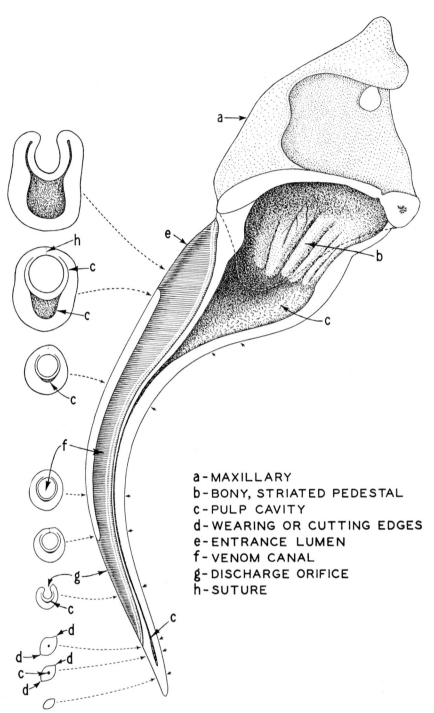

a – MAXILLARY
b – BONY, STRIATED PEDESTAL
c – PULP CAVITY
d – WEARING OR CUTTING EDGES
e – ENTRANCE LUMEN
f – VENOM CANAL
g – DISCHARGE ORIFICE
h – SUTURE

Fig. 11:17. Longitudinal and cross sections of a rattlesnake fang.

tinguished by a plane of separation. However, at the front, as the tubes approach the suture, they fuse into a homogeneous material. Toward the upper lumen, the thin inner tube is completely separated from the outer by the pulp cavity, except at the front, where, along the line of the one-time suture (*h*), the two are still fused. The relationship between the inner and outer tubes and the pulp cavity is best understood from the series of cross sections along the fang as shown in figure 11:17.

On the larger fangs there can be seen a faint yellow ridge, forming a wearing or cutting edge (*d*), paralleling the lower aperture just beyond its outer edge, and extending from the point to a short distance above the upper end of the opening (fig. 11:18 and lower cross sections of fig. 11:17). The ridge is slightly roughened. There is a corresponding ridge on the under side of the point; as a result of these ridges the point has an elliptical cross section, with the major axis at a slight angle with the plane of the curve, the upper end of the axis being tilted outward and the lower inward. Both fangs on a side have the points twisted in the same direction.

Viewed under magnification, the fang material is sometimes transparent, sometimes translucent white, but often a mixture of the two, the transparent sections being flecked and striated with white. In the larger fangs, and in strong light, the pulp cavity can be seen as a shadow, terminating in a cone-shaped void within the fang point.

Although the suture along the front of the fang is visible on the inner surface of the duct, as can be determined by an examination of fractured sections, it is less evident than on the exterior surface in front. It seems to be more of a shadow than an actual plane of separation, so perfect is the junction. Yet experiments with immature fangs, in which the suture opens smoothly and evenly, show it to be a true joint. The front junction or closing of the tube is much more perfect in the solenoglyphs (including the rattlesnakes) than in the proteroglyphs, an observation made by Thomas Smith as early as 1818 (p. 473).

THE REPLACEMENT SERIES AND FANG DEVELOPMENT

I have already mentioned the first reserve fang in connection with the replacement mechanism. Actually, the first reserve is one of a series of replacement fangs that lie in a double magazine above the functional fang (figs. 11:5, 11:6, and 11:19); there is one such double magazine on each side of the head. In each magazine the immature fangs are as closely crowded together as their dimensions and their nutritive capsules will permit. Each magazine is double, in that there is a central dividing wall of tissue that separates the immature fangs that will eventually become functional in the outer socket from those that will occupy the inner socket. The successive replacements are in a graduated order of completeness or maturity (fig. 11:20). An example series of developing fangs is of interest as an indication of the ancestral form that may have been taken by the fang, before the snake's biting mechanism reached its present high degree of specialization and perfection.

It is well known that the fangs of pit vipers, such as the rattlesnakes, might appear to be fabricated by the process of rolling a flat section so as to form a solid tube, much as butt-welded pipe is made, because of the joint or suture, evidenced

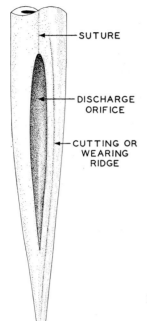

SUTURE

DISCHARGE ORIFICE

CUTTING OR WEARING RIDGE

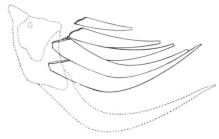

Fig. 11:19. Position of replacement fangs.

Fig. 11:18. Point of fang showing discharge orifice and cutting edge.

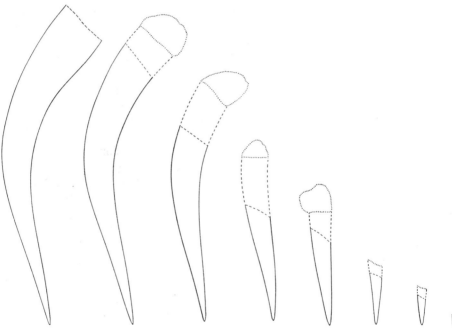

Fig. 11:20. Relative completeness of a series of developing fangs. The first replacement fang is at the left; the youngest bud on the right. Solid parts are calcified; dashed sections formed but uncalcified; dotted sections are unformed.

by the dark line along the front of the fang. Both lumens are really gaps in the suture, the upper or inlet opening being short and relatively wide, while the lower, or discharge, orifice is a long and narrow slit (figs. 11:12, 11:13, and 11:18). As the two surfaces of the hypothetical flat member are both covered with dentine, it follows that, after rolling or folding, the inner surface of the tube (the canal) is coated in the same way as the outer; however, the inner surface is found to be considerably softer than the outer. The line of the longitudinal suture or weld can be clearly seen in large fangs, but so perfect is the joint that it cannot be detected with a sharp needle, except rarely near one of the apertures. The interior line of the joint is even more perfect, for it can be seen only with a magnifier under strong light. When a functional fang is broken, there is no tendency of the break to follow this line; yet it is a real suture, as shown by studies of the immature fangs of the replacement series, for in these the fang will readily split along the suture. The material of the functional fang is very brittle and shatters under strain. The surface can be cut with fine sandpaper or a file, or scratched with a needle point. The surface of the tip of the fang seems slightly harder than the upper parts.

The fangs are developed or completed, not as a unit, but from the point upward, the point being fully formed and hardened long before the upper part takes shape (fig. 11:20). Also, while the form of the fang indicates derivation from a flat plate rolled into a tube, the actual growth does not proceed in this manner; for, from the earliest period of development in which the form can be ascertained, the tubular shape is in evidence.

Elsewhere (1939b, p. 9) I have described in detail the successive members of a replacement series, in order to show how the growth proceeds. In a typical series removed from a large western diamond (*C. atrox*) there were seven replacements in the magazine, varying in size and development from the first replacement, which duplicated the functional fang, except for having an incomplete base, down to the seventh, only a small capsule attached to the magazine wall. From this series it was observed: First, if the fang were originally developed from a partly folded, and thus grooved, tooth, the process is not now repeated in the growth of the individual fangs; second, the fangs do not grow by the enlargement of their parts; on the contrary, the first stage is the development of the fang in its full size in the vicinity of the lower aperture, followed by the completion of the point and then the gradual extension of the upper tubular section.

If there is a suggestion of a derivation from a grooved fang in the present suture or weld, and the continuity of the external dentine surface with the internal surface of the canal, it is no longer evident in the development of the tubular section of an individual fang, at least prior to the deposition of dentine. The only resemblance to a grooved fang, during the present progression of individual fang growth, lies in the appearance of the lower aperture during its formation. This is the part of the fang first formed, and, as the aperture is in reality a deep slot, we have, in effect, a short, grooved tooth. To this the upper tubular section is subsequently added.

It was found that if a mature fang be broken by the introduction of a pin into the lower venom orifice, the fracture does not follow the line of the front suture or weld, but is jagged. However, in the immature fangs, beginning with the second reserve, the introduction of a pin causes the weld, however perfect its appearance, to open quite readily and evenly.

In earlier days, some writers misinterpreted the reserve series of fangs as being auxiliary active fangs, or as teeth (like the palatines and pterygoids) to aid in swallowing the prey (Tyson, 1683, p. 45; Clavigero, 1937, but written in 1789, p. 390; Holmes, 1823, p. 257; Knox, 1826, p. 412; Lucy Audubon, 1869, p. 81). But others recognized their true purpose at once (Charas, 1673, p. 27; Areskine in Mead, 1702, p. 41; Bartram, 1744, p. 359; and Nicholls in Mead, 1745, p. 61). Fontana (1787, vol. 1, p. 15) watched the replacement under way by examining a viper at two-day intervals. Within 30 days he saw the advancement and ankylosis of a first reserve into its socket, and thus confirmed the function of the reserve series.

The rattlesnake teeth, other than the fangs, have recently been investigated by Brattstrom (see table 2:9). Although his researches are not complete, his conclusions to date are that the palatine teeth normally number 3–3 but may be 2–2. Single palatine teeth occur in *Sistrurus catenatus,* and in some specimens of *Crotalus molossus molossus* and *C. mitchelli pyrrhus.* The pterygoids are most often 8–8, but may number 9 or 7, and rarely 10, on a side. They are reduced to 6 or 7 in *pricei* and *triseriatus,* and to 5 in *intermedius.* In *Sistrurus catenatus* there are 5 or 6. The dentaries number 9 or 10 in the larger rattlesnake species. They are reduced to 6 or 7 in *C. m. pyrrhus.*

Ontogenetic Variations in Fang Length and Shape

In addition to a study of the development of the successive fangs in a single snake, the ontogenetic development within a subspecies is worthy of investigation, as are also comparisons between species. The length and shape of the fangs are matters of practical concern, since they affect several of the variables that may determine the gravity of a snake bite, as, for instance, the depth of penetration of the venom, the rapidity of injection, the amount of venom that may be lost externally in clothing, and the chance of fang breakage on contact.

To make comparisons of fang lengths, it is first necessary to establish standards of measurement. The measurement of the length of a fang is found to be a rather intricate procedure. First the protective sheath of tissue must be cleared away. The fang itself is fragile, especially in the smaller snakes. The active fang is imbedded in the maxillary socket, which hides the true base, so that its length over-all, either along the curve or in a straight line from base to point, cannot be determined without dissection. Nor can the junction, either with the edge of the socket or with the bony pedestal, be used as the proximal terminus, since this is irregular and cannot be located with accuracy. I have found the most satisfactory criterion of length to be the straight-line distance from the lower end of the upper aperture, or lumen, to the point of the fang (fig. 11:21). This is, of course, merely a convenient arbitrary criterion; the actual length of the fang to the edge of the maxillary socket is greater, and the full length, including the basal frustum, greater still.

Studies were first made to learn whether there is any sexual dimorphism in fang length (Klauber, 1939b, p. 21), but none was found.

Elsewhere (1939b, pp. 23 to 43) I have reported on studies of the fang lengths of five species of rattlesnakes, from birth to maturity, as correlated with their head lengths and body lengths over-all. It was found that the fang length bears a substantially constant proportionality to body length during the juvenile stage, but subsequently the fangs grow at a slower rate than the body. In comparison with head length, the fangs increase proportionately faster than the head in the juvenile stage, at the same rate in young adults, and slower than the head in the fully adult stage. Thus it is that adult rattlesnakes of any species have proportionately shorter fangs than the young, whether comparisons are made on a basis of length over-all or on head length. The dispersion, in terms of the coefficient of variation, of individual fang measurements about the species regression lines (which are parabolas) is of the order of 5 to 8 per cent. These conclusions were drawn from measurements of the fangs of from 44 to 588 specimens of each of the 5 species studied. Figures 11:22 and 11:23 show the dispersion of the fang lengths of 100 specimens of *C. r. ruber* about the regression lines that represent the fang–head and fang–body length relationships. These two curves are parabolic and have the approximate equations $F = -0.00186H^2 + 0.393H - 3.940$ and $F = -2.098L^2 + 13.171L - 0.666$, where F and H are expressed in millimeters and L in meters. The equations of the ontogenetic regression lines of other species will be found in Klauber, 1939b, p. 29.

To ascertain the change in fang shape that takes place as a snake grows from a juvenile to adulthood, a series of some twenty specimens of the red diamond rattler (*C. r. ruber*) at all ages were studied, measurements being made of the radius and angle of the central curve, and the thickness at the mid-point, which dimensions were correlated with fang length. It was found that the fang does not retain a form of constant proportions, as the individuals grow to maturity. The thickness at the middle does maintain proportionality up to the time the snake is a young adult. Subsequently there is a more rapid increase in diameter than in length, so that the fangs of the larger snakes are proportionately thicker, heavier-walled, and stronger. When it is remembered that the adult snakes have relatively shorter fangs, in proportion to their bodies, it appears that the diameter of the tube does increase more nearly in proportion to the body length of the snake.

The radius of the fang curvature increases gradually from the smaller to the larger snakes, but apparently reaches a maximum when the snake becomes a young adult, subsequent to which there is no further increase in this radius. The central angle of the curve in the fang also increases as the snakes grow to maturity. For instance, in the juvenile *ruber* this angle is approximately 65 degrees, while in the fully adult specimens the angle averages 72 degrees. Thus, the arc of curvature increases with age, and the larger snakes have a relatively more hooked fang, with a greater recurvature at the end. Figure 11:24 shows a series of ten *ruber* fangs taken from snakes varying in size from about 350 to 1,350 mm. (14 to 53 inches) at intervals of about 100 mm. (4 inches). The changes in the radius, the angle of the central arc, and the recurvature in the distal tangent are evident.

INTERSPECIFIC DIFFERENCES IN FANG LENGTH AND SHAPE

With regard to differences between species of rattlesnakes, there is a considerable variability in both the shape and the relative length of the fangs. Species with small heads, proportionate to their bodies, are found to have short fangs, as might be expected. Using either the head–fang or body–fang relationships as

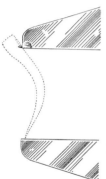

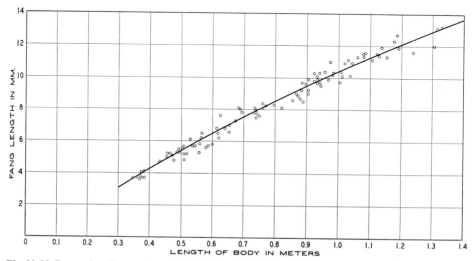

Fig. 11:21. Method of measuring a fang, with a pin point, for insertion in the upper lumen, attached to the upper jaw of the caliper.

Fig. 11:22. Regression line and dispersion of 100 specimens of the red diamond rattlesnake (*C. r. ruber*), showing the relationship between fang length and over-all body length.

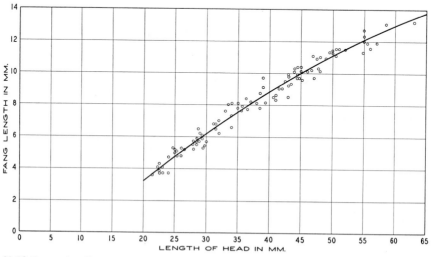

Fig. 11:23. Regression line and dispersion of 100 specimens of the red diamond rattlesnake (*C. r. ruber*), showing the relationship between fang length and head length.

bases, and restricting the data to adult rattlesnakes, we are able to deduce generic trend lines for the rattlesnakes as a group (Klauber, 1939b, figs. 41 and 42). These curves are found to be parabolic in shape. Although there are some species that deviate from these lines, certain conclusions may be drawn, particularly that the adults of small species of rattlesnakes have shorter fangs, in proportion to the sizes of their heads or the lengths of their bodies, than the adults of the larger species. In other words, the little rattlesnakes have even shorter fangs than might be expected on a basis of size alone. In table 11:1 there are presented the adult fang proportionality statistics of a number of rattlesnake species and subspecies. *C. stejnegeri, C. polystictus, C. exsul,* and *C. molossus* have unusually

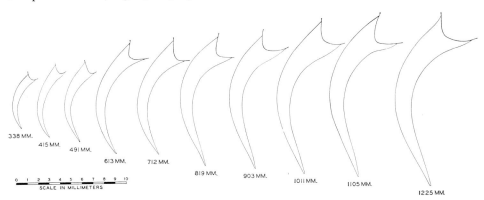

Fig. 11:24. Change of fang size and shape from juvenile to adult in a series of red diamond rattlesnakes (*C. r. ruber*). (The figure below each fang indicates the over-all length of the snake in millimeters.)

long fangs, while *C. l. klauberi, C. triseriatus, C. v. helleri,* and *C. v. oreganus* have notably short fangs, in proportion to their heads. Stunted races are like the adolescents of their prototypes and therefore have relatively long fangs.

Assuming that long fangs are an advantage, if not carried to an extreme, we may hazard the guess that proportionately longer fangs are possible in a larger species because it has the weight to drive them in, in a strike, or the muscle to imbed them in a bite, whereas the smaller snake would lack the essential momentum or muscular power. For we have been discussing linear dimensions only; whereas the weight of a rattler increases even faster than the cube of its body length, and its muscular strength at least as rapidly as the square. Thus, the larger snake is provided with the power to drive in a proportionately longer and heavier fang. Again, viewing the venom and fang as a prey-securing mechansim, we must recognize the fact that, if both prey size (weight) and required venom dosage vary approximately as the third power of the snake's length, the fang should be longer than that involved in a constant ratio with head length. The trend of the ontogenetic variation seems to be designed to give to each species its highest fang-to-head ratio at the time of the most rapid increase in bulk, that is, between adolescence and young adulthood, when presumably the rattler's food requirements are at a maximum.

There also is a tendency toward proportionately thicker fangs in the larger snakes. This is to be expected, for, if the forces (especially transverse) exerted

TABLE 11:1
AVERAGE FANG PROPORTIONS OF ADULT RATTLESNAKES

Subspecies	Length over-all divided by fang length	Head length divided by fang length
C. adamanteus	83	4.1
C. atrox	106	4.6
C. basiliscus basiliscus	125	5.0
C. cerastes cerastes	119	5.6
laterorepens	105	5.1
C. durissus durissus	104	4.4
terrificus	96	4.1
totonacus	102	4.0
tzabcan	105	4.3
C. enyo enyo	135	5.6
C. exsul	94	4.4
C. horridus horridus	107	4.6
atricaudatus	106	4.4
C. intermedius intermedius	207	9.3
omiltemanus	185	8.2
C. lepidus lepidus	148	6.8
klauberi	162	7.3
morulus	136	5.9
C. mitchelli mitchelli	151	5.7
muertensis	127	5.6
pyrrhus	107	4.9
stephensi	128	5.6
C. molossus molossus	86	4.1
nigrescens	88	4.4
C. polystictus	89	3.9
C. pricei pricei	155	7.5
C. pusillus	100	5.1
C. ruber ruber	97	4.5
lucasensis	95	4.4
C. scutulatus scutulatus	126	5.1
salvini	97	4.4
C. stejnegeri	88	4.0
C. tigris	165	6.1
C. tortugensis	112	4.6
C. transversus	196	10.0
C. triseriatus triseriatus	112	5.7
aquilus	136	6.8
C. unicolor	106	4.8
C. viridis viridis	115	5.1
abyssus	121	5.4
caliginis	110	5.2
cerberus	115	4.9
decolor	132	5.8
helleri	113	5.0
lutosus	131	5.5
nuntius	122	5.8
oreganus	132	6.0
C. willardi willardi	110	5.7
meridionalis	92	5.0
silus	92	4.7
S. catenatus catenatus	131	5.8
tergeminus	120	5.5
S. miliarius miliarius	140	6.9
barbouri	121	5.7
streckeri	130	6.8
S. ravus	108	5.7

on the fang increase in proportion to the weight of the snake (roughly to the cube of the length), then the cross section of the fang must increase more rapidly than would be involved in a mere proportionate increase in linear dimensions, which would increase the cross section only as the square. The structural problem is somewhat similar to that of the cross section of the leg bones of mammals, which cannot bear a constant proportionality, since the compressive strength would increase only as the square of the linear dimensions, while the weight to be supported increases as the cube.

As to the central curvature of the fangs, it is found that small rattlesnakes tend to have a reduced curvature. Also, the species *C. d. durissus, C. m. molossus, C. polystictus,* and *C. p. pricei* have flatter fangs than other rattlesnakes; in this character they resemble the pit vipers of the genus *Bothrops,* which have flatter and less recurved fangs than most rattlers, and hence fangs better adapted to stabbing than to biting.

Elsewhere (Klauber, 1939b, p. 54, table 30) I have given dimensional data on the fangs in adult specimens of various species and subspecies of rattlesnakes. Of particular interest is the slenderness of the fang compared to its length, thus insuring depth of penetration. Yet this is attained without serious loss of strength, owing to the density and high compressive strength of the dentine composition and the excellence of the structural design.

The maximum size of fangs attained in the rattlesnakes may be of interest. I have not had the opportunity to measure the fangs of any very large specimens of the eastern diamondback (*C. adamanteus*), the largest of the rattlers, and the heaviest of all venomous snakes. The largest available to me have been a series some 1,600 mm. (5 ft. 3 in.) long, with fangs having a length of about 17 mm. (¹¹⁄₁₆ in.) from the lower end of the upper lumen to the point. Calculations lead one to expect that a 2,440 mm. (8 ft.) specimen would have fangs about 22 mm. (⅞ in.) in length. This would make the over-all length, to the distal edge of the maxillary, about 27 mm. (1¹⁄₁₆ in.). Rattlesnakes do not by any means have the largest fangs found among the venomous snakes. The African vipers of the genus *Bitis* probably exceed all other snakes in this characteristic. The African Gaboon viper, an extremely heavy-bodied snake, is said by Pitman (1938, p. 270) to have fangs approaching two inches in length. Bogert (1943, p. 337) explains that this probably refers to the length along the curve; however, the straight-line distance from the lower end of the upper aperture to the point might well reach 1¾ inches, a formidable weapon, indeed.

The extent of the reverse curvature near the point of the rattlesnake's fang once initiated a bitter controversy between the eccentric British naturalist Charles Waterton and the friends of the American painter-ornithologist John J. Audubon. Audubon had shown in plate 21 of his *Birds of America* (1827–30; plate 28 of the quarto edition of 1841 and of the reprint of 1937) a timber rattlesnake threatening a pair of mocking birds. The plate does, indeed, invite criticism; the snake is attacking the birds at their nest up in a tree (unusual); the snake is threatening the birds with open mouth (almost incredible); the snake has two functional fangs per side (unusual); and the fangs are recurved to an exaggerated extent. The pertinent references in this acrimonious controversy have been cited elsewhere (p. 461).

SPITTING RATTLESNAKES

I have mentioned elsewhere (p. 444) the popular supposition that rattlers threaten
their enemies with open mouth. This is certainly not true of uninjured snakes.
Another somewhat related action, often attributed to rattlers, is that of spitting
venom at their enemies.

Bogert (1943, p. 341) has discussed the spitting cobras, a subgroup of the cobras
whose spitting ability has often been attested. They are able to eject a spray of
venom for distances up to six feet; they aim at the eyes, and the fine drops of
venom, if they do strike an eye, are exceedingly painful, and may, if remedies
are not soon applied, result in the loss of sight. Bogert has shown that the spitting
cobras have fangs differing from those of their nonspitting relatives, in that the
lower orifice is so modified that venom is directed forward instead of downward.
Also, cobra venom is shown to be more effective on the eyes than the venom of
some other kinds of snakes, although it is not certain that the venom of the
spitting cobras is more effective than that of the nonspitters among the cobras
(Bogert, 1943, p. 351).

The references to spitting rattlers and the question whether they actually spit,
are fairly extensive, including Audubon, 1827, p. 26; S. W. Mitchell, 1860, p. 24;
1889, p. 506; Wyman, 1861, p. 293; Dugès, 1877, p. 15; Smith, 1882, p. 636; Cope,
1892a, p. 687; 1892b, p. 538; 1900, pp. 1150, 1174; Ellzey, 1892, p. 538; 1893, p.
25; Stejneger, 1895, p. 374; W., 1894, p. 488; J. D. Mitchell, 1903, p. 36; Kennedy, 1905, p. 451; Strecker, 1926a, p. 69; 1928, p. 20; Netting, 1932, p. 4; Barbour,
1934, p. 44; Boone, 1937, p. 54; Peters, 1937, p. 23; and Wallace, 1950, p. 118.

Certainly the rattlesnakes, unlike the spitters among the cobras, do not possess
fangs designed for spitting. The lower orifice in the fang directs the venom downward, not forward. I have seen many rattlesnakes strike, but have never seen an
uninjured rattler spit, with the ejection of either venom or saliva in the course
of the strike. Only one of my many correspondents who have cited rattlesnake
experiences has mentioned spitting, this in the case of a northern Pacific (*C. v.
oreganus*), which I judge he had been annoying at the time. The snake may have
been injured.

In a number of instances in the citations that I have listed, the authors state
that rattlers spit only when they miss, or fall short of, the object of a strike, or
when they strike the wire of a cage (e.g., Audubon, S. W. Mitchell, Smith, Netting). In several others of the cases mentioned, I think it clear that the snake
had had its mouth injured before the alleged spitting was observed, which might
explain the unusual occurrence. Cope (1892a, p. 687) stated that rattlers may
threaten with open mouth and "at this time drops of the poisonous saliva fall
from the fangs, and by a violent expulsion of air from the lungs are thrown at
their enemy." When the possibility of such an effect was questioned by Ellzey
(1892, p. 538), Cope defended his position, yet there is evidence that his original
statement had been based on a single experience with a prairie rattlesnake (*C. v.
viridis*) whose head he had already injured (1900, p. 1174). Kennedy (1905, p. 451)
describes the spitting of a rattler that had been speared and was being held by a
hay fork.

In my own experience, a red diamond rattler (*C. r. ruber*) struck at me when

I was beyond its range, and I received a spray of drops of venom or saliva, I am not sure which. But this snake had previously injured its jaw slightly by striking a lamp bulb. I presume that prior to its lunging at me, saliva or venom had gathered on its lower jaw and this was thrown over me by the force of the forward lunge.

Probably the most reliable account of a spitting rattler is that of Strecker (1928, p. 20). He had a western diamond (*C. atrox*) in captivity that on several occasions, when irritated, spat for distances up to three feet through the wire of its cage. Strecker thought the ejected liquid was saliva rather than venom. He admits that the snake struck the wire of the cage in the first instance, and that some venom may have been ejected on that occasion. It would also appear that this might have caused a head injury that induced the subsequent spitting. Strecker knew that most spitting was mythical; as an example he recounts the story of a rattler that spat at a victim beyond its reach because of an intervening horse-hair rope that it couldn't cross. This involved mythical spitting over a mythical barrier. Col. M. L. Crimmins informed me that at one time when he was engaged in milking many hundreds of western diamonds that were kept in wire-screened cages, they often struck the screens upon his approach and sprays of venom resulted.

It is my conclusion from these accounts that natural spitting by rattlers, if it ever occurs, must be rare, indeed. Certainly rattlers have nothing resembling the specialized fangs and the stereotyped methods of the cobra spitters.

THE VENOM DUCT AND GLAND

THE VENOM DUCT

The course taken by the venom between the gland and the fang has been the subject of several uncertainties. In the early days it was thought that the act of biting caused the piercing of the venom gland by the fang itself, with a conse-quent release of venom into the wound (Neal, 1720, vol. 2, p. 574; Oldmixon, 1741, vol. 1, p. 188; Dumont, 1753, p. 108; Beltrami, 1828, vol. 2, p. 160; Kendall, 1892, p. 588). But other writers recognized the presence of a more positive means of delivery—a duct between the gland and the fang, serving to carry the venom directly to the upper entrance of the venom canal in the hollow tooth (Areskine in Mead, 1702, p. 43; Nicholls in Mead, 1745, p. 78; Fontana, 1787, vol. 1, p. 20). However, although the course of this duct between the venom gland and the fang could readily be traced, the method of its connection to the fang was more difficult to ascertain.

In the rattlesnakes the duct begins at the forward end of the gland, which lies below the anterior edge of the eye. It passes forward below the pit and the nostril, slightly above and outside of the maxilla. It then turns sharply downward to a point in front of the upper lumen of the fang. The course of the duct outside of the maxilla can be followed by its swelling when the gland of a rattlesnake is pressed to expel the venom.

The problem of the connection of the duct to the fang is complicated by two conditions that must be met: first, the duct must follow the rotational movement of the fang between its resting and active positions—or at least it must make a connection with the inlet orifice when the fang is in the latter position; and, secondly, there must be some provision for the maintenance of the connection despite the repeated exchange or alternation of active fangs between the two maxillary sockets.

Most of the early writers visualized either a direct entrance of the duct end into the fang, or they thought the terminus was brought to the outer edge of the fang opening and was fastened there to prevent leakage. The fang-entrance theory was the first to be discarded; one of its last advocates was Niemann (1892, p. 29, fig. 10). Actually, there is no evidence of the entrance of the duct end into the fang.

The second theory, as suggested, among others, by Burnett (1854c, p. 32) and Johnston in Mitchell (1860, p. 18), visualizes a gripping of the fang aperture by the end of the duct. With each change of fangs, the duct was assumed to shift and become fastened to the newly active fang. The difficulty of explaining how the duct end could become firmly attached to successive fangs in the alternate sockets, without a transitory interval during which the duct would adhere to neither fang, thus preventing venom delivery, caused this theory to be questioned. Furthermore, it was found that, during the transition period when a snake has two active fangs, instead of neither fang being able to deliver venom, actually both can do so, as has been verified by many observers (e.g., Fontana, 1787, vol. 1, p. 18). In 1933, while milking rattlers having two active fangs, I tried the experiment of slipping a card between the two fangs before exerting pressure on the gland, with the result that venom could be seen to squirt from both fangs simultaneously; there was no confusion between the two jets, as there might have been without the card.

The currently accepted theory of the transfer of the venom from the duct to the fang stresses the part that the fang sheath plays in the venom delivery. This has been developed with increasing accuracy and detail by a number of experimenters, including Areskine (in Mead, 1702, p. 43), Nicholls (in Mead, 1745, p. 78), Fontana (1787, vol. 1, p. 20), Mitchell (1860, p. 22, footnote), Wyman (1861, p. 293), West (1895, p. 821; 1898, p. 525), Kathariner (1897, p. 55), Langmann (1900, p. 402), Martin and Lamb (1907, p. 785), Aurich (1908, p. 11), Willson (1908, p. 528), Kellaway (1937, p. 1), Lueth (1941b, p. 15), Bogert (1943, p. 327), and Smith and Bellairs (1947, p. 356). According to this explanation, the duct passes through the fang sheath in front of the fang and terminates at a point opposite the upper fang opening. The sheath itself holds the venom in a sort of pocket and transfers it to the fang. The part of the sheath just below the upper lumen exerts a grip on the fang, thus preventing leakage and loss of pressure. This grip is essential, since otherwise the injection would be only partly effective and much venom would be wasted between the sheath and fang. Since the sheath surrounds both fangs during the interval when both an old fang and a replacement fang are active, the method whereby both may discharge venom at once is explained, as well as the reason why no duct movement is required when a new fang replaces an old.

Aurich (1908, p. 11) observed that the central fold of membrane between the two fang series tends to direct the venom toward the active fang; or, if both are active, to both fangs. Nicholls (in Mead, 1745, p. 78) seems to have had a similar idea. Bogert experimented on copperheads and rattlers having fangs in various stages of replacement, injecting the venom gland with blue latex whose course upon dissection could readily be traced. He found that the terminus of the duct in the sheath tended to widen when two fangs were active, and to narrow again after the elder of the two had dropped out (reported at the 1946 meeting of the American Society of Ichthyologists and Herpetologists). This would seem to indicate that the adherence of the sheath to the fang may be exerted in an area quite close to the fang lumen, thus restricting the size of the venom pocket and the chance for leakage. Although, when a fang is advanced in the biting position, the sheath covers it almost to the point, the sheath offers no resistance to biting, for it readily slips up the fang when the point is imbedded in the bitten object.

An attempt was made to determine whether there is any muscular action in the sheath, tending to grip the fang to prevent leakage while venom is being expelled. As far as could be seen, there was no such action; but it was observed that when a fang is rotated into the biting position, the sheath is stretched, with the result that it presses firmly against the upper end of the fang. Thus it clings so closely that the venom enters directly from the duct into the pocket formed by the widened or flared entrance to the upper lumen, and there seems to be little evidence of leakage down the fang, between it and the sheath. On the contrary, the venom spurts out of the lower orifice of the fang as if under considerable pressure, which would hardly be possible if the leakage were important.

Experiments have shown that snakes, in biting, have control of the venom discharge; they can, at will, discharge venom from either fang (on opposite sides of the head), from both, or from neither. Although the delivery on the two sides of the head is usually equal, I have noted an instance in which a red diamond rattlesnake (*C. r. ruber*), while being stripped or milked, ejected 0.9 cc. of venom from the right fang, and only 0.2 cc. from the left. The form of sphincter in the venom duct, by which this valve action is accomplished, has been discussed by Jeter (1854, p. 10), Mitchell (1860, pp. 15, 24), Langmann (1900, p. 402), Aurich (1908, p. 10), Amaral (1925, p. 5), and Corkill (1932b, p. 34). Yarrow (1888, p. 327) has mentioned the fact that a rattler can rotate either maxilla independently of the other; and Backus (1903, p. 694), James (1906, p. 8), and George (1930, p. 58) have noted a similar independence in the control of venom expulsion on either side of the head. Both of these conditions of separate control of the opposite sides of the head are commonly observed when rattlesnakes are being milked.

The muscles that produce the various movements involved in a snake bite—the opening and closing of the jaws, the erection and retraction of the fangs, and the extrusion of the venom—have been described in detail by several authors (see citations, pp. 716 and 742).

THE VENOM GLAND

In most poisonous snakes, including the rattlesnakes, the venom glands are located on either side of the head toward the outer edge of the upper jaw. Their extent and size depend not only on the size of the snake but on its genus as well. In several genera, the African night adders (*Causus*) and burrowing vipers (*Atractaspis*), and the Malayan elapid *Maticora* (or *Doliophis*), the glands of adults extend well down the neck (Noguchi, 1909, p. 60; Scortecci, 1939, p. 57; Smith and Bellairs, 1947, p. 356), but in most snakes the glands are restricted to the head.

In the early days, the location and function of the venom glands were matters of uncertainty. Redi (1664, translation of 1665, p. 160) may have confused the fang sheaths with the venom glands, although subsequently in the course of his debate with Charas (Redi in Charas, 1673, supp., p. 29), he made it clear that he did understand their location and functions. Charas (1673, supp. pp. 32, 93) certainly recognized the venom gland and its duct, although he thought the venom only a harmless saliva. Areskine (in Mead, 1702, p. 43), Ranby (1728, p. 377), and Nicholls (in Mead, 1745, pp. 65, 73) also described these organs. Thus it is that Fontana (1787, vol. 1, p. 233), although giving a more complete and accurate description of the venom-generating apparatus than had previously appeared, was not justified in claiming to have been the first to describe and locate the gland and its discharge duct with accuracy.

These early investigations, with the exception of those of Ranby and Nicholls, were made on vipers rather than rattlesnakes, but the findings are equally applicable to the rattlers. In the rattlesnakes the gland on each side extends from a point even with the anterior curve of the eye, back almost to the angle of the mouth. The gland is below the eye, but back of the orbit it increases in height so that it reaches the level of the pupil. The posterior end is rounded.

The venom gland is homologous with the mammalian salivary parotid (Kellaway, 1937, p. 1). Its histology, first described by Fontana (1787, vol. 1, p. 235), has been presented in detail by Desmoulins (1827, p. 109), Burnett (1854c, p. 33), Mitchell (1860, p. 12), Aurich (1908, p. 8), Noguchi (1909, p. 61), Acton and Knowles (1915, p. 347; 1921, p. 729), Marie Phisalix (1922, vol. 2, p. 405), Pawlowsky (1927, p. 261), Amaral (1928c, p. 1067), and others. The gland lies in a well-defined connective-tissue sheath, surrounded and invaded by the muscles that squeeze it when discharge is to take place. Within the gland, there are numerous inwardly projecting fins of tissue that support the many glandular tubules which comprise the sources of venom secretion. The muscles that squeeze the gland have been mentioned by Nicholls (in Mead, 1745, pp. 67, 74), and have been listed by Mitchell (1860, pp. 8, 22), Stejneger (1895, p. 21), Martin and Lamb (1907, p. 784), Noguchi (1909, p. 66), Willson (1908, p. 523), Aurich (1908, p. 12), and Haas (1952, p. 581). Some of the muscles that control the closing of the jaws also operate to squeeze venom from the glands; however, one muscle that operates on the gland is independent of the biting action, so that an independent means of venom extrusion is afforded, in addition to which there is further control by a sphincter muscle in the outlet duct. Van Riper (1955, p. 311) has shown by test that venom can be injected when the strike ends in a stab; a bite is not essential.

For various reasons, snakes almost never eject the full contents of their venom glands; probably they are unable to do this with a single constriction of the gland owing to its cellular construction. Fairley (1929a, p. 300), referring primarily to Australian elapids, stated that if they were able to eject the full contents of their venom glands, human recovery from a snake bite would be rare. Corkill (1932b, p. 34) expressed the opinion that there is a more efficient compression of the glands if the snake is able to fix the teeth of its lower jaw in the victim while biting.

There is apparently some difference of opinion as to whether the venom gland, in addition to its purpose as a storage vessel, generates the venom *in situ,* or acts as an agent of separation, to dissociate the venom generated elsewhere and carried by the blood. The latter is an ancient theory (Areskine in Mead, 1702, p. 43; Fontana, 1787, vol. 1, p. 235). Phisalix and Bertrand (1893, p. 1099) and Calmette (1894a, p. 11) found that the physiological action of the blood of poisonous snakes was similar to the action of their venoms; further, the first-named experimenters proved that the removal of a snake's venom glands rendered its blood nontoxic. From this they concluded that the venom was absorbed into the gland from the blood. But Kellaway (1937, p. 172) has reached a contrary conclusion; he found that the snake plasma remained toxic after the removal of the venom glands, and that the toxic quality of the snake's blood was different from that of the venom. Tyler (1946, p. 199) believes the venom (with an antivenin in combination) may be liberated into the blood stream by the liver, and that the gland then separates the two and stores the venom. Calmette (1907, p. 157; 1908, p. 151) favored the theory that the venom is generated in the gland, whose histological structure and action he has described. Noguchi (1909, p. 59) has pointed out that the gland is of a dual character, the anterior mucous and the posterior serous. He has discussed the process of secretion in detail (p. 63).

The myth that venom generation is the result of food putrefaction, commonly heard attributed to the Gila monster, is occasionally ascribed to rattlesnakes (editorial comment in Richardson, 1936, p. 59).

VENOM

From 1926 to 1938 a rattlesnake-venom project was carried on at the San Diego Zoo. Its purpose was to secure venom, both for the inoculation of horses in the preparation of antivenin, and to make material available for the study of the physiological effects of the venoms of some of the rarer forms of rattlesnakes. Neither of the latter phases of the project was carried out in San Diego; the manufacture of antivenin was undertaken at the Mulford Biological Laboratories (later Sharp and Dohme) in Glenolden, Pennsylvania, and extensive venom studies were also made there, as well as at laboratories in scientific institutions elsewhere. Our part of the project was to secure the snakes; to classify them, extract the venom, purify and dry it, and to prepare it for preservation and shipment, in lots carefully segregated by subspecies. Taxonomic studies were co-ordinated with the San Diego phase of the program. In the course of this work, I milked[1] 5,171 rattlesnakes, of 33 species and subspecies. The yield amounted to 431 grams of dried purified venom, equivalent to about 1.6 liters (3¼ pints) of liquid venom. For purposes of handling and classification, this was divided into 634 lots. Several hundred other rattlers were milked without the processing of the venom.

Although no experimental work was done in San Diego on venom virulence or its physiological effects, a considerable amount of data was obtained on venom

---

[1] However inappropriate the term "to milk" may seem for the stripping of venom from the glands of a snake by manipulation, it is so widely used in herpetological circles that I shall continue to employ it.

yields and on the physical qualities of venom, such as the specific gravity and the proportion of solids that remained after drying. This information will be summarized at appropriate places in the exposition of rattlesnake venom that follows.

ANCIENT BELIEFS

For a long time, the source of the danger from snakes was obscured by myth and misunderstanding. Pliny more often mentioned the stings of snakes than their bites; and the possession of a dangerous sting is still erroneously attributed to some snakes. Actually, no snake of any kind has a sting. The ideas that the venom of the viper is contained in the tongue, not in the fangs, or in the tail or breath, are as old as English literature (Robin, 1932, p. 143). Petrus de Abano, of about 1300 A.D. (see under H. M. Brown, translator, 1924, p. 28), said that humans might be poisoned by reptiles in any of four ways: by the bite; by the sight of a basilisk; by the hiss of a regulus; or by touch, as, for example, by the touch of the tongue of the asp, or its spittle.

From these early ideas have come a number of misconceptions, some of which were applied to rattlesnakes after their discovery in America. Wood (1634, pp. 47, 48) felt it necessary to write that rattlers did not kill with their breaths as was reported in England; neither did they sting, for the poison came from the teeth. A priest, traveling in Canada in 1658, wrote that rattlesnakes bit like dogs, but injected their venom through a small black sting, evidently a reference to the tongue (Thwaites, 1896–1901, vol. 43, p. 153). Josselyn (1672, p. 77) maintained that they poisoned with a vapor coming through their fangs. Witt (1768, p. 10) thought they must kill their prey by fascination, for if they bit and poisoned their prey before eating it, they would surely die, a myth that some people still believe. Zeisberger (1910, p. 70, but written in 1779 or 1780) thought the fangs themselves were poisonous, as well as the venom.

The most persistent of the early misconceptions regarding the source of the danger from venomous snakes was the presumption that the virulence of the venom was generated by, or was proportional to, the snake's anger. This long antedated the advent of the rattlesnake in European consciousness. Said Cleopatra to her asp (the Egyptian cobra, *Naja haje*):

> With thy sharp teeth this knot intrinsicate
> Of life at once untie: poor venomous fool,
> Be angry, and despatch. (*Antony and Cleopatra*; Act V, sc. 11, 307.)

As early as 1548, Van Helmont (Mitchell, 1860, p. 133) found it necessary to dispute the idea that the venom virulence depends on the snake's anger. This theory led to the famous Redi-Charas controversy (1664–73), in which Redi, an Italian biologist, basing his opinion on a long series of experiments, claimed that the damage was caused by the yellow liquid issuing from the fangs of the viper, while Charas, a chemist at the Jardin du Roi, Paris, maintained that the virulence lay in the anger of the snake, or, as it was put in an English translation, "in the enraged spirits of the viper." The pertinent references are: Redi, 1664, 1665, 1670a, 1670b, 1673; Charas, 1669, 1670a, 1670b, 1672a, 1672b, 1673; Platt, 1672. The more important English translations of the rival claims of the disputants will be found in Redi, 1665, p. 160; Charas, 1670b, p. 176; 1673, p. 105; Redi, 1673, p. 13; Charas, 1673 (supp.), pp. 42, 65. Since both men were scientists of repute, the controversy served to bring the question into focus, with an improvement in the general knowledge of the subject. Fontana's extensive researches were in part initiated to settle these uncertainties. Needless to say, Redi's ideas gradually prevailed, but this did not follow immediately.

It may be assumed that Charas' theory, which did not originate with him, although he was, for a time, its foremost exponent, was evolved from a not illogical ancient presumption that the danger from a mad dog emanates from its madness (Charas, 1673, supp. p. 82) as a psychological, rather than a physical, effect. Fontana (1787, vol. 1, p. 162) rationalized Charas' theory in another way, by observing that the more angered a viper, the deeper it would drive its fangs, the longer it would continue biting, and the harder it would squeeze its venom glands. There is some truth in this, but in no way does it substantiate Charas' major premise. Some of the authors who attached the Charas theory to rattlesnakes were Moore (1744, p. 59), Ferrall (1832, p. 300), and Kunkler (1855, p. 483).

Another ancient belief, dating back to Pliny (1855–57, vol. 3, p. 58; book xi, chap. 62) or before, was that the venom was nothing but the gall of the serpent conveyed to the mouth by certain veins. Brand (1781, p. 279) credits Redi with disposing of this idea; Charas also denied its truth (1673, p. 104, supp. p. 77). Mather (1714, p. 68) applied it to rattlesnakes; he maintained that the gall secretion, with additional digestion on the way to the head, formed the venom.

VENOM PURPOSE

From these early theories, we turn to modern discoveries regarding the venom gland and its secretions. It has already been stated (p. 742) that the venom gland is homologous with the salivary parotid. So, also, is the venom, at least in part, homologous with saliva. I have already referred (p. 715) to the researches that have shown that the salivas of the so-called harmless snakes—and they are indeed quite harmless to man—may have venomous qualities. Thus there is a dual homology in the gland and its secretion.

The primary purposes of the venom of poisonous snakes are to secure food and to aid in its digestion. The prey is killed by venom injection, so that it need not be held while it struggles, which avoids the necessity of holding a creature that might injure the snake—a rat, for example. The protection a snake secures against larger enemies that are bitten in its defense is important under some circumstances, but this cannot be viewed as the primary purpose of the venom, nor as its evolutionary source. Although this has been understood for many years (Tyson, 1683, p. 45; Mead, 1702, p. 6, and 1745, p. 13; Owen, 1742, p. 36) there are still doubters, owing to the presumption that swallowing poisoned prey would be fatal to the snake (e.g., Lombard, 1881, p. 88). Kendall (1892, p. 588) believed that the fang sheath must be punctured before venom can be injected; and, finding the sheath intact after feeding, he concluded that no venom was injected in the prey. Actually, in biting, the sheath slips up along the fang, thus baring it for use.

Not only is the venom of importance in procuring prey, but it serves a major role in digesting it. Snakes do not masticate their food; their teeth, by repeated bites, may serve to puncture it to permit ingress of the poisonous saliva—as is characteristic of the back-fanged snakes (opisthoglypha)—but their teeth are too thin and pointed to tear and shred it, as is done in true mastication. However, the venom is not only a killing agent, but a digestive one as well, which is particularly important where food cannot be masticated. This was suspected by Fontana as early as 1765 (1787, vol. 1, p. 63), and has since become well authenticated. Recent statements on this function are those of Calmette (1907, p. 163; 1908, p. 157), Sarkar (1923, p. 318), Fairley (1929b, p. 313), Alvaro (1939, p. 1130), and Amaral (1951a, p. 551). Kellaway (1937, p. 1) has made the point that it is especially advantageous to the snake to introduce into the blood stream of the prey a digestive agent that is dispersed throughout the body of the victim before it dies. Porges (1953, p. 50) also stresses the digestive aspect of the venom and the importance of a spreading factor in the venom that expedites its dispersion. If we view the venom from this standpoint, the evolution of the salivary gland into a venom gland becomes more logical, for there is a change in quality of secretion rather than in purpose. Meanwhile the teeth, in most animals used for preparing food for digestion by tearing and mastication, continue this major function, but perform it by injection of the digestive fluid (venom).

It might be suggested that the food of captive snakes which must be force-fed, be injected with venom before it is fed to the snakes. One of my correspondents said this had been tried, with beneficial results on the ability of a captive to thrive on the food. It has been stated that cobras are unable to digest their food if they have been milked just prior to feeding (Acton and Knowles, 1921, p. 725; Chopra and Chowan, 1932, p. 575), although this has not been borne out by the experiences in some zoölogical gardens, including our own at San Diego.

Manual Venom Extraction

The methods to be used in extracting venom from captive snakes should be designed with two objectives in view: First, to safeguard the operator; and, secondly, to secure a maximum quantity of natural or unmodified venom, properly segregated for scientific use. The details of handling must depend on the kind of snake to be milked—the danger from its bite, the character of its fangs, and its strength and agility. Also, there are differences in procedure depending on the rarity of the snake and whether it is to be milked repeatedly or only once. The methods that I shall describe have been found suitable for rattlesnakes. Modifications may be desirable in milking other kinds of snakes; some changes would certainly be required in milking the shorter-fanged elapids.

In the procedure as developed for rattlesnakes in San Diego, an assistant catches the snake immediately behind the head by means of a noose-stick (see chapter 14), and holds it with the head resting on the edge of a table (Klauber, 1928, p. 11). When the snake is so caught and held, it has no opportunity to reach any object with its fangs and thus to waste venom. The operator, by means of a short metal bar with a hook at the end, catches the snake's upper jaw under the rostral and tips the head back. Then the rim of a porcelain cup, or other suitable container, is introduced below the fang points, and the fangs are drawn downward and forward into the erect position, with the sheaths pushed upward to bare the fangs (figs. 11:25–11:27). As the head is tipped back and steadied by the hook while the cup approaches, the snake can neither see the cup nor slash at it until it is in place, pressing against the fangs and ready to catch any venom expelled.

As the fangs are drawn forward and held erect, the edge of the cup is pushed steadily against them; this tends to hold the head firmly and gives the snake a feeling of something yielding on which to bite. The hook is now withdrawn, and the operator, further forcing the head against the cup with his index finger, presses on the venom glands with the thumb and middle finger. The pressure should be exerted from the back of the glands toward the front. The snake will usually eject some venom in an attempt to bite when it feels the steady pressure of the cup against the fangs, but in all cases the flow is increased by the mechanical manipulation of the glands. The glands should be pressed several times at intervals of about 10 seconds.

Some venom losses are entailed in the transfer from the cup to the centrifuge tube in which the purification process is continued, and, in order to eliminate this source of loss and quantitative error, such snakes as have a fang separation narrow enough to be accommodated therein are milked directly into a centrifuge tube. Tubes of 15 cc. capacity, graduated to 0.1 cc. are found satisfactory for venom work. In the case of large snakes, where particularly accurate results are desired, but the fang separation is too great for a single tube, two tubes may be used simultaneously, one for each fang. In any case, if the cup, rather than the tube, be used, it is well to transfer the venom to a tube after each snake is milked to avoid loss of the entire lot, if a snake with a diseased gland be encountered. All tubes should be numbered to avoid the chance of confusing the products of different species.

A noose-stick is not suitable for the smaller rattlesnakes, whether juveniles of the larger species or adults of the smaller, since their heads will not protrude far enough beyond the holding strap to permit gland manipulation. With these small specimens (say under 800 mm. or 2½ ft. in length) an operator can work more efficiently alone. In this method the centrifuge tube must first be affixed vertically in a stand. A vise makes a convenient holder; the tube is surrounded by a loop of heavy paper, the ends of which are held in the jaws of the vise. The snake is caught by the method of pressing its head against the table with a short, straight stick, after which the operator grasps it behind the head with his left hand. Using the metal hook to tip the head back, the operator hooks the fangs over the edge of the tube, and presses the glands with the fingers of the right hand. The operator can keep the tail of the snake from thrashing about by pressing it between himself and the work table on which the vise is set. The vise holding the tube should be breast high.

Some operators prefer not to use a noose-stick regardless of the size of the snake, in the belief that it unduly slows the operation, and leads to the loss of venom if the snake strikes the stick before it is noosed. The criticism is certainly valid as far as time is concerned, but it is doubted whether the snake is more likely to strike a noose-stick than it is a hook-stick before the latter is pressed on its head. It is important not to tighten the noose until the strap is in the proper position just behind the head. I think that the increased safety in the use of a noose-stick with large rattlesnakes more than counterbalances its objectionable features.

Where it is desired to have especially accurate data on the yield from each snake, a narrow, calibrated tube, reading to 0.01 cc. and flared into a funnel at the top to accommodate the fangs, may be employed. If venom-yield studies are desired, the length of each snake should be measured after the milking, and recorded with the corresponding incremental reading on the tube. A piece of evenly meshed lace net stretched over the mouth of the tube, through which the snake can bite, may be used with very small snakes. The fangs are caught on the strands, and any venom deposited on the lace may be blown into the tube.

It may be remarked, in passing, that many operators recommend the use of a thin rubber or parchment cover for the venom cup in all cases, regardless of the

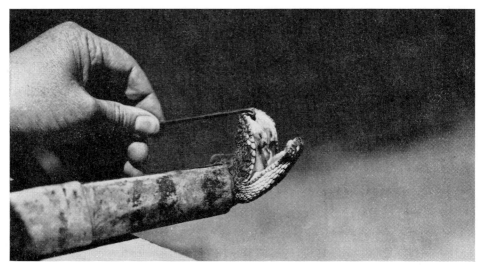

Fig. 11:25. The mouth of the snake is opened, and the jaw is tilted back by the use of a metal hook.

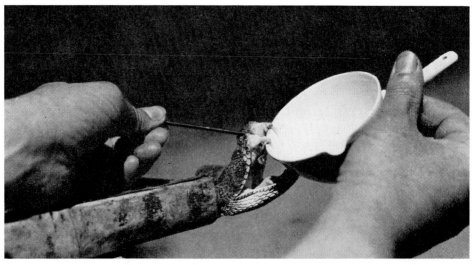

Fig. 11:26. The venom cup is slipped under the fangs, while the head is steadied with the hook.

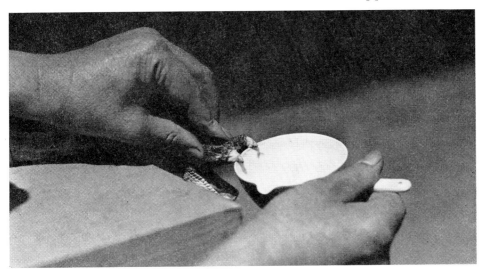

Fig. 11:27. The hook is removed, and the glands are pressed to expel the venom.

size of the snake. The purpose of the cover is to afford a yielding substance through which the snake can sink its fangs. This may be justified for short-fanged elapids, or even for small viperine snakes, but I have found it time-consuming and unnecessary when milking rattlesnakes. It is true that the stretched material induces a more natural biting action, but this is of relatively minor importance, since, by manipulation, the venom flow can invariably be increased beyond the quantity discharged in the course of a natural bite. When a diaphragm is used, venom is frequently spilled on it before the fangs penetrate, which reduces the accuracy of size-yield studies, besides wasting venom. Furthermore, as the fang points cannot be seen after they have penetrated the diaphragm, it is impossible to observe the effectiveness of the manipulation of the glands, or when the flow has ceased. Some operators (e.g., Kellaway, 1937, p. 2) believe the rubber or parchment dams to be necessary to prevent saliva and impurities from being added to the venom. The same protection is secured by the use of the metal hook, for then only the fangs and the forward edge of the snake's mouth are above the receptacle.

Because of declining yields from successive milkings, a factor that will be discussed later, fresh snakes provide much the best sources of venom. However, it is well to allow them a rest period of two weeks or more, after capture, before the first milking.

Undoubtedly a strong pressure exerted on the venom glands frequently causes some injury; and if the snake is more important as an exhibit than its venom is for scientific purposes, or if additional venom is expected from subsequent milkings after an appropriate period of rest (about a month), then the pressure on the glands should be gentle, or the snake should be allowed to bite through a diaphragm without any external pressure on the glands. Schoettler (1951c, p. 299) prefers not to squeeze the glands as this may force out immature cell contents and modify the venom quality.

An electric current to stimulate venom discharge has been tried (Sewall, 1887, p. 204; Johnson, 1938, p. 385; Lyman, 1939, p. 104) and some success has been claimed for it. Fox (1913, p. 29; see also Tyler, 1946, p. 196) used pilocarpine on Gila monsters to stimulate venom excretion. However, Tyler found that the venom was attenuated.

Anesthesia has been used to secure safety in handling (Gilman, 1854, p. 26; Calmette, 1907, p. 162; 1908, p. 156). Its use may be advisable with particularly agile and dangerous snakes, but certainly it is unnecessary with rattlers. Ditmars (1940, p. 145), when milking cobras, cooled them in a refrigerator to facilitate their being milked with safety.

At the San Diego Zoo, using the methods I have described, we handled rattlesnakes at a maximum rate of about 45 per hour. Col. M. L. Crimmins wrote me that he had milked 60 western diamonds (*C. atrox*) per hour. Ross Allen has stated (Allen and Merryday, 1940, p. 236) that he milks eastern diamonds (*C. adamanteus*) at the rate of 150 per hour, and once handled 150 in 44½ minutes. Hearst (1948, p. 7) and Hylander (1951, pl. 15) credit Allen with having milked about 73,500 venomous snakes in the years 1941 to 1945. It need hardly be said that, where individual yield–length records are kept, the process of milking is much slower than the rates here given would indicate.

Purification and Drying

If it be desired to use the venom removed from a snake for scientific purposes, or in an antivenin project, it is necessary to purify and dry it. Drying is essential as a means of preservation. During the processing, the several lots of venom, segregated by subspecies and even by smaller groups of snakes, should be assigned serial numbers in order that the records may be accurate. The methods used at San Diego are here cited as examples of a laboratory procedure found satisfactory from experience.

The crude venom was sent to the laboratory in centrifuge tubes, each corked and numbered. If a delay of more than two or three hours was to be encountered before the venom could be placed in the centrifuge, the tubes were stored in a refrigerator at about 5° C. (41° F.) to prevent bacteriological deterioration. Even at this temperature some changes in the physical character of the venom were evident, and therefore it was deemed desirable to purify the venom as soon as possible. Before being centrifuged, the liquid measure and the weight of each lot were recorded.

The centrifuge we used operated at 1,700 r.p.m. with a radius of about 180 mm. (7 in.). The venom was kept in the centrifuge until the greater part of the fluid was clear and free from opalescence. This usually required from 5 to 6 hours, although the time varied from only 15 minutes or so, to as long as 20 hours. The solid residue, comprising cell debris and other impurities, was then weighed and discarded, and the clear, liquid venom retained, both its weight and volume being again recorded. In the case of small quantities of venom from the rarer kinds of rattlesnakes, the centrifuging step was omitted.

Following the removal of the dregs, the venom was transferred to petri dishes and placed in an electric incubator, where it was dehydrated at 37° C. (98.6° F.) for 48 hours. Later in the project, this step was changed to drying at room temperature in a vacuum desiccator over calcium chloride. The lower temperature was presumed to reduce any change in the character of the venom. Upon completion of this step, the dried venom was weighed and stored in the dark in properly labeled glass vials.

Subsequent to the completion of our San Diego venom project, the dehydration method known as lyophilization came into general use and is to be recommended when venoms are prepared for experimental work. In this processs the liquid venom, after removal, is immediately and quickly frozen at a very low temperature, by the use of dry ice or other refrigerant, after which the moisture is evaporated under a high vacuum. Antivenins are lyophilized in the same manner. Quick-frozen venom (without subsequent dehydration) can be kept in a deep freeze, and apparently retains its toxicity unimpaired for a considerable time. This is a convenient means of preservation for some types of experimental work.

Venom preserved in dry form is thought to retain its poisonous properties for a long time. It can be redissolved in distilled water or normal saline solution when required for use. Amaral (1923, p. 685) has stated that dried venom is always soluble in sodium chloride solution (0.8 to 1.5 per cent), and in most cases in water, but that *C. d. terrificus* venom is not completely soluble in distilled water. Schoettler (1951a, p. 490) prefers a 0.9 per cent saline solution in redissolving dried venom. Minton (1954, p. 1079) stores reconstituted liquid venom at $-40°$ C. ($-40°$ F.) until its use is required.

PHYSICAL PROPERTIES

In the course of purifying and drying venom for future scientific use, some information was gained in our San Diego project concerning its physical properties, particularly the proportion of impurities precipitated in the centrifuge, the specific gravity of the purified liquid, and the proportion of solids remaining after dehydration.

The venom, as first removed from the snake, is always slightly cloudy. A gradual deposition of dregs begins as soon as the venom stands undisturbed, and some venoms will seem clear within an hour or so. However, despite this apparent clarification, the use of a centrifuge for purification is always advisable.

The dregs, deposited slowly in standing venom or rapidly by centrifuging, are said by Noguchi (1909, p. 77) to consist of epithelial cells, cellular debris, and some granula. These are presumed to be impurities having no part in the poisoning process. They are probably present to a greater degree in venom milked by manipulation than in the venom discharged in a natural bite, because of the more drastic treatment of the glands by external pressure. Also, in the rapid handling of many snakes, some foreign matter, not from the snake's mouth, may fall into the venom receptacle.

At San Diego we found the dregs to be deposited in two layers, the lower coarse, the upper finer. The upper layer is soluble in salt solution, the lower is not. This lower layer no doubt comprises the true dregs; the upper may be a precipitate resulting from oxidation of the venom, a presumption premised on the fact that its volume tends to increase while the venom stands, even at temperatures inhibiting bacterial action.

The percentage of dregs depends somewhat on the processing method. Particularly when the determination is made by weighing, as it should be, the presence of venom in the interstices of the debris will considerably affect the result. When no special effort is made to account for this incidental venom, the precipitate in rattlesnake venom is usually found to be between 4 and 5 per cent of the gross venom by weight. In some cases, especially with juveniles, or snakes long in captivity without food, the percentage may be much higher. In one instance, in the venom of 119 young, single-rattle *C. v. viridis,* the percentage of dregs reached 28.7; however, so extreme an increase is not the case with all young, although they do tend to have higher proportions of dregs than adults. There are no indications of consistent species differences in the proportion of debris. In the determination of the percentage of dregs in 90 lots of rattlesnake venom, it was found that 32 lots fell below 4 per cent; 28 between 4 and 5.99, inclusive; 18 from 6 to 9.99; and 12 lots had 10 per cent or more. The true dregs, obtained by first washing, and then drying the precipitate to eliminate the involved venom, fell considerably short of these percentages. Indeed, a number of tests indicated that the solids, probably comprising the actual cellular debris, as found by washing and evaporation to dryness, were only 8 to 10 per cent of the dregs as determined by pouring off the liquid venom in the centrifuge tube, and then weighing the residuum.

Specific gravity tests were run on a number of samples of the venoms of 22 different species and subspecies of rattlesnakes. It was found that the specific gravity of the venom of fresh adult rattlesnakes varies from 1.070 to 1.100. There are slight species differences. *C. v. viridis, C. v. oreganus, C. v. helleri, C. v. decolor, C. adamanteus, S. m. barbouri,* and *S. c. tergeminus* are low, usually below 1.080. *C. r. ruber, C. r. lucasensis, C. h. horridus, C. d. durissus,* and *C. d. totonacus* have high-gravity venoms, probably above 1.090. *C. atrox, C. cerastes, C. v. abyssus,* and *C. v. lutosus* are intermediate. The high record (1.100) was attained by a *C. r. ruber* sample.

The venoms of juvenile rattlers, and those from snakes being milked for a second time, have low specific gravities, usually 0.008 to 0.020 below the normal for the species. The record low was found in the venom of a newly born brood of *C. r. ruber,* with a gravity of 1.042, compared with a normal for the subspecies of 1.095 to 1.100. A series of 135 juveniles of *C. atrox* had a gravity of 1.080 compared with a species average of 1.088.

There is an obvious positive correlation between the specific gravity and the percentage of residual solids in dried venom. The approximate linear regression equation is sp. gr. $= 0.00234$ times the per cent of solids $+ 1.028$. In this equation the solids are those left by dehydration of the venom, after the removal of the dregs precipitated by centrifuging. The fact that venoms of reduced specific gravity have a correspondingly reduced solid (or venom-principle) content means that the young and remilked snakes have less toxic venoms, drop for drop. However, this comparison is not an accurate intraspecific criterion of venom strength; venom virulence cannot be judged by specific gravity, as is evident from the fact that *C. r. ruber* venom, among the heaviest, is at the same time one of the weakest.

When rattlesnake venom is allowed to stand undisturbed in a test tube, a stratification will be observed in the liquid, the upper zone yellow, the lower colorless.

There is a considerable variation in the relative proportions of these two parts of the fluid; occasionally one or the other may be absent. This stratification will occur whether or not the liquid has been centrifuged. In two tests, the following differences were found between the specific gravities of the two layers:

Species	Upper yellow layer	Lower colorless layer
C. molossus	1.088	1.094
C. tortugensis	1.064	1.080

Although the term "drop" is so indefinite a quantity as to be useless as a measure in scientific work, it frequently appears in reports of the quantity of venom discharged by a snake. Obviously, the size of a drop depends on both viscosity and temperature. In tests on about 65 cc. of venom, divided into 53 lots representing 6 different species, it was found that there are about 16 drops of venom in a cubic centimeter at 18° C. (64.4° F.). The range was from 12.7 to 24.0 drops per cc. It is known that the venoms of different genera of snakes do vary in viscosity, and it is probable that there is some diversity among the rattlesnakes.

Liquid rattlesnake venom is usually bright yellow in color. There is a considerable difference in the depth of color (from light yellow almost to orange), just as there is in the relative proportions of the two zones (yellow and colorless) when the liquid is allowed to stand long enough to stratify. Amaral (1929, p. 6) has stated that the color of the venom is correlated with the lipoid fraction. He has also expressed the opinion that there are specific and subspecific differences in color (1926a, p. 91; 1929, p. 7). I doubt whether such differences are consistent enough to be diagnostic. Fresh venoms from three species of snakes were compared, using Ridgway's *Color Standards* (1912). *C. v. helleri* venom was empire yellow, that of *C. r. ruber* apricot yellow, and of *C. atrox* lemon yellow. Reference to these color plates will show how slight the differences are.

Although its venom is normally yellow, I have observed a medium-sized *C. r. ruber* to produce colorless venom, and several adolescent *C. r. lucasensis* did likewise. Four young *C. adamanteus* about six weeks old had colorless venoms. No doubt the color is correlated with the proportion of solid residue; but although young rattlers have weak venoms, they are usually light yellow in color, rather than colorless as in these young *adamanteus*. Noguchi (1909, p. 77) found colorless venom in some captive specimens of *C. h. horridus,* but observed that this was not a species characteristic. Vellard (1938, p. 409) has written that the venom of the Neotropical rattlers from southern Brazil is white, whereas that of the snakes of Argentina, Paraguay, and northwestern Brazil is yellow. Barton (1793, p. 111) stated that rattlesnake venom is darker in color during the mating season. This lacks verification, but there may, indeed, be seasonal differences in venoms.

As observed by Mitchell (1860, p. 30; 1889, p. 511), Noguchi (1909, p. 77), and Vorhies (1936a, p. 86) rattlesnake venom is virtually odorless when fresh and unaffected by bacterial action. In recent tests at the San Diego Zoo, one out of three observers thought that a very faint sweetish odor could be detected, the others believed there was none. The venoms of three subspecies were tested: *atrox, ruber,* and *helleri.* Langmann (1900, p. 402) thought that each kind of venom had a different odor, rattlesnake venom being mousy. One of my correspondents claimed to have observed that rattlesnake venom turns green and has a bad odor when it strikes the air. These, however, are the changes resulting from putrefaction. Hollander (1948, p. 129) thought he could tell when most of the venom had been abstracted from a dog's wound by the offensive smell of the venom on a cloth, a quite erroneous conclusion.

Mitchell (1860, p. 30; 1889, p. 511) states that rattlesnake venom is tasteless. At San Diego we have noted a slight taste, astringent at first and then turning sweetish, when held on the tongue. But the taste is by no means strong. There is a slight tingling effect on the lips.

Occasionally rattlesnakes, particularly captive specimens and those previously milked, yield a thick brown liquid instead of venom, evidently the result of some pathological condition in the gland. Sometimes this emanates from one fang, sometimes from both. When venom is processed for experiments, any that has been contaminated with this brown liquid should be discarded.

Residue after Drying

As has been stated, rattlesnake venom must be dried if it is to be preserved for future use. The dried venom is presumed to contain, virtually unimpaired, all of the toxic principles originally contained in the fresh liquid. Any attempt to store venom in its liquid form, at least without the addition of preservatives that may change its properties and physiological effects, will fail at ordinary temperatures because of bacterial putrefaction, although glycerine has been used with some success. Even storage in a refrigerator is unsatisfactory, whether at 0° C. (32° F.) or 5° C. (41° F.), since a gradually increasing precipitate indicates that some change is taking place, the normal 4 to 8 per cent increasing up to 12 per cent or more in liquid venom kept for several months. Kellaway (1937, p. 3) has emphasized the necessity of using dried venom in scientific work because of the intraspecific variability in the proportions of solids in fresh liquid venoms, which obviously affects any experiments in which the liquids might be used quantitatively. He even thought it desirable to powder, and to redry in a vacuum over sulphuric acid, any venoms dried by the usual processes, to insure the removal of remaining water.

The proportion of solids remaining after desiccation varies with the genus and species of snake, the drying process used, and, finally, with the method of calculation employed. With respect to the latter, it is important to remember that the ratio of solids cannot be determined accurately by dividing the weight of the solid residue in grams by the volume of the liquid in cubic centimeters, since a cubic centimeter of venom weighs about 1.08 grams—the venom specific gravity—to say nothing of the effect of temperature upon volume. Residue tests, to be accurate, must be based on the weight of the original liquid, and this weight should be determined after the removal of the dregs by centrifuging. Also, the test should be made only upon venoms that have been kept in tightly corked vials to reduce evaporation prior to the test. Finally one must be careful in the use of terms. I am sure that when Mitchell and Reichert (1886, p. 8) write that "the losses of venom on drying" were, for *C. adamanteus*, 25.15 per cent, or when Allen and Merryday (1940, p. 238) say, speaking also of *adamanteus* venom, that "when dried it loses 20 per cent of its weight," they must mean that the loss due to drying is 75 (or 80) per cent of its weight, and that the retained weight is 25 (or 20) per cent. At least, that is my conclusion as to the proportion of dry residue after evaporating rattlesnake venom; I cannot speak from experience concerning the venoms of other kinds of snakes.

A few figures on solid residues—as a percentage, usually by weight—cited in the literature are: Calmette (1907, p. 166; 1908, p. 159) 20 to 35 per cent; Flexner and Noguchi (in Noguchi, 1909, p. 71) 50 to 70 per cent; Willson (1908, p. 531) 50 to 75 per cent; Houssay (1923, p. 450) 30 per cent for Argentine *terrificus* venom; Amaral (1928b, p. 103) 25 to 35 per cent; Githens (1931, p. 82; 1935a, p. 166) 25 to 35 per cent; Reese (1934, p. 103) 25 to 50 per cent; Kellaway (1937, p. 3) 12 to 67 per cent for the Australian black snake and 19½ to 42 per cent for the death adder. Ross Allen, in 1954, sent me some records of his experiences with *adamanteus* venom that indicated a solid residue of 24.2 per cent.

At San Diego, by use of the accurate method for ascertaining the ratio of the weight of the residue to the weight of the purified liquid venom, we found, in 112 determinations of the venoms of 23 different species and subspecies of rattle-snakes, that the solid residue ranged from 13.9 to 31.6 per cent. The mean was 24.34 ± 0.30 per cent, and the interquartile range (half the lots) 22.20 to 26.48. The coefficient of variation was 13 per cent.

No interspecific differences of note were observed, beyond those already mentioned in connection with specific gravity determinations and the correlation between the specific gravity and the proportion of solid residue. But the results did show a definite tendency toward low solid yields (and therefore weak venoms) in the case of young snakes or snakes milked for the second time. Every lot falling below a 20 per cent residue was composed of snakes belonging to one of these two categories. Seven lots composed entirely of juveniles ranged from 13.9 to 23.4 per cent, with a mean of 18.3. The tendency toward low residues in remilked snakes was not so marked. In one series of prairie rattlesnakes (*C. v. viridis*) the solid recovery was 20 per cent after 6 months in captivity, compared with 24 per cent when they were first caught; and in a series of western diamonds (*C. atrox*) the reduction was from 28 to 18 per cent, after a similar period. These reductions were probably the result of captivity and lack of food, rather than the attenuation that follows remilking after only a short period of rest. As a result of these tests, I should estimate 27 per cent as the average dry residuum to be expected from evaporation of the venom of fresh adult rattlesnakes.

Venom, in drying, cracks with irregular fractures, like a layer of gelatin. The dried residue resembles a collection of irregular crystals, but the crystalline form is one of appearance only.

The question may well be raised whether, when rattlesnake venom is dried, the moisture evaporated is pure water, or whether it may contain some volatile poison. In one test at San Diego, the venom was distilled at 35° to 36.5° C. (95° to 97.7° F.) in a vacuum at 117 mm. Hg. The distillate was condensed in an ice bath at 2° C. The *p*H of the distillate was found to be 6.9 to 7.0 and the specific gravity 0.99915. Drops on a microscope slide, after drying, showed a small trace of deposit. An injection into a rabbit of the distillate from *C. r. lucasensis* venom produced no ill effect. It may be concluded that the distillate is substantially all water, and that evaporation does not eliminate any important volatile constituent.

CHEMICAL COMPOSITION OF VENOM

As long ago as 1661, Lovell (sec. 1, p. [27]) remarked that there are as many kinds of venoms as there are serpents. He did not much exaggerate. Venoms are organic chemical mixtures of great complexity, of which gross chemical analyses have little value. Their several components may be partly differentiated or separated by chemical or physical fractioning, but eventually we must largely depend, in drawing conclusions as to generic and specific differences, on venom effects, based on animal experimentation. This is a difficult and time-consuming endeavor, in which much remains to be done, especially among the rattlesnakes. It is a field in which I have had no personal experience, so that the summary that follows is drawn entirely from published sources.

For a long time, it was thought—and hoped, for this would simplify the search for an antidote—that snake venom was a relatively simple chemical compound. The earliest studies sought to learn whether it was acid or alkaline, with the expectation of finding an appropriate neutralizer. Mead (1702, p. 10) concluded that viper venom was acid, and that the damage was caused by fine-pointed crystals that pierced the blood corpuscles; these crystals he saw in drying venom. Fontana (1787, vol. 1, pp. 43–47, 252, 260) decided that viper venom was neither acid, alkaline, nor caustic; that it contained no salts, but was, in fact, an animal gum. Brickell (1805a, p. 101; also Harlan 1835, p. 502) determined that rattlesnake venom was acid, and therefore that the cure should be sought among the alkalies. Paine (1875, p. 136) thought that rattlesnake venom was prussic acid, or at least like it. To conclude this phase of the discussion, it may be said that rattlesnake venom is slightly acid (Mitchell, 1860, p. 31; Noguchi, 1909, p. 77) but that the damage which it causes is in no way a simple acid effect, so that this fact is not of importance. At San Diego we have found rattlesnake venom to have a pH value of 5.6 to 6.2, with a mean of 5.9. We have been unable to detect any consistent subspecific differences.

Occasionally the idea has been expressed that the damage done by venom is bacterial in nature, a belief no longer given the slightest credence. Fontana, as early as 1787 (vol. 1, p. 86), reported that Buffon had attributed its poisonous effects to microscopical animalcules. Others discussing the subject have been Anon. (1883b, p. 742), Fletcher (1883, p. 136), Mitchell and Reichert (1886, p. 154), and Leighton (1892, p. 734). It is true that rattlesnake fangs are usually contaminated with pathogenic bacteria, that venom kept at ordinary temperatures putrefies from bacterial action, and that venom has an antibactericidal effect on the blood. From these somewhat related phases of the subject, there evolved various misinterpretations, with the erroneous conclusion that snake poisoning is, in itself, a bacterial infection.

Prince Louis Bonaparte (1843, p. 169) was probably the first to make a sound chemical analysis of venom (Mitchell, 1860, p. 32; Fletcher, 1883, p. 132). Gradually, as it has become known that venoms are largely composed of proteins defying any simple chemical analysis, research has been directed toward the classification of their components through their several physiological results. As stated by Corkill (1932b, p. 32), "It has been convenient in analyzing the effect of venoms . . . to denominate various principles as being responsible for certain physiological effects." Thus, at the present time, venom analyses and species differences are much more often stated in terms of physiological effects than of organic chemical constituents. Amaral (1951a, p. 551) summarizes the composition by stating that venoms are comprised chiefly of proteins, including enzymes. In another analysis (1928c, p. 1070) he presented the following summary of constituents: (a) proteins (albumin and globulin), (b) proteases and peptones, (c) mucin and mucin-like substances, (d) ferments, (e) fat, (f) detritus (absent from purified venoms), and (g) salts, such as calcium chloride, and calcium, magnesium, and ammonium phosphates. Markowitz, Essex, and Mann (1931, p. 25) determined that the characteristic activity of rattlesnake venom—they used the venoms of *atrox* and *horridus* in their experiments—is present in the purified albumin fraction, and that the globulin and protein-free fractions are inert.

Some of the early important work on the chemical constituents of rattlesnake venom was that of Mitchell and Reichert (1886, p. 51), Wolfenden (1886, p. 326), and Faust (1911, p. 244); summaries have been presented by Noguchi (1909, p. 79) and Boquet (1948, p. 91). Slotta, working on the venom of *C. d. terrificus* at the Butantan Institute, São Paulo, announced in 1938 (p. 207) the isolation of a pure principle from *terrificus* venom to which he gave the name crotoxin, the formula for which he stated to be $C_{1386}H_{2086}O_{470}N_{372}S_{41}$. Another more recent formula is $C_{1230}H_{1776}O_{432}N_{328}S_{36}$. Much additional data on the analysis of snake venoms, especially that of *terrificus,* have been presented by Slotta and his associates in a series of papers, including Slotta and Fraenkel-Conrat, 1937, 1938, and 1939; Slotta, Szyszka, Fraenkel-Conrat, and Forster, 1937–39; Slotta and Primosigh, 1951 and 1952; and Slotta, 1953. Crotoxin is said to encompass the entire neurotoxic and hemolytic activity of *terrificus* venom, with an intensity 25 per cent higher than that of crude venom. The authors dwell particularly on the importance of the sulphur in the crotoxic molecule. Slotta and Primosigh (1951, p. 696; 1952, p. 62), by the method of two-dimensional partition chromatography, determined the presence of 18 amino acids in crotoxin. Further important papers on the subject were presented at the Berkeley, California, symposium on animal venoms in 1954 (Buckley, editor, 1955, in press) by Fraenkel-Conrat, Slotta, Moussatche *et al.,* and Gonçalves.

Taube and Essex (1937, p. 43) refer to rattlesnake venom (crotalin) as if it were a single uniform substance. Faust (1907, p. 236; Efrati and Reif, 1953, p. 1086) states that two specific toxins have been isolated from venom; ophiotoxin ($C_{17}H_{26}O_{10}$) and crotalotoxin ($C_{34}H_{54}O_{21}$).

Merchante (1936, p. 35) and Micheel (1941, p. 170) also mention the fact that snake venoms are richer in sulphur than are most proteins. Micheel points out that poisons of plant origin are comprised of low-weight molecular compounds that are effective after absorption in the digestive tract. But animal poisons, including snake venoms, are high-weight molecular compounds of a protein nature, which, when taken orally, are decomposed and lose their effectiveness; they must be introduced into the blood stream to be effective. Veda, Sasaki, and Peng (1951, p. 195) disagree as to the importance of sulphur in snake venom; they found its toxicity more nearly proportional to the nitrogen content. Barnes and Trueta (1941, p. 623) comment on the effect of the high molecular weights of certain venoms on absorption. They found the molecular weight of Russell's viper venom to be over 30,000 and that of the Australian tiger snake to exceed 20,000. Some cobra venoms fall below 5,000.

Another recent paper of importance on the biochemistry of venoms is that of Porges (1953, p. 47), in which it is stated (p. 49): "Although knowledge is still limited, the enzymes are now apparently considered the real toxic principles of venoms, either through their own activity or through their influence on other reactions." According to Zeller (1948, p. 460), while the knowledge of the activity of enzymes in snake venoms is incomplete, it is evident that the enzymes are important in the syndrome produced in the bitten animal by the venoms. Some venom components profoundly influence the reaction mechanisms of others. Enzymes have an important role in the production of shock, hemorrhage, hemolysis, and blood clotting. They affect the spreading or diffusing factor (p. 475). Some of the enzymes in snake venoms are found in the digestive juices of other animals, thus verifying the usual salivary theory of venom derivation (p. 486). Some poison enzymes in snake venoms may be digestive agents, others have been developed in the direction of highly toxic substances, and some display both activities. Some of the local necrosis following nonfatal cases may result from the primitive digestive property of the venom. Ghosh (1950, p. 108) poses the still unsettled question: Do venoms act as destructive enzymes, or do they produce their injurious effects by inhibiting or changing some of the vitally important enzyme systems present in the body of the victim? Nachmansohn and Wilson have stated: "Snake venom contains a surprisingly high concentration of a great variety of enzymes" (1951, p. 270).

Gonçalves and Polson (1947), Gonçalves and Vieira (1950), and Gonçalves (in Buckley, editor, 1955, in press) have studied the composition of snake venom by the method of electrophoresis. They observed differences in the venoms of the Neotropical rattlesnake, *C. d. terrificus,* as found in different parts of Brazil. They also determined the presence of a new basic protein, crotamin, with effects different from those of crotoxin. It occurs in *terrificus* venom from southern Brazil. Other experimentalists using electrophoresis have been Neumann and Habermann, Hoxter, and Moussatche *et al.* (Buckley, editor, 1955, in press); also Habermann and Neumann (1955, col. 1966). Analysis by absorption spectra has also been suggested (Horton, 1951, p. 173).

As I have stated, most venom comparisons and lists of components are based on physiological effects, rather than on chemical composition; to analyses of the former type I shall return in due course.

DETOXICATION OF VENOM

The detoxication of venom was of interest in earlier times because of the hope that any substance that would render it harmless outside of the body might also seek it out and accomplish the same purpose within the body of a snake-bite victim. Over the years this hope has been found illusory, except in the case of antivenin, but it led to the temporary advocacy of such antidotes as ammonia and potassium permanganate. Unfortunately, venom is so rapidly absorbed by the body tissues, and is so similar to various body fluids, that it cannot be isolated and destroyed within the body. Another, and more useful, type of detoxication is that resulting from the admixture of certain substances that weaken venom without destroying its antigenic properties. This permits the more rapid immunization of animals without injuring them, in the preparation of anti-venomous sera, an effect to be mentioned again under the subject of antivenin.

In connection with the purification and preservation of venoms for experimental purposes, it is important to know what processes can be used without changing the venom quality. Experiments have shown that the application of heat at temperatures below 37° C. (98.6° F.) has little or no effect. Above this temperature, disintegration takes place in varying degrees (Mitchell and Reichert, 1886, p. 22; Noguchi, 1909, p. 94; Jackson, 1927, p. 204; Welch, 1930, p. 36; Githens, 1931, p. 82; Boquet, 1948, p. 81). Maier (1939, p. 163) states that the hemorrhagic fraction of venom is quickly destroyed by heat, but that the neurotoxic part is more stable, and will withstand a higher temperature. Where the venom has been dried at a moderate temperature, desiccation itself does not materially affect the toxic quality, as has been shown by many experiments dating from the time of Redi (1673, p. 16; see also Brand, 1781, p. 282; and Fontana, 1787, vol. 1, p. 65).

Whether the time element prior to redissolving and utilizing the dried venom is important, is subject to some question. Richards (1885, p. 33) experimented with dried venom 15 years old and deemed it unchanged. Mays (1913b, p. 1811) believed that venom he had kept for 25 years retained its original strength. Macht (1933, p. 988), in tests on plant seedlings, found some loss of strength after five years. Taylor (1940, p. 283) performed experiments with cobra venom that seemed to indicate a loss of virulence with the passage of time; he had some venom that was as much as 35 years old. Schoettler (1951a, p. 496) considered Taylor's results to be inconclusive; he found venom batches of the same age to differ as much as batches of different ages. Kellaway (1937, p. 3) believes that venom, if properly dried and sealed in glass, will retain its toxicity for many years.

Schoettler (1951c, p. 299), in further tests on the effect of age on the toxicity of dried venom, endeavored to determine the reasons for the contradictory results previously mentioned. He found that in nonhemorrhagic, neurotoxic venoms the loss is small or absent, but in venoms of other types the loss is considerable. It is particularly deleterious to permit atmospheric contacts with dried venoms; some *Agkistrodon* venom lost only 14 per cent of its strength in 8 years; but when frequently unstoppered it lost 70 per cent in one year. Lyophilized *terrificus* venom lost one-third of its strength in a couple of months. Schoettler concluded that desiccated venom cannot serve as a standard for antivenin titration without frequent retesting. He suggested the development of a method of storing with a preservative solution in sealed ampuls. Storage in an atmosphere of nitrogen has also been suggested. Pollard *et al.* (1952, p. 164; Andrews and Pollard, 1953, p. 396) reported a relatively unimportant loss in toxicity of dried moccasin venom after storage up to 2 years.

In the early days, glycerine was used for the preservation of venom in liquid form. Maier (1940, p. 354) has suggested the use of ammonium chloride. It remains to be seen whether storage in a preservative liquid is to be preferred to storage dry. In either case sealing is important.

Mitchell (1861, p. 278) reported that freezing did not affect the toxic properties of rattlesnake venom. I should consider it undesirable to keep liquid venom at a temperature below 0° C. (32° F.), even though rattler venom is found to remain liquid at –7° C. (19.4° F.). However, Oliver (*in litt.*) reported the storage of unde-hydrated *viridis* venom in a deepfreeze with no apparent loss of toxicity; and indeed, Minton (1954, p. 1079) has recommended the storage of redissolved venom at –40° C. (–40° F.).

Reports on the effects of radiation on venoms are somewhat conflicting. Jackson (1927, p. 204) stated that X rays reduced toxicity. Welch (1930, p. 37) found that although cold and light had little effect on dried venom, radium emanations destroyed its toxicity, and its antigenic quality as well. He found that it was also detoxified by ultraviolet light. Macht (1935, p. 520), on the other hand, stated that X rays and radium were without effect, but that ultraviolet light reduced toxicity. Davenport (1943, p. 25) says that dried venom deteriorates in the light (see also Boquet, 1948, p. 82). Welch (1930, p. 37) records electricity as being destructive of dry venom.

With regard to the many chemicals whose effects on venoms have been tested (see, for example, Mitchell and Reichert, 1886, p. 29), the results may be of importance in one of three ways: in aiding the analysis of venoms; in detoxication to facilitate immunization; and in the attempted development of antidotes. The two latter phases will be treated briefly elsewhere. Also, detoxication by digestive fluids will be summarized under the suction treatment for snake bite, as the hazard of swallowing venom is frequently mentioned in connection with the possible danger involved in sucking a bite.

CLASSIFICATION OF VENOM COMPONENTS BY TOXIC EFFECTS

The difficulty of making pertinent chemical analyses of snake venoms, with the object of defining their obvious differences in chemical terms, has led to an alternative formulation: the expression of these differences qualitatively, and, as far as possible, quantitatively, in terms of the physiological effects of their components.

It has long been recognized that snake venoms differ widely in their effects, and that they entail differences beyond those to be expected from large snakes as compared with small, or by reason of the fact that some venoms are stronger and others weaker, and hence that one would involve an intensification of the symptoms of the other. On the contrary, the symptoms themselves—the bodily effects—vary greatly in character. That this has long been known is evident, for example, in Lucan's famous description of the snakes of northern Africa as given in the *Pharsalia*—the history of the war between Caesar and Pompey—book 9 (Riley, 1909, p. 368; Duff, 1928, p. 557; see also Nicander, 1953, pp. 45–59, for a still earlier account). However mythical and fantastic these effects of the bites of the African snakes may seem today—they were written in the first century A.D.—we can recognize some factual differences in symptoms, beneath the blanket of folklore.

With additional study and experimentation, it has gradually been learned that there are not only generic differences in snake venoms, but specific differences as well. Of these instances, one of the most notable is found among the rattle-snakes, for the venom of the Neotropical rattler (*C. durissus* and its subspecies) more nearly resembles cobra venom, in its effects, than it does the venom of such

Nearctic species as the diamondbacks (*C. adamanteus* and *C. atrox*), or the sub-species of the western rattler (*C. viridis*).

For a time, snake venoms were divided into two broad categories, the neurotoxic and hemorrhagic, depending on whether their destructive actions were largely on the nerves or on the blood and tissues. But it was soon recognized that few, if any, venoms were purely of the one type or the other. Rather, it was often the case that one effect was more serious than the other, so that the presence of one type was masked by the more important symptoms of the other. And, finally, it became evident that each of these broad categories could be broken down into a number of smaller ones, each having a distinctive physiological pattern. A discussion of the many segregations of categories that have been proposed is quite beyond the scope of this work on rattlesnakes; the following references are cited for those who may seek further information on these principles of venoms based on their pathologic effects: Martin and Lamb (1907, p. 792), Acton and Knowles (1921, p. 745), Amaral (1923, p. 686; 1928c, p. 1070), Fairley (1929a, p. 301), Houssay (1930, p. 308), Kraus and Werner (1931, p. 127), Corkill (1932b, p. 32), Wyne (1937, p. 605), Kellaway (1937, p. 3; 1939, p. 545), Micheel (1941, p. 170), Babcock (1944, p. 83), Essex (1945, p. 158), Boquet (1948, p. 105), Zeller (1948, p. 459), Ghosh (1950, p. 102), and Amaral (1951a, p. 551; 1951b, p. 1248). As an example, the following is a list of the principal categories, primarily based on Fairley (1929, p. 301):

1. Neurotoxins acting on the bulbar and spinal ganglion cells
2. Hemorrhagins destroying the endothelial cells lining the blood vessels
3. Thrombase producing intravascular thrombosis
4. Hemolysins destroying red blood corpuscles
5. Cytolysins acting on blood corpuscles, leucocytes, and tissue cells
6. Antifibrins or anticoagulins retarding the coagulation of the blood
7. Antibactericidal substances
8. Ferments and kinases for the purpose of preparing the prey for pancreatic digestion

Elapid venoms are usually rich in principles 1, 4, and 6, and viperids, including the rattlesnakes, in numbers 2, 3, and 5. However, there are many deviations from these groupings, and variations in their relative pathological importance; variations not only in their order of importance in the venoms of different kinds of snakes, but in the effects as they vary with the kind of animal bitten. For example, some venoms may be particularly lethal to birds, others to amphibians, an intensification usually correlated with the natural prey of a species. In actual snake-bite cases, it is difficult to separate these effects, except into such broad categories as neurotoxic or hemorrhagic; more detailed classifications can be made only by animal experimentation in the laboratory. It is necessary to determine whether each of the different actions of the venoms on the body depends on the presence of a distinct poisonous substance, or whether a smaller number of such substances may exert different toxic actions in various tissues and organs (Githens, 1931, p. 82). Also, there may be an autotoxic action, in that, under the influence of certain venom principles, such as particular enzymes, body parts or organs may produce pathological substances causing a still more widespread damage. Duran-Reynolds (1939, p. 69) considers a spreading factor, which affects the rapidity with which a venom spreads through the tissues and is absorbed, to be important.

This is concurred in by Porges (1953, p. 51), and this factor, hyaluronidase, has been further discussed in separate papers by Boquet, Martirani, Favilli, and Jaques (in Buckley, editor, 1955, in press).

Kellaway (1939, p. 545) believes that this simplified classification of toxic principles is adequate: (1) proteolytic enzymes; (2) phosphatidases; and (3) neurotoxins. Micheel (1941, p. 170) presumes that snake venoms, when introduced into the blood, act in three principal ways: (1) As neurotoxins affecting the brain and nerves, centrally or peripherally; (2) as hemolysins affecting the red blood corpuscles; and (3) as hemorrhagins causing the blood-vessel walls to become permeable to blood.

The rattlesnakes may be divided into three classes, with respect to our knowledge of their venoms. These are (1) the Neotropical rattlesnake (*C. durissus*) and some of its subspecies (especially *C. d. terrificus*), which are known to have strongly neurotoxic venoms; (2) the diamondbacks (*C. adamanteus, C. atrox,* and *C. ruber*), the timber rattler (*C. h. horridus*), and the western rattlesnake (*C. viridis*) and its subspecies, all of which are known to have predominantly hemorrhagic venoms; and (3) the remaining species, about whose venoms too little is known to classify them with certainty, although most of them, with the exception of *C. unicolor, C. basiliscus, C. enyo,* and *C. scutulatus,* are presumed to be primarily hemorrhagic.

One of the best summaries of the effects of the several toxic principles contained in rattlesnake venom, with particular applicability to the species found in the United States, is that of Githens (1931, p. 82). This is as follows:

> Among the more important effects of rattlesnake venoms on the body, we may distinguish effects on the tissues near the bite, effects on the blood, and effects on distant organs and tissues to which the venoms are carried by the lymph and blood.
>
> The local effects are due to a toxalbumin which is more readily destroyed by heat than most of the other constituents. This causes locally more or less severe pain due to an irritant action on the nerves and sensory endings. It exercises a peculiar action on the walls of the blood-vessels, causing them to become permeable to the blood, which escapes from the vessels as clear lymph and as local hemorrhages, leading to marked swelling and discoloration of the tissues near the bite. A great deal of fluid may thus pass out from the blood-vessels, and if incisions are made in the skin near the bite, the fluid will ooze out as a yellowish or more or less blood-stained liquid. This liquid may carry with it considerable amounts of the venom.
>
> The action of rattlesnake venom on the blood affects chiefly its clotting powers and the red blood cells. Small amounts of venom added to blood generally tend to cause clotting, larger amounts to prevent it. Evidences of each of these effects are likely to be seen after a snake bite. The red cells are dissolved by the venom, the degree of hemolysis varying markedly with different kinds of venom. The white blood cells are less affected.
>
> Various organs are found to be susceptible to the action of the venom, which exercises a destructive effect on the functional cells. The most striking symptoms are paralytic, due to a so-called neurotoxin. The lesions include neuritis of the small nerves of the limbs. Both sensory and motor cells of the spinal cord show degenerative changes, most marked in the dorsal and lumbar cord. Changes are also found in the cells of the medulla oblongata. Paralysis results, beginning in the forelegs of animals (or wings of birds), extending to the hind legs and finally to the muscles of respiration. When these are involved, death follows quickly.
>
> The kidneys are also markedly affected by the destructive action of the venom. The secretory cells are injured, resulting in albuminuria, and the urine is often stained red by hemoglobin or blood. The blood-vessels are dilated and may be distended by altered blood.

Degenerative changes in the liver are also seen, and yellow discoloration of the eyes and skin from mild jaundice is common in severe cases when death does not occur soon after the bite.

The changes in the blood and vessels lead secondarily to hemorrhages in various parts of the body; the particular poison responsible for these effects being known as hemorrhagin. Hemorrhage may occur from the nose or in the eyes. Bleeding from the eyelids has often been reported after bites of the fer-de-lance (*Bothrops atrox*) of tropical America.

Essex and Markowitz (1930) made a number of interesting determinations using the venoms of *C. atrox* and *C. h. horridus*. They found that the immediate and marked fall in blood pressure caused by these venoms is neither cardiac nor due to intravascular thrombosis, and therefore must be peripheral in nature (p. 327); the hemolysis so characteristic of most Nearctic rattlesnake venoms results from an expansion in size of the red corpuscles, with injury to their membranes (p. 341; this had been noted by Mitchell and Reichert, 1886, p. 155); the effects, while similar in some ways to those of histamine, are not caused by the presence of histamine (p. 705). They concluded (p. 344) that *Crotalus* venom is a non-specific protoplasmic poison. Working with other associates, they determined that the increase in the viscosity of the blood caused by Nearctic *Crotalus* venom results from the swelling of the erythrocytes previously mentioned (Baldes, Essex, and Markowitz, 1931, p. 30); and that, as their efforts to separate the venom into several toxic components were unsuccessful, it was not proved that the toxic manifestations are caused by a number of separate substances (Markowitz, Essex, and Mann, 1931, p. 25).

Githens and Wolff (1939, p. 44) were impressed with the importance of the neurotoxic effects found, not only in the venom of the Neotropical rattlesnake (*C. durissus*), but in four Nearctic species or subspecies as well: *C. tigris, C. s. scutulatus, C. m. mitchelli,* and *S. c. catenatus.* These form a group having more powerful venoms than the other rattlesnakes tested. These investigators noted two different neurotoxic effects, an early respiratory failure, and a later paralysis, from which they infer the possibility of two distinct neurotoxic constituents.

Githens (1941, p. 149) has called attention to the fact that death from venom is commonly the result of the neurotoxic factors, even though the early symptoms may be predominantly hemorrhagic, a conclusion previously reached by Mitchell and Reichert (1886, p. 156) and Mitchell and Stewart (1898, p. 3). Githens believes that there are four groups of such neurotoxins found in the venom of pit vipers: (1) those that occur in most Nearctic rattlers; (2) those that occur in the rattlers having outstandingly powerful venoms (*C. d. terrificus, C. s. scutulatus, C. tigris, C. m. mitchelli,* and *S. c. catenatus*); (3) moccasin venoms; and, (4) bothropic venoms. He states that it has been repeatedly shown that there is not a close anti-genic relationship between the neurotoxins of the elapids and those of the pit vipers, but there is some relationship between the venoms of the pit vipers (Crotalidae) and the true vipers (Viperidae).

In other experiments, Githens (1941, p. 153) determined the content of the necrotic factor in pit-viper venoms to be much more constant (variation 4 to 1) than that of the neurotoxic factor (variation 10 to 1). He found variations in the clotting factor of 30 to 1 (p. 156), and in the proteolytic factor of 5 to 1 (p. 158). Species values are listed by him. Much of Githens' later work involved tests of the proportional curative effects of antivenins derived from immunization with known venoms, on envenomation by the same and other venoms. Cross antigenic methods of this type are important in immunological work, and in the determination of venom relationships and components (see, for example, Schoettler, 1951b).

Although Githens' work has undoubtedly enhanced our knowledge of rattlesnake venoms to a considerable degree, I think one of his results may be questioned, namely, the presence, in any considerable amount, of the neurotoxins of the type that he calls "neuroparalytic" in the venoms of some of our North American rattlesnakes. Were this principle strongly apparent in such species as *S. c. catenatus* and *C. s. scutulatus,* both of which are moderately common in some well-populated sections of our country, we may be sure that our medical literature would mention the symptoms of blindness and "broken neck" so well known to the physicians of Central and South America, where bites by *C. d. durissus* and *C. d. terrificus* are frequent. However, I do not doubt Githens' statement that deaths from the bites of our North American rattlesnakes are usually due to the insidious effects of the neurotoxins, rather than to the much more spectacular symptoms of the hemorrhagins. The point is that the neurotoxic principle is not the same one that causes the typical *durissus* symptoms. The late Mrs. Grace Olive Wiley wrote me that she had experienced important neurotoxic symptoms from the bites of *C. v. helleri* and *C. v. cerberus.* Paralysis was involved, but not of the "broken neck" type. Other neurotoxic symptoms that have been observed in cases involving various subspecies of the western rattlesnake (*C. viridis*) are respiratory difficulty, temporary blindness, and tingling of the scalp, tongue, lips, and the soles of the feet.

Minton (in Buckley, editor, 1955, in press) found, in tests on mice, that there is a strong neurotoxic factor in the venom of *S. c. catenatus.* Hemolysin was also high in this venom; and hemagglutinins were strong in *atrox* and *ruber* venoms but not in that of *adamanteus.* The hemagglutinins were measured by tests on rabbit erythrocytes. He determined relative necrotizing effects by measuring the necrotic area in test animals 24 hours after injection. He found a positive correlation between the toxicity of the venom (from all lethal factors) and the area of necrosis.

The following papers supply some correlations between the various chemical and physical fractions of venoms, and their physiological constituents: Mitchell and Reichert (1886, p. 51), Mitchell (1889, p. 511), Amaral (1923, p. 689; 1928c, p. 1069), Fairley (1929a, p. 301), Githens (1931, p. 82), Markowitz, Essex, and Mann (1931, p. 22), Ghosh and De (1935, p. 380), Taube and Essex (1937, p. 43), Keeley (1937, p. 537), Slotta and Fraenkel-Conrat (1938, p. 213), Zeller (1948, p. 459), Boquet (1948, p. 94), Horton (1951, p. 173), and Porges (1953, p. 47).

I shall mention these toxic effects again in connection with the symptoms of actual snake-bite cases.

Venom Toxicity Comparisons

In the introduction to this chapter, I outlined the factors that affect the gravity of a snake bite. Many of these concern the individual snake, such as its size, the quantity of venom injected in a bite, and the length of the fangs. Of factors of this type, one is characteristic, within limitations, of the subspecies of snake rather than of a particular individual. This is the venom virulence—that is, the toxicity of the venom per unit of weight or volume. Usually this is expressed in terms of the minimum lethal dose (m.l.d.), which is the smallest amount required to kill some laboratory animal such as a pigeon or guinea pig. It is further necessary, in stating the m.l.d., which is usually given in milligrams of dried venom, to specify with what animal and of what weight the determination was made, as for example, a pigeon weighing 350 grams or a mouse weighing 22 grams. Proportionate changes are made in computing m.l.d.'s, if the experimental creature weighs more or less than the specified standard weight, or the m.l.d. may be expressed in terms of quantity of venom per unit of weight—that is, per gram or per kilogram—of the test animal. And, finally, it is necessary to specify the nature of the injection, whether intravenous, intramuscular, subcutaneous, or intraperitoneal, for these, also, cause variations in the lethal dose.

In the 1930's, the m.l.d.'s, for a number of species and subspecies of rattlesnakes were determined by Dr. Thomas S. Githens and his associates at the Mulford Biological Laboratories, Glenolden, Pennsylvania, mostly with venoms forwarded from San Diego. The figures were given in milligrams of dried, purified venom for intravenous injections in pigeons weighing 350 grams. The conclusions were published in Githens (1931, p. 84), Githens and George (1931, p. 32), Githens (1935, p. 171), Githens and Wolff (1939, pp. 37, 43, and 50), and Githens (1941, p. 151).

Before summarizing Githens' results, I should like to point out that the variability is very high, for divergences of 10 to 1 in different batches of venom from the same subspecies are not at all unusual. These differences may result from a variety of causes, such as variation in the test animals, the condition of the snakes when milked (although most venom lots resulted from the pooled milkings of a number of snakes), from methods of processing, and from possible misidentifications of the rattlesnakes themselves. Under such circumstances, the m.l.d. values are far from final. One caution regarding interpretations is necessary: whenever there are wide variations in a calculated figure, as in this case, arithmetical averages should not be cited; central ranges (or medians) are much more important. I have only to point out that 0.2 is the mean of 10 determinations, 9 of which equal 0.1 while one equals 1.1, to indicate that a figure twice the probably correct one can result when a single aberrant test is included when computing a mean.

A summary of Githens' results, derived in part from his published data, and partly from information received from him by letter, is presented in three tables. Table 11:2 includes those subspecies of which there were sufficient venom lots and tests to produce fairly trustworthy values. Table 11:3 presents similar data for a second group comprising those subspecies of which several determinations were made, so that there may be a fair estimate of the median. With regard to the two grades of *C. d. terrificus,* groups A and B in this table, I can only presume that these groups either represent separate subspecies or that there were marked differences in the methods of venom purification. These *terrificus* venoms did not come from San Diego. A third series of m.l.d. values is set forth in table 11:4. These values are based on only one or two tests per subspecies and therefore the m.l.d.'s are to be considered only provisional.

TABLE 11:2
RELATIVE TOXICITIES OF RATTLESNAKE VENOMS: FIRST GROUP

Subspecies	M.l.d. for 350g. pigeons, in mg. of dried venom		
	Min.	Max.	Usual range
S. catenatus catenatus	0.006	0.04	0.015–0.03
C. adamanteus	0.12	0.50	0.20 –0.30
C. atrox	0.09	0.35	0.10 –0.16
C. horridus horridus	0.02	0.40	0.04 –0.35 [a]
C. mitchelli pyrrhus	0.40	0.60	0.40 –0.60
C. molossus molossus	0.12	0.40	0.30 –0.40
C. ruber ruber	0.30	0.60	0.50 –0.60
C. viridis oreganus and helleri	0.06	0.14	0.10 –0.12
C. viridis viridis	0.015	0.45	0.04 –0.08

[a] There were unusually wide, unexplained differences in the *horridus* data.

TABLE 11:3
RELATIVE TOXICITIES OF RATTLESNAKE VENOMS: SECOND GROUP

Subspecies	M.l.d. for 350g. pigeons, in mg. of dried venom		
	Min.	Max.	Estimated median
C. cerastes	0.09	0.15	0.12
C. durissus durissus	0.025	0.26	0.11
C. durissus terrificus (group A)	0.025	0.21	0.10
C. durissus terrificus (group B)	0.003	0.003	0.003
C. mitchelli mitchelli	0.002	0.04	0.003
C. scutulatus scutulatus	0.005	0.02	0.013

TABLE 11:4
RELATIVE TOXICITIES OF RATTLESNAKE VENOMS: THIRD GROUP

Subspecies	M.l.d. for 350g. pigeons, in mg. of dried venom	
	Range	Estimated median
S. miliarius barbouri	0.12 –0.60	0.40
C. basiliscus basiliscus	....	0.08
C. enyo enyo	....	0.10
C. lepidus klauberi	....	0.01
C. mitchelli stephensi	0.16 –0.20	0.18
C. pricei pricei	....	0.20
C. ruber lucasensis	0.024–0.40	0.30
C. tigris	....	0.004
C. viridis abyssus	....	0.06
C. viridis cerberus	....	0.10
C. viridis lutosus	0.06 –0.20	0.15
C. willardi willardi	....	0.10

The results set forth in these three tables are not sufficiently assured to determine whether relationships between rattlesnakes premised on other characters—squamation, for example—are verified by the venoms. Githens believed these data to prove that primitive rattlesnakes have powerful venoms, and that small species tend to have venoms of greater virulence than large, in partial compensation for their lack of venom quantity. I should consider the latter conclusion

TABLE 11:5

RELATIVE TOXICITIES OF RATTLESNAKE VENOMS FOR MICE

Subspecies	M.l.d. in mg. of dried venom	
	Macht, 22-gram mice	Githens and Wolff, 20-gram mice
C. adamanteus	....	0.04
C. atrox	0.12, 0.30	0.12
C. cerastes	0.06	0.17
C. basiliscus basiliscus	....	0.08
C. durissus durissus	....	0.035, 0.12
C. durissus terrificus	....	0.0026
C. horridus horridus	0.11	0.08
C. lepidus klauberi	....	0.02
C. mitchelli mitchelli	0.045	0.0035
C. mitchelli pyrrhus	0.075	0.05
C. mitchelli stephensi	0.12	....
C. molossus molossus	0.06	0.14
C. ruber ruber	0.11	0.22
C. ruber lucasensis	0.12	0.08
C. scutulatus scutulatus	0.24	0.012, 0.014
C. tigris	....	0.012
C. viridis viridis	0.045	0.025
C. viridis abyssus	0.10	....
C. viridis lutosus	0.14	0.07
C. viridis oreganus or helleri	0.14	0.045
C. willardi willardi	....	0.24
S. catenatus catenatus	....	0.018
S. miliarius barbouri	....	0.12

somewhat doubtful, although true of some kinds of rattlers. Decidedly worthy of note, if verified by future tests, are the highly toxic venoms possessed by *C. d. terrificus* (B), *C. m. mitchelli, C. tigris, C. s. scutulatus,* and *S. c. catenatus.*

Macht (1937, p. 500) has published the m.l.d.'s of a number of subspecies of rattlesnakes based on intraperitoneal injections into 22-gram mice. The venoms he used were prepared in San Diego. Githens and Wolff (1939, p. 50) have also recorded the results of tests on mice except that their standard was a 20-gram mouse. The results of the two series of tests are presented in table 11:5.

The m.l.d.'s determined by these tests do not match well. Of the 12 subspecies of rattlesnakes included in both series, 7 have values, as found by one experimenter, that are at least twice those of the other, and in two instances the discrepancy is more than 10 to 1. In 8 of the 12 duplicated tests, Macht's m.l.d.'s are higher than those of Githens and Wolff, meaning that he found the venoms less powerful. The discrepancies cannot be charged against differences in the method of purifying and preserving the venoms, for, so far as known, all of the venoms used in the duplicate tests came from San Diego. Githens and Wolff (1939, p. 48) have stated that they consider mice less satisfactory as test animals than pigeons, as mice are more subject to individual variations. Also, they are of the opinion that intravenous tests are more conclusive than intraperitoneal. They think pigeon tests should show lower m.l.d.'s because birds are more susceptible to viperine venoms; however, this does not explain the discrepancies between the two series of mouse tests.

Although there have been many investigations and tables published on the m.l.d.'s of various kinds of snakes other than rattlesnakes, the data on the latter, with the exception of the Githens and Macht results already cited, are rather meager. This has come about owing to the fact that the extent of the differences in the toxicity of the several kinds of rattlesnakes (with the notable exception of the Neotropical rattlesnake) has only become appreciated within the past 25 years; in fact, it was Githens' tests that first showed the importance of the variance among the Nearctic species. Only since these experiments has it been realized that species differences might explain results that hitherto had seemed conflicting, and that it is not satisfactory to group rattlers as if their venoms were all the same. For example, Billing (1930, p. 173) reported certain tests as having been made on *adamanteus* venom, when, in reality, it was *atrox* venom that was used. These two species of diamondbacks are not so closely related as was once supposed, and their venoms may differ in the relative proportions of several toxic principles.

In addition to the rattlesnake m.l.d. values determined by Githens and Macht, a few others are available. Crimmins (1927a; F. M. Allen, 1938, p. 1248) calculated the m.l.d. of *atrox* venom for dogs at 1 mg. per ½ kg. of body weight, when injected intramuscularly. This figure is practically the same as that of Jackson and Githens (1931, p. 1), who give 1 mg. per lb. (0.454 kg.). Billing (1930, p. 177) found the m.l.d. of *atrox* venom to be 0.025 mg. per gram of body weight of rats. Amaral (1923a, p. 686) gives the *terrificus* figure for intravenous injection of pigeons as determined by V. Brazil at 0.001 mg.

Boquet (1948, pp. 36–37) lists, from a variety of sources, the following m.l.d.'s in mg. per kg. of weight:

	Rabbits		Guinea pigs	
	Intravenous	Subcutaneous	Intravenous	Subcutaneous
C. d. terrificus	0.25 to 0.5			
C. adamanteus	0.25	0.25	1.0	4.0

Schoettler (1951a, p. 494) cites the following m.l.d.'s for mice in terms of mg. of dried venom per gram of mouse, using subcutaneous injections: *C. d. terrificus* 0.0002; *C. basiliscus* 0.0009; *C. atrox* 0.015; *C. horridus* 0.015; *S. catenatus* 0.005. To correlate these figures with the mouse determinations of Githens and Wolff, or Macht, it is necessary to multiply Schoettler's figures by 20 or 22.

For man, the m.l.d. in terms of mg. of dry venom per kg. of bodily weight has been given as 0.37 by Crimmins (1929, p. 604; Reese, 1934, p. 104), 0.37 by Allen (1938, p. 1249), 1.0 by Amaral (1923b, p. 95), and 3.0 by Wyne (1937, p. 605). The last figure is certainly too high.

Enough rattlesnake m.l.d.'s have been presented to indicate their inconsistencies, and to show how unsatisfactory this criterion is as a measure of relative toxicity, particularly because of the many variables that affect the results. Even when the species and weight of the test animal are standardized, and the nature of the injection is uniform—whether intravenous, intramuscular, intraperitoneal, or subcutaneous—there still remain differences inherent in the individual susceptibilities of the test animals, and variations in the venom batches from a single subspecies of snake, and even batches from the same snake taken at different times.

In an elaborate series of investigations of the venoms of some of the most dangerous Australian snakes, Kellaway (1929a, tiger snake; 1929b, copper-head;[2] 1929c, spotted black snake; 1929d, death adder) considered such variables as the kind of animal (among others, he and his associates experimented on horses, sheep, goats, monkeys, cats, rabbits, guinea pigs, rats, and mice), the weight of the animal of each kind, the type of injection (whether intravenous or subcutaneous), and, of course, the quantity of venom, correlated with the time interval prior to death, or, as the case might be, ultimate survival, for the greater the quantity of venom, the more rapid is the lethal result. Kellaway's detailed researches showed the importance of these variables by keeping all but one factor constant in a test series, thus evaluating a single variable. He showed that one kind of animal might be 10 times as resistant as another to the venom of a certain snake; and that intravenous injection might be 5 times as lethal as subcutaneous. It is clear that standardization is necessary if we are to draw conclusions as to the relative toxicities of the venoms of several different kinds of snakes, and even then the comparison will be valid only for the particular set of standard conditions adopted.

Even with the standardization of test procedures, it becomes essential to define certain time-dosage factors inherent in the term "minimum lethal dose" (m.l.d.), or whatever measuring unit be employed. For, in running a series of tests with gradually increasing dosages, should we take the lowest dosage (in mg. of dried venom per unit of weight of the test animal) that kills any of the series, the level of dosage that kills half the animals, or the dosage beyond which none survive? Obviously the first type of criterion is dependent on a single individual (the weakest) of the test series; and the last is determined by the dosage just higher than the hardiest individual of the test series can withstand. Lamb and Hanna (1902, p. 12) used the terms "certain lethal dose" and "maximum nonlethal dose" as two of their levels. Kellaway, in his papers already cited, to avoid the uncertainties involved in these criteria of toxicity, plotted curves—a separate curve for each kind of venom, each kind of test animal, and each type of injection—in which the dosage in mg. of dried venom (per unit of animal weight) was plotted on rectangular co-ordinates against per cent of mortality. This is a more accurate type of presentation than any other, but does not lend itself to tabular comparisons.

To overcome this difficulty, Schoettler (1951a, p. 491) suggests the integration of each curve, thus finding the true point of 50 per cent mortality, or m.l.d.$_{50}$. This is a procedure worthy of adoption by future investigators, if we are ever to

[2] An entirely different snake (*Denisonia superba*) from the American copperhead (*Agkistrodon contortrix*). Nor is the Australian spotted black snake (*Pseudechis guttatus*), a venomous elapid, related to the harmless American black snake or black racer (*Coluber constrictor constrictor*).

have comparable figures on toxicity; there will remain enough uncertainties, even then. The difficulties involved in m.l.d. determinations will be better understood when it is recalled that each point on a curve representing per cent mortality plotted against venom quantity will require a number of separate tests—each on a separate animal—and that two or more different venom lots should be used at each dosage level.

Table 11:6 is a summary of Schoettler's results (p. 494) with rattlesnake venoms. He eliminated two variables, first, by using only mice; and, secondly, by employing only subcutaneous injection in the leg. He considered this the most significant type of injection since it most nearly approximates the kind likely to be experienced in a snake-bite accident to a human being. All figures in the table represent the dosage in mg. of dried venom per gram of mouse.

TABLE 11:6

RELATIVE POTENCIES OF RATTLESNAKE VENOMS FOR MICE (mg/g)
AS DETERMINED BY SCHOETTLER

Subspecies	l.d.$_0$	m.l.d.	Mean l.d.	l.d.$_{100}$ =c.l.d.	$\dfrac{\text{c.l.d.}}{\text{m.l.d.}}$
C. d. terrificus....................	0.0001	0.0002	0.00060	0.0011	5.5
C. b. basiliscus....................	0.0008	0.0009	0.00278	0.004	4.4
C. atrox............................	0.014	0.015	0.01611	0.019	1.3
C. horridus........................	0.014	0.015	0.02490	0.036	2.4
S. catenatus........................	0.004	0.005	0.00680	0.009	1.8

Schoettler defines his dosage levels as follows: l.d.$_0$ is the highest dose causing zero mortality; m.l.d. is the lowest dose causing the first death (obviously the difference between these two columns indicates the size of the step or increment used in the test dosages); mean l.d. is the mean determined by integrating the dosage-mortality curve (often cited by other authors as l.d.$_{50}$);[3] and l.d.$_{100}$ (or c.l.d.) is the lowest dose causing 100 per cent mortality. To secure these results required an average of 81 mice for each kind of venom tested. Schoettler suggests that the ratio c.l.d/m.l.d. is an indication of the amount of variation in susceptibility between individual mice, as it is the ratio of the amount of venom required to kill the hardiest mouse to the amount required to kill the weakest.

Some other rattlesnake toxicity values are now available in terms of l.d.$_{50}$, rather than the previously used criterion of m.l.d. Minton (1953, p. 213) found the average l.d.$_{50}$ value of *horridus* venom for mice by intraperitoneal injection to be 0.00511 mg. per gram of mouse. In later papers (1954, p. 1079; in Buckley, editor, 1955, in press, table 1) he presents the following l.d.$_{50}$ toxicities in milligrams of venom per gram of mouse, by subcutaneous injection: *S. c. catenatus* 0.00525, *S. m. barbouri* 0.02425, *C. c. laterorepens* 0.00550, *C. v. helleri* 0.00356, *C. h. horridus* 0.00915, *C. adamanteus* 0.01455, *C. atrox* 0.01925, *C. r. ruber* 0.02125; also the following l.d.$_{50}$'s are shown for intraperitoneal injections: *S. c. catenatus*

---

[3] The dosage causing the death of half the test animals. This notation for the per cent of mortality seems to have been first suggested by Trevan (1927, p. 490) in a paper pointing out the necessity for mortality-dosage curves in the evaluation of poisons. See also Reed and Muench (1938, p. 493). The value l.d.$_{50}$ is now used more often in evaluating venoms than m.l.d., for the latter depends too much on the most resistant individual in the test series.

0.00022, *C. v. helleri* 0.00156, *C. h. horridus* 0.00925, *C. adamanteus* 0.00167, *C. atrox* 0.00842. Minton's results show that there is a difference between species of rattlesnakes in the ratio of the toxicities as determined by subcutaneous and intraperitoneal injections. Intraperitoneal injections usually require a smaller quantity of venom to prove fatal. Minton found the intraperitoneal $m.l._{50}$ dose to vary from 4 to 101 per cent of the subcutaneous dose, with an average of 41 per cent.

Criley (in Buckley, editor, 1955, in press, table 5; see also Pollard, 1954, p. 242) has presented $l.d._{50}$ values for 18 g. mice, when the venom is injected intravenously. The Criley results are presented in terms of the number of $l.d._{50}$'s contained in one mg. of venom. To make these values more readily comparable with those of Minton (although the methods of injection were different), I have converted the Criley figures to mg/g with the following results: *atrox* 0.0031, *adamanteus* 0.0015, *terrificus* 0.000126, *horridus* 0.0031, *viridis* 0.0011, *oreganus* [*helleri?*] 0.0025, *ruber* 0.0040, and *basiliscus* 0.011. It will be observed that the two sets of values are not uniformly correlated. It would be expected that Minton's values of $l.d._{50}$ would be higher than Criley's, since intravenous injection is more effective than subcutaneous, but a closer approximation to a constant ratio might have been anticipated. At least both sets of values illustrate the great variability in toxicities shown by different species of rattlesnakes.

Even these dosage-mortality curves and $l.d._{50}$ values do not exhaust the variables that must be evaluated in toxicity studies, for there remains the time element. Obviously larger doses kill more quickly than smaller, and certain limits must be set in the formulation of dosage-mortality curves, especially with short-lived test animals. Acton and Knowles (1921, p. 736) investigated this phase of the problem, using cobra venom. They plotted curves in which one variable was the elapsed time from venom injection to death, and the other was venom quantity. The resulting curve was found to be hyperbolic. The time to death reached a minimum—the experimental animals were rats—at about three minutes, and no quantity of venom, however great, produced a quicker death. Similarly, the curve was asymtotic along the other axis, since, with a sublethal dose, death was never produced regardless of the elapsed time. The cobra-rat curve proved to be $y = 3 + 360/(x - 0.1)$, where y is the time from injection to death in minutes, and x the dosage in mg. of venom. Thus the minimum time (x increasing to infinity) was three minutes, and the sublethal dose (y increasing to infinity) was 0.1 mg.—since $x - 0.1$ is then zero.

INTRASUBSPECIFIC VARIATIONS IN TOXICITY

There are many myths, and possibly some factual ideas, regarding differences in the dangers from rattlesnake bite at different times of the day, different seasons of the year, under different weather conditions, and other external influences. Usually these ideas are founded on the assumption that it is the quantity of venom injected in a bite that is variable, rather than its toxicity. I should like now to mention a few presumed, or actual, intrasubspecific variations in toxicity. Schoettler (1951a, p. 496) states that there could well be differences in a glandular secretion such as snake venom, as a result of climatic, seasonal, alimentary, sexual, and genetic influences. Tests to determine the extent of any venom differences resulting from these factors will, indeed, be difficult.

The relative virulence of the venom of young snakes, compared to that of adults, has been the subject of a divergence of opinion. Allen and Maier (1941, p. 250) state, based on experiments by Allen (1937, p. 71), that the venom of young rattlesnakes is more potent than that of adults (see also Maloney, 1945, p. 31, and Jones, 1947, p. 49). However, it seems to me that these experiments—there were only five—were too limited in number to be convincing. As a matter of fact, the opposite conclusion might have been drawn from the results. In San Diego, as mentioned earlier, it was found that the proportion of solid residue from the drying of juvenile venoms was less than that from adults; thus it must be less virulent on a drop-for-drop basis unless the solids from the juveniles entail a more potent quality. Crum (1906, p. 1433) expressed the opinion that such may be the case, but I know of no proof that this is a fact.

Avicenna (in Thorndike, 1923–41, vol. 2, p. 413) and Rivers (1874, p. 510) thought that the venoms of juveniles are weaker than those of adults. Bannerman and Pocha (1907, p. 810) considered their experiments on Russell's vipers in India to prove that the venom of juveniles is relatively weak. However, their experiments lacked quantitative controls. I believe that, until experiments are made which demonstrate the higher toxicity of dried juvenile venoms, we must conclude that juvenile venoms are weaker than adult venoms per unit of liquid quantity.

Experiments also remain to be made to see whether there is any difference between the venoms of the sexes, as stated by Avicenna (Thorndike, 1923–41, vol. 2, p. 413) about a thousand years ago. He thought the poison of the male viper more potent than that of the female. But whether there are any differences beyond those resulting from size is not known, although there are presumed to be none.

Witt (1768, p. 10), evidently a member of the Philadelphia Chamber of Commerce, maintained that the rattlers (*horridus*) of Maryland were more venomous than those of Pennsylvania. That there are differences in toxicity between the venoms of the same species but from different areas is unquestioned. Vellard (1938, p. 409; 1939, p. 463; 1943, p. 55), Machado (1945, p. 55), Barrio and Vital Brazil (1951, p. 291), Gonçalves and Vieira (1950, p. 141), and Gonçalves (in Buckley, editor, 1955, in press) state this to be true of *C. d. terrificus* in Brazil; and Schoettler (1951a, p. 496) has determined that there are marked differences in the venoms of the European viper (*Vipera berus*), depending on the locality where the snakes were collected. Githens found great differences between the venom of *C. mitchelli mitchelli* from the Cape Region of Baja California and that of *C. mitchelli pyrrhus*—the same species but a different subspecies—from San Diego County, California. These differences were confirmed, although to a lesser degree, by Macht.

Schoettler (1951b, p. 505; 1952, p. 294) has stated that different venom samples from the same species of snake may be neither toxically nor antigenically identical. Ipsen (1938, p. 787), discussing the venoms of vipers, said there were not only intrasubspecific variations, but that different samples of venom from the same snake were not quite the same. Pollard *et al.* (1952, p. 161; see also Watt and Pollard, 1954, p. 367) have discussed variations in the toxicity of moccasin venom. From their data, I have calculated a coefficient of variation of 15.3 per cent in the l.d.$_{50}$. Minton (1953, p. 214) found differences as great as five to one in the toxicities of the venom of adult timber rattlesnakes (*C. h. horridus*) captured at the same time and place, and of the same sex.

Somewhat the same condition as that which applies to juvenile snakes probably applies to venoms collected from snakes soon after a first milking without an adequate resting interval. With such venoms, the proportion of solid residues after drying is low, as was found in our venom-yield results at San Diego. Tyler (1945, p. 196) reported the same condition in Gila monsters. Thus it would seem that these secondary yields are weaker on a liquid basis. Kellaway (1929a, p. 353), working with Australian tiger-snake venom, found no difference in the toxicity of the primary and secondary yields on a dried venom basis; however, he did believe there was a slight weakening of venom of snakes that had been starved in captivity. This was also said of the cobra by Kanthack (1892, p. 272).

There are, as has been said, considerable differences in the susceptibility of various species of animals to a particular venom. Elliot (1933b, p. 364; 1934c, p. 210) has stated that rabbits are twice as susceptible to cobra venom as are dogs, and 25 times as susceptible as mongooses. Billing (1930, p. 195) reports that it takes six times as much *C. atrox* venom, per unit of weight, to kill a rat as it does to kill a guinea pig or rabbit. Amaral (1923, p. 686; 1935, p. 7; 1928c, p. 1069) states that such venom differences are evolutionary results from differences in the character and susceptibility of the natural prey of each species. Rattlesnake species that ordinarily feed on cold-blooded prey, which is notably less susceptible to venoms than warm-blooded, are thought to have venoms of high toxicity, an explanation of the powerful venom of *S. catenatus,* according to Netting (1929, p. 108).

Venom Yield

One of the most important factors in determining the danger from snake bite— almost equal to the unit toxicity of the venom, and in some species more so—is the quantity of venom injected in a bite. The rattlesnake milking campaign of 1926 to 1938 at the San Diego Zoo has supplied some original data on this factor, particularly with regard to average venom yields from the different subspecies, and, in a few of the more common subspecies, the variation of yield with size or age. It must be realized that whatever figures we may present are inevitably affected by the conditions of captivity; we can only hope that the intersubspecific differences and ontogenetic variations found in captive snakes are comparable with those of snakes in the wild.

The variables affecting net venom recovery in the laboratory are of three classes: (1) the character and condition of the snake as found in the field; (2) the changes in its condition entailed by capture and captivity; and (3) the venom yield as a proportion of the total venom available in the glands. As to the first item, it may naturally be expected that there will be differences in venom yields from snakes of different species. Also, it will certainly be found that there is some correlation between size and yield. Then there is the condition of the snake; if venom has recently been expended in defense or in the capture of prey, the glands will not be full. The snake may be in poor health, which might reduce gland secretion. Seasonal conditions may affect gland activity; snakes might be presumed to have more or less than a normal supply just before or after hibernation.

With the capture of the snake, the situation is further complicated. Expert, indeed, will be the field collector who can catch a snake, particularly one of the more nervous species, without the loss of some venom. The length of the rest period prior to the first milking is also important. Lastly, when the snake is milked, there remains an uncertainty as to the proportion of the available venom that is obtained, and how this amount may compare with that injected by a biting snake.

Upon reflection on all of these conditions, we cannot wonder at the wide variations in yield per snake that are noted when rattlers are milked, even when they are of the same subspecies and of uniform size. And, as many of these conditions are operative naturally in the field, the reasons for the diverse and seemingly inconsistent effects that so often follow snake bite are made apparent.

From the standpoint of the venom collector or investigator, the first group of conditions is beyond his control—he must take his snakes as he finds them, large or small, sick or well. But in the capture and handling, much will depend on the collector. Care and skill will usually get a snake into his bag without its having had an opportunity to use the fangs and thus waste venom. When the snakes have arrived at the laboratory, they should be kept in seclusion, and preferably in the dark, for at least two weeks. If they have expended some venom in capture it will be at least partly replenished; if not, what they have will remain intact until milking time. Carelessness in the field or laboratory often leads to fang breakage, which further increases the difficulty of venom collection.

When large numbers of rattlesnakes are milked, time often does not permit the measurement of each specimen as it is milked, or the separate determination of its venom yield, even on a liquid basis. Thus, at San Diego, while we did make some yield-length records that I shall mention in due course, most of our rattlers were segregated only into three categories—large, medium, and small. Obviously, these segregations were not exact, for it was necessary to classify each snake according to standards set for its subspecies, a large specimen of one of the smaller species being little larger than a juvenile of one of the larger forms. In addition, secondary, or repeat, milkings were separated from primary, or initial, milkings. From data that will be mentioned later, we found that the juveniles could be neglected in the computation of yields per snake, as the venom recovery from a hundred of them often did not equal that to be expected from a single normal adult. The medium-sized snakes were rated at half an adult; and the repeat milkings at half the primary. Applying these ratings, we have computed the average yields in milligrams of dried venom per fresh adult snake, as set forth in table 11:7.

With regard to the average yields developed in this table, it is my opinion that individual variations are so large that results premised on fewer than 10 adults, or their equivalent, are not to be deemed conclusive. The following comments apply to particular subspecies:

C. adamanteus: My average yield (666 mg.) is undoubtedly too high. Stadelman (1929, p. 29) reports an average of 492 mg. from 9 adults; and Allen and Maier (1941, p. 251) give 415 mg. as an average from 108 specimens. Recently Mr. Allen advised me that the average yield from another lot of 50 diamondbacks was 484 mg. I think these figures, or say an average yield of about 450 mg., more representative than mine.

C. atrox: Very high yields from large specimens of this important species are occasionally recorded. Stadelman (1929, p. 29) reports 645 mg. as an average of 4 specimens. However, Jackson (1927, p. 208) mentions 220 mg., and Allen and Maier (1941, p. 251) give 230 mg. as an average from 24. Hence, I believe my average of 277 is probably reasonably representative of adult yields.

C. durissus: There has been so much confusion in the literature in the application of the names *durissus, terrificus,* and *basiliscus* that some of the published yields are questionable. There is some evidence that the yield of *C. d. terrificus* averages considerably below that of *C. d. durissus.* Amaral (1923, p. 685) gives an average of 30 mg. for *terrificus;* this is probably based on specimens of all sizes. Houssay (1923, p. 450) cites the average of the same subspecies from Argentina as 23 mg. Schoettler (1951a, p. 497) milked 2,758 Brazilian specimens of *terrificus* in 1949 and got an average yield of 24 mg. As to *C. d. durissus,* from data presented by George (1930, p. 59) one may estimate a yield of 125 mg. for this subspecies in Honduras.

C. v. viridis: My figure of 44 mg. is considerably too low, as the majority of the specimens from which the yield was determined came from areas (particularly from near Platteville, Colorado) where this subspecies does not attain the size reached in other places. I should place the yield of this subspecies in Montana, Wyoming, Nebraska, and Kansas at close to 100 mg., thus conforming to the yields of the other subspecies of similar size—*abyssus, cerberus, helleri, oreganus,* and *lutosus.* The stunted races, *nuntius* and *decolor,* have lower yields, as is to be expected.

S. m. barbouri: Allen and Maier (1941, p. 251) give an average yield of 34 mg. for this subspecies. Subsequently Allen advised me by letter that the average yield from 82 specimens of this little rattler was 30 mg.

It will be noted that some of my data were gathered before the eventual division of several of the forms into additional subspecies—the species *cerastes* and *horridus,* for example. From my records, I cannot resegregate the yields.

In the course of our San Diego venom program, I encounted a few maximum yields that are worth recording. These are set forth in Table 11:8.

At the present time the high record for a rattlesnake venom yield, in terms of dried residue, is held by an *atrox* from an unknown locality. Fortunately, this specimen, which yielded 3.9 cc. of liquid venom, was milked directly into centrifuge tubes so that no venom was wasted, and the dry yield of 1,145 mg. of purified venom shown in table 11:8 was actual and not calculated. It will be noted that the percentage of solid residue was unusually high. The snake was 1,655 mm. (65 in.) long, not at all unusual for this species.

Higher records will undoubtedly be made with large specimens of *adamanteus.* Mitchell and Reichert (1886, p. 2) reported that an *adamanteus* 8½ ft. long and weighing 19 lb. on one occasion yielded about 1½ drachms of venom. I should

TABLE 11:7

VENOM YIELDS OF RATTLESNAKES MILKED AT SAN DIEGO

Subspecies	Number of snakes							Equivalent fresh adults	Total dried venom in mg.	Yield in dried venom per fresh adult, mg.
	Fresh snakes			Second milkings			Total snakes			
	L	M	Sa	L	M	Sa				
Crotalus adamanteus	10	4	8	..	4	..	22	12	7,991	666
Crotalus atrox	72	148	153	16	..	..	393	155	42,840	277
Crotalus basiliscus basiliscus	1	2	..	..	..	..	3	2	594	297
Crotalus durissus durissus	3	6	..	..	..	..	9	5	1,386	277
Crotalus durissus totonacus	1	..	..	..	..	..	1	1	514	514
Crotalus cerastes	82	57	12	9	16	..	176	119	3,987	33
Crotalus enyo enyo	13	5	..	1	..	..	19	16	458	29
Crotalus exsul	1	..	..	..	..	..	1	1	54	54
Crotalus horridus	7	6	..	..	..	..	13	10	1,392	139
Crotalus lepidus klauberi	10	16	5	..	..	..	31	18	177	10
Crotalus mitchelli mitchelli	45	7	..	12	..	..	64	55	1,775	32
Crotalus mitchelli pyrrhus	103	68	4	63	60	..	298	174	39,524	227
Crotalus mitchelli stephensi	10	3	..	..	..	..	13	11½	837	73
Crotalus molossus molossus	34	19	2	9	..	..	64	48	13,734	286

Crotalus ruber ruber	194	159	41	91	54	6	545	332½	120,920	364
Crotalus ruber lucasensis	206	45	5	115	10	1	381	288	67,246	234
Crotalus scutulatus scutulatus	66	118	10	13	20	1	228	136	10,498	77
Crotalus tigris	12	:	:	2	:	:	14	13	145	11
Crotalus tortugensis	6	11	:	:	:	:	17	11½	641	56
Crotalus triseriatus aquilus	1	:	:	:	:	:	1	1	36	36
Crotalus viridis viridis	470	752	443	11	:	:	1,676	1,070	46,697	44
Crotalus viridis abyssus	4	6	:	:	:	:	10	7	678	97
Crotalus viridis cerberus	7	8	:	:	:	:	15	11	1,239	112
Crotalus viridis decolor	4	:	:	:	:	:	4	4	86	22
Crotalus viridis helleri or oreganus	195	479	55	49	99	3	880	484	54,377	112
Crotalus viridis lutosus	38	34	11	8	7	:	98	61	6,733	110
Crotalus viridis nuntius	32	26	13	7	4	:	82	59	3,032	51
Crotalus willardi willardi	1	:	:	:	:	:	1	1	37	37
Sistrurus catenatus catenatus	5	2	:	:	:	:	7	6	183	31
Sistrurus catenatus tergeminus	1	1	:	:	:	:	2	1½	55	37
Sistrurus miliarius barbouri	5	4	:	:	:	:	9	7	125	18
Mixed lots	:	:	:	:	:	:	63	...	2,677	...
Total	:	:	:	:	:	:	5,171	...	430,882	...

a L, large; M, medium; S, small.

interpret this as being about 5.8 cc. of liquid venom, possibly equal to 1,500 mg. of venom on a dry basis. Allen and Maier (1941, p. 251) reported a yield of 4.5 cc. from an *adamanteus*. C. B. Pollard advised me that he had secured 6¼ cc. of liquid venom from an *adamanteus* at a single extraction. I have no doubt that large specimens of *adamanteus* and *atrox,* if given an adequate rest and if carefully handled in milking, should occasionally produce well over 1,000 mg., and even up to 1,500 mg., of dried, purified venom. The next highest yields are derived from *ruber, lucasensis,* and *molossus. C. b. basiliscus* may also give a liberal yield.

TABLE 11:8

MAXIMUM VENOM YIELDS EXPERIENCED AT SAN DIEGO

Subspecies	Yield in mg. of dried venom
Crotalus adamanteus	848
Crotalus atrox	1,145
Crotalus cerastes	63
Crotalus horridus atricaudatus	229
Crotalus mitchelli mitchelli	90
Crotalus mitchelli pyrrhus	308
Crotalus mitchelli stephensi	129
Crotalus molossus molossus	540
Crotalus ruber ruber	668
Crotalus ruber lucasensis	707
Crotalus scutulatus scutulatus	141
Crotalus viridis viridis	162
Crotalus viridis abyssus	137
Crotalus viridis cerberus	150
Crotalus viridis helleri	390
Crotalus viridis oreganus	289
Crotalus viridis lutosus	234
Crotalus viridis nuntius	72

I have never had an opportunity to milk one of the really large ones. The single *totonacus* I have milked suggests that this subspecies produces venom in quantity, although this would hardly be expected from its relationship with *durissus* and *terrificus*. These are thought to have smaller yields than diamondbacks of similar size, but of a very powerful neurotoxic venom that more than compensates for the lack of quantity. Houssay (1923, p. 450) reported a yield of 90 mg. from an Argentinian *terrificus,* and Schoettler (1951a, p. 497), 300 mg. from a Brazilian specimen.

Reports of some yields that are quite beyond the realm of possibility have been published. Barringer (1892, p. 295) mentions a gram of venom per kilogram of snake, which is possible if he refers to a gram of liquid rather than of dried venom. Rolker (1905, p. 201) speaks of a tablespoonful at a single bite; this is about 15 cc. and quite beyond reality. Lloyd (1925, p. 32) refers to a yield of about two ounces of venom from a large snake, or nearly 50 cc.

In contradistinction to maximum yields, it should be recorded that in every species, through some condition, often of capture or captivity, specimens are encountered that extrude little or no venom, despite the best efforts of the milker.

These differences between high and low yields in adults suggest that, in investigating the ontogenetic curve of yields, we should draw such conclusions as we may concerning the dispersion of individual yields about the regression line. These successive items of investigation—first, the toxicity differences and differences of average yield between species, and, secondly, the variations within a species because of the individual snake's age and gland repletion—all of these are fundamental to an understanding of snake bites and their treatment.

Sexual Differences in Yield.—Of the normal intrasubspecific differences that might affect the statistics of snakes in the wild, the first is sexual dimorphism. If none of importance is disclosed, then one possibly complicating variable may be ignored. The problem of investigating sexual differences is somewhat complicated by the fact that the males of most species of rattlesnakes grow larger than the females and thus one may be comparing fully adult females with vigorous and still-growing young males. I made comparisons in 6 different subspecies, involving a total of 445 snakes, and found no indication of sexual differences in 4 of the 6. In one (*C. r. ruber*), there may have been a slight male superiority in yield, but the number of snakes involved in this group was too small to prove this beyond question. The other series, the largest and best of those groups available with individual length-yield data on each snake, and of a subspecies of snake yielding enough venom so that the yield per snake could be measured with fair accuracy, comprised a series of 242 adult and subadult specimens of *C. r. lucasensis*. There were no juveniles. In this series, it was found that mature females produced more venom than the young adult males with which they corresponded in size. They were not always superior, but their mode was definitely higher. I do not know whether this condition exists in other species of rattlesnakes. Only large series—at least 100 of each sex, all with individual venom records and length measurements—will verify this sexual difference, and the snakes must be of a kind affording large enough yields so that variations of less than 0.1 cc. will be unimportant.

Even if the female superiority that I have mentioned is verified by future researches, this does not mean that female rattlesnakes are more dangerous than males. It is to be remembered that when we compare snakes of the same sizes we are comparing fully adult females with subadult males. Eventually the males reach larger sizes than are attained by the females and correspondingly exceed the females in venom yield. So steep is the ontogenetic length–venom curve, that it is probable that the largest males produce at least 50 per cent more venom than the largest females.

With this note of uncertainty regarding the reality of sexual differences in yields of venom in snakes of the same size, I next proceed to a summary of ontogenetic trends, with the sexes combined as if sexual differences could be ignored. And, indeed, other variable factors render them unimportant.

Ontogenetic Variation in Yield: Averages.—My first approach to the problem of the ontogenetic variation of venom yield will be an attempt to deduce the regression lines of average yield on length, from the two large homogeneous series of rattlesnakes that have served in other statistical studies—one series of *C. viridis viridis* from near Platteville, Colorado, and another from near Pierre, South Dakota. Of the first series, we have venom–length statistics of 754 snakes, divided into 16 groups by sizes; of the second series, 295 snakes divided into 20 groups. The dry, purified venom yield is available for each group, so that the yield per snake may be computed. When the results are plotted, it is immediately evident that the venom increases at a more rapid rate, proportionately, than the over-all length of the snake, a not unexpected development, since the venom might be expected to increase at some rate proportional to the bulk of the snake, or the cube of its length. This is not quite the case, although the venom yield increases faster than the square of the body length. The equations of these two regression lines are found to be: for the Platteville series $V = 101L^{2.33}$ and for the Pierre series $V = 80L^{2.36}$, where V is the venom yield in milligrams of dried venom per snake, and L is the length of the snake in meters.

TABLE 11:9

VARIATIONS OF VENOM YIELDS WITH SNAKE LENGTH IN *C. v. viridis*

Length of snake over-all, mm.	Yield in mg. of dried venom	
	Platteville series from Colorado	Pierre series from South Dakota
300	6.2	4.6
400	12.1	9.1
500	20.2	15.5
600	31	24
700	44	34
800	60	47
900	79	62
1,000	101	80
1,100	....	100

It should be remarked at once that the juveniles gave lower yields than indicated by these curves. The average yield of the young entering their first hibernation was barely one-tenth of expectation. There is also a slight indication of a below-expectation yield in the very large specimens, a reduction that some experimenters (e.g., Amaral, 1923, p. 685; 1925, p. 6; 1951b, p. 1247) have stated occurs in old snakes. I should make it clear that my results do not so much indicate an actual reduction of yield in the large snakes as a failure to increase at the rate indicated by the ontogenetic curves. As in the case of young snakes, so also very large specimens introduce difficulties in getting accurate yields, for their thick head muscles make it hard to apply full external pressure on the glands.

It is not easy to visualize trends expressed in exponential curves of this type, for which reason I present in table 11:9 representative lengths and yields as approximated from the curves.

The Platteville snakes are somewhat stunted, compared with the Pierre series. It would seem that they have more venom, proportionate to their sizes, than the larger snakes; usually they have about the same quantity of venom as a Pierre snake 100 mm. longer. The Platteville rattlers rarely attain a length of 1,000 mm., while the largest snakes of the Pierre series almost reach 1,100 mm. Probably the maximum amount of venom is the same in the two series, despite their differences in size. It may be noted that in either series, when the length doubles in growing from 500 to 1,000 mm., the venom yield is multiplied by about 5. Or, as another example, a young-adult snake about 750 mm. long needs to add only ⅓ to its length in order to double its venom yield.

I have already mentioned the lack of conformity of young snakes to expectation in the matter of yield. I am not at all sure that this discrepancy is real; rather, I attribute most of it to the practical difficulty of securing from these little snakes whatever venom they may have in their glands. From the regression lines that I cited, we should expect venom yields of about 6.2 mg. per juvenile snake from the Platteville series, and 4.6 mg. from the Pierre youngsters. The actual result from 170 Plattevilles averaging 299 mm. in length was 0.56 mg.; and from 72 Pierres with an average length of 329 mm., 1.26 mg. per snake. Another lot of baby South Dakota rattlers of slightly larger size, numbering 174, had an average yield of 2.37 mg. A San Patricio, Texas, series of juvenile *atrox*, of which there were 135, had an average yield of 2.2 mg., compared to an adult average of about 277 mg. It would probably be fair to assume that a baby rattler has from one-twentieth to one one-hundredth of the venom of an adult, but that the effectiveness of its bite is even less, proportionately, than these figures would indicate.

I have shown elsewhere (1937, p. 44) that, in *C. v. viridis*, the weight increases as the 3.3 power of the length, that is, these snakes get proportionately stouter as they age. The venom yield does not increase proportionately quite so fast as the weight. The exponential equations are found to be approximately as follows: For the Platteville series $V = 0.447W^{0.870}$; and for the Pierre series $V = 0.493W^{0.826}$. In these equations V is the dry venom yield in milligrams and W the weight of the snake in grams. For adults only, say above 600 mm. in length, the following more simple linear equations will be found satisfactory: for the Platteville series, $V = 0.191W + 7$; and for the Pierres, $V = 0.163W + 5$.

It might logically be expected that the venom yield would be proportionate to the capacity of the venom glands, and therefore to the cube of the head length. Actually, the venom yield increases somewhat faster than the cube of the head length. The equations are substantially as follows: for the Platteville series, $V = 1.11H^{3.15}$, and for the Pierre series, $V = 0.75H^{3.27}$, where V is the yield in mg. of dried venom and H is the head length in centimeters. These equations are applicable to the adults; the exponents are slightly higher, and the coefficients lower in specimens below 500 mm. in length. It will be observed that the yield is more nearly proportional to the cube of the head length than it is to the cube of the body length, as might well be expected.

Comparative studies of the Platteville specimens taken in the autumn prior to their entering hibernation and of those collected in the spring upon emergence indicate slightly higher yields for the latter. Some of the autumn specimens had no doubt fed recently, which was not true of those collected around the dens in the spring.

The fact that very large rattlers do not always produce as much venom as might be expected from their size has lead to a belief that has become folklore in some areas to the effect that large snakes are not so dangerous as smaller ones. Naphegyi (1868, p. 250) thought that if a rattlesnake had over 15 rattles its bite would not be serious, but one with 3 to 8 rattles would be fatal.

Ontogenetic Variation in Yield: Individual.—Thus far, by the use of yield averages in *C. v. viridis*, I have developed some typical ontogenetic trend curves. Now I shall present some data on the dispersions of individual specimens and the ontogenetic trends shown by scatter diagrams of yield–length data. In general, the results are found to be rather unsatisfactory, because of the great variations in yields at any body length. Not only do we have a high dispersion, but it is of a type not lending itself to statistical analysis because it does not follow the normal probability curve. In each snake there is an obvious upper limit to the yield—the capacity of the two venom glands—but the lower limit is zero. It is true that only rarely does a rattler produce no venom—I am assuming that the snakes have been given a reasonable rest before their first milking—but the dispersion below the mode is much wider than that above.

The curves are steeply exponential in type. I find it easier to define high yields, and what might be termed good yields, than modal yields, unless many specimens are available. As an indication of the character of variation found in individual yields, I present both the ontogenetic lines and tables of yields for three diamondbacks, the red (*C. r. ruber*), the San Lucan (*C. r. lucasensis*), and the western (*C. atrox*). These data are applicable only to subadults and adults. In table 11:10 there are set forth the constants in the equation $V = aL^b$, where V is the liquid venom yield in cubic centimeters, and L is the length of the snake in meters. Yields at various body lengths, as derived from these curves, are presented in table 11:11.

No claim is made with respect to the detailed accuracy of these data. They merely serve to illustrate how rapidly yields increase with size, and the very wide variations between good and high yields. High yields are as much as 100 per cent above the good yields in the smaller sizes, and 50 per cent in the larger. And as for low yields, which fluctuate with great inconsistency, these dwindle almost to nothing. It will be observed that these curves, setting forth as they do high and good yields, are much steeper, that is, there is a more rapid increase with growth, than was the case with the *C. v. viridis* curves previously deduced for average yields. Also, the *viridis* curves dealt with dried venom in milligrams, and these curves with raw liquid venom in cubic centimeters. The dry yield in milligrams may be approximated from the liquid yield in cubic centimeters by multiplying by 250.

Minton (1953, p. 213) found the yield in adult *horridus* to average 3.39 mg. of dried venom per inch of snake; the individual variation was from 1.86 mg. to 5.28 mg.

Venom Retention and Restoration.—Those who keep large numbers of rattlesnakes in captivity for the purpose of maintaining a continuous venom supply soon learn that a constant output is not to be expected. For various reasons, the production usually declines, so that the hope of a steady supply can be met only by continual procurement of fresh snakes.

It is not apparent that the mere restraint of captivity is important in affecting venom secretion; probably any decrease results from a combination of the conditions of light and temperature, overcrowding, inadequate food supply, and parasites and disease. No doubt the severe pressure on the venom glands in the first milking may be injurious, or the use of a common venom cup may transmit disease from one snake to another. But whatever the cause, it is a fact that dwindling yields must generally be expected in a continued milking program; and even to be moderately successful such a program should entail intervals of rest between milkings of at least two weeks and preferably a month or more. Although not definitely proved by experiments, it is probable that adequate food for the snakes will improve the yield. To be fed successfully rattlers must be separated into relatively small groups. Many will not accept food in captivity.

TABLE 11:10

Constants in the Exponential Yield Curves of the Form $V = aL^b$
of Three Subspecies of Rattlesnakes
(V is the yield of liquid venom in cc.; L is length of the snake in meters.)

Constant	C. r. ruber		C. r. lucasensis			C. atrox	
	High yield	Good yield	High yield	Good yield	Modal yield	High yield	Good yield
a	1.57	1.07	1.48	0.98	0.82	0.86	0.57
b	3.60	3.63	3.62	4.07	5.09	3.02	3.42

TABLE 11:11

Yields Derived from Exponential Yield Curves: Yields in cc. of Liquid

Length of snake over-all in meters	C. r. ruber		C. r. lucasensis			C. atrox	
	High yield	Good yield	High yield	Good yield	Modal yield	High yield	Good yield
0.6	0.24	0.16	0.23	0.13	0.07	0.19	0.10
0.7	0.43	0.28	0.40	0.23	0.14	0.30	0.17
0.8	0.70	0.47	0.66	0.40	0.27	0.44	0.26
0.9	1.07	0.72	1.00	0.64	0.46	0.63	0.40
1.0	1.57	1.07	1.48	0.98	0.82	0.86	0.57
1.1	2.20	1.51	2.10	1.45	1.33	1.14	0.78
1.2	3.04	2.10	2.90	2.05	2.07	1.48	1.05
1.3	....	....	....	....	....	1.88	1.40
1.4	....	....	....	....	....	2.36	1.80
1.5	....	....	....	....	....	2.88	2.27

What has been said about the adverse effects of captivity does not apply to the initial milking, although this will undoubtedly be increased by a resting period of a month or so between capture and the first milking. This will permit the replenishment of any venom lost while the snakes were being caught, or in precapture feeding. During this resting period, the snakes should not be annoyed. I have no doubt that a well-cared-for snake long in captivity—one that feeds readily—would give as high an initial yield as any wild snake, but these conditions are seldom met when snakes are kept in large numbers for milking, particularly when on public exhibition.

Before presenting some available statistics on successive yields in snake milking programs, I should like to offer some that compare the venom injected in a natural bite with that secured in milking, and also the effects of successive natural bites. I shall first touch on the latter, which may be of importance in actual snake-bite cases, and may afford knowledge of the rapidity with which venom is resecreted after the glands have been partly evacuated.

As early as 1673, Redi (p. 26) proved that successive bites by the same viper were decreasingly serious. In colonial times, Capt. Hall (1727, p. 310) performed similar experiments with rattlesnakes, and found that dogs and other animals were affected to a declining degree. But Clayton (1693, p. 133) claimed that, when a series of hogs were bitten, they all died, indicating that plenty of venom remained for successive bites. Lawson (1709, p. 134; Brickell, 1737, p. 145) maintained that the venom was restored slowly, because, when two men were bitten by the same rattlesnake, the second was not seriously harmed. Barton (1793, p. 103) experimented with four chickens on successive days with declining effects. Burnett (1854a, p. 314) reported similar results on eight chickens. Jeter (1854, p. 10) maintained that after about four bites, a snake is so drained of venom that it is harmless for several days. This is still a popular belief (Allyn, 1937, p. 223). Seitz (1933, p. 99) presumed that gland replenishment takes almost as long as the time required for a snake to digest its prey. Oliver (1944, p. 871) believes that full replenishment requires two weeks.

Allyn (1937, p. 223) experimented with timber rattlesnakes (*C. h. horridus*) by causing them to inflict successive bites on rats. He found that the first rat bitten died within 10 minutes, the second and third in from 10 to 15 minutes, while a fourth rat recovered. He also determined that venom replenishment was rapid enough to permit a rattler to kill a rat every day for five successive days. He allowed a rattler to bite through a diaphragm, but without external pressure on the glands, and noted that the first bite produced 0.5 cc. of liquid venom, the second the same amount, the third between 0.2 and 0.3 cc., and the fourth about 0.1 cc.

Fairley and Splatt (1929, p. 338) made a number of experiments to determine the residual venom in successive natural bites made by death adders and tiger snakes, both of which are dangerous Australian elapids. They found a great variability in the successive yields from individual snakes. If the venom yield from the first bites be considered to equal 100 per cent, the second bites in the death adder produced 46 per cent, and third 7 per cent; the corresponding figures for the tiger snake were 36 per cent for the second bite, and 3 per cent for the third. Despite these rapid declines in the yields from natural bites, subsequent milkings showed that the glands still contained considerable venom—in the case of the death adder almost as much as had been delivered in the second natural bite, and in the tiger snake, more. Another series of tests, in which the snake was permitted to bite only once and was then milked to evaluate the reserve, showed that the death adder held back from 0 to 85 per cent in reserve, with an average of 25 per cent; and the tiger snake withheld from 5 to 81 per cent in reserve, with an average of 27 per cent.

Acton and Knowles (1914a, p. 414) reported that cobras used 62 per cent of their venom in a good bite, and saw-scaled vipers 71 per cent (1941b, p. 419). These figures are not applicable to rattlesnakes, with their longer fangs and more copious supplies of less powerful venom. When a rattlesnake has bitten through the diaphragm over a venom cup, it is difficult to disengage the fangs and secure independent bites; however, it is clearly evident, from the additional flow secured when the glands are pressed, that much venom is held in reserve after the first bite. This is probably inherent in the structure of the gland and the muscles that express the venom.

The amount that a rattlesnake holds in reserve after an initial bite has been stated to be from 25 to 75 per cent of the original contents of the glands (Amaral, 1928b, p. 103). King (1941, p. 44) has expressed the opinion that it is about 67 per cent. Allyn's results, previously mentioned, indicate a reserve of 65 per cent. Stahnke (1954, p. 23) mentions the case of a man who was bitten by a 3½-foot western diamond nine days after the snake had been milked. The snake was milked immediately after the accident and yielded 20.4 mg. of dried venom. Two weeks later the yield was 87.8 mg. Undoubtedly the amount retained depends on many conditions, such as the fullness of the glands when the snake strikes, whether striking prey or an enemy, and, if the latter, the degree of its fear or injury, and, of course, the length of time it is allowed to hold on. I judge that large rattlers striking small prey expend comparatively little venom—they seem barely to touch it before retracting the head. From experiences in milking rattlesnakes, and observing, first, the flow from the initial bite, and then the flow that results from pressure on the glands, I should estimate that they usually hold considerably more than 50 per cent in reserve. But I should admit that an angered or injured rattlesnake with a good hold with both jaws—the lower jaw would increase muscular effectiveness—might easily inject up to 75 per cent of the gland contents. In reality, this would involve several successive biting pressures, including separate gland pulses, but without withdrawal of the imbedded fangs.

The effects of successive bites may be of practical importance, in that, occasionally, a victim may be bitten several times by an angered or injured snake before he can get beyond its range. Driver (1911, p. 561) tells of a child that was bitten twice; and Doughty (1928, p. 237) of another that was bitten three times. Bulger and Northrop (1951, p. 1134) treated a girl of 22 months who had been bitten by a *C. v. viridis* in each leg. Col. Crimmins wrote me of a child that was bitten and was followed up by a rattler that struck seven times altogether. Booth (1814, p. 322) tells of a rattler that bit a man 25 times on a single occasion. He was cured by the application of a plant known to the Indians of Yucatán, where the incident occurred. This last experience has all the evidence of a hearsay story that need not be credited. Fontana (1787, vol. 1, p. 166) observed, from his experiments, that several bites in the same part of the body are not so dangerous as when the same number of bites are scattered.

From what has been said concerning the additional flow secured by milking after a natural bite, it could be assumed, correlatively, that milking always produces a greater yield than a natural bite. I have no doubt that this is the case with rattlesnakes. Minton (1953, p. 213) examined timber rattlers and copperheads killed 24 hours after they had been milked and found that the stripping had been virtually complete; there was almost no venom in the glands. Lamb (1904, p. 1275; Amaral, 1923, p. 685) stated that a cobra gave 60 per cent more venom on biting than by milking. This may be true with some elapids, for the location of the glands in their relatively small heads may make milking difficult, but it is contrary to the results of Fairley and Splatt already mentioned, and certainly it is not the case with rattlesnakes.

Following a discussion of successive bites and venom reserves, the next question that arises concerns the rapidity of venom replenishment: How rapidly and completely are the contents of the glands restored after a bite or milking? The fact that venom is restored rather slowly after a forced and complete milking is well known to those who keep snakes in captivity for the collection of venom. In such institutions it is usually the custom to depend largely on fresh snakes from the wild, so limited are the secondary yields. There is, besides, the possible effect of captivity on venom quality, which might cast doubts on the results in some types of experimental work.

To the extent that declines in successive yields from the milking of captive specimens may indicate the slowness of venom secretion, the following experiences at San Diego may be cited. In one group of *C. atrox*, with 38 days between the first and second milkings, a liquid recovery of 73 per cent of the initial stripping was secured, but the quality of the venom was so attenuated that the dry purified residue represented only 48 per cent of the original quantity. Nine specimens of *C. v. oreganus* from central Washington were milked three times, at intervals of four weeks between the first and second stripping, and two weeks between the second and third. The second milking yielded only half that of the first (in liquid venom), and the third only 6 per cent of the first. In the case of three blacktails (*C. m. molossus*), the liquid venom yield after an interval of 32 days was 47 per cent of the first milking. Fifteen large prairie rattlers (*C. v. viridis*), kept at about 15° C. (59° F.) during their natural hibernating season, gave less than 2 per cent of their initial yield when milked nine days after the first stripping. Over 100 adult specimens of *C. r. lucasensis*, divided into groups, were milked in one day, and the groups were then remilked at varying subsequent intervals. The results, in terms of dried venom, were as follows:

Interval in days after milking	Dry venom recovery in per cent of initial yield
7	15
19	36
27	59
40	67
54	90

These snakes had been in captivity—but without food—for some weeks prior to the initial milking and were no longer particularly afraid of people.

George (1930, p. 59), with *C. d. durissus,* reported a secondary yield of 69 per cent on a liquid basis after an interval of about 25 days. Fairley and Splatt (1929, pp. 340, 343, 345, and 347), with Australian elapids, got secondary and tertiary yields quite comparable to the initial yields, and in some cases exceeding the first milking. Some yields continued good up to the fifth or sixth milking, but many of the specimens were subsequently not listed and presumably died after the fourth or fifth. These snakes were milked at monthly intervals.

Several experimenters have secured good results from successive milkings over long periods. Houssay (1923, p. 449), working with *C. d. terrificus* in Argentina, made four extractions per month in summer and two per month in winter. Presumably the yields must have held up well or he would have resorted to fresh snakes.

Wolff and Githens (1939b, p. 234) got a remarkable series of extractions from a group of water moccasins that were milked 16 times during a period of about two years, at intervals varying from three weeks to six months. Unfortunately, it is impossible to determine the correlation between the length of the rest periods and the corresponding yield, as the methods of stripping were not consistently uniform. But at least it was shown that the average yield in dried venom was well maintained up to the sixteenth milking. The highest yield—a record breaker for water moccasins—was secured on a second milking of one of the snakes, producing 4.0 cc. of liquid and 1,094 mg. of dried venom (1939a, p. 52). These moccasins were fed during their captivity.

Undoubtedly the rapidity of replenishment depends on the treatment of the glands in the first milking, and the conditions of captivity during the rest period. Food and water, a proper temperature, an avoidance of disturbance, an adequate interval of rest, and an absence of disease are all essential, if secondary milkings are to be at all productive.

Of course, the expenditure of venom for food, immediately before milking, is to be avoided. Clark (1942, p. 44) found that it was not worth while to milk snakes unless they had fasted for at least three weeks. Stadelman (1929, p. 29) was impressed by the copious yields from snakes dug out of hibernation, where they had not fed for a considerable time.

Harris (1932, p. 13), speaking of the ways in which various Indian tribes handled rattlers in religious ceremonies, expressed the opinion that they knew that the venom of a snake long in captivity and without food would be less toxic. Harlan (1835, pp. 495, 502) said that snake-show people prevented their rattlers from having food or water in order to reduce the danger. Palmer (1915, p. 241) thought that the absence of food made a rattler's venom pale and scant. Lamb (1904, p. 1275) mentioned the adverse effect of captivity on the venom yield from cobras.

There have been some quite unjustified statements regarding the speed of venom replacement. Wolman (1937, p. 21) thought that a three-foot rattler would produce a cubic centimeter of venom every two or three days, if well fed. Mac-Clary (1939, p. 24) estimated that it would require two or three days for a rattler to replenish its venom; King (1941, p. 44) gives a figure of three or four days. These are but guesses. One snake-pit owner, who had been bitten ten times by rattlesnakes, informed me that some of his worst bites occurred soon after a snake had been milked and presumably had been stripped completely of its venom, but this was only a matter of opinion, for he kept no accurate records. But certainly, regardless of the evidence that I have presented indicating slowness of recovery, and reduction in yield after complete stripping, no one should be so foolish as to believe the myth that a rattlesnake is not dangerous because it has recently bitten something.

Prevost (1746–89, vol. 14, p. 150; Lacépède, 1788–89, vol. 2, p. 418) states that rattlesnakes in Paraguay become so distressed from the overfilling of their venom glands, when not used, that they will bite anything for relief. In Nicaragua there is a native belief that snakes periodically wash out their venom if they have not expended it by a strike (Banton, 1930, p. 475). Unonius (1950, p. 298), writing in the period 1841 to 1858, said that in summertime the glands become so full that the snake is blinded. There is, of course, no evidence that the glands ever become overfilled, and if they did, the snake could easily release venom without biting anything.

TOXIC INDICES

It would be of general popular interest if it were possible to rate poisonous snakes in the order of their danger to human beings. Some kinds are undoubtedly much more dangerous than others; but an accurate rating is quite impossible because of the many uncertainties involved in snake-bite cases, as was pointed out at the beginning of this discussion. It is difficult to rate, with any accuracy, even so limited a group as the rattlesnakes.

It might be assumed that one criterion—the venom—should permit a fair evaluation, and it does, to a limited degree. If we divide the average quantity of venom extruded in a bite by the m.l.d., the result is a toxicity index—the number of m.l.d.'s per bite. Toxic indices of this kind are often cited in the literature (e.g., Githens, 1935a, p. 171; Stickel, 1952, p. 15), and they do have some comparative value. It would be easy to compile a set for the rattlesnakes, using the average yields set forth in table 11:7, divided by the corresponding m.l.d.'s in tables 11:2 to 11:4, or 11:5. Yet, if we recall the wide variations in yields and the equally wide variations in the m.l.d.'s—as great as 10 to 1 in different batches of venom from the same subspecies in Githens' results, and 4 to 1 in Schoettler's—to say nothing of such important qualifying factors as the kind of experimental animal and the type of injection, it seems to me that under the circumstances of uncertainty in both the numerator and denominator used in computing indices, the presentation of a table of toxic indices would suggest a totally undeserved validity and accuracy.

It is proper to arrive at certain general conclusions. The South American rattlesnake (*C. d. terrificus*) is surely the most dangerous of all the rattlers because of its combination of large size and extremely powerful venom. The Central American rattler (*C. d. durissus*) is a still larger snake and may be even more dangerous; but both its yield and m.l.d. records are uncertain because of past nomenclatorial confusion. It probably has a higher yield but of a less powerful venom than *terrificus*. *C. b. basiliscus* may also be a very dangerous snake.

Of the species found in the United States, I should give first place to the eastern diamondback (*C. adamanteus*) because of its extreme size and high venom delivery, although its venom is not a strong one. Next would come the western diamond (*C. atrox*), which results in more serious cases in the United States than any other venomous snake, rattler or otherwise; and may, in fact, cause more serious cases than all the other kinds of rattlers in our country put together. This is because it ranges over a large area, is extremely plentiful in some places, including farming districts, and is nervous, easily aroused, and, in rare cases, even aggressive. It has a more powerful venom than *adamanteus*, but the quantity is smaller. Following *atrox*, I should place *C. viridis* and *C. horridus*, particularly their larger subspecies, and *C. m. molossus*. All of these are thoroughly dangerous snakes. Nor should my not having mentioned them suggest that the other kinds of rattlers are to be trifled with. For example, if future tests of the quality of the venom of *C. s. scutulatus* corroborate the m.l.d. figures now available, this may prove to be a very dangerous rattler.

Of course, despite all the doubts surrounding the data on yields and m.l.d.'s, we can make some fair guesses concerning relative hazards. For example, there is no indication that the sidewinder (*C. cerastes*) fulfills its fearful reputation of being the most deadly rattler that crawls. Its venom yield is certainly low and the venom is not especially powerful; and as a dangerous snake, it is not to be compared with some of the larger rattlers that I have mentioned.

Schoettler (1951a, table 2) brings into his calculations of a toxic index not only yield and toxicity, but the frequency of occcurrence of the snakes, based on the numbers sent in each year to the Butantan Institute at São Paulo, Brazil. He reaches the conclusion that, although there are many species of coral snakes in Brazil, and many species of nonrattlesnake pit vipers (*Bothrops*), the rattlesnake (*C. d. terrificus*), of which only one kind is currently recognized there, is by far the most dangerous snake in that country. With that conclusion I have no reason to disagree, although I am not particularly impressed with the evaluation of the factors used by Schoettler in grading the snakes, or the applicability of similar factors to the grading of snakes in other countries.

I have mentioned elsewhere that there are elapine snakes more dangerous than any rattlers, such as the king cobra of southeast Asia, the mambas of Africa, and the taipan of Australia. These are large snakes with powerful venoms. For extreme virulence of venom, Fairley (1929a, p. 300) awards the palm to the Australian tiger snake, stating that the average yield from one of these snakes would be sufficient to kill 118 sheep. Grasset and Schaafsma (1940, p. 236) report that the venom of a South African back-fanged snake, the boomslang, *Dispholidus typus,* is more powerful than that of a cobra or mamba. But the snake is not especially dangerous because of the inefficiency of its biting mechanism. D'Amour, Becker, and Van Riper have reported the venom of the black widow spider (*Latrodectus mactans*) to be 15 times as virulent as that of the prairie rattlesnake.

VENOM UTILIZATION

Rattlesnake venom is in occasional demand for two purposes: for the immunization of animals (especially horses) in the production of antivenin; and for therapeutic uses. The latter is still in the experimental stage and there is no certainty, or even probability, that rattler venom will ever have any recognized place in pharmacology.

Production of Antivenin.—From time to time, people in areas where rattlesnakes abound—particularly in the Southwest—have been encouraged by the high prices reputedly paid for venom, to consider going into rattlesnake farming, with the expectation of a continuous and valuable crop. Actually, as I have pointed out elsewhere (p. 1010), rattlesnakes are difficult and expensive to raise in captivity, and repeated milkings are not fruitful; therefore, a steady venom supply must come from the continuous availability of freshly caught snakes. Even this might be profitable, as an off-season side line for farmers and stock raisers in a few places, were there a steady market for dry venom, but such a market does not now exist, and probably never did. It was widely reported during World War II that "the government" would buy all the rattlesnake venom available at some fantastic price, and as a result I received from hopeful farmers many requests for instructions in the art of rattlesnake culture. I do not know how the rumor started. It was probably true that large supplies of antivenin were purchased for Southern army training camps, and therefore there was an increased demand for venom for immunological purposes by the manufacturers of antivenin. With this requirement I shall deal later, in connection with the preparation of antivenin. It is probable that there is a moderately steady demand for the venoms of some species of rattlers for this purpose, but the manufacturers have their own sources of supply from depots where the snakes may be accurately identified and the venom properly purified and dried.

As to prices: in 1927, at about the time when the commercial preparation of antivenin began in the United States, some *atrox* venom in Texas was sold at $10 per liquid ounce. This would be at the rate of about $1.35 per gram of dried venom. In 1937, there were quotations from reptile supply dealers at $3.50 per gram, and in 1945 from $2.00 to $3.00, depending on the species. During World War II, a manufacturer of antivenin paid $15 per gram for *ruber* venom, $20 for *horridus,* and $25 for *viridis, helleri,* or *catenatus* venom. One commercial dealer recently quoted *adamanteus* venom at $10 per gram, dried and purified, and *atrox* at $12; *horridus* venom was $20 and *viridis* venom $25. These quotations are not to be taken as indicative of bid prices at which sales can readily be made at any time.

The Butantan Institute, of São Paulo, Brazil, procures a continuous supply of fresh snakes by exchanging with farmers an ampul of antivenin for every four snakes of any species, whether or not venomous. Shipping containers are furnished and the snakes are transported to the institute at the expense of the state (Vaz, 1951, pp. 53, 60).

In the early days of the Antivenin Institute of America (1927–30), a co-operative arrangement was made with the Atchison, Topeka and Santa Fe Railway and the Railway Express Agency, whereby large numbers of rattlesnakes were collected by the railway section crews along the rights-of-way in California, Arizona, and New Mexico, and were transported to the San Diego Zoo, where the venoms were abstracted, processed, and forwarded to the Mulford Laboratories at Glenolden, Pennsylvania. This project made available for experimental purposes the venoms of a number of rare subspecies of rattlesnakes.

Use of Venom in Therapeutics.—As I have said, aside from the use of venoms for immunizing horses for the production of antivenin, and in associated immunological and taxonomic studies, there has been a limited requirement for venom in therapeutics, although primarily on an experimental, rather than on a commercial, basis.

There is something peculiarly fascinating in the conversion of a dangerous creature such as a rattlesnake—and the essence of that danger, the venom—into a cure for disease, and so it is that experimental work looking to such a use has often resulted in sensational and premature accounts of the curative properties of venom. Today it may be that cobra venom is still used to some extent to reduce pain in cases of inoperable cancer and similar afflictions, and moccasin venom in cases of intractable hemorrhage; but for the many diseases for which rattlesnake venom has been tried, no cure has survived the test of time, although often publicized with initial enthusiasm and assurance.

The therapeutic use of snake venoms long antedated the discovery of America, so there was nothing particularly novel in similar attempts to cure diseases with rattlesnake venom when these spectacular snakes first became available. The venom treatments began on a plane of folklore, as in Europe, where viper venom had been so used; but later some really scientific work was undertaken in an endeavor to cure afflictions with these exceedingly powerful toxins. It was expected that the results would parallel the important contributions of vegetable poisons to medicine, but in this they have proved a disappointing failure.

The literature of the therapeutic uses of snake venom is quite extensive. Lists of the many diseases for the amelioration of which various kinds of venom have been tried, at least experimentally, will be found in Mays, 1909, p. 481; Chopra and Chowhan, 1932, p. 577, and 1935, pp. 445, 452; Kellaway, 1937, p. 12; Hughes, 1938, p. 689; Gessner, 1940, p. 343; Ghosh, 1941, p. 187; Boquet, 1948, p. 137; and Grundmann, 1950, p. 570. These also contain bibliographies from which the treatments given the maladies may be ascertained, especially in Boquet, who lists over 50 such references, most of them recent. The Harmon and Pollard bibliography (1948) is also rich in therapeutic references. A few articles on the general subject of venom therapeutics, but in a more popular vein than those just cited are: Cooke, 1934, p. 118; Macht, 1938, p. 34; Allen and Merryday, 1940, p. 236; Castiglioni, 1942, p. 1185; and Humphreys, 1951, p. 12.

Rattlesnake venom, either taken orally or injected subcutaneously, has been suggested for a number of maladies, and no doubt it has been tried and unreported for many more. Wallace (1827, p. 663; Paine, 1875, p. 140) prints a letter written in 1824, in which pills made of pounded venom glands and cheese were alleged to relieve palsy, rheumatism, and typhus fever. They gave a general feeling of well-being and, indeed, of "ethereal delights." The writer of the letter— no doubt under the influence of his remedy—hazarded the prophecy that rattle-snakes would one day be raised for medicinal purposes. Beltrami (1828, vol. 2, p. 186) said that rattlesnake venom was an excellent tonic for anyone with the courage to swallow it.

Rattlesnake Venom in Homeopathy.—Snake venom, particularly bothropic venom, under the pharmaceutical name "lachesis"; rattlesnake venom usually under the name "crotalus," but sometimes "crotalus horridus," or, occasionally "crotalinii";[4] cobra venom under the name "naja"; and coral-snake venom under the name "elaps"—all have long had a place in the homeopathic pharmacopeia. Their usage has been in accordance with the homeopathic theory that a medicine is efficacious for any disease whose symptoms approximate those resulting from the medicine alone (Hering, 1844, p. 369). The prescription of either lachesis or crotalus by homeopaths has been discussed by Hering, 1844, p. 369; Good, 1853, p. 9; Hayward, 1882a, p. 113; 1882b, p. 243; 1883, p. 54; 1884, p. 149; Mohr, 1901, p. 238; Stoneham, 1906, p. 453; Koch, 1925, p. 16; Fleagle, 1931, p. 808; Wyne, 1937, p. 606; Gladish, 1939, p. 554; and Dunning, 1943, p. 135.

The most complete survey of the effects and therapeutic applications of rat-tlesnake venom, using the methods and conclusions of homeopathy, is that of Hayward (1884, pp. 149–381). He followed, of course, the major tenet of home-

---

[4] Noguchi devised the term "crotalin" as a short word for rattlesnake venom when used as an immunological or therapeutic agent.

opathy, stating (p. 153): "When the symptoms which indicate a given form of disease are like those that crotalus will produce, its power as a remedy is incalculable." For the purpose of analyzing the symptoms of rattlesnake bite, he gathered all the symptoms that were available from provings—voluntary tests on human beings—(Hayward, 1883b, p. 26), actual snake-bite cases as reported in the literature, and experiments on animals. The symptoms thus secured were then reassembled into 23 categories affecting different organs or parts of the body (e.g., the throat), a total of 757 symptoms being listed, with many, of course, repeated under the various categories. Under each of the 23 categories, conclusions were drawn with respect to the similarity of the crotalus symptoms to the symptoms of any diseases affecting the same organ or body part. Where such similarities were found, the conclusion was drawn that rattlesnake venom, in quantities less than those that would cause the symptom, would ameliorate or cure the disease.

In the case of some afflictions, the cure was determined on a purely theoretical basis, but actual clinical experiences proving the value of the remedy were cited with respect to many diseases. The administration of the venom (greatly diluted) was usually by mouth, but in very serious diseases hypodermic injections were employed. Crotalus was also applied to open sores in the form of a lotion or wet compress. The general program was to administer the venom (called, as is usual in homeopathy, crotalus) in reduced quantities such that the venom would not, of itself, cause those symptoms characteristic of the disease it was sought to cure.

Among the afflictions or conditions for which Hayward recommended crotalus— these are but a minor proportion of those he included—were: delirium tremens and alcoholism, melancholia, vertigo, convulsions, meningitis, apoplexy, deafness (of certain kinds), catarrh, bronchitis, erysipelas, neuralgia, mumps, diphtheria, quinsy, laryngitis, gangrene, peritonitis, acute jaundice, dysentery, cholera, asthma, epitaxis, pneumonia, hemophilia, pernicious anemia, hematura, rheumatism, syphilis, elephantiasis, scarlatina, typhus, yellow fever, plague, epilepsy, hydrophobia, and dropsy.

Hayward's voluminous work on crotalus (over 200 printed pages) was the guide for homeopaths in their treatment of diseases by the use of this venom for many years; and this remedy is still of importance in homeopathy, as can be seen from the considerable catalogue of serious diseases listed for treatment with crotalus by Fleagle (1931, p. 809), Wyne (1937, p. 606), Gladish (1939, p. 554), and by Dunning as recently as 1943 (p. 137). Some of the diseases added subsequent to the work of Hayward have been ear infections, puerperal fever, appendicitis, goiter, rheumatic fever, endocarditis, smallpox, and typhoid fever.

Neidhard (1860, second edition, 1868; see also Hayward, 1884, p. 160) has dwelt at length on the efficacy of the venom of *C. horridus* in the treatment of yellow fever, and, to a lesser extent, of cholera and bilious remittent fever. Dr. W. L. Humboldt was said (Manzini, 1858, p. 1) to have used the treatment in New Orleans as early as 1849; and Dr. N. B. L. Manzini reported having successfully used venom in 2,000 cases in Cuba. The cure was originally devised on homeopathic premises (Holcombe, 1853, p. 465), owing to the supposed resemblance of the symptoms of yellow fever to those of rattlesnake bite, but later its use was not restricted to homeopaths. Despite the scourge that yellow fever remained for the next 40 years, little was subsequently heard of this treatment, from which it may be assumed that other physicians were unable to duplicate the favorable results of Humboldt and Manzini.

Rattlesnake Venom in Standard Medical Therapeutics.—Although rattlesnake venom has never achieved a place in the regular (allopathic) pharmacopeia, it has been used experimentally in the treatment of a number of afflictions, occasionally with some appearance of success. One of the most famous early cases was that of a youth in Rio de Janeiro, who was treated with *terrificus* venom for leprosy or elephantiasis, or both, in 1831. This was first reported by Sigaud in 1834, and subsequently by Clarke (1838, vol. 1, p. 443), Mitchell (1861, p. 284), Anon. (1874, p. 559), and Hayward (1884, p. 229). The case ended fatally within 24 hours. Goldschmidt (1901, p. 31; translation, p. 353) mentions a more recent attempt to treat leprosy with *terrificus* venom. There was also one subsequent report on the use of rattlesnake venom for elephantiasis by Dugès (1877, p. 17), who thought the patient had been somewhat benefited.

Rattlesnake venom has been recommended for alcoholism (Burnett, 1854b, p. 323). It is not difficult to trace the source of this idea. In the days when alcohol was the standard remedy for rattlesnake bite, it was believed that a patient would never become inebriated, regardless of the amount of whiskey or brandy he consumed, as long as there remained any unneutralized venom in his system. The recommendation for venom as a cure for alcoholism is an obvious corollary.

Rattlesnake Venom Treatment for Epilepsy.—Probably the widest use of rattler venom for curative purposes, and the nearest that it has come to adoption by any appreciable element of the medical profession for any purpose, was in the treatment of epilepsy. The theory of the beneficial effect of the venom was that it decreases blood coagulability and that epileptic blood is above normal in this respect (Jenkins and Pendleton, 1914, p. 1750; Chewning, 1915, p. 261).

Although mentioned incidentally by Hayward (1884, p. 379), a serious consideration of the treatment was apparently initiated through a case report by Self (1908, p. 305) of an epileptic 35 years old who had been subject to seizures at intervals of a month for over 15 years. He was accidentally bitten by a moccasin, and suffered no further attacks within the next two years. When this was reported in the medical press, it was picked up by Mays in 1908, who gradually developed an elaborate technique for treating epileptics with rattlesnake venom, and, as he thought, with considerable success (Mays, 1909, p. 481; 1910, p. 46; 1913a, p. 561; 1913b, p. 1811; 1914, p. 105). The dosage, place of injection, and intervals between treatments were all carefully considered. At one time he reported having given no less than 6,000 injections in strengths of from $\frac{1}{200}$ to $\frac{1}{50}$ of a grain, and this without any infections. He stated that he used *horridus* venom, but as he secured it in Brownsville, Texas, we may assume it to have been *atrox* venom. He gradually expanded his treatments to include phthisis, acute and chronic bronchitis, pleurisy, pneumonia, asthma, dyspnea, neuralgia, lumbago, and sciatica. Some of Mays' articles were written in reply to skeptical editorials and comments in the medical press.

Another advocate of the crotalin treatment for epilepsy was Spangler (1910, p. 462; 1911, p. 517; 1912, p. 520; 1913, p. 699; 1918, p. 727; 1924, pp. 389, 495, 138; 1943, p. 91). His dosages ranged from $\frac{1}{400}$ to $\frac{1}{12}$ grain. He believed that most cases were definitely benefited, and eventually reported on the treatment of over 600 cases. He mixed the venom with trikresol to act as both a preservative and antiseptic. He thought the degree of nervous improvement in the patient was correlated with the local reaction to the venom, which was from *C. horridus*. He also mentions having treated tuberculosis with venom, but this was incidental. With respect to epilepsy, after 16 years of experience, he stated that the treatment showed some striking benefits in the form of increased weight and improved hemoglobin and metabolism, as well as in the elimination or amelioration of seizures.

Yawger (1914, p. 1533) described a test made on the crotalin treatment at the Oakbourne Epileptic Colony in Pennsylvania. The institution undertook the trial as a result of glowing reports in the lay press, which inspired the patients and their relatives to demand the use of venom. Six patients were given the treatment; the results were generally unfavorable. Other unfavorable comments were those of Joyce, 1913, p. 535; Douglass, 1914, p. 360; Austin, 1914, p. 268; and Thorn, 1914, p. 933.

Anderson (1914, p. 893), of the Hygienic Laboratory in Washington, made tests on commercial preparations of crotalin after the death of a 15-year-old boy from an infection following venom treatments for epilepsy. He found that nearly 40 per cent of the samples received from four different commercial drug firms then marketing crotalin were nonsterile. He felt that the chance of infection was increased by the antibactericidal action of the venom, and stated that he thought it impossible either to sterilize or standardize the venom. In this valid criticism by Anderson will be found the basic reasons why rattlesnake venom, even if it had produced the benefits for epileptics claimed by its proponents, would by now have been superseded by more reliable drugs. Macht (1936, p. 537) has mentioned the further fact that venom is unstable and decomposes even at room temperatures (see also Appleby, 1942, p. 246). The editor of the *Journal of the American Medical Association,* answering an inquiry (Falk, 1939, p. 1055), thought the preparation no longer on the market for the reasons already given. However, crotalin was listed in the *American Druggist Blue Book* for 1955.

Some further references to the use of venom in epilepsy are: FitzSimons, 1929, p. 4; and 1934, p. 2; Chopra and Chowan, 1932, p. 577; Podolsky, 1934, p. 259; Macht, 1936, p. 537; Maier, 1940, p. 352; Chowan, 1941, p. 11; and Appleby, 1942, p. 246. Macht says it is now rarely mentioned as a possible cure for the disease. It is not among the 23 drugs suggested for the treatment of epilepsy in a current pharmaceutical publication (Jones, 1950, p. 380).

Miscellaneous Therapeutic Uses.—Several writers, in addition to those whom I have mentioned in connection with homeopathic practices, have presented extended lists of diseases claimed to have been successfully treated by the use of rattlesnake venom. Woodruff (1913, p. 72) used it for epilepsy, asthma, neuralgia, neuritis, lumbago, sciatica, tics, coccygodynia, laryngitis, pleurisy, St. Vitus's dance, debility, nerve exhaustion, and insomnia. Other diseases that he mentioned, but evidently not treated by him with rattler venom, were hoarseness, pneumonia, and acute and chronic bronchitis. The venom treatment resulted in a general systemic benefit, or so it was claimed. McCarty (1914, p. 660) cites five case reports of asthma, sciatica, and hystero-epilepsy. He says the case of sciatica was not improved, but that this may have resulted from too low a dosage and too early a discontinuance. Atchison (1853, p. 201) mentions a case of rattlesnake bite, during the treatment of which the patient recovered from whooping cough.

Palmer (1915, p. 243) tells of a dealer who standardized rattlesnake venom, preserved in ampuls with glycerine and alcohol, and distributed it for headache, neurasthenia, hysteria, asthma, hay fever, sciatica, lumbago, St. Vitus's dance, goiter, anemia, epilepsy, and acute homicidal mania. It was recommended that the dosage be increased gradually. Rattlesnake venom has been stated to be a folklore cure for deafness in Oregon. I do not know how it was applied.

Recently experiments have been made on the use of rattlesnake venom in the treatment or amelioration of various afflictions. Maier (1940, p. 353) mentions the successful use of rattlesnake venom in the treatment of rheumatoid arthritis. A quite contrary view of the results is taken by Anon. (1944, p. 132). Albee and Maier (1943, p. 221) claimed some success in the use of moccasin venom for the same disease.

Rattlesnake venom has been suggested as a cure for tetanus (Ameden, 1883, p. 339; Hildigo, 1899, p. 26) and for asthma (Spangler, 1925, p. 779; Alvaro, 1939, p. 1132). Alvaro (p. 1143) states that Valle in 1937 had some success in the treatment of eye inflammations with detoxified *terrificus* venom.

Some articles on the use of rattlesnake venom in therapeutics have cited its employment by Monaellesser to relieve pain in 115 cancer cases (Podolsky, 1934, p. 259; Lesser, 1938, p. 288; Maier, 1940, p. 353). It is my understanding of the report of these cases (Monaellesser and Taguet, 1933, p. 371) that only cobra venom was so used. However, Brazil (1934, p. 50) did experiment with *terrificus* venom as a pain reliever and claimed some success. Essex and Priestley (1931, p. 550) experimented with rattlesnake venom in the control (by cell destruction) of a certain type of cancer in rats. The results were negative.

Walsh, in his *Story of the Cures That Fail* (1929, p. 68), refers to cures connected with venomous reptiles as "cures with a punch" that shock people into believing in them. He attributes such improvement in epileptics as was reported as having resulted from the neurotic effect of the type of cure rather than from its substance.

I have discussed elsewhere the wide differences that exist between the venoms of the many kinds of rattlesnakes—differences not only of relative potency but of physiological effects. It is notable that the physicians who used rattlesnake venom therapeutically at the turn of the century were seldom definite as to the species of rattler from which the venom was derived; and even when the species was mentioned, we have reason to doubt the accuracy of the designations—*horridus* venom from extreme southern Texas, for example. We may assume the drug manufacturers to have been equally uncertain of their products, for there was then little appreciation of the differences in the venoms of the many species of rattlesnake. And there are even differences—maybe from sexual, climatic, alimentary, or seasonal influences, as suggested by Schoettler—in different batches of venom from the same subspecies of rattlesnake. These may lead to toxicity variations as great as 5 or even 10 to 1. The accurate identification of the various kinds of rattlesnakes requires some experience. With all of these obstacles to the standardization of venom as a drug, it is evident that the preparation of a remedy derived from rattlesnake venom, or one of the constituents of that venom, would not be a simple task. The very factors that have made it so difficult to secure uniform values of minimum lethal doses will make it equally difficult to secure uniform therapeutic products from venom, assuming that such a product were found to be efficacious in the cure of some disease, and that it could be marketed in a stable, sterile form.

Therapeutic Uses of Venom Today.—As I have stated, the therapeutic uses of snake venom that still have their advocates today are cobra venom as a nonhabit-forming pain reliever (Monaellesser and Taguet, 1933, p. 371; Macht, 1936, p. 61; Des Ligneris and Grasset, 1936, p. 512; Hughes, 1938, p. 689; Rutherford, 1939, p. 413; Leech, 1940b, p. 1196; Talkov and Bauer, 1943, p. 152; Osol and Farrar, 1947, p. 1587); and moccasin venom in the control of hemorrhage (Peck, 1932, p. 579; Dack, 1935, p. 412; Peck and Rosenthal, 1935, p. 1066; Peck, Crimmins, and Erf, 1935, p. 1525; Goldberger and Peck, 1937, p. 469; and Githens, 1939, p. 167). There is an adverse report on moccasin venom by Leech (1940a, p. 2218). These few citations represent only to a minor degree the quite formidable literature on these two uses of cobra and moccasin venoms, which have survived longer than any based on rattlesnake venom.

It may be that uniformity was one of the reasons why cobra and moccasin venoms passed somewhat beyond the experimental stage in therapy, while rattlesnake venom never did. There is but one species of water moccasin (*Agkistrodon piscivorus*) in the United States, and a supply of venom from this snake might have some degree of uniformity, even though emanating from separate sources. The cobras of the genus *Naja* seem also to yield venoms having some degree of consistency, at least with respect to certain constituents. But the term "rattlesnake," although restricted to snakes with this queer caudal appendage, nevertheless encompasses some rather diverse creatures, and venom quality is one of the characteristics in which this diversity is manifest. These venom differences (except in the case of *terrificus*) were virtually unrecognized before 1925, and are not fully appreciated today by some experimentalists. No doubt many of the unaccountable conflicting results of early therapeutic experiments were caused by an unjustified assumption that "rattlesnake venom" was a consistent and uniform product—regardless of the species of rattlesnake that produced it—which is far from the fact. This is not said with any implied regret, for I think that even if rattler venom had attained the degree of therapeutic success that certain of its enthusiastic proponents expected, its eventual replacement by some more uniform, stable, and sterile product would have come anyway.

The *American Druggist Blue Book* for 1955 lists, as available on the American market for therapeutic uses, only crotalin and cobra venom. Moccasin venom has recently been deleted. A recent general publication on pharmacology (Beckman, 1952) mentions snake venom in connection with the treatment of only one disease, hemophilia (p. 324), for which it is stated to have no proven value.

Thus, in current therapeutics, rattlesnake venom has no recognized place in regular medical practice; and the values attributed to it from time to time by enthusiasts hoping to turn this ordinarily dangerous substance to man's advantage have failed to be substantiated.

12. The Bite and Its Effects

THE NATURE OF THE BITE

Elsewhere (p. 452) I have discussed the difference between a rattlesnake's strike and its bite; the questions of whether a rattlesnake can strike without being coiled and can bite without striking have been answered in the affirmative, if there be due regard for the need of an agreement on definitions. I shall now consider only the bite, whether that bite is the terminal feature of a strike (the forward lunge of the head and body), or is the mere process of opening the mouth and sinking the fangs in the prey or in an enemy close enough to be reached without a lunge.

It is not difficult to observe how a rattlesnake bites when no strike is involved—such a bite, for example, as is likely to occur when a snake is held in restraint or stepped upon. Accidents of this kind are frequent when a rattlesnake is carelessly handled, with a sufficient length of neck left free to allow the snake to turn and bite the hand that holds it. The same thing may happen when a hiker steps on an unseen snake. Under these circumstances the snake opens its mouth wide enough to advance the fangs and to sink them into the victim, an action which the jaw muscles are amply strong enough to execute. This is a simple bite, the effectiveness of which depends somewhat on the radius of curvature of the surface bitten, as well as on the penetrability of the substance beneath. Objects of small radius—a wrist, for example—can be bitten more effectively than flat surfaces, since the lower jaw of the snake affords a viselike action that permits full use of the jaw muscles. When biting in this way, a rattler can, if one or both fangs meet obstructions, raise each fang separately to seek a new point of entrance. The curve of the fang aids in penetration.

BITE OR STAB?

The nature of the bite that terminates a strike is less easy to analyze, for the forward motion of the head is too rapid to permit seeing what the snake does. However, since the advent of high-speed photography, many instructive pictures of striking rattlesnakes have been taken (e.g., Mili, 1946, pp. 57–58; Van Riper, 1950, p. 128; 1953, p. 100; 1954, p. 50; 1955, p. 309; Van Riper, Niedrach, and Bailey, 1952, p. 1; Pope, 1952, p. 3) and further research is under way to disclose certain details of the sequence.

A rattlesnake starts its forward lunge with the mouth closed. During the advance, the mouth is opened very wide, the angle between the upper and lower jaws attaining almost a 180° opening. The plane of the upper jaw is substantially vertical; and because the maxillary mechanism permits a tilt even greater than 90°, the basal section of the fang is pointed slightly upward (fig. 11:9). Hence, despite the curvature of the fang, the points are directed almost horizontally forward, or, at most, but 15° to 25° below the horizontal. They may either be driven in by the force of the forward thrust, or they may be imbedded by a biting action produced by a hingelike closing of the jaws. It is upon this detail—stab or bite—that there has been a difference of opinion among herpetologists.

To some extent, the shape of the rattlesnake's fang favors the bite, rather than the stab theory, for the pronounced central curve in the fang (figs. 11:14 and 11:17) assists subcutaneous penetration by continued pressure—a sort of folding in—after the fang has once entered (Klauber, 1939b, p.17). This might explain why the South American rattlesnake (*C. d. terrificus*), with its very powerful venom, has straighter fangs than the Nearctic rattlers, since the injection requires a shorter time of contact for full effectiveness, and consequently a simple stab is adequate. Some pit vipers of the genus *Bothrops* have straighter fangs than the rattlers, but it is not known whether they use the fangs differently on contact. The elapids, with their shorter fangs, are known to bite; they often hold on until shaken loose, for only by this means can they sink the fangs deep enough to inject venom.

To return to the rattlesnakes: it may be suggested that they either stab or bite, depending on the conditions involved, such as whether they are biting prey or acting in defense, and depending also on the size, contour, and penetrability of the object struck. There is likewise the matter of the relative sequence of contact of the fangs and the lower jaw, an uncertain feature since rattlesnakes are rather poor shots. They often completely miss a small object such as a rat; thus it is that they sometimes strike their target too high or too low, so that either the lower jaw or the fangs may make the first contact.

Some ingenious experiments have been made with high-speed photography to get a superimposed set of pictures, the first at the instant when the fangs contact the object of the strike, followed by two others at predetermined intervals some milliseconds later. These pictures have now reached a considerable degree of perfection, although there have been difficult problems to solve, particularly with respect to the density and penetrability of the object struck and its curvature at the point of contact. The earliest photographs were taken of rattlesnakes striking balloons, which disappeared upon being struck and thus left the fangs clearly visible. However, the sequence, after the first contact, had little relation to what occurs in a natural strike, because the substance to be stabbed or bitten vanished at the very instant when it was most necessary to see how the snake's mouth and fangs would normally engage it.

Probably the best pictures produced to date—at least the best that have come to my attention—comprise a series taken by Walker Van Riper, of the Museum of Natural History, Denver, showing a number of strikes by prairie rattlesnakes, *C. v. viridis* (1950, p. 128; 1953, p. 100; 1954, p. 50; 1955, p. 309). The target in the most informative pictures was a three-inch latex bulb, a soft and flexible object.

An ingenious electric system was devised to secure accurately timed and spaced flash intervals. These intervals were varied to produce pictures at the most crucial positions of fangs, jaws, and target. Some showed two or three successive positions of the snake's head on the same plate; others showed single views to illustrate the position and action of the snake's jaws upon contact with the target (figs. 12:1 to 12:4). The resulting photographs may be judged to favor either the stab or bite adherents, depending on interpretation. In some, the indentation of the bulb appears only under the fangs; although the lower jaw is touching the target, it seems to be exerting no upward pressure, and thus the snake is stabbing (e.g., fig. 12:3). But, in other pictures, there are indentations both under the fangs and under the anterior mandibular teeth; clearly the snake is exerting a pinching action—a bite—on the fold of latex between its jaws (fig. 12:4). So both theories are in some degree verified.

It should be stated that, in the balloon pictures, the snake was seen usually to close its mouth sooner than in the latex pictures, an indication that the mouth is normally closed as the result of an endeavor to bite, which closing is more nearly possible when the balloon bursts, than in the presence of a more material substance such as latex. Mr. Van Riper attributes the variations, in the pictures that showed both stabs and bites, to individual differences in the snakes tested. Although I do not deny the existence of these differences, I think the nature of the stab or bite often depends on the composition and curvature of the object struck.

In a normal strike, as shown by the high-speed pictures, the mouth is opened to its widest soon after the forward lunge begins, and some distance before the target is reached. The head withdrawal is slower than the forward lunge. The snake's mouth is closed when it returns to the coil from which it struck, and it is now ready to strike again if necessary.

BITE PATTERNS

The question of stab versus bite is of more than academic interest, since it may have a bearing on the treatment to be rendered, and the treatment of rattlesnake bite is too serious and painful a procedure to be taken lightly. Persons in the fright that follows a snake bite may be quite incapable of judging whether or not the snake was venomous, or even of noting whether it had rattles, in which case its venomous character would be a foregone conclusion. In some accidents the snake is never seen. Under such circumstances the nature of the marks left by the snake's teeth may be of critical importance. If rattlesnakes only stabbed and never bit, then in most cases it would be quite easy to distinguish a rattler (or other pit-viper) bite by the two punctures made by the fangs, as differentiated from the rows of smaller punctures made by the short, solid teeth of harmless snakes. (I am speaking of conditions met in the United States.) But, on the other hand, if a rattlesnake bites and the harmless pterygoid, palatine, and mandibular teeth also make puncture marks, then to distinguish between rattler and harmless bites would not be so easy or certain, particularly with the complications of inter-vening clothing, partially ineffective bites on irregular surfaces, teeth scratches made when the victim jerks away, and other confusing effects.

Fig. 12:1. A striking prairie rattlesnake (*C. v. viridis*), showing the position of the jaws as the head reaches the target.

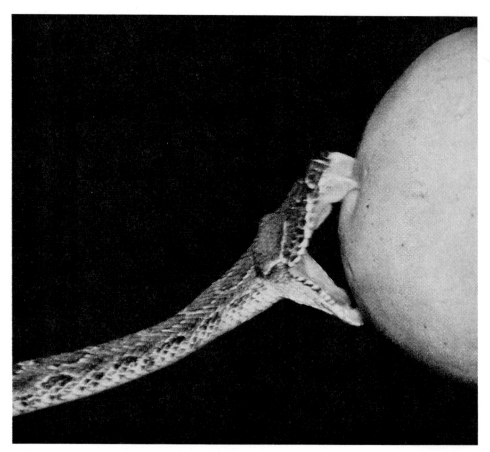

Fig. 12:2. A striking prairie rattlesnake, showing a stabbing action as the fangs reach the target.

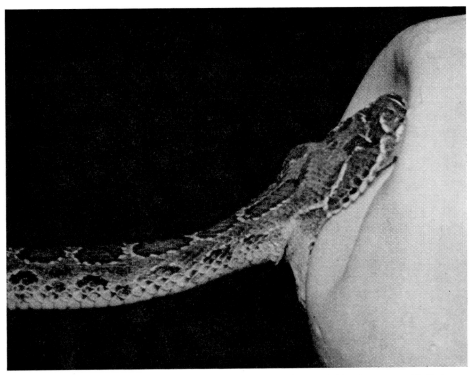

Fig. 12:3. A striking prairie rattlesnake, showing the fangs imbedded in the target with little pressure exerted by the lower jaw, 1/50 second after the fangs penetrated the latex target.

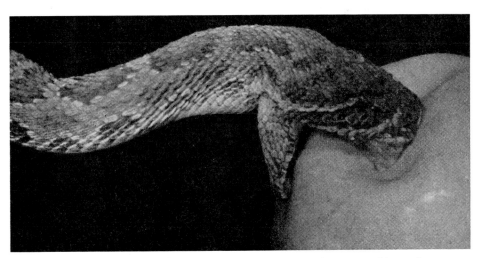

Fig. 12:4. Another strike of a prairie rattlesnake, in which there was a biting action immediately on contact of the fangs with the target.

(Figs. 12:1 to 12:4 are published by courtesy of Walker Van Riper, who took the photographs.)

Work has been done on biting patterns by Fairley (1929b, p. 321) on Australian snakes, and by Pope and Perkins (1944, p. 331) on the snakes of this country. The impressions made by snakes in biting substances such as plasticine may be readily identified, but unfortunately a similar legibility cannot be expected in actual snake-bite cases. Even under the bite theory, the initial contact is likely to be in the nature of a stab, with the bite as a follow-through, a sequence visualized by Vorhies (1917, p. 361). Some proponents of the bite theory believe that contact is first made by the teeth in the lower jaw, rather than by the fangs. Nettie Young (1940, p. 657), with much hospital experience with *atrox* bites in Texas, says that two fang marks were usually evident, although occasionally there was but one. She does not mention any marks made by other teeth. However, several of my correspondents who had been bitten said it was difficult to distinguish the fang marks from the tears made by the solid teeth when the hand was jerked away. (These were bites in the fingers.)

The bite pattern may be of some importance in judging the size of the snake and the depth of penetration, if the fang marks are clear. This is of interest to a physician contemplating incisions for drainage. Rough estimates are possible from the separation of the fang marks; however, it should be understood that they cannot be considered more than guesses. The conditions of snake bite are so variable, and the looseness of articulation of the fangs so considerable, that accuracy is not to be expected. I should say that with such typical species as *atrox* and *viridis,* the depth may approximate 75 per cent of the fang separation; and in *adamanteus, ruber,* and *molossus,* 80 to 90 per cent. Only in the rare Mexican form, *polystictus,* with its long fangs and slim head, would the depth be likely to equal the separation of the fang puncture marks. If it be recalled that the lower orifice of the fang is well above the point, and that the fangs tend to take a curved course, rather than penetrating straight inward, I should say that an incision to a depth of one-half to two-thirds of the distance between punctures should reach the deepest place of venom deposition. A rough guess may be made of the length of an adult rattlesnake (such as *atrox* or *viridis*) by multiplying the distance between fang punctures by 65.

ACTIONS AFTER A STRIKE

Rattlesnakes, in striking prey for food, seldom retain a hold on the victim. They release it and, if it travels any distance before dying, follow it by scent.

A rattlesnake, when striking an intruder in defense, usually withdraws its head and re-coils in preparation for a second lunge. However, in some instances rattlers have been observed to hang on. It is probable that this is not a part of a normal sequence, but results from an inability to withdraw the fangs because of some condition involved in the bite, entanglement in clothing, for example. That this may occur has been mentioned by Smith (1882, p. 637), Seton (1903, p. 440), and Gillam (1916, p. 134). Lyon (1910, p. 384) makes it appear that a rattlesnake's hanging on is to be expected; he gives directions for pulling it away from the victim to whom it might otherwise attach itself for 20 to 30 minutes. Although this is an exaggeration, there have been instances in which rattlers have hung on; for example, there was the case noted by Jones (1857, p. 376) in which a girl bitten in the ankle dragged a snake several yards before it was shaken loose. Ham (1861, p. 83) records a bite by a massasauga, in which the snake clung to a man's hand. Happ (1951, p. 20), in San Diego County, was bitten by a southern Pacific rattler, *C. v. helleri,* as he reached into a leaf-mold bin, and the snake was hanging on to his thumb when he withdrew his arm. Another such instance is recounted by Col. M. L. Crimmins: "Antonio Hernández was cutting Johnson grass near Frio City, 12 miles from San Antonio, at 6 P.M. August 31, 1946, when a rattlesnake lunged at him and caught him on the left forefinger and hung on until he shook it off. When a snake strikes upward it may hang on because of the curved fangs."

The question of whether rattlesnakes can bite when in, or under, water is occasionally asked. The answer is that they can bite readily enough, although, lacking the anchorage of a solid base, they cannot strike efficiently.

While there is still much to be learned about the method of biting used by rattlesnakes, we need no longer believe, as did Lindeström in 1655 (1925, p. 168; also Holm, 1702, edition of 1834, p. 53), that a rattlesnake has a head like a dog, and can bite a man's leg off as if hewn with an ax.

THE SNAKE-BITE HAZARD

The whole problem of the gravity of snake bite is not only complicated by the variable factors that attend each accident—which factors have been listed in the introduction to chapter 11—but also by the difficulty of determining whether a dangerously venomous snake was really involved. There are no simple or infallible ways of telling a venomous from a harmless snake, short of a closer examination than the ordinary person has an opportunity, or is willing, to make. The venomous snake is popularly supposed to have a short, heavy body, a broad triangular head, and cat's eyes, that is, vertically elliptical pupils. But many dangerously venomous snakes have none of these characteristics, and certain harmless species have some or all of them. It is true that some groups of venomous snakes have unfailing indicators: the rattle of the rattlesnakes, for example, and the facial pits of the larger group of snakes (the pit vipers) that includes the rattlesnakes as a component part. But the only universal test for a venomous snake is an examination of its upper jaw for hollow or grooved fangs. And who, in the excitement of a snake-bite accident, even if the culprit fails to escape, will ever make the examination necessary for such an identification? Unless a person has some general knowledge of the snake fauna of an area, he will be completely at sea in judging whether the snake was actually venomous. The effect of excitement and shock on the victim will preclude dependence entirely on symptoms; the bite of a harmless snake can cause a serious nervous reaction, and even death from fright may befall the person who doesn't know that he was bitten by a harmless snake. And so it is that innumerable people have endured painful and even dangerous treatments, in an endeavor to cure a snake bite that was quite harmless to start with. And so it is, also, that the most useless and fantastic remedies have been proved effective because they have brought recovery from a malady that never existed. As long ago as 1828, Pennock, speaking of the uncertainties and variable conditions involved in every snake-bite case, wrote (p. 21): "These results furnish additional evidence that the supposed specifics for the bite of a rattlesnake owe their reputation to their having been used in cases wherein no fatal effects would have resulted."

The relative dangers from various kinds of venomous snakes are dependent on many factors other than the toxicity of the snake's venom and the perfection of its biting mechanism, subjects that have already been discussed. Some of these additional factors have to do with the snake itself—on its disposition, and on its prevalence, habits, and habitats, and how these impinge on the human residents of the same area. And then there is the density of the human population, and its habits—whether people seek to decimate the snakes, and whether they roam about unshod and with legs unprotected. Hence we may have snakes that are quite dangerous from the standpoint of the virulence of their bites and the high percentage of the fatalities resulting therefrom; yet they may be quite unimportant hazards because of their particular natures. Such a snake, causing a negligible number of injuries, is the coral snake of the Southeastern states. Although a dangerous snake, with a moderately high proportion (probably about 20 per cent) of fatalities following its bite, it is, in fact, so secretive and inoffensive that it is not often found—although fairly common in some places—and is so peaceful that it can be handled with little danger of its biting unless it be frightened or injured. In fact, it frequently has been handled under the misapprehension that it is a harmless king or scarlet snake, and this without accident (e.g., Oertel, 1930, p. 88).

Other snakes may be dangerous but cause no problem since they inhabit remote places where few human beings ever go. And even the hazard from dangerous snakes may be somewhat mitigated where the people are snake-conscious and alert, have no inhibitions against killing venomous snakes—and, unfortunately, nonvenomous, beneficial snakes as well—and go about mostly in the daytime and well shod. Finally, there is the adequacy of the treatment available if an accident should befall. For all of these reasons, neither statistics of the number of bites in any area, nor the ratio of the fatalities to the total bites from any kind of snake, are as important as the total fatalities, or the ratio of the fatalities to the total population.

In *U. S. Army Air Forces Informational Bulletin No. 20*, April, 1945, as an indication of the relative unimportance of the snake-bite risk, the statement was made that there are more deaths in the United States each year from lightning than from snake bite; and that to a soldier, with shoes and leggings, mosquitoes are 1,000 times more dangerous than snakes. Netting (1944, p. 45) says that more people are killed and injured annually in their bath tubs in this country than by snake bite. In a way this is a reassuring statistic, but it must be admitted that a good many more people encounter bath tubs than snakes and, we hope, oftener.

The danger from rattlesnake bite has always been exaggerated, from the standpoints of both frequency and severity. It is doubtful whether bites by venomous snakes in this country ever exceeded 2 per 100,000 of population per annum, or that the fatalities exceeded 15 to 20 per cent of those bitten, even when the population was largely rural, and despite the fact that the treatments in those bygone days were often as dangerous as the bites they sought to cure. The corresponding figures for today are much lower, as I shall point out in a subsequent discussion and development.

SNAKE-BITE STATISTICS

Who has not read of the 20,000 people said to die annually in India from the bites of poisonous snakes? For this number is cited in nearly every popular book on snakes down to the present day. These statistics were originally based on reports assembled by Sir Joseph Fayrer on deaths by snake bite in parts of India in 1869 (Fayrer, 1872, p. 30; 1874, p. 30). From these reports and some extrapolations, the over-all estimate of 20,000 deaths per annum was reached. The number was confirmed by further statistics collected for the years 1880 and 1881 (Fayrer, 1882, p. 205), and later for the 10 years ending in 1890 (Fayrer, 1892, p. 620). I have no reason to question Fayrer's summaries and extrapolations, but somehow one must assume a mechanism for gathering mortality statistics, and an accuracy of case reports in rural subdistricts among a people with quite non-European views concerning snakes and snake bite, that was more than human, if the results are to be considered entirely trustworthy. Whether they can be verified under present conditions in India and Pakistan, I cannot say. Swaroop and Grab (1954, p. 58) reach the conclusion that the figure was 15,000 per year, up to the separation of Pakistan in 1947, but admit that many factors cast doubt on the accuracy of the statistics.

Said Colonel Frank Wall (1928, p. 69), certainly one who knew the relationship of men and snakes in India if anyone ever did (he was writing of the problem in India):

> In reading the reports of snake casualties, which appear from time to time in various publications, I have been forcibly and repeatedly struck with the very incomplete way in which many of these cases are recorded, and also by the fact that in many cases the diagnosis of snake-poisoning (*ophitoxaemia*) appears to have been quite unjustified. Frequently one or two of the most obvious symptoms in a case are mentioned—not necessarily symptoms of *ophitoxaemia* at all—to the exclusion of many others which though less obvious are perhaps of greater importance in establishing a diagnosis. It appears to me that the term "snake-bite" is often used as synonymous with "snake-poisoning," and the mere fact that a man has been bitten by a snake, or is reported as having been bitten by a snake, has been the only justification for considering and recording the case as one of snake-poisoning. Many cases appear to be recorded as snake-poisoning which should have been returned [as] wound punctured, or wound lacerated.

In a similar vein, Ganguli and Napier (1946, p. 847) remark that "snake bite" in India is often a convenient euphemism for death by violence. To the extent that these statistics on snake-bite fatalities in India may be accurate, they indicate a death rate of about 5½ per 100,000 of population per annum, or one-quarter of the death rate in the United States resulting from automobile accidents.

But whatever the fatalities in India, where cobras and other dangerous snakes are protected for religious reasons, where the rural people go barefooted and barelegged, and where the best remedial measures are probably not available in the rural districts, they have little relation to the snake-bite problem in countries where similar human attitudes toward snakes do not exist.

Some other foreign data on snake-bite cases and fatalities are these: Noguchi (1909, p. 75) stated the mortality rate for the Ryukyu viper on Okinawa in the years 1898 to 1906 to be 52.6 per 100,000. The fatalities were about 15 per cent of the bites. Somei To (1940, p. 130) stated that there were 839 fatalities from snake bite in the island of Formosa in the years 1904–38. This involves an annual mortality rate of 0.59 per 100,000. Fairley (1929, p. 296) estimated that 195 people died from snake bite in Australia in the years 1910 to 1926, inclusive. This is at the rate of about 0.2 person per 100,000 per annum. Rose (1950, p. 297) says that in Rhodesia in 1930 there were 10 deaths from venomous snakes in a population of 2½ million. Amaral (1923a, p. 691; 1923b, p. 90) gives the number of snake-bite cases in the state of São Paulo, Brazil, as 1,500 per annum. Before the advent of antivenin the mortality rate was 150 per year (about 3.3 persons per 100,000 per annum); this has since been cut to 3 to 5 deaths per year, or about 0.1 per 100,000. Dunn (1951, p. 753) cites the following annual death rates per 100,000: Ryukyu 5.9, São Paulo 5.1, India 5.0, Australia 0.18. Worrell (1952, p. 3) gives a figure of 5 deaths per year, or 0.06 per 100,000, for Australia. These statistics indicate the great differences in death rates in countries where dangerous snakes are plentiful, but where human factors materially affect mortality rates. Allen (1949, p. 616) gives the world-wide mortality from snakes as 30,000 per annum. This, no doubt, assumes the accuracy of the figure of 20,000 or more for India alone.

The most complete study of snake-bite mortality throughout the world, that has been made up to the present, is that of Swaroop and Grab (1954, pp. 35–76) under the auspices of the World Health Organization. They comment on the obstacles to accurate information that result from the fact that the category for reporting deaths from snake bite in the *International List of Causes of Death* also includes all other venomous creatures such as centipedes, scorpions, spiders, and insects, which, in some places, cause more deaths than snakes. Also there are the difficulties of securing accurate death reports in primitive areas where snake-bite cases are likely to be most prevalent. The conclusions of these authors as to the death rates in some countries are summarized in table 12:1.

As one reviews the Swaroop and Grab survey, which, in summary, reports that throughout the world about 30,000 people die from snake bite annually, he cannot but be impressed with the effects on mortality rates of three major factors: 1) the relative characteristics of the venomous snakes in each country with respect to the gravity of a bite; 2) the relative populations of people and snakes; and 3) the nature of the activities and clothing of the people who work and live in snake-infested areas. And it is also clearly evident that, if snake-bite statistics are ever to be accurate, it will be necessary to make a suitable revision of the categories under which deaths are reported. It may be a surprise to some to learn that in Mexico, which is plentifully supplied with dangerously venomous snakes, deaths from other venomous creatures (principally scorpions) outnumber those resulting from snake bite by about 10 to 1. This matter of the accuracy of statistics is of more than academic interest, since, in the long run, it affects the amount of time and money that will be made available for remedial researches and the development of appropriate antivenins.

FATALITIES FROM RATTLESNAKE BITE IN THE UNITED STATES

How serious is rattlesnake bite? How many people are bitten by rattlesnakes each year in the United States, and how many of these cases prove fatal? One might assume that, with the improvement in the coverage and accuracy of accident and mortality statistics in this country, it should be possible, at least, to determine the total deaths from snake bite each year, if not specifically from rattlesnake bite, but such is not the case.

The difficulty, already mentioned, lies in the death classifications used, which conform to the *International List of Causes of Death,* for the category involved— E-927, *Poisoning by Venomous Animals*—includes other animals as well as snakes;

TABLE 12:1

ANNUAL MORTALITY FROM SNAKE BITE
(Data from Swaroop and Grab, 1954)

Area	Mortality rate per 100,000 per annum
Egypt	0.20
Union of South Africa[a][b]	0.57
Canada[a]	0.02
Brazil[c]	4.10
British Guiana[a]	0.80
Colombia[a]	1.56
Costa Rica[a]	1.93
Mexico	0.94
Venezuela	3.10
India	5.40
Burma	15.40
Ceylon	4.20
Thailand[a]	1.30
Spain[a]	0.02
France[a]	0.06
Italy[a]	0.04
England and Wales[a]	0.02
Australia	0.07
Japan	0.13

[a] Includes bites or stings of all venomous animals.
[b] White population only.
[c] 2,000 deaths estimated for 1949 in a population of 48,500,000.

and although snakes are brought to mind first when venomous animals are mentioned, deaths from other creatures such as the black widow spider and certain scorpions are by no means unimportant.

I shall first discuss fatalities, both in terms of totals and per 100,000 of population, followed by such information as I have been able to gather on the proportion of rattlesnake-bite cases that end fatally.

Table 12:2 presents the statistics for death category E-927 for the United States as a whole, and for particular states wherein snake bites (as well as the bites and stings of other creatures) are important.

States not shown separately in the table, but which had 10 or more fatalities during the 10-year period 1943 to 1952, inclusive, were: Kentucky 15, Missouri 14, and Virginia 11.

To show that the bites or stings of venomous animals other than snakes are important, and therefore that the figures given in cause of death E-927 must not

TABLE 12:2

ANNUAL DEATHS IN THE UNITED STATES FROM THE BITES AND STINGS OF VENOMOUS ANIMALS

(By place of occurrence, 1924–41; subsequently by place of residence. Data through the courtesy of the Public Health Service, Federal Security Agency)

Year	U.S.	Ala.	Ariz.	Ark.	Calif.	Fla.	Ga.	La.	Miss.	N.Mex.	N.C.	Okla.	S.C.	Tenn.	Tex.
1925	76+	5	N.D.[a]	N.D.[a]	5	9	N.D.[a]	6	2	N.D.[a]	4	N.D.[a]	1	3	N.D.[a]
1926	103+	6	11	N.D.	12	8	N.D.	2	4	N.D.	4	N.D.	3	3	N.D.
1927	88+	2	10	2	7	4	N.D.	3	4	N.D.	3	N.D.	2	3	N.D.
1928	97+	2	5	5	8	8	4	2	2		2		3	1	N.D.
1929	98+	4	10	3	4	8	7		2		6	5		4	N.D.
1930	100+	6	10	2	6	11	4	3	1	2		2	3	5	N.D.
1931	115+	5	2	7	9	6	6	3	4	2	4	9	7	1	N.D.
1932	125+	4	5	6	10	7	8	3	3		5	7	6	4	N.D.
1933	155	4	5	9	6	10	10	4	3	3	3	3	11	3	N.D.
1934	147	8	6	7	8	15	6	6	5		3	7	5	4	29
1935	211	8	9	12	8	10	5	6	3	5	3	11	5	7	15
1936	162	10	7	5	6	9	9	4	8	2	4	11	3	4	35
1937	148	8	10	7	5	10	6	3	5	1	1	8	5	5	26
1938	153	3	5	3	9	10	6	3			4	7	4	2	27
1939	102	3	8	3	3	10	4	7	2	1	3	2	3		14
1940	100	6	9	3	3	5	5	6	6	2	5	3	3	2	11
1941	78	4	7	3	4	2	3	2	4	3	3	5	3	5	17
1942	98[b]	1	5		2	2		1	3		2	3	3		16
1943	77	3	3	4	4	7	5	2	5	1	1	5		1	24
1944	78	3	2	4	4	3	3	1	6	2	5	4		1	20
1945	50	3	4	3	2	5	1	2	1	2	5	1	4	2	9
1946	62	3	6		5	4	3	1	1	2	3	2	1	5	14
1947	64	3	1	2	2	3	4	2	1	2	3	1	1	5	16
1948	40	2	2	1	2	6	2		1		3		4	2	4
1949	47	2	3	5	3	4					1	1	2		8
1950	51	2	2	6	5	2	3	2			2		1		10
1951	49	2	3	1	4	3	5	2	2		3	1			5
1952	44	1	1		1	2	5		4		3		3	1	8
Total 10 yrs. 1943–1952	562	22	27	26	32	39	31	12	21	9	28	15	15	17	118

[a] No data, these states not being in the death-registration group until the dates shown. In addition to those indicated separately, Nevada was not included until 1929, and South Dakota not until 1930. As Texas, the most important state from the standpoint of total fatalities, was first included in 1933, the statistics for the United States as a whole are to be considered incomplete prior to 1933.

[b] An error of 20 seems to have been made in 1942, in that 20 deaths in this category were credited to Maine, when, in fact, there were none in that state.

NOTE.—While this work was in press, the following statistics for the year 1953 on deaths under this category became available: U.S. as a whole, 35; Tex., 5; Ala. and Ariz., 3 each; Calif., Ga., Miss., Mo., and N.C., 2 each; Ark., Fla., Kans., Ky., Mass., Mich., Nev., N. Mex., Ohio, Okla., Oreg., Tenn., Va., and W. Va., 1 each; all others none.

be offhandedly attributed to rattlesnakes, or even to snakes at all, reference is made to the statistics of fatalities in Arizona cited by Stahnke (1950, p. 26; see also Whiteman and Henderson, 1947, p. 27) and statistics for later years secured from the U. S. Public Health Service. The data cover the 22 years from 1929 to 1951, inclusive, but without 1937. The fatality causes that could be allocated were segregated thus: Scorpions 69, rattlesnakes 18, insects (unspecified) 5, spiders (unspecified) 4, black widow spiders 3, Gila monster 1, bee 1, centipede (secondary infection) 1; total 102. Thus rattlesnakes caused only 18 per cent of the fatalities listed in cause E-927. Of course, Arizona is not to be considered typical of the usual distribution of deaths in this category, because of the presence in that state of the dangerous scorpions *Centruroides sculpturatus* and *C. gertschi,* species particularly hazardous to children. These dangerous scorpions are almost confined to Arizona, as far as their range in the United States is concerned. Arizona contains more different subspecies of rattlesnakes (16) than any other state, and, as to numbers of individuals, they are plentiful in many areas; yet despite these facts, rattlesnakes caused less than 1 death per year in the 22 years enumerated. Unfortunately Swaroop and Grab (1954, p. 46) make the mistake of assuming that the Arizona ratio of snake-bite fatalities to the total fatalities from venomous animals may be applied to the United States as a whole.

In California, in the 14 years 1931 to 1944, inclusive, there were 19 deaths from rattlesnake bite (information obtained through the courtesy of Dr. Tracy I. Storer). During the same years, the total deaths under classification E-927 (or its predecessors) were 70. Rattlesnakes therefore accounted for 27 per cent of the total. It is believed that the black widow spider was the principal offender in this state. I am under the impression that today in California rattlesnakes probably cause at least 50 per cent of the fatalities under E-927 (rattlesnakes are the only dangerous snakes in the state), or 2 or 3 per year in a population of 13 million.

Although I have no statistics to prove it, I should assume that in Texas the percentage of snake-bite fatalities, in relation to the total venomous-animal deaths, would be higher than in Arizona and California, owing to the prevalence there of the large and dangerous western diamondback, *Crotalus atrox.* In Florida, in the years 1940 to 1951, inclusive, of the 46 deaths caused by venomous animals, 38 deaths or 83 per cent resulted from snake bite, most of them no doubt caused by the eastern diamondback, *Crotalus adamanteus,* the largest of all rattlesnakes. The divergent records from Arizona, California, and Florida show how difficult it is to allocate the fatalities grouped under E-927 to the several kinds of dangerous creatures involved.

Incomplete as the snake-bite statistics in the United States may be, because of the lack of a further subdivision of category E-927, it is nevertheless apparent that snake bite in this country is of relatively minor importance. Deaths in the United States now occur at the rate of about 1,500,000 per annum, and of these only about 50 are to be attributed to venomous animals, including snakes. Even among accidental deaths, snake bite is rather unimportant. In 1948, one accidental death out of 2,450 in this country was caused by the bite or sting of a venomous creature; in 1949 the figure was one in 1,917 accidents.

Death rates are usually expressed in terms of deaths per annum per 100,000 of population. At present the rate for the United States as a whole is about 0.033

per 100,000 per annum for all venomous creatures, and maybe 0.015 to 0.02 for snakes alone. In California, in the years 1931 to 1944, inclusive, the death rate from rattlesnake bite was 0.02 per 100,000 per year. With a present population (1955) of about 13,000,000, it is believed that rattlesnake-bite deaths in California will average about 2 per annum but might reach 5 in an exceptional year, or a top figure of 0.038 per 100,000. The rate in Florida may reach 0.2 per 100,000 per annum.

Table 12:2 indicates a recent decline in the number of deaths from the bites and stings of venomous animals. A peak in numbers was reached in 1935 with 211; the latest statistics indicate an annual toll of less than one-fifth of this number, despite the increased population. A number of factors may be cited as contributing to this decline: The advent of antivenin in 1927 and its subsequent improvement in quality and distribution; better methods of incision and suction treatment, and the prevention of shock; improved remedies for scorpion stings and black widow bites; the use of antibiotics and other drugs to prevent infection; more adequate information on treatments in the hands of hospital staffs; faster means of transportation from field to hospital; the mechanization of agriculture; and the urbanization of the population. I do not suggest that these factors have been given in the order of their relative importance. I also wish to call attention to the fact that all of these statistics include so-called illegitimate bites, meaning those that result from handling snakes, a subject to which I shall return.

Proportion of Rattlesnake Cases Ending Fatally

The statistics previously given have involved the numbers of fatalities in this country and their relation to population; I shall now touch on the fatalities as related to the numbers of bites or cases.

Many of the early accounts of rattlesnakes stated that the bite was invariably fatal (Marcgravius, 1648, p. 241; Neal, 1720, vol. 2, p. 574; Purry *et al.*, 1732, p. 1017; Sloane, 1734, p. 322; Goldsmith, 1774, vol. 7, p. 210). Others, however, were equally sure that the bite could be cured if some plant remedy known to the Indians were applied. Hernández (1615, fol. 192r; 1628, p. 329; Nieremberg, 1635, p. 269) stated that the bite caused great fissures in the body of the victim, and death usually ensued within 24 hours. Thompson, traveling in Oregon in 1811 (1916, p. 522), was told that the bite of a full-grown rattler would be fatal within three or four minutes unless the flesh at the bite were instantly cut out. Bigland (1844, p. 136) said that recovery from rattlesnake bite is rare, although some victims live for five or six hours. Fontana (1787, vol. 2, p. 44), who experimented extensively with vipers, reached the conclusion that rattlesnake bite was not always mortal, even though rattlers have seven to eight times as much venom as a European viper.

Gradually the extent of the danger, first cited by travelers as being one of the greatest hazards encountered in the wilds of America, has been more soundly evaluated. Vigne (1832, vol. 1, p. 90) thought the number of accidents was exaggerated. Burton (1861, p. 193) believed that, although many people were bitten, there were few fatalities; and Duval (1870, p. 16) considered the bites to be less often fatal than generally reported. However, the disparagement of the rattlesnake danger should not reach the unimportance assigned by Cist (1845, p. 17), who believed the bite no more serious than the sting of a bee. According to Ricketts (1898, p. 219), Dr. Joseph Leidy stated in 1890 that there never had been an authenticated case of death from rattlesnake bite in the United States. This led to an investigation which disclosed some, but surprisingly few, fatalities; but there seems to have been a tendency, in the survey that was made, to attribute most of the fatalities disclosed, either to infection or to excess alcohol used in the treatment, and not to death by rattlesnake bite. However, there can be no doubt that the number of fatalities has usually been exaggerated.

To the questions—How many people are bitten each year by venomous snakes in the United States? What proportion of these bites is by rattlesnakes? What percentage proves fatal?—only the most sketchy answers can be given.

First, as to the number of bites by poisonous snakes: In recent years these have usually been estimated within the range of 1,000 to 2,000 per year for the entire country: Amaral (1927aa, p. 32) 1,000; Hutchison (1929, p. 43) 1,000; Barker (1929, p. 64) 1,000; Githens (1935b, p. 163) 1,500 to 2,000; Hutchins (1941, p. 20) 2,000; Oliver (1944, p. 855) 1,500 to 1,800; Maloney (1945, p. 80) 1,800; Anon. (1947b, p. 10) 1,000 to 2,000; Breland (1948, p. 206) 1,500 to 1,800; Bogert (1948b, p. 188) about 750; Bulger and Northrop (1951, p. 1134) 2,000; Holt (1950, p. 13) 1,500; Amaral (1951a, p. 553; 1951b, p. 1253) 2,000 to 3,000; Hylander (1951, p. 10) under 1,000; Stickel (1952, p. 16) 1,000 to 2,000; Porges (1953, p. 47) 2,000 to 3,000. On the strength of these estimates—not all of which, by any means, are to be considered independent, that is, made without knowledge of the prior ones— I presume we might guess the current number of bites by venomous snakes at about 1,500 per annum. This estimate takes into consideration our increased population and the vast number of automobiles that carry inexperienced urban dwellers into remote and primitive districts on week ends and vacations. On the other hand, the mechanization of agriculture has undoubtedly reduced the incidence of snake bite among farm workers. Of the bites by venomous snakes, 70 per cent, or say about 1,000 per year, are inflicted by rattlesnakes, this proportion being derived from the statistics of distribution that follow.

Rattlesnakes are the most important venomous snakes occurring in the United States. They range over the largest areas, and in those places that they share with other venomous snakes they are often the most plentiful (especially is this true west of the Mississippi River) and probably cause the most fatalities, although not always the most snake-bite cases.

Willson (1908, p. 530) compiled the records of 566 snake-bite cases in the United States in which the offender was recognized. The division was rattlesnakes 408 (72 per cent), copperheads 97 (17 per cent), moccasins 53 (9 per cent), and coral snakes 8 (1.4 per cent). These were cases, not fatalities. Amaral (1927b, p. 81) found that rattlesnakes were responsible for 91 per cent of the cases in Texas. Hutchison, in two important papers (1929, p. 45, and 1930, p. 42), reported the distribution of snake-bite cases for the years 1928 and 1929, including only the accidents wherein the culprit was recognized as a rattlesnake, copperhead, or moccasin. The distribution was: Rattlesnakes 584 (61 per cent), copperheads 308 (31 per cent), moccasins 82 (8 per cent), total 974. There were 115 additional cases in which it was impossible to determine even the genus of the snake concerned.

Githens (1935a, p. 172) gives this distribution of cases on which he secured data: Rattlesnakes 1,088 (55 per cent), copperheads 691 (35 per cent), moccasins 194 (10 per cent). Githens' rattlesnake percentage is lower than Hutchison's because he omitted from his tabulation cases of rattler bite in which the species could not be ascertained, even though the offender was known to be some kind of rattler.

Swartzwelder (1950, p. 579) was able to determine the kind of snake in 160 out of 306 cases in the Louisiana Charity Hospital, between 1907 and 1946. In this area, the moccasin was the principal offender with 66 per cent of the cases, followed by rattlers with 27, and copperheads with 7 per cent. In Florida in 1948, 78 per cent of the bites by venomous snakes were inflicted by rattlers (Andrews and Pollard, 1953, p. 389). Wood (1954, p. 937) reported the following distribution of 134 bites in Virginia: Rattlesnakes 10.4 per cent, copperheads 88.9 per cent, moccasins 0.7 per cent.

In many areas in the United States rattlesnakes are the only venomous snakes present and therefore cause 100 per cent of the snake-bite cases. In view of these statistics, I should conclude that rattlesnakes are the cause of about 70 per cent of the cases involving bites by venomous snakes in the United States.

As to the proportion of rattlesnake bites that prove fatal, again the conclusions are largely guesses; in fact, even with perfect records only average mortality figures could be given, not an answer applicable to every bite, so much depends on the kind and size of rattlesnake, its condition when biting, the effectiveness of the bite (the depth of fang penetration and the quantity of venom injected), the size and health of the victim, and, finally, the availability and character of the treatment. Also, in judging mortality statistics, it is well to remember that the serious cases are the ones likely to reach hospitals and thus to be recorded.

Jeter (1854, p. 32), from a study of 60 cases, gave the opinion that 40 per cent of rattlesnake-bite cases would recover without treatment, and 70 per cent would be saved if proper treatment were given. Mitchell (1861, p. 276) learned of 5 fatalities in 57 cases. He further remarked (p. 290) that the physicians of that day were disposed to report only the successful cases, so there were few post-mortem records. Williston (1878, p. 203) mentioned 3 deaths in 11 cases; he thought 2 of these had been due to negligence. Ellzey (1884, p. 251) believed that 15 per cent of rattlesnake-bite cases proved fatal. Barringer (1892, p. 297) investigated 38 cases upon which he estimated the mortality ratio to be about 10 per cent. Fountain, a traveler in the West in the early seventies, was much more pessimistic; he stated (1901, p. 60) that a fatality would result 10 or 11 times out of 12 bites. Such a mortality ratio is entirely without foundation. Willson (1908, pp. 552, 554) recorded 48 fatal rattlesnake-bite cases out of 408, or a mortality of 11.7 per cent.

Crimmins collected data on 60 cases in Texas in 1926 and found the mortality to be 15 per cent (Jackson, 1927, p. 203). Amaral (1927aa, p. 32) estimated the mortality in the Northeastern, Middlewestern, and Northwestern states at 10 per cent; in the Southeast at 25 per cent; and in the Southwest at 35 per cent. Brymer (1928, p. 300) cites some interesting but rather inconsistent figures on mortality rates in southwestern Texas. He states that rattlesnake bites would be fatal 98 times out of 100 if left untreated, and that this mortality rate would be reduced to 21 per cent with the best of treatment. But later (p. 306), in discussing the statistics of types of treatment that he gathered from 150 doctors by means of a questionnaire, he recorded only 21 deaths in 2,300 cases, or less than 1 per cent fatal. Dr. J. W. Hargres, one of Brymer's correspondents (p. 304), thought the mortality rate should be below 1 per cent, unless the victim were struck in a vein.

Barker (1929, p. 64) estimated 1,000 bites per annum with 22 per cent of fatalities. Dudley Jackson (1929, p. 4) reported 2 deaths in 45 cases, or 4½ per cent. In 1936 (p. 26) he expressed the opinion that his improved incision and suction method of treatment had cut the mortality in Texas from 15 down to 1 per cent. Hutchison (1928, p. 52; 1929, p. 43) reported 15 fatal rattlesnake cases out of 399 (3.75 per cent) where antivenin was used, and 13 out of 88 (15.7 per cent) where it was not used. Not all of these cases were rattlesnake bites. Githens (1936a, p. 172) cites a mortality of 39 out of 142 cases, or 27 per cent, where antivenin was not used, and 59 out of 946, or 6.2 per cent, when antivenin was used; this is a total of 98 fatalities out of 1,088 cases, or 9 per cent without segregation as to treatment. All of these were rattlesnake cases. I think it hardly fair to credit the reduced mortality rate entirely to antivenin; in all probability the cases not treated with antivenin received a minimum of other types of competent treatment as well.

Swartzwelder (1950, p. 575) records only 2 fatalities in 306 cases of bites by venomous snakes treated at the Louisiana Charity Hospital in New Orleans between 1907 and 1946. By no means all of the bites were by rattlesnakes. Maloney (1945, p. 80) says that there were 61 fatal cases out of 347 investigated by Ross Allen in Florida during the previous ten years; this is a mortality rate of 17½ per cent. A later report for the years 1947–50 listed 10 deaths in 131 cases, or a mortality rate of 7.6 per cent. Holt (1950, p. 15) reports that, at the Green Memorial Hospital in San Antonio, 900 cases were treated without a death, by use of the Dudley Jackson methods.

Other recent figures, unsupported by case statistics, are those of Hutchins (1941, p. 20) 5½ per cent; Babcock (1944, p. 83) 9 per cent; Oliver (1944, p. 855) 5 per cent; Maloney (1945, p. 80) 8⅓ per cent; Breland (1948, p. 206) 5 per cent; Dunn (1951, p. 753) 13 per cent; Stickel (1952, p. 17) 2 per cent for patients receiving adequate care; and Porges (1953, p. 47) 10 to 35 per cent, evidently derived from Amaral (1927aa, p. 32). Vaughn (1947, p. 8) gives a ratio, quite beyond any possibility, even without any treatment, of 90 per cent.

During World War II, when very large numbers of men were in training camps along the southern border of the United States and in Southwestern areas, the snake-bite hazard was a matter of frequent public concern. There were rumors of many fatalities, and the wisdom of carrying out maneuvers in these rattlesnake-infested areas was seriously questioned. As a result of an inquiry, I was advised by the Department of the Army that there were 1,910 hospital admissions in the continental United States, among army and air force servicemen, during the years 1942 to 1945 inclusive, under the category of bites and stings of all venomous animals. This was at an annual rate of less than one man bitten or stung out of 10,000 exposed. "Stings" comprised 10 per cent of the cases, and "bites," many of which may have been snake bites, the other 90 per cent. The most important statistic of all is that there were no fatalities. So much for the truth of rumors.

A public utility company, with whose operations I am familiar, had large crews of men engaged in construction and maintenance work in areas where rattlesnakes are plentiful. Between 1931 and 1954, during which time over 8,000,-000 man-days were worked, there was one case of rattlesnake bite. This did not involve a fatality. It is probable that about 10 per cent, or say 800,000 of the man-days worked, involved some snake-bite hazard by reason of the location of the activity.

In Brazil, Fonseca (1949, p. 150) reported a mortality rate of 12.2 per cent from the bite of the Neotropical rattler (*C. d. terrificus*). Kraus (1923, p. 326) reported a Brazilian mortality rate of 9.8 per cent from the bite of this snake. This was for the years 1902 to 1922, and referred only to patients who received antivenin treatment.

The United Fruit Company, in the snake-bite cases treated in its Central American hospitals in the years 1938–51, inclusive, experienced a mortality rate of 4.9 per cent. These were the statistics of all venomous snake bites, not necessarily rattlesnakes.

Since the time when most of these statistics were compiled, the treatment of rattlesnake bite has been further improved by the availability of stronger antivenins, the use of antibiotics to combat infections, and the development of various injections and transfusions to reduce shock. It may be estimated that these improvements, when used, should reduce the over-all mortality rate for rattlesnake bite in the United States to well below 4 or even to 3 per cent. These figures are related to those previously given in terms of total fatalities from the bites and stings of venomous animals in the United States set forth in table 12:2. I think we may conclude from both approaches, the total deaths from all venomous animals and the proportion of deaths by rattlesnakes alone, that the total rattlesnake fatalities in the United States probably average less than 30 per year or 0.02 per 100,000. The figure for all snakes is probably about 0.027.

Hutchison (1929, p. 46) has presented some statistics on the frequency of snake-bite cases by states for the year 1928. The states that had more than 10 cases (not fatalities) attributable to rattlesnakes in that year were: Texas (109), California (30), Alabama (21), Florida (18), Georgia (15), New Mexico (12), Arizona (11), and North Carolina (11). These figures cannot be correlated with the fatalities in table 12:2 since the bases are not comparable.

The following statistics summarize my conclusions, as above derived, with regard to rattlesnake bite in the United States: total bites 1,000 per annum; fatal bites 30 or 3 per cent of those bitten; mortality rate 0.02 per 100,000 of population per year.

VARIABLE FACTORS IN SNAKE-BITE CASES

HUMAN VARIABLES IN SNAKE BITE

There are more snake-bite cases involving men than women because men are more often in the woods or fields, either working or hunting. Amaral (1927b, p. 81) reported 103 bites affecting men in Texas compared with 37 involving women. Hutchison's ratio (1929, p. 48) for snake bites reported in 1928 was 397 males to 176 females. Swartzwelder, in Louisiana, recorded 247 males to 48 females. Women, he found, were most often bitten while working around the home or traversing the fields. Wood (1954, p. 938) recorded twice as many male as female cases in Virginia. Ross Allen (*in litt.*) lists 61 cases affecting males to 17 in which females were the victims. Both Amaral (1930, p. 57) and Barroso (1944, p. 37) report somewhat similar ratios in Brazil. Willson (1908, p. 559) found the male fatalities to be proportionately greater in number than the female. He attributed this to the fact that the men were usually farther from treatment when a snake bite occurred, and that the women were protected by thicker clothing—this was before 1908. He did not concede any difference in susceptibility.

Statistics on the ages of snake-bite victims will be found in Willson (1908, p. 558), Amaral (1927b, p. 81; 1930, p. 57), Hutchison (1929, p. 48), Barroso (1944, pp. 37, 40), Swartzwelder (1950, p. 577), and Wood (1954, p. 940). Bites among children are proportionately more frequent than in the population as a whole. In the years 1947–50, Ross Allen (*in litt.*) reported that 46 per cent of the bites recorded in Florida were sustained by children of 10 years or younger. Wood (1954, p. 940) reported that 27 per cent of all bites were sustained by children under 8 years of age, and another 27 per cent by others of from 9 to 15 years. Rattlesnake bite is particularly dangerous in the case of children because of their lower neutralizing capacity, of the way in which the younger ones crawl about, and because, with their short stature, they are more likely to be bitten in the head or body. And sometimes they do not immediately tell anyone they have been bitten, so that treatment is delayed.

Since the earliest studies of the effects of snake venoms on animals have been made, it has been known that the smaller the animal the more quickly it succumbs to a given quantity of venom (Redi, 1673, p. 12; Mortimer, 1736, p. 317; Fontana, 1787, vol. 2, p. 33). Of course, this presupposes a single kind of animal, for it was recognized that some species were more susceptible—or less immune—than others.

And it is the same with humans; the young and the infirm are more seriously affected than adults and those in good health. De Mayerne made this observation as early as 1694 (p. 162). Willson (1908, p. 570) has estimated the mortality among children at twice that of adults. Hutchison's data (1929, p. 52) seem to bear this out. Anon. (1933b, p. 21) reported 22 rattlesnake bites suffered by children in Texas; 2 were fatal. Fonseca (1949, p. 150) reported a mortality rate of 15.7 per cent from *terrificus* bite in children, compared with 11.0 per cent in men and 12.3 per cent in women. The reason is not far to seek. The body has a capacity to cope successfully with, and eventually to dispose of, a certain quantity of venom, and each unit weight of the body undertakes its share. Thus the capacity to overcome the invasion of a given quantity of venom is proportional to the weight of the body. A child may lack the capacity to withstand a certain bite, while an adult might have it.

This consideration of capacity also governs the amount of antivenin that should be used. Ordinarily we think it natural to give a child less medicine than an adult, but the reverse is necessary with respect to antivenin. For the purpose of antivenin is to neutralize that part of a venom dose that the body cannot neutralize for itself, so the antivenin has a greater task in the child and more is required. Amaral (1951b, p. 1258) says that a child may require three to five times as much antivenin as an adult. Needless to say, such quantities should be used only by a physician with due regard to the susceptibility of the patient to serum sickness.

There are undoubtedly differences among individuals in their susceptibility to snake venom, as there are to other protein poisons. Dr. Dudley Jackson (by letter) stated that in his extensive practice he had encountered some people who were hypersensitive to venom. In some cases this condition may be in the nature of an anaphylaxis resulting from previous exposures. A case of hypersensitiveness is discussed by Zozaya and Stadelman (1930, p. 93). Another case of more doubtful authenticity, involving recurrent symptoms and susceptibility to rattlesnake emanations, is reported by Ludy (1926, p. 28).

Said one of my correspondents, C. B. Clark, Duffield, Virginia:

> As to the fatalities caused from bites, they appear to depend on the physical condition of the victim. Persons who swell very easily from insect stings or bites appear to be affected worse by snake bite, while those who seem to suffer no noticeable effect from bites or stings from insects recover very readily from snake bite.

The location of a bite on the body may be of great importance. It may reduce the depth of penetration if the fangs should strike a bone or tough tissue. If, by unfortunate chance, the venom should be injected directly into a vein or artery, the outlook will be grave indeed, since the absorption will be rapid and without the opportunity to delay or interrupt it. On the other hand, injection into fat leads to slow absorption. Bites in the extremities are less serious than in the body, for absorption is usually slower and the opportunity to delay or prevent venom diffusion by a tourniquet, or other curative measures, is enhanced. Dunn (1951, p. 744) has pointed out that hemotoxin leaks out into the tissue around a bite, and that the more distal the point of injection, the greater the amount of venom required for a lethal dose.

Willson (1908, p. 557), Amaral (1927b, p. 81), Hutchison (1929, p. 48; 1930, p. 42), Swartzwelder (1950, p. 581), and Allen (*in litt.*) have tabulated the locations of the bites in a total of over 2,000 cases in the United States. The majority of these, but not all, were rattlesnake bites. Although the segregations of body parts made by the different authors are not exactly the same, they may be assembled and grouped as set forth in table 12:3.

Where the hands are differentiated, it is found that the bites in the right hand exceed those in the left by about 2 to 1, a not unexpected result. Bites in the forearm exceed those in the upper arm about 20 to 1, and bites in the shin or calf are about 20 times as numerous as those in the thigh. Bites in the hand are about 7 times as frequent as bites in the wrist; and in the front part of the foot about twice as prevalent as in the heel. But, of course, the most important conclusion from these data is that only about 1½ bites out of 100 are in the head or body, compared with 98½ in the arms or legs, for head and body bites are likely to prove serious.

Nettie Young, from her experience as a nurse in the Robert B. Green Memorial Hospital in San Antonio, where Dr. Dudley Jackson's cases were treated, found a higher percentage of bites in the legs than that shown in table 12:3. She reported 75 per cent in the lower extremities, 22 per cent in the hands and arms, and 3 per cent elsewhere in the body. Wood (1954, p. 940) reported that in Virginia among 191 bites, mostly by copperheads rather than by rattlers, the distribution was as follows: lower limbs 65 per cent, upper limbs 33 per cent, head and trunk 2 per cent.

In the tropics, owing to the heavier ground cover and the different type of agriculture, as well as the reduced protection afforded the feet and legs by the less general use of shoes and trousers, bites in the lower limbs are higher in percentage than in the United States as a whole, with a frequency somewhat like that in Texas. In Brazil, Amaral (1930, p. 63) found the bites in the lower limbs to be 69.4 per cent, in the upper limbs 30.0, and in the head and trunk

TABLE 12:3

DISTRIBUTION OF SNAKE BITES IN THE BODY: UNITED STATES CASES ONLY

Body part	Cases	Subtotal	Per cent
Finger...............................	369	.....	18.06
Hand or wrist.........................	264	.....	12.92
Arm.................................	203	.....	9.94
Upper limb.........................	...	836	40.92
Foot or ankle.........................	724	.....	35.44
Leg.................................	451	.....	22.07
Lower limb.........................	...	1,175	57.51
Total limbs.........................	...	2,011	98.43
Trunk...............................	14	.....	0.69
Head................................	18	.....	0.88
Head and trunk.....................	...	32	1.57
Grand total.........................		2,043	100.00

less than 0.6 per cent. Barroso (1944, p. 41) gives these percentages: lower limbs 78 per cent, upper limbs 17 per cent, and the head and trunk 5 per cent. Fonseca (1949, p. 160) lists the sites of 5,980 snake bites reported to the Butantan Institute, São Paulo, Brazil. There were 1,065 in the upper limbs, 4,900 in the lower, 16 in the head, and 9 in the body. Clark (1942, p. 44), in Central America, encountered 53 bites in the arms (of which 33 were in the fingers), 1 in the shoulder, and 50 in the legs (including 7 in the toes, 17 in the foot, and 11 in the ankle). These were not all rattler bites. Picado (1931, p. 141), in Costa Rica, reported 70 per cent of bites in the legs or feet, 25 per cent in the arms or hands, and 5 per cent in the head or trunk.

As to the relative effects of bites in the different parts of the body, Redi observed as early as 1673 (p. 13) that a fatal result is more likely to follow if the bite occurs where veins and arteries are large. Stradling (1883, p. 225) considers the ankle a bad place to be bitten for this reason. There is a well-known rattlesnake story in the Southwest concerning a cowboy who was struck in the neck while crawling through a barbed-wire fence and died instantly. This is told of many times and places; it may have had its genesis in some actual occurrence wherein a man was found dead in a fence, having been unable to untangle himself after being struck. Gould and Pyle (1897, p. 717) report the case in Montana of a soldier bitten in the throat who did recover. Brymer (1928, p. 306) thought that of 21 deaths from rattlesnake bite in Texas, 15 were caused by bites at or near a large vein. He thought that bites above the knee were invariably fatal (p. 300). Otken (1942, p. 185) stated that fatal cases are usually those bitten over ulnar or saphenous veins; unfavorable sites are the ankle, inner aspect of the leg, and the palmar surface of the wrist; sites likely to prove less serious are the heel or the fleshy part of the leg. Allen (1938, p. 1248) points out that deep penetration means intramuscular rather than subcutaneous injection, with increased danger of necrosis and gangrene.

A case illustrative of the almost complete absence of penetration when a bone is struck is the following:

> The only snake-bite case I have seen was when a three-foot *C. m. molossus* I was handling twisted its head (I had gripped it not very snugly behind the head), and bit my right index finger. I saw the fang tips penetrate the flesh immediately over the second joint, then threw the snake from me. I suffered no pain, and had no swelling, although there was a very mild itching which came intermittently for nearly a day, around the two tiny punctures in the flesh. The only conclusion I could draw was that the fang tips touched bone on top of my finger, and thus were checked from deeper penetration. The skin through which they went was so thick I don't believe any portion of the poison canal entered the finger. Since I had no pain, the only first aid I gave was to swab the surface with iodine, to kill bacteria. *Earl Jackson, National Park Service, Las Vegas, Nev.*

Illegitimate Bites

One item of interest in connection with snake-bite statistics is the question of what proportion of the bites or fatalities results from the handling of snakes, as compared with those that happen to persons who have no intention of indulging in so unnecessary a risk. The latter might be referred to as legitimate bites. Hutchison (1929, p. 49), in a table describing what the victims were doing when bitten, lists 19 people who were bitten while handling captive snakes, and 3 while catching them, or a total of 22 out of 455 cases. However, the nature of the tabulation is such that there may have been duplications, with fewer than 455 cases involved.

Githens (1935b, p. 166) has furnished what are probably the most accurate statistics on this question now available for the United States. He reported: "A surprisingly large number of bites were inflicted on persons who were intentionally handling poisonous snakes. Of the 2,342 bites, 163, or more than 1 in every 15, were received in this way. Of these, 47 were in ignorant persons, often children, who picked up the snakes, not realizing their danger. Forty-eight were in professional snake catchers, about half being received while capturing the snake and half in handling recent captives. Thirty-one were showmen at fairs or carnivals, and 23 scientists studying snakes in the laboratory or extracting venom. Snakes supposed to be dead inflicted 14 bites." This figure of one illegitimate bite out of every 15 (6.7 per cent) has been often quoted (e.g., Richardson, 1936, p. 44; Hutchins, 1941, p. 20; Anon., 1951, p. 32). Kauffeld (1942, p. 90) gives the proportion as 15 per cent. Wood (1954, p. 941), in his investigation of snake-bite cases in Virginia, found that 13 per cent of the accidents occurred when snakes were being handled. Ross Allen (*in litt.*) reported 23 illegitimate bites out of 106, or 21.7 per cent, in Florida during the years 1947–50. From

Githens' figures, I should exclude children not expected to know better, which would reduce the illegitimate bites to about 6 per cent of the total.

I recently tabulated 117 reports of venomous snake-bite cases reported in the newspapers. Of these, 62, or 53 per cent, were incurred in the handling of snakes, in picking up those thought to be dead, or as a result of misidentifications. I do not cite this as a fair representation of the proportion of illegitimate bites; it merely indicates that this kind of accident usually gets more publicity than the really accidental accident. Isely (1951, p. 1), in reporting on the annual Waynoka, Oklahoma, rattlesnake hunt (a publicity exploit), stated that 55 participants belonged to the White Fang Club, composed of those who had previously been bitten. Unfortunately, we do not know what proportion of the white-fangers gained entrance to the chosen circle legitimately. Fitch (1949a, p. 573) reported that, in connection with the studies made at the San Joaquin Experimental Range in Madera County, California, five people were bitten while handling rattlers in connection with the scientific work there carried on; there were no true accidents. Minton (1950, p. 322) estimated that, in Indiana, one-third of the snake bites occurred while people were handling the snakes.

Davenport (1943, p. 19) suggests that illegitimate bites are the more likely to prove serious since a rattler held in the hand can more readily reach the body, where the bite is more dangerous than in the extremities. However, the Hutchison statistics hardly bear this out. Of a number of cases of people bitten while handling rattlers, all were bitten in the fingers or hand.

THE GRAVITY OF RATTLESNAKE BITE AS AFFECTED BY THE SPECIES

The species of rattlesnake responsible for a bite entails, in itself, many important factors affecting the gravity of the case. For on the species will depend the toxicity of the venom, and its quantity as well, two important factors that have already been treated in detail. The length of the fangs, and the force with which they are driven in, will affect the depth of penetration, again dependent on the species of rattler involved. Of course, some of these factors are variable within a rattlesnake species; for example, there are young ones and adults; also any snake, regardless of the species, may happen to have virtually empty glands at the time of a bite, or it may have broken fangs. But, by and large, it can be said that some kinds of rattlers are a hundred times more dangerous than others. Some, indeed, may be incapable of causing a human fatality.

Githens (1935a, p. 172; 1935b, p. 167), from his case-report studies, presents the following mortality rates in per cent for various kinds of rattlesnakes: *C. adamanteus* 27; *C. atrox* 11.2; *C. horridus* 6.7; *C. viridis viridis* 6.5; *C. v. oreganus* and *C. v. helleri* 6.1; *C. cerastes* 6; and *S. catenatus* or *S. miliarius* 0. Allen (1939a, p. 33) gives *C. adamanteus* fatalities as 30 per cent of the bites; *C. horridus* 4 per cent; and *S. miliarius* 0. Later, by letter, Allen reported a mortality of 15 per cent in *adamanteus* bites for the years 1947–51. Robinson (1896, p. 711) mentions a fatality from *S. catenatus*. Allen and Neill (1950b, p. 11) report that there are many bites by *S. miliarius barbouri* in Florida each year, but there have been no fatalities. But Davis (1918, p. 15) mentions a very painful and even serious case from a bite of a juvenile of this small species. Another was reported by Beyer (1898, p. 21). Oertel (1929, p. 314) thought a *miliarius* bite might be fatal to a child. Sutcliffe (1952, p. 113) found a note attributed to Hallowell, recording a fatality following the bite of *miliarius*.

Minton (1950, p. 318) expresses the opinion that the bite of *S. c. catenatus* is rarely fatal, but that *C. h. horridus* bite may be very grave. Webber (1951, p. 12) states that the bite of the copperhead is rarely fatal because of its short fangs and meager venom supply. This is mentioned only because statistics on copperheads are so often included with those on rattlers. Of course, all of these statements of the relative danger from the bites of various species of rattlesnakes must be correlated with some uniformity of treatment.

Altogether, from the statistics available, I think we may say that the eastern diamondback, *C. adamanteus*, is the most dangerous rattlesnake, and therefore the most dangerous snake in the United States, from the standpoint of the percentage of fatal cases resulting from its bite. But the western diamond, *C. atrox*, because of the large area occupied, its prevalence in agricultural districts, and its nervous disposition, together with its large size and moderately powerful venom, probably causes more deaths in the United States than all other rattlesnakes taken together.

The South American rattler, *C. d. terrificus*, as found in Brazil, is more dangerous than any species found in the United States. The mortality rate when antivenin was used was reported by Kraus (1923, p. 326) at 9.8 per cent, by Amaral (1930, p. 57) at 12.1 per cent, by Barroso (1944, p. 40) at 13.2 per cent, and by Fonseca (1949, p. 150) at 12.2 per cent. I deem this a more dangerous snake than *adamanteus* despite the discrepancy involved in the mortality ratios that I have just cited for the two species—about 15 per cent or more for *adamanteus*, and 13 per cent for *terrificus*—because I believe them to have been compiled and computed on different bases.

This matter of the relative danger from different species of rattlesnakes involves many variables. Elsewhere (p. 788), I have pointed out the difficulty of evaluating even such relatively measurable factors as unit venom toxicity and venom yield.

BITES BY YOUNG SNAKES

I have discussed elsewhere some of the factors that affect the relative hazards from juvenile snakes, such as the toxicity of their venom as inferred from the proportion of solids remaining after evaporation, and the variation of venom yield with snake length. As is characteristic of young snakes of many kinds, both venomous and harmless, juvenile rattlers are more "on the prod"—ready to bite— than adults. But the fact remains that young rattlers, with their short, delicate fangs and limited venom supply, are very much less dangerous than adults of the same species. However, they are not to be trifled with. They have both fangs and venom ready for use immediately upon birth and can inflict a very painful injury.

Beyer (1898, p. 21) allowed himself to be bitten by a young *S. miliarius* only 5½ inches long, eight days after its birth. To start with, this is a small species of rattler that, even as an adult, may not be able to inflict a fatal bite on a human being. But Beyer enumerates many painful symptoms from which he suffered, and from which he did not recover for three days or more. W. T. Davis (1918, p. 15) had an extremely painful experience with the bite of a *miliarius* only nine inches long.

Prof. W. B. Davis, of A. and M. College, Texas, gives this account of an experience with a juvenile rattler of a medium-sized species:

> The *C. lepidus* that bit me was very young, with only a button, but I can vouch that it had sufficient venom in one poison sac (only one fang was effective) to cause my hand to swell up and my side to turn green.

The late E. A. McIlhenny wrote me concerning the bite of a canebrake rattler (*C. h. atricaudatus*) less than two hours old, that almost proved fatal. I have had the experience of watching the progress of two cases of bites by juvenile southern Pacific rattlers (*C. v. helleri*), both of which were painful and even serious. Some of the neurotoxic symptoms were quite alarming.

TABLE 12:4

MONTHLY DISTRIBUTION OF SNAKE-BITE CASES IN THE UNITED STATES
(Data of R. H. Hutchison)

January	7	August	191
February	1	September	158
March	23	October	65
April	83	November	19
May	116	December	5
June	168		
July	252[a]	Total	1,088

[a] The July peak is not quite so high as shown in the table. I have changed Hutchison's statistics, which were on a weekly basis, to monthly, and it happened that there were five weekly reports in each of his Julys. To compensate for this, about 33 should be deducted from July, as tabulated, and added to August.

The following references will be of interest to those who may wish to pursue further the matter of bites by juvenile rattlers or copperheads: Rengger, 1829, p. 90; O'Reilly, 1899, p. 377; Rolker, 1903, p. 386; Viosca, 1926, p. 328; Reese, 1926, p. 357; Stadelman, 1928, p. 67; 1929, p. 81; Conant, 1938, p. 116; 1951, p. 116; Gowanlock, 1943, p. 37; Kauffeld, 1943b, p. 607; and Polaski and Polaski, 1952, p. 138.

TEMPORAL VARIABLES IN SNAKE-BITE CASES

Snake-bite cases are most frequent when there is a coincidence of snake and human activities. In most areas of the United States, the snakes, rattlers among them, are most active in the spring, May especially. (In some areas of the Southwest, where summer rains are prevalent, the snakes may reach a peak of activity later, in July or August, although their sorties then are largely nocturnal.) But the human activities are later—the vacation, hunting, fishing, and harvesting seasons—so that the snake-bite season reaches its peak in July. The most complete temporal statistics on snake-bite prevalence available for this country are those of Hutchison (1929, p. 47; 1930, p. 41), who reported the monthly frequencies of bites by poisonous snakes, for the two years, 1928 and 1929, as set forth in table 12:4.

Swartzwelder (1950, p. 576) found that the hospitalized cases in Louisiana reached a peak in September, closely followed by June, July, and August. Allen (by letter) reported a substantially equal incidence of bites in Florida during May, June, and July, followed by somewhat lesser numbers in April, October, and November. Wood (1954, p. 938) found, in Virginia, that July was the peak month, followed, in order, by September, August, and June. Barroso (1944, p. 45) reported that snake-bite cases in Brazil also reach a maximum in their summer (January–March).

Like the seasonal incidence of snake-bite cases, the hourly incidence depends on the correlation of snake and human activities, but much more on the latter, if the snakes are above ground at all; for the majority of snake bites probably involve hidden and resting, rather than active, rattlers—snakes that are not even seen by the human victim before the accident. Thus it is no surprise to learn from the brief statistics of Swartzwelder (1950, p. 580) that most accidents occur between 6 and 9 in the morning, and between noon and 6 in the afternoon. Wood (1954, p. 938) found that two-thirds of the snake-bite accidents in Virginia occurred in the daytime. The most dangerous hours were, in order: 9–12 A.M.; 6–9 P.M.; 3–6 P.M.; 12–3 P.M.; 9–12 P.M.

SEASONAL AND CLIMATIC EFFECTS ON THE GRAVITY OF SNAKE BITE

There has long been a belief that venomous snakes are more dangerous in the summer and in hot weather than in the winter. This is a presumption that was held in Europe and elsewhere long before the discovery of America, and in colonial times the theory was extended to include rattlesnakes. Whether these seasonal differences—if they exist—are to be attributed to variations in venom toxicity or to venom quantity has not generally been stated. Certainly there are seasonal differences in snake activity, and it is possible that the theory may have gained credence from the fact that a cold snake strikes slower and with less effectiveness than a warm one; and if the snake is cold enough it cannot strike at all, in fact, it cannot even bite. It may be that venom is secreted more slowly at lower temperatures, but it is doubtful whether any different results are to be anticipated from a winter as compared to a summer bite, if the snake is warm enough so that its jaw action and ability to imbed the fangs are not impaired. But certainly it is true, as a matter of practical interest to hunters and fishermen, that the rattlesnake hazard is reduced or completely eliminated in cold weather, but this is more the effect on rattlesnake habits than on a change in the gravity of the bite.

The prerattlesnake statements on the relative dangers from snake bite include those of Pliny (1855–57, vol. 2, p. 311; book viii, chap. 59), who thought vipers harmless during the hibernating season; and Avicenna (Thorndike, 1923–41, vol. 2, p. 413) and Lovell (1661, p. [27]), who considered them more or less harmless in winter but dangerous in summer. This, it should be understood, was attributed to lack of potency of the venom in winter, not to an inability to bite. A similar idea is held by the Chinese with regard to one of their pit vipers, *Agkistrodon acutus* (Read, 1934, p. 344), and a like variation has been attributed to the cobra in India (Williams, 1792, p. 226).

The same idea respecting rattlesnakes was expressed as early as 1665 by Taylor (p. 43). Clayton (1693, p. 127) said that rattler venom was more powerful in June and July than in March or April; and much the same thought was echoed, with some modifications in the months selected, and with heat mentioned as the causative factor, by Lawson (1709, p. 129), Brickell (1735, p. 144), Salmon (1744–46, vol. 3, p. 413), Kearsley (1766, p. 74), Carver (1778, p. 482), La Rochefoucault-Liancourt (1799, p. 594), Schoolcraft (1821, p. 325), Warburton (1849, vol. 1, p.

175), Moragne (1853, p. 82), Kunkler (1855, p. 483), Peake (1860–61, p. 50), Bevin (1875, p. 4), Shuler (1881, p. 292), Pollock (1911, p. 157), Strecker (1926a, p. 67), Ludwick (1930, p. 121), and Texier (1940, p. 207, but written in 1844).

There have been a number of variations on this theme. Brookes (1763, vol. 3, p. 368) thought rattler venom most powerful in March and April when the snakes were most vigorous. Brewer (1897, p. 58) said that dogs bitten in April almost always died, whereas those bitten in late summer recovered. He also cited the case of a man bitten in April who died despite drinking a pint of whiskey, but a child bitten in July recovered. Needless to say, with so many important variables unspecified in each case, this proves nothing.

Walduck in 1714 (Masterson, 1938, p. 215) said that rattlers have no venom when they first come out of hibernation. Witt (1768, p. 10) had the opinion that in winter the bite of a rattlesnake was no worse than a pin prick. Barton (1793, p. 101) reported that some rattlers have no venom, even in the active season, and that they bite with reluctance in seasons of torpor. Anon. (1832b, p. 99) said that rattler bite was instantaneously fatal at some seasons, implying less virulence at others; and Williams (1848, p. 449) thought the venom inert at certain seasons. Neidhard (1860, p. 34), who used venom for therapeutic purposes, said the venom must be taken from the snake only in summer, and when freshly caught, if possible. Wood (1863, p. 102), in the natural history that was so important in the education of Victorian children, wrote that rattlers seldom attempted to bite in the spring when the venom was comparatively mild (see also Comfort, 1878, p. 78). Paine (1872, p. 223) was greatly surprised when a copperhead bite in the winter proved to be serious. Dyche (1909, p. 313), from an examination of a single rattler in winter, concluded that snakes are without venom in the hibernating season.

Although Fontana (1787, vol. 2, p. 92) proved experimentally to his own satisfaction that there are seasonal differences in the venom of the European viper, his methods were too crude to be trustworthy. Walker (1945, p. 13) traced 50 cases of viper bite in Great Britain, and found that, despite the commonly held belief there that viper bites are serious only in spring, actually there were serious cases (with five fatalities) in all months from March to October, which means substantially all the time the vipers are out of hibernation in that climate. Houssay (1923, p. 449) reported higher yields from the Neotropical rattler (*C. d. terrificus*) in summer than in winter.

Related to the idea of seasonal variations in venom virulence is the idea that southern snakes are more dangerous than those in the north (in the Northern Hemisphere), which is well founded if the effect of snake size be taken into consideration. Lucan in about 60 A.D., discussing the Libyan snakes encountered by the Romans, said that the desert climate increased the virulence of the snake called dipsas (Riley, 1909, p. 369). The effect of latitude on rattlesnakes is mentioned by Mather (1714, p. 67), and by Cist (1845, p. 17). Ellzey (1884, p. 251) thought moccasins more fatal than rattlers—they are not—because of their southern habitat and fish diet. It is true that snakes living on cold-blooded prey, which is less susceptible to venom than warm-blooded creatures, usually have powerful venoms.

Other temporal conditions have been thought to influence the gravity of rattlesnake bites. Koster (1817, vol. 2, p. 56) records a case of rattlesnake bite in which the phase of the moon reputedly affected the bite. This was evidently a survival of an ancient belief (Pliny 1855–57, vol. 5, p. 369; book xxix, chap. 22; Topsell, 1608, p. 33). There is also an old theory that venom is stronger at noon than at night (Avicenna in Thorndike, 1923–41, vol. 2, p. 413) but I have not found a record of this as having been attributed to rattlesnakes.

Moore (1744, p. 59) reported rattler bites more dangerous in wet weather; Flack (1866, p. 319) said they were worse during thunderstorms when the air was charged with electricity, although Higgins (1873, p. 86) had an exactly contrary idea. Higgins' position was more in line with an ancient belief expressed by Seneca that when snakes are struck by lightning they lose their venom (Thorndike, 1923–41, vol. 1, p. 102). Higgins also expressed the opinion that female rattlers are more venomous when pregnant, and Williams (1848, p. 450) thought the bite worse during the mating season. Long ago (about 150 B.C.) Nicander (1953 translation, p. 37) expressed the opinion that female snakes were more dangerous than males.

Pound (1946, p. 173) records an item of Nebraska folklore to the effect that rattlesnakes will not bite in the fall; they will bite only in the spring when they shed their skins and go blind. But Flint (1832, vol. 1, p. 75; Arfwedson, 1834, p. 76; Unonius, 1950 [1841–59], p. 298) expressed the belief that rattlers were blind in summer, not because they were shedding their skins, but because they are so full of venom and absorb so much of it into their own systems that blindness results. Powell (1918, p. 329) remarked that when rattlers are blinded by skin changing, they wouldn't bite anything, not even themselves. Rengger (1829, p. 90; Gibbs, 1892, p. 48) makes the sensible observation that rattlers may be more dangerous when shedding, because, having secured no prey while blinded, they have conserved venom. Clark (1942, p. 44) stresses the importance of the reduction in the amount of poison present in the venom glands of a snake that has recently fed. There are various ancient beliefs that may have some foundation in this fact.

Pausanias (1918–35, vol. 4, p. 291), who lived in the second century A.D., said that venom virulence depends on the kind of food eaten; vipers that are vegetarians—there are, in fact, no vegetarian vipers—are particularly dangerous. Celsus (Spencer translation, 1935–38, p. 121), a century or so before, deemed snakes to be more harmful when either the snake, or the man it bit, was hungry, or when the snake was brooding. Avicenna (Thorndike, 1923–41, vol. 2, p. 413) repeated the idea of the danger in the fasting snake. As has been said, there is truth in both of these ideas—when the snake has been fasting, or is inactive while heavy with young—as they do affect the venom supply.

Harlan (1835, p. 495) said some snake-show exhibitors thought that not drinking water made a rattler's venom more virulent; but, on the other hand, Warburton (1849, vol. 1, p. 175), thought that rattlers issuing from hibernation were harmless until they had obtained water. Yarrow (1883a, p. 263) records a myth to the effect that it is safe to handle a rattler if it be deprived of water for some time.

Is there any truth in these ideas concerning the importance of seasonal, climatic, and other effects on the comparative gravity of rattlesnake bite? There is some basic truth in many of them, particularly such as may influence the venom supply. Obviously, snakes that have recently expended some venom in feeding are less dangerous than those that have conserved the supply. Snakes are more dangerous in warm weather because they are more active and alert. It is probable that, at favorable temperatures, they restore their venom supplies more rapidly after partial depletion than when they are cold and lethargic. But whether the unit toxicity of venom in any species is influenced by these factors remains to be proved. Any difference is probably of negligible importance compared with such an obvious factor as the size of the snake.

Concerning the effects of rattlesnake bite, and the fangs and venom involved, there is no sharp line between beliefs that have some basis in fact and those that may be attributed solely to myth and folklore. Some of these ideas have been included in this chapter. The more fantastic will be found at the beginning of chapter 18, which treats of myths, folklore, legends, and tall stories.

SYMPTOMS AND AFTEREFFECTS

In a discussion of the symptoms of rattlesnake bite, we have the difficulty of sifting out the variables that affect the gravity of the bite, particularly the kind and size of the snake, the amount of the venom injected, the site of the bite, and the size and health of the victim. But the source of more confusion than all of these is the superimposed effect of the treatment, and the difficulty of segregating its symptoms from those of the venom alone. Then we have the problem of differentiating the purely physical symptoms from those caused by fear and mental shock; indeed, these are sometimes so important that they may lead to the supposition that the patient had been bitten by a venomous snake when actually the bite was inflicted by one completely harmless. It is unfortunate that there is no single symptom sufficiently dependable and distinctive to leave no doubt that the bite was inflicted by a venomous snake, and that sufficient venom was injected to warrant the radical, painful, and even dangerous remedial measures that are necessary in serious cases; and, indeed, are necessary before later symptoms can have verified the early diagnosis.

In an outline of the symptoms of rattlesnake bite, it is first necessary to make a distinction between the South American rattlesnake, *C. d. terrificus,* and the species inhabiting the United States, of which such Nearctic forms as *C. adamanteus, C. atrox, C. viridis,* and *C. horridus* are typical. There is no doubt that *terrificus* venom, primarily neurotoxic, differs in its effects to a major degree from the others, which are largely hemorrhagic. There are many snakes that are not rattlesnakes, and not even pit vipers, whose venoms are more like that of *terrificus* or, alternately, like those of the Nearctic rattlers, than these two are like each other.

The degree to which the *terrificus*-Nearctic gap is bridged by the venoms of other species and subspecies of rattlesnakes is not known, for there are many forms about whose venom symptoms we have little information. Some reports have been made on the symptoms of *C. d. durissus* bite, which appears less extreme in its differentiation from the Nearctic types than is *C. d. terrificus.* Whether *C. d. culminatus, C. d. tzabcan,* and *C. d. totonacus,* to say nothing of such related forms as *basiliscus* and *enyo,* exhibit further trends toward the northern snakes, we do not know. Reports of snake-bite cases in Mexico are not plentiful, and some of the species occurring there may have venoms with peculiar symptoms, including extreme neurotoxicity.

As to the species inhabiting the United States, it is doubtful whether any of the widely distributed species could have venoms greatly different from the Nearctic mode, without its having become already apparent through case reports, although this might be possible in species with such restricted ranges as those of *lepidus, pricei, tigris,* and *willardi.* As indicated by Githens' m.l.d. tests, discussed elsewhere (p. 765), aside from expected divergences in toxicity, the only rattlesnakes indigenous to the United States that showed possibilities of having venoms differing from the Nearctic mode were *C. tigris, C. s. scutulatus,* and *S. catenatus.* The only *scutulatus* bite of which I have knowledge (information from Dr. F. A. Shannon) did develop neurotoxic symptoms, including double vision, and difficulty in talking and swallowing. As to *catenatus,* there are already sufficient reports to indicate that the symptoms in man do not greatly differ from those produced by the other more prevalent Nearctic species.

SUMMARIES OF SYMPTOMS

The symptoms of rattlesnake poisoning have often been described, both in the form of summaries, and in the reports of individual cases. Among the summaries, the following are to be recommended: Willson (1908, p. 539), Staley (1939, p. 548), Babcock (1944, p. 83), Jones (1950, p. 613), Amaral (1951a, p. 552; 1951b, p. 1252), Stickel (1952, p. 19), and Shannon (1953, p. 368). These will aid in translating the list of venom principles—elsewhere (p. 760) set forth in terms of physiological effects—into the effects in terms of external symptoms.

Hutchison (1929, p. 50) has given a frequency list of the symptoms resulting from a study of many rattlesnake-bite cases in the United States. The list, presented in table 12:5, is both interesting and important.

Other symptoms mentioned, but not tabulated in terms of frequency, were: Urticaria (hives), thirst, excitement, gastric disturbance, heart pain, enlarged glands, soreness, diarrhea, collapse, shock, convulsions, and bloody urine.

Allowing for the effects of the treatments given in these cases, which effects cannot be divorced from the later symptoms of the bites, I think we have, in the first eight items listed in table 12:5, a fairly complete picture of the most common symptoms of rattlesnake bite. Of course, in the evaluation of Hutchison's list, it must be remembered that case reports are rarely complete or fully objective, and that some symptoms were present but unrecorded in many cases.

DISCUSSION OF SYMPTOMS BY CATEGORIES

I have read many case reports of rattlesnake bite in the medical literature, as well as outlines and discussions of venom effects. With the Hutchison list as a guide, I should like to comment on some of the symptoms mentioned in these other sources. I shall touch on them in somewhat the same order as in the Hutchison list. It should be understood that all of these remarks apply to the bites of the kinds of rattlers found in the United States.

Swelling and Discoloration.—Almost all case reports dwell on the presence and importance of this manifestation. A swelling, in most cases, is pronounced at the site of the injury. Besides the swelling, there is much surface discoloration—the ecchymosis or blood extravasation listed separately by Hutchison. It may be red, blue, or black; it tends to darken with time. The discoloration is one of the most evident of the hemorrhagic effects of the venom, as the breaking down of the endothelial lining of the smaller blood vessels permits the blood to diffuse through the tissues. Smith (1950, p. 289) refers to the swelling as resulting in part from the "accumulation of a great deal of lymphatic ooze." The swelling gradually spreads toward the heart. It sometimes becomes of very large and alarming proportions; it may be severe enough to rupture the skin (Willson, 1908, p. 540).

TABLE 12:5

FREQUENCY OF OCCURRENCE OF SYMPTOMS IN RATTLESNAKE BITE
(Data of R. H. Hutchison)

Symptom	Number of cases in which it was observed
Swelling	185
Pain	149
Weakness	93
Giddiness	61
Respiratory difficulty	43
Nausea and/or vomiting	33
Hemorrhage	31
Weak pulse or heart failure	21
Gangrene	11
Ecchymosis (blood extravasation)	10
Paralysis	7
Increased pulse rate	6
Unconsciousness or stupor	3
Increased temperature	3
Perspiration	1
Nervousness	1

From the extremities, if the site of the bite is in one of these, as it usually is, the swelling may reach the trunk within 24 hours or less; the rate will depend on the quantity of venom, and on the use of a tourniquet, if any. Brewer (1897, p. 58) and others have mentioned red streaks extending proximally from the site of the bite. The swelling appears quite soon after the accident, and, if not masked by remedial measures, most of which also produce swelling, is a fairly good diagnostic indicator of the presence of venom, and therefore that the snake was venomous and that some poison has been injected. The action of the venom in causing the dissolution of the walls of the capillaries to produce extensive extravasation has been described by Taube and Essex (1937, pp. 49, 51) and Fidler *et al.* (1940, p. 363).

Pain.—Instantaneous pain—as differentiated from subsequent pain resulting from the swelling, or from incisions, a tourniquet, or other treatment—is mentioned in nearly all accounts of rattlesnake bites. Were its presence invariable, it would constitute the best single confirmation of the presence of venom in the bite, thus justifying treatment. Unfortunately, there have been a few cases, some of a dangerous character, wherein no pain was felt; but even so, pain remains the most characteristic early symptom of rattlesnake bite. It must be reiterated that this statement is only appropriate to the rattlers found in the United States; there is said to be little or no local pain from the bite of the Neotropical rattler; and there are many kinds of venomous snakes in other countries, including some of the most dangerous, whose bite produces few or no local symptoms.

The pain in rattler bite is usually almost instantaneous, although this depends on the site of the bite, which may also explain the painless cases. Clayton (1693, p. 134; Brickell, 1735, p. 145) said that one victim described it as "a flash of fire through the veins." Lee in 1691 (see Kittredge, 1913, p. 149) mentioned the great pain of a bite. Savage (1877, p. 36) referred to it as the most violent pain the victim had ever known. Shuler (1881, p. 292) called it a burning pain. Anon. (1947b, p. 10) stated that the pain, often excruciating, is evident in from three to five minutes. Githens (1931, p. 82) points out that the pain is the result of the irritant action of a toxalbumin on the nerves and sensory endings, and thus should be almost instantly apparent.

But despite all these evidences of a sharp, stinging pain as a typical symptom, there have been cases, as mentioned by Mitchell (1861, p. 280), wherein there was none. This has been confirmed by a number of persons who have been bitten by subspecies of the western rattlesnake, *Crotalus viridis,* as I shall set forth in particular case reports. Once, in presenting a paper on rattlesnakes, I commented on the almost invariable presence of this symptom. Later, several members of the audience recounted experiences of their own in which no pain had been felt, at least not until after the first curative measures had been applied.

The symptom of immediate pain is advantageous to a snake in that it should tend to draw the attention of an enemy away from the snake before the victim could injure it.

Weakness and Giddiness.—Accounts of rattlesnake bite frequently mention various degrees of weakness, faintness, and giddiness, sometimes relapsing into complete loss of consciousness or syncope. Some of the terms met in these reports are shock, dizziness, giddiness, vertigo, collapse, syncope, debility, loss of strength, pallid countenance, etc. No doubt these symptoms are strongly affected by the fright that accompanies a bite, and by the pain incident to the treatment. Great excitement, confusion of mind, and extreme nervousness are occasionally mentioned. The victim may become comatose or unconscious in the early stages, as distinguished from the coma that may be expected in the final stages of fatal cases. The various manifestations of weakness may be very serious if they affect people when alone in the field and far from help. It is always difficult to divorce any symptoms of this character that may be attributed to the physical effects of the venom from those induced by fright and mental shock.

Respiratory Difficulty.—This characteristic neurotoxic symptom is not infrequently met in cases of Nearctic rattler bite, particularly in the later stages. Willson (1908, p. 541) states the respiration may be rapid and shallow, or slow and stertorous. In one case near Jacumba, San Diego County, California, a man bitten in the ankle had difficulty in breathing for 24 hours after the accident. Judged from a numbness in the side of his face, it was thought that the snake was a southern Pacific rattler (*C. v. helleri*), but this is not certain, for two other rattlers live in that area, the southwestern speckled rattler (*C. m. pyrrhus*) and the red diamond (*C. r. ruber*). I have often found it difficult to ascertain the species of rattler involved in a snake-bite case in places where more than one kind is found, as the evidence required for identification is rarely available. Even color descriptions are usually too vague to be conclusive.

Nausea and Vomiting.—These are occasional symptoms, as are also digestive disturbances such as diarrhea or constipation. Blood may sometimes be passed. Nausea may be a relatively early symptom.

Hemorrhage.—There may be considerable oozing from the wound, owing to an anticoagulant action of the venom, and this may take place even though no drainage incisions have been made. There may also be bleeding from the mouth, nose, intestines, or kidneys.

Circulatory Disturbance.—The pulse is often rapid (double normal), feeble, and fluttery or thready. There is a concomitant lowering of blood pressure, which may have serious secondary reactions. The temperature is generally subnormal, except in cases where an infection becomes important. An anemia of considerable severity and duration may follow (Willson, 1908, p. 546), a logical effect of the hemolytic principle in the venom.

Miscellaneous Effects.—Gangrene is sometimes a direct venom effect, but more often follows the improper use of a tourniquet—that is, one that is too tight and permitted to remain too long with the pressure unrelieved. Blebs and vesicles at or near the site of the bite are common.

Various nervous or systemic disturbances are occasionally observed, including convulsions. There may be local paralysis involving difficulty in swallowing and numbness of the face, especially of the lips and tongue. There may be excessive thirst. Cold sweats are not infrequently mentioned in case reports.

As temporary blindness is a symptom of the bite of the Neotropical rattler, one must be sure that this species is not included in summaries when the symptoms mention blindness. However, Bozeman (1850, p. 739) reports a case in Alabama of a boy nine years old bitten by a ground rattler (presumably *S. miliarius*) in which the vision was seriously affected. There was pain in the head and neck, followed by inability to focus or co-ordinate the eyes. This continued for four or five months, with occasional short spells of blindness. Altogether, recovery was not complete for a year and a half. McLane (1943, p. 25) describes an *adamanteus* bite that resulted in a retinal hemorrhage. There is available the record of a bite by a northern Pacific rattler (*C. v. oreganus*), in which temporary blindness was experienced about half an hour after the bite. Willson (1908, p. 543) mentions a case of deafness of short duration resulting from snake bite.

In view of this great variability in the symptoms of bites by Nearctic rattlesnakes, it is to be regretted that uniformity is not evident in at least one symptom upon which the diagosing physician might place dependence. Initial pain comes nearest to meeting the requirement, but this fails occasionally. Studies have been made in the hope that a blood-smear test might be devised to determine accurately whether crotaline venom had entered the blood stream of the victim of a bite, but so far without success.

SYMPTOMATIC CASE REPORTS BY SPECIES

Although Hutchison's original symptom list segregated the rattlesnake species, the number of cases tabulated was insufficient to permit drawing conclusions as to specific differences in symptoms, if there are any, among the commoner Nearctic species. Only in the cases involving *atrox, viridis,* and *horridus* were there enough reports to permit even rough conclusions on this point, and in these three species the symptoms seem relatively uniform, except that weakness and giddiness were proportionately more frequent in *viridis* and *horridus* cases than in those that involved *atrox.*

There are available some case reports, either in the medical literature or among those that I have collected, wherein the species of the offending snake is known beyond question. From these we may learn whether there are any notable differences from the modal symptoms previously summarized. In these accounts the steps in the treatment are usually inserted in parentheses. They are introduced because they often modify the subsequent symptoms.

Crotalus adamanteus.—The details of a very serious bite by an eastern diamond rattler of large size have been given by MacDonald, the victim (1930, p. 34; 1946, p. 133), Allen and Merryday (1940, p. 235), and Hightower (1945, p. 9). The essential symptoms were instant pain "like two hot hypodermic needles," spontaneous bleeding from the wound, intense internal pain, hemorrhage from the mouth, low blood pressure, weak pulse, great swelling and black discoloration of the leg (the site of the bite) with accompanying severe pain. We note here no departure from the usual Nearctic symptoms, as evidenced in very severe cases. As most of Dr. S. Weir Mitchell's epoch-making experiments (1860, 1861, 1886 with Reichert, and 1898 with Stewart) were carried on with *adamanteus* venom, it is no surprise to find the strongly hemolytic and hemorrhagic symptoms evident in this case.

The following symptoms are quoted from a recent (1952) account by Everna Phillips of an *adamanteus* bite in the side of the leg, near the knee cap, suffered by Ross Allen:

> This was the worst snake bite in the history of the Reptile Institute. Due to the great quantity of venom injected, different and heretofore undescribed symptoms were experienced. Twenty-five minutes after the bite he could not walk and it was difficult to breathe. Every muscle in his body jumped and twitched spasmodically, due to the neurotoxic effect of the venom. This continued for five days and was the most dreadful and exhausting experience of any of his many injuries. The hemolytic effect of the venom caused his right leg to swell and turn black from the ankle to hip. During the fourth and fifth days, which the doctor said were the most critical, Ross was too weak to talk. The hemolytic effect also caused an anemic condition by the fourth day, in spite of four blood transfusions. On the sixth day, like a miracle, a marked improvement was evident.

The symptoms evident in this serious case have been set forth in detail by Watt and Pollard (1954, p. 367), partly in the words of the sufferer himself. Tingling of the hands, chest, and face, with numbness of the upper lip, were experienced soon after the bite. These are neurotoxic effects not usually so evident in bites by *adamanteus.* Some of these symptoms were still present when the patient left the hospital 22 days later. The pain, normally prominent in bites by this species, was apparently deadened by the large dose of venom, so that initially no pain was felt. Muscle twitching began five minutes after the accident. Paralysis of the legs prevented walking within half an hour. One peculiar symptom was that everything appeared yellow to the victim; Dr. Pollard informs me that this symptom had been observed in other bites by the eastern diamondback.

Andrews and Pollard (1953, p. 390) found some diversity in the degree of pain present in *adamanteus* cases, from moderate to very severe, depending on the quantity of venom injected. As previously mentioned, there may be so severe a reaction from a large venom injection that the pain is virtually absent, by reason of a numbing effect.

Crotalus atrox.—From the standpoint of the number of serious snake-bite cases occurring in the United States, this is the most important species, as the accidents involving its bite may exceed those from all of the other species of rattlesnakes in this country combined. Unfortunately, in no part of its range is it the sole indigenous rattlesnake, although it is the most plentiful in much of its territory. Thus, unless the snake causing the accident has been accurately identified, one can never be sure, from the locality alone, that *atrox* was the culprit.

Col. M. L. Crimmins of Texas has had extensive experience with *atrox* and *atrox* cases, and I think we are safe in summarizing his list of symptoms (1927b, p. 23) as essentially those of *atrox*. These are:

a. A fiery pain from the action of the venom
b. Profuse bleeding at the bite, owing to the anticoagulative action of the venom
c. A rapid swelling, beginning at the site of the bite, the result of an infiltration of blood and lymph through the connective tissue
d. Discoloration of the tissues from the same cause
e. A rapid pulse, sometimes double normal, followed by very low blood pressure
f. Neurotoxic symptoms, nausea, and vomiting

One *atrox* case, that of Mrs. Grace Olive Wiley, who was bitten four times in the left hand while endeavoring to give water to an *atrox*, has been fully reported by Ehrlich (1928, p. 65). The symptoms, with their times of onset, were as follows, with the treatment in parentheses: Immediate: Intense, sharp, localized burning pain; profuse bleeding from the fang wounds; bluish discoloration with localized swelling. (A tourniquet was applied above the elbow.) After five minutes: Nausea and weakness; increasing localized pain, radiating in all directions. At 20 minutes (and arrival at the hospital): Tingling and numbness in the opposite hand; thirst; an aggravation of the previous symptoms; temperature 99° F., pulse 120, respiration 26. (At 25 minutes, novocaine was injected, and incision and suction were applied.) At 30 minutes: Vomiting; cold perspiration; a feeling of suffocation; increased swelling and pain. At 35 minutes: Generalized urticaria with itching and burning; swelling reached the elbow. At 45 minutes: Further increased swelling and pain; spasms of the respiratory muscles with feeling of impending death. (At 48 minutes a 10-cc. dose of antivenin was given intramuscularly, followed by 20 cc. at 63 minutes—15 intramuscularly, 6 intravenously; also 1 cc. of adrenalin.) At 120 minutes: Vomiting at intervals; thirst; chill. The subsequent symptoms are not given in detail. The patient was improving at the end of 24 hours, and was discharged on the twelfth day. By that time only localized sloughing at the bite was in evidence.

The following are the symptoms of another *atrox* case, a bite in the right index finger: There was an instant stinging pain at the bite; one minute later the finger was stiff and black at the tip. (A tourniquet, incision, and suction were applied at 2 minutes.) At 4 minutes the stinging continued; at 11 minutes the finger was black from the end to the bite, and swelling had commenced. (The tourniquet was loosened at 15 minutes. At 24 minutes blisters near the wound were punctured; at 37 minutes, as the knuckle was swollen, the tourniquet was moved to the hand. At 42 minutes the swelling continued and the tourniquet was moved to the wrist.) Discoloration and pain were now evident at the bend of the elbow. (More blisters around the bite were punctured.) At 47 minutes discoloration was evident from the wrist almost to the elbow; there was some sweating; the arm was discolored. (The tourniquet was again moved upward.) There was a tremulous feeling. At 2 hours the soreness was less below the elbow, but was worse at the inside of the elbow; there were many large blisters below the wrist, and much discoloration on the inside of the upper and lower arm. Later symptoms were obscured by the treatment. Eventually the bite caused the loss of the end of the finger.

C. atrox symptoms are further discussed by Fidler, Glasgow, and Carmichael (1938, p. 893), and by Young, (1940, p. 657).

Crotalus ruber ruber.—Although bites by this common rattlesnake are not infrequent in southern California, I have no information on unquestioned bites by this species, in which all of the early symptoms were recorded. In one case pain, swelling, and discoloration were manifested. In another there was instant pain. Symptoms similar to those of an *atrox* bite are to be expected.

Crotalus viridis viridis.—The following summary of symptoms is abstracted from the detailed personal experience of Over (1928, p. 8), who was bitten in the middle of the index finger: Instant shooting pain up the arm; dizziness and faintness (after removal of the tourniquet 30 minutes after the bite); pulse of normal rate but weak; vomiting and bowel movements; chill; acute thirst continued for 36 hours; swelling and discoloration reached the elbow in 10 to 12 hours, and engaged the entire arm in 36 hours; later it engaged part of the body; the swelling was painful and also itched; headaches and sleeplessness were encountered.

A. M. Jackley gave the following summary of the symptoms of *viridis* bite (a composite of several experiences) in a radio talk February 7, 1946: There is an immediate sensation like the sting of a wasp; there is little or no bleeding; a spreading feeling of numbness, especially at the tongue and lips; the tips of the fingers and toes tingle; there is a tendency to faint, and thereafter to remain in a coma for some time; nausea and vomiting are usually present; swelling begins about 10 minutes after the bite, with discoloration, and continues with severe pain for 36 to 48 hours.

In a case of a man bitten in the palm of the right hand near the little finger by a young prairie rattlesnake, there was no initial pain. After 3½ minutes the lips and tongue began to tingle. There was slight bleeding at the bite. (At this time a tourniquet and ethyl chloride were applied.) After 15 minutes there was a dull pain in the arm. Later, after the injection of antivenin, there were dizziness and loss of control of the limbs. Ultimately the swelling of the arm was very severe.

In another bite by a prairie rattlesnake involving a child, there were marked neurotoxic symptoms in an arched back, hypertonic muscles, difficult respiration, vomiting, regular convulsive movements, and an inability to recognize people. A duodenal ulcer became evident four days after this bite (Bulger and Northrop, 1951, p. 1135) and was judged to be of neurotoxic origin.

Crotalus viridis lutosus.—There are available two complete and informative reports on bites by the Great Basin rattler, one by Woodbury (1945, p. 179) on a bite which he himself sustained, and another report by Woodbury and Mrs. J. D. Anderson (1945, p. 185) describing a bite experienced by her husband. Both cases show, however, despite the detailed accuracy of the records, how impossible it is to separate any but the first symptoms from the effects of the remedial measures.

Dr. Woodbury was bitten in the middle of the third finger of the left hand by a snake about two feet long, a young adult. Some of the outstanding symptoms were: Profuse bleeding from one fang puncture; swelling; vomiting; severe pain in the pit of the stomach; thirst; spreading swelling and discoloration; insomnia (from pain); sloughing and necrosis at the site of the bite; general depression. The maximum temperature rise was 1.4° F.; there was a fall in the red blood count from 5,600,000 to 3,900,000; and in the white count from 29,000 to 10,000.

Anderson was bitten in the back. His symptoms were: A stinging or burning pain; fainting; nausea, chills, and vomiting; swelling of the right arm; a rapid pulse (120); slightly elevated temperature; spreading soreness, pain, and discoloration; diarrhea; heavy perspiration; thirst; a rash (probably from antivenin); blood in the urine; excruciating pain; paralysis of the arm. There was a serious anemia with a red-cell count of 3,800,000 and hemoglobin 75 per cent. It is evident that Anderson was seriously allergic to horse serum, and it is impossible to tell to what extent some of his symptoms were accentuated by the antivenin he was given.

Crotalus viridis oreganus.—A case report is available of a man bitten on both the right and left forefingers by a 30-inch northern Pacific rattlesnake in central California. An unusually well co-ordinated record of the symptoms was kept, so that it is possible to correlate the symptoms with the treatment. For this reason the case is presented in tabular form. Times in parentheses indicate elapsed times after the bite.

Symptoms	*Treatment*
There was immediate local burning pain, followed shortly by a general tingling sensation all over the body.	
(4 min.) Swelling began almost immediately.	Tourniquets were placed on both wrists. "X" incisions were made over each fang mark. Suction was begun by mouth because suction cups were ineffective on the fingers. The fluid was swallowed to maintain constant suction. Four small incisions were made later about each major cut.
(15 min.) The head felt thick, with a heavy, woozy sensation. A marked perspiration was noted. A noticeable chill developed. The respiration had increased in rate. Moderate bleed-	A doctor was called.

Symptoms	*Treatment*
ing occurred at the bite. A considerable effort was required to walk to a car only 30 feet away, support being needed.	
(30 min.) While getting out of the car at the hospital, the patient was unable to co-ordinate his legs—they were like rubber sticks.	Arrived at the hospital.
There was severe pain in the solar plexus, and a great need for air resulted in heavy, gasping breathing. Perspiration was profuse. Temperature 103°–104°F.	On the operating table.
(±1½ hr.)	15 cc. of antivenin were given intramuscularly in the thigh. Larger incisions were made at each fang mark; these were treated with carbolic acid.
(1¾ hr.) Pronounced quivering of the lips and chest were noted. There was a slight bluish cast to the lips. The swelling extended to the forearms to a moderate degree. The patient, now violently sick, began vomiting. The drinking of any liquids resulted in immediate vomiting.	Placed in bed.
	An injection of morphine was given to relieve the pain in breathing, which had continued from the first reaction. A subcutaneous injection of 1 qt. of saline solution was given.
(10½ hrs.) The extreme illness continued to 5 A.M. The swelling greatly increased and there was a bluish cast all over the face. From the time of the first severe breathing reaction until the intensity decreased was 1½ hr. The thickheaded feeling continued but without loss of consciousness. There was continued perspiration. The throat was parched and the thirst extreme.	The arms were wrapped in compresses of hot boric acid solution.
(Next morning. ±12 hrs. ?) The sickness now passed, leaving a weak, giddy feeling. No reaction from the antivenin was noted.	A diet of liquids (fruit juice, soup) was given. A second injection of 10 cc. of antivenin was given intravenously in the left arm. Gas gangrene and tetanus antitoxins at three intervals were given to observe the reaction; there was none.
(22 hrs.) An extensive edema had developed. The right arm was swollen to twice normal size, and the swelling extended to the shoulder. In the left arm there was edema to the elbow only. The right finger was blistered by thick, heavy water blisters; there was little hemolysis throughout the finger, but some around the bite. Ecchymosis was more prominent. The finger was swollen and misshapen. In the left finger the hemolysis was extensive, characterized by blue-black edema and wound bleeding. Ecchymosis was also great. In the evening the patient was restless. Large amounts of water and fruit juices were consumed throughout the day.	15 cc. of antivenin were given intramuscularly in the right shoulder in three injections.
	A sleeping hypo was administered with a very slow reaction. Boric acid compresses were continued throughout the day and night.
The subsequent recovery was uneventful.	

Dr. Henry S. Fitch has supplied me with the data on two *oreganus* bites. One bite was in the middle of the right thumb. At first there was no pain beyond the prick of the fangs. Within a few minutes there was involuntary quivering and twitching at the site of the bite. Hemorrhagic discoloration of tissue at the bite was soon evident, quickly followed by swelling. There were tingling and numbness of the scalp and the soles of the feet. These symptoms subsided after antivenin was administered, but weeks elapsed before the swelling completely disappeared.

In the other case, a juvenile of the same subspecies sank its fangs in the middle joint of the left forefinger. Again there was tingling of the scalp and the soles of the feet. There was nausea within 20 minutes; this lasted for the rest of the day. The swelling was more rapid and severe than in the first bite, with the arm swollen to twice normal size. The hemorrhagic discoloration covered the entire arm and extended onto the body. Aching and throbbing at the site of the bite increased during the first 12 hours and became almost unbearable. The patient collapsed once while trying to stand. The swelling was evident for several weeks.

In another case reported to me of a bite in the middle finger, the following symptoms were evident: A dull stinging pain; a swelling with discoloration and partial paralysis of the arm; and severe pains in the legs and groin. In a case of a bite in the leg that ended fatally, there was little initial pain; it felt like the scratch of a briar. The snake was not seen, but *oreganus* is the only venomous snake found where the accident occurred.

Crotalus viridis helleri.—I have the data on several snake-bite experiences in San Diego County. In the case reported by Happ (1951, p. 20), a bite in the thumb by a small southern Pacific rattler entailed the following symptoms: No local pain; numbness in the fingers, mouth, and tongue; shock symptoms; profuse sweating; lightheadedness; impaired respiration; dizziness and giddiness; a drawn feeling of the scalp; continued numbness of the mouth, hands, and feet; no nausea; swelling of the arm.

In another case there were prickling of the tongue and the lips; swelling of the eyelids, with a mask-like feeling over the entire face; and a partial paralysis of the legs. In a serious case involving a large *helleri,* there were, among other symptoms, partial blindness and great difficulty in respiration. The victim recovered.

Another case involved pain at the point of the injury; a difficulty in speaking because of stiffness of the tongue and lips; a state of shock; profuse perspiration; a pallid face; the pulse rapid and thready; and drooling at the mouth. In another instance briefly reported by Wittek (1943, p. 9), who was bitten in the leg, there were great weakness, swelling, and discoloration.

An accident that I witnessed involved a man bitten in the finger by a small *helleri.* There was little local pain; paralysis of facial muscles and lips was evident; although there was little swelling at first, some few hours later the swelling was extensive and painful; the facial paralysis then decreased; several blebs appeared near the bite; eventually there were chills and fever, but these may have been caused by serum sickness.

From a bite in the thumb by a juvenile *helleri*, pain was instantly evident; there was some pain in the arm pit at 7 minutes (a tourniquet had been applied in the meantime); tingling and numbness, first in the upper lip, then in the

836   *The Bite and Its Effects*

lower lip and tongue, became noticeable 30 minutes after the bite, and were very evident at 50 minutes. Subsequent symptoms were of little interest because of the complications induced by the treatment, entailing a serious case of serum sickness. In another *helleri* bite, there was instant pain.

The following case is that of a man bitten in the calf of the leg through overalls, when he stepped on a southern Pacific rattler. Only one fang seemed to have penetrated. It felt like a hornet's sting. (The victim, a notably fearless and imperturbable individual, immediately made a lengthwise cut at the bite at least 1½ inches long and quite deep; much blood spurted out. He hunted for and killed the snake; then made a tourniquet of a strip of cloth, and walked over a mile to his mountain cabin, where he lived alone. The wound bled freely, and he washed it with carbolic-acid solution.) He felt sick and weak when attempting to stand, but comfortable when lying down. When the wound received expert attention for the first time, two days after the bite, there remained considerable swelling and discoloration. This cleared up rapidly.

Another man was bitten in the calf of the leg by a large *helleri* as he stepped out of his car. The initial pain was not extreme; he likened it to the feeling of a hypodermic needle. (As he had been taught first aid, and there was a snake-bite kit in the car, he incised the fang marks with cross incisions to a depth of about ¼ inch, and placed a tourniquet 2 inches above the wound. He also used mechanical suction and got out considerable blood. This was all done within 10 minutes or less. The tourniquet subsequently was not loosened until he arrived at a doctor's office 22 minutes after the accident.)

Almost immediately after the snake struck, a throbbing began at the site of the bite, even before the incisions were made, and there was a bluish tinge around the two fang marks. There was some tingling in the scalp, but not around the face. (The doctor gave the patient novocain and deepened the incisions to ½ inch. The tourniquet was removed and 22 cc. of antivenin were injected in a ring around the bite, after which the tourniquet was replaced.) By this time there was some swelling in the leg, and eventually the ankle swelled to 2½ times normal size. However, the swelling did not go above the knee. (The antivenin reaction was quite severe, leading eventually to swelling in the legs, partial paralysis of the shoulders, and extensive hives. The patient remained under observation in a hospital for 36 hours, and made an uneventful recovery, except for a slight deadness around the site of the bite, no doubt caused by the incisions.)

I believe the points of greatest interest in connection with these *helleri* cases, and the *oreganus* accidents as well, are the variability in the extent of the local pain and the presence of neurotoxic symptoms, particularly about the face. These were evident even when the amount of venom received was quite small. The variability of the local pain, with complete absence occasionally, is very unfortunate from the standpoint of diagnosis, for in such circumstances there is no evidence indicating—as would be the case if there were always severe pain— whether the bite has been ineffective.

Crotalus mitchelli pyrrhus.—A man was bitten in the left thumb. The only initial pain was a sharp stab as the fangs were imbedded. There was no further discomfort until after an incision had been made and antivenin had been administered. The pain was very severe about an hour after the bite. Subsequently there was much discoloration; the fingers were like red bananas. There were blebs all over the fingers and wrist, and the palm became one great blister. This case has been described by Hartnett (1931, p. 637).

Another report of what was probably a *pyrrhus* bite: The bite was in the heel, through overalls and sock, just above the top of an oxford shoe. The initial pain was like that of a thorn entering the flesh; there was a small drop of blood at one fang mark. (A tourniquet was applied after 45 minutes and a walk of 1¼ miles; also incision and suction were applied.) Four hours later the calf of the leg was considerably swollen and discolored; still later there was pain in the groin. By this time all symptoms were obscured by the treatment. The patient made an uneventful recovery in the hospital. It is presumed, from the lack of tissue at the site of the bite, that the fang penetration was not deep, and that the venom injection was probably small. In another *pyrrhus* bite, a sharp pain like that of a bee's sting was felt within about 45 seconds.

Crotalus horridus.—A man was bitten, in the finger just below the knuckle, by a young timber rattler about two feet long. There was a slight burning sensation at the site of the bite, but no severe pain. (Within three minutes two tourniquets had been applied, one at the wrist, the other on the upper arm. An incision to a depth of about ⅛ inch was made, connecting the two fang marks, and suction was applied by the use of a first-aid appliance, available and made for the purpose.) A swelling near the bite began to be in evidence 25 minutes after the accident. The patient, a man familiar with snakes, was not anxious or excited.

The patient and his companion walked slowly down the rocky cliff where the accident had happened, and reached a school where first aid was obtained about three-fourths of an hour after the bite. During this time his vision became blurred and he had a severe headache and a feeling as of "needles and pins" in the legs. The swelling had now begun to involve the hand. (At the first-aid station the wound was cleansed and penicillin was injected.) The patient had a severe thirst and drank nearly a quart of water. (After this, on the way home, suction was continued, although the tourniquets, which had previously been loosened from time to time, were now removed.) The severe headache continued, and there was a queer feeling as if the lips, tongue, and cheeks were puffing up. This continued for only about 20 minutes (it was about 1¾ hours after the bite) but the intense headache and thirst persisted. Pain at the site of the injury increased, as did the swelling above the bite. There was a weakness in the legs. (Suction was discontinued 4¾ hours after the bite, by which time little fluid was being removed.) The hand was then swollen to one-third above normal size.

On the following day, after a good night's rest, the patient felt quite well. The swelling now had progressed to the elbow, but did not encompass the entire forearm. Later in the day, pain was evident in the axillary lymphatics and in the lymph nodes in the elbow region. On the following day (48 hours after the bite) the swelling had begun to recede. Numerous small vesicles appeared on the hand and wrist. These burst when touched and exuded a viscous fluid. The patient felt good, but tired easily. Subsequently he made an uneventful recovery.

We have, in this case, an example of the amount of discomfort that can be caused by a small snake of this species—a case that further exemplifies rapid and well-administered first-aid treatment, and a patient relatively unperturbed by the experience. Particularly notable was the fact that the symptoms were not confused or obscured by fright or shock.

In another accident, in which a man was bitten in the hand, there was severe pain within a few moments, and swelling began almost immediately; nausea followed. Another man was bitten in the finger and stated that the pain went up his arm like an electric shock. A child, bitten in the leg, suffered from pain in the stomach, and from thirst and weakness. Another case involved shock and loss of consciousness. Other case reports (Wirz in Cameron, 1927, p. 74; and Mainzer, 1935, p. 376) stress instant pain, profuse perspiration, nausea, and marked swelling as the noteworthy symptoms.

Crotalus triseriatus triseriatus.—Dugès (1877, p. 18) gives the symptoms from the bite of what was probably a small individual of this subspecies. He was bitten on the back of the left index finger. He mentions instantaneous and intense pain like the stings of several bees, faintness, cold perspiration, and a painful and swollen arm.

Crotalus lepidus klauberi.—An experienced herpetologist was bitten by a 16-inch *klauberi* in the middle finger of the right hand about ½ inch from the tip. Only one fang took effect. It felt like a sharp pin prick. (Within a minute, a rubber-band tourniquet was applied at the base of the finger and was left on for about 10 minutes, after which the hand was plunged in ice water. Subsequently the hand was kept in ice water for several hours. This was the only treatment used, although after the first few hours the ice-water applications were only intermittent.) By the day following the accident, the swelling had reached the forearm, and, on the following day, the shoulder. An intense and continual burning pain developed at the site of the bite; it began on the day following the bite and became virtually unbearable two days after the bite, then lessened. (The pain was somewhat alleviated by ice packs.)

Within a day or so after the bite, a black blister about ½ inch by ¾ inch formed at the site. It was punctured daily and eventually collapsed and hardened. Some swelling was still present five weeks after the bite, with numbness and tingling sensations. In this case, as in so many others, it is difficult to distinguish venom symptoms from treatment symptoms.

Crotalus scutulatus scutulatus.—Dr. Frederick A. Shannon has written me of a *scutulatus* case in which the victim developed double vision, and also had difficulty in speech and in swallowing water. *C. scutulatus* cases are infrequently reported, as this snake is often misidentified.

Crotalus cerastes laterorepens—A man was bitten in the first joint of the index finger of the right hand. Only one fang took effect. It was no more painful than a pin prick. (A rubber tourniquet was applied, and a doctor was seen in about 25 minutes. The wound was incised and suction applied. Ten cc. of antivenin were administered. The tourniquet was continued, but with suitable releases.) At the end of 2½ hours the hand and arm swelled and the pain was violent, "as if the arm were soaking in a bucket of boiling oil."

Sistrurus catenatus catenatus.—A bite was sharply painful, until bleeding was induced by suction; there was considerable swelling. Another bite, by a juvenile a few months old, caused only throbbing. La Pointe (1953, p. 128) reported a bite from a specimen 451 mm. (17¾ in.) in length. The bite was just above the nail on the left first finger. The symptoms, somewhat masked by thorough first-aid and hospital treatments, included a strong nervous reaction, a cold sweat, faintness, and nausea. Hartnett (1931, p. 639) mentions nausea and swelling in another case.

Sistrurus miliarius.—A case involved a bite on the third finger of the left hand, near the base of the nail. The snake was a young specimen only 9 inches long. The pain was immediate and swelling quickly followed. No treatment was given at first, for the snake was so small that no serious results were anticipated. But the swelling continued until the entire arm was affected. The finger turned black. Later, the swelling extended to the body with much discoloration. On the day after the bite there were some dizziness and faintness. On the fourth day the swelling was much reduced, and had virtually disappeared 10 days after the bite. There had not been complete recovery in the use of the finger 18 months after the bite. This case (Davis, 1918, p. 15) is of especial interest because the symptoms were not obscured by treatment, and because so small a snake could cause such serious results.

In reviewing these case reports, one cannot but be struck by the frequency with which neurotoxic symptoms—partial paralysis, respiratory difficulties, and other nervous effects—are mentioned, especially in bites by the western rattlesnake (*C. viridis*) and its subspecies. But, as is typical of the bites of the Nearctic rattlesnakes, the local symptoms, extensive swelling and discoloration, are the most prominent and characteristic.

CAUSES OF FATALITIES

With all of these variable symptoms of Nearctic rattlesnake bite, what physiological effect, then, leads to an occasional fatality? It is difficult to say; with so many complicated interrelations of symptoms, it is usually impossible to select the fatal one or the organ that fails. Many of the fatalities of the past have been secondary in character—from wound infections, or gangrene resulting from such infections, or from the improper use of a tourniquet. There has been a feeling on the part of some physicians that neurotoxins are more important in Nearctic rattler bites than generally supposed, although their more insidious effects are masked by the much more apparent and dangerous-looking hemorrhagic symptoms, and that the neurotoxic effects reach a crisis later. This may have been the basis for the statement of Mitchell (1861, p. 279) that there are two kinds of effects, acute and chronic, and that acute poisoning in man is rare. Jackson (1879, p. 361) said that some doctors divided the symptoms into two stages—before and after 62 hours. Fidler *et al.* (1938, p. 893; 1940, p. 363) concluded, from experiments with *atrox* venom on monkeys, that shock was the major factor in death when the injection was intravenous, but they were less certain when the administration was subcutaneous.

The courses of typical cases are discussed by Willson (1908, p. 541). It is undoubtedly true that, in some cases in the past, there has been an encouraging subsidence of swelling and discoloration—usually after about 24 to 48 hours—that led to a premature belief that the patient was out of danger. This was followed by a sudden and fatal termination, either from respiratory or circulatory failure. Whether these fatalities have been the direct results of neurotoxins, or of the secondary effects of anemia following hemolysis, does not seem to be definitely known. With better methods of treatment—antivenin, scientific drainage, the prevention of infection, supportive transfusions, and a closer watch for any sudden onset of adverse symptoms—such unfortunate terminations should be largely avoided, where it is possible to get the victim to a hospital soon after the accident.

The data hitherto cited on individual cases were compiled from a number of personal communications, and also from various papers and published records, some of which have not been mentioned in connection with the particular symptoms discussed. For those who may wish to look up the previously uncited references, they are: Breintal, 1748, p. 144; Barton, 1793, p. 110; Bosc, 1803, p. 554; Thatcher, 1823, p. 62; Mayrant, 1823, p. 619; Philips, 1831, p. 540; Flint, 1832, vol. 1, p. 75; Trowbridge, 1848, p. 203; Jeter, 1854, p. 11; Alexander, 1855, p. 117; Oliveras, 1858, p. 225; Bogue, 1866, p. 399; Knott, 1877, p. 46; Jenkins, 1878, p. 63; Shuler, 1881, p. 292; Martin, 1882, p. 86; Bories, 1883, p. 57; Thomas, 1890, p. 123; Barringer, 1892, p. 299; Schooley, 1895, p. 356; Brown, 1899, p. 222; Lewis, 1906, p. 2012; Budge, 1913, vol. 2, p. 450; Mays, 1914, p. 106; McCulloch, 1918, p. 2; Davis, 1918, p. 15; Grinnell, 1923, vol. 2, p. 148; Atkinson and Netting, 1927, p. 40; Jackson, 1927, p. 203; Cox, 1927, p. 54; Macbride, 1928, p. 10; Pousma, 1928, p. 62; Bergman and Sabin, 1932, p. 34; Keeley, 1937, p. 537; Peters, 1937, p. 23; Allen, 1938, p. 1249; Fillmore, 1941, p. 311; Wright, 1941, p. 669; Speer, 1941, p. 640; Magee, 1943, p. 85; Macht, 1944, p. 362; Chotkowski, 1944, p. 602; Unonius, 1950, p. 297; Minton, 1950, p. 323; and Holt, 1950, p. 13.

The Symptoms of *Crotalus durissus* Bite

With respect to the Neotropical rattlesnake, *Crotalus durissus*, we find the symptoms rather sharply differentiated from those of the Nearctic rattlers with which we are more familiar, and which are the source of our rattlesnake-bite problems in the United States. As might be expected from phylogenetic and geographical considerations, the most widely differentiated form of the Neotropical rattler, in terms of venom quality, is found in the southerly part of the range, in Brazil. Northward, in Venezuela, Central America, and southern Mexico, the venoms are not so strongly differentiated from the Nearctic mode. Whether there are still further trends toward Nearctic venoms, through *culminatus, totonacus, basiliscus,* and possibly *scutulatus,* is not known. Vellard (1938, p. 409; 1943, p. 55) has found some differences in the venoms of *terrificus* from different areas in South America, and believes that the venom of the Venezuelan rattlers is midway between those of the Brazilian and Central American forms. These conclusions were reached through animal experimentation.

The symptoms of the bite of the Brazilian rattlers in cases involving human beings are summarized by Amaral (1951a, p. 552) as follows: Impairment of vision or complete blindness; paralysis of the eyelids and eyeballs; and paralysis of the peripheral muscles, especially of the neck, which becomes so limp as to appear broken. Vaz (1951, p. 32) lists visual and auditory disorders, muscular paralysis of the neck, and eventually of the respiration, with death by suffocation. Amaral comments on the lack of local pain, such as is almost invariably evident immediately in Nearctic cases. Alvaro (1939, p. 1133) believes that 60 per cent of *terrificus* cases involve ocular disturbances, sometimes followed by permanent blindness. Schoettler (1951, p. 496) points out that hemorrhagins may be present in *terrificus* venom but are completely overshadowed by the startling and serious neurotoxic effects.

I have available only two reports on the symptoms of Venezuelan cases not obscured by treatment. Baillie (1849, p. 179) mentions instantaneous pain, followed by a loss of sight, a feeling of intoxication, and loss of consciousness. In another more recent Venezuelan case, a bite in the calf of the leg produced pain, swelling, paralysis, giddiness, and slight shortness of breath. Partial paralysis of the leg, up to the thigh, persisted for over three months.

As to Central America, March (1928, p. 61) gives the symptoms of two cases of bites by *C. d. durissus* in Honduras. The first involved a large snake; the bite was in the little finger of the left hand. The symptoms observed were: Swelling; blindness and paralysis of the neck muscles; cold perspiration; heart affected; paleness and collapse; loss of consciousness; later, nausea and fatigue. In the other case, a small rattler bit a man in the hand. Seen five hours after the accident, the victim was almost blind and had severe pains in the head and spine. He lost consciousness at times. Both of these cases recovered. It will be observed that the characteristic ocular and neck symptoms of *durissus* bite are evident at least as far north as Central America.

INFECTION IN RATTLESNAKE BITE

Infection often follows rattlesnake bite—as well as the bites of other venomous snakes—for the venom contains a principle that inhibits the effectiveness of the normal antibacterial property of the victim's blood. As the snake's mouth is always contaminated with bacteria, and field remedies are seldom applied with due regard for asepsis, an infection of a serious nature may complicate and delay recovery, even leading to a fatal outcome. It is to be hoped that modern drugs—the sulfas and antibiotics—will greatly reduce the danger from this by-product of snake bite.

The understanding of the bacterial phase of snake bite went through three periods: In the first, there was no distinction between the primary effect of the venom and of the infection; in the second, the bacterial sequelae were recognized as being different from the primary venom symptoms; and, finally, the reason why the bacterial infections were so frequent and serious became evident when the antibactericidal effect of the venom on the blood had been discovered. The step between the first two phases followed naturally from the discovery of the status of pathogenic bacteria in disease by Pasteur and others; the second step was initiated by the experiments of Ewing and Welch.

Breintal (1748, p. 144) and Clavigero (1937, p. 392, but written in 1789) described bites in such detail that the presence of secondary infections may be recognized. Indeed, Clavigero understood the difference between the two phases.

The presence of bacteria in fresh rattlesnake venom, and the bacterial effect in accelerating putrefaction, were recognized by Mitchell and Reichert (1886, pp. 6, 134), and their importance in the sequence of the bite symptoms was mentioned by Mitchell in 1889 (p. 513). Barringer (1892, p. 299) stated that in 5 per cent of all bites, a chronic septicemia resulted from the pyogenic bacteria in the snake's mouth.

It remained for Ewing, working under the guidance of Welch, to prove that the bactericidal power of blood serum was greatly reduced by the venom of the eastern diamondback, *C. adamanteus* (Ewing, 1894, p. 665; also p. 1237; Welch and Ewing, 1895, p. 354). Thus was explained the virulence and speed of snake-bite infections, and the rapid putrefaction of animals killed by snake bite. Mc-Farland (1902, p. 332) believes that a letter of Kaufmann's in 1890 (*Revue Scientifique,* vol. 45, p. 180) anticipated the Ewing-Welch discovery.

The recognition of the importance of bacterial infection in snake bite led to gradual changes in treatment, without great success, however. Grandy (1903, p. 515) attempted the use of bichloride of mercury. Willson (1908, p. 535) thought that insufficient attention was being given to the effect of bacterial sequelae; that cases prolonged beyond two or three days were the result of infection and not of the venom itself (p. 540); that at least 10 per cent of the deaths were probably caused by sepsis (p. 551), and that the real percentage might well be higher. He reported (p. 545) one death from tetanus. Hartnett (1931, p. 639) mentions a case of tetanus that followed a bite. Amaral (1927, p. 80) and Strong (1928, p. 250) also mention tetanus cases. Holt (1950, p. 13) expressed the opinion that if death from rattlesnake bite occurs more than 72 hours after the accident, it is probably the result of secondary infection.

In one case of the bite of a northern Pacific rattler (*C. v. oreganus*), a man was bitten in the finger on July 8. He reached the hospital within an hour and was given antivenin and a suction treatment. He was discharged as no longer needing hospitalization on July 15, but was forced to return on August 4 by a developing infection. This caused a further hospital stay of 25 days, and a case more serious than the original bite.

Dr. Dudley Jackson, in his papers and letters in explanation of his deep-drainage method of rattlesnake-bite treatment, has stressed the importance of necrotic tissue as an ideal medium for bacterial growth, particularly of *Clostridium welchi* and *C. tetani*. He advocated the use of suitable antitoxins in all cases, as did Fillmore (1941, p. 311).

Glaser (1948, p. 245) has pointed out that rattlesnake venoms have destructive effects on some microorganisms *in vitro*. This action is probably not significant in snake-bite problems.

PERMANENT AFTEREFFECTS

Any permanent aftereffects of rattlesnake bite depend on the seriousness of the bite, and, still more, on the treatment. As in any wound treatments, necrosis may result, or nerves, tendons, or muscles may suffer permanent damage, especially in the case of inexpert field incisions. Gangrene resulting from overtight or overprolonged tourniquets may necessitate limb amputations. But permanent systemic ill effects are probably rare, notwithstanding the statement by Michaux

(1805, p. 43) that those who survive rattlesnake bite are always "sickly and sensible to changes of the atmosphere." Payne (1872, p. 223) expressed the opinion that snake bite might stunt a child. Willson (1908, p. 546) said that deformity in the fingers often follows rattlesnake bite.

Staley (1939, p. 549) presents the following summary of aftereffects: contractures (shortening of muscle or tissue) are sometimes evident, and there may be atrophy of a bitten limb; there may be a falling out of hair, but it eventually grows in again; transverse ridges on fingernails or toenails, indicating a temporary cessation of growth; seldom permanent damage to kidneys even though there may have been extensive hemorrhages; paralysis of certain nerves may be temporary or permanent; there may be secondary anemia, but it should clear up in two or three months with appropriate treatment.

The following are a few instances of damage cited by my correspondents. The reader may use his own judgment in differentiating the effects of the bite and the treatment.

> I have always been interested in cures for snake bite. Once on the desert I met a young woman who had a horrible scar on her leg between her ankle and her knee. The muscle under the scar tissue was destroyed and at that point the contour of the leg sank in. She told me that as a child running barefoot on the desert—her folks were homesteaders—she had been bitten by a rattler. Her father slashed the leg and stuck her foot and leg into a can containing coal oil. She claimed that it had saved her life as the coal oil drew the poison, though it left her leg horribly scarred. Having a naturally curious mind I asked her what the coal oil looked like when the treatment was over, and she said it had a definite greenish cast. *Margaret Darrell, Pacheco Peak Forest Lookout, Hollister, Calif.*

> There is a man in Franklin who was bitten ten years ago, and his hand was left crippled. Still another case left the individual with a stiff finger. *E. A. Schilling, U. S. Forest Service, Franklin, N. C.*

> I well remember a friend of mine of about sixteen, who was bitten on the palm of the right hand by two snakes at the same time. He couldn't use the hand for several years, but has regained the use of it by now. *Drayton Wasson, U. S. Forest Service, Española, N. Mex.*

> I have known people to be bitten and they remained cripples. *Charles J. Boudreaux, Abbeville, La.*

Despite these statements, rattlesnake bite seldom leaves any permanent effects beyond finger or limb deformities from inexpert treatment.

EFFECT OF VENOM ON THE EYES AND OTHER ORGANS

The fact that rattlers are not natural venom spitters has been touched on elsewhere. However, there may be cases in which a snake, falling short in a strike, or having a damaged mouth, may expel venom that reaches the eyes of the person at whom the strike is aimed. It is a relief to know that in such circumstances no serious effects are to be expected, to judge from instances cited by Bevan (1932b, p. 93), Allen (1937, p. 74), McLane (1943, p. 23), and Burton (1946, p. 16). The eyes become irritated and inflamed, but if washed promptly should clear up in three hours or so. Some snake venoms, especially those of the spitting cobras, may have serious effects, leading to blindness, if the venom is not quickly washed out. Bogert (1943, p. 351) experimented with diluted venom placed in the eyes of rats. The venoms of two kinds of cobras killed the rats, but rattlesnake venom (*C. atrox*) was without effect; the rats did not even show signs of pain.

According to Githens (1931, p. 82) various organs are susceptible to the action of rattlesnake venom, which exercises a destructive effect on the functional cells. There may be degenerative changes in the liver; yellow eyes and skin from a mild jaundice are common in severe cases. The kidneys, also, are affected by the destructive action of the venom; the secretory cells are injured and albuminuria results. Brymer (1928, p. 305) cites the results of autopsies in 40 fatal cases of rattlesnake bite in southwestern Texas; the spleen was usually enlarged and congested; liver congestion was not so common; there was an intense hyperemia of the duodenum and lower colon. Amorim and Mello (1952, p. 281) made detailed pathological studies of three fatal South American rattler (*terrificus*) bites and found extensive kidney damage. Bulger and Northrop (1951, p. 1135) report a case of duodenal ulcer in a child bitten by a prairie rattlesnake (*C. v. viridis*).

THE RECURRENCE OF SNAKE-BITE SYMPTOMS

Throughout the literature of snake bite, there is frequent mention of the recurrence of symptoms, usually on anniversaries of the accident, but sometimes at other intervals. The belief in this manifestation is a general one; Corkill (1949, p. 615) says that it is widely held in tropical countries.

The annual reappearance of the symptoms of rattlesnake bite was mentioned by such writers of colonial days as Catesby (1731–43, vol. 2, p. 41), Kalm (1752–53, p. 55), J. B. (1765, p. 513), Carver (1778, p. 483), and Loskiel (1794, p. 114). Kalm even records the case of a man who was badly frightened (but not bitten) by a rattler and had recurring symptoms every day for 14 days; and of a dog that had to be shot, so acute were the annual symptoms of the bite.

These early reports were not restricted to the United States. Koster (1817, vol. 2, p. 56) mentions a Brazilian Negro who was bitten by a rattler and had recurring symptoms at certain phases of the moon; and Schomburgk (1922, vol. 2, p. 103, but writing in 1847) tells of yearly symptoms following rattlesnake bite in British Guiana.

More recent accounts of this manifestation of recurrences are those of Stockbridge (1843, p. 42), Sweeney (1860, p. 318), Neidhard (1860, p. 71), Flack (1866, p. 339), Coleman (1872, p. 139), Piffard (1875, p. 62), Guild (1878, p. 50), Hayward (1884, p. 181), Wheatley (1886, p. 523), Gould and Pyle (1897, p. 717), Harvey (1901, p. 157), Crouse (1902, p. 442), Barnes (1922, p. 391), Ludy (1926, p. 28), and Randolph (1947, p. 159). The case mentioned by Stockbridge involved a moccasin rather than a rattler bite; it produced annual symptoms for 18 years. Sweeney tells of a copperhead bite, the symptoms of which returned to plague the sufferer after an untroubled interval of 30 years. (From the description, the supposed return appears to have been an entirely unrelated infection.) Gould and Pyle discuss a case report from army records in Texas, of a new and painful swelling that necessitated amputation of a finger some three years after a rattler bite. Again we may hazard the guess that a totally unrelated infection was involved. Piffard's account describes repeated abscesses at the site of a bite sustained by a woman who had been bitten in the hand by a rattler. The recurrences, at trimonthly intervals, continued for several years. Barnes (1922, p. 391) tells of a boy who became speechless at annual intervals following a rattlesnake bite. According to Randolph (1947, p. 159) there is an Ozark belief that symptom recurrences are especially probable if the wound has been treated by a doctor.

Dugès (1877, p. 18) mentions his having been bitten by a rattler without evidence of recurrent symptoms, from which it may be presumed that the idea is so widespread in Mexico, that nonrecurrence was worthy of comment.

It need hardly be said that the medical profession gives no credence to these recurrence beliefs. Willson (1908, p. 547) discussed the annual symptom idea, citing some cases, and allowing the reader to draw his own conclusions. Yarrow (1884, p. 430; 1887, p. 623; 1928, p. 75), although first somewhat credulous, finally came to the conclusion that the symptoms resulted from nervous hyperesthesia or suggestion, a theory also suggested by Piffard.

Corkill (1935, p. 253; 1949, p. 615), discussing the recurrence ideas in the Anglo-Egyptian Sudan, where cobras and vipers are prevalent, tells of the belief that annual symptoms can be avoided by recourse to a magic formula for removing the snake's teeth that otherwise would remain in the wound and cause the repeated symptoms. The likeness to some sucking cures of the American Indian shamans will at once be noted. Corkill thinks the annual recurrence belief may be founded on the fact that certain nutritional deficiencies do occur annually in the Sudan, and these might cause partly healed injuries to be worse at that season.

Accompanying the early exaggerations respecting the severity of rattlesnake bite, and the efficacy of the Indian remedies, was the generally accepted story that a bitten person took on the colors and pattern of the snake. This was reported as early as 1642 (Lechford, p. 47) and was repeated often thereafter (e.g., Kalm, 1752–53, p. 55; Carver, 1778, p. 482; Zeisberger, 1910, p. 70, but writing as of 1779; Vigne, 1832, vol. 1, p. 91; Howe, 1847, p. 297). Macbride (1928, p. 10) says this was a belief in Iowa in the period 1846–60. Philips (1831, p. 540) tells of seeing the victim of a bite whose leg was so swollen, with black and yellow spots on the skin (extravasations), that one might have fancied it resembled the skin of a snake.

SUSCEPTIBILITY, RESISTANCE, AND IMMUNITY TO RATTLESNAKE VENOM

Not only are some snake venoms much more toxic than others, but some venoms are more toxic to one kind of animal, whereas other venoms are more effective against another animal. So, in all questions of susceptibility and immunization, both the kind of snake and the kind of victim are important. In general, venoms are likely to be particularly effective on the natural prey of any species of snake.

It has long been known that cold-blooded animals (poikilotherms or ectotherms) are less susceptible to snake venoms than birds and mammals (homoiotherms or endotherms) (Fontana, 1787, vol. 1, p. 275; Russell, 1796, pp. 56, 85; Mitchell, 1860, p. 63; 1870, p. 318; Fayrer, 1872, p. 64; Noguchi, 1904, p. 4). More recent summaries of the natural immunity of various classes of animals, with appropriate bibliographies, are those of Phisalix (1922, vol. 2, p. 744), Pawlowsky (1927, p. 311), Kraus and Werner (1931, p. 143), and Boquet (1948, p. 129).

There are many beliefs, stories, and legends about rattlesnake venom—its power and the peculiar effects it is presumed to have on its victims, both animate and otherwise. These include the boot story, the ax myth, how wasps are rendered deadly, the effects on nursing children, and many others. They will be found in chapter 18, on myths and legends.

IMMUNITY TO SNAKE BITE IN MAN

Famed among the ancients were the Psylli, the Marsi, and the Ophiogenes. These tribes had a way with snakes and, best of all, they were immune to snake bite. The Psylli lived in Asia Minor near Rhodes, or, possibly, in north Africa; the Marsi inhabited central Italy, and the Ophiogenes the region of the Hellespont. Some of the same powers were ascribed to the Syrians on the Euphrates. The accounts of these peoples will be found in Pliny (book vii, chap. 2; book viii, chap. 84; book xxviii, chap. 6; or, using the pagination of the translation of 1855–57 by Bostock and Riley, vol. 2, pp. 125, 354; vol. 5, p. 286), and in Lucan's *Pharsalia* (Riley's translation, 1853, p. 374). These beliefs were repeated by many of the natural-history writers of the sixteenth and seventeenth centuries. See Topsell (1608, p. 46; 1658, p. 624), Aelianus (1615, pp. 32, 462; 1616, pp. 61, 944), and Severinus (1651, p. 398); see also Steele (1905, p. 142) and Thorndike (1923–41, vol. 5, p. 473).

To summarize the reports of Pliny and others: these peoples were not only immune to snake bite, but they could cure those bitten, by the touch of a hand or the use of saliva; they were fatal to any snake that bit them, and their odor drove snakes away; they exposed their children to snake bite to test their legitimacy. Fraser (1889b, p. 569) has mentioned peoples in other parts of the world reputed to be immune to snake bite.

It is probable that the stories of these snake people originated with travelers' tales of the exploits of the snake charmers in the countries visited. Indeed, Anderson (1910, p. 712) says that if a cobra enters a hut in India, the occupants send for a "Psylli" or snake charmer to drive it out with incantations. Celsus (1935–38, p. 115), who wrote in the first years of the Christian era, thought the powers of the Psylli were merely evidences of the boldness of experience. Elliot (1934c, p. 202) says that it is natural, when watching snake charmers in India and the carelessness with which they handle cobras, to think them immune. Suetonius (Barry, 1826, p. 87) records that Augustus ordered the Psylli and the Marsi to cure Cleopatra's wounds, but without success. Mead (1745, p. 35) thought they cured snake bite by suction, rather than with any mysterious power. Acton and Knowles (1921, p. 726) have pointed out that none of the snakes found in the countries of the Psylli and Marsi were very dangerous, which accounted for the belief in their immunity. In ancient days it was the general belief that all snakes were deadly.

Sometimes certain elements of a population were thought to be immune. Barton (1799, p. 82) says that some writers of colonial days thought the Indians immune to rattlesnake bite, but others doubted this. Richards (1885, p. 41; 1886, p. 42) mentions a report in which it was claimed that fer-de-lance bite was more fatal to whites than to other races. There is a fairly widespread myth in the South and West to the effect that Negroes are immune to rattlesnake bite. It is a fact that in a report of Florida fatalities (1940–52), it was stated that, out of 40 fatal cases, 38 were whites (Andrews and Pollard, 1953, p. 388). This is a ratio of Negro to total fatalities of 5 per cent, whereas Negroes comprised 22 per cent of the population in 1950. But it would require an occupational study of the fatal cases, as well as some knowledge of the ratio of fatalities to total bites in each element of the population, to determine whether any difference in susceptibility could have accounted for this marked unbalance in fatalities. There are enough fatal cases of rattlesnake bite among Negroes in the medical literature to nullify any theory of immunity in that race. Fleagle (1931, p. 809), a homeopath, believed that rattlesnake venom, as a homeopathic remedy, was more effective in the treatment of white than Negro patients.

Occasionally a belief in natural immunity among men is still voiced (Lewitus, 1935, p. 547), but there is no present acceptance of the idea that any people are immune, although some are more susceptible than others, as is true of individual susceptibility to other protein poisons. Zozaya and Stadelman (1930, p. 93) have reported individual cases of hypersensitivity. Fountain (1901, p. 60), traveling in the West, observed that some people seemed to be virtually immune to rattle- snake bite, whereas others suffered severely, but the variable conditions that exist in every snake-bite accident no doubt accounted for the differences observed, and not partial immunity as Fountain thought.

Acquired Immunity.—We turn now from beliefs in natural to those of acquired immunity, acquired either by eating some substance—usually a snake-bite remedy, such as some plant, a piece of snake, or some snake venom—or by the injection of an immunizing substance into the body. The advantage of taking the cure before the accident is an obvious one. We must not censure the ancients too severely for their theories, remembering that until rather recently it was generally believed that because whiskey was a sure cure for rattlesnake bite—in truth, it is worse than useless—anyone who had imbibed too freely was immune to snake bite.

Viper flesh, long one of the standard cures for snake bite in olden times, was also eaten as an immunizer (Allbutt, 1921, p. 348). Buley (1950, vol. 1, p. 267) records a belief among pioneers in the Pacific Northwest that to eat a rattler's heart would produce immunity. But although snake flesh was extensively used in the cure of snake bite, it was never as popular for immunization. On the other hand, venom was seldom taken orally as a snake-bite cure, but was more popular as an oral method of immunization, as, for example, in India (Fraser, 1895b, p. 416; Elliot, 1900, p. 221; 1933b, p. 362; 1934c, p. 207; Wall, 1906, p. 381; Thurston, 1912, p. 95; Allbutt, 1921, p. 344). It is said to be used by African bushmen (Anon., 1832a, p. 236; Harley, 1941, p. 212).

There has been a limited modern belief in this venom-imbibing method of acquiring at least a slight immunity (Anderson, 1895, p. 319; Kanthack, 1897, p. 235; Fraser, 1895b, p. 416; 1896b, p. 595; Noguchi, 1909, p. 224; Woodruff, 1913, p. 17; Elliot, 1934c, p. 210), although this cannot be justified by the results of animal experimentation, which have been almost entirely negative (Cunning- ham, 1897, p. 82; Calmette, 1898, p. 515; Elliot, 1900, p. 1146; 1933b, p. 363; 1934c, p. 208; Bonsmann, 1942a, p. 167), even though Fraser (1895b, p. 417) did cite some apparently favorable results. Most of both the beliefs and the tests have had to do with cobras rather than rattlesnakes; but Bonsmann tried *C. horridus* venom, among others, and found no resultant immunity in the animals that were fed the venom.

Corkill (1932a, p. 611) says it is believed in Baghdad that drinking water in which a snake has been boiled confers an immunity against that kind of snake. Bourke (1894, p. 140) mentions a belief along the Rio Grande in Texas that huaco bulbs (probably from plants belonging to the genera *Mikania* or *Aristolochia*) in whiskey or mescal will afford immunity against rattler bite.

That immunity may be acquired by snake-show operators through their having been bitten repeatedly is a common belief, and may, in accordance with modern theories of immunization, have some slight basis in fact. Newspaper stories from time to time report carnival and snake-show cases, with the conclusion that the accident would have been much worse if the showman had not been partly immunized by previous bites. One, who said he had been bitten 288 times, claimed complete immunity. Yet another operator wrote me that his latest bite was the most serious he had ever experienced. Peter Gruber (Rattlesnake Pete), the keeper of a museum, was said to have been bitten 30 times in 40 years (Herrick, 1953, p. 26); no mention was made of his having acquired any immunity.

Hoyt (1844, p. 243) heard in upper New York, where there are so many red adders [copperheads?] and rattlers, that if a person were bitten by one species he would be immune to the other. Fawcett (1953, p. 212) says the natives of some areas in Brazil believe that the bite of the anaconda (a nonvenomous snake) confers immunity against the bite of any venomous snake. Blackwood (1888, p. 273) told of one man who was bitten twice in a single week by rattlers; he required less treatment in the second case, probably because he was "pasteurized." Menger (1903, p. 448) reports a similar case in which—so he says—the woman patient would have died had it not been for an earlier bite that partially immunized her. Jackson (1921, p. 207; see also Brymer, 1928, p. 305, and Cooke, 1934, p. 118) says that some of Colonel Crimmins' blood—the colonel had been bitten several times—was used as an antivenin in a severe case. Elliot (1900, p. 220; 1934b, p. 802; 1934c, pp. 201, 206) finally reached the conclusion that Indian snake charmers may acquire a slight immunity through having been bitten repeatedly.

From immunity acquired through one or more accidental bites, it is a natural step to immunity secured through deliberate injections. Madame Calderón de la Barca (1843, p. 431) said she had heard that the natives near Tampico, Mexico, were in the habit of inoculating themselves with rattlesnake venom as a protection against all venomous snakes. The venom was introduced into the tongue, both arms, and other parts of the body, by the use of a snake fang. There followed a rash lasting several days, after which there was complete immunity. Collaterally there was acquired the power to call snakes, when wanted, to cure other people; or, alternatively, to cause the snakes to kill people by biting them. These last attributes are a direct inheritance from Pliny's Marsi; in fact, they tend to cast doubt on the whole story that the Indians attempted this type of immunization, notwithstanding the fact that Madame Calderón heard it from "7 or 8 respectable merchants." Something of the same kind has since been reiterated by Gharpurey (1935, p. 140), and De Lys (1948, p. 75). Stone (1932, p. 69; also Gordon, 1949, p. 11) thought that some of the Hopi and other Indians who participate in snake dances permitted themselves, as neophytes, to be bitten by young snakes with weak venoms, in order to immunize themselves against the greater risks ahead.

Wall (1906, p. 382) says that some Hindus practice venom inoculation to secure immunity; and Schmidt (1929a, p. 7; 1951, p. 10) believes it possible that Indian snake charmers may seek immunity from the effects of cobra bites by repeated small injections. William E. Haast of Kendall, Florida, states that he has immunized himself against cobra venom by repeated injections.

Immunity has also been sought through injections other than of venoms. Orfila (1818, vol. 2, p. 533; 1821, vol. 2, p. 443) repeats a report made by de Vargas in 1798 that certain South American natives inoculate themselves monthly with the juice of a plant to secure immunity from snake bite. Carnochan and Adamson (1935, p. 93) and Harley (1941, pp. 213, 225) mention a practice of certain African tribes that inject dried and powdered snake heads mixed with other ingredients. Ackerknecht (1949, p. 632) describes a method used by a tribe of Indians in Colombia, who rub snake ashes into scarifications. Other references to methods of acquiring immunity among American Indians will be found on p. 1108.

A friend of mine, an experimental pathologist, once immunized himself against rattlesnake venom until his blood had a high titer; unfortunately, he did not test for the duration of the acquired immunity.

With the problem of immunization arises also that of anaphylaxis. As early as 1892, Kanthack (p. 276) pointed out that repeated doses of venom are more dangerous than the same total amount in a single dose, as had already been mentioned by Sewall (1887). A sufficient time must intervene between immunizing doses or the cumulative effect is marked. Kanthack may actually have encountered anaphylaxis. Mendes (1952, p. 1328) mentions a case wherein a laboratory worker became allergic to *Crotalus* and *Bothrops* venoms, through having been exposed to them through inhalation. Essex and Markowitz (1930, p. 703) pointed out the similarity between crotalin shock and anaphylactic shock. This, of course, is no proof that anaphylactic shock does follow repeated injections of venom, although such would be expected from its protein character. This presumption is verified by Dr. Dudley Jackson, who, in a letter in 1933, said: "I have treated one snake dealer in San Antonio five times for snake bite. In his third bite I believe he was hypersensitive to venom, and in two minutes from the time of the bite, which was not a very severe one, he was unconscious. He went into a state similar to an anaphylactic shock. He remained in this condition for five hours; no pulse, cold and clammy, some cyanosis, but little local reaction. An intravenous injection of venom in animals produces almost instant reaction associated with a bloody diarrhea and respiratory failure. The patient did not show these symptoms. Antivenin had not been administered."

Other discussions of hypersensitivity through repeated parenteral injections of snake venoms are those of Peck, 1933, p. 312; Lounsberry, 1934, p. 658; Kyes, Markin, and Graham, 1940, p. 81; Essex, 1945, p. 163; and Schoettler, 1951, p. 495. Richards (1951, p. 189) has given a good popular account of anaphylaxis and its causes.

Is the snake-bite risk to any person sufficiently grave to justify immunization? Certainly not, except in the case of operators of snake pits in carnivals or similar places of amusement. And if these operators are frequently bitten, one can only suggest that they had better engage in some other occupation where carelessness is not so strongly penalized. Amaral (1923b, p. 96) and Anon. (1938c, p. 834) have pointed out, as observed in horses immunized for the production of antivenin, that the liver and kidneys may be seriously affected by increasing venom injections. Micheel (1941, p. 170) remarked that the effectiveness of immunization would be of short duration, so it would be better to depend on antivenin after the bite. Thus, despite the success of preventive inoculations against such diseases as typhoid and diphtheria, and however attractive it might seem to the hunter or fisherman to traverse the woods with no fear of snakes, preventive immunization is not to be recommended at this stage of our knowledge.

Susceptibility of Domestic Animals

Elsewhere (p. 964), in discussing stock losses from rattlesnake bite, I have presented a number of experiences of my correspondents who mention, in a general way, the degree to which domestic animals are affected by rattlesnake bite.

There seem to be no marked differences in the effects on cattle, as compared to horses, certainly not sufficient to warrant the information conveyed by Berkeley (1861, p. 64, 201)—this was hearsay, not experimental data—that rattlers were occasionally fatal to horses and mules, but never to cattle or buffalo, because the vaccine matter protected them from snake bite, as it does against smallpox.

Although hogs were, for a long time, believed to be immune to rattlesnake bite (Carver, 1778, p. 483), it was early evident that the supposed immunity was only the protection afforded by the layer of fat that prevented the venom from entering the circulation. Essex (1932, p. 339) found them by test to be no more resistant than other animals. Gordon (in Fayrer, 1892b, p. 114) reports the queer idea that the degree of susceptibility of hogs to rattlesnake bite depends on the color of the hog. Grasset, Zoutendyk, and Schaafsma (1935, p. 605; Pitman, 1938, pp. 35, 269) state that the hog does have some degree of immunity from the bites of elapid African snakes, not dependent on the layer of fat.

As stated elsewhere, the m.l.d. of *C. atrox* venom for dogs is about 1 mg. of dried venom per pound of dog, indicating that dogs have an average susceptibility. Certainly Kalm (1752–53, p. 58) was wrong in thinking them relatively immune. Randolph (1931, p. 133) tells us there is a folk belief in the Ozarks that dogs with dewclaws are immune. Hoit (1844, p. 243) says that dogs, having suffered a bite, are the more ready to attack rattlers, implying that they feel protected by an enhanced immunity.

Fayrer (1872, p. 64) found cats more resistant to cobra venom than dogs, on a weight basis. Corresponding results were secured by Kellaway (1929a, p. 350; 1929b, p. 359), using Australian elapids. Mitchell and Reichert (1886, p. 139) found the cat more resistant to rattlesnake venom than other laboratory animals. Sawyer (1933, p. 21) made tests indicating that cats are less susceptible to rattlesnake poison than dogs. These experiments, however, lacked adequate controls.

The belief is occasionally expressed that animals, especially dogs, if repeatedly bitten, become immune just as snake-pit operators are believed to acquire immunity. Pritchard (1940, p. 358) says that a single bite seems to confer temporary immunity on a dog. Lloyd (in Cameron, 1927, p. 70) even permitted his dog to be bitten, an exceedingly cruel expedient, in the hope that he would then have a "rattlesnake dog," that is, a rattlesnake killer unafraid of the snakes. Hamilton (1938, p. 613) and Duncan (1945, p. 172) mention instances of immunity in dogs, and my correspondents have done likewise:

> I owned a part bull dog which was bitten many times. However, the first time he almost died and each successive time it hurt him less until he finally became immune and didn't even swell. I have noted the same in horses.

◇

> Of stock and dogs, particularly dogs, which I have seen bitten by snakes—the first time is very hard on them, but later occurrences seem to be less severe.

◇

> I believe that after an animal is bitten, it never hurts it as bad any more. I had a fox terrier that was bitten on the leg in defense of my babies. A few months later he was bitten on the neck. I did not find that place in time to treat it, and he was sick for a long time. The next summer my wife found two large rattlers in the pasture several miles from home. The little dog caught one of them, and was bitten on the jaw near the ear. She had to bring him home on horseback, and was about two hours on the way. We cut the place and forced out all the poison we could. His head swelled until he could not lift it, and stayed that way for several days. He finally got well, but I think that if that had been the first time he had been bitten, he could not have lived through it.

Immunity in Mammals That Prey on Snakes

There is no doubt that mammals which regularly prey on venomous snakes do have a partial immunity—that is, it takes more venom per unit of body weight to kill them than is the case with nonophiophagous mammals.

The mongoose was long presumed to be quite immune to snake bite, particularly to that of the cobra, with which, according to an inaccurate popular belief, it is supposed to battle whenever they meet. Actually, it is not immune (Russell, 1796, p. 84; Fayrer, 1872, p. 69; 1892, p. 94; Compton, 1893, p. 173; Noguchi, 1909, p. 268). When it does attack a cobra, it escapes injury by means of its agility and fluffed-up hair (Morse, 1911, p. 295; Acton and Knowles, 1921, p. 726). But it does have a reduced susceptibility. Calmette (1898, p. 515) estimated the m.l.d. for a mongoose at eight times that of a rabbit. Elliot (1900, p. 218) stated the difference at 10 to 25 times the rabbit m.l.d. Cunningham (1897, p. 91) found the mongoose 14 times as immune as a chicken to cobra venom, and 2½ times as immune to Russell's viper venom. Later (1933c, p. 665; 1934c, p. 218) Elliot expressed the idea that Calmette's less resistant strain of mongooses may have deteriorated in venom resistance because of their having lived on the island of Guadeloupe for 50 generations or so. There are no venomous snakes on Guadeloupe.

Grasset, Zoutendyk, and Schaafsma (1935, p. 606) found the meerkat, an African mammal somewhat resembling the mongoose, more resistant to elapine than to viperine venoms. On a weight basis, the meerkat was 1,000 times as resistant as a sheep to Cape cobra venom. It took almost 100 times as much cobra venom to kill a South African mongoose as it took to kill a guinea pig, but the mongoose was no more immune to puff adder venom than the guinea pig.

Phisalix and Bertand (1895, p. 639) determined the European hedgehog to be 30 to 40 times as resistant to viper venom as is the guinea pig. Kraus (1924, p. 771) and Vellard (1945, p. 463; 1949a, p. 59; 1949b, p. 5; 1950a, p. 14; 1950b, p. 148; see also Fonseca, 1949, p. 228) studied the resistance of various South American mammals that prey on snakes and found them to possess various degrees of immunity. This was more pronounced against the venoms of the crotalid snakes on which some of them fed. Two kinds of birds that feed on snakes were found to have no special immunity.

In the United States, it is not known whether any of the mammals that eat rattlers have any conspicuous resistance. There is no mammal of which rattlesnakes comprise more than a minor or incidental part of the diet, although rattlers are occasionally eaten by coyotes, foxes, badgers, peccaries, opossums, wildcats, racoons, and skunks. So far as I know, comparative immunity tests have not been made on any of these. Hylander (1951, p. 70) states that the spotted skunk, which is reputed to feed on diamondbacks, is immune to their bite, but I have seen no records of resistance tests comparing the skunk with other mammals.

Fraser (1895a, p. 1312) believed there was a decreased susceptibility of carnivorous animals to cobra venom as compared with herbivorous. He found that rats fed on meat had their resistance increased (1895b, p. 418). Schoettler (1952, p. 303) found female mice slightly more resistant than males.

The studies of the susceptibility of partly immune mammals have been made largely to advance the knowledge of the mechanism of immunity.

SUSCEPTIBILITY OF AMPHIBIANS

Mitchell (1860, p. 54) carried on an extensive series of tests on the susceptibility of frogs to rattlesnake venom. He found them more resistant than warm-blooded animals, particularly to the hemorrhagic effects of venoms. Essex and Markowitz (1930, p. 342) found that pickerel and leopard frogs, which are frogs of moderate size, are not greatly inconvenienced by an amount of *C. atrox* or *C. horridus* venom sufficient to kill a dog. Falck (1940, p. 135) observed that a captive mottled rock rattlesnake (*C. l. lepidus*), which ate both amphibians and mammals, held onto the amphibians when it struck them but released the mammals. The mammals died more quickly than the amphibians, which, in the wild, would probably have been lost unless held.

SUSCEPTIBILITY OF REPTILES

Said Pliny 1855–57, vol. 1, p. 120; book vii, chap. 1): "The sting of the serpent is not aimed at the serpent." Gradually the truth of this statement has been verified—snakes are relatively immune to snake bite. The immunity is not a complete one, and some snake species are less affected than others, but compared with that of mammals and birds the susceptibility of snakes is low.

Among the first to test the effects of snake bite on other snakes were Fontana (1787, vol. 1, p. 39) and Russell (1796, pp. 56, 85). Later citations are: Fayrer, 1869, pp. 131, 153, 177; Yarrow, 1888, p. 388; March, 1928, p. 59; FitzSimons and FitzSimons, 1932, p. 63; Swanson, 1933a, p. 18; Allyn, 1937, p. 223; Keegan and Andrews, 1942, p. 251; Gloyd and Bevan, 1946, p. 1; Swanson, 1946b, p. 242; Philpot and Smith, 1950, p. 523; and Hylander, 1951, p. 70. Of these, the most informative are the experiments of Keegan and Andrews, and of Swanson.

At the San Diego Zoo we have seen a number of harmless snakes accidentally bitten by rattlers. Ill effects are sometimes observed. Fatalities are rare, but they do occur. The most apparent symptoms, when there are any, comprise a swelling at the bite and sluggishness.

It would be pleasingly consonant with evolutionary theory were it possible to draw the conclusion that the snakes that feed on rattlers, particularly the king snakes, *Lampropeltis,* and the racers and whipsnakes, *Masticophis,* have a higher degree of immunity than the other harmless snakes. However, this conclusion is not to be drawn from the tests thus far published. In tests made by Dr. Eaton McKay at La Jolla, California, both king snakes, *L. g. californiae,* and gopher snakes, *P. c. annectens,* survived *C. v. helleri* venom in dosages of 200 mg/kg, but specimens of both subspecies died 23 hours after receiving *C. r. ruber* venom at the rate of 1,000 mg/kg.

Immunity of King Snakes.—King snakes, the presumed deadly enemies of rattlesnakes, have long been thought to be immune to rattlesnake bite. I say "presumed enemies of rattlers" because a good deal of exaggeration has grown up concerning this relationship. There is a widely dispersed legend to the effect that king snakes spend their lives trying to clear the world of rattlers; that whenever one comes upon a rattler, usually after trailing it for weeks, he kills it by constriction, and then, taking a bow from the cheering audience, starts in quest of another.

But the truth isn't quite so felicitous. Actually, king snakes feed on snakes, as well as on mammals, birds, and lizards, and when, if hungry, one comes upon a rattler small enough to be eaten, it is swallowed just as it would have been had it been a gopher snake or some other harmless species. The story of the king snake that kills a rattler much too large to engulf is to be doubted, even if told you by one of your favorite and most trustworthy relatives. Hundreds of such stories have appeared in print; other hundreds have been told me by eyewitnesses with whom I didn't argue, but still I am unconvinced.

However, there is one feature of the rattler–king-snake relationship that may be credited, namely, the relative immunity of the king snake to rattlesnake bite, for the resistance is much greater than in mammals of similar size. I have described elsewhere (p. 1059) in some detail the stereotyped pattern followed by the king snake, *Lampropeltis getulus californiae,* in swallowing a young rattler. In four out of six cases observed, the rattler was not seized by the snout, and thus was free to bite the king snake, which it did, usually several times. These bites were ignored by the king snake, and no subsequent harm was suffered from them. Hence, although it cannot be said that king snakes are completely immune to rattler bite, we have evidence that they are unaffected by a dose of venom that would make a man, weighing about 300 times as much, seriously—and even dangerously—ill, if left without treatment as the king snake was.

Olds (1910, p. 292) records two occasions in which king snakes were bitten by rattlers without effect. Allyn (1937, p. 224) had a small king snake, *L. getulus,* bitten by a small massasauga or ground rattler (*S. catenatus*). The king snake died within an hour. Keegan and Andrews (1942, p. 252) killed a small king snake, *L. calligaster,* with copperhead venom; the dose in mg. of dried venom per kg. of body weight was 767. The king snake succumbed after 5 days. Dr. Eaton McKay, of La Jolla, experimented with *C. r. ruber* venom on *L. g. californiae* and found that it survived a dosage of 200 mg/kg, but another died 23 hours after receiving a dose of *C. v. helleri* venom at the rate of 1,000 mg/kg.

One of my correspondents wrote:

> A king snake bitten by a rattler is not entirely immune. Upon different occasions I have noticed that the muscles at the site of the bite seem sore and stiff. I remember once when a king snake in my possession carried a kink in his body for as long as three days after being bitten by a rattler.

Rosenfeld and Glass (1940, p. 482) found that when pit viper venoms (*Agkistrodon piscivorus, Crotalus adamanteus,* and *Bothrops atrox*) were mixed with king snake (*L. g. getulus*) blood and injected into mice, the usual hemorrhagic effects of the venoms were inhibited.

Philpot and Smith, 1950, proved that king snake serum (*L. g. floridana* or *L. g. holbrooki*) detoxified by heating—for snake blood, whether of venomous or non-venomous snakes is toxic to mammals—protected mice against as high as seven average lethal doses of moccasin venom. The king snake serum was less effective in counteracting *C. adamanteus* venom, but did build up successful resistance to about 2½ normally lethal doses. Philpot and Smith also investigated king snake immunity directly, by the injection of moccasin venom. One king snake survived a total of 300 mg/kg given in 4 doses within 5 days, and another 1,350 mg/kg in 5 doses within 21 days. One of these doses was at the rate of 416 mg/kg. As a comparative figure it may be noted that the average lethal dose of moccasin venom for white mice by intraperitoneal injection was 6¼ mg/kg. It is safe to say that king snakes are at least 100 times more resistant than mice to moccasin venom, and that they have somewhat the same comparative immunity to rattlesnake venom.

Immunity of Rattlesnakes to Their Own and Other Venoms.—Since colonial days it has been quite generally believed that rattlesnakes, if cornered or injured, will bite themselves with suicidal intent, and that the venom is quickly fatal, that is, within seconds or minutes.

That rattlesnakes do sometimes bite themselves when attacked or injured is unquestioned, but certainly they have no suicidal objective. They strike wildly at anything that moves, or they even lunge or bite without aiming at any particular object. Quite by accident they may hit some part of their own bodies, and, having done so, and feeling a yielding substance, they may inject venom. They are particularly likely to bite themselves if they are held down with a stick. There the likeness to the story stops. They do not die instantly; in fact, they would rarely die at all were it not for the injuries that were originally the cause of the wild strike. The nearest approach to the popular picture of a suicide occurs when a rattlesnake is kept from escaping from the hot sun. During the final moments of the 10 to 14 minutes required for the heat to kill the rattlesnake under these circumstances, it may bite itself in its violent efforts to escape the torment. Then it will die and stiffen quickly, not because of the venom but from the heat, for the heat stiffens the muscles in a way not produced by other fatal injuries, and thus the usual persistent reflex squirming of a dying snake is prevented.

Some of the early accounts of the rattlesnake's suicidal custom are those of Hall, 1727, p. 313; Brickell, 1735, p. 145; Zeisberger, 1910, p. 72, but written in 1779–80; Loskiel, 1794, part 1, p. 88; Tome, 1928, p. 114, but writing of happenings in about 1800; Audubon, 1827, p. 26; Beltrami, 1828, vol. 2, p. 186; Burnett, 1854a, p. 313; Rivers, 1874, p. 511; and Kingman, 1894, p. 488. Some merely repeat the myth, others cite particular instances, and from these it is sometimes possible to guess what really happened. In a case cited by Caldwell (1946, p. 22) the rattler was apparently fatally injured by a whip before it struck itself. In another mentioned by Grinnell, Dixon, and Linsdale (1930, p. 153), a rattler bit itself after having been wounded by a charge of fine shot. Van Dyke (1897, p. 38), discussing the legend of the roadrunner and the cactus corral, gives his idea to the effect that when a rattler bites itself, it uses its harmless, solid teeth, rather than its fangs, and therefore the cactus corral story must be mythical. Of course it is mythical, as pointed out elsewhere (p. 1251), but Van Dyke's presumption that rattlers do not imbed their fangs when biting themselves is incorrect. Schmidt (1929a, p. 3; 1951, p. 6), Vestal (1941, p. 146), and Frayne (1945, p. 32), cite the suicide stories as folklore.

The following are some accounts of snake suicides from letters I have received from forest rangers and game wardens:

> Last summer, when I hit a rattler with a rock, he repeatedly buried his fangs in his own body.
>
> ◇
>
> I have caused several rattlers to bite themselves by tormenting them with long sticks, or by throwing dirt and clods at them until they were furious and struck themselves. In all instances they became very sick in a matter of minutes, and would straighten out and die.
>
> ◇
>
> In 1933, in the Sierra, east of Sonora, California, I hit a rattler that was trying to escape with a stick. The snake was thus injured, whereupon it deliberately stopped, raised its head, opened its jaws, and plunged its fangs into its body about midway between head and tail. The movement was a deliberate one, as I was not hitting at the snake at the moment. It appeared to me that the snake was committing suicide.
>
> ◇
>
> An interesting observation made by me and three witnesses was of a rattlesnake biting itself and dying. This occurred on Chloride Cliffs, southwest of Beatty, Nevada, in 1925. We were attracted to the rattle of a small snake close by, and one of the members of the party picked up a stone and hit the snake, injuring its back. The snake became aggressive and struck about at objects nearby. Finally, it turned on itself and, opening wide its mouth, deliberately sank its fangs into its back, holding on for several moments. Then, releasing its jaws, the snake slowly assumed a relaxed position and finally died before our eyes. A stick poked at it had no effect on the snake after that.

The following observers did not stress the suicide feature:

> Once in awhile, when holding one of these reptiles down with a stick or snake-catcher, they have turned and struck at the spot where the pressure was applied. Nine times out of ten they bite themselves and often fatally.
>
> ◇
>
> In a period of years I have seen many instances of rattlers biting one another or themselves, and yet have not observed fatal results. In fact, I have kept such individuals segregated to verify this point.
>
> ◇
>
> Rattlesnakes are not harmed by their own venom, as observed in cases of snakes biting themselves while being disturbed.

I have had one experience that might have led me to believe the suicide theory. A small sidewinder caught on the road one evening bit itself while being placed in a jar. The next morning it was dead—the only one to die of several snakes caught that night. But, of course, it may have been injured before I found it. In another case a large southern Pacific rattler (*C. v. helleri*) was picked up by the tail. It tried to climb up its own body, as snakes will often do to bite and free themselves, and, when it was jiggled to shake it down, bit itself several times. It subsequently showed no ill effects.

C. B. Perkins makes this interesting contribution to the question of the rattle-snake's immunity to its own venom based on his long experience at the San Diego Zoo:

> Often when a dead rat is thrown into a cage, two snakes may see the movement. One snake may strike it; and the second snake, a bit slow on the trigger, sees the first snake strike and makes the mistake of hitting its companion instead of the rat. Usually there are a couple of drops of blood at the point where the fangs enter and that is all that happens. Some-times there is a bit of swelling that probably could not be caused by the mechanical punc-ture, but must be due to the venom. Whenever one snake bites another inadvertently in this way, a card record is made. For example, a young *C. r. ruber* struck another of the same brood in the jaw while seeking food. There was considerable swelling, but it soon subsided and there was no permanent effect. We have never lost a snake from the effects of venom, and seldom is there any evidence, a day later, that there has been an accident. Rattlesnakes certainly have a high tolerance for their own venom.
>
> Twice we have had one rattler killed by another. The first time was on May 21, 1944. While feeding a cage of red diamonds (*C. r. ruber*) one of two males in the cage bit a female, which then spun around rapidly like a top for three or four minutes, then slowly turned on her longitudinal axis. She was dead in about an hour and the autopsy showed a fang puncture between the skull and the first vertebra.
>
> The second case of death by rattler bite occurred ten years later, June 18, 1954. While some newly born young were being removed from a cage, an adult male rattler struck an-other which appeared to be mechanically hurt. It spun around rapidly for a few minutes and then relaxed. It was dead the next morning. No swelling, as might be expected had death been caused by venom, was noticeable.

The literature discussing the degree of resistance that rattlesnakes have, to their own venoms, to the venoms of rattlesnakes of other species, and to the venoms of snakes other than rattlesnakes, is quite extensive. Some immunity tests have been well conducted and are quite convincing. In general, the conclusions are: Rattlesnakes are quite resistant to their own venoms, slightly less so to rattlesnakes of other species, and still less immune to the bites of snakes of other genera. Where a fatality cannot be explained by injury or heat, we may presume either that the snake's fang punctured the spinal cord or some vital organ, or that an unusually large amount of venom was injected. Sanders (1951, p. 49), from an extensive series of tests on the Great Basin rattler, *C. v. lutosus,* concluded that the amount of venom required to kill an adult of this subspecies is greater than the amount that a single snake secretes.

The following publications contain accounts of self-inflicted and other bites, with their results: Olds, 1910, p. 292; Wooster, 1933, p. 479; Gloyd, 1933b, p. 13; Nichol, Douglas, and Peck, 1933, p. 211; Allyn, 1937, p. 223; Kauffeld, 1943b, p. 607; Gloyd and Bevan, 1946, p. 3; Duncan, 1946, p. 172; Munro, 1947, p. 57; and Loewen, 1947, p. 53. Fitch and Glading (1947, p. 121) found, about 10 feet from a mating pair, a large male *C. v. helleri* that evidently had succumbed to rattler bite.

Discussions of the extent of rattlesnake susceptibility or immunity to its own venom and that of other kinds of rattlers are those of Yarrow, 1888, p. 307; Brown, 1899, p. 222; Netting, 1932, p. 6; Bevan, 1933a, p. 59 (a short, but excellent coverage of the subject); Arnold, 1935, p. 134; Motl, 1936, p. 1; Benton, 1937, p. 211; and Gloyd and Bevan, 1946, p. 3.

Most important of the evidence, in the form of quantitative tests of resistance, is to be found in these publications: Mitchell, 1860, p. 61; 1868b, p. 314; 1889, p. 510; Mitchell and Stewart, 1898, p. 9; Welker and Marshall, 1915, p. 563; Keegan and Andrews, 1942, p. 251; Swanson, 1946b, p. 242; and Sanders, 1951, p. 47. Keegan and Andrews discuss the symptoms of snake bite in snakes, both rattlers and other kinds. Where the amount of venom injected verged on the fatal, there was immediate restlessness, swelling at the point of injection, and progressive lethargy.

Swanson (p. 248) reaches these conclusions, among others:

> At the start I had a theory that snakes might be immune to venom of their own kind, and less susceptible to venom from closely related snakes than to that of more distant relatives. Had that proven true, venom studies might aid in solving phylogenetic relationships. The experiments indicate that this theory is untenable.... There is a possibility that *S. c. catenatus* is immune to venom of its own kind. Of the other species used, none seems immune to venom of its own kind, although small doses might not affect them.... There is some indication that an individual snake may possess antibodies that can counteract the effects of its own venom, but not that of venom from other individuals of its own species, or even from its individual blood relatives.... Snakes usually seem to be able to survive what might be considered normal or average doses of venom, although they are not necessarily immune to it. It is probable that no two venom samples are exactly alike in their composition and potential effects.

Sanders (1951, p. 52) believes there are three venom effects that contribute to the outcome in fatal cases of injury to *C. v. lutosus* by its own venom: (1) Loss of blood into the tissue spaces, reducing the efficiency of the circulatory system; (2) the effect of the venom on the cellular portion of the blood, particularly the red cells, also possible clumping; and (3) extensive necrosis at the site of the injection.

It should be understood that all of the really informative tests have been carried out by the injection of measured quantities of venom. Tests in which one snake is allowed to bite another rarely prove anything, since the quantity of venom injected is never known.

The Keegan and Andrews and the Swanson experiments include, as well as tests of rattler venom on rattlers, the results of tests of *Agkistrodon* (water moccasin and copperhead) venoms on rattlesnakes. Other cases involving the effects of *Agkistrodon* venoms on rattlesnakes are mentioned by Gloyd, 1933b, p. 13; Conant, 1934, p. 382; Allen, 1937, p. 72; and McCauley, 1945, p. 134. The late E. A. McIlhenny wrote me:

> I have seen rattlesnakes, both eastern diamondbacks and canebrakes, fight in captivity and draw blood from each other without fatal results; but I had a pen of four extra large specimens, including both of these species, killed by the bites of a cottonmouth moccasin. I have often wondered why the venom of the rattlesnake was so much less effective than the venom of the cottonmouth moccasin.

Statements of interest respecting problems of self-intoxication among noncrotalids are those of Waddell, 1889, p. 57; Elliot, 1933b, p. 364; 1934c, p. 210;

Tyler, 1946, p. 196; and, especially, Kellaway, 1937, p. 159. The latter, although largely basing his conclusions on Australian elapids, has presented a most valuable summary of the reasons for, and the mechanism of, the relatively high resistance of venomous snakes to their own and other venoms. He agrees that the resistance is high, but not absolute (p. 166). He believes that the entry of venom into the blood of snakes through their biting themselves is so normal and frequent that they must be immune to survive. They may bite themselves in anger, or by closing the mouth with the fangs partly erect (p. 175). Observations suggest that the immunity of snakes to their own and allied venoms depends in large part upon the presence in their tissues of enzymes capable of destroying or utilizing the venom (p. 172).

Although the blood plasma of venomous snakes is lethal, it has a different character than the venom. There is no convincing evidence that there is normally any venom in the blood except from accidental bites. When the venom glands are removed, the plasma remains toxic. While snakes have a high immunity to their own and related venoms, it is not absolute. Based on body weight, the Australian tiger snake is 180,000 times as resistant to its own venom as is the guinea pig to this venom; it is 33,000 times as immune to the venom of the Australian copper-head (a snake entirely distinct from the American copperhead), 13,000 times as immune as is the guinea pig to the venom of the Indian cobra. Relative resistances of this magnitude to their own and other crotalid venoms are not evident in the rattlesnakes; nevertheless, their resistance is far greater than that of mammals and birds.

Tyler (1946, p. 199) has propounded a theory that, in the Gila monster, the liver produces both a venom and a complementary antivenin. The venom is separated out and remains in the venom glands, whereas the protective auto-antibodies remain in the blood serum.

Susceptibility of Miscellaneous Animals

Mitchell (1870, p. 318) tested the effect of rattlesnake venom on fish, crabs, and insects. He found them susceptible, but less so than warm-blooded creatures.

Effect of Venom on Protozoa.—Extensive tests have been made of the effects of rattlesnake venoms on protozoa, especially *Paramecium*, by Essex and Markowitz (1930, p. 343) and by Philpott (1929, 1930, and 1931). The experiments were designed to secure simpler and less expensive tests for venom toxicity, to aid in venom standardization, and to test the titer of antivenins.

Essex and Markowitz found that *Paramecium* reacted to *C. atrox* venom somewhat as do the erythrocytes in blood—they swelled and were destroyed. Philpott made tests on a number of different protozoans, in which tests he used venoms of rattlesnakes, of other pit vipers, and of cobras. He found that the several venoms acted differently on the various protozoans. Antivenin was effective in protecting them (1930, p. 180), but the titer did not correspond to that obtained when warm-blooded animals were used (1930, p. 182). In some cases the destructive agent seemed to be the hemorrhagin in the venom; in others, the neurotoxin. All protozoans were more resistant to *C. atrox* venom than to that of the cobra. There was not complete correlation in venom strength, as between the species of protozoan and the species of snake; that is, one venom might be more destructive than other venoms to one protozoan, but would be comparatively less destructive to other protozoans. Minton (in Buckley, editor, 1955, in press) found a positive correlation between the extent of the necrosis produced by different rattlesnake venoms in guinea pigs and the rapidity of the lysis of *Paramecium*. In summary, protozoans are of limited use as test animals.

EFFECT OF RATTLESNAKE VENOMS ON PLANTS

In time, current references to the effects of rattlesnake venom on plants have taken two divergent courses. Beginning in colonial days with hearsay evidence, undoubtedly descended from the Old World myths on the effects of viper venom on plants, they took the course on the one hand toward tests to determine whether venom really does affect plants, and on the other toward ever more fantastic and humorous tales devised in liar contests. The tale tellers were intrigued by the idea of wood swelling in the manner of a person's arm, as a result of a rattler bite. As an example of this type of story we have the account of the man who was chewing a toothpick that was struck by a rattler; the resultant swelling produced enough timber to build a 12-room house. Unfortunately, the swelling was cured by the turpentine in the paint as the house was being finished, so that only the cornerstone of the mansion remained. Effects of this type I have relegated to chapter 18, on myths and tall stories.

Some colonial stories, seriously believed by the tellers, of how rattlesnake venom will permeate a plant and cause its destruction were those of Mather (1714, p. 68), Beverly (1722, p. 267), Kalm (1752–53, p. 57), Breintal (1765, p. 514), and Burnaby (1775, p. 78). More recent accounts are given by Anon. (1858b, p. 472), and Flack (1866, p. 318). In these, the affected plant sometimes splits, and sometimes withers and dies. There is a relationship here with the myth of the hoop snake, that always ends its roll by driving its venomous tail-sting into some unfortunate tree, which quickly dies.

Real tests on the effects of rattlesnake venom on plants apparently began with those of Salisbury (1852, p. 337). He experimented with venom on the point of a pen knife that was inserted into the shoots of young plants. The plants withered above the cut. But he used no controls, and subsequent investigators have thought that the damage was done by the knife and not by the venom. Gilman (1854, p. 26; Mitchell, 1860, p. 47; Lewis, 1874, p. 273; Noguchi, 1909, p. 285) inoculated vegetables with venom on the point of a lancet; the next day they were withered and dead. Mitchell (1860, p. 49; Noguchi, 1909, p. 286) made a number of his own experiments on plants, first on yeast, then on higher plants. He used controls, and his findings were negative; there were no resultant differences between the poisoned and nonpoisoned plants.

Reuss (1931, p. 109) calls attention to the fact that the biting mechanism of venomous snakes is not well adapted for use on plants. If the fangs could penetrate, they could not be withdrawn. Furthermore, the dense substance would virtually close the discharge orifice of the fang and prevent venom injection.

Macht (1933, p. 988; 1937, p. 500) made experiments on plant seedlings and found rattlesnake venom to be toxic to plant protoplasm. This, of course, is not equivalent to saying that the ancient beliefs in the destruction of large plants are now vindicated.

 # 13. Treatment and Prevention of the Bite

THE TREATMENTS PROPOSED: THEIR HISTORY AND PRESENT STATUS

When I was a youngster, spending my summer vacations hunting and hiking in the mountains back of San Diego—this was in the 1890's—a new and certain cure for rattlesnake bite was announced. This was ammonia; and as soon as I, like many of my fellows, had secured a bottle to carry wherever I might go, I felt a great relief, for I knew that I had a sure protection against a danger that had previously caused some concern. So thereafter I tramped without worry in the granite and chaparral, where rattlers were moderately common.

This might be taken as an example of the way that snake-bite cures come and go, become popular and are discarded, only to be revived anew. For ammonia was not a new remedy in the 1890's; it had been advocated as early as 1738, and had been tested and found without merit in 1765. It was used again from time to time in the early 1800's. My experience was the result of only one of several rediscoveries or revivals of ammonia as an unfailing cure; and this example of my unwarranted confidence is typical of the undeserved reputations of remedies for snake bite through the ages.

As one studies the case reports of snake bites, including rattlesnake bites, one cannot but be amazed at the number of remedies that have come into prominence, that have been adopted with enthusiasm, only to be discarded eventually as worthless. Whence did these cures emanate and how were they authenticated?

They have come from a variety of sources—from pre-Columbian Indian medicine men; from European importations tracing back to ancient Greece and Rome; from the alchemists of the Middle Ages; and from the biologists and physicians of colonial and modern times. And even after they have been discarded by reputable practitioners, or have been shown by experiment to be valueless, they still persist as folklore cures in the more remote areas.

Some will wonder how these cures ever gained the confidence of so many people, and why this trust continued even after they were shown by test to have no value. As to the ancient cures, this question is not hard to answer, for in the old days all snakes, and many harmless creatures such as lizards, salamanders, and frogs, were thought to be dangerously venomous. So when an application of radishes or goat's-milk cheese—two of the hundreds of remedies recorded by Pliny—cured the bite of a reputedly fatal but actually harmless snake, they became accredited remedies.

In the case of the rattlesnakes, the explanation is not quite so simple, yet it is basically the same. All rattlesnakes are venomous, most of them to a serious degree, but many persons are unable to distinguish a rattler from harmless species, despite the infallible clue of the rattle. Furthermore, rattlesnake bite is not as serious as sometimes supposed; often it is stated to be invariably fatal, which is far from the truth. But most important is the fact that the many variable conditions involved in every snake-bite case, as discussed in the introduction to chapter 11, often reduce the gravity of the bite to such a degree that there is no real danger. So the remedies gain their reputations by saving people from dangers that never existed; and these reputations persist despite their shaky foundations.

The very diversity of the remedies that have been used for rattlesnake bite is, in itself, evidence that they were entirely or virtually ineffectual, for a truly efficacious cure soon would have displaced all others. A certain lack of confidence is shown by the fact that, in most case reports, one learns that from 2 to 10 different remedies were applied simultaneously, a sort of hopeful shotgun treatment. So, although I have listed the various remedies separately in the historical survey that follows, it is to be assumed that they were used in all manner of combinations with each other. Had one actually been effective, it might have been difficult to determine which it was, with so much confusion of treatment, although eventually it would have stood out above the others. One of my reasons for discussing in some detail the many remedies that have been tried in the past, is to preclude their being reintroduced as something new and effective, as ammonia was, in my neighborhood, in the 1890's.

Few of the rattlesnake-bite cures popular in the last century were originally devised for rattlesnakes. Most were imported from the Old World, where rattlesnakes do not occur. Today, when we know how specific antivenins must be to be effective—that is, prepared for particular snakes, or groups of snakes—we realize how hopeless it is to expect to find a universal antidote for snake bite. Even in this country in the pioneer days, rattlesnake bite was so infrequent that a standard treatment, such as those that came to be tested and used for more common diseases—diseases with a well-recognized syndrome—could not be evolved.

Another source of rattlesnake-bite remedies was in the treatments used in rural medicine for other accidents, such as cuts and bruises. Among these may be mentioned such treatments as cauterization, tobacco juice, turpentine, kerosene, iodine, salt, absorptive mud, and many others.

In discussing remedies, I have characterized some of them as folklore cures. Yet there is no well-defined or consistent line between folklore and scientific cures. We usually think of folklore cures as those founded on inadequate testing—experiments without suitable controls—and cures transmitted by word of mouth from friend or neighbor, rather than by written records or instructions. But in the case of snake bite, with its multitude of uncertainties that affect the gravity of the original bite, and the difficulty of selecting the successful remedy out of the many applied in almost every case, the verification of the success or failure of any specific

item of treatment became virtually impossible. So doctor and layman alike resorted to what we now call folklore treatments, justified by repute rather than by
objective tests.

It might be assumed that the application of folklore remedies can still be justified on the theory that every possible source of relief is warranted in the case of
so serious a contingency as rattlesnake bite. No delusion could be more unfortunate. These remedies may in themselves be dangerous; they delay the application of the truly effective medicines known today; and they confuse the course
and treatment of the malady itself. It is unfortunate that under the stress of such
an accident as a snake bite, people are likely to revert to methods that, in less
excited moments, they would ridicule. At a loss what to do, they apply some such
fantastic remedy as the split-chicken treatment because years ago there was a
family tradition that it once cured some second cousin.

In this discussion of the history and present status of rattlesnake-bite remedies,
they will be treated in the following order of categories: Elimination of venom
at the site of the bite; means for reducing or delaying venom absorption; remedies based on animal products; on vegetable products; on mineral products;
systemic drugs; bactericidals; and systemic treatments.

SCARIFICATION, INCISION, AND SUCTION

The method of snake-bite treatment, in which the wound is enlarged and suction
is applied to remove venom, is so old and so natural that its derivation is lost
in the ancient rites of medicine men and witch doctors. Undoubtedly it was invented independently in many times and places. Whether it was thought that
the danger from a bite lay in the liquid venom injected, or, as was believed by
some American Indian tribes, in the introduction by the snake of some solid
object into the wound, it was logical to try to remove the poisonous substance
at the place of entry. So the instinctive sucking of an injury, as one claps an insect
sting to the mouth, developed into more elaborate, and sometimes more successful, methods of withdrawing a part of the venom. This is one of the few of the
aboriginal treatments still considered of value.

Among the ancients who mention some form of incision or scarification, followed by suction, for the treatment of snake bite, were Nicander of Colophon,
who lived in the second century B.C. (Nicander, 1935, p. 89; Adams, 1844–47,
vol. 2, p. 159); Celsus, a Roman, born about 25 B.C. (1935–38, p. 115); Dioscorides,
of Cilicia, who wrote an important medical encyclopedia in the first century A.D.
(Adams, 1844–47, vol. 2, p. 159); and Galen, the great Greek physician of the
second century A.D. (1916, p. 85). The authority of these masters carried over into
the Middle Ages and beyond, and their recommendations were repeated by Petrus
de Abano (H. M. Brown, 1924, p. 47), Topsell (1608, p. 40), Lovell (1661, p. 243),
Jonstonus (1653, p. 24), and Redi (1665, p. 161). With the discovery of rattlesnakes in the New World, the same treatments were soon in use for their bites
(Piso, 1648, p. 41; Nieuhof, 1704, p. 15; Catesby, 1731–43, vol 2, p. 41). No doubt
the Indians, whose use of suction is discussed elsewhere (pp. 1139 and 1144), had
employed this treatment before the coming of Europeans. Other early advocates of
suction were Mead (1745, pp. 39, 42), Brand (1781, p. 297), and Barton (1793,
p. 102).

But in those days, at least for rattlesnake bite in the Americas, the miraculous curative qualities attributed to certain plants gave them precedence over the use of suction. As a matter of fact, however, it was the custom to treat snake bite with a variety of remedies all at once, and of these, suction was often one. Also, it should be pointed out that suction and bleeding were a part of the treatment of many diseases in ancient and medieval times; snake bite was a rare accident to which their application was extended. Sometimes bleeding was employed with the definite idea of withdrawing venom, but at others it was deemed more of a systemic treatment, as in the other forms of disease to which it was applied as a cure.

The extent of the scarification or incision used varied considerably at different times and places. Sometimes the scarification was more ceremonial than effective; again it might be used rather to facilitate the introduction of remedies than to withdraw venom. But often relatively deep incisions were made, and mechanical devices were used to increase the flow of blood. Cupping glasses[1] were well known to the ancients, and leeches were also employed (Nicander, 1953, pp. 89, 91; Adams, 1844–47, vol. 2, p. 159; Celsus, 1935–38, p. 115; Dioscorides in Adams, 1844–47, vol. 2, p. 159; Pliny, 1855–57, vol. 6, p. 51; book xxxii, chap. 42). More recently various piston– or rubber-bulb–operated suction devices have been employed; they are usually included as an important component of modern field-use, snake-bite kits. The most primitive of all methods—suction by mouth—I shall discuss later.

There has always been a difference of opinion as to the effectiveness of the suction treatment; it is admitted that mere scarification or deeper incision can have little value without subsequent suction to withdraw venom. It is certain that the effectiveness depends considerably on the kind of snake involved, since the character of the venom affects the rapidity of absorption into the system, or the extent to which the venom is blocked and held in the local tissues adjacent to the bite. Among others, Kellaway (1937, p. 1), Fidler *et al.* (1940, p. 363), Porges, (1953, p. 50), Shannon (1953, p. 369), and Boquet, Martirani, Favilli, and Jaques (in Buckley, editor, 1955, in press) have discussed hyaluronidase, as well as other enzymes in venom that influence the rapidity of its spread through the tissues. Suction is most likely to be efficacious in cases that involve hemorrhagic venoms, such as those of the Nearctic rattlesnakes, which cause an extensive local swelling. Fontana, who performed the first venom experiments having any real claim to scientific accuracy, was not impressed with the value of incision and suction for the bite of the European viper (1787, vol. 2, pp. 12, 15, 70; Orfila, 1818, vol. 2, p. 543; 1821, vol. 2, p. 452). However, its use continued sporadically during the period of the nineteenth century when whiskey became the foundation—a useless one—of snake-bite treatment in the United States. A few of the advocates or users of suction in actual cases were Philips (1831, p. 540), Taylor (1835, p. 540), Woodhouse (1854, p. 181), Baird (1854, p. 106), Oliveras (1858, p. 225), Marcy (1859, p. 126), Mitchell (1861, p. 291; 1874, p. 331), Gould and Pyle (1897, p. 717), and Tuten (1897, p. 896), It was a common remedy among the pioneers along the Western frontier (Terhune, 1938, p. 447; Wright and Corbett, 1940, p. 132; Bruff, 1944, p. 1176; Pickard and Buley, 1945, p. 42). But in most cases suction was used in addition to, or as an accessory of, other remedies.

---

[1] A small bell-shaped glass is heated and applied to the wound. As it cools, the reduced air volume exerts a suction effect.

In the 1920's, a more elaborate and more drastic incision–suction method was introduced and strongly advocated by Dr. Dudley Jackson of San Antonio, Texas (Jackson, 1926, p. 172; 1927, p. 203; 1929, p. 605; 1936, p. 24; Jackson and Harrison, 1928, p. 1928; Jackson and Githens, 1931, p. 1). Others who have discussed the Jackson treatment include Brymer (1928, p. 300), Bevan (1929, p. 93; 1931c, p. 12), Young (1940, p. 657), Speer (1941, p. 640), Crimmins (1946, p. 54), and Pope and Peterson (1946, p. 564). The novelty of Jackson's method involved a large number of cruciform incisions made at and around the bite, with extensions of the incised area above the bite as the swelling expanded; and also the considerable time during which suction was maintained by the use of individual rubber bulbs at each incision. In serious cases as many as 50 to 100 incisions might be made, and the suction was maintained for 20 minutes out of each hour for as many as 36 hours, or as long as the swelling continued. Besides the experience gained through the successful treatment of many rattlesnake bites (mostly by *C. atrox*) in human beings, Jackson experimented extensively with dogs, and demonstrated that the blood and lymph removed by his method contained important quantities of venom. Sometimes the flow of exudate was increased by the injection of a 1 per cent salt solution into the incisions (Allen, 1938, p. 1251).

Pope and Peterson (1946, p. 564) carried on an elaborate series of tests on dogs to determine the relative effectiveness of two elements of the Jackson method (the tourniquet and individual suction bulbs at separate cruciform incisions) and a new modification which they themselves devised, namely, a generalized suction (or, as they term it, negative pressure) applied to the injured limb. In their scheme the limb is enclosed in a container (a large-mouthed glass bottle for example) which, at the point of entrance, is sealed to the limb so that a subatmospheric pressure, or suction, can be maintained in the vessel. They experimented with negative pressures of 60 and 120 mm. of mercury below atmosphere and found that alternations between these pressures improved the results. As in the usual treatment, cruciate incisions were made in the vicinity of the point of venom injection. The authors, although admitting that the method would be applicable only to hospital treatments, with such a device as a Pavex boot, believe that the favorable results they attained justify further trials of a more generalized negative pressure.

It happened that the Jackson method was developed at the time when rattlesnake antivenin first became available in the United States. For a while there was some controversy between the advocates of the Jackson methods and those who favored antivenin, but eventually the fields of the two methods, which are not mutually exclusive, were largely composed, so that suction was advocated by those primarily favoring antivenin (Githens, 1931, p. 82; 1935b, p. 167; Allen, 1939, p. 403). Amaral (1951b, p. 1256) considers incision useful in the bites of only a few kinds of venomous snakes, of which the western diamondback (*C. atrox*) is one.

The full Jackson treatment is possible only in a hospital where extensive suction appliances, narcotics, and supportive measures are available. Incision and suction are still to be advocated in the field as a first-aid measure but to a limited extent. Staley (1939, p. 551) and Andrews and Pollard (1953, p. 394) advocate rather deep incisions involving the fang punctures. But Pope (1950, p. 6) has pointed out the dangers inherent in field incisions made by laymen, and the fact that they are seldom efficient in enhancing the extraction of venom. Stickel (1952, p. 20) advocates no incision (although a tourniquet should be applied) if a doctor can be reached within a few minutes of the accident; limited incision and suction are recommended if an hour will elapse before a doctor is at hand. He states that no deep cuts should be made in any case; there is no "venom pocket" to be cut into, as the venom is quickly absorbed and spread through the tissues. Such venom as can be withdrawn will come out with the lymph that may be extracted. Shannon (1953, p. 369; 1955, in Buckley, editor, in press) expresses somewhat the same views. It is now agreed that the abstraction of large quantities of blood is undesirable, as the patient's general condition may be weakened to an unnecessary or serious extent. Strong suction is to be avoided.

As far as possible, field incisions should be made with a sterilized razor blade or knife; at best, the risk of infection is great because of the antibactericidal action of the venom. Incisions should be longitudinal to avoid the cutting of nerves and blood vessels.

I have often been questioned as to the probable depth of venom injection as judged from the separation of the fang marks, if they are used as a guide in making incisions. I should estimate the depth at about 75 per cent of fang separation in bites by *atrox* or by *viridis* subspecies; and 80 to 90 per cent in the case of *adamanteus, ruber,* or *molossus.* However, it should be repeated that deep incisions are hazardous, not especially effective, and are unwarranted. The rapidity of absorption makes it improbable that the venom remains concentrated at the points of injection for any appreciable time, since the presence in the venom of the spreading factor, hyaluronidase, greatly expedites its dispersion through the tissues.

Although Jackson was the initiator of a regular program of multiple incisions and prolonged suction, some elements of his treatment had been advocated at earlier dates. Good (1853, p. 14) made many slits above the bite, and Stanley (1854, p. 464) applied suction cups all over a swollen arm and shoulder, and maintained the suction for several hours. Yarrow (1888, p. 431) used crosscuts.

Some folklore has crept into the making of incisions. Clavigero (1937, p. 393, but writing in 1789) said that the bite should be enlarged with lizard fangs, because they contain a counter poison—a fantastic idea. This was in Baja California. Black (1935, p. 32) says that, according to Nebraska folklore, the skin must be punctured with soapweed points to let the venom run out. In New Mexico and Texas, yucca spines are used (Dobie, 1926, p. 53; Woodhull, 1930, pp. 18, 64), as in the treatment of bites suffered by livestock.

There has been some dispute as to the danger to anyone sucking the bite of a venomous snake with his mouth. Such danger as there may be could come as a consequence of swallowing rattlesnake venom or from its entrance into a mouth sore or an ulcerated tooth. As to the first possibility, it has been known for a long time that most snake venoms are relatively innocuous when taken internally. Pliny (1855–57, vol. 5, p. 394; book xxix, chap. 18), who lived in the first century A.D., said that the venom of the asp was harmless if swallowed. Celsus (1935–38, p. 117) applied the same statement to venomous snakes in general, as did Lucan and Galen (Mead, 1702, p. 24; 1745, p. 24). Both Redi (1665, p. 160; see also Cole,

1926, p. 352) and Charas (1673, continuation, p. 59) experimented by drinking viper venom and found it harmless. Fontana (1787, vol. 1, p. 56) made a similar test with like results, but he thought large quantities might be dangerous (vol. 2, p. 322). Mead (1745, p. 22) noted that viper venom had a fiery taste and caused some swelling.

As to rattlesnake venom, Baird (1854, p. 106) swallowed the contents of a rattlesnake's gland without ill effects. Allen (1937, p. 74; Allen and Merryday, 1940, p. 238) swallowed eastern diamondback, *C. adamanteus,* venom without adverse results; and Crimmins (1934, p. 127; Davenport, 1943, p. 123) swallowed, by accident, the venom from 15 western diamondbacks (*C. atrox*) without suffering any difficulty. Valentine (1947, p. 5) mentioned a showman who regularly drank rattler venom. But Dugès (1877, p. 18) took some internally and was nauseated. Richards (1885, p. 69) discusses some of the early experiments and finds them inadequate. He believed that venom—he probably had cobra venom in mind— if taken on an empty stomach, would prove fatal. Mitchell and Reichert (1886, p. 154) stated that venom taken into an empty stomach can be dangerous; during active digestion it is harmless. Could it be that Nicander (about 150 B.C.) was right when he said that a man who sucked a bite should not have been fasting? This idea was repeated by Avicenna, Maimonides, Haly Abbas, and Rasis, although Serapion took a contrary view (Thorndike, 1923–41, vol. 3, p. 239).

Some animal experiments with rattlesnake and cobra venoms are mentioned by Harlan (1835, p. 501), Brainard (1855, p. 125), Mitchell (1868b, p. 308; 1869, p. 137), Fayrer (1872, p. 64), Fraser (1896a, p. 958), and Bonsmann (1942, p. 167). Fraser gave a cat, by mouth, the equivalent of 1,000 lethal doses of cobra venom and found that the cat was partly immunized and there were no ill effects. Fairley and Splatt (1929, p. 337) noted, when clearing snake skulls with dermestid beetles, that they would eat all the soft parts of the heads of Australian elapids except the venom glands. Beverly (1705, p. 65; 1722, p. 247) observed that no harm came to a dog that ate a squirrel which had been bitten by a rattler. But Haynes (1879, p. 484) tells of a cat that was made ill by eating parts of a rat that had been bitten.

In the opinion of Martin and Lamb (1907, p. 786), all venoms are destroyed by pancreatic digestion. Amaral (1923, p. 687; 1928c, p. 1069) believed that gastric digestion affects only a few venoms, including rattlesnake venom. Macht and Kehoe (1943, p. 31), from experiments on mice, concluded that venoms are toxic when taken internally, the elapine more than the viperine venoms. Macht (1944, p. 373) found some rattler venoms more toxic than others, when taken internally. Hayward (1884, p. 187) believed that rattlesnake venom is absorbed into the body from the intestinal tract. Such a belief was necessary to his theory of the treatment of many diseases with homeopathic doses of rattlesnake venom given by mouth. Micheel (1941, p. 170) calls attention to the difference between vegetable poisons and venoms. The former are low-weight molecular compounds and become effective upon absorption from the digestive tract. The latter are high-weight molecular compounds related to the proteins, and have a considerable sulphur content. In the stomach they are decomposed and lose their effectiveness.

If it is presumed that anyone sucking a rattlesnake bite will spit out the exudate, there is certainly no danger from the small amount of venom that might be swallowed, so that this hazard, from a practical standpoint, can be ignored. The chance of venom getting into a mouth sore or defective tooth is probably worthy of somewhat more attention; at least it has been mentioned rather frequently as involving an appreciable hazard, e.g., Moore (1951, p. 229). But even this is considered a matter of no risk by Dr. Dudley Jackson, who wrote to C. B. Perkins under date of March 26, 1934 (see also Jackson, 1936, p. 25):

> I do not believe it is dangerous to suck a wound with the mouth, even if you have cracked lips, ulcerated teeth, or ulcerated stomach. It is possible the venom would sting the lips but that is of small moment. It is barely possible it would even inflame the area if not washed out, but what is an inflamed lip among friends? The same applies to ulcerated teeth, with the exception of the danger of infection. All snake bites are infected, but infection can be treated more successfully than a snake bite. The quantity of venom that would be accidentally swallowed and reach a stomach ulcer would be of no practical danger. If we grant there is some danger in sucking the wound, it would surely be many times less for the assistants than it would be to the snake-bite victim and such a small chance should be willingly taken by any friend.

Stickel (1952, p. 21) says that a dangerous condition in the mouth would be recognized at once by pain. Some stories, probably mythical, of the dire effects of sucking a snake bite have been noted. Anon. (1766, p. 91) tells how a Negro slave sucked a rattler bite and saved his master's life, but his own head swelled to "a frightful degree" and he died. Schomburgk (1922, vol. 2, p. 104), writing of British Guiana in 1874, tells how a man who sucked a bite sustained by his son became seriously ill because he had a hollow tooth. And Rivers (1874, p. 510) mentions a man who licked venom off his own hand, after which his tongue and teeth turned black. That enough venom can get into a wound to be serious is indicated by an incident recounted by Swanson (1946a, p. 459) from the records of D. D. H. March. A woman's husband had been bitten by a fer-de-lance (*Bothrops atrox*). Her fingers had been cut by a coconut grater, and when she bathed her husband's wound, which bled profusely, she received enough venom to result fatally to herself.

Rather logically, but uselessly, it has been suggested that various presumed antidotes should be used when sucking a bite. Thus Owen (1742, p. 28) recommends that the gums and teeth be rubbed with olive oil. Topsell (1608, p. 40) suggests washing the mouth with wine, and endeavoring to keep oil in the mouth. Good (1853, p. 10) advocates salt and garlic. Collot (1924, vol. 2, p. 9) tells of using water or milk after each aspiration. Anon., with better reason, recommends washing the mouth or gargling with dilute potassium permanganate, which, indeed, can neutralize any venom with which it comes in contact, and is, besides, an antiseptic. It is to be remembered that the sucking procedure also has the objectionable feature of possibly introducing pathogenic bacteria into the wound. However, it may be doubted whether this would seriously increase the danger of contamination already resulting from the pathogenic condition of the snake's fangs and the sepsis involved in a field incision.

In this connection, several items of folklore are of interest. Clark (1928, p. 141) says it is the belief among the Negroes of Mississippi that a person with red gums can draw out venom, but if a Negro with blue gums should attempt it, disaster will follow. Hyatt (1935, p. 217) records an Illinois folklore belief that it is safe to suck a bite through a silk handkerchief. Pound (1946, p. 175) says Nebraska folklore has it that if one sucks a rattler bite, his teeth will fall out.

EXCISION OR AMPUTATION

The treatment of snake bite by elimination of the bitten part—by cutting it out or off—is an ancient remedy. It was mentioned by Pliny (1855–57, vol. 2, p. 286; book viii, chap. 35) and by Dioscorides (Adams, 1884–47, vol. 2, p. 159). It is mentioned in Chinese medicine (Read, 1934, p. 334), and was used of old in Syria (Budge, 1913, vol. 2, p. 25) and in Baja California (Baegert, 1952, p. 41, writing of 1772). It is so logical, although drastic, a remedy that it was probably tried wherever venomous snakes occur, and has been recommended and used for rattlesnake bite since colonial days, although now with decreasing frequency. Excision is mentioned by Catesby (1731–43, vol. 2, p. 41), Sloane (1734, p. 322), Winterbotham (1795, p. 406), Say (1819, p. 258), Maude (1826, p. 75), Murray (1829, p. 316), Mitchell (1860, p. 109; 1861, p. 310), Brewer (1897, p. 60), Allen (1938, p. 1252; 1939, p. 403), Bruff (1944, p. 1176), Richter (1946, p. 190; also Flanagan, 1952, p. 10), and Rollinson (1948, p. 232). It has recently been recommended for the treatment of dogs under certain conditions by Parrish (in Buckley, editor, 1955, in press).

A few cases of amputation for rattler bite may be cited: A woman who had defended her child against a rattler was bitten in the finger, and a man saved her life—so it was claimed—by cutting the finger off (Kemble, 1863, p. 168). In 1866 a man chopped off his big toe when bitten by a rattler (Halsell, 1937, p. 21). A tannery barker cut off his thumb when he was bitten by a small rattler (Schwab, 1927, p. 18). Fisher (1939, p. 49) tells the story of Three-fingered Smith of Idaho, who had seized an ax and chopped off two fingers when bitten by a rattler. One of my correspondents writes that the chief-of-party of a government surveying crew in Arizona cut off the finger of one of his men when bitten. Under date of December 26, 1948, there appeared in the newspapers the account of a young man in Mississippi who shot off the index finger of his right hand when he was struck there by a rattler.

Such experimentation as has been carried on with excision or amputation has shown that the operation must be carried out with great rapidity if any benefit is to be secured, so fast is the venom absorption (Sprengell, 1732, p. 296; Fontana, 1787, vol. 1, p. 301; vol. 2, p. 16; Russell, 1796, p. 73; Orfila, 1818, vol. 2, p. 543; 1821, vol. 2, p. 452; Fayrer, 1872, p. 102; Willson, 1908, p. 560). Modern authors who have discussed the question are Acton and Knowles (1921, p. 758) and Ganguli and Napier (1946, p. 854), who dealt primarily with cobra bite; and Allen (1938, p. 1252; 1939, p. 403; 1949, p. 616) and Keeley (1937, p. 535), whose discussions largely apply to New World pit vipers.

I think it may be concluded that the amputation of a finger or toe is never justified in the case of a bite by a Nearctic rattler, because a tourniquet, with incision and suction, will secure as beneficial a result with much less damage.

CAUTERIZATION

Cauterizing a snake-bite wound, by means of either heat or chemicals, was a drastic, painful, and damaging snake-bite remedy that had its advocates through many years, although today it is only a folklore cure restricted to remote districts. The lack of benefit from cauterization is the result of the rapid absorption of the venom into the bodily tissues—its failure to remain in a localized pocket, where it might be burned out and destroyed.

Both types of cauterization are very old. The hot-iron treatment is mentioned by Nicander (1953, p. 91; Adams, 1844–47, vol. 2, p. 159), who lived about 150 B.C. Chemical caustics are indicated among the remedies reported by Pliny, especially "nitrum," with lime and vinegar (1855–57, vol. 5, p. 518; book xxxi, chap. 46). At any rate, the origin of these treatments by burning so long antedated the knowledge of rattlesnakes by Europeans that we need give attention only to the extent of the later adoption of cauterization for rattlesnake bite, for the treatment was, from the first, a transplant from the Old World.

Cauterization with a hot iron was recommended for rattlesnake bite as early as 1648 by Piso (p. 41) as a second line of defense, if a certain herb was not to be had. Subsequently the hot-iron method was mentioned by Nieuhof (1704, p. 15), Mead (1745, p. 40), Kearsley (1766, p. 75), Winterbotham (1795, p. 406), Bosc (1803, p. 554), Say (1819, p. 258), Audubon (1827, p. 26), Marryat (1855, p. 77), Burton (1861, p. 193), Mitchell (1869, p. 138), Lanszweert (1871, p. 111), Brown (1875, p. 458), Dale (1947, p. 313), and Rollinson (1948, p. 232). Dale was writing of early days among the Midwestern settlers, and Rollinson of the cowboys of the 1870's in Wyoming. The cowboys, as a result of their frequent use of branding irons, often treated wounds with a hot iron. But hot coals were also used, according to Lawrence (1840, p. 202), Williamson (1869, p. 404), and Lanszweert (1871, p. 111).

Another method of cauterization used on the Western frontier was to sear the wound by lighting a patch of black powder placed over it (Bracht, 1849, ed. 1931, p. 48; Burton, 1861, p. 193; Crouse, 1902, p. 439; Rollins, 1922, p. 178; Rister, 1938, p. 162; Dale, 1947, p. 313). This method of cauterization for snake bite had been mentioned in a European medical treatise as early as 1792 (Moseley, p. 32). Brymer (1928, p. 307) describes a small brass or iron ring, customarily carried by miners, stockmen, herders, and Indians in frontier days, that was used to hold powder on a snake bite in order to facilitate cauterization. Powder was also recommended in Honduras (Anon., 1856, p. 597). Unexploded gunpowder, moistened and mixed with salt, was used extensively in the form of a poultice, as mentioned later in this chapter.

Good (1853, p. 10), a homeopath, favored the use of a hot coal or hot iron, but held far enough from the skin or wound so as not to cause a burn. Even a lighted cigar would suffice since, he believed, only a mild, dry heat was needed to destroy the venom.

Of the chemical caustics that were used in the treatment of rattlesnake bite, the one most often mentioned was silver nitrate (Oliveras, 1858, p. 225; Marcy, 1859, p. 130; Burton, 1861, p. 193; Bogue, 1866, p. 400; Brown, 1875, p. 458; Dugès, 1879, p. 18; Stanley, 1897, p. 38; Rister, 1938, p. 162; and Bruff, 1944, p. 1176, but written in 1849). Fontana (1787, vol. 2, p. 92) experimented with quicklime. Shapleigh (1868, p. 264) mentions nitric acid and potassium hydrate. Bosc (1803, p. 554) recommends a chemical cautery but does not specify a particular one; Lawrence (1840, p. 202) suggests an alkaline caustic. Gould and Pyle (1897, p. 717) state that carbolic acid was used in New Mexico in 1869; and Swartzwelder (1950, p. 580) mentions its having been used in Louisiana. Brown

(1875, p. 458) recommends butter of antimony (antimonic chloride). Bruff (1944, p. 1176) says that a poultice of quicklime and soap was used by the California-bound Argonauts in 1849.

The use of many of these chemical caustics for rattlesnake bite in America may have been derived originally from some of the early European medical treatises, such as that of Moseley on tropical diseases, first published in 1787. In the third edition (1792, p. 32) he recommended for snake bite (not necessarily rattlesnake bite) the following: lapis infernalis (silver nitrate), butter of antimony (antimonic chloride), corrosive sublimate (mercuric chloride), oil of vitriol (sulfuric acid), aqua fortis (nitric acid), spirit of salt (hydrochloric acid), common caustic (a mixture of calcium and sodium hydroxides), and quicklime (calcium oxide) with soap. It will be seen how completely these recommendations antedated American caustic applications for rattlesnake bite.

From the first, animal experiments with cauterization have proved disappointing, although occasionally there were sufficient indications of partial relief to confuse the situation. At least, it was shown that even a slight benefit could be obtained by the application of the cautery only if it were applied within a few minutes, at most, after the bite. Since this speed was rarely attained in the treatment of rattlesnake bite, it is probable that in almost every case so treated, the unfortunate victim suffered from this painful remedy in vain; if he recovered he would have done so without the cauterization. Unfortunately, most of the experiments showing the lack of value in cauteries were made in Europe or in India, and they do not seem to have had much weight in the United States, partly because different snakes were being dealt with, and partly because the tests, by reason of the nonquantitative methods of injecting venom into the test animals, sometimes led to conflicting results.

Fontana (1787, vol. 2, pp. 8, 92, 324, 340) performed many experiments with vipers and various chemical cauteries, and concluded that all were useless except silver nitrate. Similar tests were made by Russell in India (1796, p. 70) with both hot irons and chemicals. Other studies and comments were those of Orfila (1818, vol. 2, p. 541; 1821, vol. 2, p. 450), Whitlaw (1824, p. 258), Alexander (1855, p. 118), Mitchell (1860, p. 111; 1861, p. 292; 1868b, p. 317), and Fayrer (1872, p. 38; 1874, p. 41).

Although today most first-aid instructions specifically and strongly recommend against the use of any type of cauterization (e.g., Anon. 1951, p. 16; Stickel, 1952, p. 22), yet occasionally such a treatment is erroneously suggested (Anon., 1948a, p. 6). We may expect it to persist in folklore medicine.

As mentioned elsewhere (p. 1140), the Indians used cauterization in the treatment of rattlesnake bite, but the treatment may have been of European rather than of native origin.

Fontana (1787, vol. 2, p. 14) tried electricity, presumably a static discharge, in the treatment of viper bite but found it useless. Macht (1935, p. 520) remarked that, although venoms exposed to ultraviolet light were reduced in toxicity, the venom in a bite could not be reached because of the screen interposed by the blood serum.

The Tourniquet or Ligature

The tourniquet is a means of delaying venom absorption. It is a sort of accessory to incision and suction, since it may hold venom in tissues close to the bite where it may be withdrawn, at least in part, by suction. But, more than that, it may impede venom absorption to such an extent that the system defenses are not fatally affected. As Dr. S. Weir Mitchell has said, "The ligature obtains a reprieve." But the tourniquet, whose logic is so plainly evident to the layman, may for this very reason be misused; and it is probable that many a rattlesnake bite has ended fatally from the tourniquet rather than from the venom, without the truth ever having been suspected.

The use of a tourniquet for impeding circulation is very old, and was recommended for snake bite by Celsus, an encyclopedist of the Augustan era in Rome (1935–38, vol. 2, p. 115). Of the early British writers on natural history, the tourniquet for snake bite was mentioned by Topsell (1608, p. 40) and Lovell, (1661, p. 244). Fontana (1787, vol. 2, pp. 53–75) made the first extensive series of tests on the efficiency of the tourniquet—at least the first tests having some scientific validity—from which he concluded that it was partly effective.

For the treatment of rattlesnake bite, some Indian tribes used either actual or ceremonial ligatures before the coming of Europeans (p. 1140). The ligature was a standard element of treatment among the colonists and pioneers, particularly as an adjunct of suction. It is mentioned in such contemporary surveys of approved treatments as those of Barton (1793, p. 102), Baird (1854, p. 106), Mitchell (1861, pp. 291, 310), and Yarrow (1888, p. 431).

It might be natural to assume that so long as the venom from a bite could be restricted to some local area—a finger or a hand, for example—the patient's life would be safeguarded; therefore it would only be necessary to effect such a restriction with a tourniquet until the venom could be neutralized by some appropriate antidote. But the danger from gangrene was early recognized; it was clearly stated by Fontana in 1787 (vol. 2, pp. 26, 53, 70; Orfila, 1818, vol. 2, p. 544; 1821, vol. 2, p. 452), who said that a tourniquet should not be too tight nor be allowed to remain unloosened too long, or gangrene would result. Unfortunately, even today this danger is not given due weight, especially by laymen. Crouse (1902, p. 433) mentions a case in which an arm was lost because of gangrene, and Backus (1903, p. 692) another in which a hand was nearly lost. Brymer (1928, p. 302) refers to two leg amputations resulting from "cording." Githens (1935b, p. 167) says that out of 72 fatal cases arising from snake bite, death was caused by gangrene in 6. Keeley (1937, p. 535) mentions six fatalities of this type, and Swartzwelder (1950, p. 581) discusses some serious cases that came to his attention. Excellent recent discussions of the dangers of over-tight and over-long (in time) tourniquets are those of Milne and Milne (1952, p. 193) and Stickel (1952, p. 20). Stickel says that a tight tourniquet left on longer than eight or nine hours will certainly cause death.

As a matter of fact, the tight tourniquet is not only dangerous but unnecessary, for the venom is not diffused through the body via the blood vessels, but is carried by the lymphatics, as was early recognized by Barton (1793, p. 106) and Barry (1826, p. 88). This has been more recently discussed by Jackson (1927, p. 207;

1929, p. 606), Githens (1931, p. 85), Keeley (1937, p. 536), Young (1940, p. 657), Fidler *et al.* (1940, p. 363), Fillmore (1941, p. 312), Speer (1941, p. 640), and Shannon (1953, p. 369). Only a moderate pressure is required to restrict lymph flow and thus a tight tourniquet is not required.

Some of the criteria that have been recently suggested for judging the proper constriction of a tourniquet are these: Tighten until the pulse can barely be felt; if the limb becomes numb and cold the band is too tight (Anon., 1947b, p. 10). It should be possible to force a finger between the tourniquet and the limb (Jones, 1950, p. 613). Stickel (1952, p. 20) expresses it thus: "Tighten tourniquet until a finger can just be forced under it. This will stop circulation in lymph spaces and slow it in veins. The pulse in the affected part should not be stopped by the tourniquet but may be slightly weakened by it. It is all right for the affected part to turn pinkish, but if it becomes bluish or cold the tourniquet is too tight." Other discussions of tourniquet tightness are those of Staley (1939, p. 551), Reynolds (1952, p. 1268), and Shannon (1953, p. 370).

The tight tourniquet is still occasionally recommended in the medical handbooks (e.g., Conn, 1950, p. 703; Amaral, 1951a, p. 553; 1951b, p. 1256), but this is probably because such treatments may still be considered essential in the case of bites by snakes having venoms quite different from those of the Nearctic rattlesnakes with which this discussion is mainly concerned. I am not even sure that the loose tourniquet is to be recommended in the case of the Neotropical rattler (*C. durissus*). Dunn (1951, p. 751) has pointed out that different degrees of constriction are necessary for different kinds of venoms, and that Fayrer (1872, p. 41) may have been correct in insisting on a very tight ligature for cobra bite. The lymph-restrictive tourniquet may be adequate only for our North American viperids (including rattlers) whose venoms have pronounced local effects resulting in slow absorption. Jackson (1929, p. 606) has observed that pure fresh rattlesnake venom is too violent an irritant to animal tissue to be absorbed and eliminated, and that lymph is poured out to dilute it, thus making absorption possible. Fairley (1929a, p. 309), whose studies were concentrated on the venoms of the Australian elapids, stated that a ligature is of value only if the venom contains a thrombase which causes local clotting of tissue fluids, and thus leads to localization and the possibility of the neutralization of the venom at the site of the bite. Grassett (1933, p. 39) found, in tests of cobra venom on sheep, that the use of a tourniquet reduced the amount of antivenin required for protection by one-half to one-third. Allen (1938, p. 1251; 1939, p. 403) recommends against the use of a tourniquet in any case; and Vaz (1951, p. 50) does not favor tourniquets for *Bothrops* bites, nor do Efrati and Reif (1953, p. 1105) for the bites of Palestinian vipers. Allen's experiments that led to his conclusions do not seem to me to have been adequate in scope to justify the abandonment of this measure for rattlesnake bite in the United States, especially in view of conflicting results of other workers.

Multiple tourniquets have sometimes been recommended (Fayrer, 1872, p. 37; Menger, 1903, p. 447; Willson, 1908, p. 561).

Young (1940, p. 658) said that it was Dr. Dudley Jackson's practice to remove all field tourniquets when the patient arrived at the hospital and to place a new one of rubber tubing about one-half inch above the bite. Certainly a complete study by the hospital doctor should always be made of the position and tension in a tourniquet upon admission of the patient. Anon. (1947b, p. 10) recommends placing the tourniquet about two inches above the bite, and Holt (1950, p. 14) suggests two to three inches above the proximal margin of the swelling. Andrews and Pollard (1953, p. 394) recommend placing the tourniquet at the nearest proximal one-bone level; in the case of a finger or toe at the base of the digit; if the bite is in the hand or forearm, at mid-upper arm; if in the foot or calf, in the lower thigh; and if above the elbow or knee, in the limb proximal to the bite. At the hospital all constriction should be removed within two hours after the bite (p. 395). Keeley (1937, p. 535), Anon. (1947b, p. 10), Stickel (1952, p. 23), and Shannon (1953, p. 370) state that the ligature should be moved from time to time to keep it above the swelling.

With tight tourniquets, a periodic loosening is absolutely essential, the frequency dependent on the tightness. Some of the suggestions have been: Hutchison (1929, p. 56) 1/10–15[2]; Oertel (1929, p. 315) 0.5/10–15, (1930, p. 87) 2 to 3 sec./10–15; Hartnett (1931, p. 637) 3/20; Keeley (1937, p. 535) 1/15; Staley (1939, p. 551) 5 to 10 sec./10–15; Young (1940, p. 658) 1 or 2/10–15; Anon. (1947b, p. 10) 3/30; Conn (1950, p. 703) few seconds/5–10; Amaral (1951b, p. 1256) same; Bulger and Northrop (1951, p. 1135) 0.5/20–30; Andrews and Pollard 1/15. It is Stickel's opinion (1952, pp. 20, 23) that a tourniquet properly applied to impede only lymphatic circulation can be left without loosening for as long as 15 hours.

Broad rather than narrow tourniquets are to be preferred (Mitchell, 1861, p. 310; Stickel, 1952, p. 20). Stickel observes that rubber tourniquets often fail to maintain a constant tension. Narrow tourniquets may become buried in swellings and be forgotten. There is more danger of a ligature being too tight over a single bone, as in the upper arm, than over a double bone, as in the forearm. Corkill (1932b, p. 38) calls attention to the necessity for speed in application, probably of particular importance in the case of neurotoxic venoms and others requiring tight tourniquets. Stickel (1952, p. 20) notes that, if a person is alone when bitten, he should place a tourniquet at once, before there is a chance of his fainting.

Keeley (1937, p. 536) expresses the belief that gangrene is much more frequently the result of the tourniquet than of bacterial action, although the latter cause has been observed in some cases.

A recent newspaper report (May 13, 1953) told of a Mexican in San Diego County who made a tourniquet of the skin of the rattler that bit him.

FREEZING AND COLD PACKS

Freezing with an ethyl-chloride spray or ice has been suggested, on the theory that a low temperature will delay venom absorption and reduce the chemical activity of the venom. Crum (1906, p. 1433) was among the first to suggest ethyl chloride. Willson (1908, p. 560) thought freezing might be used when a bite on the head or body made a ligature impossible. F. M. Allen has reported on the use of freezing temperatures in three publications (1938, pp. 1248, 1252; 1939, pp. 394, 403; and 1949, p. 616) and is rather favorably disposed toward its use, as are Andrews and Pollard (1953, pp. 391, 394, 395, 396). Ganguli and

---

[2] Meaning loosening for 1 minute out of every 10 to 15 minutes.

Napier (1946, pp. 854, 859), although considering refrigeration of little service, nevertheless say that its use may be desirable in conjunction with a tourniquet when a victim arrives at the hospital, if no tourniquet had been applied in the field. Anon. (1951a, p. 32) says that an ice pack is useful when alternated with suction. Efrati and Reif (1953, p. 1107) found freezing ineffective in the treatment of the bites of various vipers in Asia Minor.

Recently there has been a greatly revived interest in the technique of treatment by chilling (called the L-C, or ligature-cryotherapy method) as a result of the activities of H. L. Stahnke in Arizona (1953a, p. 142; 1953b, p. [1]; 1954, p. 1). This method has a certain plausibility in that it is presumed to retard circulation and hence should cause a less rapid absorption of the venom, and reduce its chemical activity as well. Also, as it is a substitute for incision, it reduces the suffering of the victim, at least initially. In consequence, since the advent of Stahnke's papers, there has been a widespread uncritical advocacy of the method in nature and sportsman's magazines (e.g., Reed, 1953, p. 28; Neumann, 1953, p. 115).

In his latest instructions (1954, p. 3) Stahnke advises a temporary, tight ligature, on the nearest available one-bone site above (proximal to) the bite. Then a piece of ice should be placed on the wound, during the preparation of a suitable vessel containing crushed ice and water, in which the bitten limb may be immersed. Five to ten minutes after immersion to a depth well above the ligature, the latter is removed, and no further ligation is employed. Continuous immersion is recommended for at least 12 hours in the case of rattlesnake bite, and several days may be needed in a serious case. However, in long immersions, it is recommended that the limb be surrounded by a plastic bag, care being exercised to eliminate air spaces within the bag. The necessary length of treatment is determined by allowing the limb to warm up to see if the patient can feel the return of any venom effects. The warming is accomplished gradually by continued immersion but without the addition of ice. During the treatment, the patient is kept warm. Stahnke does not consider ice packs adequate substitutes for immersion in ice water; he also (1954, p. 11) recommends against intermittent immersion as being painful and ineffective. He does not recommend a direct application to the wound of ethyl chloride or any other refrigerant; if these are available in the field, a wet cloth should be sprayed to freeze it, after which the cloth may be applied to the bite. The cloth may be refrozen from time to time.

Shannon (1953, p. 371; also in Buckley, editor, 1955, in press) opposes the L-C treatment, and sees a serious danger in its use. He expresses the view that any external applications at the bite should be neither too hot nor too cold. He believes that the L-C treatment "should be rejected *in toto.* . . . Iced water is not only immediately painful but leaves sequelae which may result in amputation or a permanently physiologically deranged extremity" (p. 373). Shannon's opposition is in part the result of his own experiences in the treatment of soldiers subjected to freezing temperatures and icy immersions during the Korean campaigns. Certainly further experimentation and case histories are desirable before there is any widespread adoption of the L-C method. Some recent rattlesnake-bite cases treated by L-C are said to have produced permanent limb damage. More data are needed to prove any benefits from freezing; and the danger from uninterrupted applications of low temperatures for any length of time should be recognized. Shannon feels that cryotherapy is a method that cannot be tested properly by the use of small laboratory mammals, since their resistance to the damage of extremities by cold is greater than in man. It is possible that the use of ice packs in a hospital for limited periods with adequate medical guidance and control may have beneficial features without the danger attendant on the more drastic ice-water immersion. Watt and Pollard (1954, p. 369) have described a serious case involving an *adamanteus* bite, in which the patient's leg was kept in ice packs for eight days. There was no subsequent necrosis.

CURES DERIVED FROM THE SNAKE

One of the more persistent tenets of folklore medicine is that the cause of an injury will also furnish the cure, if the method of application can only be discovered. Thus, the use of snake parts to cure snake bite is both ancient and widespread.

Aristotle, in the *Historia Animalium* (Thompson, 1910, §607a), said that the body of the asp provided the only known remedy for its bite. Nicander of 150 B.C. recommended the viper's head or liver in wine (1953, p. 69). Pliny dwelt on cures of this kind at some length (1855–57, vol. 5, pp. 395, 396, 412; book xxix, chaps. 21, 22, and 38). Thorndike (1923–41, vol. 1, p. 171; vol. 2, p. 513) gives other ancient references to cures of this type. Adams (1844–47, vol. 3, p. 510) mentions some of the methods cited by Paulus Aegineta in his medical encyclopedia written in the seventh century A.D. In general, these ancient cures involved the use either of all of the snake that caused the injury (or one of the same kind) or of some part such as its head or liver, prepared in various ways, often mixed with other ingredients. The applications were sometimes external, sometimes internal.

The Old World cures of this type were carried down through the Dark Ages and emerged again in the early natural history books (Topsell, 1608, pp. 33, 43; Jonstonus, 1653, p. 24; Lovell, 1661, p. 258; Charas, 1670b, pp. 154, 176). Some of the modern writers who have dealt with this phase of medical folklore are Halliday (1924, pp. 133, 135), Robin (1932, p. 15), and Dawson (1935, p. 206).

Charas, who had at least some pretentions to the new methods of science, was one of the last of the workers to give any credence to cures of this type; in fact, he went so far as to invent improvements (so he thought) in the disease remedies derived from the bodies of venomous snakes, including cures for their bites. Afterward, tests by Fontana (1787, vol. 2, pp. 9, 13; see also Orfila, 1818, vol. 2, p. 543; 1821, vol. 2, p. 451) and Fayrer (1872, pp. 38, 121) showed such remedies to be useless. But they are still widespread, as for example, in Syria (Budge, 1913, vol. 2, p. 25), Iraq (Corkill, 1932a, p. 619), the Kalahari Desert in Africa (Farini, 1886, pp. 367, 375, 452), Bolivia (Fawcett, 1953, p. 196), and China (Read, 1934, p. 341). The discussion by Schlegel (1843, p. 105) will also be found of interest.

I have elsewhere (p. 1137) discussed the cures of this type employed by the American Indians for the treatment of rattlesnake bite. It is difficult to determine to what extent these methods were European transplants brought in by the whites, but it is probable that at least some of those encountered by ethnologists among the more isolated tribes of the Southwest were indigenous.

Whether these cures were derived from European sources or from the Indians with whom they came in contact, the early explorers and emigrants used snake parts for the cure of rattlesnake bites, and these prescriptions still persist as folklore cures in many sections of the United States and elsewhere in the Americas. Piso (1648, p. 41) prescribed the rattler's head, mashed and applied to the wound; this was in Brazil. Josselyn (1672, p. 78; 1675, p. 114), in New England, recommended that the rattler's heart be swallowed while fresh, or be dried and pulverized and taken in wine or beer; and that its liver be bruised and applied to the bite. Hennepin (1698, vol. 2, pp. 22, 117) reports a case of treatment with viper salt, clearly an imported European idea. Nieuhof (1704, p. 15) repeated Piso's remedy. According to Kalm (1752–53, p. 187), rattlesnake oil was found beneficial. Carver (1778, p. 483) prescribed rattler fat rubbed into the bite. Kercheval (1833, p. 366) and Harlan (1835, p. 497) reported the use of fresh rattlesnake flesh applied to the bite. Koscicky (1878, p. 247) mentions the use in Venezuela of rattler gall mixed with spirits. Daniels and Stevans (1903, vol. 1, p. 347) report the use of a rattlesnake skin, steeped in vinegar and bound to the bite to draw out the venom.

Coming to present-day folklore remedies in the United States, we have these methods reported: Kentucky: Bind the liver and intestines of the guilty snake to the bite (Thomas and Thomas, 1920, p. 115). Mississippi Negro folklore: The application to the bite of a piece of the snake's body, on the theory that it will reabsorb the venom (Clark, 1928, p. 141). Oklahoma: Apply the warm flesh of the rattler, or oil prepared from its fat, to the bite (Smith, 1929, p. 76; 1930a, p. 84). Texas, Mexican folk-cure: Cut the snake's body into pieces and apply to the wound to draw the venom (Woodhull, 1930, p. 64); or let the victim bite off the head of the offending snake (Nixon, 1946, p. 19). Ozark Mountains: Bind a piece of the rattler's flesh to the wound; but always kill the snake and burn it before applying any treatment (Randolph, 1931, p. 100; 1947, p. 158). Iowa: Cut the snake's body in pieces and bind them to the wound (Stout, 1936, p. 189). Adams County, Illinois: Kill the snake and wrap it around the bite, or use its entrails (Hyatt, 1935, p. 218). Nebraska: Cut the rattler into three-inch pieces, split and apply to the bite (Black, 1935, p. 32; Pound, 1946, p. 166). Merely to kill the snake and cut it in pieces, without binding to the wound, will also suffice; or the skin may be used to draw the poison (Pound, 1946, pp. 166–7). Tennessee: Drink rattler oil (Redfield, 1937, p. 15); or bind a piece of the snake to the bite (McGlasson, 1941, p. 15). Texas Negroes of about 1870: Bind the heart of the snake to the bite (Scarbrough, 1941, p. 10). New Mexico, Spanish-speaking people: Take rattlesnake oil, or apply the warm flesh of the snake to the bite to draw out the venom (Curtin, 1947, p. 15). When bitten by a rattler, grab the snake by the head and tail, and bite it in the middle, whereupon the poison in the person's mouth will kill the snake and cure the bite (Baylor, 1947, p. 150).

The Split-Chicken Treatment

One of the most widespread and uniform of the folklore cures for snake bite is that which may be termed the split-chicken remedy, for chickens were most often used, although other animals have had some acceptance. In this treatment, a live chicken is split or slit and the bleeding flesh is immediately applied to the snake bite as a poultice. According to popular belief, the chicken's flesh should turn green, or its comb blue, from the venom that it draws from the wound, whereupon another chicken should be applied until the abnormal color no longer appears, after which the patient is assumed to be cured. In some forms of treatment the chicken, or other animal, is killed in preparing it for application; in others the flesh is bared without a fatal injury. Needless to say, not the slightest benefit has ever been shown to result from this cruel method, yet it is still practiced in some backwoods areas. It is not to be considered merely a quaint, harmless custom, for its use can dangerously delay the application of really effective first-aid measures.

Some of the ancient, prerattlesnake references to the use of this type of treatment for snake bite are: Pliny (1855–57, vol. 5, p. 392; book xxix, chap. 15—split mouse; p. 400, xxix, chap. 25—split chicken; p. 400, xxix, chap. 26—split pigeon or swallow); Celsus (1935–38, p. 117, but dating from about 1 A.D.—split chicken, kid, or lamb); Galen (about 160 A.D., see Adams, 1844–47, vol. 2, p. 158); Alsaharavius (about 975 A.D., see Adams, 1844–47, vol. 2, p. 162); Maimonides (about 1200 A.D.; see Wootton, 1910, vol. 1, p. 112); Topsell (1608, pp. 40, 301; 1658, p. 621); and Lovell (1661, p. 245).

The earliest reference that I have found to the split-chicken method as having been applied to a rattlesnake bite is Budd (1685, p. 35). He mentions its use in a case in Pennsylvania or New Jersey. The split-chicken type of treatment has been reported used in the following areas or groups: New York (Evers, 1951, p. 110—Catskill Mountains); Pennsylvania (Fogel, 1915, p. 291; Brendle and Unger, 1935, p. 202—Pennsylvania Dutch); Illinois (Hyatt, 1935, p. 217); Michigan, Illinois, and Missouri (Bergen, 1899, p. 69); Southern Plains (Rister, 1938, p. 163); Nebraska (Black, 1935, p. 33; Pound, 1946, p. 167); Virginia (Speck, Hassrick, and Carpenter, 1942, p. 37—Rappahannock Indians; Martin, 1947, p. 184—Blue Ridge Mountains); North Carolina (Speck, 1944, p. 48—Catawba Indians); Virginia to Florida (Smiley, 1919, p. 379); Virginia (Beck, 1952, p. 149); Kentucky (Thomas and Thomas, 1920, p. 114); Tennessee (O'Dell, 1944, p. 4); Mississippi (Clark, 1928, p. 141); Louisiana (Peake, 1860–1, p. 51; Swartzwelder, 1950, p. 580); Arkansas (Webber, 1951, p. 13); Texas (Dobie, 1926, p. 52—Mexicans; Woodhull, 1930, p. 64); and New Mexico (Curtin, 1947, p. 81—Mexicans). Some other American references are Breintal, 1748, p. 144; Say, 1819, p. 259; Burton, 1861, p. 193; Bailey, 1876, p. 404; Yarrow, 1888, p. 431; Hoffman, 1894, p. 128; and Powell, 1918, p. 329.

In other parts of the world, this remedy is used in such widely separated places as Devonshire, England, and among the Hottentots of Africa (Black, 1883, p. 45; Radford and Radford, 1947, p. 12); in India (Thurston, 1912, p. 95); and in Syria (Budge, 1913, vol. 2, p. 687).

In the United States, for rattlesnake bite, as was the case in the treatment of the bites of venomous snakes in the Mediterranean countries, a variety of animals other than chickens were or are used, such as toads or frogs (Burton, 1861, p. 193; Fogel, 1915, p. 291; McGlasson, 1941, p. 15; Speck, Hassrick, and Carpenter, 1942, p. 37; O'Dell, 1944, p. 4; Buley, 1950, vol. 1, p. 267); rabbits (Woodhull, 1930, p. 64); and a turkey buzzard crop (Wied-Neuwied, 1843, p. 347). In the cattle country, a cow might be killed, the abdominal cavity split, and the injured arm or leg of the human sufferer plunged in and left until the body of the cow became cold (Woodhull, 1930, p. 17; Black, 1935, p. 32; Pound, 1946, p. 168).

Here is an account of a split-chicken cure from one of my correspondents in Montana. It also introduces the folklore of the annual recurrence of symptoms:

> I know of one instance of a 12-year-old boy who chased a rattler into a hole and attempted to make a tail catch. He was bitten on the wrist. We rushed him to his home. His father happened to be a farmer. We cut a live chicken in halves, applied these to the bite till the doctor arrived, who was called immediately. The doc said we saved the lad's life. This lad's hand stopped growing, shriveled, and almost every year in dog days, July and August, he has light fits, when he will froth at the mouth.

In Marjorie K. Rawlings' novel *The Yearling* (1950, p. 133) a man, when bitten by a diamondback, shoots a deer and claps the warm liver and heart to the wound, thus saving his life. Presumably this is an item of Florida folklore. It is a method also found in Mexican folklore according to Dobie (1926, p. 52). Richter (1946, p. 193; Flanagan, 1952, p. 10) mentions an early folklore cure in the Middle West in which the bloody skin of a freshly killed skunk or black cat was applied to a bite.

Some variations of the split-chicken remedy have been reported. Hyatt (1935, p. 217) writes that a chicken wing might be used; another informant stated that the chicken must be black (p. 218), as is also mentioned by Speck *et al.* (1942, p. 37), who likewise remarked that the chicken must be carefully buried after the treatment. Beck (1952, p. 149) said that, according to the folklore of Rappahannock County, Virginia, a decapitated black rooster must be used, and if the treatment were successful all its feathers would fall out. Curtin (1947, p. 81) reports that the Mexicans around Santa Fe, New Mexico, believe that several chickens (usually three) must be used, and the cure is complete when a chicken survives. Pound (1946, p. 167) says that in Nebraska as many as 12 chickens may be used in a single case.

Say (1819, p. 259) doubted the value of the split-chicken treatment; and Mitchell (1861, p. 295), the great expert of his day on rattlesnake bite, said it was unworthy of serious consideration and did not even merit testing. Curiously enough, H. C. Yarrow, the U. S. Army surgeon and herpetologist, seemed to consider it worth a trial in extreme cases as late as 1888 (p. 431).

Milk

Milk is an ancient remedy for snake bite; it dates back to Pliny (1855–57, vol. 5, p. 286; book xxviii, chap. 33). Both cow's milk (Lovell, 1661, p. 260) and goat's milk (p. 258) were used; the application was either external, in the form of a poultice, or as a drink. It seems never to have been particularly popular in the treatment of rattlesnake bite, although Barton (1793, p. 109) said it was used in the Western settlements of his day. It was also mentioned by Moore (1828, p. 342). Randolph (1947, p. 102) says that snakeweed boiled in sweet milk is one of the Ozark folklore cures. In a recent West Virginia case reported in the press, the victim was given milk to drink. As liquids in quantity are recommended in the modern treatment of rattlesnake bite, milk taken internally may be beneficial, but there is nothing to recommend its external application. Mauyduyt

(1774, p. 388) reported a Louisiana belief that a person, if bitten by a rattler soon after having drunk milk, would quickly die.

MISCELLANEOUS ANIMAL PRODUCTS

Several folklore treatments that apply animal products to rattlesnake bite are of Old World derivation. Among these is the saliva of a fasting man (Piso, 1648, p. 41), which is mentioned by Pliny (1855–57, vol. 5, p. 288; book xxviii, chap. 7). A poultice of melted cheese, said by Curtin (1947, p. 169) to be used by the Spanish-speaking people of New Mexico for rattler bite, also dates back to Pliny (vol. 5, p. 330; book xxviii, chap. 42). Another is eggs in various forms; Swartz-welder (1950, p. 580) mentions this as a Louisiana folklore treatment, and Loomis (1949, p. 119) says it was used in California in the 1850's. It is recorded in Pliny (vol. 5, p. 386; book xxix, chap. 11) and by Lovell (1661, p. 250).

The scrapings of a crocodile's tooth were used for rattlesnake bite both in Baja California in 1772 (Baegert, 1952, p. 11) and in Paraguay in 1784 (Dobrizhoffer, 1822, vol. 2, p. 308). Although Pliny suggested powdered human teeth (1855–57, vol. 5, p. 291; book xxviii, chap. 8) and fails to mention this use of crocodile teeth— but he does describe nineteen other remedies derived from crocodiles—we may be sure that so unusual a cure, noted in such widely separated places as Paraguay and Baja California (where there are no crocodiles), must have had a common European origin. Powdered crawfish were used near Niagara Falls in the late 1700's (Guillet, 1933, p. 16), and mosquito bites were also suggested (Hoit, 1844, p. 243).

Treatments that involve various kinds of excrement are of ancient origin (Pliny, 1855–57, vol. 5, pp. 330, 392; book xxviii, chap. 42, book xxix, chap. 15). They were mentioned in some of the earliest accounts of the rattlesnake (Hernández 1615, fol. 192ᵛ; 1628, p. 330; Nieremberg, 1635, p. 269) as well as in some current folk cures (Pound, 1946, p. 167).

Anon. (1873, p. 1) tells a tall tale—it is related with tongue in cheek—of a woman who was cured of the bite of a "side-wiper" by putting in her ear the blood squirted from the eye of a horned toad. This may have been one of the earliest mentions of the fact of natural history that some horned toads, when annoyed, eject a thin stream of blood from the eyes (Klauber, 1939a, p. 93).

BOTANICAL CURES AND VEGETABLE PRODUCTS

In colonial days and for a time thereafter, various plant cures for rattlesnake bite were the most popular and generally used of all treatments. Sometimes extracts or infusions of the leaves or roots were given internally; sometimes poultices or fomentations were applied; often both methods were used together. Although many of these cures were attributed to the Indians, who were supposed to have that deep knowledge of nature often attributed to primitive people, others were derived from European and Asiatic lore, for plant cures for snake bite had an extensive place in ancient and medieval pharmacology. Nicander, in about 150 B.C. listed many of these plants (1953, pp. 61–73). Pliny, in his great *Natural History,* records no less than 196 ways in which plant preparations could be used to cure snake bite; probably at least a hundred different plants were involved. Many plants are contradictorily stated by him to be the best or the most effective of all cures. Gesner (1587, fol. 15^v–17^v) has listed some 183 plant cures assembled from Pliny, Dioscorides, and Avicenna.

All of these plant cures had their reputations founded on the belief that where there is a danger the Almighty has provided a remedy, if man has the piety and wit to find it. But none of these supposed remedies has ever been shown to have the slightest beneficial effect, except a few that may have had some incidental value as stimulants, narcotics, or antiseptics. Certainly none has remotely approached being a specific antidote for the bite of a rattlesnake or any other snake, as was so often claimed by their proponents. Like all folklore treatments, their reputations were gained in the cure of cases in which there never was any danger to the patient, either because he had been bitten by a harmless snake, because no venom had been injected, or because of one of the many other variables that affect the severity of snake bite, as listed in chapter 11.

Of the hundreds of plants advocated by Pliny and his contemporaries, many cannot be recognized from his names and descriptions, even by professional botanists. Of those that can, some are still employed in folklore cures, such as onions, garlic, rue, ash, and others. Some were to be taken internally, others externally. Often they were to be mixed with such substances as wine, vinegar, honey, or grease.

As soon as reports of rattlesnakes began to come back from the New World, stories of infallible plant cures were included, usually crediting the remedies to the natives (Hernández, 1615, fol. 192^v; 1628, p. 330; Higgeson, 1630, p. 12; Wood, 1634, p. 47; Nieremberg, 1635, p. 269; Lechford, 1642, p. 47; Piso, 1648, p. 41; Van der Donck, 1649 [ed. 1909, p. 298]; Clarke, 1670, p. 42; Montanus, 1671 [ed. 1851, p. 79]; Grew, 1681, p. 227; Clayton, 1693, p. 133). Usually the terms rattlesnake weed or rattlesnake root were applied to these plants. Ashe (1682, p. 145 of 1911 ed.) described three kinds of rattlesnake root.

In the eighteenth century the accounts were much the same. Rattlesnake bite was extremely dangerous, it was reported, but fortunately various herbs wrought certain and immediate cures. These were known to the Indians, who sometimes would, but at other times would not, divulge them to the white man. Through a kindly Providence the particular plant needed was always available where rattlesnakes were found. Elsewhere (p. 1127) I have discussed at some length the plant cures used by, or attributed to, the Indians. Some additional eighteenth-century references to plant cures, not elaborated in the chapter on Indian treatment, are these: Beverly, 1705, book 2, p. 23; Byrd, 1921, pp. 188, 199 (from letters written in 1706 and 1741); Mather, 1714, p. 64 (see also Botkin, 1947, p. 286); Dudley, 1723, p. 295; Clayton, 1744, p. 153; Kalm, 1752–53, p. 188; Jefferys, 1760, part 1, p. 158; Charlevoix, 1761, vol. 2, p. 17; Smith, 1765, p. 509; Witt, 1768, p. 10; Goldsmith, 1774, vol. 7, p. 212; Smyth, 1784, vol. 1, p. 109; Brand, 1781, p. 300; Anburey, 1789, p. 231; La Rochefoucault-Liancourt, 1799, p. 137.

A few of the reports are worthy of comment. Byrd wrote in 1741 that he regretted that the root for curing rattler bite lost its effectiveness in crossing the ocean. Evidently the skeptical Britishers had tested its reputed effectiveness. Kalm gives a very complete list of the plants then in use; he was a competent botanist so that they may be recognized. Jefferys made two comments of interest to the delver in folklore: first that the plant that constituted a cure sounded like a rattler's rattle when shaken (evidently one of the plants having bladderlike pods and loose seeds, currently called rattleweeds); and secondly that the plant cure is always available near where rattlesnakes are found (see also Le Page du Pratz, 1774, p. 269; Weld, 1800, p. 150). Witt (1768, p. 10) claimed that his form of rattlesnake root (*Prenanthes*) would cure even if the patient had been bitten several days before, provided the weather had been moderate in the meantime. La Rochefoucault-Liancourt made the point that it was so easy to cure rattlesnake bite with rattlesnake root that the bite could not be so dangerous as reported in Europe. Bigelow (1817–20, vol. 3, p. 2) drew the same conclusion from the number of different plants that would cure rattler bite, according to the beliefs of that time.

Some nineteenth-century accounts of the use of plants in treating rattlesnake bite, including some case reports, are given in the following citations: Bosc, 1803, p. 554; Michaux, 1805, p. 43; Haynesworth, 1808, p. 57; Schoolcraft, 1821, p. 326; Hubble, 1825, p. 484; Maude, 1826, p. 77; Moore, 1828, p. 342; Chateaubriand, 1828, vol. 1, p. 178; Kercheval, 1833, p. 367; Williams, 1834, p. 310; Wetmore, 1837, p. 159; Parker, 1840, p. 57; Lawrence, 1840, p. 202; Bruff, 1849 (ed. 1944, p. 1176); Baird, 1854, p. 106; Whiting, 1854, p. 258; Brainard, 1855, p. 133; Logan, 1859, p. 111; Burton, 1861, p. 193; Lanman, 1863, p. 230; Irwin, 1861, p. 89; Staples, 1865, p. 279; Lanszweert, 1871, p. 111; Mitchell, 1874, p. 331; Brown, 1875, pp. 86, 115, 127; Dugès, 1877, p. 21; Jenkins, 1878, p. 64; Guild, 1878, p. 11; Kennedy, 1879, p. 328; Shuler, 1881, p. 292; O'Reilly, 1889, p. 144; Hoffman, 1894, p. 128. Their very number is an indication of the popularity and persistence of this type of treatment. In the actual case reports given by these authors, two facts stand out: many of the reports are based on hearsay; and plants gradually ceased to be the sole remedies applied—more often they were one of several remedies applied together.

Some indication of the extent to which plants have recently been used in folk-lore cures in the United States is evident from the following citations: Pennsylvania Germans (Brendle and Unger, 1935, p. 200), Pennsylvania pioneers (Wright and Corbett, 1940, p. 132), Maryland (Whitney and Bullock, 1925, p. 87), Tennessee (McGlasson, 1941, p. 15), Arkansas (Randolph, 1947, p. 102), Midwestern pioneers (Pickard and Buley, 1945, p. 42), Indiana (Terhune, 1938, p. 447; Brewster, 1939, p. 38), Illinois (Hyatt, 1935, p. 218), Nebraska (Black, 1935, p. 32; Pound, 1946, p. 166), Oklahoma (Smith, 1929, p. 76; 1930a, p. 84), Texas (Bourke, 1894, p. 140; Crouse, 1902, p. 439; Dobie, 1926, p. 52; Woodhull, 1930, p. 64; Dodson, 1932, p. 85), New Mexico (Curtin, 1947, pp. 15, 33, 34, 42, 80, 198), Southwest (Yarrow, 1888, p. 370), California (Curtin, 1947, p. 81), Northwestern pioneers (Buley, 1950, vol. 1, p. 260). Some South American plant references are those of Orfila (1818, vol. 2, p. 533; 1821, vol. 2, p. 443), Dobrizhoffer (1822, vol. 2, pp. 306, 310, but first published in 1784), Baillie (1849, p. 179), and Mitchell (1861, p. 302).

There was, of course, a great diversity in the plants recommended, sometimes owing to the lack of botanical knowledge upon the part of the reporters, but more often because a large number of different plants actually gained reputations as rattlesnake-bite remedies. Most frequently mentioned were plants of the genera *Polygala, Liatris, Asclepias, Plantago, Prenanthes, Fraxinus, Alisma, Bidens, Crotalaria, Hieracium, Astragalus, Aristolochia, Silene, Botrychium, Spiranthes,*

Polygonatum, Brauneria, Lilium, Daucus, and *Euphorbia.* Michaux (1805, p. 43) observed that most of the plants suggested as cures for rattlesnake bite were succulents.

Many of the New World plant remedies for snake bite belonged to the same genera as those used for the same purpose in Europe in pre-Columbian times. Of the 20 genera listed above, 17 were reported as being used by the Indians. To account for this correlation we may choose one of three causal factors: coincidence; a real curative value, independently discovered; or a common origin— that is, the cures were not of Indian selection, but were brought over by the explorers and colonists, although attributed to the Indians, or, conversely, were adopted by the whites from the Indians. It is my belief that, to whatever extent the American cures were related to those used in Europe, the remedy was really of European rather than Indian selection. However, it was undoubtedly true that some of the plants had been used by the Indians before the coming of the Caucasians. If these were congeneric with the European cures, it was the result of coincidence, rather than any real remedial value independently discovered by the two peoples.

When the Indian cures failed, the cause was usually attributed by them to some infringement of ceremonial detail, for their treatments often had a mystical basis. The whites were more likely to cite some botanical misidentification. Logan (1859, p. 111) said that the Indians were successful in their use of plant remedies— a matter of repute rather than fact—because they always had the remedies ready for use, whereas the whites waited too long to secure and apply them. Kercheval (1833, p. 367) told of two women who almost lost their lives by taking the wrong plant by mistake, the remedy being worse than the bite.

The value of plants fell into disrepute as methods of animal experimentation were perfected. Say (1819, p. 258) doubted their value and placed his confidence in other remedies. The guaco (or huaco) plant, so highly esteemed in tropical America, was tested early and found ineffective (Anon. 1856, p. 597). Fayrer (1872, pp. 38, 144) tested various plant cures and plant drugs popular in India, with adverse results.

Quinine, camphor, yeast, and other plant derivatives have occasionally been tried for rattlesnake bite (Oliveras, 1858, p. 225; Lanszweert, 1871, p. 111; Lacombe, 1851, p. 292; Swanson, 1952, p. 182). Some plants that had a place in the pharmacopeia for other purposes, and hence were known to physicians, were prescribed for snake bite after the use of plants based entirely on folklore had declined. Among these was echinacea, prepared from the roots of the purple coneflower. This was a staple remedy in Texas in the 1920's (Brymer, 1928, p. 306).

Caesar's Cure.—One of the most famous and romantic of the early plant cures for rattlesnake bite was Caesar's cure. Caesar was a Negro slave in Carolina in 1750. Sometime prior to that time he had devised an antidote for poisons and another for rattlesnake bite. These he agreed to divulge for his freedom and a monetary reward. Tests also were agreed upon. Evidently the tests proved satisfactory, for, in the *Carolina Gazette* of May 9, 1750, the details of the remedy were published, as commanded by the Commons House of Assembly, which had bought Caesar's freedom and awarded him a pension of £100 annually for life. The *Gazette* article was shortly after given wide publicity in the *Gentleman's Magazine* in London (Anon., 1750, pp. 342–43).

Plantain roots (*Plantago*) and horehound (*Marrubium*) were the bases of both the poison antidote and the rattlesnake remedy. For the bite, an infusion of these plants was to be taken internally, and a leaf of tobacco moistened with rum was applied to the bite. Caesar's antidote, which is quite worthless for both purposes for which it was devised, does not differ greatly from other botanical cures popular in the eighteenth century. Plantain roots of various species were used in several of the formulas of those days.

The test, by which Caesar proved the efficacy of his cure to the legislators, seems to have been made by him and some of his fellow slaves. They jumped into a tub of large rattlers and allowed themselves to be bitten. They had no fear because of their confidence in Caesar's cure. They were rewarded with a bottle of rum. We may guess that the rattlers had been defanged or milked before the test.

Whitlaw (1824, p. 257) reported that he tested the cure on animals and that it failed to work. Later he was told by a doctor in Augusta, Georgia, who claimed to have cured 150 cases with Caesar's remedy, some after mortification had set in, that he, Whitlaw, had been using the wrong plant, the water plantain (*Alisma*) being the proper one. It was pointed out to him in a swamp. It is not clear just how successful he was after his error had been remedied. Whitlaw wrote from London, whither he had moved; evidently he had little opportunity to try the water plantain on rattler bites there.

Crandall and Gannett (1945, p. 179) found a manuscript copy of Caesar's cure in an old book of records in New York that dated back to the early 1800's. They apparently did not recognize its derivation, thinking it an original folklore remedy. Others who have mentioned Caesar's cure were Smyth (1784, vol. 1, p. 109), Ettwein (1848, p. 38, but written in 1788), La Rochefoucault-Liancourt (1799, p. 595), Harlan (1835, p. 491), Nelson (1894, p. 48), Medden (1930, p. 75), Wright (1939, p. 151), and Gordon (1949, p. 422).

Even before Caesar, another colonial had been rewarded for a rattlesnake-bite cure. In 1741, one Palmer Goulding in New England petitioned for wild lands, in return for divulging a new cure for snake bite and other sores and diseases. Proof of the efficacy of his remedy was required and this he was apparently able to furnish. He was awarded 200 acres of land, on condition that he "subdue" 6 acres within 3 years (Trask, 1892, p. 215).

Onions and Garlic.—Onions and garlic were important remedies for snake bite in the ancient and medieval worlds; they were also employed as repellents. Sometimes the onions were applied in poultices, sometimes they were eaten (Dioscorides, in Adams, 1844–47, vol. 2, p. 159; Maimonides in Wootton, 1910, vol. 1, p. 112; Petrus de Abano, *circa* 1300, in Brown, 1924, p. 47; Topsell, 1608, p. 302; Lovell, 1661, pp. 245, 258). They were applied in China (Read, 1934, p. 340) and in the Sudan (Corkill, 1949, p. 615). The spread of their use to the United States might well have been expected, and they were reported to have been tried as early as 1753 (Dumont, p. 110) in Louisiana. They later became a regular folklore cure. Sometimes they are made into a poultice, or a fresh onion may be cut and held against the wound. It is the belief that when the onion turns green it is actively abstracting the venom, and a fresh one should be applied from time to time. They were used by cowboys (Stanley, 1897, p. 38), in early Pennsylvania (Tome, 1928, p. 117; Swanson, 1952, p. 182), in New Mexico (Curtin, 1930, p. 188; 1947, pp. 18, 54), by Pennsylvania Germans (Brendle and Unger, 1935, p. 201), in Tennessee (McGlasson, 1941, p. 15), by Midwestern pioneers (Pickard and Buley, 1945, p. 42), by California miners in the gold-rush days (Loomis, 1949, p. 119), and by "old" Northwestern pioneers (Buley, 1950, vol. 1, p. 260).

Tobacco.—An early and widespread snake-bite cure in the United States was tobacco. In the days when the chewing of tobacco was a much more prevalent habit than today, freshly chewed tobacco became a standard first-aid poultice for cuts and bruises, and the extension to snake bite was inevitable. Occasionally it was mixed with gunpowder (Kalm, 1752–53, p. 193). Sometimes strong tobacco juice was taken internally for rattlesnake bite, and if the patient failed to get sick from so nauseating a drink, this was taken as proof of its effectiveness, just as a failure to get drunk proved the efficacy of whiskey (Peake, 1860–61, p. 50; Grant, 1871, p. 459). Tobacco was one of the earliest of the recommended cures for rattlesnake bite, since it dates back to 1615 (Hernández, fol. 192^v).

Tobacco poultices have been mentioned as folklore remedies in Oklahoma (Smith, 1929, p. 76; 1930a, p. 84), Arkansas (Randolph, 1931, p. 99), Illinois (Hyatt, 1935, p. 218), Nebraska (Black, 1935, p. 32; Pound, 1946, p. 167), New Mexico (Curtin, 1947, p. 166), Texas (Duval, 1870, p. 11), Tennessee (McGlasson, 1941, p. 15), Louisiana (Swartzwelder, 1950, p. 580), and New York (Evers, 1951, p. 112). Pickard and Buley (1945, p. 42) report tobacco, mixed with salt, as a standard remedy of the Midwestern pioneer. In early California, the sheep-herders used equal parts of tobacco, salt, and onion (Cleland, 1941, p. 189). Dobrizhoffer (1822, vol. 2, p. 307, but first published in 1784) said the natives in Paraguay blew tobacco smoke into a snake-bite wound, put on a tobacco poultice, and took a drink of the juice. Anon. (1908b, p. 132) reports a Florida case in which a man bitten by a rattler may have died from the remedy of four cups of water in which tobacco had been steeped.

Indigo.—Indigo, a preparation derived from plants of the genus *Indigofera*, was sometimes used for rattlesnake bite a century or so ago. It was often one of the ingredients of complex poultices, as, for example, mixed with rattler flesh and salt (Maude, 1826, p. 75), with iodine (Baird, 1854, p. 106), with camphor gum and grain alcohol (Grieve, 1908, p. 75), and with sorrel (Brendle and Unger, 1935, p. 201), the last a folklore cure of the Pennsylvania Germans. It appears that powdered indigo, in the form of bluing, mixed with salt, was a favorite remedy of the cowboys in certain areas of the Southwest (Marcy, 1859, p. 129; Wheatley, 1886, p. 523; Stanley, 1897, p. 38; Rister, 1938, p. 162). Indigo, as a snake-bite cure, is also mentioned in the Chinese pharmacopeia (Read, 1934, p. 340).

Vinegar.—Vinegar, usually in combination with some plant, was often used in ancient and medieval medicine. Pliny lists 18 plants together with which it may be applied for the treatment of snake bite. It seems never to have been popular for the cure of rattlesnake bite, although a salt-vinegar combination is reported by Trowbridge (1848, p. 204). Swartzwelder (1950, p. 581) mentions another folk-lore mixture taken internally, including lard, vinegar, boiled tobacco juice, qui-nine, and whiskey. This was in Louisiana.

Echinacea.—One of the few vegetable remedies used by the Indians in the treat-ment of rattlesnake bite that retained a place in the modern pharmacopeia, at least until recent times, was echinacea, a derivative of the root of the coneflower (*Echinacea*). According to Brymer (1928, p. 306), who favored its use, it was pre-scribed extensively by physicians in southwestern Texas. It was applied both orally and by hypodermic. As a remedy in conditions other than snake bite, it was used for septicemia and boils.

Turpentine.—Turpentine was first tested for efficacy in snake bite by Fontana (1787, vol. 2, p. 9), who decided that it might be of some benefit. Today it is thought to be of no value whatever, but it is still a folklore cure in the country districts where it is so often used in cuts. One may assume that the burning pain that turpentine causes may give the victim—or, what is more important, his relatives—the feeling that something powerful is working for his good. It has recently been reported as a folklore cure for rattlesnake bite, generally mixed with camphor or gunpowder, in Texas (Woodhull, 1930, p. 63), among the Penn-sylvania Germans (Brendle and Unger, 1935, p. 201), in Nebraska (Black, 1935, p. 33; Pound, 1946, p. 167), in Tennessee (McGlasson, 1941, p. 15), and in Louisi-ana (Swartzwelder, 1950, p. 580). I was recently sent the report of a case in West Virginia treated with turpentine.

Hot pitch or tar, probably of vegetable origin, was used to treat snake bites by the ancients (Pliny, 1855–57, vol. 5, p. 17; book xxiv, chap. 23; Topsell, 1608, p. 41; Lovell, 1661, p. 247) but does not seem to have been tried in this country for rattlesnake bite.

Alcohol.—Alcohol, especially whiskey, was for a long time the most generally accepted remedy for rattlesnake bite. It differed from many of the other remedies that are no longer recognized as having value, in that it was not only accepted by laymen, but by the medical fraternity as well.

The use of whiskey for rattlesnake bite was the source of innumerable stories and vaudeville gags, particularly during the prohibition era. But the effect of its use was anything but a joke. Without doubt many a fatality was caused by the large quantities of whiskey given to the victim under the mistaken belief that no amount of alcohol could cause injury to a person who had been bitten by a rattler. There were several correlated theories that were basic to the treatment. For alcohol was not given primarily as a stimulant; on the contrary, it was believed to be a specific antidote for snake bite and particularly rattlesnake bite. It sought out the venom in the body and destroyed or neutralized it wherever it might be, whether in the blood or tissues. So antagonistic were these two substances—venom and alcohol—that neither could ever exhibit its characteristic effects until it had gained superiority over, or suppressed, the other. Thus it was thought that a person exhibiting any snake-bite symptoms was insufficiently supplied with alco-hol. And, as a corollary, a person could not become drunk, regardless of the quantity of whiskey imbibed, until that quantity was more than the amount required to neutralize the venom in his system. Naphegyi (1868, p. 252) cites a logical result of these relationships. The Pinto Indians, from near Veracruz, were so accustomed to great amounts of mescal that alcohol in large doses failed to inebriate them. Thus alcohol was ineffective as a snake-bite remedy and if bitten they were beyond cure. This bit of logic would have pleased Lewis Carroll.

Because of these theories whiskey was used very generally and in large quantities for the treatment of rattlesnake bite throughout the United States. Vestal (1941, p. 146) has stated that the rattler, more than any other cause, made the High Plains country a hard-liquor area. It is to be remembered that one who had applied the precepts of safety-first by imbibing freely was immune to rattlesnake bite until the effects had worn off. So the cure was taken as a safety measure against a possible encounter with the affliction.

The use of alcohol for the treatment of snake bite was not discovered by Americans, nor was its modern use restricted to the United States. It was mentioned by such classical writers as Nicander about 150 B.C. (1953, p. 65; Adams, 1844–47, vol. 2, p. 159), Celsus, who suggested strong wine with pepper (1935–38, p. 117), Pliny (1855–57, vol. 4, p. 474; book xxiii, chap. 23), and Dioscorides (Adams, 1844–47, vol. 2, p. 159). It was recorded by Petrus de Abano in about 1300 (Brown, 1924, p. 47) and Lovell in 1661 (p. 243).

Alcohol did not gain much popularity for rattlesnake bite until the middle of the nineteenth century. I find no case reports of massive doses of whiskey prior to that of Mayrant (1823, p. 619). By the middle of the century the alcohol treatment was well established and had supplanted all others in popularity (Baird, 1854, p. 106; Brainard, 1855, p. 132; Mitchell, 1860, p. 114; 1861, p. 307). Baird, an outstanding biologist of the time, was among those who gave impetus to the antidotal theory of the use of alcohol when he stated: "It is a singular fact that a very large dose of spirits generally fails to produce intoxication." By this time, faith in the previously accepted plant remedies had begun to decline, and there was no difficulty in turning the people to the more pleasant treatment that made large doses of whiskey not only desirable but essential. The rapid increase of popularity of this remedy is indicated by a sudden flurry of case reports and discussions in the 1850's and 1860's, such as those of Lindsly, 1852, p. 341; Hopkins, 1853, p. 389; Blackburn, 1853, p. 128; Atchison, 1853, p. 201; Burnett, 1854, p. 315; Woodhouse, 1854, p. 181; Whiting, 1854, p. 258; Jeter, 1854, p. 24; Thomas, 1855, p. 305; Alexander, 1855, p. 119; Oliveras, 1858, p. 225; Anon., 1858a, p. 471; Marcy, 1859, p. 129; Lyons, 1860, p. 52; Peake, 1860–1, pp. 487, 522; Burton, 1861, p. 193; Mitchell, 1861, pp. 300, 309; Bogue, 1866, p. 400; and Flack, 1866, p. 338.

How the theory of the direct antidotal effect of alcohol gained credence among doctors and laymen alike is not known, since there were no tests to substantiate it. Any of three related principles were taken as proof of the theory: (1) rattlesnake venom is harmless to a person in a state of intoxication; (2) a person who has been bitten, no matter how unaccustomed to alcohol, will not become intoxicated regardless of the amount administered, until the venom has first been neutralized; (3) venom symptoms are neutralized by alcohol, and any continued evidence of symptoms is evidence of insufficient alcohol. Of course, the verification of these effects was based on inadequate or misinterpreted evidence; and the general proposition that alcohol cures snake bite had its validation in the uncertainties that have authenticated all the folklore remedies of the past—the cure of cases that required no treatment, that recovered despite the treatment rather than with its help.

The theory that no one who was drunk could be injured by a rattlesnake was well stated by Flack (1866, p. 338), who believed that the snake wastes its venom on any man whose blood is diluted with whiskey. Anon. (1858, p. 471) gave the idea this peculiar twist: A man drank himself into intoxication after being bitten and then taking ash tea. This proved the powerful antidotal effect of the ash tea since the tea must have cured the bite first, for otherwise the subsequent alcohol wouldn't have caused drunkenness. In another instance the value of violent exercise as a snake-bite remedy was proved in the same circuitous way (Potter, 1870, p. 288). Other references to the antagonism between venom and alcohol will be found in Anon., 1872b, p. 643; Fletcher, 1883, p. 139; and Packard, 1886, p. 737. Blackburn (1853, p. 128) saw a drunken man rashly pick up a big rattler. He was bitten several times but suffered no ill effects. The rattler died, a proper end for so foolish a creature. Dobie (1950b, p. 1) tells the yarn of a man who would let a rattler bite him for a drink, but only if he were already drunk. This was not a case of better judgment when sober; on the contrary, he believed in the immunity conferred by anticipatory alcohol.

A modern twist to the venom-alcohol relationship is thus expressed by one of my correspondents: "The main danger from snake bites is hysteria. There have been cases of drunken people bitten by rattlesnakes, and they didn't know about it or didn't worry about it and survived. I believe if a person is bitten and relaxes, and doesn't worry, he will get all right." The same thought, but without the alcohol obbligato, was expressed by Lloyd (in Cameron, 1927, p. 72).

Some of the quantities of liquor given (or taken) for rattlesnake bite were formidable, as, for example, a quart in 10 to 12 hours (Mayrant, 1823, p. 621); 2 quarts of corn whisky in 12 hours, until, no doubt amid rejoicing, the patient finally showed signs of inebriation, and the doctor desisted (Blackburn, 1853, p. 128); 1½ quarts of whiskey for a young girl (Atchison, 1853, p. 201); 7 quarts of brandy and whiskey in 4 days (Whiting, 1854, p. 258); a quart of brandy in the first hour, and another quart within 2 hours (Burnett, 1854a, p. 315); 1 quart of brandy and 1½ gallons of whiskey in 36 hours (Thomas, 1855, p. 305[3]); 1 ounce of whiskey every few minutes for a boy of 11, until half a pint had been given (Oliveras, 1858, p. 225); 1¼ gallons of whiskey (Coleman, 1872, p. 138); one-half pint of bourbon every 5 minutes until a quart had been taken[4] (Beattie, 1873, p. 619); recommended treatment, ¼ pint of whiskey every 20 minutes until the patient becomes intoxicated (Rivers, 1874, p. 511); 1 quart of whiskey (Bailey, 1876, p. 404); pure corn whiskey in moderate doses every 10 minutes, but not enough to make the patient drunk (Shuler, 1881, p. 292); 1½ pints of brandy within a half-hour (Richardson, 1879, p. 306); 1 quart of whiskey (Spaulding, 1884,

---

[3] The doctor reported (seriously) that the patient was seen next day looking for another rattlesnake to bite him. Thus was born one of the sure-fire vaudeville gags of a later time. Jeffrey (1955, p. 251) mentions the tale of a dry town where a tired rattlesnake had ten men on its waiting list.

[4] Surprisingly enough this patient got drunk; the rattler that bit him must have been out of practice.

p. 66); 104 fluid ounces (0.8 gallon) of apple brandy in 4 hours (Blackwood, 1888, p. 272); 2 ounces of whiskey every 2 hours was the army treatment in 1869 (Gould and Pyle, 1897, p. 717). A newspaper story of 1867 said that persons suffering from rattlesnake bite, including nondrinkers, had taken up to a gallon of whiskey without showing signs of inebriation (Nixon, 1946, p. 305). Scarbrough (1941, p. 10) mentions a case in 1870 wherein the doctor had reported that the amount of whiskey given a child would have killed it had it not been suffering from copperhead bite; also, it would have died from the bite without the large dose of whiskey.

Coleman (1872, p. 138) tells of an experience in the Confederate army in which a man suffering from snake bite was given a gallon of whiskey when the current price was $450.00 a gallon. One officer protested, saying the cure was worth more than the man.

There were objectors to the use of alcohol in large quantities almost from the time when it first became popular, including Jeter (1854, p. 24), Alexander (1855, p. 121), Brainard (1855, p. 132), Mitchell (1860, p. 114; 1861, pp. 300, 307), Paine (1875, p. 129), and Crouse (1902, p. 442). Some of these doubted the value of alcohol, others thought it definitely injurious. As early as 1831, Horner (p. 397) had reported a fatality from rattlesnake bite in the case of a man who was drunk when bitten. This should have led to doubt as to the specific antidotal quality of alcohol. Bracht, in 1848 (ed. 1931, p. 48), said that the only rattlesnake-bite fatality in Texas known to him was probably caused by the treatment with large quantities of whiskey, rather than by the venom itself. Lyons (1860, p. 52) reported a patient who got very drunk on 1 to 1½ pints of alcohol, from which he questioned its value as a cure. Barringer (1892, p. 283) mentions a death from an overdose of whiskey following the bite of a harmless snake. Mitchell (1869, p. 138) records a case in which a man, bitten in the finger, was given 1½ pints of whiskey and died within 2 hours. Alcohol poisoning may be suspected, as so quick a death from a bite in an extremity would be almost impossible.

In the days of its popularity for rattlesnake bite, whiskey was sometimes injected or applied externally as well as internally (Bogue, 1866, p. 400; Spalding, 1884, p. 66; Ellzey, 1884, p. 252; Richter, 1946, p. 193). It was frequently mixed with other substances, particularly red pepper; and although it was the most trusted treatment, other remedies such as a tourniquet and suction, or various poultices were not inhibited by its use. However, it is true that the complete confidence in whiskey often estopped the use of more effective treatments.

The decline of whiskey as a cure began in the early part of the present century, and it was practically eliminated from the methods approved by reputable physicians in the 1920's, when antivenin and the incision-suction program of Dr. Dudley Jackson became available. Willson (1908, p. 566), from his survey of snake bite in the United States, had concluded that alcohol in large doses only added alcohol poisoning to snake poisoning; and that acute alcoholism may have resulted in 5 per cent of the fatalities (p. 569). Pope (1919, p. 51) gave a corresponding figure of 10 per cent. As Brymer learned from a questionnaire sent to practicing physicians in southwestern Texas, its use there had virtually ceased by 1928.

Today alcohol is not recommended in snake-bite cases except, rarely, in small quantities as a stimulant. It has the adverse effect of speeding circulation and thus increases the rapidity of venom absorption. Most first-aid manuals and doctors experienced in the treatment of rattlesnake bite oppose its use. It has been virtually relegated to a folklore status, where it is still popular.

Oils and Fats

Oils and fats, whether of animal or vegetable origin, have been popular as snake-bite remedies since the earliest days, and even now have a place in folklore medicine. The application was sometimes internal, sometimes external, often both.

Among the early advocates of lard for the bites of European snakes was Maimonides about 1200 A.D. (Wootton, 1910, vol. 1, p. 112). Cadwallader Colden wrote Gronovius in 1744 (see Gronovius, 1763, p. 26; and A. Gray, 1843, p. 95) that hog fat should be a good cure for rattlesnake bite, for hogs are immune to rattlesnakes because a rattlesnake's fangs cannot reach a hog without applying the remedy (the fat) at the same time. Thus he rationalized the cure that he attributed to the fat. Hog lard was also recommended by Kalm (1752–53, p. 192). Whitlaw (1824, p. 257) tested hog fat without success, but hog and other animal fats continued to be recommended from time to time (Good, 1853, p. 10; Lanszweert, 1871, p. 111), and fat still remains a part of folklore medicine (Thomas and Thomas, 1920, p. 114, Kentucky Negro lore; Black, 1935, p. 32, and Pound, 1946, p. 167, Nebraska folklore; Swartzwelder, 1950, p. 580, Louisiana folk medicine).

Petrus de Abano of about A.D. 1300 (Brown, 1924, p. 47; Lovell, 1661, p. 260) recommended eating old butter for snake bite, but he did not refer to rattlesnake bite, of course.

Olive oil, or sweet oil as it was also called, was a European remedy for snake bite dating back at least to 1200 A.D., and was probably used much earlier. It was recommended for rattlesnake bite by Catesby (1731–43, vol. 2, p. 41), Hill (1752, p. 108), Kalm (1752–53, p. 192), Smith (1765, p. 509), Kearsley (1766, p. 75), and Miller (1799, p. 253).

In view of the advocacy of olive oil for viper bite in England, the Royal Academy of Sciences of Paris made experiments that were reported adversely in 1737 by Geoffroy and Hunauld (see also Castellani and Chalmers, 1913, p. 277, regarding tests by Morgagni in 1761). It was found useless as a remedy by Fontana (1787, vol. 2, p. 39). Mead reported some experiments in 1745 (p. 40); see also Orfila (1818, vol. 2, p. 543; 1821, vol. 2, p. 451). Nevertheless, olive oil continued to enjoy some reputation as a cure for viper bite in Europe (Acrell in Brand, 1781, p. 299) and was recommended and used in the United States sporadically for rattlesnake bite for a long time (Ker, 1816, p. 20; Thatcher, 1823, p. 62; Trowbridge, 1848, p. 203; Williams, 1848, p. 453; Baird, 1854, p. 106; Oliveras, 1858, p. 225; Beasley, 1865, p. 559; Dugès, 1879, p. 18, in Mexico; and Earley, 1890, p. 503). When prescribed for internal use, as much as a quart was given (Thatcher, 1823, p. 62, referring to a case in 1776 at Fort Ticonderoga, New York; Williams, 1848, p. 453).

American denials of the efficacy of olive oil for rattlesnake bite were made by Moore (1828, p. 342) and Mitchell (1861, pp. 294, 301); and today it is doubtful whether olive oil is extensively used as a folklore cure anywhere in the United States.

KEROSENE

Kerosene has long been a favorite cure for rattlesnake bite among farmers and others in remote districts. They have great faith in it as a specific antidote that will reach the venom and neutralize it. The venom is presumed to turn the kerosene green, thus affording a visual proof of its effectiveness. Usually the bitten limb is immersed in kerosene and kept there, but sometimes the oil is used in a poultice with onion or garlic. Despite this belief, there is no evidence from tests that kerosene is in any way effective against the bite of the rattlesnake or any other venomous snake. The cure is probably a direct descendant of the early folklore remedies of various oils, fats, and greases.

Kerosene was patented in 1854, and came into general use as a domestic illuminant about 1860. The earliest report of a rattlesnake bite treated with kerosene that I have come upon was a case in northern California reported by Baker in 1878 (p. 163). Dale (1947, p. 313) says kerosene was used as a snake-bite remedy for children in frontier Indiana, Illinois, Kentucky, and Tennessee, in the period 1840–70. More recent sectional reports are these: Virginia (Beck, 1952, p. 149), Mississippi (Clark, 1928, p. 141), Louisiana (Swartzwelder, 1950, p. 580), Texas (Brymer, 1928, p. 301; Woodhull, 1930, p. 63; Small, 1946, p. 88; Stillwell, 1949, p. 112), New Mexico (Curtin, 1947, p. 54; Jones, 1947, p. 49), Oklahoma (Smith, 1929, p. 74; 1930a, p. 84), Tennessee (Redfield, 1937, p. 15; McGlasson, 1941, p. 15), Arkansas (Randolph, 1947, p. 102), and Nebraska (Black, 1935, p. 32; Pound, 1946, p. 167).

INORGANIC CHEMICALS

Iodine and Iodides.—Iodine, in the form of the tincture, and various iodides, particularly potassium iodide, were often used for rattlesnake bite in the middle of the last century. The application was usually by painting the wound, and much importance was attributed to the treatment by some of the medical practitioners of those days who considered it a specific antidote (Whitmire, *et al.*, 1849; 1860, p. 267; Brainard, 1855, p, 135; Ham, 1861, p. 83; Staples, 1865, p. 279; Haynes, 1879, p. 486). Others who discussed the value of iodine and iodides were Mitchell, 1861, pp. 270, 299, 310; Lanszweert, 1871, p. 111; Fayrer, 1872, p. 38; Yarrow, 1888, p. 387; Gould and Pyle, 1897, p. 717; Willson, 1908, p. 564; Castellani and Chalmers, 1913, p. 278; and McGlasson, 1941, p. 15. The only use of iodine today in snake-bite treatment is as an antiseptic (Anon., 1947b, p. 11; Vaz, 1951, p. 50).

Bibron's Antidote.—Bibron was coauthor, with Duméril, of an important French multivolume work on reptiles. His antidote comprised a mixture of potassium iodide, mercuric bichloride, and bromine or potassium bromide. It seems never to have attained the popularity in the United States that it reached abroad. It was tried or mentioned by De Vesey (1858, p. 375), Hamilton (1858, p. 95), Mitchell (1861, pp. 277, 302), Ham (1861, p. 83), Desprez (1869, p. 25), Lanszweert (1871, p. 111), and Anderson (1872, p. 366). Mitchell (1861, p. 302) and Fayrer (1872, p. 38) judged it to be worthless from tests that they made. Yarrow (1928, p. 73) stated that Bibron's remedy was once regularly supplied to Western army posts for the treatment of rattlesnake bite.

Potassium Permanganate.—Of the many inorganic chemicals that have been proposed and used as antidotes for snake bites, rattlesnake bites included, potassium permanganate probably attained the widest popularity, and this with the sanction of and use by the medical fraternity itself. For a time, from about 1900 to 1930, most of the rattlesnake-bite first-aid kits included potassium permanganate as the most essential item.

Lacerda of Brazil is often credited with the first use of permanganate of potassium as a snake-bite antidote (Lacerda, 1881, pp. 514, 561); he was, for a time, its greatest advocate (Lacerda, 1884), and had much to do with the extent and rapidity of its adoption. However, it had been tried on cobra bite without success by Fayrer in India as early as 1869 (Fayrer, 1869, p. 153; 1872, p. 95; 1874, p. 95).

One of the earliest treatments of rattlesnake bite with potassium permanganate was given in May, 1883, by a medical student named Mories (1883, p. 57) who was employed by the Northern Pacific Railroad. He had read of the use of the remedy and tried it out on a patient four hours after the latter had suffered a bite in the calf of the leg. Not only was the remedy injected into the wound, but also elsewhere in the leg, and it was likewise given internally. Despite this treatment, the patient recovered in four days.

Even from the first, and notwithstanding its subsequent wide use, doubts were cast on the efficacy of permanganate. H. C. Yarrow, the Army surgeon and herpetologist who had much Western experience, considered it a standard treatment in 1884 (p. 435), but by 1888 (p. 327) he had concluded it had little or no value, a conclusion also reached by Richards in India (1885, p. 146). But despite these and other adverse expressions, the use of potassium permanganate continued to spread in this country. However, with the availability of an anticrotalic antivenin in the late 1920's, the snake-bite treatment manuals no longer took a neutral attitude respecting the use of permanganate, but definitely recommended against it. Since that time this chemical is seldom met with in snake-bite cases, although it is sometimes employed as an antiseptic (Githens, 1935b, p. 166; Anon., 1947b, p. 11).

The rise and fall of potassium permanganate is an example of the difference between theory and practice. This chemical—in common with a number of others—will, when mixed with venom, completely destroy its toxic properties, as demonstrated by many test-tube experiments. But venom is so closely akin to bodily tissues, and its absorption by them is so rapid, that the permanganate cannot reach and destroy it in the body. Permanganate is a strong oxidizing agent, but Jackson (1927, p. 207; see also Hutchison, 1929, p. 51) has pointed out that it cannot oxidize in the presence of blood and lymph. On the contrary, it chars the tissue and prevents the natural outpouring of lymph that would otherwise wash out some of the venom. Fairley (1929a, p. 311) has stated that potassium permanganate itself may cause necrosis and gangrene.

The cases in the medical literature citing the use of potassium permanganate in the treatment of rattlesnake bite are too numerous to warrant listing here. Thomas (1890, p. 123) mentions 27 cases of his own. Brymer (1928, p. 306), in his extensive investigation of the methods of rattlesnake-bite treatment customarily employed by practicing physicians in southwestern Texas, found that potassium permanganate had been used in 1,800 out of 2,300 cases, and by 100 out of 150 practitioners. However some doctors did not favor it, because of irritation, abscesses, and sloughing. Reese (1934, p. 109) made some animal experiments seeking to revive the use of permanganate, but the benefits seemed negligible. But as an indication of how slowly some of these treatments are discarded after they have been shown to be valueless, or even detrimental, we note a recommendation by Farley (1951, p. 29) of the use of permanganate in the treatment of dogs, printed next to a U. S. Public Health Service article on snake-bite treatment for man that does not even consider permanganate worthy of mention.

Salt.—Salt has been used as a snake-bite cure since the days of ancient Rome (Pliny, 1855–57, vol. 5, pp. 497, 509; book xxxi, chaps. 33, 45). It was often mixed with some plant. It was used in the treatment of rattlesnake bite as early as 1765 (Smith, p. 509). Thereafter it received fairly frequent mention (Bonnecamps, 1920, p. 403, but writing of 1750; Thwaites, 1896–1901, vol. 70, p. 141, regarding its use in 1757; Gale, 1766, p. 244; Kearsley, 1766, p. 75; Carver, 1778, p. 483; Tome, 1928, p. 117, but writing of the early 1800's; Swanson, 1952, p. 182, reporting a case in 1824–25). Salt is without direct effect on venom, as was shown by Fontana as early as 1787 (vol. 2, p. 9). It is currently listed as being among the folklore remedies of these sections of the United States: Illinois (Hyatt, 1935, p. 218), Nebraska (Black, 1935, p. 33), Kentucky (Thomas and Thomas, 1920, p. 115, with fresh pork), Tennessee (O'Dell, 1944, p. 4), Arkansas (Randolph, 1947, p. 102, with soap), Louisiana (Swartzwelder, 1950, p. 580, with garlic), and New Mexico (Curtin, 1947, p. 15). It was used by the pioneers in the "old" Northwest (Buley, 1950, vol. 1, p. 260).

In modern hospital treatments a saline solution may be injected at the site of the bite to aid in washing out venom (Anon., 1947b, p. 12) or in a compress to keep the wound clean and sterile (Vaz, 1951, p. 50). Normal saline injections are also used as a supportive measure.

Gunpowder.—Gunpowder was not only used as a cautery by explosion, but, usually mixed with salt, was applied as a poultice to rattlesnake bites, particularly in pioneer communities. The black powder of those days was a mixture of potassium nitrate, charcoal, and sulphur. Mention is made of this remedy by Barton (1793, p. 102), Kercheval (1833, p. 367), Good (1853, p. 10), Tome (1928, p. 117, re use about 1800 in Pennsylvania), Brendle and Unger (1935, p. 202, use by Pennsylvania Germans), Wright and Corbett (1940, p. 132, early Pennsylvania), Pickard and Buley (1945, p. 42, Midwestern pioneers), and Buley (1950, vol. 1, p. 260, pioneers of the "old" Northwest).

Ammonia.—Ammonia has had a sustained life as a snake-bite remedy, although it was shown long ago to be ineffective. It seems to have been mentioned first by Le Beau (1738) for the cure of rattlesnake bite in Louisiana, and by Jussieu (1747, p. 54) and Mauduyt (1774, p. 287). It was tested by animal experimentation by Fontana (1787, vol. 1, pp. 121, 131, 239; vol. 2, pp. 3, 42) and found to be without value. Its use in those days was premised on the theory that venom was an acid that could be neutralized by the alkali ammonia. It was also tried internally as early as 1792 (Williams, p. 225). From this time on, ammonia was often mentioned in discussions of remedies for rattlesnake bite (51 references); among those who advocated it particularly were Moore (1828, p. 341), who claimed to have treated 16 cases with success, Keith (1873, p. 337), and Paine (1875, p. 132). It was sometimes applied in the form of ammonium chloride (Bracht, 1931 [1849], p. 48), ammonium carbonate, or as *eau de Luce* (Collot, 1924 [1826], vol. 2, p. 9). Today its use is restricted to the occasional prescription of aromatic spirits of ammonia as a heart stimulant (Anon., 1947b, p. 14).

Miscellaneous Inorganic Chemicals.—Although no other chemical ever reached the widespread use attained by potassium permanganate, several inorganic chemicals that were found to render snake venom harmless when mixed with it in a test tube attained some popularity. Of these probably the most important were gold chloride, chromic acid, and calcium hypochlorite (Kaufmann, 1891, p. 41; Brown, 1899, p. 224; Crouse, 1902, p. 43; Willson, 1908, p. 564). They failed for the same reason as did potassium permanganate—an inability to reach and neutralize venom already mixed with body tissues. Mitchell (1868b, p. 316; 1869, p. 138) experimented with the sulfites and hyposulfites of sodium and calcium, but they were equally ineffectual.

Many other inorganic compounds have been tried for the bites of rattlers and other snakes from time to time, most of them in the hope that the venom might be neutralized, others for their systemic effects. Because of the acid character of venom, many were either bases or the salts of the alkali elements such as sodium, potassium, calcium, or magnesium, or of the ammonium radical. Alum water (potassium aluminum sulfate) was a folklore remedy in the West (Rightmire, 1900, p. 306; Pickard and Buley, 1945, p. 42; Buley, 1950, vol. 1, p. 260). Other cures included compounds of arsenic, iron, antimony, or mercury. Of all of these, the only one having any present repute is Epsom salts (magnesium sulfate) applied in the form of a wet dressing on the incisions when suction is not in progress (Githens, 1935b, p. 166; Anon., 1947b, p. 11; Holt, 1950, p. 14). Recently Staley (1939, p. 551) and Shannon (1953, p. 371) have recommended half-gram injections of calcium chloride as possibly reducing hemolysis.

Garb *et al.* (1955, p. 580) found some amelioration against *adamanteus* venom in an unidentified fraction of a certain India ink. It was not the carbon fraction.

Washing the bite with plain running water was once a folklore treatment in parts of the country (Pennsylvania Germans: Brendle and Unger, 1935, p. 201; Tennessee: McGlasson, 1941, p. 15; California: Lloyd in Cameron, 1927, p. 72).

MUD OR EARTH APPLICATIONS

The application of mud or absorbent earth to the bite of a snake is probably of ancient origin. It is mentioned by Topsell (1608, p. 41) and is given as one of the cures for rattlesnake bite in the first printed account of the treatment of its bite (Hernández, 1615, fol. 192^r; the account is repeated by Hernández, 1628, p. 329; 1651, p. 329; Nieremberg, 1635, p. 269; Jonstonus, 1653, p. 24; and Grew, 1681, p. 51).

Whether the mud cure was of Indian origin, or came from an observation of dogs treating themselves, is not known. A few Indian tribes used the mud method (p. 1141), but it does not seem to have been popular among the colonists in the United States. There are several accounts and case reports of the use of mud packs in the nineteenth century and later (Faux, 1823, p. 249; Potter, 1870, p. 287; Beattie, 1873, p. 619; Roberts, 1888, p. 375; Richardson, 1899, p. 145; Lloyd in Cameron, 1927, p. 72; Tome, 1928, p. 117, writing of the early 1800's).

Folklore studies have attributed the mud application to the following areas: New York (Relihan, 1947, p. 167; Evers, 1951, p. 112), pioneer Ohio (Richter, 1946, p. 193; Flanagan, 1952, p. 10), pioneer Indiana (Terhune, 1938, p. 444), Illinois (Hyatt, 1935, p. 218), Nebraska (Black, 1935, pp. 32, 33; Pound, 1946, p. 167), Kentucky (Thomas and Thomas, 1920, p. 114), Tennessee (McGlasson, 1941, p. 15), Louisiana (Swartzwelder, 1950, p. 580), Texas (Woodhull, 1935, p. 63), and New Mexico (Curtin, 1947, p. 15).

There were some variations in the method of application. Sometimes the limb was buried in the mud of a swamp or creek, despite the discomfort of the patient; sometimes a more convenient mud pack or poultice was used. On occasion the victim was buried to his neck in a manure pile (Relihan, 1947, p. 167). Sometimes absorbent earth or clay was mixed with milk and applied to the arm or leg, or the wounded part might be buried in dry earth and milk poured around it. W. R. Smith (1930a, p. 84) reports the application of a paste of clay, soot, and vinegar as a folklore remedy in Oklahoma.

Fontana (1787, vol. 2, p. 92) experimented with absorbent earths applied to viper-bitten pigeons. The results were inconclusive. Certainly today the drawing power of absorbent earth would not be considered as efficient as any of the suction methods readily available.

SNAKE STONES

The snake stone, an ancient device designed to draw venom from a snake bite, has never been as important in the folklore treatment of rattlesnake bite, as it was in the treatment of snake bites in the Old World. There snake stones were often used, and great importance was attributed to them, and no doubt still is, in many backward places. They might be of animal, vegetable, or mineral origin; usually their derivation was clothed in mystery. Often they appeared to be partially calcined and porous pieces of deer horn; some comprised charred vegetable matter removed from the stomachs of ruminants, or calculi. In operation they were believed, when affixed to a snake bite, to adhere until all venom had been sucked out, whereupon they dropped off. Their power for the next bite was restored by boiling or treating with fire. Not all snake stones were applied to bites; some, particularly a mineral type with snakelike streaks, were worn as amulets or snake repellents. Some discussions of snake stones are the following: Grew (1681, p. 52), Mead (1745, p. 44), Acrell in Brand (1781, p. 303), Fontana (1787, vol. 2, pp. 51, 78, 87, 92), Russell (1796, p. 73), Fayrer (1872, pp. 38, 40), Yarrow (1888, p. 386), Castellani and Chalmers (1913, p. 277), Acton and Knowles (1921, p. 737), Thorndike (1923–41, vol. 6, p. 323), Halliday (1924, p. 139), Frazer (1935, vol. 1, p. 165), Cole (1926, p. 352), and Rosenberg (1946, p. 46). Tests on the efficacy of snake stones made by Redi, Fontana, Russell, and Fayrer have uniformly failed to show any value in their use.

In America, snake stones have never been extensively used. Their use by Indians has been mentioned elsewhere (p. 1140). As early as 1693, Clayton (p. 133) mentions the employment of a bezoar stone (of ruminant origin) for the treatment of rattler bite. A Frenchman in Philadelphia in 1745 advertised the sale of a "chemical stone" that would cure snake bite as well as many other afflictions. In 1793 a merchant of South Hampton, New Hampshire, advertised snake balls for sale. This was another name for snake stones (Johnson, 1932, p. 223). Mease (1808, p. 1) tells us that in 1805 a Virginian advertised a snake stone that would cure rattlesnake bite or rabies, and offered to sell it to the people of four or five adjacent counties for $2,000. Shares were $10 each. Evidently the sale was made, despite Mease's effort to discourage it. A more recent account of a community snake stone, this time owned by 20 farmers in North Carolina, was that of "More Anon" (1905, p. 453). The author claimed to have witnessed successful treatments with this stone, a small porous object about the size of a silver dollar. Richter (1946, p. 194; Flanagan, 1952, p. 10) mentions a snake stone in the folklore cures of the early Ohio Valley. Randolph (1947, p. 141) states that a "mad stone" is used for snake bite in the Ozarks.

Tennent (1860, vol. 1, p. 196) mentions the treatment of a rattler bite with a snake stone in Sonora, Mexico. Clavigero (1937, p. 394, but writing in 1789) reports a snake stone composed of burned deerhorn that was used in Baja California for rattlesnake bite. After each application it was boiled to remove the venom and was then reattached to the wound. Prevost (1746–1789, vol. 14, 1757, p. 150) reports the use of a snake stone in Paraguay. Picado (1931, p. 159) mentions their use in Costa Rica.

NARCOTICS AND STIMULANTS

Opiates.—In the early days of snake-bite treatment, opium, sometimes in the form of laudanum, was given as an antidote for snake bite (Whitlaw, 1824, p. 258; Baillie, 1849, p. 179; Oliveras, 1858, p. 225). Short (1869, p. 564) used opium in the case of a bite by a massasauga, *Sistrurus catenatus.* As the ordinary opium symptoms were not evident, he assumed that the venom and opium had mutually neutralized each other. More recently, sedatives, such as morphine, aspirin, or barbiturates, have been recommended to relieve the pain of the venom or the treatment, so that the patient might obtain comfort, rest, and improved morale (Staley, 1939, p. 551; Young, 1940, p. 659; Anon., 1947b, p. 14; Happ, 1951, p. 22; Vaz, 1951, p. 50; Stickel, 1952, p. 25). However it has recently become evident that some venoms may be synergistic with some drugs. For example, Stahnke, (1954, p. 12) recommends against the use of morphine or Demerol in cases that involve neurotoxic venoms.

Strychnine.—Strychnine had been suggested as a cure for snake bite at least as early as 1860, since Mitchell (1860, p. 131) mentions in his bibliography a paper by Duncan referring to its use in India. I have been unable to locate the Duncan paper.

Strychnine may have been tried on rattlesnake bite first by Lanszweert (1871, p. 108) in the form of the arsenate; in this he thought he had found a new and successful remedy. Fayrer (1872, p. 74; 1874, p. 74) decided, after experiment, that strychnine had no value in the bites of cobras or Russell's vipers. Mueller (1888, p. 196; 1893, p. i) revived the use of strychnine for the treatment of the bites of Australian elapids, and strongly advocated it. He believed that he had invented the cure. His enthusiasm caused a rather widespread use of strychnine for awhile; indeed, in the 1890's its use was considered so important that it was assigned a separate section in the second series of the *Index-Catalogue of the Library of the Surgeon-General's Office, United States Army* (vol. 15, pp. 471–72), and no less than 57 articles in medical journals on this supposed antidote were listed as references.

The treatment of rattlesnake bite with strychnine has been tried or suggested by Jones (1896, p. 145), Brewer (1897, p. 60), Crouse (1902, p. 439), Gresham (1905, p. 1735), Crum (1906, p. 1433, for copperheads), and Lewis (1906, p. 2012). It has been commented on by Stejneger (1895, p. 469), Willson (1908, p. 566), Castellani and Chalmers (1913, p. 277), Brymer (1928, p. 306), and Fairley (1929a, p. 308). Strychnine was not a successful antidote and has no present recognition in the treatment of snake bite, except that it may rarely be used—but only by a physician—as a stimulant (Staley, 1939, p. 551; Anon., 1947b, p. 14; 1951, p. 16).

Ether.—Ether has occasionally been used as a stimulant in the treatment of snake bite, including rattlesnake bite (Whitlaw, 1824, p. 258; Stanley, 1854, p. 464; Beasley, 1865, p. 559; Fayrer, 1872, p. 39; Ellzey, 1884, p. 252; and Roberts, 1888, p. 375). It has no present adherents.

Adrenalin.—Adrenalin (epinephrine), a vasoconstrictor and heart stimulant, has occasionally been recommended for rattlesnake bite, as, theoretically, it should restrict venom absorption and sustain heart action as well (Menger, 1903, pp. 263, 447; Hooker, 1903, p. 87; Rogers, 1905, p. 190; Lewis, 1906, p. 2012; Willson, 1908, p. 567; Alcock, 1914, p. 248). It seems never to have attained any great popularity.

Miscellaneous Stimulants.—As early as 1648, Piso, (p. 41) recommended the use of a heart stimulant for rattlesnake bite. Bogue (1866, p. 399) made the sensible observation that, as venom is absorbed too rapidly to be reached by local remedies that might neutralize it, the victim's vital energies should be sustained until he can overcome or eliminate the venom. Stimulants may also have a beneficial psychological result, in counteracting the depressing effects of fear and alarm. With the advent of antivenin, stimulants have the further purpose of conserving the victim's vitality until the antivenin becomes available. However, the stimulant should not be such as to speed the blood circulation to the point of causing a more rapid dispersion of the venom.

Among the stimulants that have been recommended and used from time to time are nitroglycerine (Jones, 1896, p. 145), digitalis (Jones, 1896, p. 145; Tuten, 1897, p. 896), atropine (Jones, 1896, p. 145; Crouse, 1902, p. 439), sparteine (Vellard, 1929, p. 165), nikethamide or coramine (Anon., 1947b, p. 14), tea or coffee (Staley, 1939, p. 551; Ganguli and Napier, 1946, p. 855; Anon., 1947b, p. 14; Dunn, 1951, p. 752; Anon., 1951, p. 32; Stickel, 1952, pp. 22, 24); and caffeine with sodium benzoate (Staley, 1939, p. 551). One of the popular first-aid kits of the days before antivenin contained caffeine tablets. Oxygen inhalation has been used (Keeley, 1937, p. 538; Bulger and Northrop, 1951, p. 1135). This might be of some value in cases wherein respiratory paralysis becomes an important symptom. Fayrer (1872, p. 39) suggested that galvanism (electric treatment) might be of value, but no subsequent tests have supported this opinion.

EMETICS AND PURGATIVES

Among the few snake-bite remedies of the ancients that have some basis in logic, and are still advised, were the use of emetics and purgatives, since some venom is excreted through the intestinal tract. Emetics were employed before the Christian era (Celsus, 1935–38, p. 117), and purgatives for snake bite date back at least to Dioscorides (Adams, 1844–47, vol. 2, p. 159), who flourished in the first century A.D.

Throughout the history of snake-bite treatment, emetics have been occasionally mentioned as having value (Topsell, 1608, p. 40; Mead, 1745, p. 43; Acrell in Brand, 1781, p. 299; Fontana, 1787, vol. 2, p. 9), and their use for rattlesnake bite was a natural later development (Baillie, 1849, p. 179; 1869, p. 238). Some of the plant cures for rattlesnake bite that were popular in colonial days were, incidentally, emetics (Beverly, 1705, book 2, p. 23). More recently Crouse (1902, p. 439) recommended stomach lavage with iodine, potassium bromide, and calomel, to neutralize the venom in the stomach. Willson (1908, p. 565) thought emetics useless.

Purgatives or colonic irrigation for rattlesnake bite were mentioned by Alexander (1855, p. 122), Marryat (1855, p. 77), Stejneger (1895, p. 474), Crouse (1902, p. 439), Willson (1908, p. 565), Jackson (1927, p. 208), Brymer (1928, p. 305), Young (1940, p. 659), Holt (1950, p. 14), and Stickel (1952, p. 24). Stomach washes and diuretics also have been used (Stejneger, Crouse, Willson). Sudorifics or diaphoretics have been recommended, again following Dioscorides. Byrd (1921, p. 188), writing in 1706, described a root that cured rattlesnake bite by causing profuse sweating, but that had no effect if taken by a person who had not been bitten. Dobrizhoffer (1822, vol. 2, p. 311, first published in 1784) told of herbs used in Paraguay to promote sweating in snake-bite cases. Orfila (1818, vol. 2, p. 544; 1821, vol. 2, p. 453) suggests medicines to induce sweating and sleep. More recently, and specifically for rattlesnake bite, sudorifics have been mentioned by Crouse (1902, p. 439) and Willson (1908, p. 565).

BACTERICIDAL TREATMENTS

I have discussed in chapter 12, under symptoms, the danger of infection in rattlesnake bites, since one of the effects of the venom is to reduce the normal antibacterial quality of the victim's blood, thus increasing the usual risk of infection that accompanies a puncture wound, a hazard accentuated by the invariable presence of pathogenic bacteria in the snake's mouth. Some of the supposed antidotes for rattlesnake bite, such as potassium permanganate and tincture of iodine, were incidentally antiseptics, but an appreciation of the necessity for the use of antitoxins against tetanus and gas gangrene, although not new, was given an increased impetus by Dr. Dudley Jackson as a part of his deep-drainage method of treatment. His treatment also involved the use of hypertonic magnesium sulfate compresses between suction-cup applications (Young, 1940, p. 659). More recently the newly discovered sulfas and antibiotics have become increasingly important in the treatment of snake bite, rattlesnake bite included, to avoid infection (Ganguli and Napier, 1946, p. 855; Chotkowski, 1949, p. 602; Tanner and Schellack, 1950, p. 66; Happ, 1951, p. 22; Vaz, 1951, p. 50; Stickel, 1952, p. 25; La Pointe, 1953, p. 128; Shannon, 1953, p. 371; Watt and Pollard, 1954, p. 369).

SOME NEW DRUGS

As this is written, some of the newer drugs such as ACTH, cortisone, and the antihistamines are beginning to be used in cases of snake bite, either to allay particular symptoms, or to avoid some of the troublesome allergic effects of antivenin. They may ultimately result in advances in treatment. In 1948, Trethewie and Day (p. 159) determined experimentally that histamine liberation may be important in fatalities from the bites of Australian elapids, and that antihistamines might be beneficial in treatments. Maier (1951, p. 463) reported on the use of an antihistamine in the treatment of dogs in rattlesnake bite. Dr. H. E. Cluxton, Jr., in December, 1951, described the use of ACTH in a case of copperhead bite, evidently with beneficial results. Others, who have recently commented on the use of these drugs, have been Stickel (1952, pp. 22, 23), Pradhan (1952, p. 66), Efrati and Reif (1953, p. 1108), Hoback and Green (1953, p. 236), Andrews and Pollard (1953, p. 395), Schoettler (1954, p. 1083), and Allam *et al.* (in Buckley, editor, 1955, in press). The most complete tests on these drugs so far have been those conducted by Schoettler, using the venoms of *C. d. terrificus* and *B. jararaca*. He found antihistamines, ACTH, and cortisone ineffective and in a few cases even detrimental. Yet, in their most recent work, Wood, Hoback, and Green (1955, p. 130) continued to find benefits in the use of ACTH and cortisone.

ARTIFICIAL RESPIRATION

Artificial respiration has been tried, sometimes with success, in cases of bites by cobras and other snakes whose venom, largely neurotoxic, often produces death by respiratory paralysis (Cheevers, 1870, p. 374; Acton and Knowles, 1921, p. 759; Fairley, 1929a, p. 311; Ganguli and Napier, 1946, p. 855). In such cases, artificial respiration may postpone death until antivenin or other remedial measures become effective. It may be assumed that the recent more efficient methods of artificial respiration, including the use of an iron lung, might be even more efficacious.

But in rattlesnake bites, which primarily involve hematoxins—except those of the South American rattler, *C. d. terrificus* and its relatives—it could hardly be expected that artificial respiration would be of any important benefit. Its use has been mentioned by Yarrow (1888, p. 388), Crouse (1902, p. 439), Willson (1908, p. 567), and Shannon (1953, p. 371), the last in connection with coral snake bite.

INTRAVENOUS FLUIDS

There has recently been an increasing recognition of the importance of blood transfusions in serious cases of snake bite, with the recommendation that the patient be typed immediately upon hospital entry, so that one or several transfusions can be given quickly if indicated to the attendant physician (Kelley, 1937, p. 538; Staley, 1939, p. 551; Young, 1940, p. 659; Oliver, 1944, p. 878; Holt, 1950, p. 14; Vaz, 1951, p. 50; Stickel, 1952, p. 24; Andrews and Pollard, 1953, pp. 392, 395; Shannon, 1953, p. 371; Watt and Pollard, 1954, p. 369). Early blood-level determinations should be made so that the attending staff can evaluate subsequent changes (Andrews and Pollard, 1953, p. 395).

Jackson (1927, p. 208) recommended a blood transfusion from a donor who had previously been bitten, in the hope of securing an antidotal effect; but today, with more powerful antivenins available, a blood transfusion is primarily of importance when the red blood cell count or the hemoglobin shows a marked decrease. These conditions may result from either blood destruction by the venom or loss of blood in the incision-suction procedure. Plasma may also be used. Dunn (1951, p. 753) suggests methods of washing out venom neurotoxins with the victim's own blood.

The intravenous injection of normal saline solution also has been used, often with beneficial effects (Hooker, 1903, p. 88; Willson, 1908, p. 567; Crimmins, 1930, p. 449; Githens, 1935b, p. 166; Keeley, 1937, p. 538; Young, 1940, p. 659; Oliver, 1944, p. 878; Anon. 1947b, p. 14; Bulger and Northrop, 1951, p. 1135; Stickel, 1952, p. 23; Shannon, 1953, p. 371). Glucose also has its value (Staley, 1939, p. 551; Happ, 1951, p. 22; Stickel, 1952, p. 24). Various supportive infusions and injections that were found of value in a very serious case have been listed by Watt and Pollard (1954, p. 369).

PATIENT CARE

Certain methods of care of patients who have been bitten have been deemed important. That the victim should be encouraged and reassured is self-evident. The fact that the gravity of rattlesnake bite is so often exaggerated can have a most depressing and even serious effect (Palfrey, 1892, vol. 1, p. 19; Fountain, 1901, p. 60; Crouse, 1902, p. 439; Young, 1940, p. 659; Swartzwelder, 1950, p. 587). Lloyd (in Cameron, 1927, p. 72) stresses the deleterious effects of fright in rattlesnake bite.

A liquid or bland diet for the first few days has been recommended (Young, 1940, p. 659; Bulger and Northrop, 1951, p. 1135). Later blood-building foods and injections of liver concentrates are advisable (Woodbury and Anderson, 1945, p. 188; Stickel, p. 25, 1952).

Both warm (Orfila, 1818, vol. 2, p. 543) and cooling baths (Allen, 1948, p. 127) have been suggested. Stickel (1952, p. 22) recommends keeping the patient warm, as the shaking of a chill tends to spread the venom. Massage of the bite area has been suggested (Crouse, 1902, p. 439), a very doubtful expedient, for any manipulation of the tissue at the bite should probably be confined to that incident to mechanical suction. Electric treatment of the spine was used in 1869 (Gould and Pyle, 1897, p. 717); such treatments have no present place in remedial therapy.

The formation of blisters is sometimes extensive. It is usually the practice to open them, precautions being taken to avoid infection (Philips, 1831, p. 540; Young, 1940, p. 659; Magee, 1943, p. 90; Vaz, 1951, p. 50). Young states that the blisters contain some venom in the exudate. Necrosis from secondary infections sometimes requires skin grafts (Andrews and Pollard, 1953, p. 390).

Although Walduck in 1714 (Masterson, 1938, p. 215) and Guild (1878, p. 50) recommended that a man bitten in the arm or leg elevate the limb, more recent recommendations are to place the bitten part lower than the rest of the body to retard absorption (Young, 1940, p. 659; Fillmore, 1941, p. 312; Stickel, 1952, p. 22).

EXERCISE OR REST

Exercise, or exertion of any kind, is today considered undesirable in the treatment of rattlesnake bite, since one should avoid speeding blood circulation and therefore the absorption and dispersion of the venom through the system. The victim should be brought to the hospital with the least possible exertion upon his part. However, this has not always been the accepted method. Exercise and continued activity were at one time the approved treatments for overdoses of certain opiates; and by analogy such treatments were recommended for rattlesnake bites when narcotic symptoms became evident. Potter (1870, p. 286) mentions a case in which the victim of a bite was compelled to run beside a buggy in which his rescuers rode on the way to the doctor. Blackwood (1888, p. 272) reports a similar occurrence. In India, where the neurotoxic symptoms of cobra bite frequently include lethargy, Fayrer (1872, p. 38) found it necessary to protest against treatments that involved violent exercise, with flogging, pinching, etc., which were currently a part of the folklore cures.

The desirability of rest, rather than exercise, for the victim of snake bite was voiced in the days of Augustus by Celsus (1935–38, p. 117), who advised a warm room with the bitten part lowered. Subsequently rest and warmth have been advocated by Fayrer (1872, pp. 38, 41), Richards (1885, p. 48), Willson (1908, p. 565), W. H. Smith in Brymer (1928, p. 303), Staley (1939, p. 551), Anon. (1947b, p. 14), Swartzwelder (1950, p. 587), Vaz (1951, p. 50), and Andrews and Pollard (1953, pp. 390, 394).

Efrati and Reif (1953, pp. 1087, 1106) stress particularly the desirability of immobilizing the bitten limb. The flow of lymph, and therefore the absorption of venom, is dependent on the movements of muscles. To prevent muscle movements, these authors advocate limb immobilization with plaster longettes. It is claimed that this method was used successfully in the treatment of the bites of Palestinian vipers.

A study of a number of recent case reports evidences an increasing appreciation upon the part of attending physicians that rattlesnake bite must be taken seriously, and that the great variability in prognosis, with the possibility of sudden changes in symptoms, requires close watching and supervision. Brymer (1928, p. 307) thinks that every case should be vigilantly attended for 48 hours. All available data from the victim and others at the scene of the accident should be obtained, for any information on the kind and size of the snake, how the bite occurred, the nature of the first-aid measures that were taken, with the time intervals involved, will be of value in determining remedial measures (Andrews and Pollard, 1953, p. 395). Supportive measures against shock should be emphasized (Staley, 1939, p. 551; Shannon, 1953, p. 371). Above all, the physician should be prepared for sudden reversals, even after apparent recovery is well under way. Often there is a reassuring amelioration of the startling hemorrhagic symptoms, followed by a sudden onset of much more insidious neurotoxic symptoms. If a case merits antivenin, it certainly should be under uninterrupted observation for several days. By this precaution there should be avoided such a sad, fatal case as that, recently reported in the press, of a child sent home from a doctor's office after treatment, instead of to a hospital.

EXAMPLE CASES OF FIRST AID

In the previous discussions regarding the various remedies that have been used for rattlesnake bite, it has been necessary for reasons of clarity to discuss them individually, as if, in each case, but one remedy was applied. But such a condition has been rare in the treatment of rattlesnake bite; on the contrary, it has been usual to apply several remedies, and even today multiple treatment is justified by the several effects it is desired to secure and by the protection necessary against various pathological conditions as evidenced by particular symptoms. Examples of diversified treatments are to be found in most of the case reports that I have cited; a number will be found in the tabulations of Mitchell (1860, pp. 100–1) and Willson (1908, table 2).

There is another phase of snake-bite treatment that is rarely evident in published case reports, namely, the uncertainty and alarm present in the field when such an unexpected accident happens. To remedy these omissions I give herewith some reports, especially of field treatments, sent in by my correspondents. There is, of course, no criticism or ridicule implied with respect to the remedies used.

> I once found a hunter who had been bitten on his leg by a timber rattler. I at once corded the leg at the knee, just tight enough to retard the flow of blood. I then heated the blade of my pen knife, and made slight incisions where the fangs had entered, then placed a suction pump made for just such purposes, and pumped out as much of the venom as possible. I then placed the man in my car and took him to the doctor. He recovered. If the leg above where I had corded it had begun to swell, I would have corded it higher up, and would have made an incision where the swelling had taken place, as the poison would have been at the surface of the skin. *Connie Davis, Supervisor of Game Wardens, New Albany, Miss.*

◇

> In 1942 I met a man who had been bitten by a ground rattler, and this is what he did: He was going out to feed stock about 8 o'clock in the morning. He was barefoot and stepped on the snake near its head, thus preventing it from striking with but one fang. Immediately he took his knife and cut out a generous chunk of flesh from his heel. Then he applied a tourniquet as quickly as possible, and took it off about noon only because the pain became unbearable. That evening about 6 o'clock he went to a doctor who gave him a shot of antivenin. This was told me six months later and the man still had to wear a shoe with the part around his heel cut away so that it wouldn't irritate the place that had not yet healed. Any of the three treatments would be rather serious in themselves, especially the tourniquet, but in the man's words, "Don't tell me that the bite of a pigmy rattler isn't a serious thing." *Glenn Gentry, State Division of Game and Fish, Paris, Tenn.*

◇

> In October, 1938, I was killing rats around my barn. My two small boys were helping me. One of the boys called out that something had stung him. The other boy went to investigate and found a small rattler. I got a large cord out of my pocket as quickly as possible. The snake had struck his forefinger on the inside about the middle. I put the cord around his finger next to his hand tight enough to stop the circulation, then took my knife and lanced both places to the bone, then placed the wounds in my mouth and sucked with all my might. Then I loosened the bandage until I got a mouth full of blood. Then I retightened the bandage, spit that out, put the wound back in my mouth, sucked and loosened the bandage. I kept this up for five minutes, then took the bandage off, and wet the hand in coal oil as a disinfectant. His finger swelled a little and there was a small ridge down his hand. He went to school the next day. *J. D. Bankston, Mason, Tex.*

Recently a ranch hand was bitten on the calf of the leg by a rattler. A German prisoner of war who was with him treated the bite by cutting the bite with a sharp knife, sucking out the blood and then chewing up some tobacco and spitting the juice into the wound. The bite was wrapped up and the man suffered no ill effects, other than a sore spot. He continued to work at his job. *George S. Gorsuch, U. S. Forest Service, Wheatland, Wyo.*

<>

I know of only one person being bitten where I could observe the case. We were haying on a neighboring farm when a woman telephoned to the farm where her husband and several of us were haying, saying she had been bitten. The husband, another boy, and I started for his ranch. We found that there was no way to cross the Salmon River as the boat had been taken. So a neighbor swam the river and brought the woman across and to the doctor, who had been called. This brave woman had killed the snake and cut the incision where the snake had bitten her, and then soaked her foot in five gallons of coal oil. The doctor said this was one of the best things she could have done. The woman recovered. *Ernest Gutzman, Forest Ranger, Winsper, Idaho.*

<>

I saw one man that was bitten, a sheepherder. He killed the snake and used the carcass for a poultice, then used mashed raw potato and tobacco for another poultice. He stayed in camp and cured himself. I hope nobody else tries this, though. *Floyd C. Black, U. S. Fish and Wildlife Service, Challis, Idaho.*

<>

I know of one man in this particular locality who was struck on the ankle by a rattlesnake. This incident occurred several years ago and transportation facilities were slow. He reported that a live chicken was split down the middle and bound tightly over the wound. He then traveled by buckboard for six miles to a doctor, where further treatment was administered, and within a few days he had completely recovered. Quite a few of the old-timers in this area swear by this treatment for snake bite. *Edward L. Peltier, U. S. Forest Service, Cle Elum, Wash.*

<>

In April, 1940, I was on patrol near a fishing resort, when a fisherman, who had been drinking more than was good for him, attempted to imitate a Hopi snake dancer by picking up a five-foot rattlesnake, despite the protests of his partner and myself. He was bitten on the index finger of the right hand. I placed a tourniquet on his arm and made a cut about two inches long and reaching to the bone, making three crosscuts reaching the bone in addition. This was done within 30 seconds after the man was bitten. We placed him in a car and during the 50 minutes of wild riding to a doctor, we changed the tourniquet about every 10 minutes, leaving it off about the same length of time it had remained on. Twice, during our run for medical aid, we believed the patient was dead, but we revived him by having him inhale ammonia fumes. The doctor gave him the serum treatment and he was taken to a hospital where he remained for three months, and left minus his index finger and thumb. Considering the gallant fight made by the doctor to save his arm, he was very lucky. The doctors were frank in saying that the severe bleeding of his hand was responsible for his recovery. *R. L. Neill, Arizona Game Ranger, Phoenix, Ariz.*

<>

I have known at first hand of only four actual cases of snake bite, all of them on the hand or forearm. All of these were treated but one. Two cases were treated immediately by making incisions and applying suction. The third case was treated after approximately one hour, using secondary incisions at the upper edge of the swelling. This patient had to be hospitalized and was seriously ill for some days. The fourth case was not treated, due to obstinacy on the part of the victim. He was bitten about 10 A.M., and I was informed later that he died enroute to the Fresno Hospital sometime in the late afternoon or evening of the same day. *Glen E. Sindel, District Ranger, Descanso, Calif.*

An important contribution to the history of the treatment of rattlesnake bite in the United States was made by Brymer (1928, p. 300). He sent out questionnaires to a number of practicing physicians in southwestern Texas, where rattle-snake bite was a moderately common accident, and received 150 replies. He was seeking to learn which of the treatments then in vogue was the most successful. He records brief clinical extracts from 30 of the reports, from which statistics of the use of treatments may be derived. This, it should be remembered, was during the interim after the usual Western cure (whiskey) had become outmoded, but before either antivenin was available or Dr. Jackson's intensive incision-suction method had been widely publicized. The following was the order of frequency in which remedial measures were used: potassium permanganate 22, strychnine 11, echinacea 9, kerosene immersion 5, ammonia (aromatic spirits) 4, morphine (for pain) 4, turpentine and camphor 2; and potassium iodide, potassium chlorate, alum, ammonium carbonate, chloral hydrate, digitalis, and caramel (calomel?) 1 each. This probably gives a fairly accurate picture of the relative popularity of the different remedies at the time. I have omitted a tabulation of the number of cases wherein incision, suction, and a ligature (usually called cording) were used, as these seem to have been taken for granted, and consequently were not mentioned by some of the reporting doctors who actually favored them. Besides, these first-aid measures were often applied before the doctor was called.

Despite the fact that potassium permanganate was still the most frequently used remedy at the time, a note of caution pervaded a number of the reports. Injections of permanganate had been discontinued by some doctors and weaker solutions were beginning to prevail, because of experiences with sloughing and other evidences of tissue damage. One correspondent said he had discontinued permanganate unless he was able to reach the patient within 15 to 30 minutes after the bite.

CASE DURATION

In rattlesnake-bite cases, with their many variable factors affecting severity, there is a corresponding variability in the duration of the case and the period requiring treatment or precautionary observation. Naturally much depends on the treatment and its efficacy. Complications, such as infections or gangrene, sometimes caused by the treatment rather than the bite, may also prove important.
Said Thomas Lechford in 1642 (p. 47):

> There are Rattle Snakes [in New England], which sometimes doe some harme, not much; He that is stung with any of them, or bitten, he turns of the colour of the Snake, all over his body, blew, white, and greene spotted; and swelling, dyes, unlesse he timely get some Snake-weed; which if he eats, and rub on the wound, he may haply recover, but feele it a long while in his bones and body.

Young (1940, p. 660), from experience with Dr. Dudley Jackson's cases in San Antonio, stated that in uncomplicated cases patients should be discharged from the hospital in from five to seven days after the accident. Willson (1908, p. 549) thought that in the majority of instances, recovery from constitutional symptoms should be complete in two or three days, often in a few hours, but there would be unhealed lesions of longer duration. Brymer (1928, p. 300) thought that, with good treatment, half the cases should be completely recovered in 10 to 12 days.

Some more specific case durations are shown by these examples: A man was discharged 12 days after a bite (Bogue, 1866, p. 399); recovery after a serious bite by an eastern diamondback, *C. adamanteus*, 5½ months (Mitchell, 1874, p. 331); a man bitten in the right leg by *C. adamanteus* or a canebrake rattler, *C. h. atricaudatus,* on June 1, received regular treatment until July 17, and the wound was not completely healed in May of the following year (Tuten, 1897, p. 896); a man bitten in the instep, probably by a western diamondback, *C. atrox,* was unable to use his foot for five or six weeks (Crouse, 1902, p. 439); a man bitten by a large rattler, probably *C. h. atricaudatus,* was in a serious condition for 30 hours, his arm was badly swollen for 80 hours, and he did not return to work for 30 days (Gresham, 1905, p. 1735); a boy of 13, bitten by a southern Pacific rattler, *C. v. helleri,* was hospitalized for 16 days (Wittek, 1943, p. 9); a man bitten in the back by a Great Basin rattler, *C. v. lutosus,* did not return to work for 58 days (Woodbury and Anderson, 1945, p. 187); a man suffering from a serious *adamanteus* bite was in the hospital for 10 days, in bed for 2 months, and was crippled for 3 additional months (MacDonald, 1946, p. 140); a man, after an *adamanteus* bite, was hospitalized for 10 days, and was in bed at home for 2 weeks more (Hylander, 1951, p. 20). In another serious bite by a snake of this species, a man was hospitalized for 22 days and was unable to work for 102 days more (Watt and Pollard, 1954, p. 369).

In three cases reported to me, there were these durations: A man bitten in the arm by a northern Pacific rattler, *C. v. oreganus,* was able to return to work in 6 days; a man bitten in the ankle by a rattler of the same subspecies, was in the hospital for 3 days, and was away from work for 20 days; a boy bitten in the thumb by a red diamond rattler, *C. r. ruber,* was hospitalized for 6 days. In another bite by the same species, a man passed the crisis in 72 hours, although he did not recover for several weeks. From a bite by a Great Basin rattler (*C. v. lutosus*) a man was sick for several weeks, and his weight dropped from 180 to 128 pounds. Andrews and Pollard (1953, p. 391) report the following periods (in days) of hospitalization for nonfatal *adamanteus* bites: 1, 2, 3, 5, 7, 9, 42, 86. The last two cases were prolonged because extensive necrosis required skin grafts.

Some data are available on the duration of fatal cases of rattlesnake bite. The presentation of these figures should not be taken as an indication of a high mortality rate, for fatalities involve only a small proportion of all cases, as has been pointed out elsewhere.

In the early days, not only was the danger from rattlesnake bite exaggerated, but so also was the rapidity of death. Hernández (1615, fol. 192[r]) in the first printed account giving any information on the bite of the rattlesnake, said it would be fatal in 24 hours (see also Hernández, 1628 and 1651, p. 329; Nieremberg, 1635, p. 269). Beverly (1705, book 2, p. 23) reported the bite sometimes fatal within two minutes; this was repeated by Catesby (1721–43, vol. 2, p. 41) and Hill (1752, p. 107). Kalm (1752–53, p. 308) took a more realistic view, stating that a bite in a vein would be quickly fatal, but this seldom happened. Somewhat the same opinion was expressed by Gibson (1825, p. 103).

Mitchell (1889, p. 509), usually quite trustworthy, and the greatest authority of the nineteenth century on rattlesnake bite, reported that men had died within one minute after being bitten. Jeter (1854, p. 16) claimed to know of two cases that resulted fatally within a few minutes. Two almost instant deaths were reported by Tixier (1940, p. 77) in describing his travels through the Osage country in 1839–40. There is an old (in fact, the first) American ballad entitled "The Pesky Sarpent" that tells a sad tale of a man bitten by a rattler who failed even to reach home. His bride, who was with him at the time and sucked the wound, unfortunately had a bad tooth and also succumbed. According to Margaret Boni (1952, p. 254), the ballad is thought to have been founded on an actual occurrence of August 7, 1761.

Barton (1793, p. 108) said he had heard of a man bitten in the neck who died within a few minutes. The following is quoted from a letter written some years ago: "I have just returned from the funeral of ———. He was bitten last Friday while tending an irrigation ditch about 100 yards from the house. We found him less than half an hour after death, swollen until no one could have imagined it to be ———. In some way the rattlesnake reached him in the throat, perhaps as he crawled through the brush. The doctor said he couldn't have lived more than about two minutes." Another correspondent wrote of a man who died within a few minutes when struck in the neck while crawling through a fence. A story frequently heard throughout the Southwest concerns a cowboy found dead by his fellows, with his body halfway through a barbed-wire fence. The condition of the body made it evident that he had been struck in the neck by a rattler and died almost instantly. It is true that such an occurrence is possible, but some details of the story, particularly that the culprit was a sidewinder found near the body, suggests a common origin, notwithstanding a reputed occurrence at many different times and places. This is rapidly becoming an item of folklore in the cattle country.

The following are some general statements regarding the duration of fatal cases of rattlesnake bite: Wood (1855, p. 331), in his natural history that remained for many years the basic authority in this field for Victorian youth, said that the "bite is inevitably mortal, and death always ensues within a few hours after the wound has been inflicted."

Shuler (1881, p. 292) remarked that, without field treatments, a victim might die within an hour or even within 10 minutes. Rolker (1905, p. 201) said that fatalities have occurred after 10 minutes, but some after 2 hours. Willson (1908, p. 540) gave his opinion that some fatalities occurred in less than an hour. Babcock (1944, p. 83) wrote that the bite is rarely fatal, except after hours or days; and Holt (1950, p. 13) thought that in the few fatal cases, death usually occurs in from 3 to 4 days, although a large dose of venom in a vein might result in almost instant death. Stickel (1952, p. 22) said that patients dying from rattlesnake venom often do so within 24 to 36 hours. Schomburgk (1922, vol. 2, p. 102), writing of British Guiana in 1847, said that some people die of snake bite years after the bite. This is not to be taken seriously.

Here are a few specific fatal-case durations taken from case reports or accounts in travel literature: Kearsley, 1766, p. 74, 30 hours; Home, 1809, p. 75, 18 days; Dobrizhoffer, 1822, vol. 2, p. 288, 12 and 14 days; Rengger, 1829, 13–14 minutes; Lacombe, 1851, p. 290, 2 hours; Mitchell, 1861, p. 279, 20 minutes; Shapleigh, 1868, p. 264, 40 minutes; Anon., 1869, p. 93, within one hour; Rivers, 1874, p. 511, 3 hours; Spalding, 1884, p. 66, 27½ hours; Roberts, 1888, p. 375, few minutes; Blackwood, 1888, p. 272, 10 minutes; Gould and Pyle, 1897, p. 717, 18 days; Brewer, 1897, p. 59, about 5 days; Crouse, 1902, p. 445, 6½ hours; Lewis, 1906, p. 2012, 6 hours; Barnes, 1922, p. 390, 28 hours; Rhone, 1928, p. 87, less than 2 hours; Oertel, 1929, p. 314, ½ hour; Crimmins, 1934, p. 130, 2 cases, each in 40 minutes; Gowanloch, 1934, p. 6; 1943, p. 34, 15 minutes; Lyon and Bishop, 1936, p. 255, 7 days; Otken, 1942, p. 185, 1 hour, 3½ hours, 14 hours; Uhler, 1943, p. 6, one almost immediately, one in 10 minutes; Minton, 1950, p. 320, 7 days; Hylander, 1951, p. 70, 45 minutes; Sibley, 1951, 12 minutes. Not all of these reports are completely trustworthy. It is to be noted that many involve children, particularly those that resulted fatally in the shortest times. I have had six re-

TABLE 13:1

DURATION OF FATAL CASES

Elapsed time between bite and death	Willson[a]	Hutchison	Total
Less than 1 hour	8	1	9
1 to 6 hours	13	1	14
6 to 24 hours	18	15	33
Second day	4	3	7
Third to seventh day	4	1	5
Nine days	1	..	1
Seventeen days	1	..	1
Over a month	1	..	1
Total	50	21	71

[a] Not all, but most, of Willson's cases were caused by rattlesnakes.

ports from correspondents of deaths in 45 minutes, 1 hour, 3 hours, 4 hours, 7 hours, and 14 hours.

Two fairly trustworthy statistical summaries on this subject are those assembled by Willson (1908, p. 549) and Hutchison (1929, pp. 52, 53). These are presented in table 13:1. I think we may fairly conclude that the first day, and especially the last part of it, is the most dangerous period.

Adkinson (in Brymer, 1928, p. 302) expressed the belief that in southwestern Texas most fatalities occurred about 8 hours after the bite; he thought the danger largely passed if the patient survived 12 to 15 hours. Nonetheless, Brymer himself (1928, p. 307) was of the opinion that the doctor should be close at hand for the first 48 hours. Pollard, from his experience with *adamanteus* bites in Florida, considers the interval between the third and sixth days to be the most crucial.

A recent fatality was recounted by Schmidt (1954, p. 247). The victim, an experienced snake collector, was bitten by a large western diamond (estimated length 4½ feet) in the back of the left hand. Unfortunately, despite the most approved types of treatment, both in the field and hospital, he succumbed six hours after the bite. Undoubtedly a most important factor in this case was that it took 2¼ hours to reach the hospital, because of distance and transportation difficulties.

Ricketts (1898, p. 223) was of the opinion that if death does not occur within a few hours, the fatality is from some agency other than the venom, presumably an overdose of alcohol, an infection, or gangrene. Corkill (1932a, p. 625) supplies the following presumed relationship between the interval before death in fatal cases and the principle of the venom likely to have caused the death. This table of factors was stated to be applicable to the bite of the Levantine viper, *Vipera lebetina,* which is found from eastern Europe to India, but it is of interest since there is probably a correlation between certain principles of rattlesnake venoms and the interval before death in fatal cases:

Types of death from the bite of *V. lebetina*	Interval between the bite and death
Thrombotic	Almost at once
Depressive	Few hours
Cytolytic	1 to 3 days
Vitiatory	4 to 6 days
Septic	About 14 days

It has been stated that in quickly fatal cases of rattlesnake bite, the hemorrhagins of the venom were the causal factors, but deaths after the first day—assuming no infection or similar complication—were likely to have been caused by the neurotoxins.

As a matter of reassurance, in closing this discussion of the rapidity of death from rattlesnake bite, I wish to repeat that the fatalities from this cause for the entire United States, with a population of over 160 million, seldom exceed 30 per year. Of every 100 people bitten by rattlesnakes, only about 3 will die.

Veterinary Treatments

Subsequently in this chapter I shall discuss the effects of rattlesnake bite on stock and other domestic animals, and the resulting losses. Here I shall briefly mention the remedies that have been used in their treatment. In general it is found, as would be expected, that most of the remedies that have been applied to human beings, whether of a folklore or scientific nature, have also been used for domestic animals.

Woodhull (1930, p. 43) has listed a number of remedies used in Texas by Americans and Mexicans for cattle and horses. Among these are the following:

Scarify the wound with a knife until it bleeds freely; then take 5 or 6 spikes of Spanish dagger (*Yucca*), stick them under the skin and leave them there for 24 hours. It is customary, even without the scarification feature, to insert a number of Spanish dagger points around the wound.

Apply hot lard.

Incise and apply fine salt.

If the swelling is serious, apply cold mud or clay as a poultice.

Apply cow manure, but be sure to keep it cool.

Pound up the inside of a prickly-pear (cactus) leaf, and apply as a poultice an inch thick. Keep it moist with water and change it when warm.

Jab the swellings with a sharp instrument until black blood and water come out; this is the venom. Spanish dagger spines may be used to make the punctures.

Hold a hot coal at the bite, but not close enough to scorch the hair.

Stand the animal in mud and rub the wound with kerosene.

After puncturing around the wound with Spanish dagger spines, apply kerosene and tallow.

Apply soda and vinegar.
Bathe with kerosene.
Blister with turpentine.
Tie on a tourniquet and jab in Spanish daggers.

The following are animal treatments mentioned by others; some are similar to those listed by Woodhull, although they are from areas other than Texas. Incision, with or without means of suction, is mentioned as being used in Nebraska (Black, 1935, p. 46; Pound, 1946, p. 168), California (Wagnon, Guilbert, and Hart, 1945, p. 22), and New Mexico (Curtin, 1947, p. 33). The use of Spanish dagger points seems to be a regular feature of Southwestern folklore treatment, as it is mentioned by Woodhull, Black, and Pound; also by Dobie (1941b, p. 294).

Cauterizing with gunpowder was used in early Wyoming days on animals as well as humans (Robinson, 1944, p. 396). Black (1935, p. 46) mentions the gentler method of holding a hot coal, near, but not touching, the wound. Powell (1918, p. 329) claimed to have used the split-chicken cure with success on a horse.

Plant cures for animals date back to Pliny in the days of the Roman Empire (1855–57, vol. 4, p. 256; book xx, chap. 51; vol. 5, p. 123; book xxv, chap. 64). More recent plant treatments have been reported by Post (1878, p. 360; 1879, p. 56), Bloom (1934, vol. 9, p. 423), and Hamilton (1938, p. 577). The latter's report indicates that Woodhull's prickly-pear remedy was used in the Dakotas in the late 1800's.

Drenching the animal with warm lard is an item of Nebraska treatment (Black, 1935, p. 46; Pound, 1946, p. 168). Washing with salt is a Mexican cure for sheep in New Mexico (Curtin, 1947, p. 33) as is also the mud treatment. The mud cure for a horse is mentioned by Bailey (1947, p. 706). With grazing animals that are likely to be bitten in the nose or throat, tracheotomy may sometimes be necessary (McNellis, 1949, p. 145).

The following are some of the treatments that have been given dogs for rattlesnake bite: Salad oil (Morton, 1637, p. 82); ammonia, nitrous salts, and a tobacco rub (Montule, 1821, p. 76); Bibron's antidote (De Vesey, 1858, p. 376); Bibron's antidote and whiskey (Oliveras, 1858, p. 227); a tea made from a weed (Davis, 1889, p. 183); a mud bath (W., R., 1891, p. 124); incision and suction (Jackson and Harrison, 1928, p. 1929; Crowe, 1931, p. 299; Jackson and Githens, 1931, p. 6); antivenin (Hollender, 1948, p. 129); antihistamines (Maier, 1951, p. 463). In a recent communication, Dr. H. Grady Young, of Thomasville, Georgia, has recommended calcium borogluconate reinforced with benadryl. Parrish (in Buckley, editor, 1955, in press) recommends excision.

Ross Allen has cited some of his many experiences with dogs bitten by eastern diamondback rattlesnakes (*C. adamanteus*) and has given his recommendations for treatment in two articles (1948, p. 124; 1951, p. 22). The treatments that are suggested closely parallel the latest recommendations for human beings, that is, a tourniquet, incision, suction, and antivenin. Pritchard (1940, p. 358) says that dogs may suddenly take a turn for the worse, with unfavorable cardiac and circulatory symptoms, just as human beings do.

I have had several interesting reports of folklore treatments given by some of my correspondents to their dogs. They were probably typical of what was done for dogs in the field 8 to 10 years ago.

I have had several dogs bitten by rattlers and have saved them all by slitting the fang holes with a knife and placing the wound in coal oil, and working the blood out with the hand. If a dog or any other animal is struck squarely on the end of the nose, it will die, I think, for I have never seen an animal live that was struck there. [*Montana.*]

◇

While hunting coyote dens near Dubois, Idaho, I was using a faithful hunting dog. He always hunted two or three hundred yards from me. It was an unusually hot day and in rattlesnake country. I heard my dog bark and saw him grab a rattlesnake and shake it, but the snake had been quicker and had hooked its fangs in the dog's upper lip. The dog released the snake and shook it loose. I called the dog to me, and on examining him, I found he had been bitten twice along the side of his upper lip. His head was swelling fast, so I killed the rattlesnake immediately without its biting itself, and quickly removed the skin and applied pieces of the snake's flesh to the snake bites on my dog, keeping this up for about two hours, using fresh pieces of the snake, which drew most of the poison from the dog's wounds into the flesh of the snake. On returning to camp I applied ground, raw onions to the snake bites on the dog, changing them every 30 minutes, until all the poison was drawn out. By doing this my dog was able to hunt with me again in two days. [*California.*]

◇

Quite a large dog (a black and tan hound) was bitten in the nose by a rattler. The fang marks were opened with cross incisions and kerosene poultices were put on. The position of the bite, of course, made a tourniquet impossible, and poison centered in pockets below the jowls which were both lanced with about three-inch incisions. The dog recovered and is O. K. [*California.*]

◇

I had a dog bitten by a very large rattler last summer, on the foot. I took my knife and cut each fang mark deep so that it bled well, put a tourniquet above the bite, and stood the dog in water and mud until the pain stopped, which evidently, by his howling, was severe. His leg swelled in a short time. In about three days the swelling went down and all the flesh decayed and fell away from the bone, which took about six weeks to heal over. There is only a scar to show now. [*California.*]

It has often been stated that dogs, when snake-bitten, seek a mud hole or swamp, and immerse themselves in mud until the worst reaction is past. Presumably this is done to relieve the pain. I cannot say, from my own experience, whether this is fact or folklore, but certainly it is a widely circulated bit of natural history (Kercheval, 1833, p. 368; Anon., 1889, p. 518; Matteson, 1899, p. 669; E. D. Jones, in Cameron, 1927, p. 74; Hamilton, 1938, p. 613; Tome, 1928, p. 117, related of about 1800 in Pennsylvania; Pound, 1946, p. 171; Duncan, 1946, p. 172).

The following accounts received from my own correspondents with regard to self-treatment by dogs, closely parallel the printed reports cited above:

During the summer of 1910, my brother's English setter was bitten just under the left eye, while hunting, by a medium-sized prairie rattlesnake. No treatment was given and the dog's head swelled very much, and he was in extreme discomfort. The dog disappeared about four hours after being bitten, and returned seven days later reeking with mud from a swamp. The head and face were still badly swollen, but recovery was rapid, and in about three weeks he was apparently well except for a permanently blinded eye. *W. E. Beed, U. S. Fish and Wildlife Service, Waupun, Wis.*

◇

I had a bird dog that got bitten twice by the same snake, once in the nostril and once below the right eye. His face started swelling in a very few minutes, and within three hours his eyes were nearly swollen shut. The dog left home and was gone three days. When he returned his face was nearly normal. The bite around the eye cost him a patch of hair about the size of a dollar. *Howard L. Munson, Newcastle, Wyo.*

Animals in the mountains, when bitten, seldom die if able to get to water or mud. I have seen numerous dogs that were bitten. If left alone, they will stay in mud or water and recover in a few days without any medical attention. Stockmen and other people living here in the mountains never attempt to treat a dog when he is bitten, but let him go to a mud or water hole; the animal will stay in this place at least four days before going back to his home. *Bernie I. Leas, Fire Control Assistant, Platina, Calif.*

<>

Years ago I told an inquirer that a dog or bear, when bitten by a rattlesnake, would lay still for many days. One case here was a pointer bitch that stayed in the mud for six days without food, and was a rack of bones when she did leave. This bitch had been bitten on the upper jaw near the nose by a large snake. The boys who owned the dog wanted to take her to a vet., but their father said no. She became perfectly well in a short time. *R. M. Williams, Arbuckle, Calif.*

<>

If she were bitten, my dog would go and lay in a mud hole for a couple of days and come home. *Bernie I. Leas, Fire Control Assistant, Platina, Calif.*

ANTIVENIN

HISTORICAL

Curiously enough, although snake-bite antivenins have not been so effective as some other antitoxins—such as those used against diphtheria and tetanus, for example—the first important work on this type of artificial immunity was that of Sewall (1887, p. 203), who was seeking to produce immunity against rattlesnake venom. He discovered preventive inoculation, for he was able to produce, in test animals by repeated sublethal doses, a gradually increased resistance, and this without ill effects on general health. He found that the resultant immunity did not last long. Yarrow (1888, p. 432) took notice of Sewall's experiments and thought preventive inoculation might have useful possibilities. Kaufmann (1893, p. 136), in experiments begun in 1890, also demonstrated this method of deriving immunity.

The next important step was taken by Phisalix and Bertrand (1894a, p. 356), who found that the blood of a guinea pig immunized by the method of Sewall, when injected into a second guinea pig, protected the second against venom. Thus was evolved the idea of the remedial substance, antivenin. They also made tests (1894a, p. 288) that later led to the use of anavenoms, for they found that venom partially detoxified by heat still retained its immunizing power, as was independently verified by Calmette (1894c, p. 275).

Subsequently Calmette (1894b, p. 120) developed a program for producing antivenin; and thereafter Phisalix and Bertrand, Calmette, Kanthack, Kaufmann, Bancroft, and Fraser wrote a number of important papers describing experiments, all of which contributed to the practical development of antivenin. Fraser (1895a, p. 1310) immunized horses, cats, and guinea pigs to such a degree that they could withstand three times the normal lethal dose of venom. He judged the immunity to be of rather short duration. He found that the protective principle was contained in the serum of the blood of the immunized animal, and that the protection was still retained if the serum were dried (p. 1311). He was among the first, if not the first, to use the term antivenene[5] for the protective serum (1895a, p. 1311). In testing the immunizing strength of the antivenin, he tried injecting it into test animals in several ways and sequences: before the venom was injected, mixed with the venom, on the opposite side of the body from the venom, and after the injection of the venom. Stephens and Meyers (1898, p. 620) also contributed to methods of antivenin titration. Fraser (1895b, p. 418) gave some thought to the derivation of an antivenin directly from a snake's blood, since he knew that snakes are largely immune to their own venoms, but this proved entirely impracticable. Cunningham (1897, p. 83) made the point that a snake's immunity to its own venom cannot be the result of autoinoculation, since many harmless snakes have a similar immunity.

McFarland (1901, p. 325) observed that it was more difficult to immunize horses against rattlesnake than against cobra venom, because of the intense local reaction produced by the former. This he overcame by using intravenous rather than subcutaneous injections. As late as 1904, Lamb (p. 1276) was pessimistic as to the future of antivenin; he calculated that it would require up to 350 cc. (about ¾ pint) of antivenin injected intravenously to protect against a fully effective cobra bite, and ten times as much if the antivenin were given subcutaneously. Such quantities are, of course, quite impracticable.

Calmette used horses for the production of antivenomous serum in 1895, and in the same year the first attempts were made to cure human beings in actual cases of snake bite. The commercial production of this remedy for cobra bite followed within the next few years. Most of the early work on antivenin was based on cobra venom, for it was natural that the remedy should first be developed where the need was greatest. Greval (1934, p. 365) stated that the preparation of antivenin began in India in 1901, and that 1,020 15-cc. ampuls had been distributed by 1902. Antivenins for rattlesnake bite were produced in this country experimentally by Flexner and Noguchi in 1903 (1904, p. 364) and in Brazil against *Crotalus d. terrificus* by V. Brazil in 1905, but the commercial distribution of antivenin for the treatment of rattlesnake bite in the United States was delayed for many years. Comprehensive histories of the early development of antivenins are those of McFarland (1902, pp. 329, 369, 403, 450, 492) and Noguchi (1909, chapter 23, pp. 223–32). An interesting popular article was written by Dam (1894, p. 460). This was one of the semiscientific stories in *McClure's Magazine* that rapidly increased its circulation.

Ever since the development of antivenin, there has been confusion in the popular mind between it—the curative serum from the blood of an immunized animal, usually a horse—and venom. It has become almost a folklore belief that venom itself is used in the treatment of snake bite. This is a combination of some of the old folklore cures, which used viper heads or viper flesh for treating viper bite, with the modern use of venom in the production of antivenin. The new item of folklore telescopes the process into the direct introduction of venom into the snake-bite wound as a remedy for the original bite. Southwestern folklore even has it that a second bite will cure the first, so that a rattler should be caused to bite twice (Jeffrey, 1955, p. 250).

---

[5] Alternative terms are antiserum, antivenomous serum, antivenom, antivenene, antivenine, and antivenin, of which the last is preferred in the United States. Some medical dictionaries assign slightly different definitions to some of these terms, while others consider them synonymous. Anavenin, anatoxin, and toxoid are terms used for venoms that have been detoxicated but without impairment of their antigenic properties.

AVAILABLE ANTIVENINS

Antivenins, for protection against indigenous snakes, had been prepared and distributed by governmental health departments or research institutions in a number of countries before one suitable for use against North American crotalids was produced in the United States. This was finally undertaken by a division of the Mulford Biological Laboratories, a private company at Glenolden, Pennsylvania, under the name of the Antivenin Institute of America. The organization of the Institute is described in the first number of the *Bulletin* of the Institute, which was issued in March, 1927. The final number of this interesting and important herpetological journal appeared in May, 1932.

The Institute was organized June 1, 1926, primarily through the activities of Dr. Afranio do Amaral, who brought to this country some of the techniques previously developed in Brazil. In this project he was aided by Dr. Thomas Barbour, Dr. R. L. Ditmars, Col. M. L. Crimmins, Dr. Herbert C. Clark, and others. The organization, through depots, one of which was in San Diego, served to gather snakes, and to extract and process venom, which was subsequently sent to Glenolden for experimental purposes and the commercial production of antivenin.

The commercial sale of Mulford's antivenin was authorized by the U. S. Public Health Service April 25, 1927 (Peacock, 1928, p. 752). Improvements were subsequently made in the product from experience both in the field and laboratory. Lyophilization of the serum—quick freezing, followed by desiccation in a vacuum—was adopted in 1940 (Anon., 1940, p. 684). The Mulford company was absorbed by Sharp and Dohme in 1929; and in 1947 the manufacture of antivenin was transferred to Wyeth, Inc., as being more in keeping with their other lines of manufacture than with those of the former company. Under the Wyeth label, the concentration and improvement of the product have been continued.

Besides the Wyeth antivenin produced to counteract the bites of North American crotalids, the following antivenomous snake-bite sera were being produced elsewhere in 1953 (see also Oliver and Goss, 1952, p. 270):

Place of production	Snakes whose venom the antivenin is designed to counteract
Paris	European vipers
"	Polyvalent for African elapids and viperids
"	Polyvalent for venomous snakes of West and Equatorial Africa
"	Cobras of Egypt and India
Johannesburg	Polyvalent for snakes of South Africa
Durban	Polyvalent for snakes of South Africa
Kasauli (Punjab)	Polyvalent for Indian cobra and Russell's viper
Bombay	Polyvalent for various Indian snakes
Bangkok	Polyvalent for snakes of southeastern Asia
"	Malayan pit vipers
"	Common and king cobra
"	Russell's viper
Bandung	Polyvalent for East Indian snakes
Royal Park, Victoria	Tiger snake and other Australian elapids
Mexico City	Rattlesnakes
"	Bothropic pit vipers
"	Polyvalent for both of the above

São Paulo	Polyvalent for Brazilian pit vipers
"	Polyvalent for bothropic pit vipers
"	Neotropical rattlesnake
"	Bushmaster
"	South American elapids

With the exception of the last-named, antivenins similar to the São Paulo series are also manufactured at Nictheroi, Brazil.

Captain Hugh L. Keegan (in Buckley, editor, 1955, in press) lists the following additional antivenins: *Marberg-Lahn, Germany,* for the Neotropical rattlesnake; for bothropic pit vipers; for African cobras; for African viperids; and for Near East and Indian viperids: *Vienna,* for European and Middle Eastern viperids: *Milan,* for European vipers: *Zagreb, Yugoslavia,* for European vipers: *Alger, Algeria,* for North African vipers and cobras: *Tokyo,* for Japanese pit vipers: *Manila* (place of distribution, not manufacture), for Philippine cobras: *Taipei, Taiwan,* for Formosan pit vipers. It is not known whether all these antivenins are available on a commercial basis, or whether some are as yet only experimental.

PREPARATION OF ANTIVENIN

Antivenin is prepared from the serum of an immunized animal, usually a horse or donkey, whose resistance to venom has been built up by the injection of successively larger doses of venom, until it can withstand venom in quantities that would have been quickly fatal if given initially. After the immunization course has been completed, as shown by blood tests, blood is drawn off from time to time in quantities not large enough to injure the animal; and the serum, which contains the venom-counteracting antibodies, is segregated from the rest of the blood and processed for preservation and distribution.

Lamb (1904, p. 1274) observed that some horses yield a much stronger antivenin than others. Some horses react differently to venom than others; in some it produces maladies of the liver and kidneys. A horse that has withstood the immunization course successfully, and has proved to be a good antivenin producer, represents a considerable investment and is carefully tended. There is a limit to the neutralizing power attained by the serum; as early as 1904, Lamb (p. 1275) found that after the serum antibody-content had reached a certain concentration, larger doses of venom produced no further increase, and, in fact, there might be a decline in antidotal power.

The early method of inoculating a horse with increasing doses of crude venom had serious defects; the immunizing process was slow, and the health of the horse suffered, particularly, in the case of certain venoms, from local hemorrhagic reactions at the sites of the injections. Treatments were given every three to five days and the process required eight months or more to complete (e.g., Oertel, 1929, p. 315). Subsequent improvements have entailed the use of detoxicated venoms, or venom-antivenin mixtures. As mentioned elsewhere, venoms, detoxicated by certain chemicals, were found to retain their antigenic properties, and it was possible, through the use of the resulting toxoids, to build the horse's resistance faster, usually in three or four months, and this without frequent failures by reason of pathological developments in the horse. An alternative improvement involved the injection of venom-antivenin mixtures. This hastened immunization but had the objection of using quantities of the end product (antivenin) in carrying on the process (Githens, 1931, p. 81; 1936, p. 3; Amaral, 1923b, p. 91; 1928c, p. 1073; Boquet, 1948, p. 111). For this reason the toxoid process has come to be the one more generally followed.

Many experiments have been made to better the understanding of the immunizing processes and schedules. Markowitz, Essex, and Mann (1931, p. 198) showed that the red blood corpuscles in an immunized animal are no different from those in one not immunized, the protective antibodies being contained entirely in the plasma. Dogs immunized for the first time develop antibodies slowly and the immunization disappears in about 90 days. But, upon resumption of treatments, the antibodies develop much more rapidly and are retained longer. Akatsuka (1936, p. 181) also touched on the greater duration of reimmunization. Kyes, Markin, and Graham (1940, p. 81) found an abrupt, but short-lived, increase in resistance produced by a preliminary sublethal dose. Others who have discussed some of these immunization processes were Essex and Markowitz, 1930, p. 348; Rosenfeld and Glass, 1940, p. 484; and Tyler, 1946, p. 196.

VENOM DETOXICATION

As has been stated, the immunization of animals in order to produce antivenomous sera was at first a slow and often fatal process. The successive dosages with which the immunity was built up must not only be sublethal, they must not produce serious illness. Many discouraging failures were encountered; about the time a horse had reached full immunity, it would develop a fatal liver or kidney ailment and all the time and expense of the prior treatment would be lost. And, especially in the case of snakes with hemorrhagic venoms, such as the Nearctic rattlesnakes, sores and other local reactions to the venom were very troublesome.

The problem was to speed immunization, yet to avoid or minimize the ill effects of the venom on the animal being immunized. It might well be presumed that any substance or method that would reduce or eliminate the toxic property of a venom, would correspondingly reduce the power of the venom to build up the immunity of the animal injected—that is, to render the venom less toxic would lower or remove its antigenic property. But, logical as this theory appears, it is not correct; the toxic properties of venoms can be greatly reduced by chemical or other treatments, or the venoms may be mixed with previously prepared antivenins, and these detoxified substances—anatoxins, toxoids, or anavenins, as they are called—still retain most or all of their capacity to produce antibodies in the blood of the animal being immunized. This reduces both the time required for immunization and its danger. Grasset (1933, p. 35) stated that an immunization schedule on a horse, formerly requiring 12 to 16 months, could be reduced to 4 to 6 weeks by the use of detoxicated venom.

The attenuation of toxins into toxoids was discovered early in the development of antivenins, although probably antedated in the preparation of diphtheria and tetanus antitoxins before the method was used in the preparation of antiophidic serums. Phisalix and Bertrand (1894a, p. 288) had noted that the application of heat to venom, with a subsequent reduction of venom toxicity, did not completely eliminate its antigenic property. Calmette (1894c, p. 275) also experimented with venom detoxified by heat. This was found particularly effective in reducing the local irritation so troublesome in the animal being given an immunization course. Later he used venom partly detoxified by calcium chloride. At about this time the procedure of injecting venom-antivenin mixtures as a means of hastening immunization was discovered; this was an almost automatic sequel of tests for the effectiveness of antivenin in which various proportions of venom and antivenin were injected, either separately or together, to determine the titer or neutralizing power of the latter.

A variety of chemicals and processes have been tested as detoxicants with varying degrees of success. Flexner and Noguchi (1904, p. 374) used hydrochloric acid and iodine trichloride to modify rattlesnake venom. Carmichael (1927, p. 445) suggested sodium ricinoleate; and Shortt and Mallick (1934, p. 536) methylene blue. Ferri and Guidolin (1951, p. 300) tested a number of fluorescent substances as detoxicants. Welch (1930, p. 35) found that detoxication of rattlesnake venom with ultra-violet light was not feasible, as the antigenic property of the venom was lost.

One of the most important and successful detoxicants, formaldehyde, was probably first used by Ramon (1924, p. 1437). It has an ability to detoxify without destruction of antigenic power, as shown in experiments carried out by Grasset and Zoutendyk (1933, p. 308; 1935, pp. 391, 601), Grasset (1936, p. 368; 1945, p. 463), and Akatsuka (1936, p. 147).

Schoettler (1951b, p. 504) pointed out that, since detoxication of the venom does not alter its antigenic property, the toxic factor does not play any integral role in immunization. What we call venom is a mixture of toxic and nontoxic, antigenic and nonantigenic elements (p. 505). As the toxic and the combining properties of venoms are separate, a part of the toxicity may be eliminated without reducing the antibody-binding power (1951c, p. 313). The detoxication of venom by chemicals does not involve a mere mixing of the substances. On the contrary, it requires five or six weeks of incubation, although improvements in the method may shorten the process to three weeks (Grasset and Zoutendyk, 1938, p. 447).

SPECIFICITY OF ANTIVENINS

When the efficacy of antivenomous sera was first discovered, it was thought that, regardless of the venom used in the immunization program, the resulting antivenin might be equally effective against bites by all kinds of snakes. This was soon disproved (Martin, 1897, p. 532; Cunningham, 1897, p. 72), whereupon an exactly opposite assumption was made: that monovalent antivenins—that is, those resulting when the venom of a single species of snake has been used for immunization—would be most effective for the bite of the same kind of snake. Carried further, it was assumed that the antivenin would be partly effective for the bite of the nearest relatives of the snake whose venom had been used in the immunization course that produced the antivenin, and least effective for the bites of the species most widely separated in the phylogenetic tree.

Extensive experimentation has verified this theory in certain fundamentals, but not in detail. It is true that monovalent antivenins are almost never effective for venoms of a quite different type; for example, antivenins based on venoms that are largely neurotoxic are usually of little or no value in counteracting hemorrhagic venoms. But there are many important exceptions to the applicability of the rest of the theory, including the surprising result that a monovalent antivenin is sometimes less effective against the venom used in its production than against the venom of some other snake. So the venom-antivenin correlation is by no means a simple one. Basically these inconsistencies may in part be the result of the complex nature of snake venoms in terms of physiological effects. The nature of the detoxicants used may also play a part. And polyvalency can be secured, at least to some degree, by treating the producing animal with a mixture of snake venoms.

Following the first preparation of antivenin and the hope of its being a universal remedy, the first proofs of relative specificity were advanced by Fraser (1895, p. 1310) and by Martin (1897, p. 532). Later, important papers on the subject were those of Lamb (1903, p. 1; 1904, p. 1273) and Noguchi (1909, chapter 24, pp. 233–41), who showed that antivenins are generally specific but not completely so. More recent discussions have been those of Githens and Butz, 1929, p. 71; Githens 1931, p. 83; Ahuja, 1935, p. 482; Grasset and Zoutendyk, 1935, pp. 391, 601; 1936, p. 350; Grasset, 1936, p. 367; Kellaway, 1937, p. 159; Ipsen, 1938, p. 786; Githens and Wolff, 1939, p. 33; Githens, 1941, p. 149; Micheel, 1941, p. 170; Boquet, 1948, p. 119; Schoettler, 1951b, p. 500; and Criley (in Buckley, editor, 1955, in press).

The Githens and Butz papers indicate that there are only slight differences (antigenically) between the venoms of the more important Nearctic rattlesnake species, such as *C. atrox, adamanteus, ruber, horridus, mitchelli,* and *viridis,* so that the hope of securing a polyvalent antivenin for these is good, and, indeed, the presently available antivenin for the Nearctic Crotalidae—the Wyeth product—is claimed to be strongly polyvalent. The venom of the Neotropical rattler, *C. d. terrificus,* is so different that it may require a differently derived antivenin, although attempts to make the Wyeth product polyvalent for this subspecies are said to be meeting with success (Criley in Buckley, 1955). The rattlesnake problem is discussed further by Githens and Wolff (1939) and by Githens (1941).

Grasset (1936, p. 367) indicates the lack of complete interspecific correlation thus (using the term antivenin A as the antivenin derived from immunization with venom A): Antivenin A may be highly effective for venom A and moderately effective for venom B; yet antivenin B may be useless against venom A, and may, in some cases, be less effective against venom B than is antivenin A. To make polyvalent antivenins more effective is a complicated problem of antigenic selection and trial. As stated by Grasset and Zoutendyk (1936, p. 350): "These extremes of unexpected antigenic dissimilarity and equally unexpected antigenic similarity emphasize the importance of selecting viperine venoms strictly on their antigenic characteristics for purposes of serum production."

Schoettler (1951b, p. 507), in his studies of the antivenins prepared by the Instituto Butantan, in São Paulo, Brazil, reached the conclusion that the monovalent antivenin prepared specifically against the bite of *C. d. terrificus* was not quite so effective against this particular snake as was one of the polyvalent antivenins derived in part from *Bothrops* venoms. He therefore recommended that the manufacture of the monovalent *terrificus* antivenin be discontinued.

Even if monovalent antivenins were more effective than polyvalent against the bites of the particular snakes from whose venoms they were derived, it would still be essential, in most countries, to have polyvalent antivenins, however less effective they might be. For, in practical snake-bite cases, the species of snake causing the accident is seldom known. Even if the snake is killed, which is not often the case, it cannot be identified unless the remains are brought to some scientific institution. Hence a polyvalent antivenin must be used. In the United States the problem is simplified. Except for coral snakes, which have restricted ranges and are seldom the cause of snake-bite accidents, the other venomous snakes—the rattlers, copperheads, and moccasins—have venoms so much alike in type that monovalent antivenins would have little or no advantage over the polyvalent type now manufactured. Monovalent antivenins would be commercially impracticable, and would serve no useful purpose in areas where more than one venomous species is found.

ANTIVENIN PURIFICATION AND CONCENTRATION

The treatment of the raw immunizing serum, as removed from the horse, in order to preserve and concentrate its protective properties, is an important step in antivenin manufacture. In the early days of the use of antivenins, they were distributed in liquid form in sealed vials. Storage at low temperatures was necessary, and even then deterioration was rapid. V. Brazil reported a loss of strength of 30 per cent in three years; this referred to the product as made in 1916. In 1930, the antivenin then available in the United States deteriorated 10 to 15 per cent, when kept at room temperature for 20 months. Now the lyophilizing process is used; the product is distributed dry, but ready for re-solution and use. This process strengthens the product and slows deterioration. It is stated that dry antivenin will be virtually unimpaired for at least five years, if kept at temperatures between 2° and 10° C. (35.6° and 50° F.).

The most recent improvements in antivenins have not only sought to enhance the lasting quality of the product, but, even more important, have sought to increase the titer—the neutralizing power per unit of quantity—and at the same time to eliminate, as far as possible, those portions of the product causing serum sickness in persons allergic to horse serum. This last improvement is not only important as a protection to the victim of a snake bite, but will make field use safer and therefore more effective, since an early use of antivenin increases its protective value. Various methods of fractionation and segregation of the horse serum have been devised, whereby unnecessary and even deleterious portions of the antivenin have been removed, with increased effectiveness and reduced danger in the part retained. By these means, also, polyvalency has been increased, as well as the speed with which the antivenin neutralizes—the latter called by Grasset (1933, p. 36) its avidity. These concentration and purification methods were developed in part for antitoxin sera other than snake antivenins. Some of the important papers describing the chemical processes used in fractionating, purifying, and concentrating the sera, such as the ammonium sulphate and pepsin methods, have been the following: Mallick and Maitra, 1932, p. 951; Grasset, 1932, p. 267; 1933, p. 39; Greval, 1934, p. 365; Grasset and Zoutendyk, 1938, p. 449; Pope, 1938, p. 245; 1939, pp. 132 and 201; Grasset, 1946, p. 109; Grasset and Christensen, 1947, p. 207; and Harms, 1948, p. 390. For example, Grasset and Christensen, by enzyme purification of certain polyvalent South African antivenins, increased the antibody concentration four to six times, and this with a reduced serum reaction. The present activities of the research laboratories justify the expectation of stronger and more polyvalent antivenins in the future, and with reduced reactions in patients allergic to horse serum.

According to Criley (in Buckley, editor, 1955, in press), the immunization program used by the manufacturer of rattlesnake antivenin in the United States involves increasing doses of venom until the horses are hyperimmunized. The doses start at 3 mg. and are approximately doubled at weekly intervals, until a dose of 1,000 mg. is reached in the eleventh week. The first blood for use in the preparation of antivenin is drawn off in the twelfth week. Thereafter a maintenance schedule involving venom injections, bleeding, and resting periods is continued indefinitely (Criley, table 4). The venom used for immunizing the horses is composed of a mixture of the venoms of *C. d. terrificus, C. atrox, C. adamanteus,* and *Bothrops atrox* (the fer-de-lance). This combination of venoms affords the broadest polyvalency in the product. Other mixtures had been experimented with, some of which included several additional venoms, but the titer for the excluded venoms was not diminished when they were omitted and dependence was placed on the four-venom mixture already mentioned. Gingrich and Hohenadel (in Buckley, editor, 1955, in press) give the following neutralizing values of the resultant antivenin for various crotalids in terms of the milligrams of venom neutralized per ampul (10 c.c.) of antivenin, based on the test of a representative lot: *C. atrox* 11.5, *C. adamanteus* 17.5, *C. d. terrificus* 4.25, *C. horridus* 16, *C. v. viridis* 11, *C. v. oreganus* [*helleri?*] 15, *C. r. ruber* 27, *C. b. basiliscus* 23, *Agkistrodon contortrix* 28, *A. piscivorus* 25.5, *A. bilineatus* 14, *Bothrops atrox* 24, *B. neuwiedi* 20.5, *B. jararaca* 17, *B. jararacussu* 22.5, *B. alternatus* 9, *Lachesis muta* 15. All of these neutralizing potencies are above the standard required by the National Institutes of Health. The institutes have assigned a dating limit of five years after the date of issue, if the ampuls are given a ten per cent excess fill. There is said to be no indication of loss of potency after six years of storage at 37° C. (98.6° F.).

These neutralizing values are based on mouse tests. The figures are of interest in showing relative titers for different venoms, but they cannot be applied directly to calculations of the number of ampuls of antivenin that might be required in any case of snake bite, since three paramount factors that affect every case are never known: (1) the amount of venom injected that must be neutralized; (2) the quantity of venom that the victim's body can take care of by its own inherent defenses (related to the victim's weight and m.l.d.); and (3) the quantity of venom eliminated by such accessory methods as incision and suction.

TESTING AND STANDARDIZATION

The testing of antivenins is a complicated process. It is related to the evaluation of venom toxicities, and is complicated because of the variable factors entailed— variations in the venoms against which protection is sought, in their physiological effects, and in the susceptibilities of the test animals. In general, it is the purpose of the test to determine the quantity of dried venom (in mg.) that a given quantity of liquid antivenin (in cc.) will neutralize. This is the titer of the antivenin. To be successful, antivenin must be introduced into the body of the animal to be cured in sufficient quantity to neutralize whatever venom the snake has injected, beyond that which the victim, through natural absorptive and disposal processes, can handle by himself. If a snake injects 100 mg. of venom, and the body of the victim has sufficient inherent resistance to absorb 30 mg. without fatal results, then the antivenin must be introduced in a quantity adequate to counteract the remaining 70 mg. These quantities are never known in a snake-bite case; they are only mentioned to indicate the nature of the problem involved, and the importance of the neutralizing power in terms of cc. of antivenin per mg. of venom. The antivenin first produced in this country was said to have a titer of 2 mg. of rattlesnake (presumably *atrox*) venom per cc. of antivenin. This was later strengthened to 3 mg. per cc. Studies in standardization that accompanied the development of antivenin in this country have been described by Githens (1931, p. 83; 1936, p. 3; and 1941, p. 149), and by Jackson and Githens (1931, pp. 2, 6). In tests of the effectiveness of the antivenin, the venom and antivenin are mixed in graduated proportions and then injected into the test animal whose m.l.d. of that particular venom is already known. The number of m.l.d.'s counteracted per cc. of antivenin is calculated when the test animal barely survives (Githens, 1931, p. 83). More recently the animal's $l.d._{50}$ is determined and used as a standard in terms of which the neutralizing power of the antivenin is measured. The methods of standardization and testing now used by Wyeth Laboratories have been outlined by Gingrich and Hohenadel (in Buckley, editor, 1955, in press).

Schoettler (1951b, p. 500) has pointed out that accurate information on the results of the antivenin treatment for snake bite is difficult to collect and correlate. He developed a useful method of evaluating an antivenin by plotting dosage–per-cent-mortality curves with and without antivenin (p. 501). He thought it would eventually be possible to increase antivenin concentrations (p. 507). One complication in determining the titer of antivenin, for the venom of any particular species of rattlesnake, is the variability introduced by the relative susceptibility of the species of animal selected for the tests, and the method of injection of both the venom and antivenin. Schoettler (1952b, p. 1040) studied the time element involved in administering the remedy and found that delay diminished the chance of recovery. He also showed the superiority of intravenous over subcutaneous injection of the antivenin. Other important discussions of antivenin titration and standardization by Schoettler will be found in 1951d, p. 839, and 1952a, p. 293.

Martin and Lamb had early pointed out how weak antivenins are compared with bacterial antitoxins, in that cobra antivenin had only 1/10,000 the neutralizing value of diphtheria antitoxin and 1/20,000 that of tetanus antitoxin (Alcock, 1914, p. 245; see also Minton, 1954, p. 1077). Grasset (1933, p. 35) has explained that antivenin must meet a more difficult situation than that met by antitoxin in a disease, for in a disease there is a period of incubation with a gradual increase in toxin, whereas in snake bite the toxin is introduced abruptly and at full strength. Boquet, Bussard, and Izard (1952, p. 640) have suggested that the effectiveness of antivenin might be increased by adding the spreading factor hyaluronidase to quicken its absorption and dispersion through the tissues.

USE OF ANTIVENIN

When possible, antivenin should be administered by a physician. It is rarely available in the field, so that to await a doctor's care will usually not involve any material delay in its use. In an emergency, such as when it is available in a remote camp and the case is serious, it may be used by anyone, but the instructions should be followed carefully, particularly as to the avoidance of serum shock.

In the United States, only one kind of antivenin is available. This is Antivenin (Crotalidae) Polyvalent, Wyeth. In this country, it should be used only for the bite of a rattlesnake or a large water moccasin (cottonmouth). The bite of a copperhead is rarely serious enough to justify the use of antivenin. Excepting only coral snakes that occur in the Southeastern states and in southern Arizona, these are the only dangerously venomous snakes found anywhere in the United States. The Wyeth antivenin at present manufactured is not useful against coral-snake bite. Antivenin should not be used unless there is evidence that the bite has been that of one of the pit vipers mentioned, and that some venom has been injected. To make this determination there must be some dependence on symptoms, and these symptoms must be other than those that result from fright. They must not be confused with the symptoms of the first-aid treatment, such as those caused by incisions made at the site of the bite, or by the use of a tourniquet. The symptoms of an effective bite by a rattler or water moccasin nearly always involve marked local pain—a violent stinging—soon followed by swelling and discoloration around the bite. I have discussed these symptoms at greater length elsewhere (chap. 12), but, in general, they will be evident in case of the bite of any rattler in the United States. Occasionally the bite of the subspecies of the western rattlesnake, *Crotalus viridis,* will cause little or no pain or swelling at first; the earliest sensations may be a tingling or prickling in the scalp, the soles of the feet, or in the lips and tongue.

So much has been said about not using antivenin unless there is evidence that it is really necessary, because it is not a remedy to be taken on the theory of "Take it to play safe; no harm done if it isn't needed." For antivenin is essentially a horse serum, and some people are so sensitive or allergic to horse serum that the reaction may be decidedly annoying and persistent, and even serious unless proper precautions be taken. This has been fully recognized by the manufacturers, who include, in each package of antivenin, instructions for making sensitization tests and for effecting desensitization. Such tests are not described here, since the instructions will always be available with the antivenin, and they may be changed and improved from time to time in future. All physicians, through their experience with other horse-serum antitoxins, are familiar with such tests, and the precautions to be taken where the patient is shown to be sensitive. The manufacturers are continually endeavoring to reduce the deleterious, yet antigenically unnecessary, components of their antivenins.

It also would be completely out of place for me to make suggestions as to where the antivenin should be injected, whether at the site of the bite or elsewhere, and whether subcutaneously, intramuscularly, or intravenously. These questions are fully covered in the instructions, which also recommend the number of syringes (ampuls) to use. As now prepared, Wyeth antivenin, after redissolving, comprises 10 cc. of liquid per ampul. As many as five or more ampuls may be required in a single case, dependent on the seriousness of the bite and the size of the patient, for children require more. Recent antivenin instructions emphasize the importance of the early administration of multiple doses, if there is evidence from the symptoms that more than one ampul will be required. Under these circumstances, the immediate injection of up to five ampuls given at one time will be more effective than the same number applied from time to time as the case develops and the symptoms become more alarming. These are matters to be decided by the physician, but at least he should be thoroughly aware of both the possibilities and limitations of antivenin. It is not a cure-all for the bites of snakes in our country, but it should be of great aid and importance in reducing the danger from snake bite, especially from the neurotoxic effects of the venom. Dependence should not be put on it to the extent of a neglect of other remedial measures. The manufacturer of antivenin for use in the United States is to be commended for making this clear in his instruction circular, and his discussion of the other measures is excellent.

When antivenin for our American crotalids was first made available in the United States—this was in the late 1920's—the idea was widespread that antivenin was a cure-all; that no matter how serious the bite, the victim need only take one 10-cc. shot and go about his business as if he had not been bitten. This was not the result of any statements made by the firm then manufacturing antivenin, but was, rather, caused by the uncritical newspaper publicity that greeted its availability in this country. Subsequently, when cases were lost despite the use of antivenin, there was a considerable reaction, as, for example, in the publication of R. R. Ozmer's article entitled "False Security" in 1930. Certain improved methods of the incision and suction type of treatment, particularly those advocated by Dr. Dudley Jackson of San Antonio, were recommended instead of antivenin. Today (1955) there is a better appreciation of the status of all methods of treatment, and of the value of the improved antivenin now available—its value as an important adjunct, but no cure-all. The main thing for the attending physician to remember is that, more often than not, several ampuls of antivenin, rather than a single one, will be needed, and that, having taken all necessary precautions against serum shock, he should have no hesitancy in using them, and this simultaneously rather than serially. I know of one fatal case that might have been saved had the physician not taken it for granted that a single ampul was the maximum dose needed or permissible.

Besides the sensitivity or allergy tests described in the Wyeth instruction pamphlet, the following references to the problems involved in the use of antivenin will be found of interest: Woodbury and Anderson, 1945, p. 187; Ganguli and Napier, 1946, p. 857; Pope and Peterson, 1946, p. 564; Boquet, 1948, p. 126; Richardson, 1949, p. 87; Pope, 1950, p. 7; Happ, 1951, p. 26; Devoe, 1951, p. 235; Milne and Milne, 1952, p. 193; and Oliver and Goss, 1952, p. 27. While the usual reaction of those allergic to horse serum is confined to troublesome hives, there have been reports of stiffness and swelling of the joints, swelling at the point of injection of the antivenin, fever, edema of the eyelids, and respiratory failure. It is possible that there may have been confusion in some cases between the snake-bite symptoms and the supposed symptoms of serum sickness.

Urticaria or hives comprise the most usual symptoms of serum sickness. In one case with which I am familiar, itching started three days after the use of the antivenin and continued for seven days, reaching a peak on the seventh day after the bite. In another case with the same patient 13 years later, hives became evident two days after the bite and continued for eight days. They covered the entire body and were very severe. It is to be hoped that antihistamines will benefit such cases; however, they do not seem to have been effective in Happ's case (1951, p. 26).

Some statistical indications of the value of the crotalid antivenin used in this country have been submitted by Amaral (1927b, p. 80), Hutchison (1929, p. 51), and Githens (1935b, p. 167). There is no doubt that the use of antivenin has reduced the death rate from the bites of poisonous snakes in the United States, and has speeded the recovery of nonfatal cases. But it is difficult to derive authentic differences in mortality rates, because the cases wherein antivenin was used, and those in which it was not, are so seldom comparable in other particulars. For example, the antivenin cases are more likely to have had other remedies—such as tourniquets, incision, suction, and various supportive measures—applied more efficiently than was the case where antivenin was not used. Antivenin is in itself an indication of adequate care, and often of hospitalization.

There is by no means a universal agreement among physicians who practice in areas where rattlesnake bite is an occasional occurrence that antivenin should be used. Some do not favor prescribing it because of the danger of serum sickness; they consider incision and suction equally effectual and less dangerous. Another argument against antivenin is its relatively low titer for the bite of the western diamondback (*C. atrox*), the rattler which causes a large percentage of the dangerous cases of snake bite in the United States.

Antivenins cannot do the impossible; and with their present concentrations some dangerous snakes can inject venoms in such quantities that quite impracticable quantities of antivenins would be required to counteract them. In 1904, Lamb (p. 1276), with the cobra antivenin then available, stated that it would take 350 cc. of antivenin injected intravenously and up to 7,000 cc. taken subcutaneously to counteract a fully effective cobra bite. Presumably the strength of the cobra antivenin is now much intensified. Schoettler (1951, p. 502) calculated that it would require 14 ampuls of the best antivenin then available to cure an average bite of the most dangerous snake in Brazil, the South American rattlesnake (*C. d. terrificus*), and 170 ampuls to cure a maximum-injection bite. In one case of rattlesnake bite in California, 480 cc. of antivenin were given. Minton (1954, p. 1077) has pointed out some of the weaknesses of antivenin.

In Costa Rica, where an attempt has been made to reduce the prevalence of folklore cures for snake bite, there is a law (1952) requiring specified municipal districts to appropriate not less than 500 colones per annum for the purchase and distribution of antivenin (see also Anon., 1928b, p. 50). There is a provision of the Education Code of the State of California, chapter 5, article 1, page 739, paragraphs 24, 504–5, that requires the first-aid kit to be carried on any school field trip to contain "some sort of antivenum." Presumably antivenin is meant.

RECOMMENDED TREATMENT FOR RATTLESNAKE BITE

I have some doubt as to the advisability of presenting here a set of instructions for the treatment of rattlesnake bite, for it is to be expected that such instructions as I may offer today will have been superseded by improved treatments within a few years, whereas other parts of this book should still retain their usefulness. But as someone in an emergency may look here for suggested methods of treatment, I shall offer a program that represents the present consensus of expert opinion. It should be understood that I am not a physician; neither am I skilled through experience in the treatment of rattlesnake bite. I am merely handing on such instructions as appear to represent the preferences of most physicians. The procedures recommended are selected particularly with the treatment of the bites of Nearctic (United States) rattlesnakes, and copperheads and moccasins in mind. With these limitations they can be made more specific, but they may not be appropriate for, nor involve the best practices in the treatment of, the bite of the Neotropical rattlesnake (*C. durissus* and its subspecies), or of snakes of kinds other than the northern pit vipers.

REFERENCES

Ordinarily the medical texts containing the best advice on the treatment of snake bite are the manuals or treatises on tropical medicine. Of these no criticism is offered, but necessarily their coverage must be broad enough to include all kinds of poisonous snakes in all countries, and thus they are not aimed particularly at treating the venoms, largely hemorrhagic in quality, that characterize most rattlesnakes, especially those occurring in the United States. Hence, in using them, the physician must select the details of treatment appropriate to the bites of Nearctic rattlers. Among publications of this general type that will be found useful are:

OLIVER, J. A.
    1944.   Snakes and Snake Poisoning. *In* Clinical and Tropical Medicine, by Z. T. Bercovitz, pp. 855–880.

GANGULI, S. K., and L. E. NAPIER
    1946.   Snakes and Snake-bite. *In* The Principles and Practice of Tropical Medicine, by L. E. Napier, pp. 836–859.

AMARAL, A. DO
    1951.   Snake Venation (Ophidism). *In* Clinical Tropical Medicine, by R. B. H. Gradwohl, L. B. Soto, and O. Felsenfeld, pp. 1238–1264.

DUNN, E. R.
    1951.   Venomous Reptiles of the Tropics. *In* Diseases of the Tropics, by G. C. Shattuck, pp. 741–754.

It will be observed from the titles that these chapters in the manuals of tropical medicine present summaries of the natural histories of venomous snakes as well as instructions for the treatment of their bites. They are all by experienced herpetologists.

The following are some additional manuals and instruction books that are to be recommended; most of them apply specifically to the treatment of rattlesnake bite:

YOUNG, NETTIE
    1940.   Snakebite: Treatment and Nursing Care. Amer. Jour. of Nursing, vol. 40, no. 6, pp.
             657–660. [A valuable exposition of the methods used in the hospital by Dr. Dudley
             Jackson of San Antonio.]

CRIMMINS, M. L.
    1946.   The Treatment of Poisonous Snake Bite in Texas. Proc. and Trans. Texas Acad.
             Sci., vol. 29, pp. 54–61. An older edition will be found in Military Surgeon, vol. 74,
             no. 3, pp. 125–132, 1934. [This is primarily an expositon of the incision-suction
             method developed by Jackson. Instructions for this treatment will also be found in
             the "Dudley" kit for first aid.]

PERKINS, C. B.
    1949.   The Snakes of San Diego County with Descriptions and Key. 2d ed. Bull. Zoöl. Soc.
             San Diego, no. 23, pp. 1–77. [Good instructions for field treatment, pp. 17–21.]

ANON. (Wyeth Incorporated)
    1951.   Antivenin (North American Antisnakebite Serum). Philadelphia, pp. 1–19. [A valu-
             able pamphet, not only on the use of antivenin, but on other first-aid and hospital
             measures to be taken.]

VAZ, E.
    1951.   Instituto Butantan. São Paulo, pp. 1–61. [Includes suggestions for treatment of the
             bite of the Neotropical rattlesnake, *C. d. terrificus,* as well as other tropical snakes.]

OLIVER, J. A.
    1952.   The Prevention and Treatment of Snake Bite. Animal Kingdom, Bull. N. Y. Zoöl.
             Soc., vol. 55, no. 3, pp. 66–83. Also published as a separate booklet. [Good first-aid
             instructions, p. 79.]

STICKEL, W. H.
    1952.   Venomous Snakes of the United States and Treatment of Their Bites. Washington,
             U. S. Fish and Wildlife Service, Wildlife Leaflet 339, pp. 1–29. [The most up-to-date
             manual of treatment now available. A copy of this mimeographed folder should be
             in the library of every hospital. It can be obtained free by application to the
             U. S. Fish and Wildlife Service, Washington.]

Some of the matters that I shall mention in the instructions that follow have
been discussed at greater length elsewhere in this book, particularly in the historical section at the beginning of this chapter. They are briefly reintroduced
here so that the pertinent points will be available in one place.

TREATMENT: Part 1, for the Victim and His Companions in the Field.

As a matter of reassurance to the victim of a bite, it can be said that even with
the crudest treatment, or without any treatment, rattlesnake bite would probably
not be fatal in more than 10 per cent of the cases, although greater with some
especially dangerous species. With proper treatment the mortality from rattlesnake bite should be less than 2 or 3 per cent. Snake bite is likely to be more
serious in children, since the ability of a body to absorb venom without fatal
results varies with the weight.

In an accident of this kind, be sure that the snake involved is a venomous snake.
All rattlesnakes have rattles. Many harmless snakes are blotched like rattlesnakes.
Don't jump to conclusions. Many harmless snakes will bite fiercely when trod
upon or handled, but their bites are without injurious effects; they are no more
serious than a scratch and should be given a like antiseptic treatment. Nevertheless,
there are authentic instances in which grave results and even death have been caused
by totally unwarranted fear following the bite of a harmless snake. If there is any

doubt as to the identification of the snake that did the biting, kill it and bring it in, or at least bring in the head and tail. Use a stick to push the dead snake into a box or can. However, do not consume time catching the culprit if this will delay treatment of the victim. But a sure identification may save the victim from painful and unnecessary treatment. This is said because every herpetologist has had many a snake brought to him that the bringer thought was a rattlesnake, or some other kind of dangerous snake, but which proved to be a harmless snake. You can have your snake identified by a zoo, a natural history museum, a park naturalist, or by the biology department of any high school or college.

The actual injection of rattlesnake venom into a wound is followed immediately by a sharp, stinging local pain in almost every case, and this should be used as a criterion in determining whether the bite is that of a rattler, and if venom has actually been injected. With most species a marked swelling is also evident within a very short time. In rare cases the bite of a western rattlesnake (*Crotalus viridis*) causes no local pain, but even with this kind, a local swelling usually develops quite soon. Also, a prickling sensation will be felt about the face, especially the lips.

Assuming that a person has actually been bitten by a rattlesnake, and that some venom has been injected, the following procedure should be adopted by the victim and his companions, if any are present:

(1) The victim should not become unduly alarmed or excited, and should not run, for to do so will speed the circulation and the rapidity with which the venom is absorbed. Move the injured limb as little as possible. Remember that few cases of rattlesnake bite are fatal.

(2) Immediately apply a tourniquet between the bite and the heart, about 2 inches above the bite. If no first-aid kit is at hand, use a shoe string, necktie, or any strip of cloth. Rubber tubing makes a good tourniquet. Do not tie it too tightly; you should be able to force a finger under it, and feel a pulse below it. Complete stoppage of the circulation is unnecessary and dangerous. If the affected part turns blue,[a] the tourniquet is too tight. In any case, loosen the tourniquet for 20 seconds at 15-minute intervals. This loosening is important; there is grave danger in leaving a tight tourniquet in place too long without release.

(3) With a sharp instrument, such as a razor blade or a knife, make a longitudinal incision beside each fang mark or slightly above it, that is, toward the heart. The depth should be about equal to that of the fang, say from an eighth to a quarter of an inch deep if the snake is of moderate size, and about one-half inch long. (If the fang marks are clearly evident, the depth of fang penetration may be judged to have been about three-fourths of the fang separation). Before using, sterilize the cutting instrument with iodine, alcohol, or the flame of a match. Also sterilize around the bite with iodine or alcohol before cutting. Before cutting, inject a local anesthetic if available. Omit the cutting if the snake was a small one, or if you will be able to get to a doctor within 10 or 15 minutes. If the bite is in a bony part, make no cuts until a swelling develops, then cut into the swelling.

(4) Apply suction to the wound and the incisions thus made, either with the mouth or by using one of the suction devices in the first-aid kit if you have one.

---

[a] This does not refer to the purplish blotches that may be caused by the venom.

Moisten the open end of the suction device to make it adhere better. Apply suction continuously for at least half an hour. A healthy person with good teeth need have no fear of getting venom into the mouth or stomach with untoward results, particularly if the blood is spit out at once. Even if no cuts are made, suck the bite.

(5) If antivenin is available, use it in accordance with the instructions accompanying the syringe, but only in case a doctor cannot be reached within an hour or two. If you are more than two hours from help, use it, but follow the instructions carefully. Otherwise, wait until the doctor is reached and let him administer the antivenin. Don't use the antivenin if the victim is known to be seriously susceptible to horse serum; if this is not known follow the test instructions.

(6) If swelling or discoloration progresses up the limb, additional lengthwise cuts should be made above the bite and suction should be applied there, the tourniquet having been moved to a new place above the swelling. It is best to put on a second tourniquet before removing the first.

(7) If the patient is faint, give him a cup of strong coffee, a cup of tea, or a teaspoonful of aromatic spirits of ammonia in a glass of water. Don't give any alcoholic drink.

(8) Get the patient to a doctor or hospital as soon as possible. Don't let the suction program delay doing so. Secure a physician experienced in previous snakebite cases if one is available. Be sure to see a doctor even if the case seems to be a mild one. If the patient is alone, he should drive only as far as the nearest highway, asking someone else to take over as soon as assistance is at hand.

(9) Do not do any of the following things: Do not use potassium permanganate. Do not give whiskey. Do not burn or cauterize the wound, since this will interfere with the all-important suction and drainage. Do not use folklore remedies; they are a waste of time when time is valuable, and, by confusing the symptoms, they make treatment by a doctor more difficult.

(10) If the physician in charge of the case has not had previous experience, he can telephone the county hospital for advice. Such hospitals have usually had experience with the treatment of snake-bite cases in their own areas, which is important. If you have a copy of *Wildlife Leaflet 339,* the Wyeth antivenin pamphlet, or one of the other publications cited above, turn it over to the doctor for his study. Remember that snake-bite cases are so infrequent that many doctors have never seen one. Their own libraries may be lacking in recent instructions of the most approved character.

TREATMENT: Part 2, for the Physician and the Hospital.

These suggestions are made with due diffidence, since I am not a physician. They represent a summary of recent recommendations by those having wide experience.

Antivenin.—Administer Wyeth antivenin according to the instructions, taking all required precautions against horse-serum shock. Three points should be emphasized: (1) much more than a single 10 cc. dose may be required—50 cc. or more are not at all unusual, so it should be available in suitable quantities; (2) if multiple doses are required, they will be more effective if injected simultaneously than if used serially as the symptoms develop; (3) more will be required for children than adults, since their venom-neutralizing power is less. Give particular attention to the place (whether at the bite or elsewhere) and method of injection as set forth in the instructions. Get as much information as possible concerning the kind and size of snake involved to aid in estimating the extent of the antivenin that may be required.

Tourniquet.—Field tourniquets should be removed, and a new one installed and tightened just enough to stop lymphatic circulation. It should be moved so as to keep it ahead of the swelling. The bitten limb should be kept below body level. Keep it immobilized.

Incision and Suction.—Continued incision and suction, with progressively advanced cruciform cuts keeping pace with the swelling, are still recommended, but to a less degree than was formerly the case. Usually suction for 20 minutes out of each hour for from 5 to 15 hours is recommended. Although mechanical suction devices are to be used, they should be regulated so that the negative pressure will not be extreme.

While some body fluid containing the admixed venom is removed by these methods, and also the culture media for gas gangrene and other bacteria are eliminated, it is recognized that suction involves a loss of blood that the patient can ill afford. The doctor, in judging the value of continued suction, must be guided by the extent of the local hemorrhagic symptoms. Free bleeding should not be allowed to continue. Sometimes the elimination of venom at the incisions can be increased by flushing with normal saline solution.

During the suction program, but between suction applications, the incisions should be covered with magnesium sulfate compresses. Where the incisions have been extensive in serious cases, they should be kept open and draining for two weeks, even if the patient is progressing satisfactorily.

Transfusions.—Type the patient for blood transfusions as soon as he is admitted to the hospital. Transfusions may be needed quickly if the patient shows signs of shock, or if his red-cell count and hemoglobin are dropping. Blood tests should be made every three hours.

Shock.—For dehydration and shock, intravenous normal saline, 5 per cent dextrose solution, or Ringer's solution have been suggested. An appreciation of the danger of shock in snake bite, with adequate protection against it, has been one of the major improvements in treatment during recent years.

Sedation.—Administer sedatives and stimulants as needed. Some of the symptoms of rattlesnake bite, to say nothing of the incision-suction treatment, are extremely painful. Morphine is generally recommended to reduce pain and allay apprehension as soon as the patient enters the hospital.

Septicemia.—Septicemia is more than a usual threat in rattlesnake bite, both because of the condition of the snake's mouth, and because the venom has certain characteristics tending to weaken the normal bactericidal quality of the victim's blood. Tetanus and gas gangrene antisera, separate, or combined, are to be recommended, with the regular precautions attendant on their use. Antibiotics should be used in precautionary doses or as needed by developments.

Food and Drink.—Give blood-building foods, including the usual treatments for anemia. Encourage water consumption. As kidney damage is common, frequent urine examinations are desirable.

Purgatives.—Some venom is excreted through the intestinal tract. Gentle colonic irrigations of salt and soda solutions every four hours or so are recommended.

Continued Care.—If there is one feature of rattlesnake-bite treatment wherein a herpetologist may presume to offer advice to an attendant physician, it has to do with the continuance of care and vigilance beyond what seems to be required. Often, in these cases, the spectacular hemorrhagic symptoms have a way of clearing rapidly. The patient is deemed to be beyond danger and is left unattended. Suddenly neurotoxic symptoms, such as respiratory or cardiac failure, are manifested and the patient may sink quickly beyond recovery. Those having the most experience in these cases recommend the closest vigilance for not less than 48 and preferably for 72 hours, and, of course, longer if the symptoms continue serious.

Miscellaneous Comments.—With such crotalid venomous snakes (rattlers, moccasins, and copperheads) as are found in the United States, serious bites usually develop conspicuous local symptoms within a matter of minutes, or in an hour at most. The physician should have made some effort to become familiar with the dangerously venomous snakes that occur in his neighborhood; this will aid in prognosis. Blood typing and a blood count should be ordered upon admission, since the destructive action of the venom may later affect the result. A urinalysis should be made; Shannon (1953, p. 371) advises intravenous saline and blood if hemoglobinuria or albuminuria is present. His recommendations on supportive measures will be found valuable. Remember that snake bite is particularly dangerous to children.

References.—The physician will find much pertinent information on treatment in the Anon. (Wyeth), Stickel, Crimmins, Oliver, and Young references already cited. In addition, I suggest Holt: Southwestern Medicine, vol. 31, no. 1, pp. 13–15, 1950; Happ: Bull. San Diego Co. Med. Soc., vol. 37, no. 3, pp. 20, 22, 26, 1951; Chotkowski: New England Jour. Med., vol. 241, no. 16, pp. 600–603, 1949; Magee: Military Surgeon, vol. 93, pp. 85–90, 1943; Shannon: Southwestern Medicine, vol. 34, no. 1, pp. 367–373, 1953; and Watt and Pollard, Jour. Florida Med. Assn., vol. 41, pp. 367–370. Particularly recommended are Stickel, p. 22 (follow-up care), and Anon. (Wyeth), p. 16 (instructions for physicians only).

In conclusion I should like to present these suggestions for the treatment of a case involving rattlesnake bite: If the symptoms of snake bite are not severe, don't overtreat; if they are present and severe, don't undertreat, and subsequently keep the patient under close observation.

First-Aid Kits

A number of satisfactory first-aid kits, useful for rattlesnake bite, are on the market. Generally they contain material for a tourniquet, a cutting instrument for incising the wound and an antiseptic for sterilizing it, some form of suction device to suck blood and venom from the bite, and sometimes a stimulant, a sedative, or a local anesthetic. Kits of this kind, which sometimes have trade names resembling the word "antivenom," should not be confused with the kit containing a dose of Wyeth antivenin. The kit of the first kind is purely for first-aid treatment in the field; it does not contain an antidote for rattlesnake bite, which is what antivenin is.

To anyone going into rattlesnake country in places distant from towns, on hunting, fishing, camping, or hiking trips, a first-aid kit is certainly to be recommended. Whether a dose of antivenin is also justified depends on the prevalence and species of rattlers in the terrain to be traversed, and the time required to get out to a place where a doctor and antivenin would be available.

First-aid kits for the treatment of snake bite are readily obtainable at most drug and sporting-goods stores. Among those to be recommended are the Dudley Kit, manufactured by the Flack-Hendrick Co., of San Antonio, Texas; the Compak Snakebite Kit, of the Cutter Laboratories, Berkeley, California; and the Venex Snake Bite Pocket Kit, of the E. D. Bullard Company, San Francisco, California. A type of suction mechanism that works off the windshield-wiper suction line on an automobile is also available. Some prefer kits in which rubber-bulb suction devices are used, since several of these can be attached at different incisions and will work without continued attention. Others prefer glass plunger pumps since the quantity of exudate being withdrawn can be watched. The instructions accompanying these kits are worth while in themselves.

The traveler into the remote places should also carry a copy of the latest edition of U. S. Fish and Wildlife Service *Wildlife Leaflet 339,* a free pamphlet containing much useful information on snake bite and its treatment.

THE PREVENTION OF RATTLESNAKE BITE

How may a person minimize the chances of encountering a rattlesnake, or of being bitten if he meets one? The danger from rattlesnake bite is rarely sufficient to justify anyone in changing his course or plans. Only during the spring or fall, when a man's path might take him past a rattlesnake den, would he be warranted in detouring to avoid the snakes. But there are certain precautions that may be taken to reduce the chances of being bitten if a rattler should be encountered. These include alertness and care—how one should conduct himself in rattlesnake country to avoid being bitten, and the selection of protective clothing. Snake repellents, the use of chemicals and other devices to turn away a threatening snake, once considered of great importance in more credulous days, will only be mentioned briefly here. They have no value, and so have been relegated to chapter 18, on rattlesnake myths and legends. Rattlesnake control about homes and farms is likewise a separate subject; this has been treated elsewhere (p. 982). Also, although I shall mention here some typical accidents suffered by people who were handling snakes deliberately, the methods to be used by those who seek to catch or to milk them of venom for scientific or commercial purposes are discussed in other chapters (pp. 746 and 995).

How People Get Bitten; Statistics

I know of no better way in which to impress readers with the things that should not be done than to give summaries and examples of what was being done when someone was bitten.

Several statistical summaries of snake-bite cases have been published. As the categories into which the incidents were divided by the several authors are not comparable, they must be presented separately. Amaral (1927b, p. 81) tabulated a number of case records in Texas, and information on what the victim was doing when bitten is available in some of them. They may be summarized thus, the copperhead and moccasin cases being omitted:

Children at play	9
People picking fruit, vegetables, or fodder	8
Walking in the woods or fields	6
Farming	4
Hunting	3
Stepping off the porch at night	2
Miscellaneous (not counting 2 bitten while hunting for rattlers)	5
Total	37

Hogg (1928, p. 17) gives the following percentage distribution of 1,648 accidents, mostly to hunters and fishermen:

Crawling through brush or under a fence	22½
Climbing among rocks	18
Walking with inadequate foot or leg coverings	12
Going barefooted in the open	11
Gathering firewood after dark	9
Reaching into hollow logs, under stones, into holes, or into heavy grass or brush	5
Snakes encountered in camps	3½
Bitten through "snake-proof" footgear	2
Circumstance unknown	17
Total	100

Some of these categories are not definitive and overlap others.

Hutchison (1929, p. 49) lists the following activities of persons when bitten, as reported to the Antivenin Institute at Glenolden among a total of 607 cases:

Picking, collecting, or lifting	
Cotton	8
Berries	34
Fallen fruit	12
Worms	1
Wood	10
Peanuts	3
Stones	3
Weeds, flowers, etc.	30
Subtotal	101
Reaching into or under some object	37

At play 64
At work 66
Stepped on, too near, or fell near a snake 120
Fishing 19
Hunting 14
Swimming or wading 8
Picknicking 3
Asleep outdoors 1

    Total 433
Catching or handling snakes 22

    Grand total 455

Hutchison's 1930 list (p. 42) was divided into fewer categories:

Picking up objects, such as cotton, berries, wood, weeds 110
Reaching into or under some object 13
Stepping on, too close to, or falling near a snake while
    playing, working, fishing, hunting, etc. 258
Asleep outdoors 3

    Subtotal 384
Catching or handling snakes 26

    Grand total 410

Maloney (1945, p. 80) reported that, of 347 cases tabulated by Ross Allen in Florida, 99 involved bites on the feet or legs while walking, and 34 on the hands and arms while picking up objects. What the other victims were doing was unstated.

Another compilation by Allen (*in litt.*) revealed the following activities of rattlesnake-bite victims:

Children at play 29
People handling snakes 15
Gardening 9
Farming 9
Hunting 4
Working in or around home 4
Walking 3
Fishing 1
Miscellaneous activities 12

    Total 86

Wood (1954, p. 941) reported on 77 cases (more than half copperhead bites) that occurred in Virginia. Of these, 23 accidents happened near home, 32 on farms, 12 while camping or hiking, and 10 when snakes were being handled.

The Hogg, Hutchison, Maloney, and Wood cases are not exclusively rattler bites, moccasins and copperheads being included. The following statistics, as given by Swartzwelder (1950, p. 578), cover data secured in the Charity Hospital of Louisiana at New Orleans and refer only to rattlesnake bites.

Working in cornfields 11
Gathering or moving lumber; reaching under logs or lumber;
    playing around lumber piles 3
Walking in woods 3
Picking moss 2
Fishing 1
                                                        ——
    Subtotal 20
Catching or killing snakes; showman in a cage with a snake 4
                                                        ——
    Grand total 24

Swartzwelder has also presented a table showing the occupations of the people bitten. This table includes moccasin and copperhead as well as rattlesnake bites:

Laborers   63
Farmers   36
Fishermen 22
Houseworkers   21
Trappers   18
Swampers 11
Hunters 4
Clerks   4
Showmen 2
Timber cutters 2
Machinists 2
Railroad worker 1
Engineer   1
                                                        ——
    Total 187

How People Get Bitten; Example Incidents

Before suggesting the precautions that people may adopt to avoid being bitten, I shall give brief descriptions of a number of actual occurrences. These will illustrate, better than any statistics, how accidents happen, and the kinds of actions to be avoided.

Picking Berries.—A woman was bitten in the finger while picking blackberries. Another women was struck in the lower calf of the leg as she crawled along the ground picking strawberries. A boy gathering dewberries was bitten in the thumb.

Picking Flowers.—A man was bitten in the hand by a massasauga (*S. catenatus*) as he stooped to pick a flower. A 17-year-old girl, walking in dim twilight, was bitten in the thumb by a timber rattler (*C. h. horridus*) as she picked a violet.

Picking Up Kindling Wood or Timber.—A woman in her own yard was bitten as she reached down for some firewood. A man in the desert, as he gathered sticks for a fire, was bitten in the thumb by a sidewinder. A two-year-old, helping his mother pick up sticks for a campfire, was bitten by a northern Pacific rattler (*C. v. oreganus*) that he picked up, evidently mistaking it for a stick. A man salvaging logs from a river, stepped directly on a rattler hidden in a clump of grass. A young man in a construction crew was bitten as he stooped to pick up a railroad tie.

Picking Up Game.—A man in San Diego County was bitten as he reached into a bush for a rabbit he had shot. A similar accident happened in Texas.

Reaching into Holes or Hollow Trees.—Werler (1950, p. 28) mentions two instances in Texas wherein hunters, seeking to recover small game they had shot, were bitten by rattlers when they reached into armadillo holes. A youngster in Arizona was bitten when he tracked a wounded cottontail to a hole and reached in to get it. Another hunter was struck when he thrust his arm into a hollow tree for a squirrel. A boy was bitten when he reached into a hole to catch a tortoise.

Picking Up Miscellaneous Objects.—A laborer on an electric line–construction crew reached into tall grass for a rope and was bitten by a hidden rattler (*C. v. oreganus*) that gave no warning. A man repairing a fence dropped his hammer in a clump of grass and was bitten when he stooped to pick it up. A caretaker was bitten as he picked up scraps of paper in a school yard.

Turning Rocks.—A laborer put his hand under a rock to turn it over and was bitten by an unseen rattler under the rock. A man tearing down a rock retaining wall was bitten in the middle finger of the right hand by a hidden rattler. A farmer digging a hole, cut a rattler in two with his shovel without knowing it. As he stooped to remove a rock, he was struck in the hand.

Climbing among Rocks.—A trout fisherman in the Sierra Nevada was using his hands in climbing out of a granite gorge. He was struck in the hand by an unseen rattler above him. A deer hunter put his hand on a rock to step over it and was bitten in the finger. A man, especially skilled in hunting and catching rattlesnakes, grabbed for a handhold on a rock ledge, and was fatally bitten in the left wrist by an unseen rattler. A man sat down on some rocks at the foot of a bank. He leaned back against the bank where there was a hole and a Great Basin rattler (*C. v. lutosus*) concealed in the hole, bit him in the back. A man sat down to rest beside a large boulder and was struck in the arm as he arose to leave. A fisherman was bitten while hiking through rocks looking for likely pools. A woman, wading in a creek while fishing, was struck by a rattler hidden in the rocks. A girl, clambering amid rocks, placed her hand right on a rattlesnake and was bitten.

Hunters Looking for Game.—A man in the Sierra in California, while walking around a tree and looking upward for a hiding squirrel, stepped on a rattler and was bitten in the leg. A man took off his shoes to wade out for snipe and was bitten. A hunter, aiming at a deer, heard the rattle of a snake. Without waiting to ascertain the direction of the sound, he stepped backward onto the snake, and was bitten in the leg. This case ended fatally. A man, hurrying through brush to reach a deer he had shot, was bitten just above the ankle.

Walking and Hiking.—A boy breaking his way through heavy chaparral was struck in the leg. A deer hunter walking through brush was bitten. A woman hiking through brush at Yosemite was struck in the leg by an unseen rattler. A 14-year-old boy, walking along a trail behind his brother, was bitten in the calf by a rattler hidden in small bushes bordering the path. Evidently it had been disturbed by the boy in front. A man walking on a trail slipped and put his hands out to break his fall, whereupon he was bitten in the hand through a buckskin glove.

A woman, walking toward a fishing camp along the margin of a lake, heard a rattler sound off but was too frightened to move. She was bitten in the ankle. A man walking in a ditch was struck in the thigh by a northern Pacific rattler (*C. v. oreganus*) that was hidden on the bank. A man was walking down a rocky, brush-lined trail. He had advanced his right foot, which evidently alarmed a speckled rattler (*C. m. pyrrhus*) that was hidden from him. As the left foot was moved forward, the snake struck him. He thought at first that he had been stuck by a cactus, until he saw the snake's tail disappearing in the bush. A child was bitten while carrying lunch to his father in an open field. A farmer was bitten as he traversed his cornfield.

Drinking from a Spring.—Two men, one in Wisconsin, the other in Kentucky, were struck when they knelt to drink at springs.

Stepping out of a Car.—A man on a public road stopped his car, stepped out, and was bitten by a large southern Pacific rattler (*C. v. helleri*) under the car, which he had missed seeing as he drove up. A forestry worker was bitten in the ankle as he stepped out of his car in darkness. A man stepped down from a truck and sustained a bite in the calf of the leg.

Stepping over or on Logs.—A man stepped off a log directly on a rattler that was stretched along its underside. A seven-year-old boy was struck in the palm of the hand while climbing onto a log. A man picking blackberries placed his hand on a stump and was bitten by a rattler coiled there. A man pushing some tools under a log was bitten in the palm and in the wrist.

Brush Cutting.—A forest-fire fighter was bitten in the thigh by a rattler he was trying to drive back into burning brush. A man fighting a brush fire stumbled and fell on a rattler. A man was bitten in the chest by a timber rattler when clearing brush from a ledge.

Agricultural Activities.—Bites when people are tending crops or domestic animals, or while gardening, comprise an important proportion of all bites, although somewhat reduced by the increased mechanization of agriculture. A man was bitten while gathering hay in a meadow. A laborer in Illinois was bitten in the index finger while binding oats in the field, and another when binding wheat. These are reports of times long past. Another farmer was bitten while cutting corn. One was struck while clearing obstructions from a mowing-machine blade.

A woman was bitten while feeling among some vines for melons, and a boy was struck while picking watermelons. A pea picker was bitten in the right ankle as he stood among the plants. One child was struck while picking cotton, and another while digging ginseng roots. A 16-year-old girl picking grapes was bitten in the finger by a rattler that was in the vine, coiled above ground. One man was bitten in his garden as he stooped to pick up a hose in deep grass; another as he picked up a hoe; and another as he reached into a leaf-mold bin. One gardener was struck in the chin as he stooped to examine a plant. One stepped on a rattler hidden in deep grass.

A cowboy stooping down to hobble a horse was bitten in the hand. Another was driving a stake to tether his horse when he was struck in the arm; fortunately the fangs failed to penetrate his clothing. Two men were struck by rattlers hidden in haystacks, as they pulled down hay to feed cattle. Another went out bare-footed to feed his cows and was struck in the heel. A man was feeding rabbits in a hutch; when he heard the sound of a rattle he stepped backward into a rattler and was bitten. A man was bitten as he crawled under his house to investigate a hen's stolen nest. A boy was bitten in the foot as he gathered eggs in a henhouse; another under similar circumstances was bitten in the toe. A woman was bitten when she went into her poultry house to see what the chickens were cackling about.

Accidents in the Darkness.—A hunter stepped out of his cabin in the darkness to get a rifle he had left leaning against a tree. He had removed his boots and was bitten in the ankle. A man in the desert in darkness stooped to pick up what he thought was a rope. It proved to be a western diamondback (*C. atrox*), which bit him, one fang taking effect through a glove. A boy catching insects after dark in front of his home was bitten in the heel.

Bites around the Home.—A girl was bitten while rummaging in her garage. A rancher was bitten on the left hand by a rattler coiled in an empty bucket tipped on its side. A woman hanging clothes on a line in her yard was bitten in the instep. Another was bitten by a pigmy rattler that had crawled into a dresser drawer in her home. A woman engaged in hoeing flowers in her yard was bitten in the foot. A man swung out of a cot in his home and stepped on a rattler. A woman in Texas was bitten as she slept on her porch. A boy bent over to pick up an apple at the edge of the porch of his home and was bitten in the hand.

Accidents to Children.—A boy of four was bitten when he ran into some weeds while chasing a bird. A boy playing in his own garden overturned a board and was bitten by a juvenile rattler hidden beneath. A six-year-old girl was bitten when she tried to locate something "that sounded like a locust." A boy of two was bitten when he picked up a rattler in his own yard. Another boy of two chased a kitten into the road and was bitten. A boy of seven on a bicycle rode over what he thought was a stick. He stopped to investigate and was bitten in the right foot. A 19-month-old child lifted a saw that was lying on the ground. She was bitten by a small rattler under it. The saw dropped back and covered the rattler so that the mother, who came to see why the child cried, could find nothing wrong. When the child's arm began to swell, the rattler was found, and appropriate measures were taken that saved the child's life. This is an example of the occasional cases in which young children cannot tell, or fail to tell, what has happened, which leads to delay and increased danger.

An Unexpected Second Snake.—Occasionally an accident happens when a person avoids one snake, only to fall afoul of another. A man stooped to pick up a stone to kill a rattler and was bitten by a second that he had not seen, as it lay close to his intended weapon. A man prepared to catch one rattlesnake and was bitten by another that was hidden from him.

Miscellaneous.—Of course, many accidents occur under strange and unlikely conditions. People have been bitten by rattlers in the course of such activities as:

> Changing a tire by the roadside in the evening
> Replacing a runway light at a city airport
> Picking up a golf ball in the rough
> Crawling under a barbed-wire fence
> Repairing a leaky water pipe
> Searching for supplies under a counter
> Moving sacks at a feldspar mill
> Lifting a fruit jar under a house
> Working in a living room

A man tried to kill a rattler with a shovel. He slipped, fell on the snake, and was bitten in the arm. An Indian boy was riding a burro. When the burro shied at a rattler, it bucked the boy off almost on top of the snake. The boy was bitten in the calf. A newspaper delivery boy dropped one of his papers and was bitten as he stooped to pick it up. A laborer in urban Pittsburgh was bitten while engaged in furnace repairs. The rattler had evidently been carried in by flood waters. A boy fell off a sign and was bitten by a rattlesnake immediately below. Two boys were bitten 15 minutes apart by a single small rattler coiled on the porch steps at a Halloween party. A man in a boat saw a snake swimming in a river. He knew there were no water moccasins in that area, so he seized the snake. It proved to be a rattler.

Printed Sources of Incidents

Of the snake-bite incidents that I have chosen to illustrate the ways in which typical accidents have happened, many have been drawn from my personal correspondence and from newspaper accounts. Others have been extracted from books and periodicals. For those who may do additional research on the subject, the pertinent references are listed as follows: Joutel, 1714, p. 91; Breintal, 1748, p. 147; Kalm, 1752–53, p. 53; Doddridge, 1824, p. 76; Kendall, 1844, vol. 1, p. 240; Hanley, 1854, p. 497; Jeter, 1854, p. 16; Stanley, 1854, p. 464; Anon., 1858a, p. 471; Berkeley, 1861, p. 67; Ham, 1861, p. 82; Catlin, 1868, p. 16; Duval, 1870, p. 16; Jenkins, 1870, p. 458; Anderson, 1872, p. 367; Anon., 1872b, p. 643; Knott, 1877, p. 79; Savage, 1877, p. 36; Stone, 1881, p. 473; Bories, 1883, p. 57; Roberts, 1888, p. 374; Webb, 1888, p. 267; Anon., 1889, p. 518; Thomas, 1890, p. 123; Brewer, 1897, p. 58; Lyman, 1900, p. 263; Rightmore, 1900, p. 306; Wade, 1900, p. 505; Anon., 1908a, p. 679; Grieve, 1908, p. 32; Barnes, 1922, p. 390; Schomburgk, 1922, vol. 2, p. 201; Kelly, 1926, p. 36; Amaral, 1927b, p. 81; Pousma, 1928, p. 62; Rhone, 1928, p. 87; Hutchison, 1929, p. 49; Anon., 1933a, p. 6; Lyon and Bishop, 1936, p. 255; Arrington, 1937, p. 66; Corle, 1941, p. 325; Wittek, 1943, p. 9; McCauley, 1945, p. 137; Woodbury and Anderson, 1945, p. 185; Small, 1946, p. 88; Chotkowski, 1949, p. 600; Gordon, 1949, p. 393; Barbour, 1950, p. 106; Key, 1950, p. 30; Unonius, 1950, vol. 1, p. 297; Minton, 1950, p. 320; Swartzwelder, 1950, p. 578; Werler, 1950, p. 28; and Happ, 1951, p. 20.

Lessons to Be Learned

Much may be learned from these cases that I have enumerated, which is my excuse for the repetitious nature of the stories. A few of the accidents were unavoidable;

a few involved children from whom better judgment could not be expected; a few happened to people who were inviting trouble when they sought to catch or handle snakes. But a majority fall into two categories: Either people put their hands or feet into places where a rattler might lie concealed, or their attention was absorbed in other activities, such as looking for game, so that they were not alert to their immediate surroundings. Certainly most of these accidents could have been avoided by application of this simple rule: *Watch where you put your hands and feet; don't put them in places without looking, and don't put them in places where you can't look.*

Good precautionary rules to avoid being bitten by rattlers and other snakes have been set forth many times. Some of the best of the recent publications are those of Artran (1940, p. [5]), Davenport (1943, p. 20), Keysor (1948, p. 147), Allen (1949a, p. 33; 1951, p. 20), Perkins (1949a, p. 16), Werler (1950, p. 27), and Oliver (1952, p. 70). The suggestions presented by Oliver are accompanied by especially effective photographs of posed incidents—the things one should and should not do in the field, if accidents are to be avoided. From these and other sources I have compiled the following safety-first suggestions for people in places where rattlesnakes may be found:

Don't lift a stone, plank, log, or any other object under which a rattler might be hidden, by placing your hand or fingers under it. First move it with a stick, a hook, or a pry-bar of some kind; or with your foot, if properly protected with heavy boots or puttees.

Don't gather firewood in the dark; gather all you need in the daytime, and employ the usual precautions of alertness as you pick it up.

Don't reach into a hole of any kind, whether in the ground or in a tree, for escaping game or anything else. Don't reach into holes or crevices in rock piles or under rocks.

As you walk in grass, brush, cactus, or rocks, stay in cleared spots as much as possible, and keep a sharp lookout for snakes that may lie concealed in, or beside, your path. Remember that rattlers, like most snakes, are protectively colored; it takes a sharp eye, not a cursory glance, to discover one in its natural surroundings.

Don't believe the stories you hear that rattlers are out only in hot weather; they are always hidden in the shade when it is hot. They are most active when the temperature is moderate.

Don't take too literally the tales of their shunning high altitudes, or that they can't swim or climb trees. They are found higher in the mountains than most people suppose—up to 11,000 ft. or more in the Southwest. and up to 14,500 ft. in central Mexico. In New Mexico, on December 31, 1949, a man was bitten by a rattler in the mountains only a hundred feet from a snowbank (Key, 1950, p. 30). Rattlers can climb trees and bushes, and they swim readily.

While hunting, if you are keeping an eye out for game to run or fly, learn to glance frequently at your path to avoid stepping on a rattler. And remember that the leader of a file is not the one most exposed to snake bite; he may disturb a hidden snake that will strike one of the followers.

Don't walk around your camp in darkness, for rattlers are nocturnal much of the year. If you must move about, use a flashlight to light your way, and don't remove the boots and puttees that you wore in the daytime.

Step on a log, never over it, so that you can first see whether there is a rattler concealed below the curve on the far side.

Avoid walking close to rock ledges; give them ample clearance if the path is wide enough.

Don't reach above your head for a handhold in climbing amid rocks, and avoid placing your hands near crevices into which you can't see.

When you crawl under a fence, try to do so in a cleared spot; if there is grass or brush, beat it with a stick so that a rattler will escape or make its presence known.

First examine the surroundings before sitting down to rest on a log or rock.

Learn to recognize the venomous snakes of your area, and avoid killing the harmless ones that are competitors of the rattlers for food. If you go into a new area to work, hunt, or fish, learn something about the snakes to be expected there.

When a rattler sounds off suddenly, don't move until you know whence the sound is coming; you may step onto a rattler or into its range instead of away from it. A rattler seen in time is not a dangerous snake, provided you and the other members of your party, including your dog, avoid it.

Rattlers will usually strike only at a moving object. When you back away from one rattler, make sure all is clear behind you, so that you won't trip or back into another snake.

Don't get excited if a snake gets in your boat. He's looking for a rest, not for you. Lift him out with an oar or a paddle.

Don't lay out your bedroll near brush piles, rock piles, or rubbish. Don't leave your clothes and boots lying around where rattlers can crawl into them. Pitch your camp in a clearing, if there is one.

Don't handle an injured or dead rattlesnake. Don't touch the head of a decapitated rattlesnake. Dispose of it where other members of the party can't accidentally come in contact with it. Never play practical jokes on others with dead rattlesnakes. If you must examine the head of a recently killed rattler, use sticks to handle it, not your fingers. If you must have the rattles of a dead snake for a trophy, put your foot on the snake's head before you apply your knife to its tail. All of these safety rules are required because snakes are capable of reflex actions for a considerable time after they have been fatally injured. The head of a rattlesnake has been known to bite half an hour or more after it was completely severed from the body.

If you are a snake collector, don't grab for the tail of a rattler going down a hole; the head end may already have turned and be facing outward.

For precautions around the home and children's play yard, see chapter 14 on control.

Don't let the fear of rattlesnakes keep you out of the country, or from hikes or picnics. Rattlesnakes are more plentiful in this book than in the wild. But be careful and alert.

Some interesting comments on the snake-bite hazard and its avoidance are to be found in the extensive literature of the subject. Here are some quite uncoordinated items:

Kalm (1752–53, p. 57) observed at that early date that it was not the leader of a file of men who was most likely to be bitten, but the last, because the first man alerted any hidden snake. He also advised against stepping over a fallen tree because there might be a snake lurking behind it.

With respect to the hazards of particular occupations, Doddridge (1824, p. 76) said that rattlesnakes were bothersome to harvesters in Virginia and Pennsylvania in the period 1763–83. Kane (1859, p. 265) mentioned the danger to men towing boats from a bank, an important matter in the days of the canals. According to Majors (1893, p. 105), on the Santa Fe Trail in the early days, men were sent ahead of the travelers with large whips to frighten snakes out of the pathway. Terhune (1938, p. 445) says the pioneer housewife in early Indiana, when tending her garden, hunting turkey eggs, or picking berries, carried a snake stick with which she sought to locate any snakes. Anon. (1933a, p. 6) mentions a guide on a fishing trip in Missouri, who swished the grass as he advanced in order to cause the rattlers to sound their rattles. Tome (1928, p. 31), writing of pioneer days of about 1800 in central Pennsylvania, said the settlers were careful to keep their houses closed at night, lest the rattlers gain entrance—they were very numerous. Thompson (1916, p. 521) observed that the boatmen in Oregon (he was speaking of 1811) threw their paddles ashore before they landed so that the rattlers would disclose themselves. Perry (1942, p. 88) says that the Mexicans, if they walk out at night, sweep a tree branch back and forth before them to make any rattler sound off. Chittenden (1902, p. 827) said that the only risk to the hunters and trappers of early days was in coming on a rattler unawares or stepping on one. Emerick (1951, p. 13) suggests that the best way to protect against snakes, particularly pit vipers such as rattlers, is to make a noise, as they are particularly sensitive to noise and vibrations. This is correct only as to vibrations of the ground, as rattlers are deaf to sound, that is, to air-borne vibrations. They are highly sensitive to ground-borne vibrations, which will often cause them to sound their rattles, and thus make their presence known.

Cleland (1941, p. 189), in telling of the early days in California, reported that rattlers were a real danger to the sheepherders. They were far from help should any accident befall. Crimmins (1927a, p. 199) has pointed out that one reason for the increased snake-bite problem in Texas is that formerly, when there was largely a cattle economy, everyone rode horseback, but now, with increased agriculture, many of the workers are afoot.

Gillam (1916, p. 133) suggests that you avoid moving when a rattler is crawling over your feet; probably good advice, but slightly difficult for the average person to follow. Frayne (1945, p. 32) advises against one's jumping back from a threatening rattler, as the rattler can strike faster than a person can move. This is true only if it is assumed that the rattler strikes as the move begins, for a single step will carry an adult beyond a rattler's reach. Frayne says if you do not move, the rattler will crawl away. Stillwell (1949, p. 112) makes the point that when you see a rattler in time so that it can be avoided, it is no more dangerous than a garter snake.

Hearn (1952, p. 17) says that people in Texas have learned not to leave their car doors or luggage compartments open while the car is unattended, as an occasional rattler may crawl in. One of the new items of folklore tells of the man who is annoyed by a hissing sound in his engine. When he raises the hood, he finds a buzzing rattlesnake under it.

THE CHANCE OF BEING BITTEN IN RATTLESNAKE COUNTRY

The cited illustrative examples of how people get bitten almost inevitably will convey an exaggerated idea of the danger. I think it will be salutary to cite circumstances under which people were not bitten—as told by some of my correspondents—in order to give a fairer picture of the actual risk.

> Although there were many CCC boys in camps in both the Shenandoah National Park and the George Washington National Forest, and the timber rattlesnake was common in both areas, no fatalities ever occurred from rattlesnake bites; and, if memory serves me correctly, I believe only one or two individuals were ever actually bitten. Certainly this indicates the hazards of being harmed by rattlesnakes are not very great. *A. L. Nelson, Division of Wildlife Research, Bowie, Md.*
>
> ⋄
>
> I have worked in areas more or less infested with rattlers in Wyoming, Colorado, Nebraska, Kentucky, and Tennessee, but have yet to meet the man who was actually bitten. It is always someone who knew someone who knew a man that got bitten. I know there are people who really get bitten every year but I just never happened to meet one. When I was on the Bessey District in the Nebraska sand hills, at Halsey, Nebraska, rattlers were

very thick and I probably killed 50 a season. They were quite a bother to us there, in that the entire forest is "man-made," and the planting crews always ran the risk of being bitten. I think the danger of being bitten is exaggerated, and my work there confirms this. These planting crews had to work in a stooped position with their hands right on the ground, and, as far as I know, there never was an accident. Quite often someone would set a planting basket (a small box holding trees) on a snake and get a bad scare, but that is as far as they went. *Dwight A. Hester, U. S. Forest Service, Grand Mesa, Colo.*

<>

Rattlers are common throughout this locality, but it is very seldom that any person or animal is bitten by one. *George E. Moore, Ely, Nev.*

<>

In 1939, over 1,000 men worked on a large fire in the Salmon River area in central Idaho, where there are probably more snakes per square mile than anywhere else in this western area. Crews killed as high as 30 rattlesnakes a day and not a man was bitten. *John P. Gaffney, U. S. Forest Service, Republic, Wash.*

<>

Rattlers will, as a rule, run rather than fight. They are not considered a hazard. I have heard of very few people ever having been struck by one, and no fatalities have occurred. *F. K. Lightfoot, Agness, Oreg.*

<>

Working in a rattlesnake country for the past three years with crews of CCC boys, I do not know of a single instance wherein anyone has been bitten. I have probably seen 50 snakes killed during that period in the Klamath and Trinity National Forests. *Norman J. Farrell, U. S. Forest Service, Seiad Valley, Calif.*

<>

For a number of years the Bureau of Entomology and the U. S. Forest Service have been eradicating plants of the *Ribes* family from the sugarpine belt in order to prevent the spread of the white-pine blister rust. Many men have been engaged in this work and most of them were inexperienced. They killed many rattlesnakes, yet I never heard of any of them being struck by one. *J. T. Kenney, U. S. Forest Service, Dardanelle, Calif.*

<>

Rattlesnakes are quite numerous along the line of the Metropolitan Aqueduct but they move about very little during the daytime on account of the desert heat. Prior to 1933 survey parties were in the field for a period of eight years, and subsequently from one thousand to ten thousand men were engaged on the construction of the aqueduct. During this period of several years, there was but one case of rattlesnake bite among the aqueduct forces. *T. W. Osgood, Safety Engineer, Metropolitan Water District, Banning, Calif.*

It should be remembered that the risk of being bitten by a rattlesnake, and the hazard from a bite after a person has been bitten, are two quite different things, although often confused in discussions of snake-bite problems. From statistics given elsewhere, we may conclude that, in the United States, the chance of a person's being bitten by a rattler in any one year is about 1 in 160,000. The chance of a person's being fatally bitten is less than 1 in 5,000,000. Of course, it is obvious that average figures of this kind are not particularly important, since some people are much more exposed to the hazard than others.

THE RATTLESNAKE IN THE BLANKETS

In the early days of the western migration, when the travelers often slept on the ground, there must have been a lot of worry about rattlers crawling into the blankets, to judge from the frequency with which the hazard is mentioned in the books of the day. Whether the danger was as serious as pictured may be doubted. But most of the travelers were reassured by the use of a hair rope, which, circling the sleeper's bed, was thought to be an impervious barrier to any inquisitive rattler. Although the value of this legendary protection has long since been exploded, it was, indeed, a great reliever of worry. It is mentioned as early as 1844 (Kendall, vol. 1, p. 93), and is still sporadically in use. It has been discussed in a more appropriate place, in chapter 18, on myths and legends, under repellents.

There is plenty of evidence that there was some slight risk that a sleeper might awake in the morning with a rattler for a bedfellow. It is true that on the desert the rattlers are most active in the early evening; with the coming of the midnight chill in the spring and fall, or daylight in the summer, they seek refuge, and might avail themselves of so unexpectedly adequate a concealment as that provided by a pile of blankets with a man at the core. But it may be suspected that the trapper or cowboy at the evening campfire did not minimize the risk to the attentive tenderfoot, particularly one gathering material for his next book on the hardships and hazards of Western travel.

Of course, the dangers from snakes to sleepers on the ground were not restricted to the United States or to rattlers. Paulus Aegineta, who lived in Alexandria about 640 A.D. and who wrote a medical encyclopedia, suggested these protective measures against snakes to those who must sleep on the ground: Shut up the snakes' holes with garlic pounded in water; fumigate with repellents—a number of which he enumerated, such as sulphur, bitumen, galbanum, juniper, etc.—and also strew these around the couch (Adams 1844–47, p. 155). Most of this is taken from Nicander (1953, p. 31), a herpetologist and poet who lived about 800 years before Paulus, so we see that the problem was not first met on the Oregon Trail.

Most of the accounts in the journals of the travelers in the West mention the danger but rarely recount an accident. Kalm (1752–53) said that rattlers crawled over sleeping persons without harm. Mittelberger (1898, p. 81, but writing in 1756) said the rattlers even got into the people's beds in the houses. Wuerttemberg (1938, p. 264, but writing in 1835) said it was true that rattlers got into the camps and even into the beds, but accidents were rare. Others who mentioned occurrences of rattlers being found in the beds, or the prevalent fear of their doing so, were Rengger, 1829, p. 92; Kendall, 1844, vol. 1, p. 92; Ruxton, 1848, p. 293; Rusling, 1875, p. 417; Ingersoll, 1883a, p. 41; 1883b, p. 129; 1884b, p. 104; Robinson, 1895, p. 147; Chittenden, 1902, p. 826; 1903, p. 46; Pollock, 1911, p. 152; Walsh, 1913, p. 718; Murphy, 1917, p. 67; Thompson, 1916, p. 521; Chase, 1919, p. 33; Rollins, 1922, p. 176; Dobie, 1926, p. 52; Morse, 1927, p. 233; Gibson, 1935, p. 140; Blackford, 1946, p. 10; Rollinson, 1948, p. 232; Pedersen, 1949, p. 16. Stanley (1916, p. 186), after finding two rattlers in his bed in a camp near Virginia City, Nevada, in 1864, built a scaffold so that the family could rest in peace.

As to accidents, Menger (1913, p. 144) repeats a newspaper story about two boys found dead in bed with a rattler between them. King (1932, p. 7) tells of a rattler that crawled across a man sleeping on the ground; he kicked it and was bitten. Crimmins (1934, p. 128) recounts the experience of a woman bitten while in bed, but this was no camp affair; she was sleeping on a pallet on a screened porch at home. Boatright (1934, p. 14) and Dobie (1947b, p. 91) offer two yarns of the frankly tall-story type with the rattler-in-the-blanket motif.

From my own correspondents, I have had the following:

> I once was sleeping out in the open not far from Hot Springs, South Dakota, and just as the sun was peeping up I heard the familiar sound of a rattler in my bed with me. Well, I just want to say that I never got out of a bed quicker than I did that one. This only goes to show that they will bunk with you without being invited. *Judge W. S. Owens, Cody, Wyo.*

◇

> It usually turns pretty cool here at night, so rattlesnakes move around very little during the night, although I found one on top of my bed in the morning when camping out in the badlands. *W. J. Petermann, U. S. Forest Service, Meeteetse, Wyo.*

◇

> I personally know of a sheepherder who found a rattler in his bed one morning. He struck at the snake with his knife and the snake bit him in the hand. I took him to town to the doctor within an hour. His hand puffed up tight, but he recovered in a few days. *William Lakanen, Game Warden, Rawlins, Wyo.*

◇

> A rattler in my bed wrapped around my ankle, and I didn't dare jump out of bed till it crawled off. *Marion E. Rose, Pateros, Wash.*

◇

> One fisherman, camping beside the Mad River, a mile from Ruth, found a rattlesnake coiled beneath his pillow (which was his rolled-up sweater) when he awoke in the morning. *Dr. Clarence Crane, Fernbridge, Calif.*

◇

> Twice in my life I have put my saddle blankets on brush mattresses four or five inches thick left by former campers, have slept on them through the night, and then have seen rattlers crawl out from under them next morning. The second time I had this happen I had spread the blankets on the mattress at 9 P.M. I believe the snake was there when I put the blanket on, but if so, it did not rattle. *Walter F. Emerick, Division of Fish and Game, Palmdale, Calif.*

Various suggestions have been made for campers who fear reptilian bedfellows. Hogg (1928, p. 54) says snake-proof tents are available. Kauffeld (1940, p. 54) recommends a cot. Allen (1949a, p. 71; 1951, p. 21) suggests a mosquito net hung from above and tucked under the bedding all around. Stickel (1952, p. 8) remarks that auto travelers can carry a small roll of wire screen with which they may erect a fence around their beds.

How Illegitimate Bites Happen

Just as is the case with legitimate bites, the reader can best be impressed with the things not to do—if he must handle snakes—by the citation here of some actual occurrences. Some of these accidents happened to amateurs; others involved persons who might have been presumed, through practice, to know how to handle rattlesnakes. These incidents are recounted upon the supposition that a basic recommendation that rattlesnakes should not be handled will not be heeded anyway.

Handling Supposedly Dead Snakes.—A hunter stoned a snake, and, thinking it dead, picked it up and was bitten. A man hunting rattlers shot a young southern

Pacific rattler in the neck with .22 dust shot. He put the muzzle of the rifle on the snake's head and stooped to pick it up. The rifle slipped and he was bitten. Another hunter broke a rattler's back, put a gun on its head, but too far back on the neck, so that he was bitten when he picked up the snake. A farmer, mowing a field, cut off a rattler's head, leaving about two or three inches of neck attached. He brushed aside the grass to find the head and was bitten in the thumb. A man ran over a rattler in an auto, and, thinking it dead, was bitten when he picked it up. A man started to cut the rattles off a supposedly dead snake with his pocket knife. As the knife blade cut into the snake's tail, the head flew back, and one fang was imbedded in the man's wrist. If you must have the rattles as a trophy and your feet and legs are well protected, put one foot on the rattler's head as you cut off the rattles. And even if you do this be sure the head is firmly held. Gally (1880, p. 2) told the story of a man who smashed a rattler's head, on which he then planted his foot and endeavored to pull the snake's rattles off. But, instead, he pulled the head out from under his foot and was bitten. Another man was bitten as he skinned a rattler that he had shot.

One of my correspondents, a snake man of long experience, wrote:

I have just discovered that the best way to get bitten is to put your finger in a dead snake's mouth. I decapitated a large prairie rattler, leaving only about half an inch of its body attached. I let the head lay for 15 minutes or more and then made some examinations with a small microscope. Then I propped its mouth open, intending to extract the venom, but suddenly its mouth flew wider open and came shut like a mouse trap, sinking both fangs in the end of my middle finger of the right hand. It wasn't until it had injected about all of the venom into my finger that I was able to get loose from it. There is no question but that Barnum was right. I have had a serious time, although I was lucky enough to get into a hospital in about 20 minutes, but after two weeks I am still suffering considerable pain. [For the results of experiments to determine how long the head of a decapitated rattler is dangerous, see p. 310.]

Pulling Snakes from Holes or Seeking Them in Holes.—A rattler was escaping under a rock. A collector reached down to seize it by the tail to pull it out and was bitten by another rattler, hitherto unseen under the rock. A man tried to pull a rattler from a stone wall and was bitten in the hand. A boy of 14 was bitten when he tried to pull a rattler out of a hollow tree. A man while plowing saw a rattler go down a hole. He took a wrench wherewith to enlarge the hole to get at the snake and was bitten in the index finger.

A correspondent writes:

I know of but one man's being bitten by a rattler and that was his own fault. The rattler had started into a hole and was about half in when this chap took hold of its tail to pull it out. Had he known the habits of a snake, he would not have tried it. When a rattler goes into a hole, it goes head first, true enough, but it turns its head so that it can see outside the hole, and pulls its body in the hole doubled. In other words, at least three-fourths of its length goes past its head, which is looking out of the hole. *F. C. Fitzgerald, U. S. Forest Service, Lincoln, Mont.*

Mistaking a Rattler for a Harmless Snake.—A man picked up a small rattler, thinking it harmless, and was bitten in the finger. A woman was bitten by a small rattler as she was explaining to her daughters, aged eight and nine, that it was a harmless garter snake.

Picking Up Snakes.—A collector, using a short, straight stick in the usual way, pressed a rattler's head into the ground so as to pick it up back of the head. But the ground was soft and the snake's head partly hidden, so that when he picked it up, the snake, with an inch or so of neck free, was able to bite a finger. A man put a snake stick on a rattler that was escaping under a rock. With his other hand he moved a rock the better to see the rattler he was holding. The head was not in the expected location; it was near the rock being moved and the man was bitten. A man was bitten by a small eastern diamondback that he tried to pick up when he was drunk.

Snakes Biting While Held in the Hand.—A man picked up a large rattler by the neck without controlling the posterior part of the body. The snake threw a coil around his wrist and was able to work enough of its neck free to bite the man's hand. A man holding a rattler by the neck, in order to show some visitors its fangs, had his attention distracted and was bitten in his other hand. A man holding a small rattler by the tail attempted to kill it by striking it in the body with a stick. This caused the body to whirl around his wrist and he was bitten. A boy of 15 was holding a pigmy rattler when it suddenly twisted and freed enough of its head to bite his finger.

Putting Snakes in Containers or Carrying Them.—Snake collectors usually carry their catches in flour or similar sacks, since this is a much handier method than any other. Although a rattler will rarely bite through a sack, such cases as these demonstrate the necessity for caution: MacDonald (1939, p. 35; 1946, p. 136) was bitten just above the knee by a large *adamanteus* through a sack. He was twisting the mouth of the sack when it swung against his knee. A man carrying a large *ruber* in a sack was bitten in the thumb when he took hold of the bottom of the sack to turn it upside down in order to drop the snake into a box. Another man was bitten by a *lutosus* that had been dropped into a sack. As the captor was tying a string around the mouth of the sack, the snake raised up on its tail and bit him. A man poked a red diamond (*C. r. ruber*) with his finger, and was bitten through the sack. A boy was carrying a pigmy rattler in a sack that was fastened to his belt. Even this small snake succeeded in making an effective bite through the cloth of the sack.

Hammond (1858, p. 95) tells of a man who was bitten while trying to put a prairie rattlesnake (*C. v. viridis*) into a bottle. And I can't resist mentioning the newspaper report of several children who were happily playing with a rattlesnake until one of them was bitten as they tried to force it to crawl down a hole.

Milking Rattlesnakes.—Among the snakes sent to a zoo for milking, one was found to have had its mouth sewed shut by some peculiarly inclined donor. As the last stitch was clipped, the snake, which was naturally trying to open its mouth, snapped it open and snagged the operator's finger with one fang. An operator was demonstrating the removal of venom from a snake to a small audience. He became so interested that he used one hand to gesticulate and got it within range of the subject.

Bites by "Fixed" Snakes.—Rattlesnakes purchased by snake shows from regular dealers may have had their fangs removed by order of the purchaser. Accidents happen when the fangs grow in again, or where a careless job has been done by the seller. A carnival-pit operator was bitten by a large western diamond (*C. atrox*) that was supposed to be fangless. Whether replacement fangs had grown in, or the snake had been shipped untreated, it was impossible to discover. Another was bitten by fang stumps that made a sufficient wound so that some venom entered.

MULTIPLE BITES

Multiple bites are of two kinds: those involving two or more bites in the same accident, and those in which the victim receives several bites on successive occasions. The first kind is usually of the class that I have termed legitimate bites—that is, those in which the victim was not engaged in catching or handling rattlers—while the second kind is usually suffered by people who make a business or avocation of catching and handling snakes.

Typical incidents of the first kind are these: A woman gathering strawberries was bitten three times before she could get out of range. Another woman received two bites, one on the instep, one on the great toe. A child, bitten in the leg, stooped down to grab the leg and was bitten in the hand. A 22-month-old girl was bitten in each leg. A soldier, lying down, was bitten four times by a *C. horridus* (Sutcliffe, 1952, p. 113). A boy of four was bitten four times while playing in his yard. A boy was trying to force a small prairie rattler (*C. v. viridis*) into a quart jar and suffered two bites, one in the forefinger of each hand. Booth (1814, p. 322) tells a story—certainly fanciful—of a man who was bitten 25 times on a single occasion.

Bites on many successive occasions, suffered by those who handle snakes, are the rule rather than the exception. Ironmonger (1889, p. 67) claimed to have been bitten 49 times. Tex Sullivan, a well-known collector, had been bitten many times—22 according to a letter from Col. Crimmins in 1950. Preachers of a snake-handling cult claimed to have been bitten from 250 to 400 times.

Unfortunately, these successive bites, as I have mentioned elsewhere, seem not to develop any immunity, at least not to an important degree. Sullivan's twenty-second bite was an exceedingly serious case. S. H. Walker, a collector in the Coachella Valley, who had experienced a number of bites, eventually succumbed to the bite of a rattler hidden in rocks—a snake that he had not seen before it struck him. The case of Mrs. Grace Olive Wiley is well known; she had been bitten many times before receiving a fatal cobra bite.

Under date of April 30, 1933, Douglas D. H. March, then of Philadelphia, wrote me:

> On January 20, I was bitten on the right index finger by the largest of the *C. atrox* I received from you last fall. It was a full bite and very severe in its manifestations. I was held in Jefferson Hospital for three days because of the bite; and just as I was expecting to be discharged, I developed pneumonia and spent another month there. Between the bite and the pneumonia, I mighty nearly faded out. I lost the first joint of the finger. This gives me two mutilated index fingers. The other was caused by a copperhead. I think I am now qualified to jump into any snake-bite argument that may come up. I have been bitten by *C. horridus, adamanteus, atrox, terrificus, Agkistrodon mokasen* and *piscivorus,* and *Bothrops atrox* and *schlegeli.* Curiously, it was the two *atrox—Bothrops* and *Crotalus*—that caused me the greatest discomfort and concern.

March later (April 3, 1939) succumbed to the bite of a fer-de-lance (*Bothrops atrox*) at the Panama Zoo, of which he was then curator. This was said to have been his eighteenth bite.

HUMAN ATTITUDES TOWARD RATTLESNAKES

SNAKE-HANDLING CULTS

The incorporation of snakes into religious ceremonies is exceedingly ancient and widespread throughout the world. Several American Indian tribes participated in such ceremonies, using rattlesnakes, as described in chapter 16.

A Christian snake-handling cult in the Southeastern states gained considerable newspaper notoriety in the 1930's and 1940's, when it made the handling of venomous snakes a test of faith, based on the Scriptural admonition: "And these signs shall follow them that believe . . . they shall take up serpents and . . . it shall not hurt them" (Mark 16:17–18). The sect is said to have been founded in 1909. It eventually spread to small scattered rural groups in Virginia, West Virginia, Kentucky, North Carolina, Tennessee, Georgia, Louisiana, Alabama, and Florida.

At the services, amid scenes of fanatical fervor and mass excitement, rattlesnakes and other venomous snakes were passed from hand to hand to demonstrate the faith of the disciples and converts. The adherents admitted a fear of snakes; only under the hypnosis of these emotional revivals were they able to handle them. The snakes were not restrained in a manner calculated to prevent their biting; on the contrary, they were held at mid-body so that they were free to bite the holder or anyone within range. If a man were bitten it proved his lack of faith.

No doubt most of the followers were carried away by religious piety with a touch of exhibitionism, but this could not be said of the audiences that came to see a free snake show. Later, when several of the states, or possibly all of them, had passed laws forbidding the handling of snakes in religious ceremonies, the onlookers were augmented by those who hoped to see a riot when the state police arrived to interfere.

Unfortunately, these demonstrations of emotionalism by the mountaineers were not harmless affairs, and a number of innocent neophytes, who had not yet reached an age of independent judgment, were seriously hurt. Even babies were permitted to touch the rattlers. Thus the prohibitory laws became necessary and were enforced, despite claims that they infringed the freedom of religious worship. The extent to which services of this type are still being held surreptitiously I do not know. The sect is no doubt still in existence, but with less startling rituals. While they lasted, the newspaper reports were extensive. Altogether, it is said that over 100 people were bitten, seven fatally, between 1934 and 1948. I have found newspaper confirmation of six fatalities. The record of bites may be an underestimate, as some of the preachers claimed to have been bitten from 250 to 400 times.

Recent newspaper accounts indicate a revival of snake-handling rituals, either by the same or other cults. Callahan (1952, p. 92) reports occasional attempts at renewals. A case of snake bite during church services was reported in Greenville, South Carolina, in August, 1953. Two fatalities were recorded in the Southeastern states in the summer of 1954, one at Trenton, Georgia, the other at Fort Payne, Alabama. In connection with the latter case, a lay preacher was fined $50 for handling venomous snakes and endangering other members of the congregation. In the summer of 1955 there were at least two additional fatalities; one in July at Altha, Florida, and the second at Fort Payne, Alabama, the scene of one of the deaths of the previous summer. These deaths were followed by memorial services in which the deceased were praised for their undeviating faith. In these funeral rites, attempts were made to handle the rattlesnakes that had caused the fatalities, despite the refusal of the authorities to permit these features of the obsequies. It is apparently a tenet of the cult that the deaths are justified and sanctified if the other followers carry on by a continuance of snake handling as a demonstration of faith.

There were two bites, one fatal, at services held at Long Beach, California, in April, 1954. It is not known whether the church involved in the last incident is allied to the Eastern sect. Since the accident the Long Beach authorities have stopped the use of venomous snakes in such rituals.

One court case arose when the widow of one of the participants attempted to collect under the double-indemnity clause of his life insurance policy. The court ruled that the occurrence was not like being bitten by a snake in the woods. There was a voluntary assumption of risk that was not accidental. A misconception of the language of the Bible did not excuse a person, and he (or his estate) must not be allowed to profit, said the court. So the double indemnity for accidental death was denied (Ford *vs.* Standard Life Insurance Company, Tennessee Court of Appeals, Eastern Division; reported in 12CCH789, 1947).

Data on the snake-handling cult will be found in Whitehead, 1940; Thomas, 1942, p. 164; Kerman, 1942, p. 93 (reprinted in Clough, 1947, p. 156); Baird, 1946, p. 36; Barbour, 1950, p. 106; Callahan, 1952, p. 91. The Kerman report is the most complete.

Ludwick (1930, p. 121) mentions an isolated case of a man in Idaho who allowed himself to be bitten by a rattler while in a religious frenzy.

MURDER, SUICIDE, AND WAR

In ancient days, long before the time of Cleopatra, snakes were occasionally the fatal instruments in suicides, murder, and in war. They were used in the torture and the execution of criminals. They were employed to safeguard treasure in the manner of the white cobra in Kipling's "The King's Ankus." Hannibal is said to have defeated the Romans in a naval engagement by throwing earthen jars filled with snakes into their ships; and snakes were similarly used in sieges in the Middle Ages (Cheevers, 1870, p. 380). In India there are frequent cases of alleged death from snake bite that are in reality concealed crimes. A magistrate in one district said he had had 402 such cases in 21 months (Cheevers, 1870, p. 368).

Rattlesnakes have never had any popularity for these purposes. On very rare occasions the newspapers may report a suicide attempt, but I have heard of only one success. Rattlesnakes are not deadly enough. A bite may not mean an escape from life, but a very painful and prolonged escape from death. However, according to Spaulding (1944, p. 179) a man at Colfax, California, succeeded in gaining entrance to a building one night and jumped into a snake pit housed there. He deliberately annoyed the rattlers until he had been bitten 85 times, after which he went home and died.

One murder in Los Angeles is often referred to as "The Rattlesnake Murder," but actually the victim of this sordid crime failed to die of the bite of a rattler and was drowned (Williams, 1947, p. 179).

Detective stories occasionally have had rattlers as the instruments of their plots, as, for example, in interesting stories by Thomas Beer (1921, p. 16) and W. J. Neidig (1926, p. 18). Rattlesnakes have had important parts in the plots of many books and stories, the most notable being Oliver Wendell Holmes' *Elsie Venner*, of which the plot depends on the effect on an unborn child of a rattlesnake bite sustained by the mother. Here no crime was involved; at least the bite of the first rattlesnake was a natural one.

Probably the most famous of the crime stories involving snakes is Conan Doyle's Sherlock Holmes short story "The Adventure of the Speckled Band," in which a "swamp adder" was the agent of the villain. Elsewhere (1948b, p. 149) I have inquired into the identification of this snake, the like of which has never climbed a bell-pull.

Miller (1952, p. 299) reprints an Arizona newspaper account published in 1890, according to which rattlesnakes were used by the Pima Indians both to prove the guilt of and to execute one of their number accused of witchcraft. There is every reason to believe this fantastic yarn to be entirely fictional. Various details do not conform to rattlesnake actions.

PROTECTIVE DEVICES

In ancient days much confidence was placed in certain repellents or barriers—materials and devices so hated and feared by snakes that they could be used not only to keep snakes out of homes and camps, but would protect the carrier from being bitten by a snake encountered in the field. Such were the innumerable botanical repellents recorded by Pliny—cedar berries, juniper berries, wild parsnips, garlic, rue, thyme, ash leaves, and many others. Or, one might be protected by eating a viper's liver, wearing a deer's tooth, or carrying burned vulture feathers. A favorite protective amulet of the ancients was a piece of ophite, a marble with serpentlike streaks. In modern folklore, an onion is the most popular repellent; and the hair-rope barrier around the camp is no doubt still used here and there. But all of these devices must be relegated to chapter 18, on myths and folklore, for none has ever been shown to have the slightest value.

Protective clothing is in a quite different category, for its value is unquestioned and important. Often it entirely prevents the fangs of a venomous snake from reaching the flesh of the person at whom a strike is aimed; and even when there is penetration, the clothing may absorb part or all of the venom, or reduce the depth of penetration to an important degree.

There are ample statistics to show the importance of foot and leg coverings. In this country, where most people go about well shod, there are about 40 per cent more bites in the lower limbs than the upper; but in some countries bites in the legs exceed those in the arms by three or four to one. Much of the difference is the result of leg protection. One has only to read the reports of snake-bite cases in India, such as those assembled by Fayrer (1872, p. 42; 1874, p. 42) to note how frequently deaths were caused by bites on bare feet and legs by snakes having relatively short fangs that would never have penetrated an ordinary shoe or even a thick sock. Nicholson (1874, p. 156) reported that snake-bite fatalities in the British army in India were at the rate of about 5½ per million per year, compared with 82 per million per year among the natives. He attributed the difference largely to the fact that the soldiers wore shoes and their legs were clothed. The difference could not have resulted from better treatment in the army, as the remedies available for really serious bites in those days were quite ineffective.

With the types of clothing that Americans ordinarily wear, there is, of course, a considerable variation in the degree of protection afforded. The denser and thicker the material, the greater the protection. The hunter or fisherman going into the field in rattlesnake country is certainly justified in giving thought to the snake-bite hazard in choosing his apparel. He will probably wear boots, leggings, or a shoe-puttee combination in any case, and it will pay him to give attention to their impenetrability and length as well. No hunter will be seriously inconvenienced by foot and leg protection below the knee that is virtually impervious to a rattler's fangs.

Much, of course, depends on the size of the snake. Thin and soft shoe leather will protect fairly well against young rattlers, but more is needed to stop the fangs of the adults of the larger species. To learn something of the possibility of fang penetration, I experimented with a western diamondback (*C. atrox*) 1,420 mm. (4 ft. 8 in.) long and weighing 1,475 g. (3¼ lb.). Its fangs were 12 mm. (about ½ in.) long. The snake was caused to strike a man's oxford shoe that had been stuffed with cloth so as to afford a firm target. The leather was about 1 mm. thick. The snake struck readily enough and with considerable force, for it was backed against a wall, which aided in the forward drive.

In no case—there were several strikes—did the fangs penetrate through the leather; in fact, the penetration was not deep enough to interfere with the snake's withdrawal, nor did the fangs catch sufficiently to cause them to be pulled out of their sockets. There was enough depth to cause a snapping sound as the fangs were withdrawn, and one small solid tooth remained imbedded in the leather.

A somewhat smaller snake of the same species not only failed to penetrate the shoe, but marked it so little that the point of contact of the fangs could not be located with certainty. The venom injection by this snake was uneven. There was considerable left on the shoe at the first strike, then little or none for several, and then again some in each of several strikes.

I think it clear from these tests that leather of moderate thickness cannot be penetrated by a rattler of considerable size, and that heavy boots or a heavy shoe–puttee combination will afford adequate protection from rattlers to the part of the leg covered. On the other hand, a surveyor's type of boot, with rather thin and soft uppers, would not be a perfect protection, particularly if the strike were followed up by a bite that might suffice to penetrate a fold of leather, which is impossible if the leather is thick and stiff. Yet some experienced hunters prefer a boot with the upper part loose and flexible rather than stiff, as they think the latter may be more easily penetrated. This I doubt. But, after all, thickness is the most important feature. All authorities agree that trousers should be worn outside of, rather than tucked inside of, boots, since the loose cloth will offer a greater interference with penetration. Also, the snake may close its mouth in an attempt to bite when it feels the cloth. Allen (1949a, p. 70) calls attention to the fact that the tongue of a boot may be its weakest point. In considering the protective value of boots or clothing, it should be remembered that the point of a fang is solid; the discharge orifice is above the point and may be blocked by leather, or the venom may be absorbed by cloth, even though the point of the fang may have penetrated the skin of the victim.

The following are some actual occurrences indicating the protection, or partial protection, afforded by boots and other leg coverings: A sportsman was struck on the hip, but the snake's fangs did not penetrate loosely fastened trousers (Vigne, 1832, vol. 1, p. 94). A rattler bit a boy several times, but the poison was all absorbed by intervening flannel and no harm was done (Stern, 1871, p. 557). A man wearing rubber boots was protected when struck between the knee and hip. The mother of a child picking berries was horrified when the child came running back dragging a rattler that had its fangs caught in her skirt. The child was untouched (W., 1892, p. 588). A western diamondback nearly six feet long struck a man in the calf. He was wearing caribou-hide boots with heavy stockings underneath. One fang penetrated the boot, and venom was discharged in the stocking; this fang remained caught in the leather. The other fang scarred the leather but failed to puncture it (Sanger, 1931, p. 35). A man was bitten in the leg, but heavy clothing and underwear absorbed most of the venom (Key, 1950, p. 30).

Here are the experiences of some of my correspondents:

I have never had a snake fang penetrate an ordinary boot top, although I have had many try it. Of course, I wouldn't want to let one of our big southern rattlers try it. Their fangs are long and they strike a heavy blow. I have had these prairie rattlers hang up a heavy blow on the bottoms of my Levis until I trampled them to death, but have never been scratched. Had one slap me one time squarely on my hat brim as I was climbing a rimrock while marking timber. It gave me a bad scare. *F. R. Cochran, U. S. Forest Service, Sundance, Wyo.*

⟡

I was saved from a bite in 1942 by wearing cowboy boots. A rattler struck the top of a boot. *W. C. Pallmeyer, County Agent, Benjamin, Tex.*

⟡

I am convinced that 12-inch boots are full protection against being bitten on the feet or legs while one is in a standing position. I have had rattlers strike my boots several times while killing or teasing them; and, while I jumped just as high as the next fellow, I never had one hit more than one inch above the ankle, and in no case did they mark the boot. *Dwight A. Hester, U. S. Forest Service, Grand Mesa, Colo.*

⟡

One CCC enrollee in a fire crew was struck on the leg by a rattlesnake in 1939 at the Horseshoe Bend fire on the Rogue River. He had on leather boots which prevented the snake's fangs from penetrating his flesh. The fangs did go through the leather and resulted in a slight flesh wound. *T. S. Kampmann, U. S. Forest Service, Prairie City, Oreg.*

⟡

At Camp Six a rattler struck me on the leg, hitting my boot. I had walked to my garage and was looking out across country and did not see the snake. It hit me twice. I looked down when something hit my ankle. I jerked my foot as it struck again. I killed it without paying much attention; but next morning I looked at my boot out of curiosity and drew out the two fangs which were imbedded in the heavy boot leather. They were not driven in, but buried just inside the fibre, being visible for their entire length, practically on the surface. I assume that my quick jerk and the snake's withdrawal served to tear out the fangs. *G. G. Green, U. S. Forest Service, Agness, Oreg.*

◇

I know of two cases where men were struck on the leg below the tops of their boots. Had the snakes been of the large diamondback variety perhaps the bites would have been higher on the legs, or the fangs might have been longer, and no doubt serious bites would have occurred. *L. J. Cooper, U. S. Forest Service, Merlin, Oreg.*

◇

A rattler struck at a hunter walking in the brush, the fangs piercing—in the order named—a thickness of overall leg, a leather boot top, and two thicknesses of wool sock. The skin of the man's leg was barely scratched, but enough venom entered this slight wound to make the man feel somewhat ill and nauseated for about three days; however, he did not seek the aid of a physician. *G. W. Danforth, Napa, Calif.*

Here are some shorter reports: A deer hunter was saved by his boots. The fangs remained snagged in his trousers as the snake pulled back. A man was struck in the calf through loose overalls. One fang penetrated; the other was stopped by a seam, showing what a greater thickness will do. A man stepped out of his car and was struck in the puttees he was wearing. There was no penetration. A man stepped on a rattler and was struck in the shoe, but the fangs failed to pierce it. A cowboy dismounted from his horse and was struck in the chaps, the thick leather of which afforded perfect protection.

Men who operate snake shows that require them to walk among rattlers usually wear heavy boots or puttees and then have no fear of the snakes. They are frequently struck by fresh snakes, but the regular inmates become accustomed to their keepers and pay little attention to them. However, in one instance a large rattler struck upward at a 45° angle and hit the victim at a point 22 inches above ground, higher than the protection of his snake-proof boots (Watt and Pollard, 1954, p. 368).

One hunter of rattlesnakes made it a regular practice to step on the tail of any rattler attempting to escape down a hole or into brush. He expected to be struck in his protective boots, and frequently was, but suffered no injury.

Soldiers are usually well protected by adequate leg coverings. It is said that the medical statistics of the Civil War do not disclose a single death from snake bite on the Northern side (Mitchell, 1889, p. 503; Willson, 1908, p. 530).[7] Crimmins (1934, p. 125) said that at Camp Bullis, Texas, there was one rattler bite per thousand men per year during target practice and maneuvers in heavily infested country. During the Third Army maneuvers in the Lake Charles area of Louisiana from July to October, 1941, with 225,000 troops engaged, there were only a dozen cases of snake bite. At army camps in the United States during World War II (years 1942 to 1945 inclusive) there were 1,910 hospital admissions for bites or stings of venomous animals, including, of course, rattlesnake bites. This was at the rate of one man out of every 10,000 exposed. There were no

---

[7] This throws doubt on one of the better rattler yarns to the effect that after a certain Civil War battle—was it Shiloh?—60 Union soldiers were found dead from rattlesnake bite, but no Confederates. This resulted from the well-known fact—or is it a fact?—that rattlers particularly dislike blue. But I was told by one professional collector that he always went afield in blue trousers; he had absolute confidence in their repellent effect.

fatalities. This entailed nearly 20 million man-years of exposure, many of which were spent in the rattlesnake-infested areas of the Southwest.

Some people of experience advocate special boots or other equipment under particular circumstances. Matteson (1899, p. 666) wore stove pipes over his legs and rubber boots over his shoes when experimenting to see how high rattlers might strike. Ortel (1932, p. 202) believes metal-lined leggings worthy of consideration. Bevan (1931a, p. 109) preferred rubber boots to leather. Hogg (1928, p. 53), as a test, put on an old pair of heavy leather high-top boots over several pairs of thick woolen stockings and waded among rattlers. Only one strike penetrated at all. Benjamin (1941, p. 57) believed boots to be insufficient and advocated lining them with aluminum sheeting.

Special snake-proof boots are available on the market. They are expensive and slightly cumbersome, but may be advisable for hunters in some particular areas of the Southeastern states and Texas where very large diamondbacks may be encountered (Snyder, 1949, p. 5; Werler, 1950, p. 29; Teale, 1951, p. 66; Mc-Hugh, 1952, p. 95; Oliver, 1952, p. 71). Gokey and Company, of St. Paul, makes a special snake-proof boot. Trousers impervious to snake bite are being produced experimentally; they have a removable lining of Monel wire cloth. They have the objectionable features of being heavy and stiff.

Even in colonial days the desirability of having the legs adequately protected was recognized. Moore (1744, p. 59) said the farmers wore coarse woolen cloths that hung loose around the legs; they were called Indian boots. S. Smith (1765, p. 504) reported that the colonists protected their legs with chestnut bark. Browning (1860, p. 117), in describing conditions at the turn of the century in Maryland, says that the hunter of that day made ropes of long grass, which he wrapped around his legs for protection against rattlers. At night he stuffed grass into his pants legs for the same purpose. According to La Rochefoucault-Liancourt (1799, p. 595), the field workers on the Southern plantations wore thick worsted "splatterdashes."

A few writers have commented somewhat adversely on the protective value of clothing (Kalm, 1752–53, p. 58; Daudin, 1801–4, vol. 5, p. 300; Audubon, 1827, p. 26; Schomburgk, 1922, vol. 2, p. 104; MacDonald, 1946, p. 136; Breland, 1948, p. 206; and Griffin, 1949, p. 11). Briggs (1950, p. 124) thought that a rattler might strike successfully through a boot or wader if it struck high enough, but, even so, the fangs would fail to penetrate the clothing. Ross Allen (1949a, p. 70) says the average hunting or riding boot is inadequate in Florida; he knew of two serious bites through such boots. I heard of one case in which a man was bitten through three thicknesses of denim overalls rolled into a cuff.

Bailey (1928, p. 164) has pointed out that high boots or leather leggings are important in relieving the nerve strain of people tramping through rattler country. Heavy gauntlet-type gloves are of unquestioned value for anyone doing much climbing or working among rocks.

Adair (1930, p. 62) tells of a tourist in Texas who ran over a seven-foot diamondback that punctured two tire casings before it was killed. He remarks upon the great force behind those one-inch fangs. Were there any truth in that wild story, all that has been said previously of the protective value of boots and other clothing would be completely misleading.

THE HUMAN FEAR OF SNAKES

It is generally agreed, from tests and observations, that children have no natural or instinctive fear of snakes. An interesting discussion of the subject was initiated by a contribution to *Science* in 1916 by Dabney (p. 25); his remarks called forth additional comments by McClellan (1916b, p. 387), Henderson (1916, p. 388), and Miller (1916, p. 744). The matter has been mentioned further by Ortenburger (1930, p. 423), who experimented on his own youngsters, and by DeLys (1948, p. 71) and Stimpson (1948, p. 201). Probably the children of herpetologists such as Ortenburger's are not to be taken as examples; they become so accustomed to seeing snakes handled that the fact that some are dangerous must be repeatedly recalled to their attention. It goes without saying that no child should ever be allowed to handle venomous snakes. A recent newspaper article mentioned a suit brought by a high-school science student because of a rattlesnake bite sustained while he was cleaning the snake's cage.

Since most children cannot distinguish venomous from nonvenomous snakes, the inculcation of a moderate fear of snakes is probably justified as a safety measure. But to instill such a horror and revulsion at the sight of a snake that, when they become adults, people cannot bear to look at a snake in a cage is a mistake. This insensate fear is so widespread—it is incorrectly believed to be instinctive—that many newspapers and magazines will not print a picture of a snake, nor can one be shown in the movies without public protest. A camera magazine reported that there were 40 out of every 1,000 colored films sent in for developing that showed wild life; one out of the 40 was of a snake or other reptile.

The cultivated fear of snakes has had results quite the opposite of those desired. It causes people to become so paralyzed upon encountering a rattler in the field that they cannot take the most elementary safety precautions. If bitten by a snake they are in no condition to judge whether it was venomous or harmless. This is a matter of importance in deciding whether painful and even dangerous remedial measures are necessary, for the bite of a harmless snake requires only a touch of antiseptic, as would a scratch or a splinter. Even in areas of the United States—and they are extensive—where rattlers are the only venomous snakes, victims usually cannot even report with certainty whether or not the culprit had rattles on its tail. These are the people who destroy all harmless snakes—the natural competitors, and even the destroyers of rattlesnakes—thus aiding in the protection and the increase of the dangerous snakes they so greatly fear. So children should be taught to avoid snakes, not to be terrified by them, and eventually we may have a more understanding adult population.

That the shock caused by the bite of a harmless snake can be serious and even fatal is well authenticated. It is obvious that such an eventuality is more likely to happen to persons in whom the fear of snakes is exaggerated. Two such cases have been recorded in San Diego County. In one, a man was bitten by a harmless gopher snake (*Pituophis catenifer annectens*) and almost died of fright; in the other a hunter was stuck by the barb of a wire fence, thought he was bitten, and barely survived the shock. Similar stories of near death from fright in the United States are recounted by Anon. (1896, p. 251), Lyon (1910, p. 384), Hogg (1931a, p. 172), and Kelly, Davis, and Robertson (1936, p. 100).

Schneck (1878, p. 585) made an investigation among 13 of his fellow physicians in southeastern Illinois to learn whether the hog-nosed snake (*Heterodon*) was venomous. Although none had had a snake-bite case, all thought the snake venomous, and he heard three different versions of the case of a boy of eight who had died from the bite. (Schneck believed that the fatality was caused by sunstroke.) Actually, although this snake is a great bluffer, hissing and blowing when annoyed, it is quite harmless, for it is without venom and will bite only on rare occasions. But the fear of this innocuous creature has caused much needless apprehension (see also Barringer, 1892, p. 283).

In foreign lands where the recognition of venomous snakes is more difficult than in our country, serious or fatal shocks from the bites of harmless snakes have been often mentioned (Creed, 1884, p. 244; Fayrer, 1892, p. 115; Prater, 1924, p. 164; Wall, 1928, p. 70; Corkill, 1932b, p. 35; Kahn, 1942, p. 288). In many places all snakes are thought to be venomous, as they were in Pliny's day. In some countries certain creatures are deemed to be highly dangerous, more so than the really venomous snakes that may be found there. This is true of the harmless blind snake (*Typhlops*) in Liberia (Harley, 1941, p. 102). In Sonora, and elsewhere in Mexico, a delicate little gecko (the lizard *Coleonyx*) that under no circumstances could pinch a person's finger hard enough to cause pain is as dreaded as a rattlesnake.

Isabella Bird (1881, p. 48) tells how the hardships of pioneer life in Colorado were increased by her dread of snakes. There were some rattlers about that she recognized and rightly feared, but her discomfort was unnecessarily increased by many harmless snakes that she thought as dangerous as rattlers.

On November 1, 1952, near San Diego, a wetback (a Mexican agricultural worker illegally in the United States), because of his fear of rattlesnakes, refused to sleep with his companions in a railway culvert where they were hiding from the immigration officers. Instead, he preferred the tracks, where no snake might be hiding, and was killed by a train. In another accident near Blythe, California, a boy, sleeping on the pavement of a road to avoid snakes, was run over and killed. In a recent accident near San Diego, the rescue of four people trapped under an overturned car was delayed because the ravine was "infested with rattlesnakes." (Two rattlers were seen by the rescuers.)

B., J. (1765, p. 513) tells a fantastic story of a man who put on his son's jacket by mistake. It was too small and he thought he had been bitten by a rattler and had swelled up. He became seriously ill, but recovered when he found himself able to don his own jacket. A prospector was struck at by a rattler that missed its target. The man walked away and fell dead of heart failure. I have mislaid the source of this story; it may well be folklore.

Some of the exaggerated fears of rattlesnakes arise from equally exaggerated stories of their prevalence, their viciousness, and the inevitable fatalities from their bites. In truth, they are rarely as common as people think; they are timorous creatures that will bite human beings only if hurt or frightened; and a bite is rarely fatal if properly treated. Bosc (1803, vol. 6, p. 550) said that if the travelers' tales of the danger from rattlesnakes were true, America would be uninhabitable. But Blome, as early as 1686 (p. 86), had said the fear of rattlesnakes was "worse than their hurt"; and Purry *et al.* (1732, p. 1018) said that people in the Carolinas were seldom bitten. Yet European travelers have been taken in by the tall-story artists down to the present day. Voelgyi (1926, p. 140), returning to Europe from Texas, reported that people there are often found in the woods and fields dead from rattler bites.

Of course, there can be too much complacency, as is shown by the frequency with which carnival snake-pit men are bitten. Nicholson (1874, p. 137) tells of a friend who handled cobras with jaunty carelessness because he thought he had a perfect antidote, which, in reality, was worthless. Hilton (1947, p. 130) handled a coral snake that he did not learn was venomous until long afterward. This is not unusual, as coral snakes will rarely bite unless injured. Oertel (1930, p. 88) mentions a similar incident.

THE EFFECT OF THE RATTLESNAKE THREAT ON PEOPLE'S ACTIONS

A question arises as to whether the hazard from rattlesnakes is considered by explorers, hunters, fishermen, ranchers, and other outdoor people, to be serious enough to affect their actions. We are dealing here, not with the actual risk, but with what people think the risk to be. If the historians and travelers are to be believed, the rattlesnake hazard has been taken seriously by many.

Galineé, in his account of a journey in Canada in 1669–70, claims that La Salle was so frightened by seeing three large rattlers that he was taken with a high fever (Galineé, 1903, p. 41; Kellogg, 1917, p. 189). Church (1716, p. 15; Anon., 1804, p. 202) maintained that in King Philip's War the soldiers were more afraid of rattlers than of the Indians they were fighting. Once, in going through the woods in search of the enemy, they changed their route when they encountered a rattlesnake. Byrd (1929, p. 110, but writing of 1728) said that on the survey of the Virginia–North Carolina boundary, when they discovered that the rattlers had come out of hibernation, they postponed further work until fall. In 1736, in an exchange of letters between the naturalist Peter Collinson and John Bartram, the latter is warned of the hazards of travel and collecting, and "above all the danger of rattlesnakes" (Darlington, 1849, p. 87).

Ettwein (1901, p. 212), speaking of his travels in Pennsylvania in 1772, said that he almost stepped on a rattler, and his fright was such that for days he took every step with dread. This was in a wild, unsettled part of the state, where the other hardships of travel must have been great. In Pennsylvania in 1799, Hill (edition of 1890, p. 196) killed a rattler and was badly frightened by it. Later, although pressed for food and knowing that he could kill a deer if he hunted, he was too fearful of the possibility of meeting other rattlers to do so. Browning (1860, p. 340), another experienced hunter, was so frightened when he saw some rattlers moving about that he ran for a considerable distance. Fanny Kelly (1872, p. 30) tells how her husband escaped from the Sioux Indians, when they were frightened away by a rattlesnake that sounded its rattle. Howitt (1820, p. 24) tells how his party refused to pitch camp in a certain canyon because of their fear of rattlesnakes.

Marryat (1855,[8] p. 77) writing of a hunting trip into the Sacramento Valley of California says: "The dread of rattlesnakes destroyed in great measure the pleas-

---

[8] In 1855 my father was making his living hauling freight from Sacramento to the mines in Amador County. The rattlesnakes did not impress him enough to be worthy of mention, but he told me of the great quantities of game then present in the valley and the foothills of the Sierras.

ure of our sport, for we lost many a good shot from looking on the ground—which men are apt to do occasionally when once satisfied of the existence of a venomous reptile, the bite of which is by all accounts mortal."

Weld (1855, p. 79), a European visitor on a hunting trip, seems to have been taken in by the boys around the campfire. He was told that the woods swarmed with rattlesnakes "a circumstance that paralyzed my energies, and kept me in a state of constant apprehension." He wore low shoes, which did not add to his pleasure. Anon. (1858b, p. 471) mentions a farmer who was in misery through fear of rattlers. Wyman (1892, p. 588), having found rattlers up to 7,000 or 8,000 feet in California, always endeavored to camp above that altitude. (Actually, they are found as high as 11,000 feet in California.) Gauldt (1896, p. 303) tells a weird yarn, probably a campfire tall story, of a cavalryman who drowned himself in disgust when a rattler struck him (without damage) in the leggings. Matteson (1899, p. 665) reports the abandonment of a ranch because of the prevalence of rattlesnakes. Chittenden (1902, p. 837), the historian of the hunters and trappers of the Missouri Basin and the Rockies, says that these hardy men feared rattlesnakes out of all proportion to the real danger. They were considered a greater hazard than grizzlies. As a matter of fact, deaths among the men were rare, but the snakes were bothersome to their pack mules and horses.

Gillette (1949, p. 3) maintains that when outlaws of the early days in the Southwest failed to return to their hide-outs it was assumed that they had been bitten by rattlers. Stillwell (1949, p. 112) mentions some quail hunters who abandoned a trip after one had almost stepped on a rattler. Stauffer (1952, p. 16) tells of a turkey hunter who was so paralyzed by fear upon finding himself within 2½ feet of a large rattler that he remained immobile for 15 minutes, not even using his gun on the snake. Finally he flung himself away from the rattler. He abandoned the hunt and spent a sleepless night. Dobie (1926, p. 52) said that deer hunters in southwestern Texas sometimes gave up hunting until the advent of cold weather, because of the fear of rattlers. Hudgens (1953, p. 48) got such a fright from accidentally stepping on a rattler that it still interferes with his sleep. Spaulding (1944, p. 159) says a single fright from a rattler during his boyhood has preyed on his mind ever since. Holland (1953, p. 38) tells several stories of the reactions of hunters in Florida and Texas when they have encountered large rattlers. A farmer is said to have kept trespassers out of his farmyard by hanging rattler skins on his barn, as an evidence of the presence of the snakes roundabout (Shorey, 1953, p. 26).

People are known to have abandoned the purchase of property when they learned that rattlers were occasionally found in the vicinity; and instances are not unknown when they have disposed of homes already owned, upon the discovery of a rattlesnake in the vicinity. Upon the advent of antivenin in the United States in 1927, a commercial reporting agency sent out a statement to its clients advocating that publicity be given to the remedy, as it might make areas popular, either for settlement or vacations, that had hitherto been shunned because of the actual or reputed presence of rattlers.

Dobie (1926, p. 52) has vividly described the horror and savage hatred that a rattler instills in most people. Oliver Wendell Holmes referred to the sound of the rattle as "the dreadful sound that nothing which breathes, be he man or brute, can hear unmoved" (*Elsie Venner*, 1861, vol. 1, p. 238).

RATTLESNAKES AND DOMESTIC ANIMALS

ANIMAL FEARS OF SNAKES

A few tests have been made to determine the natural fear of snakes evidenced by monkeys and apes (Brown, 1878, p. 226; 1900, p. 463; Mitchell and Pocock, 1908, p. 793; Mitchell, 1922, p. 347). The tests apparently indicate that they do have a natural fear.

In the early natural histories, it was stressed that all animals, including the European horse, were frightened intuitively by the sound of the rattlesnake's rattle (Pennant, 1787, p. 89; Winterbotham, 1795, p. 406; Bosc, 1803, p. 553; Rees, 1819, p. 1; Wetmore, 1837, p. 159; Townsend, 1839, p. 69; Brainard, 1855, p. 124; Wood, 1863, p. 101; T., 1882, p. 6). B., J. (1765, p. 512) tells of some men with 10 horses who were riding in the woods when they came upon a rattlesnake. This so frightened the horses that every one of them screamed or roared. But other, more objective modern writers, with the exception of Rutledge (1935, p. 519; 1936, p. 139; 1938, p. 19; 1946, p. 230), state that much depends on the conditions under which the horse discovers the rattler. Horses are generally alarmed at sudden sounds or movements, and so are likely to be frightened if a rattler nearby suddenly rises into its striking coil and sounds its rattle. James (1823, vol. 3, p. 63) reports that the horses on Major S. H. Long's expedition to the Rocky Mountains were not afraid of rattlers but a mule was. Murphy (1917, pp. 57, 67) observed a horse and a mule to step over a large western diamondback (*C. atrox*) without seeming to see it; at least they paid no attention to it. Barnes (1933, p. 429) thought that neither horses nor cattle sense danger from rattlesnakes. Others giving some information on the subject are Ingersoll (1883b, p. 129), Hudson (1893b, p. 451; 1919, p. 173), Lumholtz (1912, p. 117), Dabney (1916, p. 25), Thompson (1932, p. 108), and Dobie (1952b, p. 115). One of my correspondents wrote:

> I have noticed that some horses are alarmed at rattlers and others show no concern at all. In the Salmon River mountains (where rattlers are very plentiful), I saw a whole pack-string pass a rattler on the very edge of a trail without noticing it. A man on the last horse saw the snake and captured it alive. He then walked by the whole pack-string with the snake in his hand and not one horse showed concern. *Glen R. Jones, U. S. Forest Service Bridgeport, Calif.*

C. M. Bogert advised me that he held a rattling rattlesnake in his hands and paused in front of each of 25 horses in a stable. Only one, a rather "spooky" horse that often shied at paper, showed even a mild interest; it snorted and retreated a couple of steps. I have mentioned elsewhere (p. 963) how the curiosity of horses, especially colts, sometimes leads to their being bitten. Austin (1906, p. 126; Towne and Wentworth, 1946, p. 278) describes the reactions of sheep to rattlers.

Dogs show much the same variability in their reactions to rattlesnakes as do horses. As I have mentioned elsewhere (p. 1042), some become confirmed rattlesnake killers. T. (1882, p. 6) said that he had a fighting dog but it was afraid of rattlers. Gowanloch (1943, p. 38) said he found dogs curious but not afraid of snakes. Sibley (1951, p. 47) thought his dogs could distinguish between harmless snakes and rattlers. They would bark at rattlers. It seems probable that this was merely their reaction to the sound of the rattle.

Maddox (1940, p. 271), repeating the yarns of an old-timer, said that most animals except buck deer give rattlers a wide berth. Dorsch (1929, p. 4) said there was no foundation to the belief that only split-hoofed animals would pass a rattlesnake. Wagnon, Guilbert, and Hart (1945, p. 22), on the San Joaquin Experimental Range, in central California, found that cattle were not afraid of rattlers even after they had been bitten.

Teale (1951, p. 64; see also J. D. Oliver, 1951, p. 38) observed a kitten to show no fear of a diamondback. Urich and Mole (1894, p. 297) found that prey-sized mammals introduced into a rattler's cage showed no sign of fear, which duplicates our experience at the San Diego Zoo, as mentioned in chapter 9. Coahoma (1902, p. 345) reported that a young squirrel did show fear when introduced into a rattler's cage. Linsdale (1946, pp. 67, 267) and Fitch (1948a, p. 555) have discussed at length the reactions of ground squirrels to rattlesnakes in the wild. The squirrels have a characteristic warning motion of the tail which calls the attention of other squirrels to the presence of the snake. This is effective, as the other squirrels nearby repeat the motion (a vertical tail thrashed from side to side) and thus the whole colony is alerted against the danger.

STOCK LOSSES FROM RATTLESNAKE BITE

Next to the frequency and mortality of rattlesnake bites among human beings, the most important phase of the rattlesnake's life history to man is the economic loss suffered through damage to his livestock and domestic animals. Of course, there is no question concerning the desirability of killing rattlesnakes about human habitations and farms, but whether the stock raiser will be benefited by having the rattlers killed on the open range is a matter of doubt. The increased rodent population may well do more damage to the grazing value of the range than the rattlers that would have kept them in control might do to the stock. Some statements that have appeared regarding rattlesnake damage have come from persons with some monetary interest in rattlesnake-control programs or methods, and have undoubtedly been exaggerated. They have tended to overlook the rodent-control phase of the problem.

Some years ago I circularized a number of cattlemen, forest rangers, and game wardens in the Western range areas, asking for opinions on the extent of the rattlesnake damage to livestock. Subsequently, in 1952, I sent a post-card questionnaire to the county agents in Texas. I had no expectation of securing statistical information, but thought the consensus of views might be of some value, and this, I think, has proved to be the case. Because of the economic importance of the problem, I have cited many of the statements, even though they may seem repetitious, for the very repetition serves to emphasize the important factors. Some are interesting in that they record specific instances of deaths of stock from rattler bite. As might be expected, there is much variation in the opinions expressed, and some of the views conflict with others.

First, I present a series of statements segregated by states, followed by other series segregated by animal activities, by symptoms, and by kinds of animals affected. These, in turn, are followed by brief citations from the literature.

STOCK LOSSES BY AREAS

Stock damage in central and northern California, Nevada, Utah, Colorado, and Kansas, and the states to the north of them, is largely or entirely caused by subspecies of the western rattlesnake (*Crotalus viridis*). In Arizona, New Mexico, and Texas, the western diamond rattler (*C. atrox*) is by far the worst offender, but other species are present in these states, so no particular incident can be assigned to any species without an identification of the snake, which is usually not available. The same is true of southern California, but here other species replace *C. atrox* in most areas. The first series of extracts from the letters follow:

British Columbia.—The bite of the rattlesnake, though dangerous, is seldom fatal, except to horses, which are peculiarly susceptible.

Washington.—Rattlesnake bite causes cows and horses to swell up badly, but I have never seen one actually die. Lambs are killed but seldom older sheep.

Oregon.—Hogs and sheep are immune. Horses are usually bitten while feeding in cheat grass or heavy patches of grass.

◇

Horses on the ranch are occasionally bitten in the legs without serious effects. Cattle are bitten while foraging, and I remember one instance where a steer became so badly infected about the nose and jaw that it was necessary to kill the animal.

◇

I have heard of cases in which horses and cattle have been bitten by rattlesnakes. Considerable swelling occurred and the animals became sick, but, so far as I know, snake bites did not result in death in any case. Damage to stock is rare here.

◇

Most stock are bitten in the head as they try to smell a rattler, and the head swells up, but they seldom die; however, a bite on the front leg is almost always fatal.

◇

I have seen horses, cows, and dogs that have been bitten by rattlers, and this spring the first fatality, a cow struck in the belly.

◇

Rattlesnakes constitute no particular threat to stock, although I have known of one case of a cow dying from rattlesnake bite, and of several valuable cougar hounds being killed in this manner. I have seen horses struck on the nose and several dogs bitten in the head, but they recovered, although with some swelling of the affected parts for some days. The main damage to horses is that ever after being bitten they shy at any small moving objects, or moving shadows in front of them.

California.—There is a considerable loss of stock from rattlesnake bite. Probably not over 20 per cent of the bites are fatal.

◇

Occasionally, we have had animals bitten. We lost a young government mule that was bitten on the leg and was not found in time for treatment.

◇

As far as losing any stock from rattlers is concerned, I believe it's safe to say we lose none. Once in a great while we find a cow or steer that looks as though it has been hit by a rattler, but inside of two weeks they get well without any attention.

◇

I have known very few cattle to be bitten by rattlesnakes and have never seen one die. However, there have been several cattle that became very sick as a result of snake bite. I have seen a few horses die from snake bite. I do not consider rattlesnakes a hazard to livestock.

I have had but one horse bitten by a rattler and he recovered. I would say that they cause little loss to stock. They do sometimes strike grazing stock on the nose.

◇

In this locality it is quite common for livestock to be bitten by rattlers. No treatment is given, but to my knowledge only one horse has ever died from snake bite, and it lived seven days. It was bitten on the nose while feeding.

◇

From reports that I have had, the damage to stock has been very small. I know several people who are grazing stock in the hills. Some say that rattlers are becoming a nuisance and are taking a toll of their livestock. Others say that they are never bothered. Those who claim a toll on their stock are people who always exaggerate. I have inspected sheep and calves that have reportedly died from rattlesnake bite, but in every case the carcass has been too far gone to prove anything.

◇

I have seen horses, cattle, and dogs bitten by rattlers. They swell up badly, and as a rule die if you do not do something for them. If you find them in time and cut the bite open so it can bleed and drain, it helps a lot.

◇

One horse that was bitten on the leg suffered considerable swelling but did not die.

Nevada.—I heard of a mare that had been bitten on the jaw by a rattler. She was grazing on open range at the time. Her head swelled to about twice its normal size and she died within about 48 hours. Her suckling colt also died a few hours after its mother.

Idaho.—I have seen some horses and dogs that were bitten by rattlesnakes but their bites are seldom fatal.

◇

As to stock: I know of about five different cases where dogs, horses, and cows have been bitten by rattlesnakes, but none was fatal.

◇

Rattlers occasionally bite and kill horses and sheep, but only two cases of each have come to my attention.

◇

I have known several sheep to die from rattlesnake bite while being driven across a snake-infested area. Also, I have known of several horses being bitten but all lived, only one showing any aftereffects.

◇

I have only known of two saddle horses being bitten. They were laid up for about two weeks with a badly swollen foot and leg.

◇

The forest service has had two cases of snake bite of horses. They have owned an average of 70 head and their use has been 90 per cent in rattlesnake country. Neither case was fatal.

Montana.—I have known rattlers to kill a number of calves when they wandered too close to a snake.

◇

I have never known a rattler to kill a cow or horse, although they are frequently bitten.

◇

The stockmen complain quite a lot about losing a steer or a horse. Usually the head swells up to an immense size, but, as a rule, they get over the bite in time. A rancher friend had a bull killed about two weeks ago.

◇

Livestock bitten by rattlesnakes suffer for a short period but seldom die.

◇

The aggregate loss of livestock from rattler bite through the infested area is admittedly heavy. Sheep growers agree that rattlesnakes kill more sheep than coyotes do.

Wyoming.—Cattle, except young calves, do not get bitten as often as horses do. They swell up pretty bad and most of them die. Old sheep get bitten quite often and about half of them die. Lots of small lambs get bitten and nearly all of them die. Horses, cattle, and sheep do not seem to go for the mud when bitten as dogs do.

<>

I have known several dogs to be bitten; also horses, cows, calves, and one cat. None died.

Utah.—I do not believe rattlesnakes cause serious damage to livestock. I only know of one occasion where stock was killed. A few years ago a cow lying in the pasture was bitten on the udder by a rattlesnake. This proved fatal.

<>

Horses and cows swell up and go lame from rattlesnake bite, but sheep are not usually injured, probably because of the wool stopping the fangs.

Colorado.—Some cattle are apparently struck by rattlers in this area. As often as not, they are struck well up on the back or side, which I am sure is the result of the animals' lying down on the snake. In one case a bull was struck several times high up on the shoulder and apparently refused to get up until he was ready.[9] In all cases that I am sure of, the animal struck was quite sick but recovered. I doubt that more than one animal out of every 2,500 grazed in a snake country gets bitten. This figure is just a guess, but the death loss—if any—is very light.

<>

In spite of the fact that livestock constantly range in heavily infested country, I have never heard of an authenticated case of any kind of ranging livestock being killed by a rattlesnake. I have heard of ridden horses being bitten and dying as a result, although I have never actually seen it happen.

<>

I have only rarely heard of any damage to horses or cattle by rattlers in this section, and I do not recall of ever having heard of any losses caused by snake bite.

<>

I do not think that rattlesnakes are a menace to domestic stock, but the main trouble is that people are often bitten by not following a few simple safety rules, when in areas where rattlers occur. I believe rattlers do more good than harm.

<>

Rattlesnakes bite sheep on the nose, but I never knew a sheep or lamb to die from the bite.

<>

A sheep man keeping his sheep down by the Rio Grande vicinity in the early spring and late fall, stated that he had an average of about three sheep bitten by rattlesnakes each year. Two of the three die as a result. The bites are on the cheeks of the animal and the swelling of the head, neck, and shoulders is pronounced. The band contains an average of 900 to 1,000 sheep.

<>

I've seen horses and cows that have been bitten but never knew one to die from the bite, although they will swell up to enormous size.

<>

Damage to stock is limited to an occasional death of a colt.

South Dakota.—A man with close to 1,000 head of sheep on the range told me that he lost 15 lambs from rattlesnake bite.

Nebraska.—A colt died from a rattler's bite in this county two weeks ago.

Arizona.—Although this is a livestock area, I have never heard of any loss from rattlesnake bite.

---

[9] Sometimes *C. v. viridis* bite causes no immediate pain.

The damage to stock by rattlers is very slight. An occasional saddle horse gets bitten while being ridden, and once in a great while a cow while grazing.

◇

I have had both dogs and horses bitten by rattlesnakes, and while they usually swell up and get somewhat sick, I do not know of a case that resulted in the death of the animal. I had a saddle horse struck while in pasture this spring.

◇

During 1920 I had occasion to observe five cases of horses being bitten by rattlesnakes on their heads, and death occurred in all cases.

◇

I believe that the loss from rattlesnake bite among stock is light, as I have seen stock at different times that have been bitten; they usually swell up and are sick, and fall off in flesh, but, after a time, recover from the bite.

New Mexico.—Damage to livestock varies with the terrain. In rough, rocky, or brushy areas there is much more damage than on level ground where there is smooth turf.

◇

I have had one horse and one dog struck, both of which survived. The horse evidently stepped on the rattler and was struck inside the hind leg about 20 inches from the ground. I was unable to work the horse for about two weeks.

◇

The damage to stock here is not serious. I have seen several animals bitten by rattlers without fatal results.

◇

There is no record here of livestock suffering from rattlesnake bites.

◇

As to the seriousness of damage to stock, I have seen cattle that have been bitten by rattlesnakes, some of which have died and some lived. I have known cases where they have struck a saddle horse while the horse was being ridden.

◇

An occasional cow is killed by being bitten by a rattler. In one instance a rather valuable bull was killed. Despite the number of stock grazed, and plentiful as the snakes are, only a very small fraction of one per cent of stock is ever injured by them.

◇

I lost my beautiful riding filly last Monday. I had all my horses on pasture and she was bitten by a rattlesnake on the nose, and we found her too late to save her. I felt terrible over losing her.

Texas.—There are many reports of rattlers striking dogs, domestic animals, and chickens. One under a box in a neighbor's milk-house struck a hen that came too near. The hen soon turned black and died.

◇

When a horse or head of cattle is found dead, quite often it is blamed on a rattler. But there is seldom positive evidence.

◇

The rattlesnake population is high in Medina County, but there is little loss. A few animals are bitten each year but most recover.

◇

A higher proportion of horses are struck on the nose than cattle, because of the more inquisitive attitude of the horse.

◇

Ranchers expect occasional losses from rattlesnakes, but pay little attention to them.

◇

I believe that many unexplained losses of livestock are due to rattlesnakes.

There are very few animals reported killed by rattlesnakes in Real County, although there is a large population of rattlers. Most of the animals recover without treatment. The warning rattle is respected by man and beast.

◇

Occasionally an animal is bitten but it is seldom fatal. Usually they recover in from four to six weeks.

◇

Our native animals don't get bitten as often as the northern-bred animals.

◇

The livestock losses in Travis County are about $5,000 to $7,500 per year.

◇

Most of the horses bitten are colts or others under five years old.

Mississippi.—I know of one horse that was bitten by a diamondback. It was being ridden at the time and was bitten on the leg. The horse was hot and was seriously hurt, but was given two shots of antivenin and recovered. I don't believe a rattler can hurt a fat hog or a bear, as the layer of fat is so thick that venom has no effect on them.

◇

I know of one mule killed in a three-year period.

West Virginia.—It is my opinion that rattlers won't bite stock except when they are stepped on. These woods have been full of sheep and cattle, and a few horses, yet in 40 years I have only known of one horse being bitten. He lay down on a rattler and was bitten in the hip.

Virginia.—I have known of horses being bitten but this is not a common occurrence. I don't believe rattlesnakes are a serious menace to stock anywhere in the county.

◇

Although much stock is being grazed in the woods here in southwestern Virginia, I have never heard of any snake-bite injury to stock.

WHAT ANIMALS WERE DOING WHEN BITTEN

In the quotations already given, there have been a number of incidental remarks on what an animal was doing when bitten by the rattlesnake. There follow some additional extracts from letters on this phase of the snake-bite problem. It will be noted that horses and cattle are usually struck in the head by rattlers while grazing. Colts and calves seem to have a fatal curiosity that causes them to sniff a snake, and their elders, also, are sometimes too curious. Here are the views of some of my correspondents:

Most stock are bitten in the head as they try to smell a rattler.

◇

Stock get bitten around the nose and mouth while feeding.

◇

A horse is usually struck by a rattlesnake when he has his head to the ground nibbling grass.

◇

An incident I recall was when a horse was bitten on the nose by an average-sized rattlesnake. While riding out to get the horses one morning I got about 50 yards from my own personal horse. He had his head down and was sniffing. Just then a snake struck him on the nose, and the horse jumped and pawed. Naturally, I rode over to see what kind of a snake it was, and found the rattlesnake.

◇

I had a colt struck on the nose, the result of too much curiosity on the colt's part.

The curiosity of colts is a large factor in their being bitten by rattlesnakes.

◇

Colts and young steers are bitten, as they are the most curious.

◇

A horse lay down on a rattler and was bitten in the hip.

◇

A saddle horse walked up to a haystack and started to eat hay and was bitten by a rattler hidden in the side of the stack.

Symptoms of Rattlesnake Bite in Animals

Most rattlesnake-bite cases in animals, with the exception of those suffered by riding horses or by dogs, occur without the presence of a human witness. However, stockmen and farmers are so familiar with rattlesnake-bite symptoms in stock that their diagnosis of snake bite is usually correct.

The following descriptions of rattler-bite symptoms, segregated by kinds of stock, are taken from letters of stockmen and forest rangers. Nearly all stress swelling as the most noticeable symptom, as has been evident in many of the quotations already given. Where the locality affords a certainty or strong presumption as to the kind of rattler causing the bite, I have supplied this information.

Stock in General

The usual result of a rattlesnake bite is that the head is swelled to nearly twice its normal size for a few days.—Montana (*C. v. viridis*).

◇

The stockmen complain a lot when they lose a steer or a horse. Usually the animal's head swells up to an immense size, but as a rule they get over the bite in time.—Montana (*C. v. viridis*).

◇

I have known of horses and cows being bitten and they swell up to enormous size.—Colorado (*C. v. viridis*).

◇

Horses and cows swell up and get lame from rattlesnake bite.—Utah (*C. v. lutosus*).

◇

Most stock are bitten in the head as they try to smell the rattler, and the head swells up, but they seldom die.—Oregon (*C. v. lutosus*).

◇

Cows and horses swell up badly, but I have never seen any actually die from snake bite.—Washington (*C. v. oreganus*).

◇

Snake-bitten animals seldom die, but they get thin.—Washington (*C. v. oreganus*).

◇

Stock usually swell up, get sick, and fall off in flesh, but after a time recover from the bite.—Arizona.

◇

When cows and horses are bitten in the head, there is a bad swelling and they may be partially blind for a while; also, they have spasms, become jerky, and have a running nose.—Arizona (probably *C. v. cerberus*).

Cattle

Cows that are bitten sometimes peel off and lose their hair, and get terribly thin.—Montana (*C. v. viridis*).

The reaction varies from severe swelling to severe bleeding with no swelling, depending on the location of the bite.—Wyoming (*C. v. viridis*).

❖

A steer was bitten by a rattler, and there was a pus sac about six inches in diameter on his side.—Wyoming (*C. v. viridis*).

Horses, Mules, and Burros

One of my horses showed up one day with a badly swollen head and nose—so large that the horse resembled pictures of a hippopotamus. I concluded the horse had been bitten by a rattlesnake, perhaps a day or two before.—Montana (*C. v. viridis*).

❖

A horse I was riding was struck on the leg just above the hoof. There was considerable bleeding, but no swelling and no lameness.—Wyoming (*C. v. viridis*).

❖

The horse's nose, where he was struck, swelled up to twice normal size in about seven hours. I had no medicine but kept the horse in. He could not eat for three days; only drank a little water. He lost about 150 pounds and had a high temperature. On the fourth day he showed signs of improvement; on the fifth day he began to eat; and in 10 days was completely recovered but still short on good flesh.—Wyoming (*C. v. viridis*).

❖

I have seen several horses bitten on the nose by rattlers. Their heads swell up to nearly twice their normal size, but they seem to get over it. The hair comes off their heads and nose up to their ears. A horse bitten on the leg will be more sick and suffer more than one bitten on the nose. I believe this is on account of the larger blood vessels in their legs.—Wyoming (*C. v. viridis*).

❖

I have known cases where a rattler has struck a saddle horse, and the horse has gone lame immediately; and in a few moments his leg was so swollen it was hard for him to travel.—New Mexico (probably *C. v. viridis*).

❖

A horse usually swells up, and the swelling lasts several days.—Idaho (*C. v. lutosus*).

❖

In each case of horses bitten by rattlers, the flesh decayed and dropped out, leaving a sunken place after the wound had healed.—Idaho (*C. v. lutosus*).

❖

I saw a horse bitten just above the hoof. The leg swelled, and an infection followed, with lameness for a year. He got thin, and the hoof never did get normal.—Idaho (*C. v. lutosus*).

❖

I have known of only two saddle horses being bitten. They were laid up for about two weeks with a badly swollen foot and leg.—Idaho (*C. v. oreganus*).

❖

Sometimes the bites cause running sores that fail to heal.—Oregon (*C. v. oreganus*).

❖

A horse was bitten on the shoulder. He had no treatment but recovered in about a week. There were no serious signs of illness, but he was logy.—California (*C. v. helleri*).

❖

A burro that was bitten by a rattlesnake had an enormously swollen head, and was very sick for several days.—California (*C. v. helleri*).

❖

I have seen horses that were bitten around the head, and the head swelled one-third above normal size.—California (*C. v. helleri*).

❖

I had a saddle horse that was struck just above the mouth on the left side while in pasture. His head was swollen for about a week.—Arizona.

Sheep and Goats

Sheep are usually bitten on the cheeks, and the swelling of the head, neck, and shoulders is pronounced.—Colorado (*C. v. viridis*).

◇

I have seen rattlesnakes bite sheep. Their heads swell to almost twice normal size, and in some cases their eyes swell shut for several days.—Idaho (*C. v. lutosus*).

◇

I have seen rattlesnakes bite lambs on the nose; they swell up in an hour's time and usually die.—Idaho (*C. v. lutosus*).

Hogs

A hog was bitten by a rattlesnake. It recovered but was in bad condition for some two months.—Utah (*C. v. lutosus*).

PERMANENT EFFECTS OF RATTLESNAKE BITE

Several of my correspondents have mentioned the fact that stock, especially horses, although they recovered from rattlesnake bite, were permanently affected:

One case of rattlesnake bite left the horse of little value thereafter.

◇

I have heard of a horse having been bitten that recovered, but he never did regain his former usefulness.

◇

I have seen horses that had been struck, but never knew of a horse dying. The horse usually swells up all over with the swelling lasting several days. The owner claimed that the horses really never fully recovered; they didn't have any strength or stamina.

◇

Most horses will live after being bitten, but a horse will usually be crippled if bitten on the lower leg. A heavy use of a saddle horse with an old snake bite will generally cause swelling and lameness.

Dobie (1952b, p. 306) tells of a horse that had been bitten as a colt, and subsequently traveled through the world listening for the warning rattle.

PUBLISHED ACCOUNTS OF STOCK LOSSES

In colonial days, and in the days of emigration to the West, livestock was of paramount importance for food and transportation. Rattlesnakes were troublesome, but not a hazard comparable to the others that faced the settlers. Here are a few condensations of statements in the literature: In 1660, a woman in New England was accused of witchcraft when, despite her objection, a man borrowed an ox, which subsequently was "wrattle snake bitt" in the tongue and died—*Johnson, 1932, p. 12*. A horse, bitten by a rattler with 24 rattles, died in 4 days even though it was kept in a swamp—*B., J., 1765, p. 513*. Horses were frequently bitten and died, because of being bitten on the nose, where the blood vessels were large and numerous. Cattle seldom died—*Kercheval, 1833, p. 386*. Horses and cattle were frequently killed by rattlesnakes in Texas—*Holley, 1836, p. 103*. Cattle and horses were sometimes bitten and killed by rattlers—*Lawrence, 1840, p. 201*. Men were sent ahead of wagon trains to kill the rattlers and protect the stock—*Gregg, 1844, vol. 1, p. 66*.

Horses died from rattlesnake bite almost as often as people—*Jeter, 1854, p. 32.* On the Mexican Boundary Survey, two horses were bitten; one died—*Bartlett, 1854, vol. 2, pp. 342, 557.* A horse was bitten and dropped blood from many places where the veins burst through the skin. This happened about 1810 in western Maryland—*Browning, 1860, p. 376.* Among the Indians, men, women, children, horses, and dogs, were bitten and died—*Catlin, 1868, p. 12.* The worst annoyance on a ranch at San Ramón, in Baja California, was the rattlesnakes. Three or four horses a week were bitten—*Gabb, 1869, p. 110.* Two horses were bitten, probably in the under-lip, while feeding in long grass—*Bell, 1869, vol. 2, p. 16.* Horses and cattle were generally bitten in the jaw and died in from one to three days—*Anon., 1872b, p. 643.* Although prairie rattlesnakes (*C. v. viridis*) were very commonly encountered on a railroad exploring expedition through the Dakotas and Montana, more than 2,000 having been killed, not a man or an animal was bitten—*Allen, 1874, p. 69.* Rattlesnakes were usually not fatal to horses and cattle on the plains—*Williston, 1878, p. 203.* On the Santa Fe Trail in the early days, rattlers were a great annoyance, often biting the mules and oxen as they grazed—*Majors, 1893, p. 105.* In Pennsylvania in 1772, a horse and a colt were lost from rattlesnake bite within a month—*Ettwein, 1901, p. 210.*

Among the Western hunters and trappers, deaths of mules and horses from rattler bite were more common than fatalities to men—*Chittenden, 1902, p. 837.* Two horses were bitten—*Pollock, 1911, p. 158.* Observations led to the belief that the danger to stock, in eastern Wyoming and western South Dakota, was not important—*Bateman, 1918, p. 501.* Rattlesnake bites endangered thoroughbred colts and other livestock, but there were no fatalities—*Haywood, 1929, p. 87.* A horse, bitten on the lip by an eastern diamondback, swelled until it looked like a hippo—*Schrenkeisen, 1930, p. 70.* A mule bitten by a massasauga (*S. c. catenatus*) died in 48 hours—*H., 1933, p. 61.* In the early 1870's on Crooked Creek near Ft. Washakie, Wyoming, so many horses and cattle were bitten that stock was removed from that region—*David, 1937, p. 265.* The loss of a single cow from rattlesnake bite by a frontiersman in the Dakotas was deemed worthy of remark in his autobiography—*Hamilton, 1938, p. 577.* Rattlesnakes caused occasional losses of stock to the emigrants on the way to California in 1850–51. "The number of rattlers we assassinated was from three to five a day, taking no pains to find them nor killing all we saw." This was in Pottawatomie County, Kansas, in May, 1850—*Moorman, 1948, pp. 12, 119.*

Rattlers caused many fatalities among the Indians' horses in the Osage country in 1839–40—*Tixier, 1940, p. 156.* A cow was bitten by a pigmy rattler (*S. m. barbouri*) and was hurt sufficiently to cause her to run off bawling. Three days later she showed no ill effects—*Carr, 1940, p. 95.* On a trip to Salt Lake City in 1846, an ox and a horse were bitten on April 15, and two horses were lost by rattler bite on May 7. This was in Iowa or Missouri— *Young, 1946, p. 136.* A. M. Jackley, who for many years was rattlesnake-control officer in South Dakota, thought that losses often blamed on poisonous weeds, coyotes, or black-market rustlers, were really caused by rattlesnakes—*Koller, 1946, p. 13.* In northwestern Nebraska, four young stallions were bitten in a single night, all in the head, and one case was quite serious—*McNellis, 1949, p. 145.* In a book on range management, rattlesnakes are not considered to be worthy of mention as a hazard to stock, although their control of rabbits and rodents is noted—*Sampson, 1952, p. 495*. Cattle losses from snake bite are estimated at 0.3 to 1.0 per cent per annum—*Stickel, 1952, p. 27*. Losses are estimated at 50 to 100 head of stock per year in an undefined area of Oklahoma—*Isely, 1951, p. 1*. A six-year-old Brahma bull, while foraging for food in a cactus clump, was bitten under the right eye by a seven-foot western diamond. The bull fell to its knees. A cowhand attempted to lance the wound, but the bull was threshing about too much. It died within 15 minutes. A steer was struck on each side of the jaw simultaneously by two rattlers and leaped away with the snakes clinging to him. The steer dropped dead within a few hundred yards—*Vessels, 1954, p. 28*. [I presume that it's dangerous for a Californian to question any remarks by a Texan, so I shall only say that Vessels did not claim to have witnessed these happenings; they were related to him.]

A Nevada newspaper report in 1948 recounted the death of a valuable Hereford bull from rattlesnake bite. It was said to have died in a few minutes after being bitten—a most unusual case, if true. Beadle (1879, p. 133) tells a Kansas yarn—which he doesn't believe himself—of a horse that was bitten and fell dead. The upper and lower [*sic*] fang marks were four inches apart. Stickel (1952, p. 26) says that adult horses have been known to die within 25 minutes from the bite of a prairie rattler.

The damage to sheep does not appear to have been material. W., R. (1891, p. 124) says that sheep were frequently bitten in Montana in 1876; the ones hurt were mostly lambs, as the adults knew enough to avoid rattlers. Brewer (1930, p. 93) said that wolves, bears, and rattlers, caused considerable damage to sheep in California in the 1860's. But Wentworth (1948), in his exhaustive history of the sheep industry in the United States, which includes a chapter on predators, mentions rattlesnakes only once, which indicates their relative unimportance in causing losses. Stickel (1952, p. 26) says that about 9 per cent of a sheep flock were lost from snake bite near El Paso, Texas.

Despite the ancient myth that hogs are immune to the bites of venomous snakes, including rattlers, it has long been known that they succumb as readily as other domestic animals if the venom enters the circulation, instead of being deposited in a layer of fat, as is often the case (De Kay, 1842, vol. 1, p. 57; Mitchell, 1889, p. 510; Bevan, 1931b, p. 78). Essex (1932, p. 339) made extensive tests with rattlesnake venom and found hogs to be without any specific immunity. Flack (1866, p. 185) claimed to have seen a hog, struck in the eye, die within 10 minutes.

I have discussed stock losses under several categories—by states, by symptoms, and by classes of stock—as set forth in letters from correspondents, but aside from a general picture of the nature of the damage that rattlesnakes do to stock, there is, in reality, nothing definite as to the extent of the losses incurred. There are available no country-wide statistics, as far as I know.

RECORDS FROM THE SAN JOAQUIN EXPERIMENTAL RANGE

The most authentic records of rattlesnake damage to stock known to me are those of Wagnon, Guilbert, and Hart made on the San Joaquin Experimental Range of the University of California, in Madera County, California (1942, 1945, 1946). The only rattlesnake occurring on the range is the northern Pacific (*C. v. oreganus*). Of the relationship between rattlesnakes and cattle, the authors have this to say (1942, p. 73):

The range land at the time of purchase was heavily infested with rattlesnakes; and despite a more or less continuous campaign against them, a study discussed in a later section has shown a population of approximately one snake per acre. In two instances grazing animals were observed to walk directly over rattlesnakes while grazing without either's paying any attention to the other; the snakes did not rattle. A defanged snake was released near a group of cattle. Its movement and rattling attracted the attention of the animals, which approached and smelled it. The snake then actually struck the animals without their manifesting any fear.

A total of 21 cattle were known to have been bitten, of which 3 yearlings died; 5 developed abscesses requiring treatment; and 2 were so disabled that they were culled from the herd. Of the 21 animals bitten, 18 were struck about the head, 1 on a front leg, 1 on a hind leg, and 1 on the udder.

In one instance loud breathing called attention to a six-months-old calf partially hidden in a clump of brush. The animal had evidently been bitten by a rattlesnake a short time before, and the enormous swelling about its head and throat made breathing difficult. Its eyes were swollen shut, and blood trickled from the inner canthus of both eyes. The tongue protruded from the mouth. Although death then appeared imminent, 1½ hours later the calf had improved; and 8 hours later it was out of danger and recovered completely without treatment.

The San Joaquin Experimental Range comprises about 4,600 acres. In the years 1936 to 1948, inclusive, there were 44 cases of snake bite. The annual snakebite frequency was about 1.4 per cent. The rattlesnake population was computed by Fitch (1949a, p. 546) at about 1.2 rattlesnakes per acre. Of the 44 snake-bite cases, 7 ended fatally, a mortality rate of 16 per cent, and an annual percentage of 0.22 for the herd. The cattle usually recovered without treatment, unless the swelling closed the respiratory tract or the venom was injected directly into the blood stream. Abscesses at the site of the bite were sometimes troublesome (Wagnon *et al.,* 1945, p. 22; 1946, p. 27). Of the bites, 35, or 80 per cent, including all of those that proved fatal, were on the head and neck. Seven were bitten on the legs, 1 on the udder, and 1 on the brisket. Some of the nonfatal cases were quite lasting, and involved loss of weight. The fatalities included 3 steers, 2 heifers, 1 calf, and 1 adult cow (Fitch, 1949a, p. 573). Mr. Wagnon believes that the incidence of snake bites may have been somewhat higher than the stated figure of 1.4 per cent per annum, as some of the animals (there were about 190) were not seen oftener than every two weeks. More recently he wrote me:

> While studying grazing cattle habits, I watched a cow grazing as she encountered a large rattlesnake crawling toward a squirrel hole. The cow moved aside. In this instance I know that the cow saw the snake. On two previous occasions, when grazing cows were seen to pass over rattlesnakes, I have no proof that the cows saw the snakes. I have not been able to detect any proof that horses smell rattlesnakes. On at least two occasions, horses that I was riding walked over snakes that were rattling, crawling, and striking, without showing any interest in them. Another horse I was riding almost stepped on a large rattlesnake, and for the rest of the day he jumped away from every object and stick that had the least resemblance to a snake.

STOCK DAMAGE IN TEXAS

Probably the most extensive stock damage by rattlesnakes is to be found in Texas. Some years ago Amaral estimated the loss in Texas at over a million dollars per year, but there are no statistics that validate this figure. Brown (1950, p. 218) states that studies are needed to establish the extent of the stock mortality, which most rangers consider quite serious. The western diamond rattler (*C. atrox*), which is plentiful throughout central and western Texas, is undoubtedly the most destructive of the Nearctic rattlers. It is a large and nervous snake, with long fangs and a moderately powerful venom.

In the hope of learning something factual regarding stock losses in Texas, I sent out return postal-card questionnaires to the county agents (agricultural commissioners) of the 254 counties in the state, and asked whether the damage from rattlesnakes could be rated as serious, moderate, unimportant, or negligible; and what animals were most affected. Replies were received from 134 agents, and may be summarized thus:

Extent of damage

Serious	0
Moderate	26
Unimportant	31
Negligible	77
Total	134

Animals most affected

Cattle	80
Horses	34
Sheep	10
Goats	3
Hogs	3
Total	130

Not much information that could be translated into relative frequency was given. One agent estimated that 1 per cent of the stock was bitten each year, and that the mortality among those bitten was 25 per cent. Another estimated rattlesnake losses at only ½ of 1 per cent of all deaths. Another gave the mortality at 10 per cent of those bitten; another at 0.06 per cent of the herd. In general, the damage was heaviest in the southwestern counties, because of both the prevalence of cattle-raising there and the presence of the western diamondback (*C. atrox*).

Stickel (1952, p. 26) has stated that county livestock inspectors reported an average loss of 1 per cent from snake bite. As none of the counties that I heard from considered the losses serious, and only 20 per cent called them moderate, I judge the actual figure to be lower, probably below 0.2 per cent per annum for the state as a whole.

RATTLESNAKES AND DOGS

I have not attempted to present the dog-rattlesnake data in the same manner as that of the stock-rattlesnake because the reports of the dog-rattler affrays are complicated by more than the usual uncertainties. There is, first, the great variability in dog sizes, and the almost equally important factor of hair length and density. There are many accounts of dogs being bitten, both in my correspondents' letters and in the literature, but the breed of dog is not often mentioned. Some dogs that were bitten died, others recovered; but the danger to a dog cannot be judged unless something is known about the size and kind of dog, as well as the size and kind of rattlesnake. Jackson (1927, p. 204) and Jackson and Githens (1931, p. 1) have given a figure of 1 mg. of dried *atrox* venom per pound of dog as the minimum lethal dose for dogs.

Elsewhere I have discussed two other phases of the rattlesnake-dog conflict: The method of attack of dogs that become rattlesnake killers (p. 1042); and the mud-bath treatment adopted by dogs to cure themselves of rattlesnake bite (p. 909). I have already discussed the remedies applied by man to his dogs and domestic stock.

Dogs are most susceptible to rattlesnake bite when they are engaged in some activity that is absorbing their attention and senses, so that they are not fully alert to the danger of a hidden snake. Although the odor of a rattlesnake is imperceptible to a human being, it is no doubt evident to a dog. Thus it is that hunting dogs and sheep dogs, because they are bent on assigned duties for their masters, are the ones most often bitten. Others are bitten in protecting children; and many that have become rattlesnake killers eventually lose their caution and make a careless move. O'Reilly (1899, p. 378) thought it possible to assess the snake-bite risk in any area by finding out how many dogs were bitten and how seriously.

Here are a few dog incidents as related by my correspondents:

I've seen dogs kill a number of rattlesnakes. Some dogs, especially the collie type, will learn to kill them and very seldom get bitten. If the dog is bitten on the front leg or neck or shoulder, it is nearly always fatal—if he is bitten by a large snake. If bitten on the nose or top of the head, he nearly always gets well. I've seen this many times.

<><

A farmer living 5 miles from Cody, Wyoming, has had two dogs bitten in the past 25 years. These dogs were bitten on the nose and in each case the dog was dead in a very few minutes.

<><

I have been told by dog handlers that the diamondback rattler is a menace to their dogs in night hunting. While located at Thomasville, Georgia, I heard of several dogs having been bitten or killed by rattlers. It is reported that when bitten on the tongue, a dog may die within a few minutes; but when bitten elsewhere about the head or front legs, the chances of recovery are about as good as for a human being.

<><

A dog stuck his head under the edge of a log and a rattler struck him near the end of his nose.

<><

I know dogs to have been bitten while following trails through rock slides and shale rock.

<><

I had an Airedale that was bitten. He was protected by the heavy fur along his neck, where he was struck, and eventually recovered.

<><

On one occasion in Virginia, upon going to a large Airedale dog that was barking in the forest, I found that he had cornered a large rattlesnake that was coiled around a gray squirrel. The dog had been severely bitten on the nose and after killing the snake, I lanced the dog's nose and administered potassium permanganate. After experiencing a severe swelling of the head, the dog recovered in several days.

<><

A fox terrier was bitten on the jaw. His head swelled until he could not lift it up, and stayed that way for several days. He finally got well.

<><

When dogs are bitten they swell up at the site of the bite, and turn black. They get listless and sort of dazed.

<><

A dog, a large mongrel about 18 inches high, was bitten in the foreleg by a southern Pacific rattler, *C. v. helleri*. At first it paid no attention to the bite, but some minutes later it whined and trembled, and acted as though the leg was injured. Finally it lay down, showing suffering, and was dead in about 20 minutes.

⟨⟩

A large hound was bitten in the nose. The nose swelled, blood, pus, and serum oozed from the wound, and the dog was very sick but recovered.

⟨⟩

An English setter was bitten just under the left eye by a medium-sized timber rattlesnake. The dog's head swelled very much, and he was in extreme discomfort.

Ross Allen (1948, p. 124; see also Allen and Neill, 1950c, p. 35) says that many valuable hunting dogs are lost in Florida from diamondback (*adamanteus*) bites each year. He estimated that 800 were bitten in 1947 and that 300 died. He thought many could have been saved with adequate treatment. He estimated a 20-per-cent mortality despite treatment, and that 30 per cent would survive without treatment. Other dog references are: Murray, 1829, p. 316; Linsley, 1843, p. 44; Alexander, 1855, p. 117; Rivers, 1874, p. 506; Mitchell, 1889, p. 514; Beyer, 1900, p. 30; Crouse, 1902, p. 443; Maddox, 1940, p. 271; Manu, 1947, p. 53; and Hollender, 1948, p. 129.

COYOTES

It seems appropriate to touch on coyotes (although not domestic animals) after the dog discussion. The extent to which coyotes eat rattlers will be found mentioned in chapter 15 on enemies. Dobie (1949, p. 118) states that, among coyotes trapped in Texas, a noticeable proportion had been bitten by rattlers. The scars are unmistakable, for the hair never grows back; the wound, when healed, is covered with bare, dark tissue. Most of the bites were on the shoulders and front legs, and less often on the hind legs. In south Texas it was estimated that 20 per cent of the coyotes showed rattlesnake scars. One coyote trapped by F. F. Gander and L. M. Huey, in Baja California, had evidently been bitten by a rattlesnake just before or after being trapped. It was dead when found.

SMALL DOMESTIC ANIMALS

Mammals and birds, whether domestic or wild, that are of sizes that the rattlesnake seeks for food, if struck squarely, usually die in less than 10 minutes. But there is much variability in the time, depending on the size of the snake and the effectiveness of the bite, so that some may survive for as much as an hour, or escape entirely. The effects of rattlesnake bite on prey-sized animals are discussed in chapter 9, on the food of the rattlesnake. Animals of such sizes have been used extensively in the research programs seeking solutions of problems of the physiological effects of venoms, their relative toxicities, the immunity and susceptibility of different kinds of animals, and, most important of all, remedies for snake bite.

14. Control and Utilization

INTRODUCTION

Rattlesnakes are of economic value by reason of their destruction of small mammals, such as rabbits, ground squirrels, and gophers, that would otherwise cause even greater inroads on agricultural fields and grazing ranges. However, the rattlers are a menace to both man and his stock because of the danger from their bites; and were it possible to replace every rattler with an equally useful, but harmless, bull snake, king snake, or racer, the balance of nature would be preserved, yet with the elimination of the risk of snake bite. Failing in this, the agricultural and other authorities in each area must determine whether the damage by the rattlesnakes outweighs their usefulness, and therefore warrants their destruction. Of course, there can be no question regarding their elimination near towns and cities; here the possible danger to persons, especially children, is such that every rattler should be destroyed. At the same time, educational campaigns should be instituted to discourage people from killing harmless snakes, for every one killed makes room for an additional rattler in the scheme of nature's economy.

Various methods of rattler control or elimination have been proposed, such as bounties, poisons, traps, the destruction of food supplies and refuges, and the encouragement or importation of competitive predators. Other means of suppression that are not the result of any conscious or organized effort are such conditions as fires, the casualties of traffic, and agricultural developments unfavorable to snakes. The relative effectiveness of these factors, organized or incidental, will now be considered.

Rattlesnakes may be hunted solely to achieve their destruction, or to effect their capture alive for such commercial or scientific value as they may have for snake shows and zoos. The methods of finding the quarry do not differ greatly for these divergent objectives, except that few people are willing to use the time and effort required to catch a rattler, as compared with that needed merely to kill it. The raiding of dens is almost the sole method of rattlesnake hunting that is sufficiently fruitful to attract those who wish only to destroy the snakes, but this is only one of the methods used when live snakes are sought. In the initial part of this chapter, I shall discuss den raids when snake destruction is the objective, returning again to this field of activity, with a more detailed discussion of the methods used in picking up the snakes, when the raid is for the purpose of catching them alive. Other methods of collecting, seldom used except in the capture of the quarry alive, will conclude this chapter.

ECONOMIC ADVISABILITY OF CONTROL

Before any methods of rattler control are adopted, except close to human habitations where the safety of people is paramount, a careful consideration should be given to the economics involved, to determine whether rodent depredations on agriculture and the chance of their spreading disease, may not outweigh the dangers from the rattlers themselves. This question of choice was thus expressed by the late Dr. Joseph Grinnell, of the Museum of Vertebrate Zoölogy, University of California, in reply to an inquiry from a rancher in 1927:

> With reference to rattlesnakes, all of my own experience corroborates yours, that these reptiles are vigorous and effective destroyers of rodents. We have known of their killing ground squirrels, pocket gophers, and rats and mice. Just as you say, there is no doubt but that the rattlesnake figures importantly in keeping down these rodents which are so troublesome to the farmer and orchardist. However, we have to grant that, by accident, perhaps, rattlesnakes are dangerous to people. Furthermore, many people are instinctively so fearful of rattlesnakes that they suffer immeasurably simply because of the danger they think threatens. For these reasons, we cannot ordinarily recommend that rattlesnakes be conserved for their usefulness in killing rodents. But in your case, where, I gather, you live away from any town, I think you are justified in letting the snakes alone, to help you fight the destructive rodents.

Other comments in the same vein are the following:

> I live on a ranch near the forks of the Red Deer and South Saskatchewan rivers, and about four miles due east of Empress. Here we annually kill anywhere from three to ten or a dozen rattlers, and this within a mile of the buildings. But a great many ranchers around here do not molest them because they keep down the gophers. *James W. Chapman, Empress, Alberta, Canada.*
>
> <><
>
> Personally, I believe rattlesnakes are far more beneficial than harmful; but I don't like them. *Bruce Torgny, U. S. Forest Service, Montrose, Colo.*

Upon this subject the U. S. Fish and Wildlife Service has this to say: "Poisonous snakes have no place in a settled country, no matter how beneficial their food habits may be" (Uhler, 1944, p. 7).

Reese (1935, p. 593; 1937, p. 349) inveighs against indiscriminate "vermin" campaigns as sometimes carried on by sporting magazines or ammunition companies. These condemn harmless and often useful creatures upon the most inadequate evidence; and, although in my younger days I was a hunter, I confess these commercially instigated campaigns were never beneficial to my blood pressure. A typical case of such a condemnation of the economically useful bull snake, based on prejudice and distorted data, is that of Whitby (1920, p. 188). This is admittedly somewhat foreign to the subject of rattlesnakes, except that, as pointed out elsewhere, the soundest of all methods of rattler control is to replace them with harmless snakes, such as bull or gopher snakes.

In summary, let me say that I hold no brief for rattlesnakes, and always recommend their destruction where they constitute any menace to human beings, or where possible damage to stock or game animals outweighs their beneficial destruction of rodents. A. M. Jackley believed that stock damage by rattlers exceeds their value as rodent suppressors in South Dakota. Wright and Bishop (1915, p. 190) found the diamondback rattler to be a seriously adverse economic factor in a part of Georgia. But most of my correspondents indicate that damage to stock is relatively unimportant. I have presented elsewhere (p. 958) the data available on this phase of the problem. I would suggest that county agricultural agents be consulted before any drastic programs of rattler suppression be adopted in any purely agricultural or grazing areas, and that some program of rodent control be co-ordinated with the rattler suppression. And even the rodents have their defenders, owing to the beneficial effects of their burrowing habits on the soil in some situations (Hardy, 1946, p. 29; 1947, p. 165), although this, also, may be more than offset by an increase in erosion (Howard, 1953, p. 429), and by their disease-carrying proclivities. These problems of prey and predator control are complicated, and require, for solution, the best judgment of experts based on all factors.

METHODS OF CONTROL

CAMPAIGNS FOR KILLING AT DENS

As has been stated, one of the most effective methods of rattlesnake control is to organize campaigns for killing them when they are concentrated at their dens, either as they gather to hibernate in the fall or when about to leave in the spring. Here the rattlers may be taken alive, or clubbed or shot, in great numbers. This method is possible only in the colder sections of the country where the rattlers are gregarious and the annual concentration draws individuals from considerable distances. This was the system employed by the late A. M. Jackley, rattlesnake-control officer of South Dakota, where probably the most successful[1] rattlesnake-control campaign ever instituted was carried on. Not only did Jackley himself destroy great numbers of snakes at their dens (fig. 14:1), but he multiplied his efforts by instructing the farmers in how to locate adjacent dens and in the use of the most efficient methods of killing the snakes. Where Jackley found it impossible to visit a den at the critical time, or to have one of his collaborators do so, he used traps, which I shall describe elsewhere. I have already touched, in chapter 8, on the physical nature of the dens, and the condition of the rattlesnakes living in them.

When the snakes are found concentrated at dens, they can easily be dispatched with clubs or sticks. There is almost no danger to those whose legs are properly protected with puttees or heavy boots. The more timid can use shotguns or .22 rifles. A .22 repeater, using dust-shot shells, is to be recommended as it minimizes the danger to one's companions. The dust shot will disable even a large rattler, so that it cannot escape until killed with a stick or hoe. Repeated visits are neces-

---

[1] I use the term "successful," which does not necessarily connote "desirable." Whether such wholesale destruction is to the best interest of the farmer or stock raiser only time will tell.

sary as the snakes come in on successive days, and some may escape into the holes and crevices. Mr. Jackley wrote:

> When you find the rattlers lying about a prairie-dog town and you place yourself between them and the holes, they will streak for the holes as fast as racers. You have to work rapidly to keep them from holing up.

Jackley's methods and results have been described in a number of his publications (1933, p. 58; 1939, p. 11; 1943, p. 1; 1946b, p. 16; 1947, p. 1).

People seeking dens usually locate them by watching for snake migrations to and from the place of refuge, although many are found accidentally if the snakes

Fig. 14:1. Dead prairie rattlesnakes (*C. v. viridis*), destroyed in a raid on a den near Timber Lake, Dewey County, South Dakota, October 22, 1937. (Reproduced by courtesy of A. M. Jackley.)

are come upon while they lie about in the sun, preparatory to beginning or ending their winter seclusion.

> Anyone with experience can readily detect the location of a den by watching the directions taken by the snakes in September and October, even though the den is a quarter of a mile away. *A. M. Jackley, Pierre, S. Dak.*
>
> ◇
>
> There is probably a den in the Klamath River gorge about 1½ miles upstream from the head of Topsy Creek on the east bank, judging from the annual "fan out" of snakes from there. *Fred R. Starr, Game Warden, Dorris, Calif.*
>
> ◇
>
> From the heavy migration of rattlesnakes across the road in Cuddy Canyon, it seems apparent that there is a den in the limestone bluffs on the north side of the canyon, about three miles west of Frazier Mountain Park. *R. J. O'Bryant, U. S. Forest Service, Frazier Park, Calif.*

Some den-raiding experiences are the following:

> The best method of killing rattlers is by finding them at the opening of a den, early in the spring before they leave for the summer, or in the fall after they have come to the den for the winter. On nice, warm days they crawl to the opening of the den and enjoy the warmth of the sun for a few hours. The temperature must be up to 80° F., or more, for them to come out. *Glenn Flathers, U. S. Forest Service, Camp Crook, S. Dak.*

I have been hunting rattlesnakes each of the past three years, and have killed well over a thousand close to Butte. We have located the dens in several different spots during April and May. Just as they are leaving their dens, they are easily found and dispatched. *William T. Sweet, Butte, Mont.*

◇

I have seen several rattlesnake dens, one with 90 snakes under a rock cliff, or slide of rocks. At the base of one rock, with a slope of about 35° and a face of 15 feet, the snakes were among prickly-pear cactus. The snakes first seemed to try to get as far back as possible into the den. We fished them out with a wire hook on a pole. We would put the wire hook into the hole and around a snake, and then jerk the snake out. On sunny days in the fall of the year, these snakes would be in one solid mass at the mouth of the den. One could approach quietly and watch them. There was not much movement among them; they just lay there to sun themselves. But as soon as they saw us, one or more would rattle, and down the hole they would go. The strongest would knock the weakest ones to the side to take care of themselves, and you could hear them buzzing in the hole. *Gustave W. Koski, U. S. Fish and Wildlife Service, Windham, Mont.*

◇

I found one den in the lava rocks—a small hole only about six inches wide. I got 27 rattlers coming out of it in one hour. They just kept coming out. *Albert Madarieta, Oakley, Idaho.*

Rev. A. C. Mackie, in describing a vendetta against rattlesnakes that he carried on near Vernon, British Columbia, wrote:

In the earlier years I went armed with a long stick having a short fork at its smaller end, partly for pinning a snake down and partly for use as an alpenstock on the treacherous and steep rocks. I also carried a .410 shotgun, but this proved unnecessarily heavy and cumbersome and was discarded in favor of a light .22-caliber pistol, firing dust shot and capable of killing or disabling a rattlesnake at a range of five yards and under. I now have a nine-shot automatic .22 pistol, and a stick shod with a steel three-pronged spear. I wear stout leather leggings underneath my trousers, which, being loose and baggy, form an excellent first line of defense, and light rubber- or crepe-soled boots which are the best for traveling on loose stones or for climbing.

Several of my correspondents have written that groups of men in their communities make a regular practice of raiding nearby rattlesnake dens in the fall or spring:

On rattlesnake-hunting days, we would gather up a party of from 10 to 50 or 75 people and go out to hunt. We took along our lunch and made a picnic of it. We got plenty of snakes and you would hear rattlers singing all day. *Hugh Ayres, Albany, Texas.*

◇

A rocky ridge near Newcastle, Wyoming, is a denning ground. Each fall and spring, when the rattlers are approaching or leaving the den, they have to cross a section of oiled highway, and the citizens of Newcastle make a regular game of driving on this stretch and killing them. *F. R. Cochran, U. S. Forest Service, Sundance, Wyo.*

◇

Each spring, rattlesnake hunting is quite a sport of the people around Fort Jones and Etna. *John Williams, U. S. Forest Service, Fort Jones, Calif.*

These seasonal, community-wide rattlesnake-control campaigns are by no means a recent development; they have been popular and effective since colonial times. Such a project even became known as a "rattlesnake bee" (Mathews, 1951, p. 1361). Babcock (1925, p. 8) states that, in Massachusetts as early as 1680, men were employed at two shillings a day to kill rattlers, and in 1740 a day was appointed for a general snake hunt, presumably at hibernating time. Mather (1714, p. 67), Dudley (1723, p. 295), Kalm (1752–53, p. 313; 1758, p. 287), and Kerr (1802, vol. 4, p. 270) have all reported that snake killing around the dens was a regular practice in colonial days. The same procedure was followed in the early Middle Western settlements, interesting accounts of community den raids being those of Atwater (1838, p. 68); Howe (1847, pp. 297, 480), who said that in early Ohio each party killed from 300 to 800 rattlers; Browning (1860, p. 383) describing events in western Maryland about 1820; Bull (1934, p. 22) writing of early days in Canada; Pickard and Buley (1945, p. 31); and Buley (1950, vol. 1, p. 256) on snake drives in the old Northwest. Anon. (1951b, p. 162) reports on a Madison County, Iowa, rattler hunt in 1849. The people were divided into two contestant groups. Each participant put up two bushels of corn, to be won by those getting the largest numbers of snakes. Every able-bodied man took part. Two men got 90 rattlers in an hour and a half, and the total killed in one year was 3,750.

Today, some of the large rattler kills at dens receive extensive publicity, with stories syndicated in newspapers throughout the country. Generally the reports are exaggerated, making it appear that the rattlesnakes have attacked the human intruders. Some of these newspaper accounts have listed the following catches: 485 prairie rattlesnakes (*C. v. viridis*) at Olney Springs, Colorado, 140 at Fort Lupton, Colorado, 115 at Riverton, Wyoming, and 67 at Great Falls, Montana; 121 Arizona prairie rattlesnakes (*C. v. nuntius*) at Lees Ferry, Arizona; about 180 Panamint rattlers (*C. m. stephensi*), near Tonopah, Nevada; and 130 timber rattlers (*C. h. horridus*) in eastern Iowa.

Catlin (1868, p. 23) tells of an extensive raid on a den in New York in 1810, and how he and his comrades tied a powder-horn bomb to a rattler's tail, then lit the fuse and let the snake crawl into the den, where an explosion followed, presumably with good results (p. 36). Sullivan (1852, p. 174) describes another den blasting. The blasting of snake dens with dynamite has recently been tried in various places. It has the disadvantage of not permitting the effects to be ascertained; also, any harmless snakes in the den will be destroyed. A further disadvantage is that the shattering of the rocks may open up new and better refuge crevices. Uhler (1944, p. 8) calls attention to the desirability of adopting control methods that will discriminate between venomous and harmless snakes. Rattler dens are occasionally blasted in connection with the building of roads, dams, and similar works—an unintentional control.

In summary, I should say that raiding dens is much the most effective method of control in those sections of the United States where freezing conditions exist for several months. This is particularly true with *C. viridis* and *C. horridus,* and their subspecies, in the northern half of the United States. Elsewhere, except in mountain regions, the snakes do not congregate, but seek their winter seclusion in smaller groups, or even in individual refuges.

TRAPS

Since a snake's feeding intervals are widely spaced and irregular, baited traps cannot be used with the same efficacy as for mammals and birds. Occasionally a rattler may be found trying to swallow a mouse already killed in a snap trap, and they have been caught accidentally in both rat and coon traps. Pits have been tried with indifferent success, since it is difficult to cause a snake to fall into one, and harder still to keep it there unless the sides are both steep and smooth.

Catlin (1868, p. 13) tells of a trap used on his farm in 1810. It consisted of a hollow log with a tapering aperture into which the rattler crawled seeking a deceased mate, a highly improbable episode. Campbell (1950, p. 44) has described the catching of two western diamonds in a wire fence. They were too large to crawl through the spaces into which they started, and were prevented from backing out by the ratchet effect of their scales catching in the wire.

Cage traps, with wing or drift fences to guide the snakes into them, have been tried with considerable success on bull snakes (Imler, 1945, p. 270; Dargan and Stickel, 1949, p. 264). Fitch (1951, p. 77) has described a wire trap used with some success for lizards and snakes, including rattlers. Walter E. Howard recently reported the successful use at the San Joaquin Experimental Range of drift fences of the type used by Imler. The fences were of ¼-inch wire screen, 18 inches high and 100 to 150 feet long. A funnel trap of wire screen was placed at the apex where the two drift fences came together. It was found advantageous to install wooden boxes opening out of the wire trap, wherein the captives might take refuge from the heat. Many rattlers, as well as other snakes, were caught.

But the most successful trapping of rattlers can be effected at dens, particularly when the snakes are issuing from hibernation in the spring. The simplest method is to block all exits but one, and pipe this into some such receptacle as an oil drum. This scheme has been used by several collectors, as, for example, Hudson (1942, p. 88; see also *Outdoor Life,* vol. 97, no. 4, p. 53, April, 1946).

The use of a pit in conjunction with a den has also been tried:

> At the Kortes Ranch, about 72 miles northeast of here, there was a den of rattlers. A square pit was dug at the entrance to the den, and in the spring there were well over 300 snakes in this pit, although they were not all rattlers. *William Lakanen, Rawlins, Wyo.*

Rev. A. C. Mackie of Vernon, British Columbia, had rather indifferent success with traps at dens:

> For three years I tried trapping rattlers but was only moderately successful, as the majority of the inmates of a den found other avenues of escape. I cemented the exit, leaving only a circular hole three inches in diameter in which was inserted a tube leading into a box, with a sliding glass shutter at the far end and well lighted by windows of mosquito netting. The entrance to this box was high up, and a snake, once in, was unable to regain the den and was compelled to endure the chilly nights until I could visit the trap. My annual catches were only 15, 6, and 7, so I discontinued the experiment.

Subsequently he tried artificial refuges, a scheme that has been used successfully to catch such small harmless snakes as ringnecks:

> I put up sun parlors outside of likely crevices; these consisted of flat thin slabs of stone resting on two side-stones, leaving a space eagerly sought by snakes as affording them shelter from the sun.

Hillcourt (1950, p. 148) recommended that squares of linoleum, tar paper, or cardboard be left scattered about, so that the snakes would take refuge under them and so could be caught.

The most successful trap and trapping campaign of which I have heard was that devised by the late A. M. Jackley, who, by the installation of traps at dens, made it unnecessary to visit them at the exact times when the snakes were entering or leaving. He wrote:

> The trap I have perfected is simple and effective in all cases where the entry or entries to the den can be closed snake-tight. All but one of these holes are closed, and from this a chute leads into the trap. The principle of the trap is to provide a small opening into a cage, over which opening is hinged, as a vertical trap-door or flap-valve, a sheet of mica or some plastic that will not warp, so that after a snake crawls through the hole, the flap quickly falls closed again behind him.
>
> The compartment or cage the snake enters must have a floor well below the trap entry, so that a snake, after getting in, won't block the door and interfere with the entrance of the next snake. It requires scarcely any pressure to open the mica flap, and the snakes enter with little or no hesitation, because the flap is transparent and they see the open space beyond.
>
> One naturally would think, after looking at the trap, that most any contrivance embodying this principle would suffice, but this is not so. For example, if the chute is made too long, too roomy, or with the hole at floor level, it will not work satisfactorily. When it is quite long or roomy, snakes like to coil inside and block the passage. Having it only long enough to shade the hole is just right. Then when a snake pokes his head into the chute the hole shows very clearly and as a rule the rattlers crawl through with scarcely any hesitation whatever.

Jackley's trap in action, and details of the trap door, are shown in figures 14:2 and 14:3. Further discussions of his traps have been published (Jackley, 1933, p. 58; 1943, p. 1; 1946b, p. 16; 1947, p. 4; Koller, 1946, p. 46).

Jackley wrote on one occasion:

> During the past few days I have emptied four more traps. Three of them contained numbers of dead snakes, as they had been frozen. However, yesterday I took local parties to a trap and removed from it fully 100 rattlers. There were 92 live ones and a few dead.

It will be observed that Jackley's trapping methods are only suitable for a spring campaign, since all the exits except one are closed and the snakes must be inside to be caught. But he subsequently described a variation that permits trapping in the fall. It is well known that for several days at this season the snakes take advantage of any remaining good weather to come out daily to sun themselves at about noon, before finally taking refuge for the winter. Jackley found that if one entrance were piped to his trap, a number of snakes that had entered through other holes would come out to sun themselves via the trapped hole, and thus would be caught. He made several good catches by this method, which he described thus:

> Nearly all dens where large numbers of rattlers hibernate have a number of entries, but one is likely to be used more than the others. The trick is to set a trap at the main entry just as you would in the spring, but leaving the other entries wide open. Then build a protection from the wind around the cage, allowing the sun to make the cage a comfortable place in which to rest. Then these snakes, after getting into the den by one of the other entrances, will unhesitatingly enter the trap when they go out to sun themselves. A few years ago I would have considered setting a trap like that a waste of time, but now I find from experience that it is an easy way to catch rattlers in the fall.

Further discussions of trapping campaigns will be found in Gloyd (1946, p. 88) and Bogert (1948b, p. 187).

Fig. 14:2. Trap valve devised and used by A. M. Jackley.

Fig. 14:3. A. M. Jackley's rattlesnake trap in action.

FENCES

Fences may be of some value in rattlesnake control if the area to be protected is relatively small, as for example, a children's playground. However, only adequate maintenance will assure even a moderate degree of exclusion.

A rattlesnake-proof fence (I do not say snake-proof) should be of one-fourth-inch mesh from the ground line to a height of at least two feet; above that the mesh may be one-half inch. The fence should be carried to a total height of at least six feet. The posts should be on the inside, and every effort should be made to make the exterior as smooth as possible to eliminate climbing holds. Werler (1950, p. 28) recommends slanting a fence outward. There should be no overhanging bushes or trees, for although rattlers do not climb as readily as many snakes, they do climb to some extent. The clearance of brush from the fence should be at least two feet at the bottom and four or five feet at the top.

The fence should be carried at least one foot below ground level, although the mesh of this section may be increased somewhat, since the purpose is to keep mammals from burrowing under, thus eliminating holes through which the snakes might gain ingress. Examinations should be made, from time to time, to determine whether tunnels have been made; this is another reason for having the ground clear along the fence. Where deep-burrowing rodents are present, even two feet below ground line may be found inadequate, and holes must be plugged upon discovery. Special attention must be given to the gates of snake-proof fences, both to see that they are not left open, and that the clearance is not sufficient to permit a rattler to enter. Electric fences have been suggested, but offer some practical difficulties, aside from possible dangers. Necessarily, the part below ground must either be a nonconductor or insulated from the electrified section.

Fences are occasionally used to guide snakes toward traps. Imler (1945, p. 270) found fences 12 to 15 inches high satisfactory to turn bull snakes toward the traps. A. M. Jackley, in his control work in South Dakota, on some occasions used three-foot-high snake-proof fences around dens to restrain the dispersing snakes in the spring until he had an opportunity to visit the dens and dispatch them. The fences were tipped in at the top. Later this scheme was abandoned in favor of traps. Methods of snake-proofing buildings are of much the same nature as rat-proofing, that is, by the elimination of all places of ingress. This is further discussed in U. S. Fish and Wildlife Service, *Wildlife Leaflet* 257 (Uhler, 1944, p. 7).

GASES AND POISONS

The killing of rattlers at their dens by the introduction of a poisonous gas, such as hydrocyanic acid, has been tried with some success. But snakes are not so susceptible to poisoning as are mammals, and there is always a difficulty in finding and plugging all of the crevices so that the gas will not escape. Obviously, so dangerous a poison should be handled only by persons of experience.

> I have destroyed several rattlesnake dens with cyanide gas. These dens held from 300 to 500 rattlers and bull snakes. The dens were found mostly in rocky ledges and crevices. *Fred W. Barnes, U. S. Fish and Wildlife Service, Hines, Oreg.*

About 5 years ago, 97 rattlesnakes were killed at a den here within a couple of miles of La Veta. Since that time poison gas has been turned in some of the holes, after which they were stopped up. This fall there were only 31 rattlers killed there. *Roy C. Spangler, Predatory Animal Hunter, La Veta, Colo.*

A. M. Jackley was doubtful of the advisability of using gas. He wrote:

Snakes may be destroyed by the use of gas when they are in small cavities, such as prairie-dog burrows, but in dens with larger spaces, in which large numbers of rattlers hibernate, and with more chances for unlocated openings, the gas must be heavier than air. For my purposes I have found hydrocyanic acid gas relatively ineffective. Another disadvantage of gas is the killing of whatever harmless snakes may be in the dens with the rattlers.

The last is a very valid criticism of the method. Later (1946b, p. 16) Jackley reported that about 40 harmless snakes (10 bull snakes and 30 blue racers) would be killed to every 100 rattlers destroyed. He mentioned experiments with chlorine, formaldehyde, methyl bromine, and carbon bisulphide. The costs of using these poisons in control were stated to be low, but the results were uncertain.

Uhler (1944, p. 8) gives the following information on the use of poisonous gases:

Snakes seem to be immune to the effects of certain kinds of poisonous gases, including phosgene, chlorine, and tear chemicals. Tests conducted in a cave near San Marcos, Hays County, Texas, approximately 50 miles north of San Antonio, failed to produce any results when phosgene[2] and chlorine fumes were forced under pressure into the recesses of a rocky cave infested with rattlesnakes. On the other hand, in the State of Washington, when mustard gas was pumped into the crevices of a bed of lava rock, rattlesnakes were driven out in a dazed condition and were easily killed with clubs.

Field employes of the Fish and Wildlife Service have had much success in destroying rattlesnakes with crude calcium cyanide. It has been found that two ounces of calcium-cyanide dust (about two tablespoonfuls) are required to kill a rattlesnake that has taken refuge in a ground-squirrel or prairie-dog burrow. The cyanide should be placed well down in the burrow by means of a ladle or long-handled spoon and in a mass rather than scattered. A stone or piece of sod should be used to cover the entrance rather than soil, which might slide into the hole and interfere with the formation of the gas. Under ordinary conditions a snake will be killed by about 30 minutes' exposure to the cyanide gas.

Calcium cyanide is a deadly poison. It should be kept in the original air-tight container and out of reach of irresponsible persons, children, and livestock. Small quantities of cyanide may be carried to the area to be treated in a can fitted with a tight top. All handling of the material should be done in the open air.

The effectiveness of calcium cyanide gassing depends on relative humidity, for moisture in the air combining with the cyanide liberates hydrocyanic-acid gas, which remains active in the burrow for several hours, diffusing in all directions. Unsatisfactory results may be expected, however, when calcium cyanide is used in rainy weather. Temperature is not a limiting factor, provided the snakes are not hibernating. The quantity of calcium cyanide necessary to kill snakes in a den or cave depends on the number of cubic feet of air space to be saturated with the poisonous gas. In general, it appears that two ounces of cyanide will liberate a deadly concentration of gas in a space not exceeding five cubic feet, provided there is no leakage.

It has long been known that snakes, rattlesnakes included, are much less susceptible to gases than are warm-blooded creatures. Stradling proved this with hydrocyanic acid as early as 1883 (p. 225). He found chloroform moderately effective, as did also Dugès (1877, p. 16) and Matteson (1899, p. 668).

---

[2] Prof. Malcolm Dole, of Northwestern University, reported one instance in which a Great Basin rattler (*C. v. lutosus*) suffered no ill effects from 30 minutes' exposure to a phosgene concentration that would have killed a man in about 10 seconds.

During World War II there was some fear that rattlesnakes would crawl into the airplanes parked in large numbers around the landing fields in some of the wilderness areas. It was rumored that some pilots were bitten in planes that had long stood unattended. It was suggested that fumigation by heavy concentrations of hydrogen cyanide be used to clear such planes of rattlers before they were flown. I am not certain that this was found to be either necessary or effective.

Ringle (1924, p. 20) tells of putting carbon tetrachloride in a hole that a prairie dog refused to enter; this drove out a prairie rattlesnake. Herrick (1953, p. 23) claimed that there was enough sulphur gas along the ground in the sour gas fields of west Texas to kill the rattlers or drive them out.

The slow metabolism of rattlesnakes (in common with other snakes), as compared with that of mammals, not only makes them less susceptible to poisoning by gas but permits them to withstand a reduced oxygen supply for some time. Simpson (1915, p. 279) put a rattler in a glass jar for a week without fresh air and reported that it suffered no ill effects. Payne (1938, p. 65) placed one in an atmosphere of carbon monoxide for half an hour, from which it emerged unharmed.

Bergman and Sakin (1932, p. 34) have repeated the statement so frequently made (e.g., Long, 1791, p. 160; Briggs, 1950, p. 124) that snakes are particularly susceptible to nicotine. Flattery (1949, p. 16) found that nicotine sulfate in water was effective in killing garter snakes. C. M. Bogert has suggested that snakes may be susceptible to nicotine, but not in the concentrations found in the natural plant.

Since ancient times, repellents of various kinds, but mostly of vegetable origin, have been thought to provide a valuable protection against snakes. Usually they were strewn about to keep snakes away from human habitations; but, in addition, they were used to protect a person walking in the woods, or to kill such snakes as could be brought in contact with the repellent. These are folklore devices without actual merit; they have been discussed in chapter 18 on myths (p. 1231).

Rollinson (1944, p. 167) reported that the cowboys in Wyoming put unslaked lime down rattler holes, and then poured in water to cook them.

Poisoned baits might possibly be used to kill rattlers, since snakes will occasionally eat dead food; but the infrequency of their meals, compared with those of mammals and birds, renders this scheme inefficient and also dangerous to other creatures. Brereton (1917, p. 91) reported finding a northern Pacific rattler writhing and half dead; it had swallowed a squirrel that had eaten strychnine. He thought there were fewer rattlers in one district after a mammal-poisoning campaign, but this may have resulted from the reduced food supply. Campbell (1953, p. 184) reported that a prairie rattler had died, apparently, from eating a strychnine-poisoned rodent. Poisoned eggs in chicken houses have been used with some success in the case of snakes that regularly eat eggs. This would not be a feasible method of rattlesnake suppression since they rarely eat eggs.

ENCOURAGEMENT OF COMPETITIVE PREDATORS AND ENEMIES

One of the most practical methods of rattlesnake control is the encouragement of competitive predators. The rattlesnake population in any area depends largely on the available food supply, and the more rodents that are consumed by other animals—harmless snakes, for example—the fewer there will be to support the rattlesnakes. One would think that this obvious fact should serve as a protection to the harmless snakes, since, every time one is killed, room is thereby made for another rattler. Unfortunately, many people are so mentally lazy that they are unwilling to spend a few moments to learn how to distinguish a venomous from a harmless snake. In many parts of the United States where rattlers are the only venomous snakes, so that the presence of rattles is an instant criterion of whether the snake is, or is not, dangerous, one still finds that a large part of the population adopts the rule: "I play safe; I kill every snake I can find." Certainly such a thoughtless person is not playing safe, for every time he kills a harmless racer, gopher, or king snake, he is only making life easier and safer for some rattlesnake. It is astonishing how impossible it is to convince such people that it is quite easy to distinguish rattlers by merely looking at their tails; there seems to be a widespread opinion that they frequently leave their rattles home on the hatrack.

Fortunately, in most agricultural districts the farmers have become fully alive to the economic value of harmless snakes, especially gopher or bull snakes, both as rodent destroyers and rattler competitors, and remove them only when they become a threat to poultry or rabbits. Webber (1951, p. 12) claimed that every bull snake was worth $50 per year to a Texas farmer as a rodent destroyer. The essential thing to remember about harmless snakes is that they have all the beneficial economic characteristics of the rattlers without any accompanying danger to man or beast.

It has been frequently stated that there is a law against the killing of harmless snakes in California (e.g., Lloyd, 1925, p. 32) but this is not the case. I do not know whether any state has such a law, but it is doubted whether one could be enforced even if it were on the statute books. Dependence must be placed on education.

The encouragement or importation of rattlesnake enemies has been suggested as a means of control. Among domestic animals, hogs have been most frequently and successfully used for this purpose; among wild mammals, deer and badgers would probably be effective; of the birds, the red-tailed hawk; and, of the snakes, the king snake (various subspecies of *Lampropeltis getulus*) would serve both as a rattlesnake enemy and as a competitive predator. The degree to which these various creatures destroy rattlesnakes has been discussed elsewhere in chapter 15, on rattlesnake enemies (p. 1032), but as Bogert (1948b, p. 186) has pointed out, no bird (and, indeed, no mammal or reptile) in the United States feeds habitually on snakes, to the exclusion of other food. Rattlers are not even mentioned by Latham (1950, p. 1) as a major item of diet of any predator in the northeastern United States. So if we are to secure any measure of rattlesnake control through the activities of other wild creatures, it must be through their competition for the rattlesnake's food, rather than through their direct predation on rattlesnakes.

Of the domestic animals, the hog has most often been credited with being effective in rattlesnake control. In the early days, as the Atlantic Coast and then the Middle West were being settled, a decline in the prevalence of rattlesnakes was stated to occur as soon as domestic hogs roamed about (Anburey, 1789, p. 385;

Blane, 1824, p. 88; Atwater, 1838, p. 68; Kennedy, 1841, p. 134; Hall, 1848, p. 124; Chamberlain, 1850, p. 15; Peake, 1860–1, p. 50; Flack, 1866, p. 334; Brown, 1871, p. 40; Hurter, 1893, p. 258; and Uhler, 1944, p. 9). It is probable that the hogs did have an effect on the rattler population in some areas, although Kennedy was overly optimistic when he wrote, more than 100 years ago, that Texas would soon be cleared of rattlers because of the activities of the hogs. Barringer (1892, p. 298) deplored the depredations of bears, which killed the hogs that otherwise would have destroyed the rattlers. Although the efficiency of hogs as rattlesnake destroyers may have been exaggerated, it is probably true that they may be counted on to eliminate the rattlers within a limited area.

A Texas county agent wrote: "We keep a good many turkeys in our county, which is a fast way to rid a place of snakes." Turkeys, and chickens as well, do kill and eat small snakes, rattlers among them, but it is probable that their greatest value in rattlesnake control lies in their stereotyped noisy reaction which calls the attention of their owners to the presence of a rattlesnake, thus inviting its destruction. As the birds actively forage about their ranges, they are likely to discover every snake above ground.

The question is frequently asked why the mongoose is not imported into the United States to destroy rattlesnakes. Such an importation would be dangerous and contrary to law (Uhler, 1944, p. 8). Kipling's Rikki-tikki-tavi and the movies present a mistaken notion; the mongoose does not live exclusively on venomous snakes. It is omnivorous and may become a serious pest. Even as a snake destroyer, it is partial to elapine snakes such as the cobra, and avoids viperine snakes. Thus, there could be no expectation that the mongoose would become a serious predator on rattlesnakes.

The results, usually unfortunate, of the importation of mongooses for the control of snakes or other pests have been pointed out by several authors with respect to the following areas to which they were brought and turned loose: Jamaica (Robinson, 1901, p. 22); Trinidad (Williams, 1918, p. 181); Martinique and Trinidad (Cochran, 1944, p. 288); Hawaiian Islands (Walker, 1945, p. 396; Baldwin *et al.*, 1952, p. 335; Oliver, 1955, p. 427); Martinique (Swanson, 1946a, p. 459). Whether the mongoose was imported to destroy snakes, as in Martinique, or rats, as in the Hawaiian Islands, the native birds and other beneficial creatures, as well as poultry, have always been the chief sufferers. As Bogert (1947a, p. 96; 1948b, p. 186) has pointed out, one cannot judge from what animals do when placed together in captivity—as in staged mongoose-cobra fights—what they will do when turned loose, especially in surroundings that are new to them. Upsetting the balance of nature by transplanting a predator such as the mongoose is always a dangerous expedient; in the United States it would probably be ineffective as a means of rattlesnake control, but would be disastrous to the smaller native wild life, to say nothing of poultry and rabbits.

Elimination of Food Supply and Cover

One of the most effective methods of eliminating rattlers in specific areas, such as around homes, is to curtail their food supply and cover. Since most species of rattlesnakes feed largely on mammals, the elimination of the rats, mice, gophers, ground squirrels, and other rodents that attract rattlers, will naturally discourage them. Similarly, as the snakes are by nature secretive, the removal of brush, rocks, boards, trash, and other hiding places tends to keep them away. Mammal holes should be plugged wherever found in an area one wishes to protect. Stoddard (1942, p. 436) recommends plowing and burning; the use of fire to destroy cover is discussed elsewhere.

BOUNTIES

The eradication of venomous snakes by the offer of bounties for their destruction is a method that has been tried with some success, although it has certain objectionable features. It is even now being used to a limited extent in some states for the control of rattlesnakes.

Interesting discussions of bounty systems used in attempts to control vipers in France, and cobras and other venomous snakes in India, will be found in Nicholson, 1874, p. 161; A. J. Wall, 1883, p. 155; Buckland, 1888, p. 644; Fayrer, 1892, p. 103; Stejneger, 1895, p. 482; and Hamilton, 1946, p. 134. Stejneger presents statistics of the snakes brought in for a reward of 25 centimes each in the Haute-Saône Department of France, a district the size of Delaware. There was a material increase in the number of bounties claimed up to 1890 (the last year given), in which year the number reached 67,620. There was evidence that the thrifty peasants were going in for snake raising; also they brought in vipers from adjacent departments. Nicholson tells of a small district in India having an area of some 150 square miles, from which 44,450 snakes (probably not all venomous) were brought in for bounties between May 29 and December 7, 1869. Fayrer (1892, p. 104) quoted a government report on the bounties paid in India in 1889. In those districts maintaining bounty systems, 578,415 snakes were turned in for rewards in that single year.

In the United States, bounties for rattlesnakes at the rate of sixpence each were offered by the towns of Medford, Dedham, North Brookfield, and Canton, Massachusetts, as early as 1719 (Babcock, 1925, p. 8). Kimberly (1954, p. 59) stated that in Worcester, Massachusetts, in 1728, the bounty was threepence per rattlesnake with an additional pound if 80 or more were killed.

As far as I have been able to learn, bounties are now being, or were recently offered, in certain counties in Texas, Florida, Iowa, Minnesota, Vermont, New York, Pennsylvania, and Wisconsin. In Texas, bounties at the rate of 20 cents per snake were paid in Bell County. The rattle attached to one inch of flesh from the tail was required to prove the claim. State-wide bounty systems have been proposed in Texas, but failed of passage.

In Pinellas County, Florida, bounties were paid from June, 1935, to October, 1938. The snakes brought in were as follows:

Year	Rattlesnakes	Coral snakes	Total
1935	1,399	296	1,695
1936	2,287	572	2,859
1937	2,099	594	2,693
1938	1,786	496	2,282
Total	7,571	1,958	9,529

TABLE 14:1

RATTLESNAKES OFFERED FOR BOUNTIES IN IOWA BY COUNTIES

County	Years of record (inclusive)	Total snakes	Average per year	Maximum		Minimum	
				Number	Year	Number	Year
Allamakee	1941–1952	4,898	408	860	1941	188	1948
Chickasaw	1932–1952 (except 1945)	2,331	119	256	1939	13	1946
Clayton	1925–1952	8,095	289	788	1932	39	1951
Delaware	1928–1952	495	20	67	1939	0	1950
Dubuque	1926–1952	7,249	268	1,643	1940	49	1947 & 1948
Fayette	1930–1932 and 1949–1952	681	97	426	1932	1	1952
Johnson	1927–1952 (except 1936)	253	10	31	1933	0	1952
Lee	1925–1931 and 1948–1952	321	27	56	1927	2	1950
Madison	1948–1950	498	166	189	1948	121	1949
Plymouth	1938–1949 (except 1944) and 1952	299	25	95	1946	1	1947
Wapello	1938–1952	43	3	9	1942 & 1943	0	1952
Winneshiek	1944–1952	1,215	135	308	1944	58	1949

Note.—In addition to the above, Davis County paid a bounty on 1 rattler in 1945; Harrison County paid bounties on 2 rattlers in 1952; Henry County on 2 in 1952; and Jones County on 1 in 1951, and 71 in 1952. Bounties have also been offered in Ida, Louisa, Monroe, and Page counties.

The bounty per snake was originally $2.00 but was later cut in half. Subsequently (according to Swalm and Swalm, 1947, p. 5) the bounty system was superseded by the employment of a paid collector, who agreed to catch annually at least 4,000 venomous snakes, mostly rattlers and moccasins.

Ross Allen wrote, in 1946, that De Soto County, Florida, had paid a bounty on eastern diamondbacks (*C. adamanteus*) for one year. There were 2,462 taken, which Allen bought from the county. Stoddard (1942, p. 436) reported that about 1,000 eastern diamondbacks were killed annually in the Tallahassee region of Florida on seven large hunting preserves, as a result of a bounty payment of $1.00 per rattler. This bounty was evidently offered by the private estates rather than by a county. Stoddard thought the snakes remained fairly numerous, although they seldom were seen during the quail-hunting (bobwhite) season in winter.

At present, Iowa probably has a more extensive bounty system than any other state. It was initiated on an individual county basis in 1913. The early results have been discussed by Guthrie (1924, p. 417; 1926, p. 189; 1929, p. 352). More recent statistics have been secured through the courtesy of Dr. Reeve M. Bailey of the University of Michigan, Paul Leaverton, Superintendent of Game of Iowa, and by direct communications from county auditors. The data on the snakes offered for bounties are neither complete nor, when available from different sources, entirely consistent. Therefore, instead of attempting to present annual figures, I have set forth in table 14:1 the summarized results by counties, using my own judgment in composing discrepancies. The bounties paid, although usually 50 cents per snake, have varied from 25 cents to $1.00. To collect a bounty, it is required to present two inches of the tail of a snake, with the rattle attached. In the case of certain injurious animals or predators, Iowa counties are required by law to offer bounties. This is not the case with rattlesnakes, for each county has the option of offering or not offering a rattlesnake bounty at 50 cents per snake. The total rattlers turned in for bounties and the amounts paid in the state as a whole, for several recent years, were as follows:

Year	Number of rattlesnakes (in part estimated from sums paid)	Total payments
1946	735	$326.50
1947	740	357.00
1948	629	325.50
1949	720	355.00
1950	978	509.75
1951	867	454.00
1952	727	436.50

In nearly all counties a gradual decline in the number of snakes brought in for bounty payments has been evident. Although one might be disposed to credit this trend to the bounty system, there is no certainty that the reduced rattler population, if there is one, has resulted from the bounties. Changing ecological conditions may have been even more important; and the improvement in economic conditions would certainly have lessened the urge to hunt rattlers for a small bounty.

Certain counties in Minnesota have been paying bounties on rattlesnakes at 50 cents each (lately raised to $1.00 in some instances), the heads and rattles being required to prove a claim. Table 14:2 presents the available statistics on the rattlers turned in for bounties. Where figures are entered, they represent the proper totals, but the blank spaces do not necessarily indicate an absence of bounties in that year.

I have been advised by the Department of Natural Resources, George W. Davis, Fish and Game Director, that Vermont has paid bounties on rattlesnakes

TABLE 14:2

RATTLESNAKES OFFERED FOR BOUNTIES IN MINNESOTA BY COUNTIES

Year	Houston	Fillmore	Olmsted	Wabasha
1935	234	...	...	...
1936	2,557	990	...	...
1937	2,003	581	...	...
1938	1,688	687	...	...
1939	2,300	564	11	306
1940	6,553	1,092	0	...
1941	5,957	561	39	...
1942	517	328	5	...
1943	554	359	9	130
1944	508	406	9	75
1945	800	171	0	20
1946	780	222	0	8
1947	1,240	99	0	39
1948	1,160	86	0	125
1949	720	126	0	128
1950	520	101	0	130
1951	600	119	0	155
1952	612	179	1	89

Note.—Winona County paid bounties on 2,473 snakes in 1937; no subsequent data are available from that county.

off and on since 1891. The greatest amount paid in any year was $117 in 1903. From 1942 to 1944 the payments were less than $40 a year, at $1.00 per snake. The rattlers presented for bounties from 1947 to 1953, by years, were 80, 43, 5, 11, 29, 34, and 4. All the snakes came from along the New York border near Whitehall, New York, especially from West Haven, Rutland County, Vermont. The head and rattles of a snake are required as proof. Rice (1895, p. 389) thought the bounty offer would encourage rattlesnake farming, but there is no indication that it has.

In New York State, rattlesnake bounties have been paid for many years by several counties, including Warren and Washington, bordering on Lake George. In Warren County, the bounty was raised from $3.00 to $5.00 per snake in November, 1950; in Washington County it remained at $3.00, according to the latest information available. The rattles and three inches of tail are required to collect the bounty. The take in Washington County is said to run about 80 snakes per year, but a recent newspaper report from Fort Ann in that county stated that 157 were turned in for the year 1953 up to October 1. There are rumors that rattlers are sometimes brought in from adjacent nonbounty-paying counties

(Shorey, 1953, p. 26), and that some hunters are deliberately sparing the females to assure an annual crop. According to Carmer (1936, p. 317) the females are collected and kept in captivity until the young are born and can be offered for bounty.

In Pennsylvania, bounties have been paid from time to time by sportsmen in Cameron, Tioga, and other counties (*Pennsylvania Game News*, vol. 21, no. 2, p. 36, March, 1951). Hamilton (1949, p. 6) and Hogan (1950, p. 9) mention unofficial bounties of this type paid in Tioga and McKean counties at $1.00 per snake. Cameron County is said to have paid bounties on 900 rattlers in 1949, and 1,100 in 1950 (Herrick, 1953, p. 23). A bill proposing a state-wide bounty of $1.50 each for rattlesnakes and copperheads was presented in the Pennsylvania State Legislature in 1951 but failed to pass.

MacQuarrie (1941, p. 82) stated that Elmer Keitel, a professional snake collector, was paid a bounty of 50 cents per rattler by Sauk County, Wisconsin. Messeling (1953, p. 21) also mentions having collected rattlers for bounties in Wisconsin. He claimed to secure about 1,000 per year, including broods and unborn young.

In lieu of bounties, regular employees are sometimes hired by a state or county to destroy rattlesnakes. Such a position was held for several years by the late A. M. Jackley, rattlesnake-control officer of South Dakota. I corresponded with Mr. Jackley for some 15 years, and secured from him much interesting information on rattlesnakes and their habits that he had acquired while carrying out control measures. I have quoted many statements from his letters and published reports, in this and other chapters. Jackley's work in South Dakota is being carried on by a successor under the same title.

The principal objections to the bounty system as a method of rattlesnake control are the following:

1. Snakes are brought in from beyond the borders of the bounty district.
2. Snakes may be bred and raised for bounties.
3. Females are held until they have given birth to young, thus increasing the bounty.
4. Claims are made for snakes found dead on the road.
5. Snakes are gathered in wild areas, where they do no harm, rather than around human habitations.
6. Harmless snakes are killed under the mistaken impression that they are venomous and eligible for bounties.

W. C. Jacobsen (1945, p. 53) and Latham (1951, p. 60) have discussed the difficulties of administering any bounty system for predator control. References to rattlesnake bounties, in addition to these already given, are Anon. (1932, p. 4), Beck (1939, p. 94), Trapido (1941, p. 26), and Breckenridge (1944, p. 156).

EFFECTS OF SETTLEMENT AND AGRICULTURE

Since the advent of white men to this continent, there has naturally been a continuous campaign to kill off rattlesnakes around habitations, and this has been so effective that the snakes are greatly diminished in numbers about cities; in some districts where they were once found, they have now been completely exterminated.

It is surprising to learn that, even in early colonial times, the comment was frequently made that rattlers were becoming absent or rare around settlements. Thus, John Bartram (1744, p. 358) stated that they had almost disappeared from the vicinity of Philadelphia; Kalm (1752–53, p. 132; 1758, p. 286) and Pennant (1787, p. 88) reported that they had been virtually extirpated in populous sections. Beverly (1705, p. 63) comments on their rarity in Virginia; and Purry, Richard, Meuron, and Raymond (1732, p. 1017) make the same statement with respect to South Carolina. Engelhardt, Nichols, Latham, and Murphy (1915, p. 3) have commented on the extermination of the timber rattlesnake, *C. h. horridus,* on Long Island. Similar reports have been made by Beyer (1900, p. 29; see also Fitch, 1949b, p. 89) on their disappearance from some sections of Louisiana, and by Wiffen (1913, p. 950) on the diminished population of massasaugas in New York. Harry E. Miller has written me of the gradual elimination of rattlesnakes from many areas contiguous to towns in New England. Of these effects of settlement there can be no question.

But with respect to the effects of agriculture, there are conflicting influences and consequently divergent opinions. It is probable that agricultural development has resulted in more rattlers in some sections and fewer in others. For, on the one hand, agriculture may increase the rodent population and thus the rattler food supply: whereas, on the other, cultivation may destroy cover, refuges, and dens; snakes are destroyed by the plow and mowing machine; livestock, particularly hogs, will kill them; and, finally, there is the never-ending enmity of the farmer and his helpers. On grazing land, the effect is no doubt always adverse; some grazing animals trample rattlers either deliberately or by accident; and, in any case, the food available to the rodents is reduced, so the rattler population in turn declines. Since, except in the rare instances when hogs are run to eliminate rattlers, the farmer's activities are not primarily designed as rattlesnake-control measures, I have discussed the effect of agriculture on rattler populations more fully in chapter 8.

FIRES

Forest, brush, and grass fires, as a means of destroying rattlers, have been suggested. It need hardly be said that the destruction of the watershed cover, to say nothing of harmless and useful wild life, would cause damage far outweighing the possible benefit of killing off the rattlers, some of which would surely escape into ground holes or rock crevices. I once found a live red diamond rattler in the center of a large burned area only a few months after the fire. However, fires would no doubt somewhat decrease the rattlesnake population, temporarily at least. But no burning program should be attempted without consultation with the proper authorities.

A few years ago, rattlesnakes were found in practically every section of Lincoln County. Due probably to range and brush fires over an extensive area in the southern part of the county, these snakes appear now to be confined largely to a half-mile strip of land on either side of Big Wood River, and Little Wood River, north and east of Shoshone. *George B. Haddock, Shoshone Rod & Gun Club, Shoshone, Idaho.*

◇

I know of one den burnt out in a forest fire in 1935. The den was in a mass of broken granite boulders, brush covered. *Philip B. Lord, U. S. Forest Service, Susanville, Calif.*

This area is frequently subject to large grass fires, many thousands of acres in extent; these apparently destroy many rattlers, and drive others outside the burning area where they are killed by fire fighters. *George A. Fischer, U. S. Forest Service, Tulelake, Calif.*

Many of my correspondents point out that the snake population has increased because of the protection of forests and chaparral from fire:

The rattlesnake population seems to be increasing since this area has been protected from fire. *D. J. Morriss, Wilma, Fla.*

◇

The natives maintain that rattlesnakes are greatly increasing since we are keeping forest fire out of the woods, but I see no evidence to substantiate this claim. *B. A. Eger, U. S. Forest Service, Buena Vista, Va.*

There are reports of fires started as a means of rattlesnake control:

Some of our forest and brush fires are caused by people trying to burn a rattlesnake out of a bush and having a fire get away from them. *Robert W. Gardner, U. S. Forest Service, Minden, Nev.*

◇

Some trouble has been caused in this locality by fires set to control snakes. This practice is naturally not approved by the Forest Service due to our conservation policy, and it is our belief that snakes can elude fire by taking refuge in the ground. I have never seen a dead snake in the burn of a big fire; but several days after a fire has cooled down, snakes were shown to be there by the trails seen in the ashes. *Nelson S. Stone, U. S. Forest Service, Camptonville, Calif.*

I have thought that fire-suppression crews might see many snakes endeavoring to escape, but such is evidently not the case. A couple of our local Reptile Club members trailed the edge of a fire near Banner, San Diego County, for five hours and reported seeing no snakes come out; nor were any burned snakes seen in the desolated area later. However, Pequegnat (1951, p. 32), in the Santa Ana Mountains of southern California, found several partly burned red diamonds among the rocks after a brush fire.

I was on a big fire (about 1,200 acres) Sunday, but did not see a sign of a snake, although it was good snake country—down toward Roosevelt in Buckhorn Canyon. *P. Bruce Centerwall, U. S. Forest Service, Tonto Basin, Ariz.*

Occasionally rattlers are encountered at fires, as indicated by the following:

I have had the experience several times while fighting forest fires, as have others, of hearing snakes rattling when the fire, or men, disturbed them, and I have found their burned bodies after fires. But, I have never known of any man or animal to have been bitten by a snake under these conditions. *A. L. Alexander, U. S. Forest Service, Roosevelt, Ariz.*

◇

I heard of a man being chased by a rattler that had been burned in a fire. *W. N. Ward, U. S. Forest Service, Tollgate, Oreg.*

Brewer (1930, p. 524) tells of starting a fire in some dry logs and unexpectedly driving out a rattler.

The following are some references to published accounts of the effects of forest and brush fires on rattlesnake populations: Flint, 1832, p. 291; Doddridge, 1824, p. 78; Williams, 1827, p. 28, and 1837, p. 67; Parker, 1840, p. 57; Hall, 1848, p. 124; Chamberlain, 1850, p. 15; Browning, 1860, p. 383 (but writing of 1820, or thereabouts); Yorris, 1881, p. 126; Tome, 1928, pp. 31, 34 (but writing of 1800); and Rutledge, 1938, p. 18. In some instances, fires were deliberately set as rattler-control measures.

Control by fire recalls an interesting echo of the past: Pliny (1855–57, vol. 5, p. 397; book xxix, chap. 22) says that Aesculapian snakes, a kind of harmless snake found in southern Europe, were brought into Rome and reared in the homes in such numbers that, had it not been for the frequent fires that burned the contents, they would have overrun the city.

FLOODS AND FREEZES

Floods are not likely to be an important factor in rattlesnake control since rattlers swim well and usually find some floating debris on which they can take refuge. No doubt floods do affect rattlesnake dispersion, as discussed elsewhere. Miss Cook (1943, p. 4) has reported a reduction of snakes in Mississippi as a result of the freeze of 1940. A. M. Jackley and others have mentioned the fatal results of a sudden freeze, whereby snakes returning to their dens may be prevented from reaching their winter sanctuary.

TRAFFIC CASUALTIES

In earlier publications, I have discussed at some length the serious inroads made in snake populations by automobile traffic (Klauber, 1931, p. 53; 1939, pp. 25, 60). In these days of fast, multiple-lane traffic over smooth-surfaced roads, on which snakes cannot secure adequate traction and therefore progress slowly and with difficulty, every major road is an almost impassable barrier, for scarcely a snake ever crosses in safety during hours of heavy travel. Thus the borders of the highways soon become virtually denuded of snakes, although the adjacent areas, through population pressure, continuously feed new material into them. Some years ago (1931, p. 58) I estimated the traffic casualties in San Diego County, California, at over 10,000 snakes per year. This figure has now increased because of the greater density and speed of traffic, so that I should now place the casualties at about 15,000 per year. Of these, roughly 8 per cent, or 1,200 per year, are rattlesnakes. A corresponding figure for the entire United States would be well over 800,000 rattlesnakes per annum. Obviously, there are great local differences because of variations in both rattlesnake and traffic density. Eventually the road casualties will decline—this is already true of major highways—because of past destruction.

Ditmars (1927, p. 5) expressed the opinion that rattlers and other venomous snakes cross highways infrequently, owing to the odor of asphalt, oil, or exhaust gases. My own experience, except with freshly oiled desert highways, has been quite different. Although snakes hesitate to cross open spaces in the daytime, they have little or no fear of crossing at night, and it is to be remembered that rattlesnakes are largely nocturnal much of the year. There is, in fact, evidence that in the spring, when temperatures are below the optimum, and when black-surfaced highways may have absorbed more heat in the daytime than the surrounding ground, the snakes find the roads warmer, and therefore especially attractive, during the early night hours.

METHODS OF CATCHING RATTLESNAKES

HUNTING RATTLESNAKES

As is true of all pursuits, one becomes skilled at hunting rattlesnakes through experience. Not only is success in hunting dependent on a knowledge of seasons and terrain, and the types of refuges sought by the snakes, but also on an ability to see the snakes when they are within sight. Usually, when intruded upon they will lie quietly, instinctively relying on their concealing coloration to escape detection. Here experience—a knowledge of what a coiled rattler looks like

Fig. 14:4. A catch of prairie rattlesnakes made by A. M. Jackley in Harding County, South Dakota, October 5 to 7, 1942.

against a natural background—is of the greatest value in the discovery of the quarry. I have, upon occasions when hunting with an inexperienced friend, pointed to a small patch of ground only 15 to 20 feet away, where a rattler lay coiled in plain sight. It was astonishing how long it usually took my companion to distinguish the snake.

CATCHING RATTLESNAKES AT THEIR DENS

As I have said initially, by all odds the most productive method of collecting live rattlers is to locate them at their dens at the time of their entering hibernation in the fall, or of leaving it in the spring. Here the concentrations are often surprisingly large, and substantial catches may be made in a relatively short time, even numbering hundreds in a single day (fig. 14:4). At these seasons, it is the habit of the rattlers to come out for a few hours on each of several successive days, either to take advantage of the last sunny days of autumn or the first warm hours of spring. They lie about at the mouths of their retreats; and collectors, properly equipped with handling tools and containers, especially if they co-operate in pairs or trios, can catch a large proportion of all the snakes they see. Of how the dens are located, and of the habits of the rattlers at the dens, I have elsewhere (chap. 8) given an account that need not be repeated here.

C. B. Perkins, then of Denver, has thus described his operations in the vicinity of Platteville, Colorado, where, in time, he collected some 860 prairie rattlesnakes (*C. v. viridis*), which he kindly shipped to me for study:

We had scouted around all summer looking for prairie-dog towns which were probably being used as winter refuges by the rattlers, and finally staked out three that seemed promising.

On October 12th, my three children (two girls, 8 and 10, and a boy, 12—all accustomed to snaking) and I got to prairie-dog town No. 1 about 10 A.M., and caught two rather small rattlers in the first half hour of work, and then nothing more for another half hour. In the next 15 minutes or so we got 13 large ones (about 30 inches), but no more till noon. None of these snakes was very near the holes.

We ate our lunch while driving to town No. 3. While the boy and I were at the north end, a mile away, the girls got two medium rattlers at the extreme south end. We got nothing, although we covered the ground pretty thoroughly. It was a fairly new town with lots of sage brush. We didn't try town No. 2, which is small, and as it was getting late (about 2 P.M.) and a cool breeze blowing, we wanted to get back to town No. 1 before the snakes had gone in for the day, but we arrived there too late.

The next day, October 13th, Mrs. Perkins and I got to town No. 1 before 10 o'clock, but could find no snakes for 15 to 20 minutes, after which we really got to work. The total catch for the day was 93 rattlers. Two snakes came from town No. 3, 30 odd from town No. 2, and the rest from town No. 1. Among them was a little albino. Very few snakes were out in the open, although those that were seemed unusually large. Most were within a few inches of the prairie-dog mounds, and a great many were coiled in the entrances to the holes themselves, so they had to be tossed out quickly to keep them from sliding down into the holes. We lost a good many at first until our technique improved, but we failed to keep track of our losses. Several times we tossed out a number at once from the same hole. As they would rush back, one of us would guard the hole while the other would work inward, taking first those that were farthest out. One might think the snakes were attacking, but as a matter of fact they paid no attention at all to the person at the hole, trying only to get back to safety. We could find no more snakes after a few minutes past 2. Anticipating no such catch, I failed to take along enough sacks, and 18 were dead when we got home. I don't believe any were hurt in the catching. The road to Platteville is fairly rough, with a paved road from there to Denver.

Next day, October 14th, Mrs. Perkins and I were again at town No. 1 before 10, but had no luck for about half an hour. The total for the day was 64. Possibly 10 were from town No. 2, none from No. 3 (although we wasted almost an hour there), and the rest from town No. 1. Catching was over, as usual, about 2. The total catch was 174 in three days.

I was unable to go the next day, and on the 16th of October we had our first cold snap. I went out again alone on November 3rd, and got 16 rattlers, mostly from town No. 1; again there were none from town No. 3.

Town No. 3 is possibly twice as large as town No. 1, and I am unable to account for the scarcity of snakes there. It is in a hollow—much higher ground all around, except to the north, but the holes go up the sides. Town No. 1 is flat and town No. 2 slopes gently toward the north.

Only once did we fish a snake out of a hole after he had gone in, although we tried 4 or 5 times, but as this took 10 or 15 minutes, we didn't try it again. But, as I said, after the first half hour our losses from escaping snakes were not too heavy.

We used leather-looped sticks with hooks at the other end, and, as a carrying sack, an alfalfa-seed bag fastened on a 10-inch barrel hoop, with a short handle. By using this sack it was not necessary to catch the snake behind the head; it could be held anywhere along the body, and dropped in the sack. Several times it was easier to scoop one up with the bag itself, and I have now straightened the front of the loop of metal to facilitate this. We caught very few with our hands.

Rapid work at the dens is essential, if a majority of the snakes are not to escape down holes or into rock crevices. For this reason two or three people can work more efficiently and safely than one alone. If there are three, one can rake, or hook out into the open, such snakes as are endeavoring to scramble down their holes. A second, with a hook or long-handled tongs, picks them up and drops them into a container carried about by the third member of the party. All should be shod with heavy boots or puttees so that they need exercise no particular care in walking around among the snakes.

Interesting accounts of experiences in catching rattlesnakes at their dens will be found in Matteson (1899, p. 666), Martin (1930, p. 77), and Anderson (1947, p. 1). Anderson caught 66 *viridis* in less than an hour at a den in South Dakota.

Of late years, widespread newspaper publicity has been given to two annual rattlesnake-catching drives at Okeene, Blaine County, and Waynoka, Woods County, Oklahoma. These drives, ostensibly to rid the surrounding country of dangerous snakes, and to profit from their sale, are really publicity projects evolved by Junior Chambers of Commerce. The Okeene event is said to date back to 1939, and the Waynoka drive to 1949. The hunts are carried out at the time of the spring emergence of the rattlers (April 12 at Waynoka and April 19 at Okeene, in 1953), which are probably mostly western diamonds (*C. atrox*), although prairie rattlers (*C. v. viridis*) and western massasaugas (*S. c. tergeminus*) are also found in that part of Oklahoma.

The hunts are highly organized and are said to be subsidized by adjacent ranches, which contribute two cents per acre, to reduce the danger to their cattle. The catch is variously stated to be from 1,500 to 3,000 rattlers per year in each hunt, and the participants number several thousand. The catch at Okeene in 1954 was stated to have been 1,576 rattlers, of which the largest measured six feet three and a half inches. The 1955 hunt produced only 550 rattlers, but the weather was inclement. The hunters dispose of their catch to the organizing group, which, in turn, sells it by auction or otherwise to snake shows and dealers. The price per pound at Okeene in 1953 was said to be 50 cents. The methods used are devised to stimulate sensationalism, with prizes for the largest rattlers and for a marked snake that has been turned loose. Also, there is an award of the Order of the White Fang to any participant who may be bitten. Whether the control achieved is beneficial may be questioned, but there is no doubt as to the success of the events in securing national publicity for the communities involved. Accounts of these hunts will be found in Anon. (1947a, p. 7), Armstrong (1947, p. 2), Hughes (1947, p. 4), Ludrick (1948, p. 11), Gillette (1949, p. 3), Isely (1951, p. 1), Mote (1952, p. 42), Polaski and Polaski (1952, p. 138), Anon. (1953, p. 14), and Anon. (1954, p. 9).

Elsewhere (pp. 552 and 975) I have discussed the effects of repeated den raids on rattlesnake populations.

COLLECTING METHODS AFIELD

When collecting is done in areas having mild climates, where the rattlesnakes seek individual retreats, rather than communal dens, other means of hunting must be used. Even in these areas, spring will be found most fruitful, since it is mating time and also because the snakes are hungry after their winter fast, and therefore less cautious in roaming about. The late fall is also a good season for hunting, as the young of the year are to be found, and occasionally an entire brood may be discovered. The exact times when these hunts will be most fruitful depend on climate and other local conditions. To be successful, the collector must become familiar with his territory to discover the seasons when snakes are most active, in what surroundings, and at what time of day or night they are most likely to be found. The important thing to remember is that rattlesnakes are naturally secretive, and, unless actively in search of food or mates, are likely to be partially or entirely hidden. Thus, in the Southwest, the hunter looks for them under bushes, in clumps of cactus, in rock crevices, or under flat stones or over-hanging banks. In this kind of collecting his equipment should include not only the means of catching and carrying his snakes, but also tools for investigating these hiding places without danger to his hands or feet. For this purpose he needs a long-handled prospector's pick, a hook on a broom handle, or a long steel bar, with which flat stones or debris may be overturned.

In desert areas, where most snakes are nocturnal, an efficient method of collecting is to drive on the paved roads at night, picking up the snakes seen crossing in the glare of the headlights. Even grayish or brownish snakes stand out conspicuously against the black background of the road surface. This has been a fruitful means of collecting such rattlers as western diamonds, red diamonds, Mojaves, speckled rattlers, tiger rattlers, and sidewinders, as well as harmless snakes. The roads must be paved, as it is quite difficult to see any but the largest snakes against the shadow-flecked and neutral background of an unpaved highway. Yet little-traveled roads are to be preferred to major highways for a number of reasons: the snake population is not so likely to be already decimated; fewer headlights will be shining in your eyes (an approaching car makes it almost impossible to see a snake); and there will be less danger from other cars when one stops suddenly or backs up[3] to pick up a snake. I have elsewhere described in considerable detail this method of collecting and its results (Klauber, 1939a, p. 7; equipment p. 15; see also 1944, p. 112).

In some sandy areas in the Southwest, professional collectors regularly catch rattlers by following their tracks. The species concerned are usually the western diamondback (*C. atrox*), the Mojave rattler (*C. s. scutulatus*), and the sidewinder (*C. cerastes*). The hunter gets out at daybreak, for he must do his hunting before the morning wind has obliterated the tracks, and before these nocturnal desert snakes have taken refuge in holes against the heat of the day. He hunts either among mesquite-crowned dunes, or along sandy dry washes, especially under the steep banks of the latter, where there is scattered brush cover. Almost every fresh track leads to a capture, unless the snake has crossed intervening hard ground. It is easy to tell from the nature of the track—whether the continuous trail of the western diamond or the interrupted series of the sidewinder—in which direction the snake has headed. The quarry is usually found coiled or stretched out under some bush or at the entrance to a mammal hole. So adept do these hunters become that their areas are soon depleted of rattlers, and they must either widen their ranges or seek new fields.

---

[3] There is no truth in the story that, when a highway patrol officer protested my backing so far and so fast, I told him I was on my way to a dentist appointment.

The following are extracts from communications received from S. H. Walker, then of Indio, California, who for years maintained a roadside snake pit and marketed snakes to dealers. His usual method was to go out on the desert early each morning and follow the tracks the snakes had left in their nocturnal excursions.

I am still occupied with the diamondback rattlers, having just got back this morning from a hunt. I got a few, but have found June the hardest month of the year to catch them in the desert. There are four months of the year when I can really get them; these are April and May, and September and October. Those are their main feeding and mating times. June finds them through breeding and feeding, and they are lazy and don't move much. But when I find a track I nearly always get a snake, because it is easy to tell which way a rattler is going, whether a diamondback or sidewinder. I follow it until I find it bedded, or where it went into a hole.

I have caught thousands of snakes since I saw you. It takes about a year to rid a place of, say, 4,000 acres, of sidewinders or rattlesnakes,[4] depending upon how much one hunts. A larger area would take more time.

I will tell you of experiences I had over at Blythe. There is a lot of salt brush in that country, and some sand. I would take a female snake and get the musk out of her in mating time. This I put on my boots, then would walk around the heavy weeds in the afternoon, and go back the next morning and find that the rattlesnakes had trailed me, sometimes for quite a way. Then I took their trails, and got as many as 25 or 30 in a morning. One morning, south of Blythe, I got 35 by 10 o'clock.

Some years later, in eastern San Diego County, Walker was climbing amid rocks and was fatally bitten in the hand by a rattler he presumably had not seen before it struck him. This was a strange accident—a chance in a million—to happen to a man as familiar as he was with the ways of rattlers.

Some collectors have made good catches by following tracks in the desert at night—particularly around mesquite hummocks—aided by the light of a powerful gasoline lamp, such as a Coleman. Occasionally, in the coastal region, a rattler may be caught, if the collector be traveling on an unpaved road in the daytime, and will stop and hunt where a crossing snake track is observed in the dust. I have caught both southern Pacific rattlers and red diamonds in this way. Under some circumstances, burning clumps of brush may be effective in driving out rattlers, although it may be presumed that many fail to come out and are killed. This scheme is said to be moderately successful for capturing the eastern diamond-back rattler (*C. adamanteus*), hidden in prairie hammocks in Florida. Burning should never be undertaken without the knowledge and consent of the proper authorities.

The following notes on collecting in Florida, by the method of burning small palmetto clumps, were received by me more than 20 years ago from J. S. C. Boswell of Virginia:

It is not unusual to get 30 big rattlers in a day's trip if you use my system. We burn the small palmetto clumps and wait with a noose on the outside. Several months ago my wife, who is equally interested and capable, took 14 in two hours. Here are some records taken from my log, showing how common *adamanteus* is in some sections of south-central Florida. *First clump:* Almost round, very dry and thick, about 70 feet in diameter. Four diamond-backs, 1 pigmy rattler, 1 four-lined chicken snake, and 2 cottonmouths. *Second clump:* Nothing. *Third clump:* About the same size and area as the first. Six diamondbacks, 1 king snake. *Fourth clump:* About 30 feet across and 200 yards long. Four diamondbacks, 1 cotton-mouth, 1 gopher snake, and 2 pigmy rattlers. All this was between 7 A.M. and 1:30 P.M.

---

[4] Meaning the western diamond (*C. atrox*).

Fig. 14:5. "Yaller Gal," a hound trained to find and "bay" rattlesnakes without endangering herself, points an eastern diamondback (*C. adamanteus*).

Fig. 14:6. Horace Schultz, owner of "Yaller Gal," prepares to catch the snake.
(Figs. 14:5 and 14:6 published by courtesy of Edwin Way Teale.)

J. R. Slevin, when hunting the banded rock rattlesnake (*C. l. klauberi*) among talus slides in the Huachuca Mountains of Arizona, found that if he rapped with a stick on the rocks a rattler hidden beneath would sometimes advertise its presence by rattling (Van Denburgh, 1922, vol. 2, p. 963). This scheme had been employed as early as 1905 by Dr. Henry Skinner, as reported by W. Stone (1911, p. 232). It was also successful in locating *C. tortugensis* on Tortuga Island.

J. K. Paulding (1817, vol. 2, p. 10) was told of a place where rattlers were common. A gentleman hired a guide to take him there and searched but found none. Then he stamped on a flat stone and about a dozen rattlers came out. This story has at least a faint tinge of possibility, but as the gentleman went on to tell Paulding that, when the first snakes rattled, several thousand came out of the rocks and all rattled and hissed in unison, we become faintly suspicious that Paulding was being taken in.

When rattlers are hunted in woods, brush, or fields, the problem is to get them to declare their presence by rattling or moving, for otherwise their concealing coloration renders them hard to see. I was told by L. M. Huey that the Mexicans in central Baja California, when gathering wood, first kick sand into a bush so that any rattler will disclose its presence by rattling. Of course, the Mexicans are seeking only to avoid hidden snakes, but the same method might be used to catch them.

Although many dogs are rattlesnake killers, some, with their keen sense of smell, can be trained to find rattlers without attacking them, and thus become efficient adjuncts in their capture. A hunting dog in San Diego has been said by his master to point rattlesnakes, and Harrington (1905, p. 9) mentions an English pointer in Missouri that would regularly point rattlers, attracting attention with short barks. W. W. Brown (1906, p. 178) mentions a small pack of foxhounds trained to hunt rattlers and to bark without endangering themselves when one was located. C.A.V. (1913, p. 498) believes a rattler senses the impossibility of escaping detection by a dog, hence rattling more readily upon the approach of a dog than a man; this is to be doubted. Others discussing the finding of rattlers by the use of dogs are G.A.I. (1908, p. 972) and Anon. (1909, p. 32). Through the courtesy of Mr. Edwin Way Teale I am able to present figures 14:5 and 14:6, showing the hound "Yaller Gal," which has been trained to trail rattlesnakes and "bay" them when found. In two years she is said to have located about 500 eastern diamondbacks for her owner, Horace Schultz of Fort Green, Florida.

Rattlesnakes can sometimes be located by means of watching for the specialized rattler-warning chirp and posture used by ground squirrels, as described by Linsdale (1946, p. 67) and Fitch (1948a, p. 555; 1949a, p. 517). Domestic poultry, especially turkeys, have characteristic ways of reacting to the presence of snakes, which their owners soon learn. H. M. Smith (1946a, p. 63) tells of a Texan who caught rare snakes by watching his turkey flock.

Hopkins (1905, p. 354) stated that if a rattler were seen to enter a prairie-dog hole it could be made to emerge if some earth were thrown in the hole. The rattler would come out, it was claimed, to avoid being walled in by prairie dogs, such being the prairie dog's reputed defense against rattlers (see also Brons, 1882, p. 565; Ringle, 1924, p. 20; Brown, 1936, p. 24; Duncan, 1945, p. 167; and Osborn and Allen, 1949, p. 330).

In Florida, if a diamondback is presumed to be in a gopher (tortoise) hole, it is said that the snake can be caused to come out without any laborious digging by plugging the entrance with earth for a short time (Hylander, 1951, p. 114) or with rags (Teale, 1951, p. 67). It is claimed that when these temporary barriers are removed the hidden rattler will immediately emerge.

Rattlesnakes may sometimes be located in abandoned mine tunnels or caves, in which they may take refuge from the heat in summer. Also, a fruitful place is said to be any deep trench with vertical sides dug for water pipes or gas transmission lines through desert areas. Into these trenches the snakes fall at night and are often to be found on the following morning.

In former days, haycocks and grain shocks were favorite hiding places for rattlers. Anon. (1887, p. 137) tells of a threshing machine that was suddenly plugged by rattlers. A dozen were removed from the machine and 54 more were found in the shocks.

Tools and Equipment

Where the snakes to be captured are well concentrated, as they are about the dens when entering or leaving their winter refuges, the best tools are first, a hook, or a narrow rake with not to exceed four or five teeth, for the member of the party who is to keep the snakes from escaping. The handles should not be so long as to be clumsy—not over five feet at most. A "potato rake" conforms closely to these specifications.

The "picker-up" may use a hook or a pair of forceps or tongs; for either a forked stick, or a loop-snare, such as may be employed in the capture of a single snake, is much too slow for this operation. If the weather is moderately cool and the snakes not too excited, a hook works very well; for when it is placed under a rattler at mid-body, the snake will usually drape itself over the hook, and then can be raised into the container. If this does not work well, long-handled forceps or tongs should be used. They must be stiff enough so that the blades will not twist sideways when closed to hold a rattler weighing a pound or two. An old-fashioned placental forceps will be found suitable for the smaller snakes. Satisfactory tongs can be made of hardwood; however, their operation will require both hands, as compared with one hand in the use of a forceps. Franklin (1947, p. 143) suggests fastening an extension stick to one handle of a forceps and a lead weight and a string to the other. The weight serves to keep the jaws apart, until the string is pulled to close them on a rattler.

Rattlers need not be picked up behind the head unless it be desired to prevent their wasting venom by biting themselves in their struggles to escape. If picked up behind the head, a heavy snake must also be supported at mid-body or it may be seriously injured. Some collectors have used nets, made like a butterfly net, but of heavier material. These are not satisfactory in stony places.

The container should be a deep can or sack into which specimens can be dropped without their being brought near the hands of the man holding it. A can should have a depth equal to the length of the largest snakes to be caught, to discourage their climbing out. The cover should either be self-closing when a snake is dropped in, or be one that may be manipulated at a distance of two or three feet. Other containers—either sacks or boxes—should be at hand so that when a fair-sized catch has been accumulated in the container carried around by the collectors, it may be emptied into the others. There should not be too much crowding in the storage containers or the younger snakes will be crushed.

If a sack be used as a portable container, it should be arranged with its mouth held open by a steel hoop, which is, in turn, fastened to a broom handle. This makes a convenient and safe arrangement; after a snake has been dropped in, with the handle still held horizontally, the shaft is rotated through 90° or a little more, thus closing the mouth. Attached to the bottom of the sack, on the outside, there should be a short length of tape or cord hanging loose, so that, when the sack is to be turned upside down to dump the snakes into another container for transportation, it will not be necessary to touch the bottom of the sack itself. Also, inside the sack all loose threads and ravelings should be cleared away, for otherwise the snakes will become entangled with them.

When a hunter is operating in areas where his quarry is much more scattered than is the case around the dens, somewhat different equipment will be found more suitable. For picking up the snakes, various devices are preferred by different collectors. Some use a forked stick, although this simple device is less often employed than published accounts would lead one to suppose. While in theory the fork may be pressed on the snake's neck just back of its head, so that the snake can then be grasped in safety with the other hand, actually, as the snakes' necks are not of uniform size, on hard ground it is difficult to pinion a snake with assurance, or to pick it up with safety, for the fingers may be too far from the head. Some prefer for the purpose an L- or T- or J-shaped metal hook at the end of a stick (Klauber, 1928, p. 12; Hightower, 1945, p. 8). Such a tool may be used either to press a rattler's head to the ground while it is being seized by the neck, or to hook under the snake at mid-body so that it may be lifted into a box or bag. Still others use only a short length of straight rod. The latter is held parallel to the ground, only an inch or so above the surface, and the end is then pressed on the snake's head or neck, so it may safely be picked up with the other hand. The straight rod has the advantage of allowing one to watch the head more readily. This method is not safe for the capture of very large rattlers.

Most hunters will find some form of snare both safe and useful. For example, a jointed, wooden shotgun cleaning rod—tipped with the usual eye for the swatch of cleaning cloth—is handy, since it takes up little space when not in use. Through the eye, a loop of cord is allowed to dangle, the two outer ends of the cord being held in one hand by the operator. The loop is dropped over the snake's head and the ends are then pulled, thus closing the loop around the snake's neck by pulling it against the eye.

More formal snares may be fashioned by attaching one end of a cord or strap to a point near the outer end of a stick—a broom handle, for example—with the loose end brought back to the operator's end of the device through a staple or keeper. A strap is better than a cord, since the snake is not so likely to have its neck cut by a strap. Another improvement is to have that part of the device along the stick composed of a stiff wire passing through staple guides, and terminated at the operator's end by an eye in which he can crook a finger. The wire makes it possible to open and close the strap loop at the outer end by pushing or pulling the wire (Klauber, 1928, p. 12; Bevan, 1934c, p. 64).

Whatever the form of stick or snare used, the handle should not be made unduly long, since by its clumsiness this will increase, rather than reduce, the danger. The snake stick should not exceed five feet at most, and four feet will be found better for all but the very largest rattlers.

The catching of very large rattlers by the neck offers an additional problem, in that, if held vertically, suspended from the neck, their struggles will frequently cause serious or fatal injuries. An operator of skill and experience will raise the snake slightly and then grasp its posterior end with his other hand to prevent its struggles and also to take some of the weight off its neck. The snake must be prevented from throwing enough coils around the collector's arm to endanger the operation. Reese (1910, p. 367) tells of a collector who was bitten as the snake thrashed about while being placed in a container.

If space be at a premium, one need carry only a piece of string to capture a rattler. When a snake is discovered, break off a short, stiff branch from the nearest bush and strip it of leaves and twigs. Tie one end of a string about one and a half to two feet long to an end of the stick and make a running noose in the outer end. The string must be stiff enough so that the loop will stay open, permitting it to be dangled over the snake's head so that it can be noosed. After the snake has been caught and placed in a container, the string may be cut safely at the stick end, whereupon the loop will be loosened sufficiently to permit the snake to free itself and avoid being choked.

Some collectors dispense with all collecting tools. They merely seize the snake behind the head with one hand and with the other grasp it near the tail, and then by stretching it out, render it helpless. If a snake is coiled ready to defend itself, it is worried until it uncoils in an endeavor to escape. Other collectors pick up a rattler by its tail and hold it at arm's length to prevent its slashing at its captor. The rattler may attempt to climb up its own body to reach the hand that holds it, which can be prevented if one jiggles the tail. This scheme is most dangerous with half-grown snakes. It is interesting to note that this method of picking up rattlers was reported to be used by the Indians long ago (Hernández, 1615, fol. 192[r]; Nieremberg, 1635, p. 269). It need hardly be said that the writer recommends none of these foolhardy practices, but prefers some form of snare-stick.

Whatever the means for picking up the snake, some container must be readily available. If the collector is afoot, a sack will best serve the purpose, otherwise boxes with hinged lids, or cans are to be recommended. In any case, if other snakes have already been collected, it should be expected that they will try to escape or may even strike, when the container is opened to drop in the new captive. Therefore, one must be alert to see that the prior occupants are not in a threatening position when the box is opened. Mixing rattlers with harmless snakes should be avoided, not because they may injure each other, but because the more active snakes, particularly racers, may be so difficult to control that they will increase the normal hazards of bagging the rattlers. If excelsior is put in the bottom of the collecting box, the occupants may hide under it and be less likely to rear up in an endeavor to escape when the box is opened.[5]

---

[5] One of my more pleasurable hunting memories is of the time during prohibition days, when I was stopped on a lonely road just north of the Mexican line, by two men of the Border Patrol. They opened the rear doors and leaned in on either side to examine my gear, particularly a hinged box on the floor. Said one: "What might there be in the box?" When I replied: "Rattle-

Although rattlers will rarely bite through a muslin sack, it is unnecessary to take chances, and therefore sacks should not be allowed to dangle against one's body when they are being carried. G.A.I. (1908, p. 972) states that a Negro was bitten while carrying a snake in a sack over his shoulder. A severe bite was suffered by MacDonald from an *adamanteus* he was carrying in a sack (1939, p. 35; 1946, p. 136). A similar accident with a red diamond occurred in Los Angeles several years ago. In tying the mouth of a sack, twist up the end so that the fingers do not come into contact with a snake, with only muslin between, while the knot is being tied. Draw strings may be used, but if they are, the mouth of the sack should be doubled back so there will be no possible chance of egress. Snakes can enlarge and squeeze through a surprisingly small hole. For the same reason the coarse weave of burlap or jute bags is not to be trusted. Canvas is satisfactory if not too heavy and stiff.

Gillam (1916, p. 132) suggested wrapping the rattles of captured specimens, thus curtailing the sound produced so as to prevent confusion with other snakes one may meet. I confess I have sometimes been startled by the sound of a rattle nearby, only to find it was a sudden activity upon the part of a snake I was carrying beside me in a sack.

Swanson (1945, p. 215; 1946, p. 458) sometimes milks captive specimens in the field since, from past experience, he thinks it safer to carry venomous snakes with as little venom in them as possible. I should hardly agree with this program, except in special cases, believing it more dangerous to undertake the handling necessary for milking under field conditions, than to carry a fully armed snake.

A method of collecting available to persons of little experience, who may wish to catch an occasional snake, is to take an empty barrel, or other suitable container, and place it open end down over the snake. A board or piece of sheet metal is then slipped under the snake and the entire assembly turned upside down. The snake is then safely in the barrel (Loennberg, 1894, p. 336).

COLLECTIONS OF PRESERVED SNAKES

Live rattlers are, of course, interesting exhibits in zoölogical gardens and snake shows, and some useful observations of their habits may be noted there. But studies are also made on preserved specimens—studies of morphology and anatomy, of rattles and fangs, stomach contents, of reproductive cycles and sex differences. In fact, most of the important information now available respecting rattlesnake phylogeny and taxonomy has been based on studies of preserved specimens accumulated in natural history museums. Some of these collections are large, with extensive series taken at single localities, so that conclusions may be drawn with regard to the degree of variation within a single population. Again, there are specimens of a single subspecies from a variety of locations and ecological niches, from which one may gain some idea of the differences produced by these varying conditions. And finally, there are specimens of different subspecies, species, and genera, so that students may determine and assess the differences between

---

snakes," they grinned at each other as if to say: "This is the best one we've heard yet." So they lifted the lid, and a couple of big red diamondbacks that I had caught an hour or so before, rose up on their tails with enthusiasm for prospective freedom. The examiners suffered nothing more serious than a couple of bumped heads, for even in those days car doors were low. The only remark I heard was (excessively expurgated): "My goodness—they *were* rattlesnakes!"

them. For all these basic studies preserved specimens are of fundamental importance, and their collection and preservation constitute an essential activity in herpetology.

For these purposes ordinary dried snake skins, such as are so often used for decorative purposes, are virtually useless, although Beebe (1947, p. 205) recommends them under certain circumstances. Dependence is had on specimens preserved "in the round," and the value of the specimens for scientific purposes is partly dependent on the care with which they are initially preserved. Accurate locality data are important; a specimen labeled with incorrect information is worse than useless, since it is misleading.

Specimens for scientific collections are preserved, either in formalin (37 per cent commercial formaldehyde diluted about 10 to 1), or in about 75 to 80 per cent ethyl alcohol. Formalin has the advantage of being cheaper, and is more certain in its results, so that spoiled specimens are less often encountered. On the other hand, working with a formalin specimen is painful to eyes and hands, so that most museums make it a practice, when field-preserved formalin specimens are received, to wash out as much of the preservative as possible and then transfer the specimens to alcohol for permanent storage. In an emergency, a saturated salt solution may be used to preserve a specimen. Later the salt can be leached out and the snake transferred to alcohol. A deepfreeze refrigerator may be used for temporary preservation.

It requires somewhat more experience to produce satisfactory alcoholic specimens, as compared with formalin, but there is little trouble if care be used. The principal requirement is that the preservative gain entrance to every part of the body cavity, and that specimens be not crowded during the setting period, which takes about a week or more. To gain these ends, the freshly killed specimen should either have the abdominal cavity thoroughly impregnated with the preservative by means of a hypodermic syringe, or slits should be cut in the belly. In the latter case, in such specimens as rattlers, I recommend a single row of longitudinal slits, each about three to four inches long—somewhat shorter in smaller snakes—separated by one inch (Klauber, 1935, fig. 2). The specimen should then be neatly coiled belly up in a suitable jar and the coils should be pressed with a blunt stick to expel the gas. This pressing of the specimens should be repeated daily for a week. During the setting period it is best to put only one specimen in a jar, except in the case of juveniles; after the specimens are fully hardened they may be placed one on top of the next until the jar is filled within an inch or so of the top. Since light fades preserved specimens badly, the jars should be kept in a dark room or under a black cloth.

If one is handicapped by limited equipment in the field, and a large rattler is collected, a fairly useful specimen can be prepared by the process of slitting the specimen on the underside from the neck almost to the vent, then cutting the body at these points, pulling it away from the skin, and discarding it, thus leaving for preservation the head and tail in the round, still attached to the skin of the body. Where large numbers of specimens from a single locality are collected, and it is desired to conserve preservative, the viscera may be removed from the bodies.

Every effort should be made to have the specimens harden in neat circular coils fitting around the periphery of the jar, for otherwise much space will be wasted in final storage. If a specimen has been placed in the preservative before all involuntary motion has ceased, it will twist up and kink. After about an hour it should be removed once more and the body restretched and straightened by holding it by head and tail and giving it several sharp jerks. This will remove the kinks, after which it may be recoiled in the container.

While the specimens are fully limp, it is advisable to measure the length over-all and the tail length, since this can be done more accurately while the specimen can still be stretched out, and there will be no inaccuracies resulting from shrinkage. It is also desirable at this time to ascertain and record the number and condition of eggs or embryos, and likewise any food contents in the digestive tract.

Snakes found dead on the road (DOR) are often sufficiently fresh and uncut to make useful preserved specimens; it is well to stop and examine any seen on collecting trips. Even if badly smashed, they sometimes yield food notes and other information of value.

If specimens are to be killed for preservation anyway, and provisions for field preservation are available, then the snakes may be collected by shooting with .22 dust-shot shells. It is best to shoot at the neck, where even a tiny charge of shot will disable a large snake, and this without sufficient injury to reduce the value of the specimen for a preserved collection. However, a specimen shot in this way, although unable to escape, is still quite capable of biting, and should be handled with all the caution one would give an uninjured snake.

In collecting specimens, unless all come from a single place, one's memory should never be depended on for the locality or other field data; a slip of paper carrying this information should be dropped into the container with each specimen. If one be collecting along a road by automobile, each specimen may be identified by the speedometer reading, which is later correlated with the mileage readings at towns or other locality points along the route. Museums differ somewhat in their methods of cataloguing and recording their preserved collections. Example systems will be found described by Slevin (1927, p. 231) and Gloyd (1938, p. 49).

SHIPPING RATTLESNAKES

No attempt should be made to ship live rattlesnakes—or any other live snakes, for that matter—by mail, since this is contrary to postal regulations. Rattlesnakes, as well as other live snakes, may be shipped by express, if placed in containers prepared in accordance with specifications of the Railway Express Agency (see p. 1012). Several rattlers may be sent in a single container, if first put in muslin bags. It is inadvisable to mix juvenile specimens with adults, as the youngsters are likely to be crushed in transit. Excelsior or shredded paper, placed loosely in the box, will aid in preventing injury. Neither food nor water is required en route.

The greatest hazards to a successful shipment are overcrowding and overheating. Under no circumstances should the boxes be so small that large snakes will be piled more than three or four inches deep, if evenly distributed over the bottom; and in the case of small snakes not over two inches. With rattlesnakes, there is not only the chance of their being crushed if too crowded in shipment, but occasionally their tails become entangled at the rattles. I have had this happen in the case of large shipments to such an extent that an hour or more was required to untangle them, and some were fatally injured.

It is well to place on every shipping container a note to keep it in a cool place. A box left on a station platform, exposed to the sun in summer, will result in many fatalities. Small specimens may be safeguarded by moist moss in the container. This expedient is also useful when specimens are transported by auto in the course of a desert hunting trip.

When specimens within a box are to be segregated because they are from different localities, they may be tied up in separate muslin sacks, such as flour or meal bags, with an appropriate locality memorandum dropped in each sack. The snakes will get sufficient air through the cloth of the sacks. In fact, some shippers prefer to use sacks in every case, for this method has other advantages. The separation of the snakes reduces the likelihood of their piling up in one corner and crushing each other; even if the box be damaged the snakes cannot escape; and the unpacking is safer. Where sacks are used, one must remove all loose strings and ravelings from the inside seams, otherwise the snakes will become entangled with them in transit and may be strangled. I have received some shipments seriously depleted from this cause.

COMMERCIAL UTILIZATION OF RATTLESNAKES AND THEIR BY-PRODUCTS

Because of the emotional reactions of many people toward snakes, rattlesnakes particularly, publicity dealing with the commercial utilization of these reptiles or their by-products is usually tinged with sensationalism and exaggeration. A single instance of the sale of a few snakes or their venom is likely to be exploited in the newspapers as a regularly established business with a sound future. The press is by no means the sole offender, for those participating in such uncertain ventures are often exhibitionists by nature, and may, indeed, profit from the lurid publicity. Unfortunately, however, people who read these exaggerated reports are struck by the profits to be gained from creatures that otherwise are considered liabilities around their homesteads, and they are thereby encouraged to undertake snake farming as a business. So every time the wire services carry one of these stories to the effect that it pays better to milk rattlesnakes at $12,500 per quart of venom, than cows at 20 cents per quart of milk, the reptile departments of the museums and zoos are besieged for advice on this lucrative but hitherto neglected source of income.

Here are some extracts from letters from people at whose earnestness, I assure the reader, I have no desire to scoff. My complaint is directed at the misleading publicity that gives them such unwarranted encouragement:

> I am writing in the interest of my son who will shortly be back from the war. He has always been interested in snakes, and I think he would like to raise them for their poison, because I see it is valuable. Please tell me how to start a rattlesnake farm and how much ground you need.

There is a rockpile above my house that is full of rattlesnakes. I kill a dozen or more there every year. I see there is money in raising them for their skins and virus. Can you tell me how to raise them, what their feed is, and how to get the virus out? Can they climb over a fence?

◇

Can you give me some information in regards to raising rattlesnakes, that is, about their care, feeding, breeding, etc.? Also, the markets for their meat and venom? How do you tan the hides? Is it safe to take out the poison teeth?

◇

I read in the paper where a woman in Casa Grande is making lots of money raising rattle-snakes in a snake farm. How many rattlesnakes do you need to start a farm? Could I start with one pair? How do you tell the males from the females? Do you have to have an incubator for the eggs and how long before they are full-grown? How do you get the oil and the gall, and where can I sell them?

The answers to all these queries follow the same pattern: There are no successful rattlesnake farms in the United States, because such live snakes or by-products as may be marketed are secured from a continuous accession of fresh snakes newly caught in the wild. In general, snakes are not easy to care for in captivity; they require much attention, expensive food, are subject to epidemic diseases, and do not reproduce readily. For all of these reasons, snake farming does not pay; it is much easier and cheaper to replace sales and losses by catching fresh stock. As to markets for snakes and their by-products, these are variable and sporadic. Such buyers as there are naturally look to sources that can be counted on to furnish material at any time and in any quantity. So the business has gravitated to a few firms that enlarge and equalize their sales by dealing in other animals as well as in snakes. Even among these dealers, the failures have been many, for the snake business, divorced of sensationalism, needs, like any other, capital and a knowledge drawn from experience. To succeed, one requires both unusual sources of raw material and an acquaintance with markets for the finished products. In the section that follows, an attempt is made to summarize the several fields of rattlesnake utilization, at best a business notably lacking in standardization.

THE LIVE-SNAKE MARKET

In any snake show, rattlesnakes are a major attraction, rivaling in public interest the pythons and boas, whose size is their drawing feature, or such famous creatures of literature as the cobras. So it is that every snake display, from the scientific exhibits in the reptile houses of the larger zoos to the snake pit in some traveling carnival, requires a foundation of rattlesnakes. These are generally secured from commercial dealers, some of whom have been engaged in the business for a considerable time, and have become well known in the various strata of the amusement trade. Most of the dealers are to be found in Texas, with a few in Florida, Arizona, and California; for the availability of stock as well as climatic conditions afford these states an advantage with respect to both local and exotic species. None of these dealers handles rattlesnakes exclusively, nor, indeed, are their outputs restricted to reptiles, for they also supply other kinds of animals for exhibitions or the pet trade, and deal generally in animals and their by-products.

Although the dealers are sometimes said to operate snake farms, they are not farms at all in the usual sense of the word; that is, places where animals are bred and raised for the market. There is, in fact, no such thing as a snake farm in the United States; the so-called farms are, in reality, only assembling depots—classification yards between the field collector and the customer. As long as full-grown snakes are as easily obtainable in the unsettled areas of this country and adjacent Mexico as is now the case, no one could possibly raise snakes profitably in competition with field collectors. Only in the case of a few rare species, obtainable solely in distant and inaccessible places, is an attempt made to breed and raise captive snakes. And this is usually undertaken by zoos with the experience and facilities for such a venture, not by the commercial dealers, who generally concentrate on the species common in their localities. So, whatever the extent of the live-snake trade, its wants are supplied by the capture of adult field stock. Most dealers destroy whatever young rattlers happen to be born in their enclosures, for there is little demand for them, and they would be prohibitively expensive to rear. Stillwell (1939, p. 16) states that one Texas dealer killed 100,000 little western diamonds in his pens in the course of 30 years.

Because of its size and ready availability, the western diamond rattlesnake (*C. atrox*) is the staple furnished by the dealers along our southern border, from Texas to southeastern California; it is more often seen in snake shows than all other species combined. Next in importance, commercially, is the eastern diamondback (*C. adamanteus*), which, by reason of its large size and showy pattern, also makes an excellent exhibit. These two species are always obtainable from well-established dealers in Texas and Florida, respectively.

Other species are not such staple commodities. The southeastern pigmy rattler (*S. m. barbouri*) is to be had in Florida. One Louisiana dealer has handled the canebrake rattler (*C. h. atricaudatus*); and its northern relative, the timber rattler (*C. h. horridus*), is often obtainable from eastern animal dealers who do not specialize in reptiles. The larger Texas dealers generally have for sale the rattlesnake known in the trade as the Mexican green rattlesnake. This is the Mexican west-coast rattler (*C. b. basiliscus*), the commercial specimens generally coming from the vicinity of Colima, in southwestern Mexico. They bring a higher price than domestic species.

Arizona dealers have a more varied stock, although much of their trade is in western diamonds. From them it is occasionally possible to secure blacktails (*C. m. molossus*), one of the showiest of all rattlers, Arizona black rattlers (*C. v. cerberus*), tigers (*C. tigris*), sidewinders (*C. c. laterorepens* or *C. c. cercobombus*), and a beautiful, pink color-phase of the speckled rattler (*C. m. pyrrhus*). However, with so varied a choice it is almost necessary to visit the dealers' pits to pick the snakes desired, as the species are not always properly identified. The Mojave rattlesnake (*C. s. scutulatus*) is usually obtainable, although often confused by the dealers with western diamonds and sometimes with blacktails.

In California, most of the trade is in Pacifics (*C. v. oreganus* or *C. v. helleri*), sidewinders (*C. c. cerastes* and *C. c. laterorepens*), and red diamonds (*C. r. ruber*). The latter are showy and desirable exhibits, and are sometimes sent to the Texas and Florida dealers for redistribution.

Few other species are regularly quoted by the dealers; and because they have little time to waste on the possible sale of the rarer species, these, when they do come to hand, are seldom saved if, indeed, they are recognized as being unusual. Furthermore, the commercial dealers do not have the facilities to segregate and keep records of incoming specimens, so that the locality of collection of any individual rattler is usually unknown. For this reason, scientific institutions desirous of securing the rarer species of rattlesnakes for their study collections are dependent on their own field expeditions, or on collectors located at strategic places who specialize in scientific material. For, without dependable locality data, rattlesnakes are of little interest to scientific institutions.

The prices of rattlesnakes fluctuate with other commodity markets, and, in addition, vary with conditions in the amusement trade. In the early 1930's carnivals and snake shows, like other entertainments, came upon hard times; there was a distressed market in snakes, and rattlers could be picked up at 25 cents a pound or less, field run. At this rate even a big five-foot rattler brought hardly more than a dollar, packed and ready for shipment. The list prices on western diamonds—always the "blue chips" of the snake market—in those days were about $1.00 for a two-foot snake, $2.00 for a three-footer, and $1.00 per foot for larger sizes. Seven-foot snakes were the largest quoted, and I suspect it would have been difficult to secure delivery of this size. By the pound, in assorted sizes, prices quoted F.O.B. express office varied from about 60 cents per pound in 25-pound lots, down to 25 cents for lots of 500 pounds. And anyone with cash could wangle a liberal discount off these lists.

Today (1955) the market is stronger. Western diamonds are generally quoted at $3.00 to $18.00, the smaller sizes selling at $2.00 per foot, and the larger, which always command a premium, at $3.00 per foot. All of these quotations are for fresh stock, packed and ready for shipment. Eastern diamonds have similarly advanced. Twenty years ago medium-sized snakes sold for $2.00, and large ones for $4.00; the corresponding prices today are $8.00 and $16.00.

Mexican green rattlers (*C. b. basiliscus*) before the war brought from $1.00 to $1.15 per foot, depending on size; or in assorted lots from $1.00 to $2.00 per pound. Today they are about twice as high, if obtainable at all. Recently, large specimens were quoted at $12.00 to $15.00 each. South American rattlers are being quoted at from $8.00 for a 2½-footer to $20.00 for a 5-footer. Other rattlesnake species formerly sold at from $1.00 to $10.00 per snake, depending on size, showiness, and rarity. These prices also have advanced materially. The prices on the less representative species never have been sufficiently standardized to warrant quotations here.

In the translation of prices per pound into prices per foot or per snake, the following table of approximate weights and lengths will be useful:

Length of rattlesnake	Weight
1 foot	¼ ounce
1½ feet	1½ ounces
2 feet	¼ pound
3 feet	1 pound
4 feet	2¼ pounds
5 feet	5 pounds
6 feet	9 pounds
7 feet	15 pounds
8 feet	23 pounds

As has been stated, the prices I have mentioned have been for fresh snakes boxed in accordance with express company regulations for venomous snakes; that is, in a wooden box, with ventilating openings covered with metal fly screen.[6] An amateur, coming upon a big rattler in the brush and looking upon it as a $10 commodity, is doomed to serious disappointment, whether he sells the snake to a dealer—if he can—or goes into business for himself. For there is a big spread—and rightly so—between the raw material under a mesquite bush and the packaged goods in the express office. The commercial dealer must develop both sources and markets. Since he must be able to ship at any time, he must carry a stock and sustain the losses thereby involved. He must advertise in the trade papers. Necessarily, his overhead is considerable. Unfortunately, sensational newspaper articles fail to distinguish between field and retail prices, thus encouraging those unfamiliar with the trade, or its uncertainties, to expect high returns. This is especially true of someone who, finding a large number of rattlers at a den, counts them as so many five-dollar bills, and wonders why this gold mine has been so long neglected. He soon learns it is much easier to catch rattlesnakes than to sell them; for, after all, the market is a thin one. Buyers are hard to locate, and anyway prefer to deal with established concerns that can be counted on to ship whenever fresh stock is needed. And such firms, far from being dependent on a den that can be tapped but twice a year, have more widespread sources of supply.

Rattlesnake collecting and selling, because of its supposed danger and unusual character, is one of the few activities having a sufficient public interest to get free newspaper publicity. Often the sale of a single snake by some youth may lead to an article intimating that he has successfully adopted this singular means of defraying his college expenses. The next thing one hears is that others, attracted by so lucrative and exciting an occupation, have accumulated a large stock of an unsalable commodity.

In the past the major commercial dealers paid their collectors from 10 to 25 cents per pound for live snakes. Today (1955), according to reports, the market may be as high as 35 or 50 cents. The dealers are less dependent on occasional hunters than on those who can be counted on to bring in rattlesnakes regularly—men whose normal occupations take them into the fields or wilds for other purposes, such as farmers, trappers, cowboys, or woodcutters. Naturally their operations are concentrated in the spring and autumn when the rattlers are more easily collected, but a few are brought in at all seasons.

As an indication of the extent of the rattlesnake business in certain areas, Crimmins (1927b, p. 23; see also Duncan, 1945, p. 168) reported that from June 1 to September 1, at Floresville, 30 miles southeast of San Antonio, Texas, H. C. Blanchard assembled and shipped 3,500 western diamonds weighing 7,500 pounds,

---

[6] The regulations read (1953) as follows: "Snakes and other reptiles must be in wooden boxes securely nailed or screwed together and material not less than ⅜ in. in thickness when measurements do not exceed 24 in. in length and 12 in. in width and height, or 30 lb. weight per container. Material not less than ⅞ in. in thickness to be used for boxes of greater dimensions or weights. Boxes in which shipped shall have all ventilating holes fully covered by wire cloth of not less than 16 mesh per inch, securely stapled about openings. Each snake shall be placed in a cloth bag inside the wooden container. All boxes in which snakes are shipped must be distinctly marked to indicate if poisonous or harmless. *Exception:* Harmless or non-poisonous snakes will be accepted when enclosed in strong bags or sacks and placed in one gallon tin cans, with lid securely wired to the top of the cans, and when plainly marked to indicate contents of can as harmless or non-poisonous snakes."

and other operators added a third to this total. Most of the field men were said to be Mexicans, and the price 35 cents a pound. Later the price was said to have advanced to 50 cents per pound.

In San Diego County, in the early spring when the red diamonds (*C. r. ruber*) congregate around the granite outcrops, one occasionally hears of lots of 100 to 150 being collected, and adults bringing $1.00 each, wholesale. As this is a large, handsome species, restricted to a relatively small area in southern California and less accessible Baja California, the price does not seem unreasonable. Maloney (1945, p. 30) stated that dealers paid $2.00 to $5.00 each to field collectors for eastern diamondbacks in Florida. Snyder (1949, p. 4) lists the following prices as paid by E. Ross Allen for eastern diamondbacks: babies 25 cents; one and a half feet, 40 cents; two feet, 75 cents; three feet, $1.00; four feet, $5.00; five feet, $6.00; six feet, $8.00; seven feet, $25.00; eight feet, $200.00, with no claimants for the latter offer. Hylander (1951, p. 13) wrote that Allen was offering $1.00 per foot in that year. Bashaw (1946, p. 11) mentioned a price of 10 cents per foot, certainly an underquotation. In the Southwest, some dealers, especially those who operate roadside snake pits, are their own collectors. They go out before sun-up and track down the rattlers before they have gone underground for the day.

I myself have been offered rattlers in large quantities at prices ranging from 15 to 35 cents per pound. But it is a quite different matter to secure them when one has need of snakes from a particular place to settle some taxonomic question. Under such circumstances I have advertised in the local newspapers, offering $5.00 per snake; and, although what I sought were small, easily captured rattlers, reported to be fairly common round about, none was forthcoming. This is a reminder of the fact that, in some newspaper accounts of the type that encourage amateurs to engage in the rattlesnake business, a rattlesnake is a rattlesnake; there is no indication of the differences in rarity and value between species. To many a scientific institution some small rattler such as a ridgenose (*C. willardi*) would be worth more than any big diamondback; and some of the little rattlers found in out-of-the-way places in Mexico would be much greater prizes than any common rattler having 50 times their bulk. This may be less the result of any real rarity of the little snakes than the difficulty of finding someone willing to collect them in their remote habitats.

Rattlers can be bought from dealers either "hot" or "fixed," the latter term meaning with the fangs removed. Fixed snakes are generally purchased by carnivals or snake pits where the show, as staged, involves handling the rattlers (Bevan, 1932c, p. 93). Fixed snakes are not wanted by zoos, since the mouth is likely to be injured, and fangless rattlers are short-lived. Some dealers charge extra for fixing—about 50 cents per snake—whereas others include this in the regular price.

The safety procured by fixing depends upon the method used. The commercial dealers usually jerk out or break off the functional fangs. This renders the rattlers fairly safe for a few days or weeks at best, that is, until the next replacement fangs grow into place, after which the removal must be repeated, or the snake is hot.

Simple fang removal is not at all difficult. The snake is caused to open its mouth, the fang sheaths are slipped up, and the fangs are broken off with snips or tweezers as close to their bases as possible. The points of the next reserve set usually protrude from the sheath, and these also may be easily pulled out. If one fears to handle a snake for fang removal, its functional fangs may some-times be drawn by causing it to strike a piece of leather or cloth, which is then jerked while the fangs are still entangled in it (Crèvecoeur, 1783, p. 100; Coues and Yarrow, 1878, p. 269). However, this is not a trustworthy scheme.

The removal of the magazine of reserve fangs is possible, but requires the skill of a delicate operation and is seldom attempted; besides, a snake so treated would usually survive only a short time. The suturing of the duct between the venom gland and fang is also possible but may well have fatal results. Jaros (1940, p. 49) has suggested electrocoagulation of the venom duct. Tait (1938, p. 10) has demon-strated the feasibility of removing the venom glands in their entirety, although the shape of the snake's head was changed by so doing. According to S. Pope (1919, p. 50), some snake handlers slit the venom glands and swab them out twice monthly with hydrogen peroxide. But none of these delicate operations is attempted by the commercial dealers. The user in the pit show who buys the fixed snakes must depend on repeated fang removals as the replacements grow in, or an even more frequent venom milking, which decreases but does not obviate the risk. Stanley (1897, p. 28) claimed to have been bitten hundreds of times without ill effects, as he kept his rattlers depleted of venom by letting them bite rubber balls. Webber (1951, p. 13) believed (incorrectly) that most of the rattlers in snake shows were not defanged, but were merely docile from much handling.

The trade in rattlesnakes is a rather ancient one. John Evelyn, in his *Diary*, mentions having seen live rattlers in England as early as 1657 (Evelyn, 1901, vol. 1, p. 318; Flower, 1925, p. 976). Tyson had one available for dissection in 1683 (p. 26). Hockley (1903–4, pp. 26, 28, 36, 39), writing in 1742, mentions several rattlesnake shipments abroad. He bought them from Indian traders and had difficulty filling the demand. Some were sent "dryed"; it is not clear whether many were shipped alive. Buckingham (1842, vol. 2, p. 178) mentions a dealer who collected over 300 rattlers in South Carolina for shipment to Europe. Prince Wied-Neuwied (1843, p. 43) in his Western travels in 1832 wrote that he bought a rattler from the landlady of a public house for $2.50.

SNAKE SHOWS

Snake exhibitions are of several kinds: the varied exhibits at the zoo; the life-like groups at the natural history museums; and the traveling pits of the circus side-shows, the carnivals, and the county-fair circuits. The latter are probably the largest customers of the live-snake dealers whose operations I have discussed. These shows, to attract a crowd, often incorporate various sensational features beyond a mere handling of the snakes, such as "swallowing" small snakes, drink-ing venom, or allowing rattlers to bite the pit keeper. Some of the snake-show operators have had interesting experiences with rattlesnakes and have a consider-able knowledge of their habits, but it is difficult to learn anything of value from them. For the spirit of showmanship eventually gets the upper hand, and they will not, or cannot, differentiate what they have seen from what they think the listener would like to hear, or what would most amaze or shock him.

Various methods of deceit are practiced in these shows. According to Bevan (1932c, p. 93) most rattlers in pits of the traveling type are either fixed, or have had the venom pressed out of the glands before each show. Rattlers that still retain their fangs are referred to as "hot," "green," or "unfixed." Stillwell (1939, p. 14) tells us that the man in the pit is a "geke," while a snake swallower is a "glommer." Glommers, so he says, are former glass blowers, whose throat pockets are so stretched that it is easy for them to retain a small snake there during the act.[7] When a geke shows spots of blood on his wrist or arm, where a rattlesnake has bitten him, it is the rattler's short solid teeth that have drawn the blood, for the fangs are absent. It is said that there are laws in some states requiring the removal of the fangs of rattlers on exhibition, but I suspect that most of these may be like the well-known California law protecting king snakes, which is really a mythical one, not to be found in the statutes.

While on the subject of snake shows, it may be stated that fang removal and other methods of deception by snake charmers are ancient practices. Pulling out the fangs is mentioned by Pliny (1855–57, vol. 3, p. 38; book xi, chap. 62), writing in the first century A.D. Owen (1742, p. 28) and Clavigero (1937, p. 389) repeat Galen's statement, made about A.D. 165, to the effect that the fang apertures were plugged with wax. Discussions of fang removal, as a common practice of the Hindu snake charmers, will be found in Russell (1796–1801, p. 2), Simson (1886, p. 242), Fayrer (1892, p. 97), Elliot (1900, p. 220), and Bogert (1945, p. 2), Mosauer (1931, p. 16) maintained that the snake charmers of northern Africa did not defang their snakes, but depended on their knowledge of snake psychology for safety. Tennent (1860, vol. 1, p. 192) thought the charmers of Ceylon depended on the natural timidity of their snakes.

What with fang removal, lack of food, and generally rough treatment, rattlesnakes in pit shows are usually short-lived. The operator takes this wastage as a routine expense; he has no facilities wherewith to feed the snakes, nor would they be likely to accept food under the conditions in which they are kept. Standing orders calling for periodical shipments of fresh snakes are usually placed with the suppliers, and it is by this means that a presentable exhibit is maintained.

One special fake occasionally seen in snake shows is the horned rattler. This creature—not to be confused with the true horned rattlesnake, or sidewinder (*C. cerastes*), which has a short hornlike scale-covered projection above each eye—has a vertical horn in the center of the head (G.A.I., 1908, p. 972; Bevan, 1926, p. 412). Actually, the snake is a western diamond, and the horn a rooster's spur held in place by the skin of the snake's head that has been slit and allowed to grow around the base of the spur. Or it may be attached with collodion. At one time these reptilian unicorns sold for $10; I presume they are now higher. Benton (1945, p. 80) and Erwin (1946, p. 28) mention having seen horned rattlesnakes in their native habitats, in Arizona and Alabama, respectively. I am at a loss to know whether these are tongue-in-cheek accounts or not; maybe I am the victim. At any rate, the single-horned rattler is a made-to-order affair. This deception was practiced in Texas in pioneer days (Kelsey, 1952, p. 164). In Egypt, it was undertaken with vipers 200 years ago (Anderson, 1895, p. 243). Maybe such creatures were what Herodotus had seen when he mentioned little snakes with a single horn (Rawlinson, 1942, vol. 1, p. 291).

A type of snake show whose popularity has lately caused it to multiply is the roadside pit, like the motor court, a product of new modes of travel. These

---

[7] Glommers are also small snakes of a size suitable for swallowing. Another place of concealment is under the tongue.

exhibits vary greatly in size and excellence; many are well worth stopping to see, particularly those that specialize on the local fauna. Lectures are sometimes given. Usually the pits are adjuncts of such other activities as gas stations, cold-drink stands, and the like. Both the snakes and their by-products, such as skins, rattles, and vertebrae necklaces, may be offered for sale; in fact, some pits are merely the showcases of a general reptile business. Often the shelves around the cages are decorated with jars filled with fangs, dried venom, and rattles, the results of past extensive operations. The advertisements of these shows take the form of roadside billboards with such legends as "World's Largest Rattlesnake," "Reptile Exhibit 10 Miles," or, "Stop at Smith's for Rattlesnakes and Gas." Generally the intervals between signs become shorter as the exhibit is approached, and the signs themselves more startling. Shows of this kind are especially numerous along the southern border, from Texas to California, although by no means restricted to this section. But it is here that the signs are a most conspicuous part of the barren desert landscape.

In recent years, snake lectures have become sufficiently popular, particularly at high schools, to encourage some naturalists to undertake lecture tours as a means of livelihood. With a few live specimens, some sample by-products, and either stills or movies, a program both instructive and entertaining can be staged.

However unnecessary it would seem, I judge from inquiries I have received that I should warn parents not to permit their children to keep live rattlesnakes in their vivariums. Almost anything that is to be learned from observations of captive snakes can be learned as well from the harmless species. Rattlesnakes are dangerous creatures; familiarity breeds contempt; and, to judge from an accumulation of newspaper clippings, even the most experienced reptile-house keepers and snake-show demonstrators occasionally have cause to regret a single moment of carelessness. There is a streak of exhibitionism in every boy, and it should not be encouraged by his being allowed to show off to his friends his fearlessness with rattlesnakes.

Rattlesnakes sometimes provide the basis for a community attraction having the nature of a fiesta. Such an event can usually count on more free publicity than many a more entertaining celebration. For example, there are well-advertised gladiatorial combats between rattlesnakes and black snakes, rattlesnakes and king snakes, or rattlesnakes and Gila monsters. These generally end in an endeavor of all combatants to escape, after showing a decided lack of interest in each other. The humane societies are surreptitiously warned in advance, in the hope that they will publicize the affair by trying to stop it.

Another entry in the attempt to draw the wandering motorist is the rattlesnake derby. The contestants are released in the center of a 500-foot ring and then roused into motion by an electric shock. Without repeated urging they will not move far from the starting point. The audience is attracted by the hope that the rattlers will streak for the other side of the ring and scare the daylights out of their fellow observers. But they never do. One of the early derbies was that held at McCamey, Texas, in April, 1936. It became an annual event and remained so for a while at least. (*American Guide Series, Texas,* 1940, p. 505).

The Hopi snake dance has been described elsewhere (p. 1113). There is now staged annually at Prescott, Arizona, a so-called Smoki snake dance, supposed to be a replica of the ancient Hopi rite, for the purpose of perpetuating the details and spirit of the original Indian ceremony. The performers are white men, and Arizona bull snakes (*Pituophis catenifer affinis*), instead of rattlers, are held in the mouths of the dancers (Arnold, 1933, p. 4; Stanley, 1947, p. 8). This fiesta started about 1920, with a strong publicity-promotion odor (Hall, 1938, p. 1). Today it may have a more serious objective, or, at least, so it is claimed (Henderson, 1952, p. 42). I have mentioned elsewhere (p. 997) the annual rattlesnake roundups conducted at Okeene and Waynoka, Oklahoma, Junior Chamber of Commerce affairs that attract many visitors.

Berkeley, California, has an ordinance, in effect since 1940, that controls the keeping or transporting of venomous snakes within the city limits. It requires a permit to exhibit venomous snakes or keep them for experimental purposes, and they may be transported only in approved containers. Suitable penalties, involving fines and/or imprisonment, are provided for infractions.

In connection with a television show in which live rattlesnakes were used, it was observed that the liability insurance carrier required signs to be placed at all entrances to the studio, warning of the presence of the rattlers. Some life insurance policies require the payment of an extra premium by those engaged in handling venomous snakes, the penalty of a hazardous occupation.

VENOM

The venom market is another phase of rattlesnake utilization, the possibilities of which have been overstated in newspaper and magazine articles. Relatively high prices are reported paid for all venom offered; as one popular writer put it, large snakes yield a dollar or more at each milking. During World War II, which did lead to a temporarily increased demand, it was generally rumored that the "government" had made a firm offer of $50 per gram for dried venom. I know of no such price paid by any branch of the Federal Government, nor, indeed, of any regular demand. But the rumor persists; and inquiries concerning the big profits to be made in this phase of snake farming continue to reach the herpetological departments of our scientific institutions.

I have discussed elsewhere the purification and use of snake venoms (p. 746). Since it is difficult and expensive to feed rattlers in captivity, and their venom yield declines markedly with repeated milkings, rattlesnake farms, as such, would not be commercially feasible, even were there a steady demand for venom. Only the rarest kinds of snakes are worth milking more than once or twice; and what production of venom there may be depends on a continuous acquisition of fresh specimens, which, after milking, are used for other purposes. Also, although dried poison, as a curiosity, is easy to produce, to prepare venom suitable for scientific purposes, such as the production of antivenin, introduces complications. First, it is necessary to segregate the venoms of the several species milked, and the accurate identification of rattlesnakes, in areas inhabited by more than one species, requires some study and experience. Secondly, although the actual removal of venom from the snakes is simple, its purification is difficult and requires expensive apparatus (p. 750). It is obvious that if a market be available, venom production is most likely to be profitable when combined with the sale of live snakes or their by-products, such as rattlesnake meat and skins. An all-round operation of this kind is described by Anon. (1933b, p. 3) and by Snyder (1949, p. 3). Those who have snake shows can stage an added attraction by milking the snakes in public, and this is sometimes done, though the venom may not be used for scientific purposes, as is usually claimed.

During World War II, when large numbers of men were in training amid wild and rough country along our southern border, the antivenin requirements increased, and venoms from certain particular species of rattlesnakes were in actual demand at $15 to $25 per gram, dried. The Philadelphia and San Diego zoos, as well as several other scientific and commercial organizations, co-operated in supplying the need. Unfortunately, an inquiry for rattlesnakes of one particular species reached the newspapers, resulting in a flood of inquiries from would-be operators of snake farms, and the snakes continued to accumulate in back-yard pens long after the need had been met. At present the demand for venom is once more sporadic, with an occasional requirement for antivenin production, or for experimental medicinal work.

Recently, one Florida dealer advertised venom at the following prices per gram: *C. adamanteus,* $10; *C. atrox,* $12; *C. h. horridus,* $20; *C. v. viridis,* $25; *S. miliarius,* $40. These prices reflect relative yields, rather than rarity, since all the snakes listed are fairly common in some localities. Coral snake venom was quoted at $1.00 per milligram. This snake has a very small yield, and, because of the short fangs, it is difficult to collect the venom in the container. This dealer states that venom is produced only from fresh specimens; no snakes are remilked. In order that he may guarantee both the species derivation and the purity of the venom sold, he purchases no venom from outsiders, a point of interest to prospective free-lance producers.

RATTLESNAKE OIL AND FAT

Rattlesnakes have long been used as the bases of various medicinal preparations. Some of these originated with the Indians and have been discussed in chapter 16 (p. 1163); others were employed, and in fact still are, by the white population, especially in rural areas. These I have treated in chapter 18 under folklore (p. 1215). These pharmaceutical uses do not produce any regular demand for snakes. Aside from an occasional purchase of rattlesnakes by the Chinese in America, the only medicinal use today, involving any market of commercial significance, is for the production of rattlesnake oil. It is, therefore, appropriate that this preparation be discussed in this chapter on commercial utilization.

The use of snake oil is neither new nor confined to the Americas. It was, in fact, both ancient and widespread; it was a well-known remedy long before rattlesnakes had been brought to the attention of Europeans, viper oil being commonly recommended for the same afflictions for which rattlesnake oil was subsequently favored (e.g., Pliny, 1855–57, vol. 5, pp. 363, 396, 412, 435, 447, 457; book xxviii, chap. 77; book xxix, chaps. 21, 38; book xxx, chaps. 12, 23, 35; Topsell, 1608, pp. 34, 305; French, 1651, p. 99; Owen, 1742, p. 53).

As the Indians had applied rattlesnake oil in pre-Columbian times and were using it in the days of the explorers (see p. 1164), it was natural that the earliest descriptions of rattlesnakes should stress these beneficial properties, for the information of European physicians (e.g., Hernández, 1615, fol. 192ᵛ; 1628, p. 330;

Nieremberg, 1635, p. 269; Josselyn, 1672, p. 38; 1675, p. 114). Thus the colonists, with the precedent of the use of viper oil in their former homes, soon adopted rattlesnake oil as a sovereign remedy for various ills, particularly as an ointment or liniment to reduce stiffness or pain. No doubt the snake's fundamental lithe-ness led to the assumption, upon the part of primitive practitioners, that the creature's oil must contain the synthesis of its graceful flexibility which might, therefore, be transferred, at least in some degree, to a human user. It is a prin-ciple of primitive medicine that every animal and plant has at least some property beneficial to mankind, and that it is the duty of the scientist and physician to discover it. Rattlesnake oil, which was thought to be particularly penetrating—it was believed that it would go right through a man's hand—seemed to satisfy this requirement of an otherwise antisocial reptile.

These are some of the ills for which rattlesnake oil or fat has been used: To absorb tumors or swellings (Hernández, 1615, fol. 192^v; Dobrizhoffer, 1822, vol. 2, p. 290); for relief of frozen limbs, lameness caused by falls, bruises, aches, and sprains (Josselyn, 1672, p. 38; 1675, p. 114); pain and sprains (Kalm, 1752–53, p. 187); snake bite (Carver, 1778, p. 483); rattlesnake and mosquito bites (Lacépède, 1788–89, vol. 2, p. 412; Kerr's translation, 1802, vol. 4, p. 268); wounds (Dumont, 1753, p. 109; Bell, 1932, p. 212); rheumatic and other pains (Beauvois, 1799, p. 368); various diseases (Weld, 1855, p. 79); elephantiasis (Dugès, 1879, p. 17); rheumatism (Dumont, 1753, p. 109; Wilhelm, 1873, vol. 2, p. 353; Inger-soll, 1883, p. 43; Anon., 1894, p. 124; Herrick, 1953, p. 23); internally for hydro-phobia, and externally for ringworm, sties, sore eyes, rheumatism, and sprains (Anon., 1898, p. 159); sciatica (Bosc, 1803, p. 555; Griffith and Pidgeon, 1831, p. 344); toothache, by insertion of fat in the cavity (Dodson, 1932, p. 84); deafness (Surface, 1906, p. 195; Herrick, 1953, p. 23); goiter, deafness, croup, rheumatism (Thomas, 1954, p. 11); sciatica, rheumatism, arthritis, gout, lumbago, neuralgia (recent newspaper advertisement). In fairness to the authors I have listed, it should be stated that many expressed grave doubts and even definite disbelief in the value of this remedy for these ills; they were merely recording its pur-ported benefits, as I am doing.

Rattlesnake oil was one of the standard remedies sold by those primitive vaude-ville acts, the traveling medicine shows, often operating under such designa-tions as Blank, the internationally famous doctor, or Eaglefeather, the Indian medicine man, whose flaring torches lit the first theatrical performance ever seen by many a Western boy. Here we heard "the great soprano just come from Covent Garden," the guitar virtuoso from the Deep South, and witnessed the unexpected discomfiture of the comedian's straight man. Then followed the appearance of the great doctor himself at the tail of his wagon, and the rush of the shills in the audience to buy the almost—but never quite—last available bottle of snake oil. Who could deny his family this sovereign cure for every serious ill, when it cost only a dollar?

Clark Stanley (1897, p. 26) tells of graduating from a traveling show and set-tling down at the World's Fair in Chicago in 1893, where he killed rattlesnakes and prepared the oil in full view of his audience. Later the demand became so great that he was compelled to establish an Eastern factory for the manu-facture of his "Snake Oil Liniment," made from a combination of oils, "the principle [*sic*] oil being Rattle Snake Oil." It was advertised as a cure for stiff joints, bruises, sprains, rheumatism, inflammations, deformities (= arthritis), pains in the back, sciatica, neuralgia, headache, deafness, partial paralysis, lumbago, muscular weakness, toothache, sore throat, cold in the chest, frostbite, chilblains, cold feet, corns and calluses, and the bites of animals, insects, and reptiles. At 50 cents a bottle it was recommended for man or beast. They must have had powerful rattlers in those days. But overindulgence in the use of the oil might cause a man to become so "soople" that he could hardly stand (Thompson, 1916, p. 524, but writing as of 1811; Carmer, 1936, p. 316). Several years ago a fraud order was issued, under the food and drugs law, against a firm that claimed its rattlesnake oil would cure deafness.

Since colonial days, rattlesnake oil has had its place in regional folklore medicine. The following tabulation presents some appropriate references:

Area	Diseases treated	Reference
Ohio	Rheumatism	Bergen, 1899, p. 73
Louisiana	Rheumatism	Roberts, 1927, p. 167
Texas	Rheumatism, stiff joints	Woodhull, 1930, pp. 65, 68
Ozark Mountains	Rheumatism	Randolph, 1933, p. 3
Pennsylvania Germans	Many	Brendle and Unger, 1935, p. 200
Nebraska	Rheumatism	Black, 1935, p. 20
Tennessee	Earache	Redfield, 1937, p. 13; Odell, 1944, p. 3
Upper Rio Grande	Rheumatism, snake bite	Curtin, 1947, p. 15
Illinois	Rheumatism	Allison, 1950, p. 311
Catskill Mountains	Rheumatism	Evers, 1951, p. 110

Today, rattlesnake oil is principally used as a pain reliever for rheumatism, and as a liniment for circus performers, acrobats, and the like. From the frequent inquiries I receive as to places where it may be obtained, I judge it is still a popular home remedy. Usually rheumatism is given as the ill to be cured, both by those who seek it and those who are looking for outlets for its sale. Sometimes the inquiry does not reveal the purpose for which it is to be used, such as: "Where can I secure the pure rattlesnake oil that has not been adulterated? I want this oil for a very particular purpose and it must be pure. One ounce will be sufficient for my purpose."

In view of the stress put by advertisers on the purity of their product, the practice of adulteration must have long been prevalent. W. A. Bevan in his column "Snake Lore" in *Outdoor Life* stated repeatedly (vol. 69, no. 3, p. 55; vol. 72, no. 2, p. 59; vol. 73, no. 2, p. 61) that most commercial rattlesnake oils were only liniments containing enough of the genuine article to legalize mail shipments; and that snake oil is, at best, only a lubricant having no greater efficacy than goose grease or any other animal fat.

Root and Connelley (1901, p. 579) relate that a customer entered a store in Atchison, Kansas, in the early 1860's and asked for half a pint of rattlesnake oil. After the satisfied buyer had left with his purchase, the druggist remarked that prescriptions for rattlesnake oil, bear oil, and lard oil were all filled from the same barrel, so all customers' requirements were easily satisfied. Anon. (1885, p. 4) gave a humorous account of the rattlesnake oil trade in Pennsylvania. Every timber raft carried a barrel of it to market.

Rattlesnake oil has also nonmedicinal uses. Kemsley (1928, p. 55) says that snake oil makes an excellent gun oil that will not clog or run. One of my correspondents mentions the same application:

Many years ago, two of my cousins had a good business selling rattlesnake oil to a gunsmith in Chicago at $5.00 an ounce. Rattlesnakes were plentiful then in Montana, and they were killed, skinned, and the fat rendered for oil. Many of the rattlesnakes there were 36 inches in length and produced considerable quantities of oil. *W. G. Willson, Los Angeles, Calif.*

Rattlesnake oil is rendered like any other oil derived from animal fat. If the snakes are freshly caught and healthy, they have a rather plentiful supply of fat that lies within the body cavity along the sides in the form of white flakes or lobes. It is not difficult to separate the fat from the flesh. The hibernating season in the fall is the best time in which to catch the rattlers, because they are both congregated and fattest at that time.

Anon. (1898, p. 160) suggests the following method of preparing the oil: Stretch a piece of muslin over the mouth of a jar and spread the fat over the cloth. Place it in the sun and the oil will drain into the jar as it is rendered by the sun. It has the consistency of machine oil and is almost clear. A large snake yields 2½ ounces of fat. Kemsley (1928, p. 56) suggests the same method, but adds that the oil may be clarified by dropping in lead shavings or shot, after which it is drained off the deposit. Dorsch (1929, p. 3) says the oil may be prepared by boiling the entire bodies and skimming the rendered grease from the surface.

Kalm (1752–53, p. 187) says it is essential that the oil be taken from a snake that has not bitten itself. Anon. and Kemsley, carrying out the same thought, give the following prescription for determining whether the oil is safe or is poisoned: Drop a little oil in a glass of milk; if it floats in a single film it is good, but if it separates into beads and the milk gathers into flakes, then it has been made dangerous by the poison and should be discarded. This is evidently a widespread folk belief. As a matter of fact, if the oil had any beneficial qualities, they would not be interfered with by venom, whose dangerous properties would, in any case, be destroyed by the boiling.

The oil that I have seen is slightly cloudy. The odor was neither pungent nor unpleasant. Pollard and McLaughlin (1950, p. 393) and Pollard and Young (1952, p. 135) have tabulated the physical characteristics of real *viridis, adamanteus,* and *atrox* oils. About 70 per cent of the material of the fat lobes is oil. The specific gravity is approximately 0.915.

As to prices, the following have been mentioned: Ingersoll (1833a, p. 43; 1884b, p. 104) $4.00 per ounce; Davis (1889, p. 183) $1.25 to $1.50 per ounce; Surface (1906, p. 195) $4.00 per pound; Anon. (1909, p. 32) $3.00 per ounce; Curtin (1947, p. 15) $1.00 per ounce. Bevan stated in 1924 (*Outdoor Life,* vol. 3, p. 233) that a certain firm selling snake oil would give $2.00 to $3.00 a quart for the rendered fat. Present quotations are highly variable. One recent newspaper advertisement quoted pure oil at $16.00 per ounce. A well-known dealer in snakes and accessories lists rattlesnake oil at $1.00 per ounce or 50 cents in 12-ounce lots.

Unfortunately, when some enterprising reporter comes upon a snake collector who has taken up snake-oil preparation in a small way, he finds a descriptive article acceptable to his editor, and it is even likely to be picked up by the wire services. Then once more the zoos and natural history museums are deluged with inquires concerning the supposed profits to be had in this modern manifestation of folklore medicine. I should say that such a business could be profitable only if carried on in conjunction with the sale of other rattlesnake by-products such as meat or skins. The demand is too fluctuating and uncertain to provide a steady income.

RATTLESNAKE FLESH AS FOOD

As I have pointed out elsewhere (p. 1185), the Indians ate rattlesnakes to some extent, either as a matter of necessity, when food was scarce, or in conformity with some tribal ceremony. Similarly, today, rattlers sometimes may save some hunter or trapper stranded in the wild without food; or serve as a sensational course in some back-yard barbecue. But they are not to be deemed an important food source. Although the flesh is quite palatable, only a relatively small quantity is secured, even from a large snake.

The only serious use of rattlesnake flesh has been as an emergency ration, a not infrequent occurrence at the time of the covered-wagon and other westward movements. For rattlesnakes dwell in barren places; they are easily hunted down and killed, even by people weakened by starvation, and therefore they were sometimes the only available food for those caught in precarious situations.

Beverly (1705, p. 65) was one of the first to report eating a rattlesnake. Joutel (1714, [p. 105 of 1906 ed.]) says that La Salle's men ate rattlesnakes and found them satisfactory. Timberlake (1765, p. 45), another early traveler among the Indians, tells us that, having eaten a rattlesnake through want of other provisions, he subsequently ate several by choice. Chittenden (1935, p. 827), writing of the fur trappers in the West, said they occasionally ate rattlesnake by compulsion; he thought it would rank with other flesh for palatability, were the animal itself not so repulsive. Forbes (1821, p. 170) mentions rattlers as being eaten by hungry travelers. Howe (1847, p. 477) recounts an incident that occurred in 1789, when men lost in a wood ate a rattler and came to prefer it to salt meat. George C. Yount (in Camp, 1923, p. 27) tells of a hunter, wounded to immobility by a grizzly and deserted by his companions, who was saved by a rattlesnake that came within his reach. He subsisted on its meat until be gained strength enough to crawl to a settlement. Ruxton (1849, p. 144) mentions two hunters, short of ammunition, who prepared to eat a rattler, but were saved from having to do so by the timely arrival of another party. Bieber (1937, p. 40), writing of the road to California as it was in '49, says "Intense heat, a scarcity of water, dusty trails, and a lack of provisions resulted in severe physical handicaps for a number of outlanders, some being forced to eat horse flesh, mule flesh, and even snakes to avoid starvation." C. C. Cox (in Martin, 1926, p. 212) tells, in his diary, of one party in 1849 "reduced to the necessity of eating several of their mules and horses, and many snakes." Tex Sullivan told Fenley (1940, p. 4) that in his boyhood days they ate rattlers in hard times. Other references to rattlesnakes as food are: Bosc, 1803, p. 555; Maude, 1826, p. 69; Coke, 1852, p. 142; Anon., 1858a, p. 325; Perrine, 1928, p. 195; and Tixier, 1940, p. 77.

Rattlesnakes were sometimes eaten as a cure for disease (e.g., Mordecai, 1860, p. 66), a prescription no doubt resulting from contacts with Indians, who indulged in this practice in various parts of the country (p. 1163). More recently, this remedy has been attributed to the Chinese on the West Coast. Also, one of my correspondents wrote before the war:

> Rattlers are relished as food by the Japanese; I have seen them making drives for them near Mono Hot Springs, Fresno County. *Philip B. Lord, U. S. Forest Service, Susanville, Calif.*

Whenever rattlesnakes have been eaten, it has been agreed that the meat is not only palatable, but definitely appetizing. Hernández (1615, fol. 192^v; Nieremberg, 1635, p. 269) said that the Indians preferred them to poultry, and there have been few dissenting opinions since. Anburey (1789, p. 228) said he liked rattlesnakes better than eels; also, they made a fine, rich soup. Cist (1845, p. 18) enjoyed rattlers more than opossum or rabbit. Dugès (1879, p. 17) thought the flesh much like frog's legs; however, he preferred iguana. Rattlesnake meat has been likened to a number of different kinds with which we are more familiar, the following being some of the similes applied: Kearsley (1766, p. 75)—veal or chicken; Faux (1823, pp. 249, 286), Audubon (1827, p. 28), Pollock (1911, p. 156), and Gordon (1936, p. 95)—chicken; Domenech (1858, p. 49)—frog or tortoise; Gabb (1869, p. 109)—eels, but less greasy; Mitchell (1903, p. 41) and Attwater (1928, p. 6)—quail; Smith and Smith (1927, p. 123)—fish; Benjamin (1941, p. 53)—chicken or quail; and Hogan (1950, p. 9)—frog's legs. Two of my own correspondents likened the meat to frog's legs. Some, with whom I talked, thought it more like canned tuna. Personally, I have found it more like rabbit than chicken. Much, of course, depends on the method of preparation.

Cooked rattlesnake has been given several euphonious names. Anon. (1839, p. 47) in *Penny Magazine* claimed it was on the menu of a frontier inn at Kaskaskia, Illinois, as "musical jack" (see also Martin, 1851?, p. 276; Anon., 1858a, p. 325; Wall, 1906, p. 376). Davis (1868, p. 300) said that when eaten on the plains it was called "prairie eel." Anon. (1907, p. 337; Masterson, 1946, p. 183) tells of a traveler in colonial days who was fed "cold eel," which he hugely enjoyed. But, upon being told on the following day what it was he had eaten, he became violently ill, lost his hair, and subsequently sued the landlord, recovering 20,000 pounds of tobacco as damages.

The newspapers lately contained an account of a hoax in which rattler was served as chicken. There were several psychological casualties when the source of the "chicken" was later divulged. Even without practical jokes of this kind, rattlesnake lunches are usually good for dog-day newspaper publicity, which, too often, is their sole purpose, for seldom is enough rattlesnake meat available to give each guest more than a mouthful. Anderson (1951, p. 6) mentions a yearly rattlesnake dinner at Allentown, Pennsylvania. Sometimes the meal is an advertisement for some wayside snake exhibit (Davenport, 1943, p. 121). The Sunday-supplement stories of rattlesnakes raised for food are just stories, for it is both cheaper and easier to catch full-grown, wild snakes.

Rattlesnake may be cooked in a manner similar to rabbit or chicken. It should be soaked in brine overnight before cooking. It may be fried, baked, or served as a stew or soup. It is tasty fried with bread crumbs. Dorris (1944, p. 16) gives the following recipe for rattlesnake steaks: Required to serve six persons—five pounds of rattlesnake meat, flour, salt and pepper, Louisiana red hot, fat, and vinegar. Use only large, healthy rattlesnakes (three to five pounds live weight preferred).[8] Decapitate with an ax about six inches behind the head. Remove the skin and viscera, cut the remaining body section diagonally into one-inch thick steaks. Soak the steaks in vinegar for 10 minutes, remove and sprinkle with hot sauce, salt and pepper, roll in flour. Fry in deep fat. Serve immediately. Other recipes will be found in Hogan (1950, p. 9) and in Hutchison and McCain (1950, p. 1), the latter solely of humorous intent.

Articles on eating rattlesnakes often caution against eating one that has bitten itself, which, so it is said, would render the meat highly dangerous. Among those mentioning this precaution have been Kalm (1752–53, p. 187), Lacépède (1788–89, vol. 2, p. 413), Bartram (1791, p. 225), Cox (1832, p. 206), and Morton (1938, p. 212). Since the poisonous quality of snake venom is destroyed by heat, this precaution may be ignored. However, even though the bite involves no danger, the bitten part is best cut out, just as one cuts away the damaged meat in an animal that has been shot. Dugès (1879, p. 20) got a big rattler to bite itself three or four times. It lived 19 hours and seemed unhurt. He then cooked and ate it without ill effect.

If about 50 per cent of a rattlesnake is assumed to be waste, the following quantities of meat should be available from large snakes: length 4 feet, 1 pound; 5 feet, 2½ pounds; 6 feet, 4½ pounds; 7 feet, 7½ pounds; 8 feet, 11½ pounds. However, no one should be so foolish as to kill such a rarity as a seven- or eight-foot snake for food; it would be better saved for a zoo or snake show.

"Ransacker" (1899, p. 264) states that a cat and dog refused to eat cooked Pacific rattlesnake. This is difficult to believe, unless, by the use of the skin or some such method, they were deliberately given the opportunity to connect the meat with the snake. Even then it is hard to credit, since wildcats and coyotes are known to prey on rattlesnakes.

George K. End established a rattlesnake canning business in Arcadia, Florida, in 1931. The product, advertised as "genuine diamondback rattlesnake with supreme sauce" was given much publicity because of its sensational implications, and enjoyed quite a vogue as a fad. Selling at $1.25 for a five-ounce can, it could hardly fall in the category of a grocery staple. Benjamin (1941, p. 53) stated that 15,000 cans were sold in the previous year; 2,500 diamondbacks were canned, which would give a yield of somewhat less than two pounds of meat per snake. Fifty people were said to be employed as hunters and canners. The by-products were skins, rattles, venom, and oil. Other references mentioning the cannery are Duncan (1945, p. 168), DeLys (1948, p. 71), Clark (1948, p. 98), and Snyder (1949, p. 16).

End was subsequently bitten by a rattler and died. The business was purchased by Ross Allen of Silver Springs, Florida, who has continued the sale of canned rattlesnake meat. In keeping with the prices of other food items, the price has been advanced and is now $1.50 per can. I was informed by Mr. Allen that in 1946, sales continued at the rate of 15,000 cans per year.

During World War II, when many youngsters were in training in Texas camps,

---

[8] Snakes of this large size are usually obtainable only in a few species (*adamanteus, atrox,* and *atricaudatus*) in the southern United States.

it was said that the roadside stands catering to servicemen made a specialty of "rattleburgers." This invited the usual newspaper publicity, and fears were expressed that the rattlesnakes might be exterminated.

SKIN PRODUCTS

Rattlesnake skins, like those of many other snakes, because of their beauty of color and pattern, have long served for various ornamental purposes. Only their relative fragility and small size have prevented their wider use where ornamental leather is required, for no snake is more decorative than such rattlers as the southwestern speckled rattler (*C. m. pyrrhus*) or the northern blacktail (*C. m. molossus*). With improved tanning methods and better distribution, rattlesnake-skin products may yet be developed beyond the stage of mere curiosities. Such has already been the history of other reptile leathers, the recent commercial exploitation of which has been described by Anon. (1928, p. 1), Gershenfeld (1930, p. 209), Lloyd *et al.* (1933, p. 1), and Anon. (1948b, p. 4). Before World War II, more than 4½ million reptile skins were shipped annually from India and the Netherlands East Indies. However, a comparable demand for rattlesnake skins is not to be expected, since their leather is in smaller sections and is thinner than that of the larger tropical reptiles, whether snakes or lizards. I was advised by a large tannery, handling some of the foreign reptile skins in quantities of 5,000 to 10,000 skins at a time, that rattlesnake skins, obtainable only in lots of 500 to 1,000 at a time, were not quantitatively attractive for a really commercial development, comparable with some of the more abundant species.

The use of rattlesnake skins for ornamentation is an old one; I have told elsewhere (p. 1175) how the Indians employed them, when not prevented by taboos. Kalm (1752–53, p. 188) describes their use as scabbards for swords and bayonets. Audubon (1827, p. 28) mentions rattler-skin shoes, and Chittenden (1935, p. 827) the ornaments with which the fur trappers adorned themselves in the pioneer days. Later, rattlesnake-skin belts and hatbands were standard equipment for the cowboys.

There has been much improvement lately in skin preparation, and it is a far cry from the stiff, parchmentlike skins of those days to the soft leathers of the finished products today. It is to be hoped that the wearing qualities are equally improved. Formerly, one dried a skin by tacking it, flesh side out, to the barn door, scraping it, and applying salt or alum. To prove that the snake was a big one the skin was usually overstretched; the central areas of the scales flaked off, and fading was the rule. Better methods are now recommended.

Bevan (1933b, p. 61) answered an inquiry about curing a snake-hide trophy as follows:

> There are many different tanning formulae with many variations of each to suit different skins. Tanning is an art which can be learned only through experience and I hesitate to advise you to start on a skin you particularly wish to keep. You can experiment by placing a snake skin in a solution of two ounces of sulphuric acid to a gallon of water with a couple of handfuls of salt. Leave the skin in the solution for five or six days, stirring it daily, then place it in a strong solution of baking soda and water until all the acid is out as indicated when bubbles cease to come out of the solution. The skin should be dried by laying it flat between two layers of sawdust. Before tanning, all the flesh should be removed by carefully scraping toward the tail, taking care not to stretch the skin at all times. The skin will be the softer for working over a beam as it dries.

The dried skin without tanning will keep indefinitely and can be sewed on an old belt. The skin itself will not do for a belt....

Acid-tanned skins are apt to disintegrate in a few years and I would not advise anyone to start on snake skins without a fair knowledge of and some experience with different tanning formulae.

Another formula is one used by Mr. Albert E. Ball of Los Angeles, who has courteously permitted me to reprint it here. The samples that I have seen were soft, pliable, and unfaded. The instructions follow:

Use a skin that has never been dried. If it has been salted, it must be washed salt-free. Squeeze most of the water out, and with the scale side down, spread the skin out on a board but do not stretch it. It is not always necessary to tack the skin down, but tacking will prevent curling of the edges. Apply glycerine (USP) generously to the flesh side and spread it with your fingers or a small brush. After an hour or so you will notice that the skin is becoming somewhat dry in spots. Apply more glycerine to keep it wet. Repeat this operation as long as the skin shows signs of drying. The intervals required to absorb the glycerine will become progressively longer and finally the skin will take no more. This will require one night or more. Soak up the excess glycerine with a soft cloth or tissue, and wash the skin very lightly with a small quantity of water. Allow it to drain five or ten minutes and soak up the excess water as before. Now it must be allowed to dry thoroughly, over at least one night. Then the skin may be slightly "tacky" to the touch but should not feel oily. Sprinkle with talcum powder.

Other tanning formulas for snake skins are given by Kemsley (1928, p. 55), McClary (1939b, p. 31), Decker (1936, p. 72; 1949, p. 140), Pratt (1942, p. 24), Hillcourt (1950, p. 161), and Sibley (1951, p. 47). Various up-to-date processes will be found in taxidermists' manuals. Anyone with a skin he particularly prizes as a trophy should place it in the hands of an experienced taxidermist. Such a skin should be mounted on a sheepskin or other suitable backing. Some preparators will tan snake skins for 50 cents per foot; others will furnish tanned skins at from 50 cents to $2.25 per foot, depending on width and rarity.

Although the sale of rattlesnake-leather devices is increasing, there is no ready market for skins, since the producers have their own sources of supply. Because of their size and availability in quantity, eastern and western diamondbacks (*C. adamanteus* and *C. atrox*) are most often used. Smaller species yield skins both too small and too thin to be serviceable, although for a few purposes, where there is an adequate backing, as in a belt, such highly colorful species as the speckled rattlesnake (*C. m. pyrrhus*)—gray, burnt orange, and pink; the Mojave rattler (*C. s. scutulatus*)—green; mountain specimens of the blacktail (*C. m. molossus*)—green and sulphur yellow; and the red diamond (*C. r. ruber*)—brick red, will be found both serviceable and highly ornamental. If one's own trophies of the hunt are to be shipped to a preparator for permanent processing, he should be consulted as to the method of preliminary preservation.

Leather products of rattlesnake skins are now available in great variety (Blanks, 1932, p. 30; Gordon, 1936, p. 95; Benjamin, 1941, p. 53; catalogues of Ross Allen), the most popular being belts, hatbands, wallets, billfolds, purses, handbags, key containers, comb cases, watch fobs, cigarette cases, and tobacco pouches. Articles of clothing such as sport jackets, caps, and neckties are made, but these are too showy to be considered more than fads.[9] On the other hand, snake-skin-covered

---

[9] Peter Gruber, known as Rattlesnake King in the Pennsylvania oil fields in the early days, wore a rattlesnake-skin suit that was said to have cost $650.00 (Herrick, 1953, p. 23). For a biographical note on Gruber see Thomas, 1954, p. 11.

coat buttons, and shoes for women, are quite attractive and appropriate. Some of the more bizarre articles fashioned from rattler skins have been holsters, gauntlet tops, lamp shades, book covers, and table runners. Souvenir knife cases, playing-card cases, and bookmarks are occasionally seen. Botkin (1949, p. 637) mentions the use of a rattlesnake skin to cover a banjo.

MISCELLANEOUS PRODUCTS

Miscellaneous rattlesnake products offered for sale by dealers include such things as skulls, rattles, and fangs. One merchant makes a specialty of vertebrae strung into necklaces; these are said to be used as charms to facilitate the teething of infants. Preserved specimens in alcohol or formalin are sold to educational institutions. Plaster casts are also prepared, as well as photographs and slides showing species differences and typical postures. Even tools for catching and handling rattlers are among the items listed by the larger dealers (e.g., King, 1941, p. 55; Ross Allen's spring price list, 1954, p. 7).

Popular accounts of the activities of some of the commercial dealers have been written by the following: Blanks, 1932, p. 30; Gordon, 1936, p. 34; *American Guide Series, Florida*, 1939, p. 521; Stillwell, 1939, p. 14; Duncan, 1939, p. 14, Fenley, 1940, p. 4; *American Guide Series, Oregon*, 1940, p. 328; Benjamin, 1941, p. 53; Maloney, 1945, p. 30; Valentine, 1947, p. 5; Snyder, 1949, p. 3; Hylander, 1951. While some of the firms or individuals mentioned are already out of business, the scope of their operations, with due allowance for some exaggeration, is interestingly described.

Rattlesnake rattles, always popular trophies when a snake has been killed, were extensively used for personal and home adornment in early days in the West. Sometimes the bead portiere of the better homes of the 1880's became a rattle portiere, a noisy affair in the slightest breeze. Pasted on boards to conform to suitable designs, rattles comprised a type of art so fantastic that it hasn't even yet returned to popularity, as have most of our bygone crudities. Menger (1913, p. 292) has illustrated and described a notable series of these pictures. They were exhibited in a Texas saloon at the turn of the century, and represented, in several panels under glass, a deer, an Indian brave and squaw, an eagle, and a number of insignia and appropriate mottoes. The deer panel was 5 feet 4 inches wide, by 4 feet 6 inches high, and used the rattles of no less than 637 snakes. The eagle required 574. Only in one detail did the artist play unfairly: the three-feather headdress of the Indian maiden was formed of rattlesnake skins, rather than rattles. Altogether, more than 14,000 rattlesnakes died to decorate this early cocktail lounge; and a shipment of 18,460 additional rattle strings had been received from a ranch on the Mexican border as Menger went to press. These were subsequently used in additional designs, and the entire collection of pictures and insignia was eventually transferred to the Buckhorn Curio Store in San Antonio, where they still are (1955). More than 32,000 rattle strings were used in the composition of the various panels, two of which are shown in figures 14:7 and 14:8, through the courtesy of the owners.

Fig. 14:7. A panel representing a deer made up of the rattles of 637 rattlesnakes.

Fig. 14:8. Eagle-cactus panel made of the rattles of 847 rattlesnakes. The pointed eagle feathers required unbroken rattle strings, including the buttons.

(Figs. 14:7 and 14:8 published by courtesy of the Buckhorn Curio Store, San Antonio, owner of the panels, and the San Antonio Zoo, which provided the photographs.)

PHOTOGRAPHING RATTLESNAKES

If possible, the field collector should always carry a camera to record the rattlers in their natural surroundings. On rare occasions he will be fortunate enough to find rattlers feeding, mating, or indulging in the male combat dance. Necessarily, however, these field pictures seldom include the detail essential to illustrate rattlesnake patterns. For reproduction in more formal papers, it is necessary to depend on laboratory shots. In these, it is inadvisable to simulate natural backgrounds, since they tend to obscure the patterns that are the primary objectives of this type of picture. I prefer snakes photographed on a glass base, thus eliminating confusing shadows. L. C. Kobler, who has made a large number of excellent photographs at my request during the past 25 years, has prepared the following description of the equipment and methods that have proved effective:

The equipment consists of an 8- by 10-inch view camera with double-extension bellows and any good lens of 10- to 12-inch focal length. The camera iris should have a rod fastened to the operating lever and then run across the front of the lens board to an indicator scale on the right side of the camera. This enables the operator to open or close the iris without placing his head or hands within striking distance of the snake. The camera is equipped with a 5- by 7-inch and a 4- by 5-inch reducing back. This permits one to take important photos at the full 8- by 10-inch size; whereas heads, tails, or sections may be shot on 5- by 7-inch or 4- by 5-inch film, thus cutting the expense of incidental photos. A sturdy tripod, with tilt-top and adjustable-height features, is necessary. I use three filters to emphasize colors or scale patterns, K2, G, or A, as required by the color of the specimen.

The auxiliary equipment can be constructed by anyone, and consists of the following items: A frame of 1- by 2-inch wood, approximately 30 inches square, with a piece of clear ¼-inch plate glass inset, and mounted on four 30-inch legs, thus making a glass-top table, on which the specimen is placed for photographing. (An old card table with the top cut out of the frame will do.) A short stepladder and two snake sticks are needed. These snake sticks are 30-inch pieces of broom handle with a heavy wire hook on one end to lift or move the snakes. Also, a 36-inch square of ¼-inch wallboard, painted with flat-white paint or calcimine is required. For lighting the subject, two 10- or 12-inch and one 6- or 8-inch adjustable clamp-type aluminum reflectors are needed, the small one having a reducer socket to take a No. 5 bayonet-base flash bulb. The three uprights to hold the reflectors can be made from broom sticks set into wooden bases.

The procedure is as follows: The glass-top table is set up in some room with plenty of clear floor space and not too much daylight. The camera, mounted on the tripod, is set at one side of the table. The camera is pointed at a 45-degree angle downward toward the center of the glass, with the lens about 30 inches from the center of the glass. The white wallboard is placed under the table, approximately parallel to the ground glass, where it serves as an out-of-focus background. The ladder to stand on is at the rear of the camera. One large reflector with a No. 22 flash bulb is set slightly above lens height, 24 to 30 inches to the right of the lens and pointed at the center of the composition. The other large reflector with a No. 50 flash bulb is set just below table height at right angles to the lens, just outside of the frame. This reflector is pointed at the center of the white background card. The small reflector with a No. 5 bulb is set to the left of the frame at about lens height, opposite the center of the composition. With the lens wide open, the camera is focused on a pencil or similar object for the first rough focus and to define the picture area. Then the pencil is replaced with the snake. At this point the snake either wriggles wildly off the glass, or rests quietly and poses. Much patience and persistence are necessary in some cases to get the subject to pose. I have generally found rattlers much easier to pose than the harmless species. After you have your snake quieted and posed in the proper natural coil, mount the ladder slowly, and do the final focusing and moving of the camera up or down to fill the negative. Close the aperture down to F45, for sharpness of definition, with the remote-control rod on the front of the camera, close the shutter, insert the film holder, and remove the slide.

All of the lights have been previously connected to a hand-type flash gun, and just after the snake has taken a breath, open the shutter, fire the bulbs, and close the shutter. This exposure is right for Isopan film with a K2 filter at F45. Minor adjustments in the placement of the lights may be necessary, but once set, one can be sure of obtaining uniform negatives. I find Isopan film, developed in Permadol to a contrast such that the white background will not print through a No. 3 or 4 glossy contact paper, to be excellent for snake photography.

I think the most essential thing in snake photography is a patience as long as a python, and the ability to move slowly and steadily no matter how anxious you are to snap a pose.

The results of Mr. Kobler's efforts are to be seen in figures 2:11 to 2:61, with the few exceptions credited to others. He has minimized, rather than exaggerated, the patience necessary to secure successful shots. Time after time, when all adjustments have been made for field and focus, the snake will again endeavor to escape and a new beginning must be made. Rattlesnakes, having some confidence in their ability to defend themselves, are more ready than most snakes to rest quietly in a watchful coil. Sometimes a snake may be soothed by placing a dark cloth over it. This gives it a chance to settle down in what seems to be obscurity. Holding a snake firmly in a confined position, sometimes in the exact pose desired, for a minute or so will often cause the subject to remain quiet for an extended period. Few living objects are more difficult than snakes to keep entirely in focus, because of the sharp details comprising scales and pattern over every part of the body.

Particularly troublesome subjects may sometimes be quieted by an initial cooling in a refrigerator. We have also used ether with some success, although too much will lead to an unnatural pose. Karlstrom and Cook (1955, p. 57) have discussed the problems of anesthetizing snakes, including rattlers.

References to photographing snakes will be found in Backus (1902, p. 212), Bevan (1930, p. 93), and Brownell (1934, p. 694; 1939, p. 368; and 1947, p. 47). The high-speed, stroboscopic photography of rattlesnakes in the act of striking, in order to determine the sequence of jaw and fang movements, has been mentioned elsewhere (p. 798). In addition to the methods of Van Riper (1950, p. 129; 1953, p. 100; 1954, p. 50; 1955, p. 308; and Van Riper, *et al.*, 1952, p. 1) an ingenious system for taking very high speed motion pictures in color of a striking rattlesnake, by means of synchronized lighting, has been described by Lester (1955, p. 22).

Photographic Fakery.—It is rarely possible to get action pictures of rattlesnakes in the wild. Occasionally a rattler will be found eating prey, but a picture of one striking prey in the wild could only result from the shot of a lifetime.

Some 25 years ago there appeared a widely syndicated pair of action shots in newspapers and pictorial-news displays. One showed a rather desiccated rattlesnake striking at a rabbit; the other the same rattler, in exactly the same position, in a battle with a roadrunner. Of course, the pictures never appeared together, for the precise conformation of the two rattlesnake poses would at once have shown the snake to be stuffed. Herpetologists, who naturally look twice at such pictures, readily connected the two and were undeceived, although the duplication was hardly necessary to expose the fraud, so dried and moth-eaten was the appearance of the snake. But not only were newspapers taken in, but reputable magazines as well (Simpich, 1928, *National Geographic Magazine*, vol. 53, no. 6, p. 677; Strong, 1928, *International Medical Digest*, vol. 12, p. 244). Bevan (1934b,

p. 65) fully exposed the fake when he found the stuffed snake and rabbit in a San Antonio museum; he was photographed holding the rattler and rabbit in their easily recognizable poses. In spite of this, the rattler-rabbit picture was exploited in a photographic magazine as recently as 1941 (L. Ward, p. 72) and in a book in 1948 (Ritchie, p. 303), and it is to be presumed these nature-faking prints will eventually attain the durability of first-rate folklore. There is a similarly immortal cobra-mongoose picture (Attwater, 1928, p. 5; also *Natural History*, vol. 59, no. 7, p. 289).

15. Enemies of Rattlesnakes

INTRODUCTION

The principal natural enemies of rattlesnakes are such mammals as deer and badgers, certain birds such as hawks and roadrunners, and, among the snakes, king snakes and racers. Various domestic animals also destroy rattlers. When the extent of control exercised by these animals is surveyed, it must be remembered that, with the possible exception of badgers, they never kill for fun, or with the altruistic idea of dispatching a creature dangerous to man. Some, such as deer and antelope, kill rattlers for their own protection or that of their young; whereas the carnivores nearly always kill for food.

One difficulty, when the rattler-killing proclivities of some animals are to be determined, is to know whether the victims were actually killed by these enemies, or were found by them on the road already crushed by passing automobiles. Since the advent of the automobile this factor has made life-history notes of this kind increasingly questionable, for the auto toll of snakes of all kinds, including rattlers, is very large.

The greatest destroyer of rattlesnakes is man himself. The nature and relative success of his activities have been discussed under control (pp. 975 *et seq.*).

Newspaper stories of rattlesnake enemies are strongly concentrated on dogs,—which, in these reports, almost invariably save the life of some child—king snakes, and cats. Staged king-snake–rattler battles—especially if the S.P.C.A. attempts to prevent them—are usually good for widespread publicity. The participants, being in strange surroundings, generally fail to react as expected, and the scheduled battle seldom comes off, even though the authorities do not intervene.

Some of my correspondents have made general statements on the subject of rattler enemies:

> The main enemy of rattlesnakes is man; the other natural enemies are hawks, eagles, and probably coyotes. I have seen both hawks and eagles carrying rattlesnakes, and have found portions of them at their nests. *W. J. Petermann, U. S. Forest Service, Meeteetse, Wyo.*

⬦

> Hawks, hogs, antelope, white-tail deer, dogs, coyotes, cats, horses, mules, and badgers seem to be the enemies of rattlesnakes. *F. R. Cochran, U. S. Forest Service, Sundance, Wyo.*

I have found rattler remains in coyotes, skunks, and badgers; I have seen hawks, magpies, and crows eating them, but I don't think they killed them. *Lawrence Kelly, Harper, Oreg.*

◇

As any given area becomes inhabited, the number of rattlers gradually diminishes, for every rattler found is usually killed, either by man, hogs, or dogs, and the odor of goats tends to cause rattlesnakes to move out of a given area. There are a few rattlers still scattered over the level part of the Estancia Valley but they are now mostly confined to rocky or brushy areas. *Drayton Wasson, U. S. Forest Service, Espanola, N. Mex.*

◇

The rattlers we have in this district are mostly timber rattlers. In all my experiences with this species of snake, I have seen only three killed other than by man; one by a large rabbit hawk, one by a king snake, and the other by a hog. *Roy W. Dennis, U. S. Forest Service, Troy, N. C.*

I now proceed to some detailed accounts of the part played by various kinds of animals in the suppression of rattlesnakes, as supplied by my correspondents, or as found in the accounts of travelers and naturalists.

Within the past few years, studies of the stomach contents, pellets (indigestible remnants of food disgorged by birds), and scats (excreta) of predators, have added much to the knowledge of their food habits. In no case have rattlesnakes been found to comprise more than a minor part of the diet of any animal. Among the recent researches, those of Fitch and Glading (1947, p. 120) at the San Joaquin Experimental Range in Madera County, California, should serve as a model. They point out, in explaining how such potentially dangerous creatures as rattlesnakes can fall prey to seemingly weaker creatures, that many birds and mammals are quicker and more alert than rattlesnakes, and can seize and render them helpless without danger to themselves.

MAMMAL ENEMIES

DEER

Deer have long been reputed to be rattlesnake killers, and a number of my correspondents have had personal experiences fully verifying these reports:

I once saw a deer kill a rattler; he accomplished this by leaping onto the snake with his front feet and off again. The deer repeated this operation several times, and, so far as I was able to determine, without the snake ever striking the deer. *Connie Davis, Supervisor of Wardens, New Albany, Miss.*

◇

Through a field glass I watched a deer running around and around, and, at times, jumping up and down. After he left, I went over to see what he had been doing and found a rattlesnake all cut to pieces. *Charles J. Boudreaux, Trapper, Abbeville, La.*

◇

At 9:15 A.M., a doe was seen to jump on a spot of ground, and then jump off at least ten times. She would stand and look, then make a high jump and light on the same spot, repeating this every ten to fifteen seconds. Finally she walked off as if nothing had happened. I went over and found a five-foot five-inch rattlesnake with its head mashed and the body cut nearly in two in several places. The snake was about dead, or so badly injured that it could not have lived. *T. T. Waddell, State Game Warden, Eagle Lake, Tex.*

Once, while hunting coyotes in the latter part of June, I noticed five buck deer kicking up quite a dust. As I looked they spread out, and then one buck, taking the lead, made a stiff-legged jump, and one by one the others followed, jumping almost exactly in his tracks. At first I thought they had got wind of me, but as they didn't run off, I went over to see what had been going on. Upon looking around I found a beaten up rattlesnake lying there. It looked almost as though someone had been working on it with a hammer. *Morgan L. Hall, U. S. Fish and Wildlife Service, Dillon, Mont.*

<>

I have seen buck deer kill rattlesnakes on three different occasions. They just back up and run and stomp them; then they turn and do it again. After a buck deer gets through, there isn't a piece of rattlesnake over one inch in length. A buck deer really makes sure that they're dead. *Albert Madarieta, Oakley, Idaho.*

<>

Once I saw a doe with a fawn kill a rattlesnake by striking it with her front feet. The deer virtually cut the snake to shreds. *F. E. Williams, U. S. Forest Service, Riggins, Idaho.*

<>

One of the most interesting sights I have witnessed was watching a doe and her two fawns kill a rattler. First there was much snorting, stamping, and hair raising, as the doe seemed to be instructing her fawns. Then they started a wide circle around the snake with the mother in the lead and the little fawns following her. As they came to the snake they leapt high in the air and struck with all four feet together on the snake with such speed that the snake apparently had no time to strike back. I dare say it had little to strike back with, after feeling twelve sharp hoofs on just one trip. However, this went on many times until it was difficult to recognize the victim as a rattler, it was so badly cut up. After killing the rattler they stood and looked at it for about a minute, apparently to make sure it was dead, and then went on about their feeding. I examined the pieces and found it to have been a good-sized Pacific rattler. The fawns were not over three months old, but they did their part of the killing. This happened in the Mad River country, Humboldt County, California. I have found two other kills that were made by deer, as could be told from the hoof marks. I have seen deer startled by nonpoisonous snakes but they did not bother to kill them.[1] *R. J. Yates, Game Warden, San Rafael, Calif.*

That deer may actually affect the rattlesnake population is evident from the following:

Deer were once relatively abundant in these mountains, but later they became almost extinct. A restocking program was carried on during the years 1935–42 and the population is now back to a level that permitted a three-day hunt in the fall of 1944. The decline in the number of snakes, especially rattlers, has been remarked upon by many of the woodsmen working for me, and I hold the same opinion. *M. Leitch, Staunton, Va.*

Several other correspondents have supplied eyewitness accounts of deer killing rattlers, always by jumping on them; and a still greater number have reported finding the cut-up bodies of snakes, surrounded by deer tracks, which left no doubt as to what had happened. A typical account is as follows:

I observed some years ago, when deer were most numerous in Pennsylvania, where a deer had evidently killed a rattler, for the snake was literally chopped up by something and the earth where the snake was had been tramped into dust. The loose earth was a mass of deer tracks; although I did not see the killing, I am confident the deer did a spendid job. *C. V. Dong, State Fish Warden, East Waterford, Pa.*

---

[1] Charles M. Bogert has informed me of a gopher snake (*Pituophis*) killed by deer. Wall (1906, p. 386) mentions the killing of snakes by deer in Ceylon. Nicander described the killing of snakes by deer as long ago as 150 B.C. (1953, p. 37).

Besides the often repeated general statement in the literature that deer kill rattlesnakes, e.g., S. R. Brown, 1817, p. 79; Kennedy, 1841, p. 134; J. G. Wood, 1863, p. 102; Flack, 1866, p. 334; Coues and Yarrow, 1878, p. 264; Humfreville, 1903, p. 445; Santleben, 1910, p. 49; Crimmins, 1931, p. 46; Maddox, 1940, p. 271; and Fenley, 1940, p. 4, there are a number of instances giving some details, such as that of Seton (1929, vol. 3, p. 288), who tells of the tactics of a buck white-tailed deer in killing a rattler; and Aldous (1938, p. 111), who watched a deer kill a rattlesnake on a farm near Wilcox, Pennsylvania. Moore (1930, p. 92) found a rattler injured by a deer. Pequegnat (1945, p. 7; 1951, p. 32) left the bodies of several speckled rattlers out overnight in the Santa Ana Mountains; the next morning he found them trampled by deer, as was evident from the tracks.

It is clear, from the accounts, that rattler killing is indulged in by both bucks and does, and not by does alone, as is sometimes supposed. It was thought by the ancients that deer ate the snakes they killed (Pliny, 1855–57, vol. 5, p. 328; book xxviii, chap. 42) but there is, of course, no truth in this. Presumably deer destroy snakes as a protective measure, particularly in the case of does with young. Evidently the practice has become instinctive for both sexes. The same reasoning holds for the other herbivores that destroy rattlers.

That deer in captivity may not readily attack rattlers is indicated by the following:

> About two years ago the Pennsylvania Game Commission had several eastern white-tailed deer in a small enclosure near Williamsport, Pennsylvania. One day the subject came up about deer killing rattlesnakes, so a couple of boys went out and caught two rattlers, some three feet long, and brought them into the pen where the deer were confined. As soon as the deer were left alone, they advanced toward the snakes. I don't mean all eleven of them, but two did. When they got within about 15 feet of the snakes the deer started to blink and slow up, and at 10 feet their eyes seemed to become dazed. They stopped and then, very slowly, veered away from the snakes. We noted as soon as the deer were a short distance away, their eyes assumed their normal expression. *T. J. Cox, State Fish Warden, Coudersport, Pa.*

ANTELOPE

The antelope, or pronghorn, a wide-ranging ruminant of the Western plains, is also an occasional killer of rattlesnakes.

> I have watched several antelope kill rattlesnakes. They just run up and stamp them with their front feet, and their hoofs cut the snakes to pieces. Doe antelope kill the rattlers if they get anywhere near their fawns. Once I was sitting on a ridge and across the wash opposite me was an old buck antelope lying down. I wasn't paying much attention to him but I saw him jump up and turn away from me. He walked about 10 feet, stopped, pawing the ground and shaking his head, and then jumped sideways about 5 feet. That was when he hit the snake. He hit the snake with his front feet, thrashing the ground and snake, too, for about 30 seconds, then ran off a few steps, shook his head again, walked off and started grazing. I went over to see what the fracas was about and found a rattler badly smashed and cut into three pieces. The snake, to begin with, had been around 2½ feet long. The wind was blowing from the snake to the antelope and I think he smelled the snake behind him. I have seen a doe deer kill a rattler but she seemed to use all four feet to stamp on the snake instead of just the front feet, as did this antelope. *Eddie Buchta, U. S. Fish and Wildlife Service, Moneta, Wyo.*

⟡

> One day I noticed a bunch of antelope acting queerly. They were running in a circle and all seemed to jump and land on all four feet in one certain place. I rode down to see what

it was all about and found a rattler all chopped to pieces on this spot where they had been jumping. This happened about 20 miles west of Casper, Wyoming. *Fred W. Barnes, U. S. Fish and Wildlife Service, Hines, Oreg.*

⬦

If you were to come out to Gillette, Wyoming, sometime and spend a few days on the antelope range, especially in July and August, I am sure you would have an opportunity to observe either a doe or buck antelope savagely stamping and cutting a rattler to pieces with its sharp hoofs, which are brought down in a tight bunch on the snake. I have observed this three times, and it is a common occurrence on a snake-infested antelope range. The size of the snake is of no importance to an antelope when it determines to eliminate the snake. The ones I observed were average-sized prairie rattlers. *F. R. Cochran, U. S. Forest Service, Sundance, Wyo.*

⬦

I have seen rattlers killed by both deer and antelope. The latter, particularly, will attack them on almost every encounter. They kill by striking with their front feet. *Norman R. Tripp, U. S. Forest Service, Slater, Colo.*

Ingersoll (1883b, p. 153), Holder (1892, p. 214), and Rollins (1922, p. 175) mention the killing of rattlesnakes by antelope. The first two accounts include pictures showing an antelope in action against a rattler.

SHEEP

Domestic hoofed animals are also reported to kill rattlesnakes occasionally. Some correspondents call attention to the fact that rattlers are scarce or absent on sheep or goat ranges. This might be caused by actual destruction by these animals, particularly of juvenile rattlers; or it might be because the sheep reduce the feed available to rodents, thus, in turn, starving out the snakes.

Very seldom have I seen a rattlesnake on a range regularly used by sheep. *Yale A. Mitchell, U. S. Forest Service, McCall, Idaho.*

A sheep may actually kill a rattler occasionally, according to these statements:

About six years ago, C. L. Miller, a game warden, made a trip a few miles down the Great Calfpasture River below his home. At the edge of a pasture field near the woods he noticed a sheep, an old one, very much animated and stamping violently at an object on the ground not visible to the observer. The sheep was using her front feet in repeated actions of this sort. Mr. Miller went to the spot for a closer view and found a rattlesnake nearly dead, with its entrails knocked from its body on the ground beside it. The ewe had moved a short distance when Mr. Miller arrived, but there was too short an interval of time between his first observation and reaching the place for the snake to have been killed other than by the sheep. This was a common timber rattlesnake, *C. h. horridus*. *M. Leitch, Staunton, Va.*

⬦

Sheep kill quite a few snakes. The snakes strike at the sheep and get hung up in their wool. *Glen Jorgensen, Heppner, Oreg.*

Kalez (1954, p. 76) claimed that rattlers fled over the sides of a canyon down which a herd of sheep was being driven.

GOATS

In the Southwest I have often heard it stated that rattlers are scarce or absent in areas browsed by goats, although this cannot be universally true, as rattlers have been found to be common in some areas where goats graze. Motl (1936, p. 3) says that rattlers are likely to be more prevalent where cattle browse than where sheep or goats range.

In 1915 at Wall's Well, south of Ajo, Arizona, I spent several days with a herder and his flock of Angora goats, and twice saw goats kill rattlesnakes. On both occasions the goat made a series of very rapid jumps, coming down on the snake stiff-legged with all four feet close together. Neither goat was bitten, but both snakes were so cut up that I thought it not worth-while to skin them. *Richard M. Bond, Soil Conservation Service, Portland, Oreg.*

<>

I have seen goats kill snakes in Napa County. The goats stand on their hind legs and use their front feet to kill the snake. They go up in the air and come down with their front feet. *Robert Wiley, Eureka, Calif.*

<>

Goats and deer kill rattlesnakes by striking them with their front feet, or jumping in the air and coming down on them with all four feet together. *Richard Ray, Clovis, Calif.*

Perry (1942, p. 62) mentions the fact that goats kill rattlers by striking them with their forefeet, used as lances.

Evidently goats sometimes avoid rattlers:

There are lots of things told about different animals killing rattlesnakes, but in all the years that I have spent in the woods, I have never seen anything except a dog kill one. A goat will calmly walk by on another trail. Once I was walking and driving several hundred head of goats. I noticed that they circled around a big rock that had lovely grass all around it. I wondered why, and went there to see. A huge rattler struck and hung his fangs in the flap of my chaps. From the way it threshed around my legs, it was as anxious to be loose as I was, but I dragged the thing several yards. *John W. Buchanan, Game and Fish Warden, Leakey, Tex.*

HORSES

Occasionally a horse may kill a rattler:

A few years ago a forest worker had his horse tied in an open shed, directly behind a cabin where he and I were eating our dinner. Upon hearing a noise in the vicinity of the shed, we rushed out to see what was going on. The horse was excited and trying to break away. In front of the horse was a dead rattler that had been pawed several times. Horseshoe marks on the ground were plain evidence that the snake had been pawed to death by the horse. *John P. Gaffney, U. S. Forest Service, Republic, Wash.*

<>

The only animals I ever saw kill a rattler were a horse and an antelope. *Calvin A. Bowman, U. S. Forest Ranger, Deer Lodge, Mont.*

In the *San Diego Tribune–Sun,* March 24, 1951, appeared an account of a mare, which, while grazing in a corral, was seen to snort, rear, and stamp down with her front feet. She sniffed the spot and then resumed browsing. Her owner, who had been watching, went over and found a three-foot rattlesnake, mangled by the horse's hoofs.

CATTLE

It is presumed that cattle often kill rattlers by stepping on them inadvertently. However, one of the members of the San Diego Reptile Club reported that he had seen a cow jump on and kill a rattler with her forefeet; it seemed to be done with intention. Gibson (1940, p. 112) reported that cattle sometimes kill rattlesnakes deliberately. Fitch and Glading (1947, p. 120), on the San Joaquin Experimental Range, found several northern Pacific rattlesnakes (*C. v. oreganus*) that had been trampled to death by cattle.

Hogs

Hogs have long been reputed to be killers of snakes, rattlesnakes particularly, and I have received several firsthand accounts of such incidents:

I have seen pigs kill and eat rattlesnakes with no harm to themselves. *Frank E. Brink, Fish Warden, Milford, Pa.*

◇

In sections of the country where there are hogs, they kill many rattlers and seem to enjoy them as food. *C. B. Clark, U. S. Forest Service, Duffield, Va.*

◇

A neighbor of mine has seen domestic hogs kill rattlers. In analyzing the stomach contents of wild boars, I have found segments of rattlesnakes. *E. A. Schilling, U. S. Forest Service, Franklin, N. C.*

◇

On one occasion, while hunting squirrels, I saw a large sow with pigs kill a rattler by the simple expedient of stepping on it with her front feet and grasping the head of the snake with her mouth. The sow and pigs then finished the job by eating the rattler. *R. J. Mc-Cormack, Tennessee State Division of Game and Fish, South Pittsburg, Tenn.*

◇

I have only once seen hogs killing a rattler. This was a large timber rattler (*Crotalus h. horridus*), which a number of Duroc-Jersey hogs had found and were eating, when I came upon them. The rattler was still squirming, and I was attracted by the excessive grunting of the hogs. Thinking, from the noise they made, that they had attacked some animal, I rode my horse into the woods and found that they were destroying a rattler about six feet in length. As I sat on my horse, the hogs actually ate this snake up. This occurred on May 12, 1912. Previous to that time rattlesnakes were quite common on the hills of Avery Island. In the early part of that year, about fifty head of hogs were liberated in the woodlands of the place, and during the next two years the rattlesnakes completely disappeared from the high land, and it was many years thereafter before I again found them in any numbers in the timber section of the island. *E. A. McIlhenny, Avery Island, La.*

◇

I exterminated rattlesnakes two summers ago at a ranger station by turning two hogs loose in the yard and pasture. Rattlers have no effect on the hogs, which eat them up. *B. A. Goodman, U. S. Forest Service, Stanford, Mont.*

◇

One day as I rode along on an inspection, I noticed some young pigs in a huddle and a sow shaking a rattler. This was during the latter part of July. When I saw them the rattler was torn near the head and wounded in several places. I don't know whether the sow ate the snake. I know of one ranch adjacent to my district that used to have an abundance of rattlers. The ranch was stocked with hogs and it is now rare to see a rattler within a mile of the hog pastures. *Milo T. Dyches, U. S. Forest Service, Monroe, Utah.*

◇

I have seen hogs just pick rattlers up and eat them, and if they were bitten, it didn't affect them. *Lawrence Kelly, Harper, Oreg.*

◇

The only snake-killing pig that I actually saw was on a ranch in the Deschutes country in Oregon. I was talking to the rancher when I heard a pig squealing angrily, and looking around saw its head and forequarters going up and down rapidly. It was pivoting around one spot as its forefeet lit on the ground. We walked over to the pig, which by this time was sniffing at a mangled rattlesnake. As I looked, he took it up in his mouth and began eating it. The rancher said the killing of rattlers by hogs was a common occurrence, but was not sure that the hogs always ate them. *Richard J. Grace, Portland, Oreg.*

On our ranch in eastern Oregon, where we had between seven and eight hundred head of hogs, I remember hearing some of the ranch hands tell about seeing hogs kill rattlesnakes. Within a few years after this ranch was converted to running hogs instead of cattle, there was a noticeable decrease in the number of rattlesnakes seen. *L. J. Cooper, U. S. Forest Service, Merlin, Oreg.*

◇

I have seen evidence of sheep and deer having trod rattlesnakes to death, and have also seen hogs kill rattlesnakes. In one instance, the hog seemed to fly into a rage, jumped on the snake and trod on it with his hoofs and bit it apart with his teeth. Due to the amount of fat on the hog, he did not seem to be bothered by the snake's bite. A hog will kneel down on a snake, grab it and start eating. He will be unhurt if the snake bites him. *E. C. Holder, State Game Ranger, Winslow, Ariz.*

◇

I saw a hog kill a rattlesnake. He came up on the snake and just shied a little; then he took the snake near its middle and began eating. The snake bit the hog twice on the side of the head, but the bite did not bother the hog, because it was fat. *Richard Ray, Clovis, Calif.*

◇

I had an uncle who raised hogs for his own use and to supply the section hands along the railroad, as well as to clear the area around the ranch home of rattlesnakes. On more than one occasion, I have seen hogs grab a snake and, while consuming it, the rattlesnake would bite the hog, but apparently without ill effects, as the venom was deposited in the fat without reaching the circulatory system. *W. G. Willson, Los Angeles, Calif.*

In these eyewitness accounts of the killing and eating of rattlesnakes by hogs, three general themes are to be noted: (1) the readiness with which hogs attack rattlesnakes; (2) the absence of serious results if a hog is bitten; and (3) the importance of hogs in clearing an area of rattlesnakes. These comments of my correspondents confirm what had already appeared in print on these phases of the rattlesnake-hog relationship.

The early natural histories mentioned the eating of snakes by hogs. Aristotle called attention to their doing so (Cresswell, 1862, p. 233) and so did Pliny (1855–57, vol. 2, p. 551; book x, chap. 95; vol. 3, p. 97; book xi, chap. 115). This propensity is often mentioned in popular natural histories, such as those of Wood (1863, p. 192), and Figuier (1869, p. 86). Beverly (1722, p. 248) tells of seeing a sow eat a rattler's head without harm. Barcia (1952, p. 281, but originally published in 1723) thought the rattlesnakes that the hogs ate in Florida gave their meat a flavor equal to the choicest pork in Spain. Hall (1727, p. 314) fed a hog with a rattler, which it ate readily. Martin (1859, p. 110) tells how some hogs excavated a snake den in January and ate the occupants, including many rattlers. Guild (1878, p. 53), writing of old times in Tennessee, said it was customary to drive the hogs to the snake dens in the fall to fatten them on the rattlers gathered there.

Occasionally hogs do not feed readily on rattlers, as indicated by this observation of a correspondent:

I have heard that hogs would kill rattlers, but once I saw a snake thrown into a pen where there were hogs that had been raised in a snake country, and they gave it a wide berth; wouldn't even go close to it. *W. D. Royster, Paulina, Oreg.*

Many writers have mentioned the use of hogs in rattlesnake control, e.g., Kalm, 1752–53, p. 67; Anburey, 1789, p. 385; Blane, 1824, p. 88; Atwater, 1838, p. 68; Kennedy, 1841, p. 134; Hall, 1848, p. 124; Chamberlain, 1850, p. 15; Peake,

1860–61, p. 50; Flack, 1866, p. 334; Hurter, 1893, p. 258; Klauber, 1930, p. 41; Uhler, 1944, p. 9. This means of extermination has also been dealt with in the chapter on control (p. 985).

It has often been stated that hogs are immune to rattlesnake bite. Gronovius (1763, p. 26) believed this was caused by the carrying of the hog's fat into the wound along with the venom, thus introducing an antidote. But it is now known that fat, once considered an important remedy, has no value in snake bite. Bergen (1899, p. 83) recorded the folklore belief that a hog eliminated the venom through the sebaceous glands of the forelegs. Actually, Essex (1932, p. 339) has shown that hogs are no more immune to rattlesnake venom than other mammals of similar size. Such protection as they have comes from their thick hides, or, more importantly, from the protective layers of fat, which prevent the venom from entering the circulatory system (Lacépède, 1788–89, vol. 2, p. 414; Weld, 1800, p. 150; Kerr, 1802, vol. 4, p. 269; LeConte, 1858, p. 666, Griswold, 1884, p. 54; and Devoe, 1945, p. 486). But DeKay (1842, p. 57) and Wright and Bishop (1915, p. 190) mention cases in which hogs have died from rattlesnake bite. Sometimes hogs rush a rattler and stamp on it to avoid being bitten (Flack, 1866, p. 185; Vinson, 1946, p. 406).

PECCARIES

The peccary, Mexican wild hog, or javelina, is frequently cited in the literature as being the enemy of the rattlesnake (Goldsmith, 1774, vol. 7, p. 210; Wood, 1863, p. 102; Coues and Yarrow, 1878, p. 264; Santleben, 1910, p. 49; Rollins, 1922, p. 176; Crimmins, 1927, p. 199; 1931, p. 46; Seton, 1929, vol. 3, p. 732; Fenley, 1940, p. 4; and Duncan, 1945, p. 167). Few confirmatory field notes have been reported to me.

> I found one place where a javelina had evidently killed a rattler, but I did not actually see it happen—the dead snake was there and all indications were that the javelina had made the kill. *P. Bruce Centerwall, U. S. Forest Service, Tonto Basin, Ariz.*

Herne (1858, p. 327; Dobie, 1947a, p. 6) has given a detailed account of the killing of a rattlesnake by a band of peccaries. They jumped on the snake and cut it to pieces with their hoofs, and then ate the remains.

COYOTES

There seems no question that coyotes occasionally kill rattlesnakes, usually for food:

> I have seen a good many dead rattlesnakes around coyote dens, although I have never seen any that the coyotes had fed on. *Eddie Buchta, U. S. Fish and Wildlife Service, Moneta, Wyo.*

⋄

> Coyotes kill rattlers, snapping and shaking them until the snake is literally shredded. This I have observed several times. *F. R. Cochran, Forest Ranger, Sundance, Wyo.*

⋄

> I have seen dead rattlesnakes close by a coyote den, from which it appeared that the coyote had killed them to protect her pups. *Vaude L. Wintersteen, Longmont, Colo.*

⋄

> Coyotes eat rattlesnakes, I am sure, for I have found the remains in their stomachs. *Robert M. Parkhurst, U. S. Fish and Wildlife Service, Weiser, Idaho.*

I have seen dogs kill rattlesnakes by shaking them in their mouths. Coyotes will kill them the same as a dog. I think they do this mostly to protect their young ones. *Frank Ivie, U. S. Fish and Wildlife Service, Bellevue, Idaho.*

◇

I was hunting coyote dens one warm day in May, and found a den where there were several dead rattlesnakes lying around that had been bitten in the neck. There were also a number of rattlesnake heads, of which the bodies had been eaten by the coyote pups. The pups seemed to know enough to leave the poisonous heads alone and not eat them. *Everett W. Norris, U. S. Fish and Wildlife Service, Malta, Idaho.*

◇

I have found the remains of rattlesnakes in the stomachs of coyotes, and dead rattlers at coyote-den sites, the old coyotes having brought them in to feed their pups. *Andrew S. Poland, Loomis, Calif.*

Some trappers use rattlesnake remains (decomposed) in preparing scents for coyote traps:

I use dead rattlers to scent traps for coyotes. When I put them up in jars for scent, I leave the head on. The smell sure holds. *Joe R. Bachlet, Wildlife Trapper, Wheatland, Wyo.*

◇

We use rattlesnakes in preparing some very good bait for trapping coyotes. *Floyd McTimmonds, Alturas, Calif.*

◇

Coyotes are very fond of dead rattlesnakes. I use them for coyote bait. *Clarence R. Ousley, Napa, Calif.*

◇

Once while I was changing a flat tire I heard a rattlesnake. I found it under a flat rock about 2 feet across, and a coyote had been digging all around the rock trying to get at the snake. I killed the snake and put it back under the rock, and made trap sets there for coyotes. I caught 15 in the next two months. I have found parts of rattlesnakes in coyote stomachs many times, but I could not say whether they killed them or found them dead and ate them. I have never seen a coyote kill a rattlesnake. *Fay Clark, U. S. Fish and Wildlife Service, Mt. Hebron, Calif.*

In addition to these reports from my correspondents of relationships between rattlesnakes and coyotes, there have been several published accounts containing confirmatory data. Sperry (1941, p. 56), in his detailed report on the food habits of the coyote, has recorded the finding of rattlesnake remains in 30 coyote stomachs from 9 different states, out of a total of 8,339 stomachs examined. Fitch and Glading (1947, p. 120) found 3 rattler remains in 944 recognizable items in coyote scats. Ferrel, Leach, and Tillotson (1953, p. 301), in California coyotes, found rattlesnake remains in 12 out of 2,222 stomachs that contained food. Gally (1880, p. 1; Dobie, 1952a, p. B-6) watched, through field glasses, a coyote attack and kill a rattler. This it did by teasing the rattler until it stretched out, whereupon the coyote seized it by the neck, shook it to death, and ate it.

L. M. Huey, of the San Diego Society of Natural History, has told me of finding a trapped coyote that evidently had been bitten by a rattler. Dobie, in his *The Voice of the Coyote* (1949), says that, of the coyotes trapped in Texas, some 20 per cent show rattler scars (p. 118). One trapper noted that a coyote had rolled on a long-dead rattler, and buried or partly buried rattlesnake remains are used as bait by trappers. [Dog owners will note a characteristic trait of their pets, here used to the coyotes' doom.] Dobie tells of a sidewinder that was kept by a coyote from reaching shade until it died from the heat, and was then eaten by the coyote (p. 119). Rattlers placed in coyote pens were killed by the captive coyotes, which used the same tactics as those employed by dogs, as will be described later.

FOXES

There is evidence that foxes may sometimes kill rattlers.

> This year on the road between the fish hatchery and Tuolumne—five miles—I saw a fox cross the road in front of my truck with a rattlesnake in his mouth. The snake did not show any life. *Ross A. McCloud, Tuolumne, Calif.*

Richard G. Zweifel reported that a gray fox had eaten a speckled rattlesnake (*C. m. pyrrhus*). Fitch and Glading (1947, p. 120) found rattlesnake remains in gray-fox scats.

One captive fox evidenced a fear of rattlers:

> I have observed a young fox's reaction to the rattle of a rattlesnake we kept several weeks in a burlap sack. The fox was about three months old. It was unafraid of any object or sound with which I saw it come in contact, except the rattlesnake. When we placed the fox near it and caused it to buzz its rattle, the fox showed signs of fear and ran to the other side of the room. We amused ourselves frequently this way and the fox's reaction was always the same. Having been taken from the den when only a few weeks old, the fox probably had never seen a rattler before. Therefore, we assumed that it was born with an instinctive fear of rattlesnakes. *James S. Durell, Wills Point, Tex.*

DOGS

I have been surprised at the large numbers of sheep and farm dogs reported to be rattlesnake killers, some with a considerable regularity. We see in the following reports a somewhat standardized method of attack. The dog dances around the snake, barking and making threatening advances. As soon as the snake abandons its defensive coil and stretches out to crawl toward some refuge, the dog rushes in, bites the snake, sometimes on the neck behind the head, but often at mid-body, and then, before the snake can retaliate, relinquishes his hold by tossing the snake in the air. This maneuver, rapidly repeated, soon finishes the snake.

A few of the incidents described by my correspondents are as follows:

> I have seen stock dogs of the shepherd breed kill rattlers. These dogs were often bitten by the snake on their first encounter, but after that they learned never to try to take hold of the snake while it was coiled, but would play around until the rattler started to crawl away, then grab it right behind the head and shake it and throw it a few feet, usually tearing the body and putting the snake out of action. *Walter F. Emerick, Division of Fish and Game, Palmdale, Calif.*

> One of my dogs killed 13 rattlesnakes in one day at haying time, in eastern Oregon. His method of killing them was to circle while they were coiled and, by backing off a short distance, allow the snake to try to get away. He would then dash in and grab it back of the head and shake it to pieces. If the snake should suddenly coil and take the defensive, the dog would shy away and go through the same tactics until he saw a chance to grab the snake without being struck. The snakes were of various sizes and it made no difference to the dog whether they were large or small, although it seemed to me he handled the larger snakes more quickly and easily than the smaller. The dog was a black shepherd such as we used for handling cattle and sheep. *L. J. Cooper, U. S. Forest Service, Merlin, Oreg.*

I knew of one dog that would kill rattlers. He would not attempt to kill a rattler when it was coiled; if he found one coiled, he would bay until someone came. But if the dog found a rattler traveling he would pick it up on the run and beat it to death by whipping it from side to side. *Floyd E. McKee, Medford, Oreg.*

⬦

Dogs kill rattlers by getting them to strike, jumping back and then grabbing and shaking them while they are uncoiled. *Lawrence Kelly, Harper, Oreg.*

⬦

I had a fox terrier that killed all the rattlesnakes he could find. He would bark and jump at a rattler until it struck at him; he would jump back, and then before the snake could coil up to strike, he would grab it back of the head and shake it to death. He would always throw it from him when he let go of it. *Ed Rose, U. S. Fish and Wildlife Service, Chilcoot, Calif.*

⬦

I have seen dogs kill rattlesnakes. A smart dog won't tackle them while they are coiled, but will torment them until they start crawling, then grab them and shake them until they are dead. *Riley R. Osborn, Game Warden, Torrey, Utah.*

⬦

I have seen several dogs kill rattlers. Their method is to watch the snake carefully, then grab it on the body with a quick pinch, then drop it and watch carefully, attacking again in the same manner. Every attack seems more vicious. The dog will always flip the snake, then let loose very quickly, not giving the snake a chance to strike. *Vernon Leovitt, Gunlock, Utah.*

⬦

I have seen several sheep dogs that would kill rattlesnakes, but quite a few leave rattlers alone. One dog that I saw kill rattlesnakes would wait till a snake was stretched out and then grab it in the middle and shake the snake, breaking it to pieces. Once I saw a dog tackle a rattlesnake nearly three feet long. The snake was coiled ready to strike, and when the dog made a grab for the snake's head the snake bit the dog below one eye. The dog jumped back and the snake coiled again; the dog came in again and the snake hit the dog on the side of the nose, but the dog grabbed the snake that time and shook it to pieces. I put coal oil on the dog's head and he lay in the water and mud in a water hole for several days, but finally got over it. He would bark at snakes after that, but was never known to get near one. *Eddie Buchta, U. S. Fish and Wildlife Service, Moneta, Wyo.*

The above account is one of a number in which the attacking dogs were not so fortunate as to escape unscathed. L. M. Huey of the Natural History Museum, San Diego, had a dog that was bitten while killing a rattler, but, far from being cowed by this experience, became an even more persistent snake killer than before. The effects of the bites in such cases are discussed elsewhere (p. 970).

> With regard to the way dogs go about killing rattlers, as a rule, they grab the rattler and give it a sling somewhat similar to popping a whip. They are not always successful at doing this and are sometimes bitten in the attempt. *Abner Casey, U. S. Forest Service, Bridgewater, Va.*

Dr. C. O. Tanner, of San Diego, has told me of the method of attack used by his dog, five years old and weighing 50 pounds, that has killed at least three rattlesnakes. The dog stalks them and dances around until they make a break for the nearest bush. Then, when they are stretched out, he runs in and bites them, tossing them into the air, and jumps back to avoid being within range when the snake hits the ground. He does this repeatedly until the snake is done for. Only once was he bitten, this time when another dog tried to help, but only succeeded in upsetting the method used. He had a serious time, but recovered.

Other encounters between dogs and rattlesnakes will be found in Maddox (1940, p. 269) and Duncan (1945, p. 172). Newspaper stories of rattlesnake-killing dogs are quite frequent. Usually, so the story goes, the dog saves the life of a child, which generally results in nationwide publicity.

Elliot (1900, p. 219; 1933c, p. 672; 1934c, p. 232) described the methods adopted by dogs in killing cobras in India. These are similar in detail to the scheme of attack employed by our dogs on rattlers. Hudson (1910, p. 71) has described how a sheep dog in England attacked an adder. The method was the same. Evidently this snake-killing pattern is very ancient and deeply ingrained in the canine family.

BADGERS

I now return to natural enemies in the wild. A. M. Jackley believed badgers to be the most important rattler killers in South Dakota. He wrote:

> Badgers are the chief enemies of the rattler in this section of the country. Not only do they feed upon them generally, but they destroy these snakes in large numbers without eating them. Where badgers dig into prairie dog holes it is mainly for rattlesnakes, and not for rodents and prairie dogs, as is sometimes thought. A trapper for the U. S. Wildlife Service told me the other day he had gone to a snake den where he had seen a large number of rattlers congregated last fall, and found that badgers had played havoc with them. He said he counted ten sets of rattles and pieces of snakes in the dirt that had been dug out.

Mr. Jackley published two accounts of his observations on the destruction of rattlers by badgers (1938, p. 374; 1944, p. 2).

Other comments on the badger's snake-killing activities are as follows:

> We had a pet badger that loved to kill rattlesnakes and drag them all over the place. *Charles G. Holzworth, Kremmling, Colo.*

<><

> I have seen evidence where a badger had killed and eaten part of a rattlesnake. The badgers appeared to dig them out and kill them. *Vaude L. Wintersteen, Longmont, Colo.*

<><

> Badgers are known to eat rattlesnakes. When they are digging into a den, it is claimed that the nose is the only part of the badger vulnerable to the rattler. *Glenn Flathers, U. S. Forest Service, Camp Crook, S. Dak.*

<><

> Badgers will grab rattlers anywhere and walk away with them, apparently indifferent to their striking. I presume the badgers eat them. *B. K. Crane, U. S. Forest Service, Austin, Nev.*

A. Pierce Artran told me of digging out two badgers in Arizona that had partly eaten a rattler he had tracked to their den. He found half the body as well as remains in the excreta. Follett (1927, p. 220) has reported that a badger dug up and ate all but the head of a rattler that the writer had buried. Crimmins (1931, p. 47) mentions a badger that broke into a box containing rattlers and ate them, in preference to rabbits in another box. Benton (1945, p. 80) states that badgers kill every rattler they encounter.

OPOSSUMS

The opossum may be at least an occasional rattlesnake killer:

> An opossum which contained rattlesnake remains was found dead (run over) at night along the road about one-fourth of a mile west of the Mt. Scott Campground. There is the pos-

sibility that the rattlesnake may have been carrion, the opossum having found an injured or dead specimen alongside of the road or in the public campground. *Frank B. McMurry, U. S. Fish and Wildlife Service, Yuma, Ariz.*

⟡

Our records show only one stomach of an opossum collected in the Wichita Mountains Wildlife Refuge which contained the remains of a rattlesnake. This constituted essentially 100 per cent of the contents, with incidental fragments of a scorpion, a centipede, and a few insects. The opossum was collected in Comanche County, Oklahoma, on October 25, 1939. *E. R. Kalmbach, Wildlife Research Laboratory, Denver, Colo.*

Brimley (1923, p. 4) has recorded the eating of a timber rattlesnake by an opossum in captivity. Schrenkeisen (1930, p. 70) states that when an opossum was put in a cage with an eastern diamondback and a brood of young, the opossum ate the brood of 18 young rattlers the first night, and on the second killed and ate a part of the mother snake.

Cats, Domestic and Wild

The following account of a house cat that killed rattlers was sent me by Col. M. L. Crimmins of San Antonio, Texas:

The first rattlesnake that we saw in the cat's possession was only about two and a half feet long. While we did not see her kill it, it was still moving when she brought it to the house. A short time afterward she brought in a little rattlesnake about eleven inches long which had been dead for some considerable time. The actual record of rattlesnake killing is as follows: In August, 1924, an employee of the Apicultural Laboratory at San Antonio came to the office and asked if we would like to see "Momsie Cat," as she was called, kill a rattlesnake. The entire office force proceeded to a piece of flat ground not very far from the Laboratory building, where we saw the mother cat with three half-grown kittens in a battle with the rattlesnake, which was approximately four feet long. The employee said that his wife had heard the rattlesnake making a great deal of noise near their house and on looking out of the door saw the cat watching it. The cat waited till the rattlesnake was coiled and then made a spring toward it. When the rattler struck, the cat dodged the blow and as the snake stretched itself with the blow the cat would bite at the back of its neck. At the time we were called the rattlesnake lay stretched out on the road and was rattling as best he could and attempting to get into some brush. The old cat would walk up slowly until she was about a foot from the rattlesnake's head and then would suddenly jump on the snake's back and bite its neck and then run. She repeated this a number of times. Each attack left the snake in a much weaker condition and at last he coiled up and ceased to rattle. The old cat approached cautiously and catching him by the back of the neck started to drag him toward the house. When she became conscious she was being watched, she left the rattlesnake and came over to where we were watching. She seemingly was exhausted by the fight she had had with the snake. On examination, the back of the snake's head was found to be full of punctures from her teeth. *H. B. Parks, San Antonio, Tex.* (See also Crimmins, 1931, p. 47; and Dobie, 1946b, p. 8c.)

⟡

I noted one particular incident of a house cat's killing a rattler some years ago that was of interest to me. The mother cat had young in a nearby corncrib and happened on this snake in a path near her home. She set about to do away with the intruder and would attack viciously by feinting at the rattler just out of its striking range, and as the snake was uncoiled she would deftly claw it just behind the head and then repeat the maneuver until she finally cut the head nearly off and then finished the job by sinking her teeth through the spine behind the head. This snake was not large, yet it was quite a feat for kitty. The snake had three rattles and a button. *V. A. Shaffer, State Conservation Officer, Murray, Iowa.*

> The only animal I have ever seen kill a rattler was a domesic cat, about half grown. He would make the snake strike until it was tired out, then rush in and seize the snake by the back of the neck. I saw him find one by chance; the other two were caught for him. I have also found the remains where a wild cat had killed a rattler. *R. M. Williams, Arbuckle, Calif.*

> —

> Our two house cats have killed several rattlers, to our knowledge. *John W. Warren, U. S. Forest Service, Hamilton, Mont.*

Newspaper accounts of the killing of rattlers by domestic cats are not infrequent. I have seen such reports from Escondido, El Centro, and Los Angeles, California; and from Rawlins, Wyoming. Ala Jones (1947, p. 50) mentions a house cat that killed a rattler and fed it to her kittens. Adair (1930, p. 62) believes that cats eat rattlers because they taste like fish, a doubtful conclusion. Kalez (1954, p. 76) thought cats would be effective in keeping rattlers away from one's home. Mrs. J. Schlenker (1952, p. 60) has observed that a domestic cat accustomed to kill harmless snakes was afraid of a dead copperhead. *West Virginia Conservation* (vol. 19, no. 6, p. 29, August, 1955) contains an account of a tomcat that chased a four-foot timber rattler.

Pequegnat (1945, p. 74; 1951, p. 50) records an interesting experience which leaves no doubt that bobcats or wild cats occasionally attack and kill rattlers for food. He found a bobcat (*Lynx rufus californicus*) eating a speckled rattler (*Crotalus m. pyrrhus*) on the road, in the Santa Ana Mountains. As no other car had passed that way, the snake had not been run over, the evidence indicating that the cat had pounced on the rattler from a hiding place in the chaparral. When discovered, the cat had eaten the anterior half of the snake, head and all. Blair (1954, p. 255), near Lamesa, Texas, saw a bobcat (*L. r. baileyi*) circling around a bush in which a western diamondback (*C. atrox*) was rattling violently. The cat was frightened away by the observer, who thought it had intended to kill the rattler for food.

RODENTS

That rodents may occasionally attack rattlers is evident from the following accounts:

> I witnessed an interesting encounter between a rattler and woodchucks. A patch of wild peach (*Prunus andersoni*) on the side of a small but steep-sloped gully harbored a large woodchuck family.[2] The flat but narrow bottom of the gully was a rather slushy meadow with a small stream running through it, and sagebrush on all sides. I was accustomed to sitting up on the gully wall and watching either the woodchucks, or the only mockingbirds I ever saw in the immediate vicinity of Reno, with whom the spot seemed a favorite. After 20 minutes browsing from the gully slope, I started down, skirting the wild-peach patch. Abreast of the woodchuck burrow, and only three or four feet away, I straddled a small rattler, and before I could do any rapid co-ordination, he whipped to the mouth of the burrow and disappeared inside. I hadn't seen the woodchucks while sitting on the slope, and they had probably taken their outing before I arrived. About half a minute after the rattler disappeared down the burrow, I heard a muffled commotion, a thumping noise such as wood-rats make with their hind feet. Shortly afterward, the female chuck backed rapidly out of the burrow, dragging the inert rattler behind her. She worried it into the wild-peach thicket surrounding the tunnel, saw me, and dashed for the nest with a loud chattering of teeth. When I examined the snake I found it had been severely bitten about

---

[2] *Marmota flaviventer.*

the head and neck, the neck being almost severed in one place; all wounds were confined to the anterior one-fourth of the animal. The rattler (*Crotalus v. lutosus*) measured nineteen inches in length. Apparently, it caused no observable damage, for I subsequently saw the female chuck on many occasions, none the worse for wear. *Ira La Rivers, University of Nevada, Reno, Nev.*

On July 9, 1944, about 5:30 P.M., a most unusual scene was witnessed on the highway near Ballena. A small button rattler (*C. v. helleri*) was found on the pavement being attacked by a full-grown ground squirrel. Apparently the rattler had been hit by a car, but not crushed. It could not travel but enough of its body was movable to allow it to strike. The squirrel would circle around and around the snake, trying to nip it, and was agile enough to dodge the short strikes of the snake. Twice the squirrel left the road when a car passed. Finally it forgot the battle and left. Just what the attraction could have been was unknown, but the squirrel's action at times reminded me of a cat when sighting game, as its tail would twitch up and down and from side to side in nervous tension. There is a possible chance that the snake had had its tail smashed and the ground squirrel smelled fresh meat to eat. *L. M. Huey, San Diego Society of Natural History, San Diego, Calif.*

Those who keep rattlers in captivity soon learn that it will be fatal to the snakes to put live rats or mice in with them for food, unless the rodents are also well supplied with food for themselves, for otherwise at night they will attack and kill the lethargic snakes. Occasionally they will eat the snakes' tails off without otherwise injuring them. Sometimes they eat the rattles. It is amazing how defenseless a snake is in such a situation. The following accounts are quite typical:

I recall an interesting incident that took place on the north rim of Grand Canyon National Park. I had found an adult rattler, somewhat sluggish in its actions. The snake was placed in a large box with plenty of light for observation. A live wood rat was captured and placed in the box as food. It was with some astonishment that I came back a short time later and found the rattlesnake dead with his head almost eaten away. The wood rat was observed for some time thereafter but showed no ill effects of his experience, indicating that he was not even touched by the rattler during the encounter. This is the second time that I had seen a wood rat kill a snake, the previous victim being a bullsnake. *Russell K. Grater, National Park Service, Estes Park, Colo.*

We have a record in our files of a captive rattlesnake being killed by a mouse. The snake did not appear aggressive when the mouse was dropped into the cage as food. The next morning the snake was found dead with a wound in back of the head, and the mouse alive. *Louis Schellbach, National Park Service, Grand Canyon, Ariz.*

In our novice days (1922–23) at the San Diego Zoo, we lost a number of rattlers before we learned that mice and rats, if put alive in the cages for snake food, would kill the snakes when they got hungry; see also Bell (1839, p. 62), Figuier (1869, p. 87), Kunzé (1879, p. 312), Stradling (1881, p. 148), Quelch (1891, p. 9), Walls (1906, p. 386), Guthrie (1929, p. 351), Seton (1940, p. 84), and Hylander (1951, p. 155). During the week when this paragraph was written, there appeared in a Los Angeles paper an illustrated story of the killing, by a "mere" mouse, of a large captive rattlesnake belonging to a local college. Evidently each institution must learn from its own experiences.

There is a story, current in the Western Plains states, that prairie dogs destroy the rattlers that invade their homes by plugging with tamped earth any hole that they have seen a rattler enter (Brons, 1882, p. 565; Hopkins, 1905, p. 354; Ringle, 1924, p. 20; Pawlowsky, 1927, p. 288; Brown, 1936, p. 24; Duncan, 1945, p. 167).

In view of the fact that prairie dogs seem to abandon towns that rattlers have taken over as hibernating dens, this story requires confirmation.

MISCELLANEOUS MAMMALS

A variety of other mammals attack rattlesnakes, presumably to eat them.

> I can record the finding of a small ground rattler (*Sistrurus miliarius streckeri*) in the stomach of an adult nine-banded armadillo. This was in Houston County, Texas, in early June, 1935. I examined the stomach myself, and found a small undamaged snake, probably swallowed only a little while before. East Texans believe that armadillos attack and kill large snakes, but I have found no corroborating evidence. Also, from east Texas comes the once-heard tale that pileated woodpeckers kill rattlers, but I don't believe it at all. *Sam D. Hinton, La Jolla, Calif.*
>
> ◇
>
> I have known raccoons to eat rattlesnakes. *Frank E. Brink, Fish Warden, Milford, Pa.*

C. H. Pope (1944, p. 224) had a pet raccoon that seemed to fear rattlesnakes. M. G. Netting (1932, p. 6) mentions weasels among other enemies of rattlesnakes. Ariza (1948, p. 60) suggests that minks may kill diamondbacks. Dudley (1723, p. 294) mentions bears as being rattlesnake eaters. This, not having been verified in the intervening years, may be considered highly questionable.

Skunks are said to eat rattlesnakes. Cowles (1938, p. 15) found that rattlesnakes exhibited a defense reaction when a skunk odor was present. A spotted skunk (*Spilogale gracilis phenax*) readily ate a live sidewinder, seizing it by the neck. Yet wild striped skunks (*Mephitis mephitis occidentalis*), accustomed to feed in a garden, recognized the sound of a rattler rattling, and showed fear.

"Buckskin Harry" (1892, p. 135) claims to have watched (with field glasses) a skunk attack a rattlesnake. The skunk danced around the rattler, which struck at it again and again. Finally, the skunk charged in and bit the snake's neck almost through in a single bite. Unfortunately, the observer did not wait to see whether the skunk would have eaten the snake, which measured three feet six inches. The skunk was uninjured; although Harry thought it had been struck several times, the fangs may not have gone beneath the fur. There are species of skunks (*Conepatus*) in South America that regularly attack venomous snakes, including the Neotropical rattler (Vellard, 1949a, 1949b, 1950a, 1950b).

> A hunting companion and I were sitting on a deer stand when a large northern Pacific rattler crawled out from beneath a rock. My friend, being a pistol crank, shot the rattler through the head. While it was in its death throes, a pair of ring-tailed cats[3] ran out from under another big rock and promptly dined on the rattler. Aside from this, when I stated that ringtails and wild cats kill rattlers, I was judging by episodes that could be reconstructed from tracks. *R. M. Williams, Arbuckle, Calif.*

Taylor (1954, p. 61) confirms the rare inclusion of a rattlesnake in the diet of the ring-tailed cat.

Even the lowly rabbit will defend its young:

> One Sunday afternoon I heard a rabbit squeal, and looking in the direction of the sound, I saw a mother rabbit jump onto a spot and give a terrible rake with her hind feet. Hurrying to the place, I saw a large rattlesnake swallowing a small rabbit. Blood was oozing out of marks on the snake's back caused by the toenails of the mother rabbit. I killed the snake and found three young rabbits inside. *W. W. Britton, Chambersburg, Pa.*

---

[3] *Bassariscus astutus.*

BIRD ENEMIES

EAGLES

As might be expected, birds of prey that feed in part on snakes occasionally take rattlesnakes. Among them are eagles, although snakes form a smaller part of their diets than is the case with some of the hawks.

In the Rio Grande National Forest and east of that forest are rocky cliffs that were the nesting areas of golden eagles. The remains of rattlers were found at the base of these cliffs under five different nests. The remains of three rattlers were found under one nest. *M. R. Hickel, Salida, Colo.*

◇

I have seen two golden eagle's nests in which young rattlesnakes had been fed to the young. There were pieces of the snakes lying around the edges of the nests. *Eddie Buchta, U. S. Fish and Wildlife Service, Moneta, Wyo.*

◇

I have watched a bald eagle kill a rattlesnake and try to carry it away to its nest. The eagle would grab the rattlesnake with his claws and try to fly away with it, but the rattlesnake was large and the eagle could not seem to raise it more than a few hundred feet in the air. Whereupon it would drop the snake and go down and try the process over again. *Lloyd L. Bernhard, U. S. Forest Service, Okanogan, Wash.*

W. A. Allen (1903, p. 87; Dobie, 1946d, p. 7c) tells in detail of an encounter between a bald eagle and a large prairie rattlesnake. The eagle attempted to beat the snake with its wings; also to injure it by dropping it from a moderate height. The eagle eventually won, and flew away carrying the rattler. In another eagle-rattler battle (McReynolds, 1906, p. 80; Dobie, 1946d, p. 7c) the eagle's tactics failed, for the rattler eventually landed a fatal strike and killed the bird. Dobie (1949, p. 119; 1952a, p. 6) has stated that eagles carrying rattlers to their nestlings first tear off the snake's head, as has also been reported by Oberholser (1906, p. 29).

One may wonder whether an eagle would defend its nest against an encroaching rattler:

Once I found a rattler on the same ledge with an occupied golden eagle's nest; the snake was about 10 feet from the nest and on the same level with it, so it could easily have entered if it had cared to. *Ed N. Harrison, Encinitas, Calif.*

Carnie (1954, p. 7) studied prey remains at the nests of 17 pairs of golden eagles, between 1947 and 1952, in the central Coast Range of California. He found 28 snakes among 503 food items; there were 26 gopher snakes (*Pituophis catenifer catenifer*), one king snake (*Lampropeltis getulus californiae*), and one northern Pacific rattlesnake (*Crotalus viridis oreganus*). King snakes are not nearly so common in this area as gopher snakes and rattlers, which are present in substantially equal numbers. The predominance of gopher snakes suggests discrimination on the part of the eagles.

HAWKS

Hawks, especially red-tailed hawks, prey quite regularly on rattlers, as will be observed from the following extracts from letters:

I have often found the remains of snakes in the nests of western red-tailed hawks (*Buteo jamaicensis calurus*). Most of them have been gopher or king snakes but several times the remains of rattlesnakes were seen. Once when collecting birds' eggs in Otay Valley, an adult red-tailed hawk flew close overhead carrying a red rattlesnake (*C. r. ruber*) in its talons. No doubt the snake had just been captured, for it was buzzing violently. The bird must have had the reptile securely gripped in its talons well toward the head as there seemed to be a long length of snake dangling as it flew over. *L. M. Huey, San Diego Society of Natural History, San Diego, Calif.*

I have seen one instance in which a western red-tailed hawk was carrying a rattler in its claws, and the hawk and the snake were having a very lively time. The snake was not full grown, but was making so much noise with its rattles that my attention was called to the bird passing on the wing nearby. I very much doubt if a western red-tailed hawk could manage a full-grown rattler of the kinds we have locally.

On the desert, the Swainson hawk feeds largely on horned toads, lizards, and various snakes, and I have seen dried skeletons of snakes at the tree base where nests were located. The Swainson hawk is a large hawk, nearly as large as the western red-tailed hawk, and is migratory, and I believe they would feed on the desert sidewinder along with all the local species of lizards. I have found nests with young of this hawk in which the principal food supply was horned toads.

The red-bellied hawk is a major enemy of the garter snake. They do not hunt where rattlers would be likely to be found, and we have never seen any rattlers brought to their nests while taking pictures of them. *J. B. Dixon, Escondido, Calif.*

I have found two red-tailed hawks with fresh-killed rattlers close to the nest; in both cases, the heads were nearly cut loose from the bodies. Apparently they take the heads off before taking the snakes to the young birds in the nest. I have found in one case, the same hawk with a gopher snake at the nest, with the head still on and uncut. *C. E. Holladay, State Game Warden, San Jose, Calif.*

I saw a large hawk fly overhead with a snake dangling from its claws. When I shot at the hawk, it dropped the snake, which I found to be a large, freshly killed rattler. *Clarence R. Ousley, Napa, Calif.*

In 1918 a red-tailed hawk was seen flying with a snake near Wellton, Arizona. The hawk was making heavy weather of it because of the weight of the snake. I shot close to the bird with a .22 rifle, causing it to drop the snake, which I recovered. It was a rattler 4 feet 2 inches long,[4] that had been caught by the head and neck, which were thoroughly punctured. *Richard M. Bond, Soil Conservation Service, Portland, Oreg.*

Twice I have seen hawks swoop down and pick up rattlers and fly away with them. I don't know whether the hawks killed them or not, but I presumed they did. *E. C. Holder, State Game Ranger, Winslow, Ariz.*

I have seen hawks flying with rattlesnakes. I do not know how the birds caught the snakes. *F. E. Williams, U. S. Forest Service, Riggins, Idaho.*

Once in Utah, at about 5:30 P.M., I saw a large hawk dive down, catch a snake back of the head and fly into the air with it. I watched the hawk land on a small rocky ledge. Being afraid the hawk might fly away with the snake, I pulled my rifle and killed the hawk. I found the snake was a rattler with three rattles and a button. The hawk had pushed its claws completely through the snake, about one inch behind the head. *Wm. V. Connary, Bancroft, Idaho.*

---

[4] A rattler of this length would weigh about 2½ pounds.

I have seen many rattlers destroyed by hawks—the hawk known as the chicken hawk. This hawk seldom, if ever, destroys chickens. *Ellen Johnston, U. S. Fish and Wildlife Service, Shelby, Mont.*

◇

I once destroyed a hawk's nest in which there were two dead rattlers, partly eaten. There were two large young hawks in the nest. *W. S. Owens, Cody, Wyo.*

◇

One of the animals which preys on the Great Basin rattlesnake in the vicinity of Reno is *Buteo jamaicensis calurus*, the western red-tailed hawk. I have found two nests of this species containing rattlesnake remains, both nests near a large snake den on Peavine Mountain. Both snakes would have been classed as medium sized for the area, neither appearing to exceed 24 inches in length. I never saw a hawk make a capture, but the possibility that these birds had picked up dead snakes seems to me too remote to be tenable, in the light of what I know of their feeding habits. I know they are quick enough to catch such agile lizards as the leopard lizard (*Crotaphytus wislizeni*), so they probably do not have much trouble with the occasional rattler they attack. *Ira La Rivers, University of Nevada, Reno, Nev.*

◇

I saw a red-tailed hawk eating a rattler once, but I cannot say whether he killed it or not. *Paul D. Wilcox, State Fish Warden, Wyalusing, Pa.*

I have received several accounts of hawks picking up rattlers and then dropping them as if to kill them, as, for example:

Near Aladdin, Wyoming, in 1944, I observed an American rough-leg hawk in flight with a snake dangling from his feet. Watching him, I saw him release the squirming snake and swoop to the ground to follow it. I rushed to the scene of action and found a badly torn and still fighting-mad prairie rattler about 28 inches long with eleven rattles. I killed the snake that I am sure would have died of its wounds which, because of their lacerated character, could hardly have been made by other means than the hawk's talons. Whether this was a case of fresh meat for the hawk or a quarrel over a chipmunk, ground squirrel, or other rodent, I cannot say. *F. R. Cochran, U. S. Forest Service, Sundance, Wyo.*

◇

Hawks and eagles have been seen carrying rattlesnakes while flying. After getting up to a fair altitude they let them drop, and then swoop down after them again. Probably this fall either kills the snake or stuns it. *Glenn Flathers, U. S. Forest Service, Camp Crook, S. Dak.*

◇

I have seen a hawk swoop down, pick up a rattlesnake, and drop it immediately after having inflicted deep flesh wounds. *Ivan L. Gyreng, U. S. Forest Service, Ephraim, Utah.*

◇

I have seen nesting hawks pick up rattlers, carry them up for several hundred feet, and then drop them on rocks, after which they dive down and pick them up again. We opened up one hawk and found that he had cut one snake in sections of about 3 or 4 inches and swallowed it. *W. G. Miller, U. S. Forest Service, Enterprise, Oreg.*

◇

I saw a chicken hawk pick up a rattlesnake off the ground and fly straight up in the air with it. When the hawk got about 300 feet up in the air, it dropped the snake and let it fall about 100 feet and then caught it with its talons. This went on for some time, until the snake had most of the life taken out of it, and was ready to make a meal for the hawk. *Ollie Cox, U. S. Fish and Wildlife Service, Eureka, Nev.*

From these accounts it appears that, of all the American hawks, the redtail is probably the most persistent rattlesnake eater. Yet even this hawk occasionally finds a rattler too much to handle with safety.

In 1922, while hiking in the foothills east of Fresno, California, I found a dead rattlesnake and five feet away lay a dead adult western red-tailed hawk. The snake, which was about two feet long, was partially eaten. Between the snake and the hawk was a mass, about a cupful, of rattlesnake meat and skin that appeared to have been regurgitated by the hawk. The snake and hawk had been dead only a few hours when found.

Possibly the hawk had been struck while killing the snake but proceeded with its feast. When the poison began to take effect, it regurgitated its meal and died shortly after. There was one bit of evidence that made me question the snake-poison theory, and that was the fact that I could find no local swelling on the hawk. However, there was no evidence of external injury that may have caused its death. *A. E. Borell, U. S. Fish and Wildlife Service, Albuquerque, N. Mex.*

A. M. Jackley, who, in connection with his rattlesnake-control work in South Dakota, was accustomed to leave many dead rattlers scattered about the dens that he raided, was convinced that some of these bodies were carried away by hawks.

In addition to the observations supplied by my correspondents, there is considerable information in ornithological and other literature on the extent to which hawks prey on rattlesnakes. Jensen (1926, p. 368), near Santa Fe, New Mexico, saw a red-tailed hawk drop down to the base of a cliff. Through his glass he could see that some kind of battle was being waged, the bird waving its wings and continually changing its position. As he approached, the hawk took wing, carrying a medium-sized rattlesnake.

Stanley (1917, p. 39) also described the capture of a rattlesnake by a hawk. It is stated that a blow of the bird's wing so crippled the snake the bird was able to make off with it. Duncan (1945, p. 167) has stated that an eagle or hawk will feint at a rattler until it uncoils, whereupon the bird will seize it with one foot, just behind the head.

Hinman (1951, p. 46) watched a large grayish hawk making determined swoops at something on the ground. After the fourth dive, he went over and found the hawk trying to make off with a rattler that was too large for it to lift. The snake's head was nearly severed from is body. Fitch and Glading (1947, p. 120) reported three rattlers in red-tailed hawks' nests, and one redtail that was carrying a rattler. Also, they saw a Cooper hawk flying with a small rattler in its talons. Ospreys are said to catch swimming snakes, including rattlers, in Florida, but no eye-witness account has been available to me. J. D. Mitchell (1903, p. 39) says that the so-called Mexican eagle, the caracara—really a hawk—is a killer of rattlesnakes.

There is also the corroborative evidence of stomach and pellet (regurgitated indigestible remnants of prey) contents on the rattlesnake-killing proclivities of hawks, especially redtails. Anthony (1893, p. 234) found a large rattler coiled in the stomach of a red-tailed hawk; this was in the San Pedro Mártir Mountains of Baja California. Fisher (1893, p. 60) reported rattler remains in two red-tailed hawks, out of 562 stomachs examined. Bent (1937, p. 158) includes rattlesnakes among the food of red-tailed hawks.

On the San Joaquin Experimental Range, in Madera County, California, Fitch, Swenson, and Tillotson (1946, p. 222) report that out of 625 red-tailed hawk prey items at 14 different nests, there were two rattlers. In 2,094 pellets there were rattler remains in 70 (p. 225). But the redtail certainly does not discriminate in favor of rattlers. Quite the contrary; on the Experimental Range, rattlers were encountered by humans five times as often as gopher snakes (*Pituophis c. catenifer*), but in the nests and pellets the gopher snakes outnumbered the rattlers almost three to one. The authors conclude that even the redtail has an instinctive caution with regard to rattlers (p. 230). Altogether, it is inferred that rattlesnakes comprise about 2.1 per cent of the redtail's prey by weight (p. 232).

Audubon (1827, p. 24) asserted that he watched snakes hide under rocks to avoid being seen by vultures or falcons flying overhead. Like others of Audubon's observations on snakes, this is hardly to be credited.

Owls

A survey of owl food habits indicates that rattlesnakes, even in an area where these snakes are common, are seldom included in the prey of owls.

> The reptile records resulting from the examination of the Wichita great horned owl food-habit material disclosed no rattlesnakes. Over 1,054 pellets and packages of nest debris were examined over a 4-year period. In a number of the records, it was impossible to determine the reptile species, for frequently only a scale or two were found. But the writer has never found an identifiable segment of a rattlesnake in any of the nests of the Wichita great horned owl, or in any of the pellets analyzed, although many snakes could be identified. This may be of interest, for the western diamondback (*C. atrox*) is one of the most abundant snakes there, and it is most active at night, especially during the warmer season. *Frank B. McMurry, U. S. Fish and Wildlife Service, Yuma, Ariz.*

> ◇

> I have seen a large owl eating a freshly killed rattlesnake, but have never seen a snake actually being killed or carried off. *Ben Nelson, U. S. Forest Service, Mayer, Ariz.*

Fitch (1947, p. 140) reported the horned owl (*Bubo virginianus pacificus*) to be plentiful on the San Joaquin Experimental Range. A study of pellets revealed the remains of 4 rattlers out of a total of 37 snakes and a total of 1,014 pellets. No snake constituted as much as 1 per cent of the prey of the horned owl (Fitch, 1947, p. 140; Fitch and Glading, 1947, p, 120). No evidence was found that the barn owl preys on rattlesnakes. Various other authors report owls as eating rattlers but without giving details, e.g., Barton (1799, p. 111), Dannaldson (1937, p. 31). FitzGerald (1907, p. 352) mentions a burrowing owl in South America that is said to prey on young rattlers.

Roadrunners

The roadrunner (*Geococcyx californianus*) is the most famous rattlesnake killer in the Southwest, but many of its exploits are quite mythical. Of course, the story (see p. 1251) of the roadrunner that builds a wall of cactus around a rattlesnake, so the latter will be stuck by the thorns and thus be angered into committing suicide, is a myth for several reasons, among which we need mention only that rattlers often crawl into cactus beds as places of refuge and seem undismayed by the spines. There is no doubt that roadrunners dispose of young rattlers as they would feed on other young snakes, but adult rattlers would be too large for a roadrunner to cope with. A variant of this story is to the effect that roadrunners kill rattlers by so annoying and confusing them that they are prevented from reaching the shade and thus are killed by the sun. It is possible this may occasionally happen.

> There has been much discussion relative to the roadrunner or chaparral cock killing rattlesnakes. I don't know whether one bird would attack a snake or not, but I once saw an

old hen and a cock bird kill a snake. It took about a half hour to accomplish the task and I still doubt that they actually killed the snake. In my opinion, the snake died of exhaustion. I examined the snake's body and found the skin broken only in one place. But in the stomach contents were two small chaparral birds. In this battle, each time the snake would strike or attempt to crawl away, a bird would take a peck at it. *L. E. Crawford, State Game Ranger, Lawton, Okla.*

◇

I witnessed one roadrunner killing a 3-foot[5] rattlesnake; this bird flew into the air about 3 feet and grabbed the snake just back of its head and ran off with it. *Phil Kennedy, U. S. Forest Service, Douglas, Ariz.*

◇

In the vicinity of Mojave, California, I came upon a roadrunner with an 18-inch sidewinder. Instead of dropping the snake, the roadrunner scuttled off with the snake trailing over its back, as a fox is said to carry a goose. As it would have been awkward to run with a partially swallowed snake dangling in front, the slinging over its back must have been deliberate. *Josiah Keely, Huntington, N. Y.*

◇

In the Coast Range I have seen roadrunners kill and eat small rattlers. *M. D. Morris, U. S. Forest Service, Pollock Pines, Calif.*

◇

When a roadrunner comes upon a rattlesnake it drops its wings and approaches cautiously. The snake coils for striking. The roadrunner jumps at the snake, back and forth, teasing the snake to strike, and, when it does, the roadrunner jumps in and pecks the snake on the head just over the brain, and this it continues until the snake is dead. I have seen this done while working in the field as a predatory-animal trapper. *Richard Ray, Clovis, Calif.*

◇

The roadrunner is plentiful in Wyoming and parts of Nevada. As an eyewitness, I've never seen one of these birds licked. I've watched several fights with rattlers; I either shot the rattlesnake or the bird killed it. But I have seen evidence in several places after a battle, that the rattler killed the roadrunner. *William Conway, Bancroft, Idaho.*

◇

The roadrunner is an active enemy of rattlesnakes, especially the young. The young snakes are eaten by the roadrunners; and in turn, the young roadrunners are preyed on by rattlesnakes. *Ben Nelson, U. S. Forest Service, Mayer, Ariz.*

◇

Upon one occasion I found two young rattlers (with a button and a single segment to their rattles) dead and lying in a roadrunner's nest. *K. R. Halstead, San Bernardino, Calif.*

◇

The roadrunners here kill many rattlers. I have found young in the nest that had parts of a rattlesnake protruding from their bills. *R. M. Williams, Arbuckle, Calif.*

◇

Ben L. Clarey, who was then living in Coachella, California, found a roadrunner nest, with three eggs, in a date palm. That was in May, 1930. When the young were 10 days old we caught a young rattler and turned it loose at the foot of the tree. Just as soon as we released the snake, the roadrunner, which had been watching us from the date palm, saw the snake on the ground. It jumped down, ran to the snake, and faced it; the snake seemed to fear the bird. The roadrunner would run up and stop quickly, using its tail as a brake. After a number of rushes at the snake, the roadrunner made one quick strike with its bill on the back of the snake's head. Then it ran off with the snake dangling from its mouth. With field glasses we watched the bird swallow the rattler head first. I should judge the snake was about 30 inches long.[6] I repeated the experiment when I found another nest with young in a tree in Glendale Cemetery. I put the snake on the ground near the nest. The roadrunner would stop the snake, but would not attack it, probably because the snake was too large and lizards were too plentiful. *I. H. Johnston, Los Angeles, Calif.*

---

[5] Probably an overestimate; such a snake would weigh about a pound, too heavy for the bird to carry. An adult roadrunner weighs slightly less than a pound.

[6] No doubt an overestimate.

As Mr. Johnston's second experience indicates, roadrunners will not invariably attack rattlers.

In the summer of 1942 I released a 2-foot Pacific rattler near a roadrunner. The bird danced around the snake for a time, but made no actual attack. *Frank F. Gander, Escondido, Calif.*

⟡

As to roadrunners killing a rattlesnake, I will say I don't believe there is anything to it. I have seen hundreds of these birds and watched them feed, but have never seen one even close to a snake. They would no doubt kill a baby snake of any kind, just as they do lizards large and small. *Walter F. Emerick, Division of Fish and Game, Palmdale, Calif.*

⟡

I think it doubtful that roadrunners kill rattlesnakes, unless the snake is small enough for them to eat. *Walter T. Pew, U. S. Fish and Wildlife Service, Hemet, Calif.*

⟡

In south Texas, 35 years ago, rattlesnakes were thick. In all my experiences there as a kid and young man, I never saw a rattler killed by a roadrunner; neither have I ever seen a pen, or trap of cactus and thorns, that they are supposed to build around a rattler so that they can kill it at their leisure. *Dow Jones, District Game Warden, Palisade, Colo.*

Partly because of the rather quaint antics of the roadrunner, and also owing to the widespread cactus-corral myth, the roadrunner is frequently mentioned in the literature as a rattlesnake enemy, yet few of the accounts are eyewitness experiences. Gregg (1844, vol. 1, p. 195) and Bartlett (1854, vol. 2, p. 563) give two of the first accounts of the killing of rattlesnakes by roadrunners. Wadham (1882, p. 27) contains one of the earliest reports in which the roadrunner kills a rattlesnake by picking out its eyes.

Bryant (1916, p. 37) had a report from E. A. Goldman of finding several young rattlesnakes in the stomach of a roadrunner. However, he believes the reputed enmity of roadrunners for rattlesnakes to be exaggerated. Johnston (1929, p. 3) tells of a roadrunner killing a 20-inch rattler. Motl (1936, p. 4) claims that roadrunners kill rattlers by picking out their eyes.

Dobie (1937, p. 137; 1939, p. 78) details several accounts of rattlers killed by roadrunners. In these, rattlers 3½ and 3 feet long were killed. One rattler was killed by having its head pecked and only the brain was eaten. Blanchard (1940, p. 32) says roadrunners are interested only in rattlers of a size small enough so that they can be killed and eaten, and that they probably dispose of numbers of young ones. E. Jackson (1940, p. 11) gives a fictional account, but based on observation, of how a roadrunner would proceed to kill a rattler. In a second article (1943, p. 14) he describes how a roadrunner attacked a snake 5 feet 6 inches long. Nabers (1953, p. 2) found a roadrunner that was attacking two rattlers at once, by diving at them alternately. Ramsey (1945, p. 37) states that roadrunners dispatch rattlers by keeping them from reaching shade, so that they are killed by the heat. This has at least some element of possibility.

Benton (1945, p. 81) reports that roadrunners tease rattlers into striking repeatedly; then when the venom is exhausted they rush in and kill the snake by pecking its head and neck. A similar statement is made by Duncan (1945, p. 167). Fitch and Glading (1947, p. 120), on the San Joaquin Experimental Range, reported that roadrunners were seen while carrying young rattlers on three occasions. In two, the rattlers may have been road casualties, but in the third case a bird was carrying a squirming 2-foot rattler. McKenna (1936, p. 225) says that prospectors always kept an eye out for rattlers if they saw a pair of roadrunners around. Some years ago a popular moving picture, *The Adventures of Chico*, contained an episode in which a roadrunner killed a rattler.

WILD TURKEYS

Wild turkeys, particularly when in flocks, will sometimes destroy a rattler:

> I observed four turkeys on the Custer Forest march around a coiled rattler and kill him, then pick the rattler to pieces. When the rattler struck at the turkey in front of him, one or two behind would dart in and peck him in the head. *R. J. Bowers, U. S. Forest Service, Philipsburg, Mont.*

Santleben (1910, pp. 48–49; Crimmins, 1931, p. 46) gives the following account of an attack by turkeys on a rattler:

> Rattlesnakes were found in great numbers in west Texas, and they were enemies that had to be guarded against at all times. Wild turkeys always show a great antipathy to them and never fail to make a deadly and persistent attack until the reptile is destroyed. An opportunity to witness such conflicts is seldom offered, therefore I will notice one instance of the kind that came under my observation. I was traveling the road near Uvalde, when I saw a large flock of wild turkeys in an open glade near the highway. I stopped when I saw the gobblers had congregated in a circle where they seemed to be fighting; but soon, I perceived they were killing a large rattlesnake. One after the other, would spring into the air in rapid succession, and come down on the reptile, which they struck a hard blow with one wing that might have been heard quite a distance. Apparently, all the gobblers took part in the fracas, and they seemed to be greatly excited; but the hens fed quietly in the vicinity and seemed to be indifferent to what was going on.
>
> I watched them about ten minutes before they observed my presence and became alarmed. After they disappeared in the brush, I approached the place and found the snake coiled up and almost dead. Evidently, the gobblers had engaged in killing him for some time before I appeared on the scene; and, if they had not been disturbed, the victim would have provided a feast for the whole flock because it was their custom to eat the snakes killed in that way.

Rutledge (1935, p. 521; 1936, p. 139) states that turkeys will attack a small rattler, but will only dance around a large one. Duncan (1945, p. 167) describes the killing of rattlers by gobblers that strike the snake with their wings and peck at its head. Hubbard (1948, p. 232; Dobie, 1947c) tells how a gobbler, with wings, spurs, and bill, killed a rattler that had fatally bitten a poult in the flock.

DOMESTIC POULTRY

Domestic turkeys react toward rattlers in somewhat the same manner as the wild ones, except that they rarely will attack a rattler:

> We have had occasion numerous times to observe the activity of turkeys upon discovery of a rattler in their pens. The turkeys will circle the snake but do not make any attempt to peck it or kill it. The snake's reaction to so many clucking heads is frequently to coil up and hide its head under its body. I have never seen a rattler strike at the turkeys. The snakes we speak of have ranged in size from eighteen inches to three feet long. Because of our love of turkeys, we are alert to their habits and can tell immediately by their peculiar clucking that they have a snake circled. We proceed to kill the snake, of course, when this happens. *A. P. Holly, Ramona Turkey Growers' Assn., Ramona, Calif.*

◇

> I saw turkey gobblers kill a rattlesnake about two feet long. *Huston Cline, Ramona, Calif.*

When turkeys see anything move, they gather around and make a complete circle. When it moves again, you should see them run and they cause so much excitement that we go to see what is wrong; and if it should be a rattler, we always help the turkeys and kill the snake. We have raised many thousands of turkeys the past ten years, and they have never killed but one snake; that was last year, and it was not a rattler. *E. C. Walton, Ramona, Calif.*

◇

I don't believe turkeys, either hens or gobblers, ever kill rattlers. I have seen them gather around snakes often, yet I never saw them touch one—they always kept their distance. *M. W. Durham, U. S. Forest Service, Pasadena, Calif.*

◇

In 1935 or 1936, there was a severe grasshopper infestation in eastern Colorado and turkeys were herded in bands like sheep over the infested areas. In the foothill area north of Ft. Collins, a region well known for its rattlesnakes, turkeys played an important role in reducing the numbers of both grasshoppers and rattlesnakes. They didn't eat the snakes, but when one was discovered by the feeding turkeys they immediately started to gobble and half a dozen or more turkeys would surround the snake. This commotion could be heard or seen by the herder, who carried a hoe for the express purpose of killing snakes. One woman herder, using this method of discovery, killed over 400 rattlesnakes in one season, and a man herder in the same general area was reported to have beaten this record. *Bruce Torgny, U. S. Forest Service, Montrose, Colo.*

Stillwell (1949, p. 112; see also Spaulding, 1944, p. 167), who herded turkeys for a while, reported that they would always surround a rattler and set up a clamor, to which he would respond by killing the snake. In the San Francisco *Call* of Sept. 13, 1911, p. 1, col. 2, there is a report that the gobblers would not only surround a rattler, but would peck it to death.

Chickens also occasionally dispose of young rattlers.

I had two of my 3-pound chickens kill and eat two young rattlesnakes they caught in my back yard in San Antonio. *Col. M. L. Crimmins, San Antonio, Tex.* (See also Crimmins, 1931, p. 47.)

◇

I have caught another fine pigmy rattler, the second in 10 years from this locality, Berkeley County, South Carolina. It was caught under unusual circumstances. I was standing in my yard (my place is located in thick woods, 5 miles from town), when, suddenly, one of my chickens came running from the woods in the yard with what looked like a spotted garter snake hanging from its head. I took after it. The chicken ran in the woods and would not drop the snake until I had overtaken it. To my surprise, I saw it was a fine pigmy rattler, striking right and left, unharmed except for a few rattles missing. So after searching for years for one while on snake hunts, one of my chickens carried one into my yard for me. *H. Ellison Mitchell, Amazon Zoölogical Institute, Charleston, S. C.*

As long ago as 1799, Barton (p. 111) reported he had seen chickens eat young rattlesnakes. McGee (1879, p. 841) watched turkeys and chickens circle around a dead harmless snake, showing that movement is not necessary to attract their attention. Sometime ago there was a report from Healdsburg, California, of a young rattler killed by a hen. E. Jackson (1942, p. 42) states that both turkeys and chickens will kill and eat small rattlers. Burum (1944, p. 3) tells how a game hen battled a rattlesnake with little damage to either contestant. Kelsey (1952, p. 162) mentions the commotion made by a lot of hens surrounding a rattler they had found.

MISCELLANEOUS BIRDS

On several occasions I have noted ravens eating young rattlers by the roadside, but these probably were traffic casualties, and I cannot be certain whether these birds would attack a live snake. In one instance the snake had been dead so long as to be quite dried up. The raven was jumping on it, seizing it in his bill and then dropping it again.

I have seen crows bothering rattlesnakes but do not know that they kill them. *R. L. Kloppenburg, U. S. Forest Service, San Luis Obispo, Calif.*

<>

In 1915, while plowing sod with a tractor, I saw a flock of bobolinks attack a rattler. They left him blinded and his head and neck raw. The snake was on the plowed ground and had no place to hide. In an hour's time the snake was dead. *Charles G. Holzworth, Kremmling, Colo.*

<>

I believe birds will kill and eat young rattlers, as I saw a Ward's blue heron catch a small moccasin; he got it crosswise in his bill, and kept his own neck stretched and so the snake couldn't bite him. Finally he got the tail straight in his bill and the moccasin, about 2 ft. of him, disappeared down the heron's throat.[7] *Joseph T. McCullough, U. S. Forest Service, Brooklyn, Miss.*

<>

On June 26, 1945, as we approached Girvin, Pecos County, Texas, a rattlesnake crossed the road, and my companion, Dr. Henry Slavik, saw a killdeer attacking it while I was busy getting my snare-stick and bag. It was a western diamond rattler about three feet long, with seven rattles and a button. *Col. M. L. Crimmins, San Antonio, Tex.*

<>

In June of 1941, the sixteenth to be exact, I located the nest of a loggerhead shrike in Cobb County. I was interested in the type of prey the bird would bring to the nest. After several days of observation, I saw only the usual things: young mice, small birds, etc. I did not go near the nest for about ten days. One afternoon, I doubled back on a hike and saw what appeared to be an old rope near the base of the bush in which the nest was located. Upon closer examination, it proved to be a very dilapidated specimen of the pigmy rattler, *Sistrurus miliarius miliarius*. The head plates were pretty well demolished but not crushed, which indicates to some extent that the snake was not killed by man. The entire length of the body was picked to pieces in the manner of a shrike eating. The snake was about 225 mm. long. In order to eat, the shrike must have its prey in a strongly fixed position. Therefore, since the snake would probably weigh a bit more than the shrike would be able to carry in its bill for any great distance, it must have been taken near where it was found. *R. E. Gordon, Atlanta, Ga.*

Ramsey (1945, p. 37) also states that young rattlers are the prey of shrikes.

In view of the readiness with which mockingbirds attack cats that approach their nests, it should cause no surprise to learn of their attacking rattlers. Two such accounts, in one of which a rattler had its eyes pecked out, are repeated by Dobie (1946c, p. 10C) and Bedichek (1947, p. 207). I have no doubt a mocker would dive-bomb a rattler, for I see them at frequent intervals from my window as they make the neighboring cats miserable, to say nothing of an occasional dog. Anna Minici (1955, p. 77) tells how a pair of mockers drew attention to a rattler by their calls of alarm. After the Minicis had killed the snake, the mockers dived at and pecked the writhing body. But I think the blinded-eye story needs verification, as do the similar accounts from my correspondents that I have cited on the effects of the attacks of other small birds on rattlers.

---

[7] Sutton, 1946, p. 97, and Moore, 1951, p. 230, also report on the killing of snakes by herons.

Several early writers tell of vultures preying on rattlers, probably through confusion with hawks. An interesting early tale is to the effect that turkey buzzards kill rattlers by means of their intolerable stench (S. R. Brown, 1817, p. 79).

REPTILE AND AMPHIBIAN ENEMIES

KING SNAKES

It is well known that certain snakes, particularly king snakes and racers in the southern United States, will eat rattlesnakes. Such occurrences have often been noted in the wild, and the remains of rattlers have been found in the stomachs of predatory snakes found run over on the road. But no one should think that the harmless snake goes about looking for rattlers to demolish, as an act of altruistic heroism. On the contrary, a young rattler looks like a good meal and will be attacked and eaten. But it is doubtful whether one of these snakes would disturb a rattler too large to handle or to be engulfed.

In order that we might observe the method whereby a king snake attacks and swallows a rattler, young rattlers were fed to king snakes on five occasions during the spring and summer of 1945 at the San Diego Zoo, and on another occasion in 1947. The pattern of procedure is sufficiently standardized so that, while full notes were made on each occasion, only two reports are presented herewith in full, the noteworthy deviations of the other four being only summarized.

Case 1. The following notes describe how a king snake ate a rattler, May 4, 1945.

The king snake was a *Lampropeltis getulus californiae* (ringed phase), a male, about 4 feet long. It had been in captivity since 1936. A smaller striped-phase cagemate was removed. The cage temperature at the floor level was 90° F. During the king snake's captivity it had been fed mice at fairly regular intervals. These it accepted readily. Once it had been fed a fledgling swallow. It had been fed no snakes.

When the door of the cage was opened to take out the other king snake and put in the rattler, the one to be tried out came quickly to the door and rose up for about half its length, showing that it expected food. The rattler, a young female southern Pacific rattler (*C. v. helleri*) with a complete string of 3 rattles, and therefore about 8 months old, was about 16 to 18 inches long. It seemed to be heavy-bodied and well fed.

When the rattler was placed on the ground the king snake, expecting its usual mouse, seemed somewhat at a loss. It first came up to the rattler, which was lying quietly, and stopped with its snout about an inch from the rattler's mid-body. It remained thus for a minute or more. Then it moved ahead slightly until its head was resting on the rattler's body. At this moment C. B. Perkins, in charge of the snakes, returned from feeding the other king snake, whereupon the snake again came to the door and rose up for its prospective mouse. It then lowered as if looking about the cage for the mouse.

The rattler was then moved slightly with a stick, to attract the king's attention. The rattler elevated its body somewhat as in the beginning of the king-snake defense reaction. Immediately the king snake seized the rattler at mid-body.

This was 12:16 p.m. The rattler bit the king snake at once; and, as the king snake threw two coils around the rattler's body, posterior to its head-hold, bit it again toward the neck. The fangs could be seen to take effect. The king snake now threw a third coil around the rattler's body, and then began to work its mouth along the rattler's body toward its head. At 12:17 the rattler, with only a part of its neck and head still free, bit the king snake in the head. The king snake, working its upper and lower jaws alternately and laterally, almost let go of the rattler in these successive motions, which were thereby facilitated, but never quite did so. From the first it had not paused to see whether it was working its own head toward the rattler's head or tail, seeming to know the right direction.

As the king snake reached the rattler's snout, it turned over slightly to rub accumulated sand from its face. At 12:20 the king straightened its neck in front of the rattler so that it was directly facing the prey and started to swallow the head. Behind the straight portion of the king snake's neck, there was a U-shaped bend so that the king's body was parallel to and wrapped around the rattler. At this point, the king snake straightened the rattler's anterior part of the body by pulling back with its own head and neck, the rattler being still held by the coils at mid-body. The rattler's neck was seen to stretch appreciably by the tension, but it is doubtful whether it was injured. There was no evidence that the rattler's neck was broken, as is sometimes stated (probably inaccurately) to occur. At 12:22 the rattler's head had been swallowed; it was still alive but was not moving.

The king snake now started a protracted swallowing process, during the first part of which the rattler's anterior half was kept taut by pulling on its head against the hold of the king snake's coils at the mid-section. As the swallowing proceeded, the coils would be loosened from time to time to permit the rattler to slip forward slightly, yet the tension was maintained, until, with the rattler less than half swallowed, its body was no longer held by the coils, but hung loosely out of the king snake's mouth. Thereafter the swallowing seemed to be more difficult than when the victim's body had been held in tension, but this may have been because the king snake was tiring. After the rattler's tail had been turned loose the king snake did not again throw a coil around the rattler, nor did it attempt to hold the rattler's body down with its own. The rattler did almost no squirming until little more than the tail remained visible.

The king snake's method of working the rattler down was to move its own head from side to side continually, but always keeping it horizontal. There was at this stage little or no evidence of a peristaltic action of the neck muscles, the engulfing of the rattler being largely the result of jaw action. The lower jaw could not be seen, but the upper jaw advanced continuously with alternating cross holds, each one being a little forward of the last. At each loosening of the upper teeth for a new hold, a distinct snapping could be heard as if the teeth pulled loose with difficulty.

The rattler was somewhat over half-way down at 12:25. It was quite motionless and upside down. Meanwhile the king snake was slowly crawling forward around the cage always as if to get a better purchase, but as there was a U-loop in the neck of the king, its *head* was always moving *back* from the rattler. At 12:31 about 5 inches of the rattler were still protruding from the king snake's mouth, and the rattler wriggled its tail slightly. The king snake was still operating its alternating cross holds and the teeth snapped audibly as they pulled loose.

The king snake rested at 12:32, and although it worked a little during the next 3 minutes, it seemed quite tired and some rests lasted a half minute or more. At 12:38 the rattler's tail still protruded and was squirming. Suddenly there was an eversion of the rattler's scent glands and a discharge, after which they were again reverted. The king snake, with the rattler almost engulfed, did not seem to use its neck muscles to work the prey down the throat.

At 12:41 only the end of the tail was showing; it continued to squirm to the last. Now the neck muscles were brought into play and the rattle finally disappeared at 12:44. After this the neck muscles were seen to work much more actively so the rattler was forced down the gullet. When it seemed well down, the king snake made an angle or fold in its neck, and sent this backward as a wave, thus settling the rattler better in the stomach. At 12:46 this was completed and the king snake opened and closed its mouth as if to test it and get it settled properly in place after the strain. The tongue was protruded in a natural way several times. There were still some side motions of the body as if to adjust the meal. The king snake yawned again at 12:48, and then lay extended along one side of the cage. The swallowing had required 32 minutes. The king snake in the following days showed no after-effects from the bites it had received from the rattler.

Case 5. This fifth experiment to demonstrate the king snake's method of eating a rattler was made on August 11, 1945. The purpose of the present test was to determine how a king snake of moderate size would handle a somewhat larger rattler than that eaten in the previous tests. The rattler was a southern Pacific rattler (*C. v. helleri*) weighing 129 grams, with an over-all length of 22 in. It had a complete string of four rattles and was a male, collected in San Diego County. The test was made at the San Diego Zoo on a concrete floor.

The rattler was first put down alongside a king snake (*L. g. californiae,* ringed phase) about 4 feet long. The king snake first watched the rattler at a distance of about 6 feet, putting out its tongue frequently, and gradually coming nearer. The king snake clearly sensed the presence of the rattler, approaching it more closely, and moving each time the rattler moved, but remaining with its head about 4 inches away. Then it approached still closer until its head was about one inch from the rattler's neck. At this time both snakes remained motionless for about 10 minutes. Then the king snake and the rattler separated, and all further attempts to get the king snake to attack the rattler failed.

Another king snake was then brought out. This was of the same subspecies, and had been brought in from Alpine, San Diego County, a few days before. It was a male weighing 256 grams, with a length over-all of 44 in. The rattler was motionless along the wall and once raised its body slightly, giving the standard king-snake reaction, but at no time did it raise its body high enough to give the king snake a blow. The king snake was motionless, facing the wall, and then, as the rattler started crawling slowly along the wall, it passed the king snake and was seized about 4 inches behind the head. This was at 2:09 P.M. The rattler immediately bit the king snake on the neck. The king snake promptly threw five complete coils around the anterior part of the rattler's body just behind where it was holding the rattler with its teeth. The coils were constricted very tightly at or about the rattler's heart. In the twisting, the king snake's anterior was now upside down, but it did not release its jaws. The rattler became stationary without attempting to move its head.

The king snake held on, taking long, deep breaths at intervals. From time to time it seemed to tighten its coils. The rattler made virtually no movement. The king snake could breathe easily, as its holding coils were posterior to the lung, but the rattler, being looped around its single lung, could not breathe. The rattler stuck out its tongue and moved its head slightly at 2:17. The king snake waved its tail and squeezed harder at 2:19. At 2:23 the king snake made its first jaw movement, but then desisted without further movement until 2:28, when there was a second jaw movement. At 2:29 the king snake, with the usual U-loop in its neck, pulled on the rattler, but the location of the jaw hold was so close to the point where the loops circled the rattler's body, that there was virtually no portion of the rattler's body to be stretched. The king snake rolled over at 2:30 so that the anterior part of its body was upright, but it released neither its mouth hold nor the hold of the loops. The rattler's head was now upside down.

There was a slight jaw movement of the king snake at 2:36, and again at 2:39, but there was no particular attempt to work the jaws toward the head. The rattler's lower jaw, but not the fangs, seemed to be caught in the king snake's body; it was making no attempt to bite. The rattler's tail came loose at 2:43, and the head hung as if the rattler were dead. At this time the king snake made several attempts to stretch the rattler out, but as before there was little or no body to stretch, for the hold of the mouth was still about 3 inches from the rattler's head, with the loops very tight just posterior to that point. At 2:45 the king snake made an attempt to free its jaws and then again pulled strongly. There was no movement upon the part of the rattler, which seemed to be quite limp. Finally, at 2:47, the king snake got its teeth free of the rattler's body—that is, the lower jaw; the upper teeth were not completely free until 2:50. The king snake now completely released its mouth hold on the rattler, although not releasing the loops.

At 2:51 the king snake made a short, violent lunge at the rattler's head but missed, notwithstanding the fact that the rattler was completely limp. It did not at this time release in the slightest degree the loops around the rattler's anterior section. The king snake now sniffed along the rattler's body until it reached the tail, and then went back and forth, touching its tongue along the posterior end of the rattler several times; then, passing its own loops, it again reached the neck section of the rattler and bit the neck but did not take hold. Again it returned to the tail section, sniffing about but being unable to determine where to take hold; all of this without releasing the central coils. Finally it located the rattler's head at 2:58, and with a quick lunge seized it at 3:00. It had the rattler's head in its mouth but not quite head-on. At 3:01 it started to swallow and almost immediately had a head-on hold. Swallowing proceeded very slowly, obstructed in part by the width of the rattler's head and by the fact that the king snake was turned in such a way as to come up against a part of its own anterior body. It attempted to work the rattler's head down by twisting its own head, first to one side and then to the other.

The rattler suddenly struggled violently at the tail end at 3:13, which caused the king snake to compress its four coils around the rattler's body as much as possible. The rattler again struggled at 3:15, whereupon the king snake threw another coil around the rattler with its own neck. At 3:20 this additional inter-lock was so complete it was difficult to see how the two snakes would ever become untangled. At this time the king snake appeared to have the rattler's head com-pletely swallowed, but then came up against a section of its own tail with which it had thrown an extra coil around the rattler's neck. This tail coil was held in such a way that it was very difficult to loosen.

They were still in this position at 3:30. The rattler waved its tail and rattled feebly at 3:36, which caused the king snake to tighten its coils. It is to be remem-bered that at this time the king snake had had four tight coils around the rattler's body in the region of the heart and lung for nearly an hour and a half. At 3:40, with the rattler still struggling and waving, the king snake was seen to have the head completely swallowed on the left side, but not quite on the right. Up to 4:01 the same condition existed without change, with the rattler waving posteriorly. The king snake now tried to straighten out its neck and succeeded in pulling an inch or so of the rattler's neck through its own tail coils. It then rested and at 4:08 began again in earnest to try to swallow the head.

There were considerable jaw movements of the king snake at 4:09, 4:10, 4:12, and 4:20, but the angle of the rattler's jaw was still lodged in the angle of the king snake's jaw on the right side, so that it could not be dislodged. Finally, by working its jaw laterally from side to side it seemed to get the rattler's head com-pletely engulfed at 4:23. Immediately it came up against its own tail coil, which it finally loosened at 4:25. Upon doing this it made the usual U-loop in its own neck and pulled strongly on the rattler, drawing some 2 inches of the latter's body through its own coils. It then started swallowing and at 4:27 pulled again, freeing 2 inches more of the rattler. At 4:28 it swallowed rather regularly, moving the head from side to side, and pulled 4 inches of the rattler out of its coils at 4:29. At this time the king snake had a part of its own coils on top of its head, thus weighting down its head, but it could not be determined whether this was done intentionally.

From now on, the swallowing continued with periodical releases of the hold-ing coils, until at 4:30 only two coils were holding the rattler posteriorly. At 4:33 the king snake deliberately stretched part of the rattler's body by pulling against a single holding coil thrown around the rattler's tail section. By 4:40 one-half of the rattler had been engulfed and the swallowing action was continu-ing quite steadily. The snapping of the king snake's teeth as they were released, first on one side and then on the other, could be distinctly heard. Posteriorly the rattler was distended with air, which increased the king snake's difficulties. The rattler's body caught in one angle of the king snake's mouth at 4:44, and it was only with difficulty that the swallowing began again, since by this time the posterior hold had been completely released and the king snake had no way of straightening out the rattler's body.

At 4:50 about 8 inches of the rattler still remained to be swallowed. The king snake, in continuing its swallowing, occasionally waved its head from side to side, thus waving the rattler's tail, and this helped to free the tail when it be-came caught in an angle of the king snake's mouth. I pinched the rattler's tail at 4:58 and it seemed quite dead. The king snake rested for two or three minutes, but again began to work at 5:00, when there were still 3 inches of the rattler's tail protruding. The king snake now began neck movements as if to pull the rattler's body in more readily and completely. It was working slowly as if it had little more space for the rattler inside.

At 5:05 two inches of the rattler's tail still showed. At 5:07 only the rattle itself protruded and the king snake continued a considerable neck action. It now started moving across the floor, with the rattles still protruding. Finally, at 5:09, it closed its mouth over the rattle. At 5:10 it opened its mouth with a yawn and then continued to work the rattler in with backward-moving waves of the neck. It first protruded its tongue at 5:10 and seemed to be completely settled at 5:11— having consumed slightly over three hours in swallowing the rattler. I took the king snake home in a sack and it still retained the rattler at 5:45, but when I returned home at 10:30 the rattler had been disgorged. It was dead.

The following notes will summarize the other three cases in which king snakes ate rattlers during the summer of 1945.

Case 2, July 21. The king snake, a ringed *L. g. californiae* about 4 ft. long ate a small speckled rattler (*C. m. pyrrhus*) about 16 in. long, a male with 2 rattles. The king snake was undisturbed by 7 persons standing about. In this case the king snake seized the rattler posteriorly and threw the holding coils around it anteriorly. This caused considerable difficulty; it released its mouth hold several times but had trouble locating a place to seize the rattler anteriorly. Meanwhile the rattler bit the king snake several times and the fangs were seen to be imbedded. When the king snake finally secured a biting hold anterior to its own coils it had no difficulty in working its jaws down to the rattler's snout, after which swallowing proceeded rapidly. The king snake maintained the customary U-shaped loop in its own neck and stretched the anterior part of the rattler's body very severely during the swallowing process. The total elapsed time was 34 minutes.

Case 3, August 4. In this case a female king snake (*L. g. californiae,* ringed phase) 44 in. long, from San José, Baja California, which had recently laid eggs, ate a young southern Pacific rattler (*C. v. helleri*) about 12 in. long from Palomar Mountain, San Diego County. The temperature was somewhat over 80° F. In this case the king snake got a mouth hold in advance of its holding coils and had little difficulty, although tired enough by the operation to take frequent rests. After seizing the rattler it worked its jaws to the rattler's snout within 4 minutes, so quickly, indeed, that it frequently almost released the rattler in working its jaws along. The king snake had the customary U-shaped loop in its own neck and stretched the rattler violently by pulling against its own holding coils. The entire operation took 36 minutes. The king snake was then put in a sack and carried to my home. Sometime within the 20 minutes en route it regurgitated the rattler, which was entirely unhurt, notwithstanding the severe stretching it had received.

Case 4, August 5. The same snakes were used as in the previous experiment. The temperature was 78° F. The king snake followed the rattler along a wall, passed it, and then suddenly turned and seized it by the head. This was the only instance out of the five in which a head hold was secured initially. Another deviation in this case, possibly owing to the advantageous hold, was that the king snake threw no holding coils around the rattler's body. As a result the rattler did considerable squirming so that its body frequently caught in the angle of the king snake's mouth. When this was done the king snake would open its mouth very wide, completely releasing both jaws, thus disengaging, but not disgorging, the rattler; it would then attempt to draw the rattler in with peristaltic movements of the neck muscles. When a dog approached and sniffed the king snake, it vibrated its tail, although it had previously paid no attention to my leaning over it only a foot or so away. The rattler was completely swallowed in 16 minutes. The lump in the king snake's stomach indicated that the rattler may have been doubled back on itself.

The first excreta appeared August 9, or 4 days later. A few rattler scales were evident. The king snake was preserved on August 12. In the remaining unexcreted material only a few scales, including some ventrals, were recognizable. Neither the rattle nor fangs were evident. The total undigested material was quite small.

Case 6. This test was made in 1947. The king snake was an adult *L. g. californiae* of the longitudinally striped phase. The rattler was a juvenile *helleri* with only a button. The king snake became alert when about 6 feet from the rattler; it approached and suddenly seized the rattler by the nose. With this unusually fortunate hold, it did not trouble to throw body coils around the victim, although several times it pressed its body on the rattler to steady it. The rattler was completely swallowed in 22 minutes.

These six experiences indicate that the king snake, in feeding on a small snake, has the following pattern: It endeavors to seize the victim anteriorly with its jaws, at the same time throwing several holding coils around the body of the prey, posteriorly. The jaws are then worked transversely toward the head of the victim. No attention is paid to any bites if the snake is a rattler, nor have any subsequent ill effects from a bite been observed. When the head is reached, the king snake turns and faces along the body of the prey and swallowing begins. The king snake has a U-shaped curve at the neck, thus facing backward along its own body. Usually it crawls slowly along in a direction opposite to that toward which its head is facing. From time to time, as the swallowing proceeds, the king snake very deliberately pulls strongly on the victim, thus stretching and straightening the unswallowed section between the king snake's mouth and its own holding coils around the posterior end of the prey (fig. 15:1). Repeatedly, as the king snake's snout reaches its own holding coils, several inches of the victim's body are allowed to slip forward through the coils. The coils are usually released entirely when somewhat more than half the prey has been swallowed. A wave motion of the neck muscles is seldom in evidence until the tail has disappeared down the king snake's throat.

Although it is often stated that rattlesnakes swallowed by king snakes are killed, either by constriction or by having their necks broken, this is to be doubted. Only in one of the six cases witnessed at the San Diego Zoo did the rattler appear to be seriously hurt before it disappeared into the king snake. This was in Case 5, which took more than 3 hours for the swallowing process, during most of which

Fig. 15:1. A California king snake (*Lampropeltis getulus californiae*—ringed phase) subduing and swallowing a young southern Pacific rattlesnake (*Crotalus viridis helleri*). (Sketch made by Mrs. Alma Froderstrom from photographs.)

time the king snake had several coils wrapped tightly around the rattler's heart-lung section. In Case 3 the rattler was disgorged unhurt, although its neck had been severely stretched in the 36-minute swallowing process, after which it had spent about 10 minutes in the king snake's stomach. Two episodes in Case 2 are shown in figures 15:2 and 15:3.

On several occasions, in examining the stomach contents of king snakes found run over on the road (DOR), I have found them to contain southern Pacific and red diamond rattlers. In one instance I thought the king snake contained two small rattlers but their condition was such that I could not be sure.

James Deuel found a California king snake (ringed phase) eating a young sidewinder at 8:30 A.M., September 25, 1938, at the foot of Borrego Mountain, in eastern San Diego County. The head had been swallowed. When the young rattler was released it was found quite unharmed.

Many of my correspondents have reported rattlesnake–king-snake battles, but as these have been given from memory, rather than from detailed notes taken at the time, I shall not supplement my own accounts with them. They have come from all sections of the country where subspecies of the large king snake, *Lam-*

Fig.15:2. A California king snake (*Lampropeltis getulus californiae*—ringed phase) about to seize a young speckled rattler (*C. m. pyrrhus*).

Fig. 15:3. A king snake seizing a young speckled rattler, simultaneously biting it and throwing coils around its body.

propeltis getulus, are found. I have received no reports which would make it certain that other king snake species are involved, although, as several include snakes in their diets, they no doubt eat rattlers as well. Ingles (1946, p. 45) was reported as having seen a rattler eaten by a California coral king snake (*Lampropeltis zonata*). However, I learned from correspondence with the author that the article had been changed by the editor of the periodical; the snake involved was really *L. g. californiae,* the common king snake of my own experiments.

Notwithstanding published statements, there is no definite indication that rattlesnakes are preferred to other snakes by king snakes. King snakes have a varied diet, readily eating mammals, birds, birds' eggs, lizards, and snakes. A rattlesnake of the right size is just another meal to a king snake, which probably does not distinguish rattlers from other snakes when they are of proper size. Certainly no attention is paid to the rattler's bite.

This matter of size brings up a point that requires further discussion. Both the literature and my correspondence contain reports of rattlers that were attacked and killed by king snakes of such size that they could not possibly have swallowed the rattlers, and it even is difficult to see how they could have killed them by any method, constriction or otherwise. At the San Diego Zoo we have repeatedly offered rattlers of moderate to large size to hungry king snakes without success. I am disposed to think that many of the lurid accounts of these altruistic king-snake–rattler battles, in which the urge for food plays no part, depend too much on memory, particularly with respect to the relative sizes of the combatants. The hardest thing to believe is that a king snake, after killing a rattler and thus having done his good deed for the day, would crawl contentedly away without making any attempt to swallow his victim.

It may be that a king snake occasionally essays to eat a rattler too large to swallow and finally gives it up after a trial. This may have been the case in the instance reported below by Mr. Hastings, although he has presumed that the rattler was disgorged because of the disturbance caused by spectators:

> At about 10:00 A.M. a king snake 44 inches long was discovered under the edge of a pile of metal posts on the south side of a garage. The king snake was in the process of swallowing a western diamond rattler and only about 15 inches of the tail end were protruding. The snake was moved to a better location for photographing and some Kodachromes were attempted. Several watchers were in attendance when the king snake decided to disgorge the rattler and crawl placidly away. The rattlesnake was found to be 31 inches long with eight rattles and button. After the rattlesnake was ejected, some blood was noted on its head but whether from the rattlesnake or the king snake could not be determined. *Homer F. Hastings, Montezuma Castle National Monument, Camp Verde, Ariz.*

Two example reports on king snakes undertaking to subdue rattlers too large to eat are as follows:

> One of the most exciting things I ever saw along that line, was a battle to death between a diamondback, almost five feet long, and a king snake, about three and a half feet.[8] I've always been sorry that I did not see the start of the fight, but arrived on the scene soon after. I did see the big snake strike at the king twice; and the next thing I knew, the king had the rattler by the throat close to his head, and very quickly threw a coil or two around him. There was plenty of action for the next several, I would say about ten, minutes; then

---

[8] A rattlesnake of this size would weigh about four pounds, the king snake about ½ pound.

the big snake was about all in. In the meantime, the king had thrown several coils around the rattler, and you could see him gradually draw them tighter. In about twenty-five or thirty minutes the big snake was dead.

◇

One of our men reported seeing a small king snake kill a large rattler. This was done by the king snake's grasping the rattler behind the head and wrapping around the rattler and holding on like a bull dog, while he squeezed the life from the rattler. The party who volunteered this information stated he watched the battle until the rattler was dead and the king snake crawled off. This was out in the open and the king snake was the aggressor.

Some published accounts of king snakes engaging in battle with rattlesnakes too large to eat are the following: D. S. Jordan (1900, p. 371), J. D. Mitchell (1903, p. 39), Bealer (1921, p. 69), Rollins (1922, p. 175), Scoville (1929, p. 143), Gibson (1940, p. 113), Rutledge (1947b, p. 128; 1953, p. 28), and Hylander (1951, p. 94). To say that some of the king-snake stories are highly fanciful is to underrate the literary powers of the writers. Rolker (1903, p. 289) goes so far as to say that within five minutes a king snake could kill the biggest python that ever lived. Assuming that a king snake could even annoy a python enough to be noticed (and it would be equally impossible to assume that the king snake would try), we must remember that the python would only have to crawl a foot or so to scrape off the king snake.

Some of these published accounts speak of "crushing the rattlesnake to a pulp" or "breaking every bone in its body," such damage being done to rattlesnakes much larger than the king snake. I think this quite incredible, and beyond the muscular power of a king snake. In only one of the six cases I have reported did the rattler seem to be seriously injured by the king snake before it was swallowed. In this instance the king snake was twice as long and twice as heavy as the rattler, and had maintained uninterrupted pressure on the rattler's heart-lung section for nearly an hour and a half. It will be remembered that in another case the rattler emerged uninjured after a squeezing and swallowing that lasted 36 minutes, plus several additional minutes spent in the king snake's stomach. In some of the stories heard of rattler–king-snake battles, the rattler, sometimes outweighing the king snake by at least 10 to 1, is crushed to shapelessness within a few minutes. In considering the evidence, one should remember that a king snake cannot remotely approach the squeezing pressure that a man can exert with one hand. It is not true that "a king snake is the strongest living thing of its size known to man, being able to crush the bones of a man's hand when angered," as reported in a letter to a newspaper. An angered king snake cannot even exert sufficient pressure on one's hand to be painful.

More factual accounts of king snakes that killed rattlers that they could and did eat are those of Brown (1911, p. 219), Chapin (1917, p. 404), Russell (1929, p. 3), E. Smith (1933, p. 55), Coggeshall (1942, p. 89), and Duncan (1945, p. 167). A. M. Woodbury (1931, p. 6) shows a photograph of a California king snake (ringed phase) eating a young Great Basin rattler (*C. v. lutosus*).

With regard to the following report, with its unusual ending, it is, of course, possible that the king snake was misidentified, although, if a rattler wants to eat another snake, I presume it would as readily eat a king snake as a gopher or garter snake. It will be noted that both snakes were relatively small.

I was working for the U. S. Forest Service in Trinity County, in northern California, on a bridge construction, where one day I got a live rattlesnake. I had heard that a king snake would kill a rattlesnake whenever it found one, so I thought I would find out. It took about 3 weeks before I got a king snake. In the meantime I fed the rattler mice and gophers. In 3 weeks the rattler ate two mice and one gopher.

The king snake was shorter than the rattlesnake by 3 inches, the rattler being 28 inches in length. I dropped the king snake into the box with the rattler. Like a flash the rattlesnake caught the king snake sideways, back of the head, then coiled itself around the king snake. It held it that way for about 15 minutes then gradually uncoiled, took the king snake's head in its mouth, and the king snake started to disappear down the rattler. In about 12 minutes the rattlesnake had swallowed the king snake. It then started to crawl around the box, looking for a hole to get out. *E. H. Mortensen, U. S. Fish and Wildlife Service, Corning, Calif.*

Naggiar (1954, p. 20) gives a fictional account of a king snake that attacked a big eastern diamondback, upon which the rattler retaliated by eating the king snake. I have been unable to learn whether there was a factual basis for this story.

Cowles (1938, p. 13) was the first to interpret correctly and to describe in detail the peculiar defense mechanism that rattlers employ toward snake enemies, especially king snakes. This involves the rattler's raising the central portion of its body into an inverted U, with only the neck and tail resting on the ground. The loop is then brought down laterally onto the offending snake like a club. It is conceivable that a large rattler might seriously injure a king snake by such a blow; certainly it might well drive the king snake away. Bogert (1941b, p. 329) made a further investigation of this peculiar defense mechanism. He found that it was not initiated by the sight of a king snake, but by the odor of glandular secretions from the back of the enemy snake. Rattlesnakes, after the removal of their tongues, failed to react. One interesting result of Bogert's tests was the positive reaction of a prairie rattler, from an area in Montana where king snakes do not occur (p. 340). Some rattlers failed to react to king snakes. Some reacted to other snake genera, including the red racer, as well as to *Lampropeltis*. Meade (1940, p. 165) has reported on the reaction of the canebrake rattler to the king snake of that Southeastern area.

I noted once that a small Pacific rattler exhibited the king-snake defense reaction when placed in a jar with a shovel-nosed snake (*Chionactis occipitalis annulata*). However, it is possible the jar may previously have been contaminated with king-snake scent. Kauffeld (1943, p. 609) found that neither the Arizona twin-spotted rattlesnake nor the banded rock rattlesnake followed the characteristic king-snake reaction.

Elsewhere (p. 853) I have discussed the immunity of king snakes to rattlesnake bite, and also the myth of the lifesaving plant that a king snake is supposed to eat when bitten (p. 1241).

RACERS

Racers or whip snakes of the genus *Masticophis* occasionally include rattlesnakes in their diet. The following is an account of the method used by the red racer or western whipsnake, *Masticophis flagellum piceus,* in swallowing a young diamondback rattler, *Crotalus adamanteus,* at the San Diego Zoo, September 2, 1945. The racer was from Pacific Beach, San Diego County, and had been in captivity since May, 1938. It had been fed nothing but mice for several years, the last reptile (a lizard) having been given it in May, 1941. The last mouse had been eaten August 13, 1945. The diamondback rattler was a recently born juvenile about 14 inches long.

The rattler was placed in front of the racer in the latter's cage at 10:22 A.M. The racer approached the rattler, as if it expected a mouse, and then backed away. By the scent, it seemed to sense the difference from the expected mouse. The rattler was then moved in front of the racer with a hook, and its attention was again attracted. Suddenly, at 10:36, the racer seized the rattler about six inches behind the head. The rattler quickly bit the racer three times, and then, after a moment, a fourth time. The rattler rattled continuously. The racer immediately started to work its jaws toward the rattler's head with a jerky motion. It made no attempt to throw any coils around the rattler. The action of the jaws was much faster than that of a king snake, and it made less of an attempt to keep a tight hold on the rattler with its jaws. By 10:40 it had the rattler's head in its own mouth, although sideways.

The racer seemed to open its mouth much wider and more freely than does a king snake, and had little trouble in getting the rattler's head down, although the rattler's jaw caught in the angle of the racer's jaw for a moment. At this point the rattler began to struggle, upon which the racer held the rattler's body down with its own. This was done twice, quite deliberately. At no time did the racer attempt to throw a coil around the rattler as does a king snake, for such is not the racer method. However, it did make a U-shaped loop in its body just as a king snake does, so that the racer's body extended posteriorly far beyond the rattler's. At 10:43 the racer was swallowing the rattler fast with a sideways motion something like that of a king snake, but with the mouth opening more widely and freely so that the rattler went down faster. Also, there was a slight wave action in the racer's neck to expedite swallowing.

The rattler was half down at 10:45, but was still squirming and rattling. The racer continued to steady the rattler by the weight of its own body, allowing the rattler to slip through just as the king snake permits its victim to slip through its body coils. At 10:48 the racer appeared somewhat tired and the movements became slower and more jerky. At one time the rattler, puffed up with air posteriorly, caught in the angle of the racer's mouth, thus causing some delay. At 10:55 all but the tail had disappeared. There was a rest between 10:56 and 10:58, with somewhat longer pauses between jaw movements. Finally the rattler disappeared at 11:02. Peristaltic neck action began to be evident at 11:04 and was increased from 11:05 to 11:07. At that time the rattler seemed to be settled in the racer's stomach. The racer then put out its tongue at 11:07. The total elapsed time was 45 minutes.

Another young diamondback, this one somewhat stunned, was offered to a black phase of the same racer subspecies, *M. f. piceus,* slightly larger than the red racer. The black racer had been collected near Ensenada, Baja California, in July, 1939. The racer seized the rattler almost immediately (11:25), about 6 inches behind the head, but, instead of working toward the rattler's head, started to swallow the rattler doubled. It worked fast in spite of having to swallow two thicknesses of rattlesnake at once. At 11:27 the rattler's head caught in the angle of the racer's mouth; by pulling the rattler in with its neck muscles and opening its mouth wide, the racer got past this obstruction at 11:28. From here on the rattler was swallowed very quickly, as the racer did not hesitate to loosen both jaws at once and to use its neck muscles continuously. The rattler's tail squirmed just before it disappeared at 11:32. The racer used its neck muscles very deliberately at 11:33, and its tongue was then put out for the first time. There was considerable neck action until 11:34, when the racer yawned twice. The elapsed time was 9 minutes.

Another red racer from Blythe, California, was placed in a sack for transportation with a young Pacific rattler from Buckhorn, California. The racer measured 5 feet 2 inches, the rattler 17 inches. By next morning the racer had swallowed the rattler. The racer was immediately preserved. In the intervening time (about 18 hours) digestion had proceeded to an unexpected extent. The head and first 6 inches of the rattler's neck were almost devoid of scales; the markings were no longer evident at all. Some areas were quite bare. The ventral scales were almost detached. The head was quite shrunken with the skin partly gone. Toward the tail of the rattler no digestion was evident.

My correspondents have supplied several good accounts of racers that ate rattlers in the field:

> One time I saw what we call a blue racer, a snake which is about bronze color with white stripes running full length of the body, and about 4 feet long, eating a rattlesnake. The rattler was all down the racer's neck but about 4 inches, with the rattle end out of the racer's mouth still rattling. *Ollie Cox, U. S. Fish and Wildlife Service, Eureka, Nev.*

From the description, this was a desert striped racer (*Masticophis t. taeniatus*), rather than the blue racer, which is one of the subspecies of *Coluber constrictor*.

> *Masticophis t. taeniatus*, the desert racer, is the only one that I have ever seen in the act of killing a rattler. I chanced upon the scene after the decision had been reached, and the racer had ingested one-third of the rattler. The racer was a 35-inch specimen, and the rattler (*C. v. lutosus*) measured 20 inches. I had been inspecting a blackbird plot, and fortunately spotted the incident in a clearing through an opening in the abundant mountain mahogany (*Cercocarpus ledifolius*) without disturbing the racer. After eighteen minutes, the racer had managed to ingest the remaining two-thirds of the rattler, and lay sluggishly in the warm clearing for an additional twenty minutes; the rattler's only motion during the procedure was an occasional twitch of the tail. When disturbed, the clumsy-looking racer made off with surprising speed, and was caught only with difficulty in the heavy brush. After considerable rough handling, he disgorged the rattler, which was beyond revivification. *Ira La Rivers, University of Nevada, Reno, Nev.*
>
> ◇
>
> In May, 1935, on the W. M. Schmidt Ranch, Mason County, Texas, I saw what we call a white racer catch a small rattlesnake about 14 in. long; it shook him several times, then started swallowing him. The racer had caught him middle ways of his body, shook the life out of him, and swallowed him doubled. In April, 1938, on the Millman Ranch, Mason County, I caught another white racer and saw he was swallowing something. I looked at his mouth and saw the tail of a small rattler. *J. D. Bankston, Mason, Texas.*

The name "white racer" probably refers to the western whip snake, *Masticophis flagellum flavigularis*.

> A few weeks ago a party of five of us spent a week in Bear Canyon in the Catalina Mountains. The elevation was probably between 4,000 and 4,500 feet. The three men in the party were away from camp the whole morning, but when we returned my wife told me she had

seen a racer eat a rattlesnake. The racer was about 3 feet in length while the rattler was young, probably about 14 to 16 inches. I cannot say what species of rattler it was. The same day, however, I did find a specimen of the black-tailed rattler (*Crotalus molossus*) about half a mile farther up the stream. My wife's attention was first attracted to the struggle by a rustling of the leaves on the bank a short distance from her. The racer had bitten the rattler in about its mid-section and was gradually working its jaws up toward the rattler's head. In the meantime the rattler was striking the racer continually. Finally the racer reached the head of its victim and swallowed it, then made off into the rocks and bushes. I am certain that no mistake was made in the identification of the snakes, for the rattler rattled incessantly during the struggle, and last fall I had two of the racers around the house as pets and my wife got to know them well. *R. R. Humphrey, U. S. Forest Service, Tucson, Ariz.*

Fig. 15:4. A California striped racer (*Masticophis lateralis lateralis*) attacking a young northern Pacific rattlesnake (*C. v. oreganus*) near Coalinga, California. (Photograph by courtesy of the California Academy of Sciences.)

As Mr. Humphrey says, the rattler was probably a blacktail (*C. m. molossus*); no doubt the racer was the Sonoran racer *Masticophis b. bilineatus*. A. Pierce Artran informed me he had once seen a racer of this species attacking a young Mojave rattler (*C. s. scutulatus*).

My brother saw a red racer (*M. f. piceus*) eat a young rattlesnake near El Capitan Dam, San Diego County. I found a red racer that had eaten a sidewinder at Dry Lake, Clark County, Nevada. Ortenburger (1928, p. 129) reports a black phase of *M. f. piceus* at Tucson, Arizona, found in the act of swallowing a good-sized rattler (*C. atrox*), while only its head and neck protruded from a hole. Van Denburgh (1922, vol. 2, plate 69; fig. 15:4, this book) shows a photograph of a California striped racer (*Masticophis lateralis*) in the act of eating a young northern Pacific rattlesnake (*C. v. oreganus*). Stebbins (1954, p. 380) records the eating of a small western diamondback (*C. atrox*) by a desert striped racer (*Masticophis taeniatus*). Other reports of racers or coachwhips eating rattlers are those of "Red Wing" (1884, p. 203) and "Manzanita" (1906, p. 374). From these several instances it is quite evident that racers or whip snakes of the genus *Masticophis* frequently consume young rattlesnakes.

Needless to say, there is no truth in the statement of Lawson (1709, p. 132; 1714, p. 137; Berridge, 1926, p. 94) that racers kill rattlers by whipping them with their tails.

BLACK SNAKES

From the earliest days of the white settlers along the eastern seaboard, black snakes have been reputed to be deadly enemies of rattlesnakes. Not only have they been reported as eating rattlers, but we hear stories about them similar to those about the king snakes, that is, of their killing rattlers much too large to swallow.

There are no less than four subspecies of snakes in the Eastern and Southeastern states that are commonly referred to as black snakes. These are the eastern black snake or black racer, *Coluber constrictor constrictor;* the pilot black snake, *Elaphe obsoleta obsoleta;* the southeastern whip snake or coachwhip, *Masticophis flagellum flagellum,* which is often black anteriorly; and the indigo snake, *Drymarchon corais couperi.* The last two are certainly ophiophagous, and the first two may occasionally eat other snakes. Since neither *Drymarchon* nor *Masticophis* occurs north of the Carolinas on the eastern seaboard, any black snake reports to the northward must have reference to one of the others. It is regretted that the uncertainty of the appellation "black snake" does not permit of a more certain determination of the aggressors in the following accounts:

> Several years ago, in southern Arkansas, I saw a black snake kill a rattler. The black snake did not attempt to eat or swallow the rattlesnake in this case, but crawled away. I have heard of cases of this kind where the black snake did attempt to swallow the rattlesnake after killing it. I remember that during the early 1920's there were a few rattlesnake–black-snake fights staged for public exhibition. They were not successful from a financial standpoint as quite frequently the snakes would refuse to fight and the money had to be refunded. *Abner Casey, U. S. Forest Service, Bridgewater, Va.*

◇

> My father and a forest supervisor were walking along a trail in the Cherokee National Forest in Tennessee, when, about ten feet ahead, they saw a black snake leaving the trail. On reaching the spot left by the black snake, they found a four-foot rattler dead, and it appeared that a struggle had taken place between the rattler and the other snake. I have heard stories like this many times, but I have never found a black snake, or any other species of snake, fighting a rattler. *John H. Stanley, U. S. Forest Service, Andrews, N. C.*

◇

> I recently saw a small black snake swallowing a pigmy rattlesnake, a small species of rattler seldom more than 18 inches long. *Herbert P. Rice, U. S. Forest Ranger, Meadville, Miss.*

◇

> About the year 1902 I was cutting timber in West Virginia, when I witnessed a fight between a large black snake and a rattler. I first saw the black snake crawling along a log; it would crawl a short distance and raise up and look over the log. By its actions I was sure it was looking at something on the other side of the log, so I moved cautiously around to see what it was. About that time I heard a rattler sound his alarm, and I saw a big rattlesnake all coiled up and ready for a fight. The black snake went around the log, and very cau-

tiously approached the rattler. It kept moving in until it got the rattler to strike at it, but dodged back, and before the rattler could coil for another strike the black snake came in and caught the rattlesnake on the back of the neck and immediately started rolling and winding itself around the rattler; then, it started squeezing and contracting it and kept this up for almost an hour. When it started to let go, it began to unwind from the coil, but did not let go of its hold on the back of the rattler's neck until it was completely unwound. When it let go of the rattlesnake it did it very quickly and left as fast as it could go. I examined the rattler. It was quite dead. *A. A. McCoy, Hines, Oreg.*

<>

Three years ago, while driving alongside a grassy fence row, I noticed a slight commotion and stopped the car and backed up to see a three-foot coiled rattlesnake on the ground, and crawling away from the rattler was a slightly longer black snake. The black snake moved off about 30 feet, but when I killed the motor and was quiet, the black snake turned back with his head raised high up in the air and came directly back to the rattler and began circling the rattler but gradually closing in, which caused the rattler to keep turning his head to face the black snake all the time. The rattler did not move his whole body, causing him to twist his neck. After three or four circles the black snake struck as quickly as lightning and nabbed the rattler by the head. There was considerable squirming of the rattler in trying to free himself, but the black held fast. I then got out of the car and walked up within five feet of the fight and took out my watch and timed the match, and in just six minutes from the time he nabbed him, the black snake had completely swallowed the rattler. I thought sure the black snake would bite off the rattles, but he swallowed the rattles with the rest of the snake. I know two other ranchers here who have witnessed a similar capture of a rattler by a black snake. After that I issued positive instructions to the boys on my ranch never to kill a black snake. *D. C. Abney, Edinburg, Tex.*

Some of the statements on the enmity of black snakes for rattlers are the following: Lawson (1714, p. 137), Burnaby (1798, p. 71), Mease (1807, p. 389), Ord (1815, p. 358), Latrobe (1836, vol. 2, p. 46), Byam (1849, p. 179), Flack (1866, p. 335), Chalmers (1878, p. 422), Morris (1897, p. 204), Humfreville (1903, p. 447), and Bailey (1919, p. 166).

Most of these tales are of the highly debatable character in which the black snake crushes to death a rattler of such size that it cannot be swallowed, often in a struggle lasting only a few minutes. It then leaves to search for another victim. Lugger (1883, p. 267) even went so far as to say that the unfortunate rattler was pulled to pieces by the black snake, and Clarke (1881a, pp. 27, 86, 187) tells how a gopher snake (in this case probably an indigo snake) bit a rattler's head off.

One of the largest of the harmless snakes of the United States is the indigo snake (*Drymarchon corais couperi*) which, with its near relative the Texas indigo snake, or blue bull snake (*D. c. erebennus*), is found in the Southeastern states from South Carolina to central and southern Texas. It is definitely known that these snakes eat rattlers, as well as other kinds of snakes and mammals, and, being larger than king snakes, could certainly engulf a rattler larger than any king snake could handle. Keegan (1944, p. 59) experimented with a captive indigo snake nearly 7 feet long; he tried both rattlers and a copperhead as prey. The indigo snake seemed to be more careful to seize a poisonous snake by the head than when feeding on nonvenomous species. Also, it chewed the head. In swallowing rattlers, one of which was 40 inches long, it was able to stretch the rattler's body as does a king snake, but held the rattler by pressing the victim to the ground with the weight of its own body, rather than by throwing coils around it, as does a king snake.

Babis (1949, p. 147) found an indigo snake in Florida that had eaten two southeastern pigmy rattlers (*Sistrurus miliarius barbouri*). Allen and Neill (1952, p. 45) believe that pigmy rattlers comprise the main diet of indigo snakes. They report that a 3-foot eastern diamondback (*C. adamanteus*) was swallowed by a 5-foot indigo.

Other accounts of indigo snakes that ate rattlers are those of Teale (1945, p. 30) and Clifton and Bowchey (1953, p. 31). Both stress a chewing action by which the indigo snake is said to pierce the rattler's brain and also damages its biting mechanism. Jasper Maris, an exhibitor of snakes, reported that a captive indigo attacked a southern Pacific rattler and chewed its head to such an extent that the rattler died on the following day. S. C. Wilson (1954, p. 16) published photographs of an indigo snake attacking a western diamondback (*C. atrox*). While swallowing the rattler, the indigo lay alongside of its victim, making no attempt either to coil about it as does a king snake or to hold it down as a racer would.

Often snakes that might feed on each other in the wild live peaceably together in captivity.

> I have seen rattlers, copperheads, and black snakes all together in a large box, and that knocked the old tale of black snakes killing rattlers as far as I am concerned. However, there might have been some difference if they met in the open. *W. W. Britton, Chambersburg, Pa.*
>
> ◇
>
> I have, in a couple of instances, seen rattlers, black snakes, and king snakes together without any evidence of hostility on the part of either; although some maintain that the black and king snakes will attack and kill rattlers. *B. A. Eger, U. S. Forest Service, Buena Vista, Va.*

We have had many experiences of the same kind at the San Diego Zoo, with large rattlers, king snakes, and racers living peaceably in the same cage.

BULL SNAKES

The belief that the large snakes known in the West variously as bull, blow, or gopher snakes (genus *Pituophis*) are deadly enemies of all rattlers is widespread, particularly in the upper Missouri Valley. Yet these snakes not only den with rattlers regularly, but they are primarily feeders on mammals, with birds and birds' eggs next in order. In Texas, Langford and Gibson (1952, p. 53, but recording pioneer days) were surprised to find that the presence of a bull snake in a tent failed to keep the rattlers away. Certainly bull snakes eat snakes and lizards much less often than do king snakes, and their eating rattlers must be of rare occurrence.

Most of the reports I have received on this subject have been general in nature, merely stating that bull snakes are known to be enemies of rattlers or that rattlers are scarce where bull snakes are found. Occasionally I have received reports of bull-snake–rattler battles, but they have been from nonherpetologists who might well confuse bull snakes with racers or king snakes. However, the following is certainly authentic:

> A specimen of the desert gopher snake (*Pituophis catenifer deserticola*) was found whose stomach contained two very small one-button Great Basin rattlers. This was in the spring of 1934 not far from a rattlesnake den. *Ira La Rivers, University of Nevada, Reno, Nev.*

At the San Diego Zoo we have tried to feed young rattlers to bull or gopher snakes without success. In one case a young rattler was presented to the bull snake with a pair of forceps. The snake was hungry and came to the door of the cage as soon as it was opened. It reared up as it would when expecting a rodent. However, upon smelling or seeing the young rattler it immediately backed away. This was done twice, showing that the bull snake readily recognized the difference between the young rattler and a mammal. When a rat was offered, it was seized immediately.

Motl (1936, p. 4) found a bull snake with about six inches of a rattler swallowed. He came back later to find the bull snake gone and the rattler dead. Dr. W. A. Hilton of Pomona saw a San Diegan gopher snake (*Pituophis catenifer annectens*) eat a small rattler in captivity. Mrs. Madge V. Ratcliffe informed me that bull snakes (*P. c. sayi*) in captivity will eat young dead rattlers. Velikanjke (1950, p. 14) tells of bull snakes being imported to control rattlers in eastern Washington. As bull snakes (*P. c. deserticola*) are native there, the story is highly doubtful, especially as it is stated further that the bull snake is the kind of snake that destroys rattlers for sport.

MISCELLANEOUS SNAKE ENEMIES, INCLUDING CANNIBALISM

Rarely rattlesnakes are cannibalistic, usually through the unnatural conditions of captivity. I once received a shipment of small western diamond rattlers and found that one 312 mm. long had swallowed another measuring 282 mm. This was later regurgitated. Occasionally snakes may swallow each other through starting to eat the same prey simultaneously, e.g., Hyde (1923, p. 448).

Von Parkinson, then of Salt Lake City, told me that a captive Great Basin rubber snake (*Charina bottae utahensis*) ate a young Great Basin rattler (*C. v. lutosus*). A captive California boa (*Lichanura roseofusca roseofusca*) ate one of a brood of sidewinders at the San Diego Zoo. This snake normally eats mammals or birds. Allen and Swindell (1948, p. 5) list rattlesnakes (presumably *Sistrurus miliarius barbouri*) in the diet of water moccasins. Allen and Neill (1950b, p. 10) report that coral snakes (*Micrurus f. fulvius*) also eat young *S. m. barbouri*.

LIZARDS

Lizards may occasionally kill small rattlers, as suggested by the following incident:

> An item which may be of interest is the killing of a small 20-inch Great Basin rattler by a large 11-inch leopard lizard, *Crotaphytus wislizeni* (a female) while both were in an open air terrarium with a number of other lizards. The incident occurred during the summer of 1934. I had a large screen terrarium 5 by 6 feet in my back yard with a variety of local lizards. This particular leopard lizard had eaten smaller lizards such as *Sceloporus*, small *Crotaphytus* of both species, and *Uta* on several occasions. I had noticed on previous occasions when snakes were introduced to the cage that the lizards usually showed immediate signs of alarm, reacting according to their sizes and individual natures. *Phrynosoma*, *Sceloporus*, *Uta*, and *Callisaurus* invariably scuttled for cover. The larger *Crotaphytus* usually vacillated between fear and fight, and I have several times had small *Thamnophis* killed by them. However, their attitude usually depended upon the size of the snake, a large *Pituophis* invariably sending them all for cover. On this occasion the rattler wandered quickly about the cage, paying no attention to the other occupants, as is usual with an animal newly caged. The lizards showed various reactions, most scurrying out of reach. The large female leopard lizard, which I had had for some time, was a perfect pet, never

once offering to bite after the first day or two. She was generally slow and deliberate of movement except when feeding, and on this occasion she sized up the snake thoroughly, pacing around the cage with it at a distance of seven to eight inches, cocking her head at various angles. Twice she tested the snake's tail with her tongue as it glided past her; this was in the late afternoon, just before sundown. I left the cage and came back just before dusk, and found all the lizards holed up for the night, the rattler lying coiled in one corner. Returning the following morning at 9, I was very much amazed to find the rattler stretched out on the sand and moving feebly, with the large leopard lizard firmly attached just behind the head. The lizard kept its hold for twenty minutes, during which time the snake apparently died from suffocation; finally, the lizard, which had been motionless alongside the snake, chewed a bit at the neck, then released its hold, looked around in the rather droll attitude they often strike, tested the snake with its tongue a couple of times, and eventually crawled up on a nearby rock to sun. However the fight began, it was probably initiated by the lizard, in the light of what I learned previously when *Thamnophis* were killed by the lizards; apparently it got one hold, the right one, and maintained it to the end, which is their way. Such a meeting would probably be rare in nature, but the possibilities are interesting. *Ira La Rivers, University of Nevada, Reno, Nev.*

Strasser (1931, p. 41) has given an account of a collared lizard, *Crotaphytus c. collaris*, that was found with a neck hold on a banded rock rattler, *C. l. klauberi*. When the author endeavored to catch both, the snake got loose and bit the lizard, which died in five minutes.

Menger (1905, p. 29) mentions a traveler who found a Gila monster chewing on the head and neck of a recently killed rattler. Benton (1945, p. 81) says it is thought in Arizona that Gila monsters kill rattlers by biting them and hanging on until they are dead. Such battles are said to have been staged in captivity.

Alligators

Swimming rattlers sometimes become the prey of alligators:

> One of the interesting things regarding the association of alligators and rattlesnakes is that if an alligator catches a poisonous snake, it will shake the snake vigorously from side to side, after grasping it in its jaws, in order to kill it completely, before attempting to swallow it. I have seen alligators thus perform with copperheads, cottonmouth moccasins, and rattlesnakes. When I had the body of one of the large canebrake rattlesnakes, that was killed early this week, thrown in to one of my big thirteen-foot alligators, although the body was devoid of head and skin, the alligator evidently sensed the variety by the odor, and immediately after grasping it, began to shake it violently before swallowing it. If it had been a racer or other nonpoisonous snake, the alligator would have simply crushed it in its jaws and swallowed it without shaking it. *E. A. McIlhenny, Avery Island, La.*

Turtles

J. Lawson (1714, p. 137; Nelson, 1740, p. 350) mentions the killing of rattlers by terrapin. There have been no recent confirmations of this statement, which was probably based on hearsay. It may be supposed that a swimming rattler might occasionally fall victim to a snapping turtle, but in any case it is doubtful whether any turtle regularly preys on rattlers. However, Crebs and Holtzapple (1951, p. 47) found a "large land turtle" that had caught a 30-inch rattler back of its head and was holding it by the neck when found, the tracks in the road indicating a considerable struggle.

AMPHIBIANS

Goodman (1952, p. 35) has given an account (with a photograph) of a bull frog (*Rana catesbeiana*) that swallowed a young diamondback (*C. adamanteus*). The frog had been put in the cage as food for some large snakes. Thus it is indicated that small rattlers may in rare cases become the prey of bull frogs.

MISCELLANEOUS ENEMIES

FISHES

Since, as discussed elsewhere, rattlers swim quite readily in streams, ponds, and lakes, young ones may become the prey of fishes:

> Large-mouthed bass will no doubt eat young rattlers if they are found swimming, for they take small moccasins. My brother caught a bass with a moccasin in him. *Joseph T. McCullough, U. S. Forest Service, Brooklyn, Miss.*
>
> ⟡
>
> One of our local fishermen caught a 4-pound rainbow trout with a 9-inch Pacific rattler in it. *R. M. Williams, Arbuckle, Calif.*

The *San Diego Union* of June 5, 1933, contained a photograph of a large-mouthed bass and a 14-inch rattlesnake that it had swallowed. The fish was one of seven caught at nearby Barrett Reservoir.

SPIDERS AND INSECTS

Krumm-Heller (1910, p. 418; translation in Lane, 1951, p. 90) tells of a spider that killed and partially consumed a small rattler in the state of Coahuila, Mexico. Gudger (1931, p. 425) also describes this occurrence, as well as another in Brazil reported by Brazil and Vellard in 1926. It is evident that large venomous tropical spiders (*Grammostola*) have sufficient venom to kill a small rattler in a few minutes. Consuming the snake by sucking, as is the way of these spiders, takes many hours, if not days.

The *New York Times* of July 27, 1938, contained a dispatch from Ely, Nevada, stating that swarms of Mormon crickets killed and ate 3 rattlers. Anon. (1804, p. 202) attributes to Indians the statement that there were no rattlers near Compton, Rhode Island, because, should they come there, the ants would eat their eyes out.

PARASITES AND DISEASES

Although reptiles, including rattlesnakes, are subject to various diseases, and are afflicted with many internal and external parasites, researches on these parasites have been less intensive than on the parasites found afflicting other groups of vertebrates, since they affect man less directly. Of those that may be of importance to man, as far as the rattler parasites are concerned, there appear to be only two: The linguatulids or tongue worms, which have been occasionally transmitted to human beings, probably from rattlesnakes; and some of the Salmonelleae, a group of bacteria causing certain poultry diseases, of which snakes, including rattlesnakes, are intermediate hosts. Aside from these, the parasites and diseases of rattlesnakes are of interest only to people who keep live snakes. To those concerned with the treatment of diseases of captive specimens, the following references will be found of interest: Conant and Perkins, 1931, p. 36; Schroeder, 1934, p. 1004; Glidden, 1936, p. 3; Bryan, 1939, p. 49; Howden, 1943, p. 41; Book, 1945, p. 37; Nelson, 1950, p. 57; Allen and Neill, 1950d, p. 5; and Goodman, 1951, p. 67.

Sick rattlesnakes are not often encountered in the wild. I found a red diamond at Dulzura, San Diego County, in 1926 that seemed ill, and also an emaciated sidewinder in the Little San Bernardino Mountains. Jackley, in his control work in South Dakota, noted only about five sick rattlers among the thousands he encountered; one of these had the beak of a meadow lark sticking through an intestine. But with captive specimens the condition is different. In the earliest days of the San Diego Zoo, we learned that the acquisition of specimens from other collections brought in various parasites and diseases, such as mites and mouth canker, to which our freshly captured wild specimens were particularly susceptible, resulting in a high mortality. Efforts to cure the snakes by means of various solutions and emulsions are seldom successful and are justified only with the rarest species. Usually it is best to destroy the snakes and thoroughly sterilize the cages with a blow torch or some other method of applying a high temperature. Unfortunately, it seems impossible ever to eliminate completely the common snake mites once they have spread through a large collection; but if there be plenty of water in which the snakes can bathe, and certain disinfectants are used from time to time, their ravages may be minimized.

There follows, in zoölogical order, a summary of some of the parasites that afflict rattlesnakes.

Sessile protozoa of the genus *Haemogregarina* have been found in rattlesnakes. *H. crotali* was described from *C. viridis* by Laveran in 1902 (p. 1036), and *H. digueti* from *Sistrurus ravus* by Phisalix in 1914 (p. 167). The latter was also found in *C. atrox* by Roudabush and Coatney (1937, p. 294). Wood and Wood (1936, p. 518) found an unidentified haemogregine in a *C. v. helleri* from Glendale, California. Book (1945, p. 38) has discussed amebiasis in snakes, caused by the protozoan parasite *Endamoeba invadens*. Rattlesnakes are probably susceptible.

Flukes or trematodes of the genus *Renifer* (or *Neorenifer*) have been found in rattlers of the genus *Sistrurus*. *R. kansensis* was reported by Harwood (1932, p. 20) in *S. miliarius;* and *N. glandularis* was described by Byrd and Denton (1938, p. 392) from a Florida *S. m. barbouri;* see also Hughes *et al.* (1941, p. 39; 1942, p. 123), Nelson (1950, p. 57), and Goodman (1951, p. 65). These flukes usually live in the mouths, respiratory systems, or intestines of snakes. According to Goodman (1951, p. 65) the fluke cycle is snail–amphibian–snake, which may be the reason why they have been reported in *S. miliarius* but not, as yet, in other rattlesnakes.

Beyer (1898, p. 24) mentions a flatworm in the pericardium of a rattlesnake. Tapeworms or cestodes have been noted in rattlers. One was found in the lower intestine of a South American rattler (*C. d. terrificus*), and L. W. Arnold found *Proteocephalus* in the intestines of rattlesnakes from near Tucson. Loewen (1940, p. 515) described *Oochoristica gracewileyae* from a western diamond (*C. atrox*) from Texas. Marr (1944, p. 488) also mentioned a tapeworm in *atrox*. Voge (1953, p. 249) lists *C. v. oreganus* as one of the hosts of a larval cestode, probably *Mesocestoides variabilis*.

As early as 1683, Tyson (p. 32) found worms, presumably round worms, or nematodes, in the stomach of a rattlesnake. J. D. Mitchell (1903, p. 36) reported what he called wireworms in a rattler. I have seen worms in *C. polystictus;* in *C. atrox, C. p. pricei,* and *C. v. nuntius* from Arizona; and in *C. m. nigrescens* from the state of Durango, Mexico. The worm from *nigrescens* was identified as *Ophidascaris labiatopapillosa* by Dr. A. C. Walton.

Barringer (1892, p. 296) mentions a nematode infection at the fang of a rattler. Viquez (1933, p. 201) designates *Capillaria crotali* as a parasite of the Central American rattler (*C. d. durissus*), and Morgan (1943, p. 180) lists *Physaloptera obtusissima* as a parasite of the northern Pacific rattler (*C. v. oreganus*) in California.

Ticks and mites are often found on rattlesnakes collected in the wild, and mites are extremely troublesome to captive specimens, among which they spread rapidly, unless impervious barriers are interposed between cages. Captive specimens seem particularly vulnerable, either because of a greater susceptibility to anemia, or because they lack a natural immunity to such diseases as the nonindigenous ticks and mites may transmit.

The most devastating mite is one variously known as *Serpenticola serpentium, Ophionyssus serpentium,* or *Ophionyssus natricis;* the last is its presently accepted name (Camin, 1949, p. 589; 1953, p. 4). It was first noted on a captive snake in Florence, Italy, in 1823, and was subsequently described by Gervais in 1844, and by Hirst (1915, p. 383) from a captive indigo snake in the London Zoo. It is probable that *O. natricis* became widespread at an early date, through the interchange of live snakes among zoos throughout the world; and wild populations have probably been infected by snakes that escaped or were turned loose, so that it is no longer possible to determine the area to which it was originally indigenous. C. B. Perkins believes it to be found on live wild snakes in San Diego County, but there is a question as to its being indigenous here. Some of the first snakes we had at the San Diego Zoo came from other collections, so although *O. natricis* became a serious pest almost at once, and has remained so ever since, we cannot be certain of its origin. Its life history has been investigated by Schroeder (1934, p. 1004). Camin (1948, p. 351) calls it a restless, fast-moving arachnid that travels constantly from one feeding spot to another, never fixing itself permanently as does a tick.

The importance of these mites lies not only in the debilitating effect of their blood-sucking proclivities, but because they transmit a disease that is usually serious and often rapidly fatal (in 6 to 12 days) to the many captive snakes that are not immune. According to Camin (1948, p. 345) one of the bacteria involved is *Proteus hydrophilus,* which produces a hemorrhagic septicemia. Rattlesnakes are as susceptible as any snakes to this disease. Some of the precautions that may be taken against the spread of mites have been discussed by Conant and Perkins (1931, p. 36), Schroeder (1934, p. 1011), Glidden (1936, p. 7), Howden (1943, p. 42), Book (1945, p. 40), Camin (1948, p. 353; 1953, p. 69), Allen and Neill (1950d, p. 9), and Goodman (1951, p. 67).

Ewing (1924, p. 179) described a lung mite, *Entonyssus rileyi,* from a rattle-snake of unstated species from Texas; and Hubbard (1939, p. 657; see also Turk, 1947, p. 22) described *Entonyssus ewingi* from an Oklahoma *atrox.*

A tick from a Honduran *durissus* was identified at the University of California, Los Angeles, as *Amblyomma dissimile.* Two other snakes of the same species had ticks—one had eight—thought to belong to the genus *Dermacentor.* Bishopp and Trembley (1945, p. 7) reported *A. dissimile* on *C. adamanteus* and *S. miliarius.*

Loomis (1951, p. 83) was of the opinion that chiggers (larval mites of the genus *Trombicula*) cause an accelerated shedding by rattlers, particularly when the infestation and damage are concentrated around the sensory pit. Wolfenbarger (1953, pp. 656, 665) reported two species of *Trombicula,* subgenus *Eutrombicula,* on *C. h. horridus* in Kansas.

Among the internal parasites from which rattlers (as well as other snakes) suffer, are tongue worms or linguatulids. These soft, wormlike creatures belong to the same order as the mites. They may attain a length of 60 mm. I am told by Dr. Howard R. Hill, of the Los Angeles Museum, who has made an intensive study of these parasites, that three forms have been recognized in rattlesnakes. These are: first, *Porocephalus crotali,* which has been found in the western diamond rattler (*C. atrox*), the eastern diamondback (*C. adamanteus*), the prairie rattler (*C. v. viridis*), the timber rattler (*C. h. horridus*), the South American rattler (*C. durissus terrificus*), the Mexican west-coast rattler (*C. b. basiliscus*), and the Tortuga Island diamond rattler (*C. tortugensis*). It is particularly common in the last two. The other two are *Kiricephalus coarctatus,* afflicting the eastern dia-mondback, and *Raillietiella furcocerca,* often found in the Tortuga Island dia-mond rattler. Linguatulids have been found in the El Muerto Island speckled rattlesnake (*C. m. muertensis*) but the species remains unidentified. Among the pertinent references on linguatulids in rattlesnakes are Humboldt, 1811, p. 298; Diesing, 1851, vol. 2, p. 431; Leidy, 1884, p. 140; Sambon, 1922, p. 197; Hett, 1924, p. 131; Hill, 1935, p. 226; 1948, p. 56; and Self and McMurry, 1948, p. 21. R. C. Schwenkmeyer, in an unpublished report, found the lungs of *tortugensis* to be damaged by linguatulids. They infest the ridged areas of the functional part of the lung, and leave the tissue leveled and thin. In some dens in Oklahoma housing *C. atrox,* Self and McMurry found half the rattlers infected. One rattler contained 158 parasites. They found at least one host of the larvae to be *Peromyscus leucopus aridulus,* a local white-footed mouse.

I have observed linguatulids to be particularly prevalent in the Tortuga Island diamondback (*C. tortugensis*). Some collectors have found these rattlers extremely plentiful on Tortuga Island, whereas others have encountered but few. It is pos-sible that this large parasite may cause cyclic fluctuations in the rattlesnake popu-lation of this isolated Gulf of California island. The intermediate host is probably the indigenous white-footed mouse, *Peromyscus dickeyi.*

Goss (1939, p. 178) and Clark (1948, p. 59) found cases of tongue worms in the lungs of human beings who had been accustomed to handling snakes. Goss be-lieves the parasite would probably be walled off in the human lung.

Dr. Howard R. Hill has advised me that the nymphs of the linguatulids para-sitic in the timber rattler and the diamondbacks have been found in the muskrat, opossum, and striped skunk. In South America, the nymphs of *Porocephalus crotali* have been observed in marmosets, bats, rats, opossums, armadillos, and raccoons. The nymphs are taken into the mouth of the final host, along with the flesh of the intermediate host. The life cycle has been discussed by Hett (1924, p. 131), Penn (1942, p. 277), and Goodman (1951, p. 66).

One of the most serious bacterial diseases of snakes in captivity, including rattlesnakes, is one variously known as mouth rot, mouth canker, or osteomyelitis. It has been discussed by Burtscher (1943, p. 59), Glidden (1936, p. 4), Howden (1943, p. 42), Book (1945, p. 37), and Allen and Neill (1950d, p. 10), and is mentioned by almost every work on the care of captive reptiles. Kauffeld (1953b, p. 132) recommends a sulfamethazine preparation, Sulmet (Lederle), for its treatment. Whether more than one disease or causative agent is involved in the terms mouth rot, mouth canker, and osteomyelitis is not definitely known. Burtscher (p. 59) attributed mouth rot to a bacillus related to *B. fluorescens.* Glidden (p. 5) says osteomyelitis in reptiles is caused by a species of *Staphylococcus.*

A pneumonia affecting rattlesnakes has been mentioned by MacCallum (1921, p. 279), Glidden (1936, p. 5), and Allen and Neill (1950d, p. 11); and tuberculosis by Book (1945, p. 38) and Glidden (p. 4). Book believes the agent to be allied to that causing tuberculosis in man. L. J. Goss has advised me that the tubercle bacillus isolated from reptiles is *Mycobacterium marinum.* Aronson (1929, p. 223) described *M. thamnopheos,* said to produce tuberculosis in garter snakes.

Hinshaw and McNeil (1944, p. 252; 1945, p. 264; and 1946, p. 397) have discussed snakes as carriers of salmonellosis and paracolon, which cause serious infections in poultry, especially turkeys. A paracolon (type 10) was found in certain rattlers, including *scutulatus, helleri,* and *cerastes,* at the San Diego Zoo. Gopher snakes (*Pituophis*) are more important carriers of these diseases than rattlers. They also mention a bacterium, *Pseudomonas,* found in the feces of rattlesnakes. Bryan (1939, p. 52) states that the usual bacterial flora are largely absent from the intestinal tracts of healthy snakes, because snake digestion is principally through the medium of digestive juices with little bacterial decomposition. The extremely powerful salivary and gastric secretions may inhibit bacterial growth.

Tumors in snakes are discussed by Glidden (1936, p. 3), Ball (1946, p. 134), and Dewhurst (1951, p. 25). Dr. Ball, in a subsequent communication, mentions a fibrosarcoma found in a prairie rattlesnake (*C. v. viridis*) from South Dakota. Stradling (1881, p. 148) mentions a tropical rattler with a tumor. J. R. Wadsworth, in a paper as yet unpublished, mentions fibrosarcomas found in the prairie rattlesnake (*C. v. viridis*) and the western diamondback (*C. atrox*).

I once found a live southern Pacific rattlesnake with a serious wound that was infested with maggots. It might be thought, erroneously, that the poisonous quality of the rattlesnake's blood would have inhibited such an infestation.

Kauffeld (1955, p. [2]) has expressed the opinion that skin abrasions incurred while a snake is shedding may prove serious, as snakes are susceptible to infection when in that condition. He also believes (p. [3]) that wounds or abrasions tend to decrease the intervals between sheddings, a conclusion likewise reached by Neill (1949, p. 115) although doubted by Perkins (1950, p. 35).

 # 16. Indians and Rattlesnakes

INTRODUCTION

Since one of the purposes of this book is to discuss the various contacts between rattlesnakes and humans, I shall outline in this chapter the attitudes that the Indians held toward these snakes, as far as may be judged by the accounts of explorers, the findings of ethnologists, or the customs and legends that some tribes have still retained.

Rattlesnakes, although they were never so important economically in the pre-Columbian Indian communities as were many other animals—particularly such mammals and birds as furnished major components of food supply, clothing, or shelter—nevertheless played their part, especially in medicine, myth, and legend. As do all primitive peoples living close to nature, the Indians duly observed each animal and fitted it into their scheme of life and religion, and in the case of the rattler this position was accentuated by its venomous nature.

Generally speaking, the Indian attitude toward rattlesnakes varied from mere aversion or toleration, through appeasement and propitiation, to reverence and even worship, always tinged with the animism that colored the Indian view of nature. Besides its place in tribal myths, the rattler had a place in war, in medicine, in art and decoration, and even, to a minor extent, in food supply. In all of these contacts and reactions there were major tribal and territorial differences, so that examples rather than generalities must be cited. Usually the rattlesnakes were given a status apart from and above that of other snakes, for, in extensive areas of the western United States they were the only seriously venomous snakes, and throughout the country they were the most dangerous. Besides, the presence of the rattles simplified recognition, and also gave them a distinction above others of the serpent tribe.

A question naturally arises as to the accuracy of the published reports of the Indian–rattlesnake relationships—of the Indian's knowledge of rattlesnakes and his reactions to them. Without doubt the reports of the early explorers and colonists on the Indian attitudes toward rattlers were deficient and erroneous for the same reasons that their accounts of the rattlesnakes themselves were inaccurate: they were untrained in observation and given to emphasizing the lurid; they were credulous and passed on, as firsthand observations, stories based on hearsay and the deliberate exaggerations of the campfire. Their statements of Indian ideas and attitudes were often colored by their own preconceptions or misconceptions.

By these standards the modern ethnologist is a paragon of accuracy, yet he, too, has suffered from handicaps, although of another nature. For by the time he was able to study the Eastern tribes, they had already been torn from their ancient haunts, and their ways of life were changed by white contacts and associations. In the West the Indians adhered longer to the customs of primitive days; but even here the investigator had often to deal with dwindling or almost extinct groups, where only a few aged informants still retained hazy memories of the olden ways and ceremonies. Much that we now have is dependent on the accuracy and objectivity of their memories; furthermore, to bring the Indian ideology unchanged through the filter of translation has proved difficult. Some intratribal variations in reports no doubt result from these handicaps—the differences in the memories of the informants and in the interpretations of the ethnologists.

Many Indian myths and usages with respect to rattlesnakes have now found their way into white American folklore, beliefs, and customs. This is particularly true of methods of snake-bite treatment and ideas concerning rattlesnake habits. And as Indian beliefs have influenced white folklore, so also white contacts have affected the Indian beliefs. There are probably few tribes that still retain unchanged their pre-Columbian attitudes toward rattlesnakes.

Today it is difficult to determine the sources of these beliefs—whether the Amerind developed them independently, or whether they were brought in later by white or Negro immigrants, for many of them have resemblances to folklore in other parts of the world. But at least we may be sure that such beliefs as involve the unique rattle could only have developed on the American continent. Undoubtedly the Indians had many other ideas respecting snakes that were original with them, however similar they may have been to primitive beliefs on other continents. Such independent but parallel concepts are common in myth and folklore.

Some of the Indian beliefs are applicable to rattlesnakes in one tribe, but to other kinds of snakes elsewhere. Much depended on the prevalence of rattlers where a tribe lived. Many of the reports are general in nature, the species of snake being undisclosed by the narrator. Often, since the snake is described as venomous, and this in a territory where only the rattlesnake falls in this category, its identity is certain.

It should be clearly understood that this presentation of the ideas of the Indians respecting rattlesnakes is only an effort to assemble these ideas for review. Their inclusion is not to be taken as an acceptance of their accuracy, for many, if not most, are obviously fantastic, as was well known to the ethnologists from whose accounts they have been abstracted.

RELIGION, SUPERSTITION, AND FOLKLORE

RATTLESNAKE WORSHIP

Serpent worship has been, and still is, widespread among many peoples and races. There is an extensive literature on the subject; it is, indeed, the greatest of all animal cults, according to Cesaresco (1909, p. 111). The extent to which the rattlesnake was worshiped in the pre-Columbian theologies of the New World can be determined only if we are able to draw distinctions between worship and respect, between veneration and fear; and, finally, if we can judge when a god, having certain characteristics of an animal but likewise many which the animal lacks, ceases to be that animal and becomes a separate entity. With these distinctions I shall not be particularly concerned. In most Indian tribes religion took the form of animism[1]—the assignment of supernatural powers to many creatures and objects—and the rattlesnake usually occupied a position of some importance in the polytheistic hierarchy; but the Indian attitude should probably be considered one of reverence or respect rather than worship.

That Mayans, Toltecs, or Aztecs can be said to have worshipped the rattlesnake is doubtful. It is evident from the decorations on buildings and monuments in Yucatán that serpents, often embellished with rattles, were important in the Mayan religion (Spinden, 1913, p. 32; Howey, 1928, p. 294; see also the section of this chapter on art and decoration). According to J. E. Thompson (1933, p. 161) a serpent with feathers attached to its scales was the commonest art motif in aboriginal Middle America. But although some of their gods assumed the form of the rattlesnake, including its unique caudal appendage, the possession of other attributes such as horns, wings, and plumes—especially the latter—shows that they had long since graduated from an identity with the lowly rattlesnakes still remaining in the wild. For example, Quetzalcoatl, meaning the quetzal-bird–serpent (Thompson, 1933, pp. 20, 157), an exceedingly important Mexican deity, may be shown as a serpent with rattles, but it can hardly be claimed that this plumed serpent is primarily a rattlesnake, even though "Yolcuat," or "rattlesnake," is one of his alternative names. The rattle is only one of his attributes; he had others that the rattlesnake lacks. He is more often shown as a man than as a serpent, and his name, at least, if not all of his attributes, was derived from a human hero.

In Peru, it is said the god of riches was worshipped in the image of a rattlesnake, horned and hairy, and embellished with a tail of gold (Brinton, 1896, p. 142). However, modern ethnologists express doubts concerning this practice, since there is no evidence of it among Peruvian Indians today.

Swanton (1911, pp. 159, 160; 1946, p. 618; see also Chateaubriand, 1828, vol. 2, p. 163) quotes Charlevoix and Pénicaut concerning the Natchez Indian worship of a wooden figure of a rattlesnake. Dorman (1881, p. 265) states that the Cherokee worshipped the rattler. No details of the extent or nature of this worship are now available, if, indeed, it could be so dignified. Collot (1826, 1924 ed., vol. 1, p. 299) and Priest (1840, 1882 ed., p. 28) mention tribes in New York and on the Missouri River that revered the rattlesnake as a manito.

Something nearer actual rattlesnake worship may possibly have been practiced by some of the Pueblo tribes of our Southwest, where rites of propitiation are said to have reached even the point of human sacrifice. Here live rattlesnakes, rather than images with some rattlesnake characteristics, were the objects of ven-

---

[1] The following is a good expression of this theology: "The Apache, whether he is praying, or hunting, or acting the craftsman, is not dealing with dumb animals and inanimate objects as the white man would have it, but is concerned with natural objects which know well his intentions, how to thwart the impious and reward the deserving." (Castetter and Opler, 1936, p. 16).

eration. During Mrs. M. C. Stevenson's investigations among the Tewa (Anon., 1914, p. 79) she was informed that such rites were still practiced in two villages, the youngest female child being the annual victim in one, and an adult woman in the other. The subjects were drugged and allowed to die in the presence of the sacred snakes. Elaborate ceremonies were involved, showing the religious nature of the sacrifice. Curtis (vol. 17, 1926, p. 19) also calls attention to the possibility of human sacrifices among the Tewa; there were stories to the effect that they had an exceedingly large rattlesnake to which newly born babes were sacrificed. When a Frenchman, quarrying rock in the vicinity of one of their villages in 1884, killed a big rattler—it was said to measure 7 feet 6 inches— there was great excitement among the Indians, which led to the belief that it was one of their sacred snakes, which had escaped. Helen H. Roberts (1932, p. 359) has published a story telling how the Indians at Pecos, New Mexico, having lost a large sacred rattler, abandoned the town. She feels that this adds to the evidence of snake worship at Pecos. Other references to this supposed practice of the Pueblos are Espinosa (1910, p. 403) and Bloom (1933–38, vol. 11, p. 268). In all fairness, it should be stated that these reports of worship of, and sacrifices to, rattlesnakes in the past among the Pueblo are now considered by competent ethnologists to be of doubtful accuracy.

Usually among the North American Indians the regard for the rattlesnakes was on a lower plane. They were believed gifted with supernatural powers, usually for evil, but this was also true of many other animals. They were cast as characters in innumerable myths and legends, and were the subject of extensive taboos. But seldom were they accorded major positions in any tribal religion, being usually objects of propitiation rather than veneration, although it is true the rattlesnake did have a superior place, compared with more ordinary snakes, in the Amerindian cosmography. To this, the following quotations testify: "Many of the North American Indian tribes entertain a superstitious regard for serpents, and particularly for the rattlesnake" (Squier, 1851, p. 222; also quoted by Jennings, 1889, p. 67); "This worship paid to the rattlesnake was universal among all tribes, but the worship was not conferred exclusively upon that serpent. All snakes of the country enjoyed a share of it, though to a less degree" (Dorman, 1881, p. 265); "The rattlesnake was the serpent almost exclusively honored by the red race" (Brinton, 1896, p. 130; Spence, 1914, p. 113); "Reverence for the rattlesnake was universal among the Indians, and has been repeatedly remarked by travelers in every part of the country" (Mooney, 1900, p. 294); "The rattlesnake was highly venerated, and tribes as far north as the Moki [= Hopi] country in the West, and perhaps as the Ohio in the East might correctly be called the Snake People" (Dellenbaugh, 1901, p. 63); "It was an animal of great importance to the Amerinds from the 38th parallel down" (*ibid.*, p. 188); "Certain animals, especially the wolf and the rattlesnake, were treated with anxious reverence" (Debo, 1941, p. 24). Ingersoll (1883a, p. 45) expressed the opinion that rattlesnakes were most venerated where they were scarcest, a doubtful conclusion.

A summary of the man–serpent relationship in the Indian cosmography, and particularly the supremacy of the rattlesnake among snakes, is given by H. B. Alexander (1953, p. 92).

RATTLESNAKE PROTECTION AND APPEASEMENT

In reviewing the preternatural relationships of Indians and rattlesnakes, I find it difficult to segregate the published reports into clear-cut categories, so interwoven are religion and legend, veneration and propitiation, myth and story. But there is one practice almost universal among the Indians, from coast to coast— a rather surprising taboo against killing these dangerous creatures, particularly surprising among an outdoor and nomadic people to whom rattlesnakes were a not inconsequential hazard. This attitude of avoidance and even protection seems to have stemmed from three somewhat distinct assignments of the rattlesnake as an avenger: (1) avenging a hurt done a brother rattler; (2) avenging an affront to the gods of weather—involving also a supplication for favorable weather, rain especially; and (3) avenging, as an agent of a higher god, infractions or derelictions in religious duties. Examples, based on these motivations, will be given in this order.

As early as 1709, J. Lawson (p. 210) reported that the Tuscarora Indians of North Carolina were afraid to kill rattlers lest the snakes' relatives return to wreak vengeance. Adair (1775, p. 237) says the Indians considered the rattler to be the king of snakes, and if one were injured other snakes would avenge it. Once, a Chickasaw chief, having protected his hands with a snakeroot infusion, picked up a rattler and put it in a hollow tree, lest Adair harm it. On another occasion, when Adair killed a rattler whose fangs had been removed by a drunken Indian trader, the red man was exceedingly angry, claiming it would bring misfortune to them both (p. 238). Again, when Adair disposed of a big rattler, an astrologer of 20 years' standing among the Indians prophesied disaster (p. 271). Kalm (1752–53, p. 186; also Lacépède, 1789, vol. 2, p. 408; Kerr, 1802, vol. 4, p. 262; Daudin, 1801–4, vol. 5, p. 309) says that while the Indians in the early days dared not destroy rattlers, through superstitious dread, they were now beginning to follow the example of Europeans in killing them off. A Seminole informed Bartram (1791, p. 256) that there was a large rattler in their camp that they would like to have destroyed. But when he had done this they tried to scratch him, evidently in symbolic propitiation, for they feared the spirit of the dead snake would incite its living kindred to avenge the injury.

Henry (1809, p. 175) had a somewhat similar experience among the Ojibwa in 1764. He found a rattler and wished to kill it, but the Indians protested. They surrounded the snake, calling it "grandfather," and blew smoke toward it, which Henry says the snake appeared to enjoy. They asked the snake to take care of their families in their absence, and to cause Sir William Johnson, the British agent, to supply their canoe with rum. Later, when they were caught in a severe storm on Lake Huron, they blamed their predicament on Henry's having threatened the rattlesnake. They sacrificed two dogs to it by throwing them overboard, and likewise offered some tobacco. They prayed to the rattler-god. In this case the snake seems definitely to have been deified (see also Drake, 1850, p. 300; F. Parkman, 1870, vol. 2, p. 181; Bourke, 1892, p. 470; Mooney, 1900, p. 458). Heckewelder (1819, p. 245) says the Tuscarora had a similar respect for the rattler. They called it "grandfather" and would not permit him to kill one. They said it gave them notice of impending danger with its rattle, and, if they killed one, all rattlers would rise against them. This was their explanation of why white men were bitten. Heckewelder said further—he was writing of the late 1700's—that this attitude was then on the decline, for the younger Indians destroyed rattlesnakes without ceremony.

Keating (1824, vol. 1, p. 128) reported that the Potawatomi Indians had a high degree of veneration for the rattlesnake, not as a spirit, but rather because of the warning it gave. They seldom killed these snakes. If a young man required a rattle for decorative purposes, he would kill a snake to get it, but would apologize to the snake and leave a propitiatory offering of tobacco beside the body. Forsyth (1912, p. 228), writing in 1827 of his experiences among the Sauk and Fox nations, said those tribes spared the lives of rattlesnakes through fear of offending them. They wished them to remain friendly; they threw tobacco to them, and even laid scraps of tobacco near the heads of dead rattlers. William Jones (1911, p. 214) said the Fox would kill no snakes because snakes were manitos; their death would be avenged by illness or accident. Dorman (1881, p. 265) reported that the Winnebago reverenced rattlesnakes and never killed them. C. A. Murray (1839, vol. 1, p. 318; third edition, 1854, vol. 2, p. 41) met a large rattler but was prevented from killing it by his Indian guide, who said it would be bad medicine.

McKenney (1846, p. 101) gives an interesting account of the ceremonial killing of a rattlesnake by the Menominee—a mixture of propitiation and profit. The finder of a snake made a proprietary signal. He then welcomed the snake as a messenger from the spirit land. Tobacco powder was sprinkled on the snake's head as an offering. The snake was then seized by the neck and tail, and every vertebra broken by a single quick jerk. The fangs were removed, and the snake's body was cut into small pieces, which were distributed among the rest of the Indians to be carried in their medicine bags as amulets against evil agencies. The skin of the rattler was attached to the hair of the finder and worn as a trophy.

Irvin and Hamilton (1853, vol. 3, p. 273) reported that many individuals of the Iowa and Sauk tribes, particularly such as professed to be snake doctors, would not kill rattlers. If they met a snake, they stopped to talk with it, often making an offering of tobacco. In one instance when a youth found a rattler, a snake priest went out to confer with it as an emissary of friendship; after that the people could travel in safety. Bourke (1884, p. 200), quoting Major S. C. Roberts, says the Sioux greatly feared a certain ravine in which rattlers abounded—no doubt the location of a den—and left propitiatory offerings of small eagle feathers tied to twigs nearby.

Washburn (1869, p. 208) supplies an incident in which an Arkansas Cherokee refused to kill a rattler; in explanation he repeated a long legend, of which the general tenor was: "I let them alone and they let me alone." J. Curtin (1922, p. 414) tells us that among the Seneca there is a similar legend accounting for the protective attitude of the Indians toward the snakes. Once a man tormented a rattlesnake. This led to a great battle between the snakes and Indians. The first man killed was the original tormenter. Finally, the king of the snakes said, "We will go away if you cease injuring or tormenting us." To this the Indians agreed and they still maintain their part of the peace pact. Emerson (1884, p. 44) reported the Indian belief that, if one of their tribe were bitten, it was in revenge for his having killed another rattler.

Mooney (1891, p. 352) tells us that in the sacred formulas of the Cherokee, the rattler is a supernatural being whose favor must be propitiated; great pains must be taken not to offend him. The Chickasaw would not kill rattlesnakes (Swanton, 1946, p. 776); nor would the Indians of Florida, who feared revenge by kindred snakes (Dorman, 1881, p. 265). Conard (1890, p. 122) said the Comanche would kill a rattler only when it was sluggish and failed to rattle when approached. Then it was presumed to be on the warpath and lying in wait for an enemy, which justified its death. McKnight (1951, p. 22) reports that the Seminole will not kill a rattler and are in awe of any white man who will.

Bourke (1892, p. 470) reports that, although the Apache would not allow a snake to be killed within the limits of a camp by one of their own people, they would not only permit a stranger to dispose of the intruder, but would even invite him to do so, as they did Bourke on several occasions. We are told by J. O. Dorsey (1894, p. 479) that some Dakota would not kill snakes by hitting them. He who violated this rule would dream horrible dreams about snakes and might have his horse bitten.

The Franciscan Fathers (1910, p. 508) say the Navaho will not kill rattlers; if the snakes disturb people they are brushed aside. Reichard (1928, p. 144) gives as the reason the Navaho belief that the snake was once a man. Babington (1950, p. 205) reports that snakes are not killed by the Navaho; if one uses a rattler's skin he will die a violent death. Some whites keep the Navaho off their premises by hanging rattler skins on their gates.

Lumholtz (1902, vol. 1, p. 310) wrote that the Tarahumare believe rattlesnakes to be the companions of sorcerers, who meet and talk with them. When a Mexican killed a rattler, an Indian expressed anger because the snake had been the protector of his home. The Tarasco believe that rattlesnakes must never be touched, much less killed.

Gifford (1932, p. 240; 1936, p. 318), writing of his investigations among the Yavapai, says that when his interpreter killed a rattlesnake, he was reprimanded by an aged Indian who said the interpreter's child might sicken as a result. This would come from the snake's supernatural power. Not only the Yavapai, but the Walapai, Maricopa, and Shivwits Paiute all have taboos against killing rattlers (Drucker, 1941, p. 104). The Yaqui believe that a rattler must be killed quickly and painlessly, if at all; otherwise the snake people will retaliate (p. 174).

Among the Tolowa of Oregon, as a penalty for killing a rattler one must drink and eat from separate vessels for five days, for the "rattlesnakes are people" and this is the same method of purification required of an Indian who has slain an enemy in battle (Drucker, 1937a, p. 266).

Powers (1877, p. 325) tells us that the Nisenan of central California had a genuine terror of rattlers. If one of their people were bitten, he would be excluded from camp for several days, for otherwise the snake, having tasted blood, would follow him in. Beals (1933, p. 394) says that when two Nisenan killed a rattler near a house, they burned the snake with live oak twigs and stones that popped, to prevent retaliation by avenging snakes. The Yokuts never destroyed a rattler. One Indian caught one on the plains and turned it loose in the mountains, where it would be less likely to be found and killed by white men. Another, seeing a white man about to dispatch a rattler, frightened it into the rocks so that it might escape (Powers, 1877, p. 379). Among the Atsugewi it was believed that if one did not bother snakes they would do no harm. A person who made a practice of killing rattlers was likely to be bitten (Garth, 1953, p. 141).

These many reports of Indian tribes in every section of the country indicate how widespread was the fear that to kill a rattlesnake was to invite the retaliation of its brothers or of supernatural associates.

The second basis for the propitiatory or protective attitude of the Indians toward rattlesnakes stems from the close connection between rattlesnakes and weather in the Indian cosmology.[2] This has been remarked by a number of ethnologists. It is implicit in the details and paraphernalia of the Hopi Snake dance, as well as in lesser-known rituals of other tribes. In the arid areas of the Southwest, which often suffer from insufficient rainfall, the ceremonials usually had the purpose of assuring an adequate water supply; in more favored sections having adequate rainfall, floods might be caused by angered rattlesnakes, and this could be prevented by propitiation. The resemblance of lightning to the snake's strike, and of thunder or the hiss of rain to its rattle, made inevitable the connection, by the symbolically minded Indians, of the rattlesnake with the rainstorm.

Brinton (1896, p. 136) points out the association between snakes and thunder and lightning in the beliefs of several tribes. "Because the rattlesnake, the lightning serpent, is thus connected with the food of man, and itself seems never to die but annually to renew its youth [by changing its skin], the Algonkin called it 'grandfather,' and 'king of snakes'; they feared to injure it; they believed it could grant prosperous breezes, or raise disastrous tempests; crowned with the lunar crescent it was the constant symbol of life in their picture writing" (Brinton, 1896, p. 142). "The snake, besides being symbolized by lightning in many American mythologies, is also symbolical of water, which is well typified by its sinuous movements" (Spence, 1913, pp. 74, 76).

Brinton (1896, p. 201) calls attention to a Chippewa pictograph in which a manito brandishes a rattlesnake as a lightning symbol. Dorman (1881, p. 264) said the Algonkin considered lightning to be a great serpent. According to Hagar (1897, p. 104) the Micmac had a legend to the effect that thunder is produced by seven flying rattlesnakes, crying to each other and waving their tails as they crash across the sky. A flash of lightning is produced when they dive for their prey.

Mooney (1900, p. 294) says the Cherokee feeling toward snakes is one of mingled fear and reverence, because they are thought to have an intimate connection with the rain and thunder gods. Every precaution is taken against killing or injuring one, especially a rattler. He who kills one will see others, and when he kills a second, more will come until he is driven crazy. To destroy a rattler is to destroy one of the most prized ornaments of the thunder god. As the rattlesnake is regarded as the chief of the snake tribe, he is to be feared and should be killed only under extreme necessity; one must ask the pardon of the snake's ghost or another will come to avenge him. The rattles, teeth, flesh, and oil are greatly prized for occult and medicinal purposes, but the snakes may be killed for them only by certain priests after appropriate ceremonies. When a rattler is killed, the head

---

[2] The association of snakes with weather—rain especially—is both ancient and world-wide; it is by no means confined to rattlesnakes, or to the New World.

must be cut off and buried an arm's length deep in the ground, and the body hidden in a hollow log. If they were left out, rain would come in torrents and the streams would overflow their banks. Mooney (1900, p. 458) states that the belief in an association between the serpent and the rain gods is almost universal among primitive peoples. Gilbert (1943, p. 183) says there is the usual linkage in Cherokee thought between snakes and lightning. It is a Sauk-Fox superstition that rattlers come out of hibernation at the first clap of spring thunder (Webber, 1951, p. 30).

According to Dorman (1881, p. 264; Hudson, 1894, p. 537) the Shawnee (Algonkin) thought thunder was the hissing of a great snake. McGee (1897, p. 180) says the Sioux connect the lightning stroke with the rattlesnake's strike. The Flathead believe that if one whips a snake it will rain (Turney-High, 1937, p. 27).

At Isleta, New Mexico, Parsons (1932, p. 277) found it a Pueblo custom to put fetishes under any tree that had been struck by lightning seven or more years before; one of these sacred objects represented a rattlesnake. Also she states (1939, p. 927) that one of their deities was Ikaina the Rattlesnake, associated with war, lightning, and the sun.

Just as the elaborate Hopi Snake dance is a prayer for rain, so also the whole protective attitude of the Hopi toward snakes, and rattlesnakes in particular, is premised on a desire to safeguard their precious water supply. Says Don C. Talayesva (Simmons, 1942, p. 17): "Serpent deities live in the springs and control the water supply"; and "They [the Snake and Antelope ceremonies] are for the propitiation of the Snake deities and to insure plenty of spring water and abundant rain for maturing crops" (p. 21); "When snakes were pleased with their treatment they were quiet and would bring rain as a reward" (p. 42).

The Keres and Tewa also have snake dances that are primarily prayers for rain, there being, in the mythology of these tribes, the same relationship between rattlesnakes and weather. While the Navaho do not have a snake dance, they, too, link snakes with lightning and rainfall, and under no circumstances will they kill one (W. Mathews, 1898, pp. 230, 233). An object that protects from lightning also protects from snakes; so long as a man carries his shell and turquoise charm, a snake may enter his hogan but will not bite him (Morgan, 1931, p. 401).

Bourke (1889, p. 186) found that the rattlesnake doctors among the Mohave were rain doctors as well. Kroeber (1908, p. 315) recounts a Mohave myth regarding a great rattler that is responsible for rain and thunder. The Klamath of Oregon believe that the rattlesnake makes the rain, and thunder is caused by his rattling (Spier, 1930, p. 119). In California, the Kato sing rattlesnake songs to stop excessive rain. Among the Chukchansi, a man who had been bitten by a rattler could stop excessive thunder and lightning by shouting for it to desist (Gayton, 1948, p. 198).

The same intimate connection between weather and rattlesnakes is evident in Mexico. The *Rudo Ensayo,* written in 1763, said the Opata believed that if one were bitten by a viper [rattlesnake] it meant he was to have been struck by a thunderbolt. He was required to give away everything he was wearing when bitten or he would be bitten again (1894, p. 172). The Huichol had the belief that lightning is a powerful serpent, and fire is another, namely, the rattlesnake (Lumholtz, 1900, p. 20; 1902, vol. 2, p. 202). Dorman (1881, p. 264) states that

Tlaloc, the Toltec thunder god, held in his hand a golden serpent representing lightning. J. E. Thompson (1933, p. 140) thinks this prevalent association, also a part of Mayan and Mexican beliefs, may result from the fact that rain brings snakes out of their hiding places.

Finally, as a third basis for the Indian treatment of rattlers, an attitude of protection was adopted because the rattlesnakes were thought to be agents of higher deities. Among some tribes, particularly in southern California, the rattlesnake was an officer of punishment, carrying out the penalties imposed by other gods. The southern California Shoshoni believed, when a rattler bit a dog near one of their homes, it must have resulted from a neglect of religious observances. Stewart (1938, p. 191) was told the story of a young Paiute who failed to take the proper religious course after a nightmare. Having dreamed that he was attacked by a rope, he should have taken a cold bath and communed with the spirits on the following morning. Failing this, on that day he was bitten by a rattler, and, despite treatment by the most skilled tribesmen, he succumbed on the third day.

The rattlesnake had this role as an avenger of dereliction of religious duties among the Luiseño and Diegueño of southern California, worshippers of Chinigchinich (Chungichnish), a superhuman being who used such instrumentalities as bears, wolves, mountain lions, rattlesnakes, and nettles to punish those disobedient to the faith or neglectful of religious observances (Boscana, 1933, pp. 29, 131; first English ed. 1846; DuBois, 1908, pp. 75, 303; Waterman, 1910, p. 275; Kroeber, 1916, p. 20). Thus, rattlesnake bite was attributed to some transgression of this kind (DuBois, p. 83), and its prevention could best be assured by the performance of ritualistic dances (Waterman, p. 276). If several people were bitten, the priests were blamed for not holding these ceremonies oftener. The Luiseño, like the Paiute mentioned by Stewart, believed that a failure to take ceremonial precautions following a dream would be avenged by a rattlesnake bite (DuBois, p. 179). The Eastern Pomo thought if a man were bitten by a rattler, it proved he had broken some taboo (Loeb, 1926, p. 316). Among the Karok, the rattlesnake was an agent of ill luck, used by fate to punish the infringement of a rule (Kroeber and Gifford, 1949, p. 40).

Lumholtz (1900, p. 12; 1902, vol. 2, p. 202) reported that the Huichol of Mexico believed the rattlesnake to be one of the animals ruled over by Elder Brother, messenger of the gods.

With children, rattlers were sometimes used as bogies. Among the Pima (F. Russell, 1908, p. 264) if a child puts his foot in an olla-head ring, or in a mortar, the mother says, "A rattler will bite you." Opler (1941, p. 37) says the Chiricahua Apache early warned their children against snakes. We are informed by Gifford and Block (1930, p. 58) that, in instructing the Diegueño children, the priests told them if they were good and got bitten they would succeed in getting home, but if they were bad they would never return. According to Sparkman (1908b, p. 222) much the same information was imparted to the Luiseño boys at their puberty ceremony. If they did not follow instructions and were bitten by a rattler in the field they would die right there, but if they heeded their elders and were bitten they would recover.

An occasional belief in the rattlesnake as an instrument of punishment is heard of among tribes farther east. Among the Meskwaki (Fox), one who had more than four skunk-cabbage roots in his possession at one time would have his home invaded by rattlesnakes, which would bite his family (Huron H. Smith, 1923–32, p. 203). William Byrd, in 1728, was told by a Saponi guide of an underworld judge of evildoers, a New World Medusa with tresses of writhing rattlesnakes (Rights, 1947, p. 96).

Rattlesnake venom sometimes was employed in intratribal punishments. Among the Omaha a sharp stick, poisoned with dried venom, might be jabbed into an offending brave in the confusion of a crowd as a punishment for disturbing the peace or disputing a chief's authority. Sometimes the man was first given a chance to reform by the poisoning of his horse, as a threat of worse to come (Fletcher and La Flesche, 1911, p. 213).

Pucher (1945, pp. 57, 59) says that rattlers were used by the Incas (or pre-Incas) in Bolivia for three purposes: to guard treasure, to test the veracity of witnesses, and to punish offenders.

Miller (1952, p. 299) reprints a newspaper story of 1890, probably fanciful, wherein the Pima Indians used rattlesnakes to test one of their tribe for witchcraft. He failed to pass the test and was fatally bitten. Dobie (1941b, p. 224) has described the torture of prisoners by the Yaqui, by the use of rawhide bonds and rattlesnakes.

It should be observed that, in segregating these instances of the protection of rattlesnakes by Indians into three categories, I have included in the first several examples wherein the reason for the protective attitude was not stated by the reporting investigator; in some of these it is possible the allocation should have been made to one of the others, were all the facts known.

Among the few tribes not fearing to destroy rattlesnakes were the Huchnom, who simply killed them as dangerous pests (Foster, 1944, p. 226).

A seasonal postponement of certain ceremonies, or the avoidance of relating particular myths and legends during the rattlesnakes' season of activity, seems to have been common methods of forestalling the snakes' resentment. Speck (1935, p. 25) says the Penobscot share the almost universal American Indian belief that legends must not be related in summer lest the snakes overhear and bite the offender. Speck also tells us (1946, p. 358) that the Catawba of the piedmont of northwestern South Carolina will not talk about snakes after dark, lest it invite annoyance from them. If a snake hears such tales he will lie in wait in the path. If he hears travel plans he will also wait along the way; to deceive him you must say you are leaving day after tomorrow when you really mean tomorrow. Mooney (1900, p. 295) tells us that certain dances of the Cherokee, being deemed possibly offensive to the snakes, were held in the late fall after the rattlers had gone into hibernation. With regard to the Omaha, Dorsey (1889, p. 190) records that myths must not be told during the day, or in summer, as a violation will cause the advent of snakes.

In the Southwest, F. Russell (1908, p. 206) found somewhat the same taboo among the Pima, who reserved their rattler myths for the season when the snakes would be away in their winter refuges. Leighton (1892, p. 736) said the Zuñi refused to recite their rattlesnake legends out of doors for fear the snakes might hear and retaliate. Concerning the Navaho, Tozzer (1908, p. 28) reported that certain long ceremonies could be held only in the late autumn or early winter when rattlesnakes and other dangerous creatures would be in hibernation. According to O. C. Stewart (1942, p. 291), among the Navaho and Ute, cat's cradle could not be played in summer since to do so would invite snake bite. He also states (p. 326) that some Ute and Paiute believe anyone telling myths in summer would be snake-bitten. In California the Kato do not sing rattlesnake songs in summer for the same reason (Loeb, 1932, p. 46).

There were a number of customs governing the terms to be used in speaking to or about rattlesnakes in an endeavor to appease them. Apologetic phrases and figurative names were often employed, the latter as a method of concealment or evasion.[3] Some even approached the formality of rituals.

The Ojibwa (Henry, 1809, p. 175) called the rattlesnake "grandfather." Parkman (1870, vol. 2, p. 264) says the Cherokee honor the rattler with a name that signifies "the bright old inhabitant." The Cherokee also avoid saying that so-and-so had been bitten by a snake; rather, it was said the victim had been scratched by briers, thus deceiving the listening rattler spirit (Mooney, 1891, p. 352). Even the common name for the rattler means "the admirable one," a propitiatory term (Mooney and Olbrechts, 1932, p. 184). When a Chickasaw had killed a snake he would say, "Well, I helped you all I could, but the Father-above has come and killed you, and I throw you away" (Swanton, 1928c, p. 252).

In the Southwest the Tewa (Curtis, 1926, vol. 17, p. 24) and the Zuñi (1926, vol. 17, p. 155) caught rattlesnakes and decorated them with stripes of red paint, after which the snakes were turned loose with suitable ceremonies of propitiation. Opler (1941, p. 227) says the Chiricahua Apache have a dread of rattlers that goes beyond a mere fear of snake bite. If they meet one they address it as "mother's father," or sometimes "mother's mother"; they request it to keep out of their way. They never mention rattlers except in invectives; and even when one says, "I wish a snake would bite you," the wisher may get a sore mouth for saying it (p. 228). According to Reagan (1930, p. 306) the White Mountain and San Carlos Apache fear snakes because of their evil powers; when they see one, they say, "Go into your hole, you evil creature, and take the evil world with you." The Navaho have sacred names for rattlesnakes and other animals (Franciscan Fathers, 1910, p. 176).

In California it is the custom of the western Shasta, if one of them kills a rattlesnake, to make an apologetic speech and cast the body in the direction of an enemy tribe (Voegelin, 1942, p. 172). The Hupa avoid the use of the term "rattlesnake" (Goddard, 1904, p. 257). The Yuki use the apologetic term "grandmother" when they have narrowly missed stepping on one (Kroeber, 1925, p. 198). Their figurative name for the rattlesnake indicates that to them the source of the rattlesnake's danger lies in menstrual blood, which they consider the deadliest of all poisons (Foster, 1944, p. 215).

The Wailaki hunter (Wintun tribe of California) never killed a rattler, but said "greeting" as he passed it by (Curtis, 1924, vol. 14, p. 93). Among the coastal Pomo the name of the rattlesnake was never mentioned, nor was the snake even talked about at any season of the year (Loeb, 1926, p. 315). It was, of course, forbidden to kill a rattler. The eastern Pomo, when coming upon a rattler, said,

---

[3] The same idea prevails in parts of India where a snake may not be mentioned, but is referred to as a "tiger" or a "string" (D. McKenzie, 1927, p. 113).

"Grandfather, I am not going to bother you; let me pass safely" (Gifford and Kroeber, 1937, p. 202). The Kato thought it unlucky to speak the rattlesnake name (Loeb, 1932, p. 46), and so did the northwestern Maidu (Loeb, 1933, p. 158). The Miwok spared rattlesnakes (Curtis, 1924, vol. 14, p. 135), and the Yokuts had specific ceremonies wherewith to placate them and thus forestall their bites (p. 161). One Diegueño shaman referred to a rattler as an "old man with a basket hat on his head" (Spier, 1923, p. 313). Such euphonious terms were thought to improve the rattlesnake–Indian relationship and understanding.

Necessarily, in this outline of rattlesnake protection and appeasement by the Indians, I have included only the citations that refer to rattlers. But it should not be thought that these practices were restricted to rattlers or, indeed, to snakes. On the contrary, propitiative and ritualistic treatments, protection, and terms of kinship, were often applied to other animals, such as the bear, deer, puma, and eagle, to name a few. The kinship term "grandfather," for example, was not restricted to rattlesnakes. Hallowell (1926) has discussed at length the Indian ceremonialism connected with the bear.

Some of the names used for rattlesnakes by the Indians were less propitiatory and more prosaic. The Cayuga referred to the massasauga as the "picture of the sun" or "dappled" because of the round spots in its pattern. They also knew, by hearsay, of another, larger rattler—no doubt the timber rattlesnake—which was called the "forked tongue" (Speck and Dodge, 1945, p. 308). The Menominee call the rattlesnake the "rattling-tail," while to the Lenni Lenape (Delaware) it was the "frightener" (Chamberlain, 1901, p. 679). Speck (1946) reports the following names in use by Southeastern tribes: The Catawba refer to the timber rattler as "rattlesnake bristling," and the ground rattler is the "rattle tail containing 1,000" (p. 355) or "snake at home in the ground" (p. 357). Both the Catawba and Creeks called the timber rattlesnake "snake chief," "king," or "greatest rattlesnake" (p. 357). The Cherokee (p. 360) call the timber rattler "now you see snake" and the ground rattler "the rattle"—the same word used for the gourd rattle. Mary R. Haas (1941, p. 129) supplies the following meanings to the terms used for the rattlesnake by various tribes: Choctaw—"supernatural or supernaturally dangerous snake"; Biloxi—"chief snake, governor snake, supernatural snake"; Tunica, Alabama, Koasati, Yuchi, and some Choctaw and Biloxi—"big snake"; Natchez and Creeks—"'snake chief." According to Dorman (1881, p. 264) the Dakota, Shawnee, and Sauk used the same word for spirit and snake.

The Franciscan Fathers (1910, p. 155) interpret the Navaho word for rattlesnake as "sounding snake." In the Havasupai and Maricopa languages, the term for rattlesnake is the same as the term for snakes in general (Spier, 1946, p. 115). The Maricopa refer to the sidewinder as the "left-handed snake." White (1947, p. 238) says the name for the prairie rattler used by the Keresan Pueblo means "he has rattles" and for the western diamond "snake with diamond pattern."

Although not propitiative, terms of this type do bear out the ideas expressed by Emerson (1884, p. 43), Brinton (1896, p. 130), and Mooney (1891, p. 352; 1900, p. 295) that many Indian tribes considered the rattlesnake to be the chieftain of the snakes.

LEGENDS AND TALES

The Indians, lacking a literature, were much given to the recitation of tales and legends, many of which were passed down as oral traditions unchanged through the generations. Some purported to be of a religious or historical character; others were repeated solely for entertainment through the long winter evenings. Many were creation myths; others sought to explain natural phenomena or animal life. In a considerable number of these, the rattlesnake appears as one of the characters, although much less often than several other animals, notably the coyote in the West. Other favorites included the buffalo, fox, raccoon, and raven, the choice varying between tribal groups. For example, the buffalo was a favorite character of the plains Indians (Wissler, 1941, p. 109), and the raven on the north Pacific Coast (Goddard, 1945, p. 134). But throughout a great area in the West and South, among divergent tribes, the coyote was the hero of many of these tales, sometimes wise, often stupid, and usually a trickster with more humor than morals.

I know of no tribal saga in which the rattlesnake is a continuing primary character to be compared with these other favorites, but this snake often appears in one guise or another. Sometimes it is an important figure in a drama, sometimes only one of a large cast of characters. In some tales the activities of the rattlers are related to the physical attributes of rattlesnakes in real life, particularly where they are instruments or agents of action; in others there is no such relationship, and the character is merely named "Rattlesnake" as one might apply any name to a character in a story.

Many of these tales have now been painstakingly transcribed by the ethnologists, after they had listened to the recitations of informants in their native tongues. The tales have contributed much to an understanding of tribal relationships and Indian psychology. The following is an alphabetical list, by Indian tribes, of references to some of those legends, tales, and songs that include rattlesnake characters or some other mention of rattlesnakes:

Achomawi (or Pit River): De Angulo, 1953, pp. 12, 134
Alabama: Martin, 1946, p. 67
Algonkin: Logan, 1859, p. 91; Young, 1903, pp. 239, 240
Apache (Jicarilla): Opler, 1938, p. 365
Apache (Lipan): Opler, 1940, p. 275
Apache (San Carlos): Goddard, 1919b, p. 183
Apache (White Mountain): Goddard, 1919a, pp. 135, 136; 1920, pp. 395, 399; Goodwin, 1937, pp. 148, 149
Arapaho: Kroeber, 1902–7, p. 421
Assiniboin: Lowie, 1909b, p. 48
Blackfoot: Grinnell, 1893, p. 45
Caddo: Weltfish, 1937, p. 51
Cahuilla: Hooper, 1920, pp. 322, 324; Curtis, 1926, vol. 15, pp. 108, 119; Strong, 1929, p. 136
Chehalis: Adamson, 1934, p. 77; Clark, 1953, p. 168.
Cherokee: Washburn, 1869, p. 208; Mooney, 1900, pp. 253, 294–306, 436; Swanton, 1946, p. 772
Chickasaw: Swanton, 1928c, p. 251
Chitimacha: Swanton, 1911, p. 357; 1917, p. 476
Choctaw: Bushnell, 1910, p. 533
Coeur d'Alène: Reichard, 1947, pp. 120, 175
Creeks: Speck, 1907, pp. 122, 149; Swanton, 1929, p. 57

Crow: Lowie, 1922, p. 339; 1942, pp. 3, 5
Cupeño: Joughlin and Valenzuela, 1953, p. 18
Dakota: Beckwith, 1930, p. 417; Deloria, 1932, p. 80
Diegueño: DuBois, 1904, pp. 227, 231
Fox: Lasley, 1902, p. 177; Jones, 1911, p. 214
Hidatsa: Pepper and Wilson, 1908, p. 310; Lowie, 1942, pp. 3, 5
Hitchiti: Swanton, 1929, p. 87
Hopi: Stephen, 1888, p. 109; 1929, p. 35; Voth, 1905, pp. 30, 35, 216; Curtis, 1922, vol. 12, p. 76; Parsons, 1933, p. 34
Hupa: Goddard, 1904, pp. 196, 263, 318; Driver, 1939, p. 414
Iowa: Skinner, 1925, p. 429
Iroquois: Converse, 1908, p. 110; Fenton, 1953, p. 81
Isleta: Parsons, 1932, p. 384
Kalapuya: Jacobs, 1945b, p. 121
Kalispel: Curtis, 1911, vol. 7, p. 100
Karok: Curtis, 1924, vol. 13, p. 63; Gifford and Block, 1930, p. 161; Driver, 1939, p. 414
Kato: Goddard, 1909, pp. 175, 234; Curtis, 1924, vol. 14, p. 166; Loeb, 1932, p. 46
Keres: Stevenson, 1894, pp. 44, 156; Judson, 1912, p. 178; Boas, 1928, p. 41; Benedict, 1930, p. 78; 1931, pp. 146, 239; Parsons, 1939, p. 296
Kiliwa: Meigs, 1939, p. 78
Kiowa: La Barre, 1947, p. 111
Klikitat: Jacobs, 1934, pp. 4, 22, 283
Koasati: Swanton, 1929, p. 201; Martin, 1946, p. 67
Luiseño: DuBois, 1906, p. 54; 1908, p. 113; Sparkman, 1908a, p. 35; Kroeber, 1916, p. 20; Gayton and Newman, 1940, p. 100
Maidu: Dixon, 1902b, pp. 41, 55, 110; 1903, p. 34; Spencer, 1908, p. 243; Gifford and Block, 1930, pp. 90, 248; Loeb, 1933, p. 204
Mandan: Beckwith, 1937, pp. 8, 85, 89, 266
Maricopa: Spier, 1933, pp. 135, 348
Menominee: Skinner, 1925a, p. 300
Micmac: Hagar, 1896, p. 176; 1897, p. 104
Miwok: Merriam, 1910, p. 56; Gifford, 1917, pp. 285, 306, 311, 331, 335, 336, 337; Barrett, 1919, p. 16; Gifford and Block, 1930, p. 135
Mohave: Kroeber, 1906, p. 315; 1925, p. 775; 1948, pp. 4, 10, 66
Mono: Gifford, 1923, p. 329; Gifford and Block, 1930, pp. 188, 256, 286; Gayton and Newman, pp. 78, 100
Navaho: Matthews, 1887, p. 405; Kluckhohn, 1944, p. 76
Nez Percé: Curtis, 1911, vol. 7, p. 162; Phinney, 1934, p. 224; V. Fisher, 1939, p. 145
Nisenan: Kroeber, 1929, p. 275; Beals, 1933, pp. 375, 391; Voegelin, 1942, p. 236
Ojibwa: Tanner, 1830, p. 351; Simms, 1906, p. 334 (Bungi)
Okanagon: Spier *et al.*, 1938, pp. 167, 226
Omaha: Dorsey, 1890, p. 322; Fortune, 1932, p. 137
Osage: La Flesche, 1921, p. 104; 1930, p. 663
Oto: Curtis, 1930, vol. 19, p. 171
Paiute: Sapir, 1910b, pp. 457, 463, 464; 1930, p. 481; Kelly, 1932, p. 200; 1938, pp. 387, 390, 392, 394; Steward, 1936, p. 430
Papago: H. R. Kroeber, 1912, p. 96; Neff, 1912, p. 58; Densmore, 1929b, pp. 97, 98; Underhill, 1946, p. 10; Matson, 1953, p. 53
Passamaquoddy: Leland, 1884, p. 110; Fewkes, 1890a, p. 261
Patwin: Kroeber, 1932, pp. 307, 308
Paviotso: Lowie, 1924, p. 298; Curtis, 1926, vol. 16, pp. 137, 139
Pawnee: Dorsey, 1904, p. 40; 1906, pp. 148, 492; Densmore, 1929c, p. 107
Pima: F. Russell, 1908, pp. 215, 248, 309, 310; Neff, 1912, p. 58; Judson, 1912, p. 175
Pomo: Curtis, 1924, vol. 14, p. 171; Barrett, 1933, pp. 67, 76, 85, 89, 91, 94, 214, 332, 373; DeAngulo, 1935, p. 237
Ponca: Dorsey, 1890, p. 322

Sarsi: Curtis, 1928, vol. 18, p. 144

Sauk: Lasley, 1902, p. 177

Seneca: Curtin and Hewitt, 1918, p. 505; Parker, 1923, p. 306

Shasta: Dixon, 1910, pp. 24, 26, 365; Frachtenberg, 1915, pp. 211, 212

Shoshoni: Ingersoll, 1883a, p. 35; 1884b, p. 91; Lowie, 1909a, p. 284; H. B. Alexander, 1916,
   p. 133; Steward, 1943a, p. 258

Tachi: Gifford and Block, 1930, p. 187

Takelma: Sapir, 1907b, p. 42

Tewa: Curtis, 1926, vol. 17, p. 77; Parsons, 1926, p. 250; Harrington and Roberts, 1928, p.
   395; DeHuff, 1931, p. 73

Thompson: Teit, 1916, p. 308

Tunica: Swanton, 1907, p. 288

Tuscarora: Lawson, 1709, p. 213

Ute: Lowie, 1924, p. 298; Sapir, 1930, p. 511

Wappo: Radin, 1924, p. 113

Wasco: Sapir, 1909, p. 301

Winnebago: Radin, 1909, p. 292

Wintun: Curtis, 1924, vol. 14, p. 174

Wishram: Sapir, 1909, pp. 97; Curtis, 1911, vol. 8, p. 125

Yana: Sapir, 1910, pp. 73, 93

Yavapai: Gifford, 1933a, p. 414; 1936, pp. 310, 315

Yokuts: Kroeber, 1907a, p. 364; 1907b, pp. 207, 209; 1925, p. 506; Curtis, 1924, vol. 14, pp.
   166, 171, 174, 175; Latta, 1936, pp. 36, 71, 79; Gayton and Newman, 1940, pp. 18, 19, 22, 100

Yuchi: Wagner, 1931, p. 78

Yuki: Foster, 1944, p. 217

Yuma: Harrington, 1908, p. 334; Gifford, 1926a, p. 67; Gifford and Block, 1930, p. 110; Forde,
   1931, p. 176; Spier, 1936, p. 15

Yurok: Curtis, 1924, vol. 13, p. 186; Driver, 1939, pp. 343, 412; Spott and Kroeber, 1942, p. 206

Zuñi: Cushing, 1901, pp. 150, 285; Curtis, 1926, vol. 17, p. 177; Benedict, 1935, vol. 2, p. 224

Some of these tales are quite amusing, such as that of the Pima (Judson, 1912, p. 175) telling how the rattlers learned to bite; the Algonkin story (Young, 1903, p. 240) of how a deity fixed a string of wampun to the tails of rattlesnakes, thus forming the rattles and making it impossible for them to move without sounding a warning; the Tewa (Harrington and Roberts, 1928, p. 395) on why rattlers will not bite in summer when the moon shines, and how the rattle can be heard two miles away; the Pawnee story (Densmore, 1929c, p. 107) of the little rattlesnake crying because his rattle wouldn't make a noise; the Wishram (Curtis, 1911, vol. 8, p. 125) on how the rattlesnakes ate some kind of grass in summer to make the bite more venomous. Also, this tribe had a myth (p. 126) to account for the immunity of the raccoon to rattler bite, an immunity to which Curtis apparently subscribes, although I know of no verification of such an idea.

MISCELLANEOUS SUPERSTITIONS AND BELIEFS

The Indians had a number of rattlesnake myths not essentially religious or propitiatory in character. Among these was that of the rattler with a jewel in its head. This has been described by Timberlake (1765, p. 47), Adair (1775, p. 86), and Bossu (1777, p. 86). Timberlake was told by the Cherokee that their most treasured and brilliant stone came from a snake's head. This was an enormous snake, protected by a number of followers. A brave Indian, encased in leather armor, succeeded in killing the snake and securing the stone. Adair's story, also told by the Cherokee, recounts the finding of a great carbuncle where a huge rattler lay dead. Bossu writes of a great rattlesnake seen swimming in the Mississippi with a carbuncle in its head. It made a brilliant flash of light in the sunrise. The snake was shot, but although the body floated, the stone was lost. Dobie (1925, p. 9) mentions the myth of the great rattler of the Arbuckle Mountains, with a diamond in its head, and others studding its sides. The myth of the serpent with the jewel in its head is restricted neither to rattlesnakes nor to the American Indians (Halliday, 1924, p. 139; also see Oldmixon, 1741, vol. 2, p. 188; Hudson, 1894, p. 537; Brinton, 1896, p. 137; Mooney, 1900, p. 297; and Krappe, 1930, p. 258).[4]

Carver (1778, p. 43; also Emerson, 1884, p. 42) repeats the story, told him by a French trapper, of one Indian who had a tame rattler that he worshipped as a god, calling it his "Great Father." The rattler was regularly liberated in October and returned to its cage of its own accord the following May. Peter Pond, a fur trader (see Gates, 1933, p. 38) stated that Carver was imposed on by the man who told him this yarn; there is, in fact, reason to believe that Carver himself doubted its truth.

Brinton (1896, p. 133) tells how a Count Zinzendorf, about to be attacked by Indians, was saved when the superstitious savages, watching through a window, saw a great rattlesnake crawl across his feet, as he sat unperturbed before his fireplace.

Swanton (1911, p. 357) recounts an interesting myth of the Chitimacha of southwestern Louisiana. In ancient times two Indians saved a pair of rattlers in a great flood. Ever after, the rattlesnakes remained the friends of man. Each home was watched over by a rattler in the owner's absence; when the owner returned, the rattler went about its business.

The Cherokee believed that seeing a snake at the start of a journey was an omen of death (Gilbert, 1943, p. 368). Should you stretch your hands toward a rattlesnake, and it appeared cross and evil, it meant you had not long to live. But if it were calm, you might pick it up and set it down; then if it crawled west it signified death; if east, a long life. These snake omens, although ancient in origin, are still believed.

The Omaha (southern Sioux) believed that some rattlesnakes could shoot or project venom for a distance of at least a hundred feet. Such a supernatural rattler was any snake one met under unusual circumstances (Fortune, 1932, p. 137).

The Hopi and some Pueblo tribes thought the smell of a woman to be highly offensive to a rattlesnake; it angered him so that he would bite (Stephen, 1936, pp. 709, 756, 766; Parsons, 1939, p. 1056).

Russell (1908, p. 264) tells us the Pima Indians credited the rattler with the ability to select the direction toward the best mesquite beans. The author wonders at the source of this idea. (It might be guessed that the densest mesquites would have the most abundant beans, and would likewise be chosen by the snakes as the best refuges from the heat.) Russell also says the Pima considered it unlucky to come upon two rattlers, one after the other, while searching for something.

---

[4] S. C. Williams, editor of the 1927 edition of Timberlake, says that the use of the term "diamond rattlesnake" may have originated from this myth (p. 75). This is quite different from the usually accepted derivation of the name, which is presumed to be based on the diamond-shaped marks along the snake's back, particularly evident in such species as *adamanteus*, *atrox*, *durissus*, and some others. Certainly this is what Beauvois had in mind when he selected the name *adamanteus*.

They greatly dreaded the magic power of the snakes, although snakes occurred less often in Pima thought than in Hopi.

Opler (1940, p. 275) reports that the Lipan Apache have a myth regarding a rattler with hair on its head.

According to Spier (1933, p. 135) the Maricopa believe jackrabbit blood contains rattlesnake venom, for the cottontail, a relative of the jack, was bitten by the rattlesnake in the tribal creation myth.

In the Yuma demonology (Gifford, 1926a, p. 67) ghosts may appear either as whirlwinds or as rattlesnakes. Such rattlesnakes are distinguished by their large size and the black and white bands encircling the tail. (Contrasting tail bands of this type characterize the western diamond rattlesnake, *Crotalus atrox*, the largest and most dangerous rattlesnake species found in Yuma territory). To kill one would result in the killer's becoming a cripple. Some rattlers can live under water for a month.

A number of unrelated rattlesnake superstitions and beliefs were prevalent among the California tribes. Beals (1933, p. 393) lists the following Nisenan beliefs: While bull snakes are hatched from eggs, rattlers are born by way of the mother's mouth—a belief obviously related to the swallowing-the-young myth (p. 1244). Rattlesnakes and squirrels may interchange bodies. An Indian killed one in the process of transformation; it had a squirrel's head and a rattlesnake's body.[5] The wood dove is the rattler's niece; if you mock her a rattler will bite you. If one person in a family is bitten, another will be (the narrator, and his grandmother before him, had been bitten). When one recovers from rattlesnake bite, he must give away everything he had with him when bitten or be doomed to bad luck forever. The Nisenan tell of a man who boasted he would eat a rattler's heart. He did so and ever afterward was quick-tempered like a rattlesnake (Beals, 1933, p. 375).

The Yurok believe that an eclipse is caused by a rattlesnake swallowing the sun (Driver, 1939, p. 343). After biting a person, a rattlesnake recuperates by steaming itself on hot rocks (p. 412).

The Maidu think rattlesnakes are harmless while drinking, as they lay aside their poison until finished (Spencer, 1908, p. 243). This fantastic theory is well known in white folklore (p. 1216).

We are told by Steward (1933, p. 307) that the Owens Valley Paiute believe that if one is bitten by a blind rattler (while shedding) he also will become blind. One who has been bitten will become sick at the same time next year (this is also an ancient white myth [p. 844]).

The Northfork Mono hold that if one keeps rattles in his home or sings a snake song, rattlesnakes will be attracted and move in (Gifford, 1932b, p. 53).

According to the Cocopa (Gifford, 1933b, p. 305), if a rattler tries to enter a house or an arbor where there are people, and he fails to rattle or to try to bite when annoyed, it is a signal that someone will soon die. Witch doctors derive their powers from the vulture, hawk, or rattlesnake (p. 312).

The Maya believe that if you see a green snake—not necessarily a rattler—and fail to kill it, you will die within a year. This disaster may be avoided if the snake is caught and cut into nine pieces (Steggerda, 1941, p. 64).

---

[5] A rattler, while swallowing a squirrel tail first, would have just such an appearance.

The Paviotso have the curious belief that the horned toad speaks the Paviotso language and is able to kill rattlesnakes (Lowie, 1924, p. 298). The Ute have the same theory. It is stated that a rattler sometimes finds a young horned toad and kills it, whereupon the mother horned toad, in furious revenge, kills the big snake with her horns. The Surprise Valley Paiute think the horned toad looks like a doctor. He is often seen to kill rattlesnakes by coming up behind them, getting underneath, and cutting them in two with his horns (Isabel Kelly, 1932, p. 201).

The Northeastern Yavapai believe the green lizard [no doubt the western collared lizard, *Crotaphytus collaris baileyi*] is more poisonous than the rattlesnake and can kill rattlers (Gifford, 1936, p. 268). As a matter of fact, this voracious lizard has been known to eat baby rattlers, although it is nonvenomous. Venom is attributed to a number of lizards by the Southwestern Indians (e.g., Yavapai, Gifford, 1932, p. 240; Chemehuevi, Kelly, 1936, p. 137), but, among all the lizards in the world, only the Gila monster and a close Mexican relative are actually venomous.

According to Conard (1890, p. 136) the Navaho, like the Apache, believed in transmigration, and that the spirit of an especially mean Indian would find lodgment in a rattlesnake. Gershenfeld (1930, p. 193) says there was an Indian tradition that the number of rattles borne by a snake recorded the number of people it had killed. Certain Paraguay Indians believe that young snakes grow from the bodies of dead adults, so the bodies should always be taken far away (Dobrizhoffer, 1784, 1822 ed., p. 299).

Although changed by time and white influences, the Indian superstitions respecting rattlesnakes are still retained by many tribes and individuals. Debo (1941, p. 298) reports that the Creeks still treat rattlers with respectful friendliness, and if one crawls into camp during a ball game, he is sure to bring success to that side (the side at bat?).

Without doubt many of these Indian superstitions have now been contaminated by European and African importations, some dating back to Pliny. It is difficult to separate those having parallel but independent sources from others that diverged from a single origin. Some of these derivations have been discussed by Milling (1937, p. 43). Of course, beliefs involving the rattle itself could only have originated in the Americas.

DREAMS

I have discussed elsewhere certain relationships thought by the Indians to exist between rattlesnakes and dreams: First, the acquisition, through dreams, of the shamanistic power to cure rattlesnake bite (p. 1151); secondly (p. 1150), the necessity of treating a dream bite with the same remedies as a real one (see, for example, Mooney and Olbrechts, 1932, p. 176, respecting this practice among the Cherokee).

Snake dreams, and especially rattlesnake dreams, were usually deemed ill omens. The Cherokee believed that sickness might result from dreaming about a snake (Gilbert, 1943, p. 368). The Oto held such a dream to mean that other tribes were about to attack, and that the camp should therefore be moved at once (Whitman, 1937, p. 86). The Kalekau, Kato, Lassik, and Yuki all believed that it was a threat of ill fortune to dream of a snake (Essene, 1942, p. 38). Loeb (1926, p.

316) says the Pomo thought it good luck to dream of a rattler or bull snake, but bad luck, on the contrary, if the snake left you in the dream. Gayton (1948, pp. 115, 243) has discussed rattlesnake dreams among the subtribes of the Yokuts and Western Mono.

The Tübatulabal thought rattler dreams were sent by witches. Anyone who dreamed of a rattlesnake was required to go out into a canyon on the following morning to make a speech to the creature, whereby the bad dream might be rendered ineffective (Voegelin, 1938, p. 62). The Paiute had a closely related belief as illustrated by a story told to Steward (1933, p. 316; 1938, p. 191). A man on a hunting trip dreamed of being attacked by a rope. Next morning he failed to make the proper ritualistic gestures of appeasement. That day he was bitten by a rattlesnake and died, despite the best ceremonial treatments. Among the Mohave, to see a rattler in one's dreams forewarns of aches and pains in old age.

The Cocopa believe that to dream of a rattler means that the dreamer will be struck in the foot (Gifford, 1933b, p. 304). The Navaho think it is not serious to dream of snakes unless one is bitten in the dream (Reichard, 1928, p. 145).

The Maya have a queer dream sequence: If a man sees snakes in a dream he will quarrel with his wife; if he dreams of an unclad woman he will see a rattlesnake next day (Steggerda, 1941, p. 59).

PROTECTIVE MEASURES

REPELLENTS, CHARMS, AND TABOOS

So intimately is the avoidance of rattlesnake bite related to its treatment, in Indian procedures, that it is difficult to separate preventive from curative measures. The Indians naturally extended their remedies to uses as repellents, for to them the idea was obvious that a substance which counteracted rattlesnake venom should also be objectionable to the snakes themselves. Hence, to keep rattlers away from camps or to avoid them when traveling, the tribes that depended on plant cures carried with them some of the same plants used in snake-bite treatment.

We learn from Arfwedson (1834, vol. 1, p. 376) that the herb called the "rattlesnake masterpiece," which was used in snake-bite treatment, was considered to be so effective that, if it were rubbed on the hands, any snake encountered would be unable to move. McKenney (1846, p. 114) was told by the Menominee that they had a root which they pounded up and put on a stick; the snake would bite at this and be killed by the poison of the root. According to Densmore (1928, p. 376; 1929a, p. 112) the Chippewa (Ojibwa) prepared a combination of powdered plantain root (*Plantago major*) and vermilion (evidently some red mineral); this was carried on the person as a protection against snake bite, and was, in fact, thought so powerful as to prevent even the appearance of the snakes. The Menominee had several plant repellents (H. H. Smith, 1923–32, p. 38).

Fenton (1942, p. 521) states the Iroquois constantly carried dried roots that they chewed and spit on their hands to repel snakes, as well as to apply to the wound in case of a bite.

Among the Southeastern tribes, Mooney (1900, p. 295) tells us the Cherokee believed that if a hunter carried a small piece of the root of the "rattlesnake master," *Silene stellata*—no doubt the same as Arfwedson's "rattlesnake master-piece"—the snakes would avoid him in terror.

The Chitimacha thought ash leaves and cane (*Arundinaria*) poisonous to the rattlesnake; if a piece of cane were run through any part of the snake's body it would paralyze the whole (Swanton, 1917, p. 478). The Catawba, according to Speck (1937, p. 191), believed that the rattlesnake root, or rattlesnake masterpiece (in this case *Agave virginica*, the American aloe), if kept on the person while passing through the woods, would ward off rattlesnakes.

In the Southwest, the Maricopa had a plant known as "rattlesnake afraid"—an aromatic shrub resembling rhubarb; this was chewed and spat on horses' hoofs to protect them on journeys (Spier, 1933, p. 290). The Kaibab tied pieces of the root of *Ligusticum pringlei* (lovage), wrapped in buckskin, to their moccasins to prevent snake bite (Kelly, 1939, p. 153). According to Wyman and Harris (1941, p. 66) the Navaho prepare an infusion of *Conioselinum scopulorum*, reinforced with four other plants, which is so strong that if any falls on a snake it will die. These plants are also chewed and applied to the body for protection when the individual is away from home, particularly when attending distant ceremonials. Wyman and Harris (1951, pp. 23, 31, 34) mention several plants used by the Kayenta Navaho as repellents. The Hopi were stated to safeguard themselves in their Snake dance by chewing and fumigating their clothes with *Iris versicolor* (H. H. Smith, 1923–32, p. 430). For other plant products said to be used by the Hopi for protection in the dance see Coleman (1928, p. 97) and Whiting (1939, pp. 32, 39, and 77).

Bard (1894, p. 11; Corlett, 1935, p. 314) reported that the Indians of southern California thought the odor of the plant they called "chucupate" so repugnant to snakes that they habitually carried a piece of its root for protection. "Chucupate" or "chuchupate" has been identified as *Ligusticum porteri*. The Nisenan put on their feet a medicine whose smell would keep rattlers away (Kroeber, 1929, p. 274). Beals (1933, p. 388) said the shamans of this tribe from near Placerville, California, claimed the smell of their preparation would cause the snakes to rattle, thus permitting one to avoid them. According to Essene (1942, p. 48) the Lassik rubbed their feet and legs with angelica, the Yuki with pepperwood, whereas the Kato used dried seaweed and octopus, all for protection against rattle-snakes. Chestnut (1902, p. 371) said that angelica was used by the Pomo, Yokia, or Yuki, near Ukiah. The Atsugewi, according to Garth (1953, p. 141) used angelica root; also they rubbed turtle liver on their legs, and the women attached turtle heads to their skirts. The northern Miwok carried a certain snakeroot around as a charm. When they were thus protected, if they met a snake it would rattle as a sort of salutation and then go on its way (Aginsky, 1943, p. 458).

In Central America, the Muskito chewed a few guaco leaves—also called huaco, probably meaning the hempweed, *Mikania*—daily as a preventive against snake bite (Conzemius, 1932, p. 137). If it were spit on a snake's head the creature would be stupefied by this infusion.

Various tribes used plant preparations to permit the handling of rattlers with safety. Charlevoix (1761; reprint of 1923, vol. 1, p. 339) wrote that the Indian medicine men had some method of stupefying rattlers so that they might be safely handled, whereby the populace would be impressed. The bones and skins were used in divining. Adair (1775, p. 237) said he once saw a Chickasaw chief chew some snakeroot, blow it on his hands, and then pick up a rattler without fear of injury. Dumarest (1919, p. 158) claimed the snake-priest assistants of the Cochiti rubbed their hands with grease and tobacco so that the rattlers required in a ceremony might be caught without danger. Corlett (1935, p. 196) reports that the shamans of Santa Marta, northern Colombia, would handle venomous snakes after a special treatment with a certain powder. A. D. Raudot, about 1710 (Kinietz, 1940, p. 404), stated the Miami Indians could catch rattlers and defang them, if they had first rubbed their hands with the same root used in the treatment of snake bite. The rattlers would not strike because of the odor.

Repellents were sometimes used about habitations to keep the rattlers away. Pope (1792, p. 98) mentions the use of *Serpentaria virginiana* (*Aristolochia serpentaria,* Virginia snakeroot?) for this purpose; the snakes were supposed to dislike its odor. Densmore (1928, p. 376; 1929a, p. 112) says that the Chippewa (Ojibwa) sprinkled around their camps a decoction of calamus root mixed with wild sarsaparilla; they also used an infusion of rattlesnake fern sprinkled about the wigwam. According to Wyman and Harris (1941, p. 66) the Navaho splatter the floor of a hogan with *Conioselinum scopulorum,* a plant of the parsley family, as the snakes are supposed to dislike its odor. Other plant repellents are mentioned by Dorsch (1929, p. 3) and Webber (1951, p. 30).

Several tribes used tobacco, about both their persons and living quarters, on the theory that it is deadly or unpleasant to rattlesnakes. Long (1791, p. 160) and Washington Irving (1836, p. 151) mention this custom in the Northwest. A Wukchumni woman, when going seed gathering, first smeared herself with tobacco, because the rattlers would smell it and go away (Gayton, 1948, p. 115). McKenney (1846, p. 114) states that the Menominee thought the smell of tobacco made rattlesnakes sick, thus rendering it easy to catch them. The southeastern branch of the Yavapai, when moving into caves, burned strong tobacco to keep the snakes from issuing from the crevices (Gifford, 1932a, p. 240). According to Bennett and Zingg (1935, p. 128) the Tarahumare attribute great repelling power to tobacco, and often smoke before going to sleep, to keep the rattlers away at night.

Various animal and mineral products were also used for protection, although these are to be viewed more as charms than repellents. According to McKenney (1846, p. 114), among the Menominee a piece of flesh from the neck of a turkey buzzard was dried and applied to the body as a powder. When an Indian was so protected, a rattler would not come near—much less bite him. According to Cotton Mather in 1716, the Indians anointed themselves with fat of the kite, a bird that feeds on rattlers, and then handled rattlers as safely as they might have handled eels (Kittredge, 1916, p. 39). Dobie (1937, p. 168) says that some tribes wear feathers on their moccasins, so that the rattlers, fearing roadrunners, will flee. Daniels and Stevans (1903, vol. 2, p. 696) say the Cherokee believed that moccasins that had absorbed smoke from a fire would make a rattler hurry away. Skinner (1921, p. 128, fig. 5d, p. 129) noted a silver bracelet etched with a fine rattlesnake figure that was considered a charm against snake bite in this tribe. A picture of a rattlesnake on an Indian's body was a good repellent (Walduck, 1714, in Masterson, 1938, p. 214).

Dorman (1881, p. 264) states that the Potawatomi wore rattlesnake fangs as a charm against rheumatism, but Ingersoll (1883a, p. 43) says they were worn as talismans against snake bite. Dobrizhoffer (1784, ed. 1822, vol. 2, p. 304) mentions tribes in Paraguay that used crocodile teeth in antisnake amulets. According to Kanner (1928, p. 279) the Cholones of Peru have the same custom. The Cora of northwestern Mexico wrap a rattler fang in an oak leaf and wear it as a love charm, and rattlesnake venom is used as an aphrodisiac (Lumholtz, 1902, vol. 2, p. 339). Morgan (1931, p. 401) tells us that the Navaho protect themselves with shell and turquoise charms; a rattler might enter a hogan but will not bite as long as the tenant has his charm. The Shuswap of western Canada carry rattles to avoid meeting a snake (Ray, 1942, p. 130).

According to R. Brown (1871, p. 40) the Indians of the Rogue River Valley, in Oregon, knowing the antipathy of rattlers for hogs, used to ask the settlers for pieces of pigskin to be placed around their ankles when gathering berries. (These might be of some service, not because of the hog-rattler aversion but, rather, the mechanical protection afforded by the leather.) D. Thompson wrote in his diary in 1811 (1916, p. 525), while traveling through the Umatilla country, that his hunters wore anklets of hog teeth to protect against rattlers, but it is doubtful that the Indians originated the practice. Spier (1930, p. 129) reports that the Klamath of northern California wore a turtle head around the neck to ward off rattlesnakes. Nearby, the eastern Shasta protected themselves by putting crushed abalone shell inside their moccasins, but the Atsugewi preferred a turtle shell suspended from the belt (Voegelin, 1942, p. 247) or a turtle head (Garth, 1953, p. 141). The Round Valley Indians of northeastern Mendocino County, California, eat devilfish flesh to prevent rattlesnake bite, for a rattler will flee from any person who has eaten this when young (Nomland, 1938, p. 117). They also use seal and sea-lion teeth as charms (p. 113). The Yokuts, Western Mono, and Miwok wore abalone pendents, usually around the neck, as amulets against rattlesnakes (Driver, 1937, p. 77; Aginsky, 1943, p. 416; Gayton, 1948, pp. 38, 115, 162, 173). Corlett (1935, p. 314) was told that in southern California it was believed that if a person carried salt, rattlers were made harmless.

Charms may enter the Indian–rattlesnake relationship in two forms: first, as protective amulets against the snakes; and, secondly, as charms formed of rattlesnake parts or effigies worn to ward off other evils. I shall now pass to the second category.

Skinner (1921, pp. 62, 311, 312) tells us that when approaching the enemy, the Menominee warrior would take a snake skin from his war bundle to give him the serpent power of stealthy approach. Skinner also illustrates (1923–25, plate 9) a weasel-skin amulet of the Kickapoo, that includes a decorative rattle. In *Idaho Lore,* edited by Fisher (1939, p. 204), it is said the Nez Percé Indians invoked a charm against evil by placing a rattler's head on hot coals in the earth and covering it with fresh liver and gall from wild beasts. During the steaming the liver was thought to absorb venom from the head, which was then carried as a talisman in a buckskin bag.

The Tolowa wore rattles on the head as a charm against attack or poisoning; the Karok as a charm against illness, since the rattlesnake never gets sick (Driver, 1939, p. 398). The same author also states (p. 398) that rattles were shaken by the Sinkyone to keep illness away. Among the Zuñi the rattle was worn as a protection against human enemies; the fat or oil of the snake was rubbed on the face on the theory that the enemy would fear and flee from this as he would from the snake itself (Stevenson, 1904, p. 599; Parsons, 1939, p. 415). A medicine of snake droppings was given to Acoma war captains, both to increase their strength and to give them power to foretell events (Parsons, 1939, pp. 415, 452, 595). In the Rain ceremonial of the Snake and Kapina societies of the Keresans at Sia, New Mexico, snake rattles were among the sacred objects placed on the altar (Parsons, 1939, p. 688).

According to the Wintu, a charm not properly cared for may avenge itself (DuBois, 1935, p. 83). Rattlesnakes and rattle charms are definitely associated with eye troubles and blindness. For example, a man whose wife was pregnant found and kept a rattle—something he should not have done. The son became blind two or three months after birth, and died when still young. In another instance, carrying a bright rock that looked like a rattle caused rheumatism and blindness (p. 84). Yet a shed rattlesnake skin could bring good fortune, if wrapped in grass and propitiated with smoke and acorn meal.

There were many Indian charms based on snakes other than rattlers. For example, Teit (1900, p. 371) says that the tail of the rubber boa (*Charina bottae*) was worn by the Thompson Indians to keep them safe from danger when hunting grizzlies. Speck (1935, p. 30) reports the Penobscot wore a snakeskin headband that was thought to have the power to drive away one's enemies.

The protective values of various charms were in some instances based on actual or fancied resemblances to rattlesnakes. Thus the Wintu of California (DuBois, 1935, p. 82) attributed good luck to ammonites having a coiled shape suggesting a rattler, and the same was true of stones having a similar shape. Among the Yana certain small round stones having bright-colored bands were interpreted as being rattlesnakes, and were much sought as charms. They were supposed to cure disease, and to bring luck in gambling and hunting (Sapir, 1908, p. 42; Sapir and Spier, 1943, p. 282).

Aside from the widespread ban on killing rattlesnakes that I have discussed elsewhere, several tribes had interesting taboos. The Modoc, and some of the Shasta, Maidu, and Nisenan, believed it dangerous to whistle around elderberry bushes, lest the whistler be bitten by a rattlesnake (Voegelin, 1942, pp. 95, 203). The rattler was much feared by the Maidu; the skin and rattles were never used, as the rattler was the cause of the first death in their creation myth (Spencer, 1908, p. 243). The Nisenan also considered the skin and rattles dangerous (Beals, 1933, p. 393). Among the Maidu the marriage of first cousins—considered incest—would surely be punished by rattlesnake bite. This recalls to mind the position of rattlesnakes as avengers in the Diegueño and Luiseño mythology.

Although rattlesnakes were said to have been killed by the Kato whenever met, they had to be clubbed rather than shot with an arrow, or lameness would befall the offender (Loeb, 1932, p. 46). The Yuki would not use the topknot of the California quail in their feather regalia because the topknot is used as a club to kill rattlers by the quail (Essene, 1942, p. 60). (Actually the topknot is feather-soft and delicate.) Among the Pomo, it was taboo to kill rattlesnakes except in the spring when they were mating, and then both must be killed or the survivor would avenge its mate, as well as in resentment through having been found in a compromising situation (Loeb, 1926, p. 316). The Navaho would not look at a dead snake or touch a shed skin (Franciscan Fathers, 1910, p. 155).

IMMUNIZATION

Various methods of immunization as a protection against snake bite have been attributed to the Indians. Señora Calderón de la Barca (1843, p. 431) was told that the Indians near Tampico, Mexico, inoculated themselves with rattlesnake venom as a precaution against future bites. A similar statement was made by Hoit (1844, p. 243). DeLys (1948, p. 75) reported that some Mexican Indians understood immunization by use of increasing doses of venom. Gordon (1949, p. 11) thought the Indians may have used this protection in colonial days. Acker-knecht (1949, p. 632) said that certain Colombian tribes inoculated themselves with snake ashes. Lloyd (1954, p. 28) saw an Indian bitten by a rattler. Little or no attention was paid to the bite, although the Indian claimed there had been enough venom injected to kill five men. Lloyd was told that the Indian was a professional snake catcher who had been immunized as a boy. Other data on the actual or supposed immunization of human beings against rattlesnake venom will be found on pp. 846 *et seq.*

SOCIETIES AND CEREMONIES

CLANS AND SOCIETIES

Most Indian tribes were divided into a number of rather confusing subgroups such as clans, societies, septs, moieties, or fraternities. These were often of great importance, particularly with respect to the permissibility of intermarriage. Some of these groups were delegated the duties of carrying on certain tribal ceremonies, or of providing the actors for specific parts.

In the present discussion these tribal groups are of interest primarily in con-nection with their participation in ceremonies in which rattlesnakes or their effi-gies were introduced, or when they took the name Rattlesnake. In certain cases the name was significant of some relationship of that particular group to rattle-snakes, such as the inclusion of snake-bite specialists or shamans, or the partici-pants in some snake ceremony; but often the name was a mere title without special significance. The shamans will be mentioned again in the discussion of snake-bite treatments. The titles assigned to the subgroups (clan, society, or fra-ternity) are often confusing; I shall usually adhere to the designations of the ethnologists from whom these data on the Indian-rattlesnake relationships are abstracted.

Stevenson (1894, p. 76) says the rain ceremony at Sia, New Mexico, was carried on by the Snake society, just as is the case in the Hopi dance. This relationship among the Pueblo is also discussed by Hodge (1896, p. 133). Stevenson (1904, p. 392) notes that, among the Zuñi, the Galaxy fraternity, rather than the Rattle-snake, was skilled in the cure of snake bite. The Rattlesnake fraternity did par-ticipate in planting prayer plumes in April at a rattlesnake shrine south of Zuñi, but so did others (p. 423). The Rattlesnake fraternity seems to have been so named because of its acquisition of a carved rattler, and also because the members quarreled like angry snakes (p. 528). Curtis (vol. 16, 1926, pp. 86, 124, 144, 241) mentions the Rattlesnake clan of the Keres, whose particular duty was the treatment of snake bite, although they belonged to the Flint society. The Zuñi Rattlesnake fraternity members caught and decorated snakes, and then liberated them (vol. 17, 1926, p. 155). Swanton (1928a, p. 169) says the taboo against killing rattlers among the Creeks was not activated by the Snake clan (see also Swanton, 1928b, p. 490).

L. A. White has discussed the status of the Snake societies or clans at the Keresan pueblos of San Felipe (1930a, p. 40), Santo Domingo (1935, p. 68), and Santa Ana (1942, p. 320), in New Mexico. These societies are merely groups of men who have been cured of snake bite and so have themselves become snake priests skilled in the application of cures, although no one is forced to join after being cured. They do not have the formal status of other societies.

At Santo Domingo, the home of the head of the society is their headquarters. Here a man is brought who has been bitten, and here he is kept for four days in a room with the snake that bit him, together with others freshly caught, so that he may become acquainted with them and they won't bite him. The head priest also stays with them. On the fourth day following the bite, a meal painting is made on the floor; the patient is placed beside it and the snakes in front. After a ritual the patient is presumed cured, and the snakes are taken out and liberated. The priests return to a supper provided by the patient's family. Women are treated in the same way, except that no snakes are kept in the room with them; also, they do not become society members but only helpers.

When a man was bitten at Santa Ana, where the Snake society had become inactive through lack of members, a messenger was sent to San Felipe for a snake doctor. None could be found, so that evening the patient himself was taken to San Felipe. However, it was now too late and he died the following morning. It is noteworthy that, although the deceased was educated and spoke English, in this emergency he fell back on primitive medicine (no doubt influenced somewhat by his fellows) rather than go for scientific treatment to the Albuquerque, New Mexico, hospital, which would have been more quickly available than the treatment at San Felipe. For a further discussion of the scope and relationships of the Pueblo rattlesnake clans, see White, 1930b, pp. 605–7; 1947, p. 238; and Parsons, 1939, pp. 868, 893, 900, 910.

Gayton (1948, pp. 46, 156, 164) has mentioned rattlesnake clans or moieties among the Yokuts and Western Mono of California.

DANCES AND EXHIBITIONS

Rattlesnakes were used by the Indians in a number of dances, either actually, or through effigy or symbolism. Samuel Lee mentions such an effigy in a letter written from New England about 1691 (Kittredge, 1913, p. 149). Wied-Neuwied (1843, p. 374) reported a Mandan dance in which two participants represented rattlers, as symbolized by transverse black stripes on the back.

We are told by Powers (1877, p. 160), in his account of the California Indians, that the Pomo of the north coast had a dance, including an episode in which a large defanged rattler was waved in the faces of the watching women to frighten them. Among the Nisenan there was a dance to keep the rattlers from biting the people in summer, but there is no mention of snakes being used in it (p. 324). The wizards of the Yokuts tribe held a rattlesnake dance each year. Four of them capered about with live rattlers in their hands, chasing and threatening each other. It was presumed by Powers that they had either defanged the snakes or had denied them water for several days, which he apparently believed would render them harmless. The credulous tribesmen thought the priests invulnerable and pressed forward in an endeavor to secure, from the dancers, immunity from snake bite during the coming year (p. 381).

Kroeber (1925, p. 504) has described this rattlesnake dance of the Yokuts in considerable detail. It was essentially a demonstration of magic power by the rattlesnake priests or shamans. It was celebrated early in the year before the rattlers had come out of hibernation; in fact, it may have been coincident with the snakes' egress, in order to facilitate the capture of many rattlers. On the first evening the priests danced while each carried a snake in a bag, and tests were made to determine which of the audience would be the victims of snake bite during the ensuing year. Next day these victims were treated in advance by suction of the prospective bites, and by the process of securing the emission therefrom of the tiny rattler that causes the pain—usually represented by a rat's tail or a small dead snake transferred from the mouth to the hand of the officiating priest. This was followed by an episode in which the real rattlers were danced with; they were so teased and annoyed that they were frequently seen to bite their tormentors, hanging by their fangs to fingers or hands. Dr. Kroeber makes no suggestion as to the source of their immunity from serious results. There followed another rite in which the shamans—contrary to the usual custom—were assessed goods for the ransoming of their snakes; and then a final episode to insure that the rattlers in future would rattle before striking. Altogether, this was a rattlesnake ceremonial of considerable intricacy, second only to the Hopi dance in elaboration of detail, and even more basically related to the snakes themselves, in that it was carried out to prevent snake bite, rather than as a prayer for rain, as is the Hopi dance.

Gayton (1948) has pointed out the various ramifications and themes of the snake dance among the subtribes of the Yokuts and Western Mono of the San Joaquin Valley in California. Not all subtribes had such a ritual (pp. 42, 136); among those that did were the Chunut and Tachi (p. 39), the Paleuyami (p. 47), Wukchumni (p. 122), Yaudanchi (p. 123), and Choinimni (pp. 152, 243, 247, 285). Some subtribes or village groups that had no dance, attended at other places where they were held. Usually the purpose of the ritual was to prevent people from being bitten or to cure those who would be bitten, in advance of the event. Sometimes the participants were bitten and cured during or after the ceremony. Although the local variations in the rituals were extensive, that of the Wukchumni may be outlined as an example. The ceremony was held in April, when the snakes (northern Pacifics, *C. v. oreganus*) were coming out of hibernation. Some choice was made in catching the snakes; the first out were not taken. The snake shamans put the captured snakes in a pit at the place of the dance, and the populace put money in the pit in payment for the dance. After a clown-coyote ceremony, each participant took his rattler from the pit, holding it in his left hand, with the tail in the right, and joined with his fellows in an intricate dance. Then more money was put up by the audience, maybe $50 or $60, to see a shaman bitten. He would throw his snake on the ground to anger it, then permit it to bite him and dangle from his arm by its fangs, after which his fellow doctors would cure the bite with a sucking ceremony. An additional description of the Yokuts dance is that of Riddell, 1955, p. 94.

Loeb (1926, p. 375) has described the Pomo dance first mentioned by Powers. It seems to have been devised by members of a secret society to impress outsiders. It involved an extensive ritual centering on a single rattler, after the latter had been fed beads and feathers, which it was expected to eat with enjoyment. The ritual concluded with the supposed swallowing and regurgitation of the snake by a priest trained and designated for the purpose. Following the ceremony the snake was turned loose, for it was taboo to injure it. Once a man killed a rattler that had been used in the ritual and died in consequence. This ceremony was less elaborate than the dance of the Yokuts, but seems to have had the same purpose. According to Goldschmidt (1951, p. 365), the Nomlaki, a Wintun sub-group, sometimes held an emergency dance to cure rattlesnake bite. The Luiseño and Diegueño also had a ceremony designed to keep rattlesnakes from biting people (Drucker, 1937b, p. 42).

Mooney (1896, p. 1033) tells us of a violent dance of the Cheyenne and Arapaho in which venomous snakes—which must have been rattlesnakes—were sometimes handled. This is likewise mentioned by Curtis (vol. 6, 1911, p. 147), who also described a war dance held by the southern California Shoshoni to pray for recovery from snake bite or other afflictions (vol. 15, 1926, p. 16). Liette (1947, p. 150, but written in 1702) briefly described a dance of the Illinois in which defanged rattlers were used, and another in Louisiana was mentioned by the Duke of Wuerttemberg (1835, ed. 1938, p. 265). Speck and Brown (1951, pp. 21, 62) mention a snake-mask dance of the Cherokee, which was intended to dramatize defiance of supernatural enemies by wearing a mask in the image of a rattlesnake.

The most famous of all dances involving rattlesnakes is that of the Hopi Indians of northeastern Arizona. This elaborate ceremony, a prayer for rain, in which some of the participants dance with live rattlesnakes dangling from their mouths, was first brought to the attention of Americans by Charles A. Taylor's brief account in 1881 (p. 276), followed shortly by Bourke's extensive description (1884). This dance has evoked so much interest, particularly with regard to the supposed immunity of the dancers, that I have devoted a separate section to it.

There have been other rattlesnake dances besides those previously mentioned. We know that there were, and still are, dances carried on by the Pueblo of New Mexico, who are related to the Hopi (Swanton, 1953, p. 339). These dances were mentioned by some of the early Spanish explorers, as, for example, by Gallegos, the clerk of the Rodríguez-Chamuscado expedition in 1581–82 (ms. in the Newberry Library, Chicago). He tells us that the natives handled live rattlers (*biboras*) that had *cascabeles* on their tails. Other references to the early Spanish reports on these ceremonies are: Twitchell (1914, vol. 1, p. 461), Bolton (1916, p. 183), Mecham (1917, p. 58), Hammond and Rey (1927, pp. 247, 346), Bandelier (1930, p. 378), and Bloom (1933, p. 228). One may judge from these brief accounts that the dance seen by the Spaniards in the sixteenth century was similar in many respects to the Hopi ritual today; that it included the handling of live rattlesnakes and was a prayer for rain.

In recent times, studies of the Pueblo ceremonials have been renewed. Stevenson (1894, p. 76), Fewkes (1895a, p. 118; 1897, p. 309), Reagan (1907, p. 268), Parsons (1939, p. 976), and White (1947, p. 238) have presented the details of the ritual followed by the Keres at Sia (or Zia) Pueblo in New Mexico and also at Jemez Pueblo. As with the Hopi, these rituals were prayers for rain, and rattlesnakes implemented the supplication. The Tewa Indians likewise had a snake dance (Curtis, 1926, vol. 17, p. 79). Parsons (1939, p. 545) mentions a dance at Isleta, New Mexico, in which a mythical rattlesnake was brought in to purify the town. Less specialized or intricate dances were known from California, Mexico, and Central America (Arlegui, 1851, p. 165; Fewkes, 1893, p. 285; Hodge, 1896, p. 133; Fewkes, 1897, p. 311; James, 1902, p. 59; Lumholtz, 1902, vol. 1, p. 355; 1910, p. 194).

The extent to which snakes were handled by Indians, aside from the formal occasions of dances and other ceremonies, probably varied considerably between tribes, and on the propensities of individual Indians. Several of the colonial travelers speak of Indians who claimed to have the power to charm rattlesnakes. It is difficult to tell now whether these were based on misunderstood religious formulas or on the exhibitionist tendencies of a few individual Indians. Clayton (1693, p. 127) tells us that, as one Indian was about to pick up a rattler, a Colonel Cleyborn, who had requested the demonstration, struck the snake with his crutch, whereupon the snake bit the Indian. Clayton calls this a "pleasant" story, the archaic meaning of this word being "humorous." Many a snake-show operator since that day has suffered from the sportive inclinations of spiritual descendants of Colonel Cleyborn. Brickell (Brit. 1737, p. 143) also mentions the power of charming rattlers that the Indians claimed to have; they kept secret the extent and nature of their ability to handle the snakes without danger to themselves.

Many rattlesnake medicine men or shamans demonstrated their ability to handle rattlers at times other than formal rituals or when effecting cures. No doubt this was to keep themselves before the public. Gifford (1936, p. 310) tells of a Northeastern Yavapai shaman who would pick up a rattler and put it in his shirt; he would then take it out and terrify people. In picking up a snake he would first draw a circle with dust across the snake's back. Once a shaman was bitten as he picked a snake up. He quickly tore it in half.

A Paviotso shaman (Park, 1934, p. 101), as soon as he had acquired his power from a dying brother, was able to catch rattlers without trouble. He put sage brush in their nostrils.[6] Sometimes he put them around his waist next to the skin. He used to ride home like this, and had rattlers about him all the time. Beals (1933, p. 375) tells of a young Nisenan who boasted he could kill a rattler with his heel. He was bitten and died; his failure to make good his boast seems to have shocked his family more than his demise.

Brinton (1896, p. 130) thought that certain Indians indulged in snake handling to demonstrate their intercourse with unseen powers and thus impress their fel-

---

[6] It may have been the sensory facial pits that he plugged, in the belief that the rattler would be less likely to strike.

lows. Influenced by the lore of the Hindu snake charmers, Brinton states that the Indians knew of the snake's susceptibility to rhythmic sounds—a susceptibility modern science has every cause to doubt.

Díaz del Castillo, a companion of Cortes, writing in 1568 (1632, fol. 69r), described a zoo kept by the Aztecs that included rattlesnakes among the exhibits. Says Díaz: "Moreover, in that accursed house [the temple of sacrifice] they kept vipers and venomous snakes, who had something at their tails which sounded like morris bells, and these are the worst of vipers. They were kept in cradles and barrels, and in earthen vessels, upon feathers, and there they laid their eggs and nursed up their snakelings, and they were fed with the bodies of the sacrificed, and with dogs' meat." This translation is by Maurice Keatinge (Díaz del Castillo, 1800, p. 142; see also Jennings, 1889, p. 60; Goode, 1901, p. 369; and Howey, 1928, p. 311). Díaz' description of the food and reproductive habits of the captive rattlers is, of course, pure imagination. It is probable that he attributed a totally unwarranted religious aspect to the presence of these snakes in the Aztec zoölogical collection, since they were exhibited with other animals having no religious significance.

THE HOPI SNAKE DANCE

The Hopi Snake dance is the best known of all Indian rituals. The widespread publicity it has received results from a single spectacular episode that occupies but a half hour during an elaborate nine-day ceremony, only a few other parts of which are ever seen by the public. In this fantastic episode, which so greatly fascinates the spectators, some of the participating priests execute a form of dance around a ring while each holds a live snake in his mouth, gripping the snake at the neck with his teeth and lips. Some of the snakes are rattlers. The dance is held annually at two or three of the Hopi pueblos in central Navajo County, Arizona. Each year people come in large numbers and from great distances to see it, and the argument as to why the participants are not fatally bitten is unending. The whole relationship between men and rattlesnakes, and the popular beliefs about these snakes are exemplified by the public reaction to this dance, so that no work on rattlers would be complete without its description. That which follows represents a summary from the reports of a number of ethnologists and other scientific witnesses, together with my own observations.

Fewkes (1896b, p. 694) calls this "A serious, precise ritual which has survived from prehistoric times to our present day," and, further (p. 698): "No Hopi priest lives who understands the meaning of all the details, nor does he care for an explanation of them." He is content merely to cling to the rites of his ancestors because, through experience, they have been proven good.

It should be understood that the dance, with accompanying ceremonials, differs in detail as practiced at the several Hopi pueblos, of which there are five that hold dances. That is to say, although the ritual, in all details, is rigidly observed at each pueblo, there are certain differences in schedule, paraphernalia, and performance among the pueblos; however, such differences are of a character important to the ethnologist rather than to the casual observer.

The dance is carried on through the co-operation of two fraternities, or secret societies, known as the Snakes and the Antelopes. These societies are not to be confused with the names of clans. There is, for example, a Snake clan that is separate from the Snake society; members of other clans may be enrolled in the Snake society, although it is understood that the chief priest of the Snake society is always a member of the Snake clan.

The dances are held at the pueblos of Mishongnovi and Walpi in the odd-numbered years, and at Hotevila, Shipaulovi, and Shimopovi in the alternate years. (There are many variations in the spelling of these pueblo names.) The dates are selected by the priests based on astronomical observations and are announced seventeen days in advance of the culminating Snake dance. The usual time for the dance is during the third or fourth week in August, and the occurrence is generally on consecutive days in the pueblos, as for instance in 1936 at Hotevila, August 22, Shipaulovi, August 23, and Shimopovi, August 24; and in 1937 at Mishongnovi, August 22, and Walpi, August 23. Within the last 20 years, the earliest and latest dates that have come to my attention have been August 19 (Mishongnovi, 1937 and 1951) and August 30 (Shipaulovi, 1952). For many dance dates see Forrest, 1929, p. 347.

The snake ceremonial, of which the Snake dance is a culmination, involves a co-ordinated program lasting nine days. Much of what happens is never seen by the public or by the nonfraternity Hopi; but the more important of these secret rites have been witnessed and carefully recorded by scientific observers, who had won the confidence of the participants, and this, fortunately, in the days before white influence had been seriously felt, that is, before 1905. Of the ceremonials seen by the public, the four important rites are: The Antelope race in the morning and the Corn dance in the evening of the eighth day, the Snake race early on the morning of the ninth day, and the Snake dance itself, occurring in the late afternoon of that day. It is this concluding rite that has given the entire ceremonial its name, and this, as far as the public is concerned, is the all-important feature of the ritual. However, it should be understood that the Snake dance, although the culminating rite, is only a single half-hour episode of the elaborate nine-day ceremonial. (For a schedule of all the events see Klauber, 1932a, p. 65.) The importance ascribed by the public to this fantastic feature has been rather unfortunate in that it gives an inaccurate picture of the solemnity and symbolism of the ritual as a whole.

Four days of the nine are given over to a ceremonial hunting of the snakes. This is done, not only by catching those found in the open, but also by following their tracks to holes, and digging them out with hoes and other more primitive digging sticks that have been consecrated for the purpose. The snakes may be either rattlers or of nonvenomous species. The search is conducted with great energy. No observer appears to have accompanied the Indians on these hunting trips except for short periods, for they are much averse to being watched while catching the snakes. The snakes are sought in the area surrounding the village, one day at each of the four cardinal points, invariably in the order north, west, south, and east. During these hunts the novitiates, some of whom may be only boys, are initiated in the capture and handling of snakes. If not enough snakes are found on the four official or ceremonial days, the hunts may continue informally for several additional days; on these the search may lead anywhere, unrestricted as to direction.

There are certain accessories to which Indian names are applied that must now be briefly explained. First, there is the kiva, an underground or semiunderground vault, entered by means of a ladder through a hatchway in the roof; this serves the combined purposes of a lodge room and the scene of various religious rites. There are separate kivas for the various secret-society groups; in each of the pueblos there is one for the Snake society and one used by the Antelope society, and, usually, several others besides. The *bahoki* (or *pahoki*) is a permanent stone shrine erected near the center of the town plaza, or other public ceremonial place, where the Snake dance and other rituals are performed. Then there is the *kisi,* a temporary bower of cottonwood branches shaped like an Indian tepee, but much smaller. This is erected near the center of the plaza (in the direction of greatest dimension) but close to one side, so as to leave a dancing space before it. The entrance to the *kisi* is covered with canvas or a blanket. In front of the *kisi* a hollow is dug, over which is placed a board. This is the *sipapu,* the entrance to the underworld. The *kisi* is used only for the Snake ceremonial.

The snakes that have been captured are placed in sacred clay jars, and are stored in the kiva of the Snake priests. Here, when not actively engaged in hunting, and particularly after the fourth ceremonial day of the hunt, the Snake priests live and engage in the making of prayer sticks (*pahos*), in observing various sacred rituals including ceremonial smokes, and in the preparation of their costumes.

Similarly, while these rites are proceeding in the Snake kiva, the Antelopes, who are relieved of the necessity of hunting snakes, are carrying forward even more elaborate ceremonies in their retreat; for the Antelopes, although they do not dance with snakes, have a part in the ritual which is superior, rather than inferior, to that of the other fraternity. An altar is prepared in their kiva, consisting of a beautiful colored-sand mosaic, symbolic of a rain storm, with clouds and four snakelike lightning strokes, surrounded by a variety of ritualistic objects (fig. 16:1). Prayer sticks and other sacred paraphernalia, of great diversity and particularity, are manufactured and appropriately used; many are sent by official couriers and deposited at four shrines of the rain gods. A tableau is enacted with a Snake Youth and a Corn Maiden, dramatizing the ancient snake myth upon which the dance is based, accompanied by traditional songs and chants. There is imitation thunder produced by a whirling stick on a string (called a bull-roarer); lightning is simulated by the shooting out and retraction of an extensible rack, like a long pantograph; clouds by ceremonial smoke; and rain by water asperged from sacred vessels. (These devices are also used in some pueblos in the subsequent public dance.) Sacred corn meal and corn pollen are used extensively by sprinkling, to sanctify objects and actions.

During the ceremonies in the kivas, appropriate insignia are attached to the tops of the entrance ladders above ground as a notification to the nonfraternity townspeople that the ritual is in progress; these serve also as a warning against trespassing into the secrecy of the ritual.

Among the sacred paraphernalia there is one item of particular interest to the herpetologist; this is the snake-whip or snake-wand, a wooden shaft about eight inches long, to which is attached a pair of eagle feathers. From the first hunts to the final dance, these serve a practical purpose in soothing the snakes, or in herding them when it is desired to have them go in a certain direction, or to cause them to straighten out when they have coiled for defense. Eagle feathers are used because eagles are the masters of (prey on) snakes.

On the morning of the eighth day, at an early hour, occurs the first feature of the ceremony that the public—whether Hopi or white—may witness; this is the Antelope race, in which the young men of the village compete.

On the evening of the eighth day occurs the Antelope or Corn dance, which resembles the Snake dance in method, except that wands of corn stalks, twisted

Fig. 16:1. Sand mosaic of the Antelope priests at Shimopovi, Arizona, a feature of the Hopi Snake dance. The sand colors are indicated by the diagram at the upper right-hand corner. The semicircles represent rain clouds, from which snakelike lightning strokes descend. The mosaic is surrounded by various ceremonial devices.

(Drawing from J. W. Fewkes, 1897, plate 72, courtesy of the Smithsonian Institution.)

together with melon vines, are used in place of snakes. Further, the respective roles of the Antelope and Snake priests are somewhat different in the Corn dance, as compared with the succeeding Snake dance. This ceremony is not a rehearsal of the Snake dance, as has been occasionally stated, but is a definite part of the ritual, a prayer for the growth of corn and other crops upon which the Hopi rely for sustenance.

Early on the morning of the ninth day occurs the Snake race, in which young men of this and adjacent villages participate. The race is said to be for a distance of four or five miles and ends in a steep and exhausting ascent to the mesa on which the dance is to be held. The prize to the winner consists of some small sacred offerings, which he buries in his corn field as a blessing of the crop.

Other young men and boys, most of whom have accompanied the racers only up the final slope, come into the village carrying corn stalks and melon vines.

These are now the cause of a good-natured wrangle with the women and girls, who snatch them from the boys and bear them to their homes as trophies.

At noon on the ninth day occurs the secret rite of washing the snakes, in anticipation of their part in the dance. This takes place in the kiva of the Snake society. It has been witnessed and carefully reported upon by a number of ethnologists, especially Fewkes *et al.* (1894, p. 83), Dorsey and Voth (1902, p. 247), Voth (1903, p. 339), and Stephen (1936, p. 577, but written in 1892). It is an extremely elaborate ritual and differs in detail among the towns. In general, the snakes, after removal from the sacred storage jars, where they have spent most of the time since their capture, are taken in handfuls by the chief Snake priest, before the assembled members of his fraternity, and are dipped in an effusion contained in an earthen bowl, the liquid having previously been the subject of a suitable ceremony. After the washing, the snakes are dried by allowing them to crawl on sand; they are permitted partial liberty in the kiva for as much as two hours, following which they are placed in cloth sacks awaiting the ceremony.

All reporters who have witnessed the washing state that the snakes are handled gently but fearlessly, except at Walpi, where they are hurled quite violently on a sand mosaic. There is no report of anyone having been bitten. During their brief freedom they are guarded by boy priests.

The Snake dance itself occurs at sundown on the ninth day, the time fixed by precedent. Prior to the dance, the snakes, carried in several cloth bags, are placed in the *kisi* by the Snake priests.

On the afternoon of the dance, the audience, which consists of the local Hopi, visitors from adjacent pueblos, Navaho, and, with improvements in roads, an increasing number of whites, has been circulating through the village and about the plaza engaged in sight-seeing. Long before the dance most of them have selected vantage points from which they expect to view the ceremony. Many, especially the more timid, are perched upon the housetops in double and triple rows on the side facing the plaza. On the ground there is another group, completely surrounding the plaza, seated in the doorways of the Hopi homes or on a sort of stoop built into the fronts of most of the houses. Competition for vantage points is sufficiently keen so that members of the audience are content to remain stationary for an hour or more before the dance, in order to hold their places.

The number of participants in the final ceremony varies in the several pueblos, and at different times in the same pueblo. There may be as few as five Antelopes and eight Snakes, or as many as twenty-five Antelopes and thirty Snake priests.[7] The number of reptiles used varies from about 15, where the priests are few, to 60 or more at Shongopovi, where the largest dances are currently held. At the turn of the century there were reports of as many as 100 snakes being used at Walpi. From a quarter to half of the snakes are generally reported to be rattlers; the others are harmless bull snakes, racers, or, occasionally, some rarer species.

The dance begins at about sundown[8] with the entrance of the Antelope priests.

---

[7] When I saw the dance at Mishongnovi in 1931 there were 8 Antelopes and 8 Snakes; at Walpi in 1933 my son reported 8 Antelopes and 16 Snakes; at Mishongnovi in 1943, Paul L. Breese reported 9 Antelopes and 18 Snakes. Some low and high numbers of participants during recent years have been 5 Antelopes and 9 Snakes at Hotevila in 1938; 7 Antelopes and 8 Snakes at Shipaulovi in 1954; and, as a high mark, 23 Antelopes and 25 Snakes at Shongopovi in 1954.

[8] The time of starting the dance during recent years has varied from 4:45 P.M., at Mishongnovi in 1939, to 6:00 P.M., at Hotevila in 1938. The average starting time for 16 recent dances was 5:13 P.M. The appearance of the Antelopes is taken as the starting time.

They come from their kiva in single file, dressed in elaborate and symbolic costumes, complying in detail with the ritual. The stragglers among the audience find the best remaining places. Indian police generally aid in a somewhat haphazard way in keeping the central area cleared. The Antelopes hold rattles made of buckskin in one or both hands and carry pouches filled with sacred corn meal. Rather slowly and sedately they make four circuits of the central area, scattering a pinch of meal on the *bahoki* (shrine) and on the *sipapu,* the board before the *kisi,* as they pass; they also stamp with the right foot on the board. Their march is accompanied by a rhythmic shaking of the hand rattles and the jingle of their trappings. Finally, having completed the fourth circuit (always in the direction north, west, south, east), they stand in a single row, either upon each side of the *kisi,* or with their backs to it, facing the central area.

After a short pause the Snake priests emerge from their kiva. They are headed at some distance by one or two of the chief priests. They are not dressed or painted uniformly, for there are certain differences, not only between pueblos, but between individuals, in symbolic representation of mythological characters and occupations. One or two priests enter the *kisi,* while the rest make four circuits of the central area as did the Antelopes. The Snake priests move, however, at a considerably more rapid gait than did their predecessors, and there is a certain aggressive intensiveness in their actions not evident among the Antelopes. Each time an individual passes the *kisi* he stamps violently with right foot on the board, which, being over a hole, gives forth a hollow sound. Thus the rain gods of the underworld are advised, by this imitation thunder, of the impending ceremony. At the completion of the fourth circuit the Snake priests line up in a row facing the Antelope priests.

Then follows a ceremony of considerable length involving a slow, weaving dance with rising and falling chants and incantations. Among other paraphernalia each Snake priest carries at the back of the right knee a hollow turtle shell against which dangle small objects, said to be sheep hoofs; thus, when the right leg is stamped, the turtle shell gives forth a deep rattling sound, and this keeps time with the dance and the hand rattles shaken by the Antelopes.

Now the Snake priests—but not the Antelopes—break up into trios, each containing one man who is usually referred to as the "carrier," a second called the "hugger," and a third known as the "gatherer." As the first carrier passes before the *kisi* he stoops and is handed a snake by one of those within. This snake he puts into his mouth, holding it with teeth and lips from six to twelve inches behind the head.[9] The hugger now puts his left hand on the carrier's right shoulder, or about his neck, and together, the carrier continuing to hold the snake, they slowly dance, with a shuffling step, around the area, with the carrier on the inner side of the circle. Each pair is followed by a gatherer. After approximately one and a half times around, the carrier puts the snake on the ground and, in passing the *kisi,* receives another. In one of the pueblos the carrier holds the snake with his hands as well as lips; elsewhere, however, it dangles unsupported from his mouth. The exact position and action of the hugger, with reference to the carrier, differ in the several pueblos.

---

[9] Langley (1945, p. 8) reports that the carriers have their mouths filled with clay to avoid injuring the snakes with their teeth. Other observers have failed to note anything of this character.

Fig. 16:2. The Snake dance at Oraibi, Arizona, in 1902. A carrier with a snake in his mouth in the central foreground; Antelope priests before the *kisi* at the right.

Fig. 16:3. The Snake dance at Oraibi, Arizona, in 1902. A carrier in the right foreground with a hugger immediately behind, and a gatherer some steps to the rear.

(Figs. 16:2 and 16:3 by courtesy of the Museum of Anthropology, University of California, Berkeley.)

Meanwhile, other trios have followed the first, and there is a circle of dancing priests, who are receiving, carrying, and putting down snakes in more or less confusion. The hugger, while dancing around at the right hand of the carrier, from time to time brushes the snake's head or the carrier's face with the eagle feathers of a snake-wand. This is presumed by some to be for the purpose of engaging the snake's attention, to keep it from biting the carrier. The hugger acts as guide, as well as protector, for the carrier's eyes are generally closed.

The gatherer belonging to each trio has been following his two fellow priests. When a snake has been put on the ground by his carrier he picks it up, usually six to eight inches behind the head, sometimes at once, but more often after sprinkling it with sacred corn meal. Or, if it coils, as if for defense, he brushes it with his feathered snake-wand or snake-whip, and, as soon as it has straightened out to escape, he seizes it. After he has accumulated several snakes in this way, some are handed to the Antelope priests, who hold them until the termination of the dance. The Antelopes have not left their place by the *kisi*, but have continued, with chants and rattles, to furnish the rhythm for the Snake priests. At one point in the ritual a group of women approach with white meal held before them in shallow baskets; pinches of this meal are scattered on the snakes and dancers.

When all the snakes have been danced with and are now held by the gatherers or the Antelopes, one of the priests draws a circle on the ground with corn meal. Immediately all the snakes are piled into this circle in a seething mass; thence many try to escape but are carried or herded back within the ring. The women scatter the rest of their sacred meal upon the snakes. This is the part of the dance causing the most excitement among the audience, particularly those nearest the circle, since some of the snakes may reach them before being caught.

Now the Snake priests as a group rush to the squirming pile and seize the snakes by the handfuls until all have been picked up. Then they run in the four cardinal directions off the mesa and down the steep trails onto the plain below, where the snakes are liberated at some distance from the bases of the cliffs, usually at specified shrines, and thus the messengers to the gods are sent upon their way. The Snake priests return to the mesa more slowly. An emetic is taken as a purifier, and then the dance closes with a great feast of celebration and with merrymaking that lasts four days. Meanwhile, the audience has dispersed, the Indians to their homes, the whites to their adjacent automobiles or camps.

It should be repeated that there are considerable variations in many details as the dance is practiced in the several pueblos; not variations caused by carelessness or indecision, but rather the result of gradual divergences in paraphernalia and ritual, as the dance has been handed down from generation to generation through the centuries. Most of these differences are of importance only from an ethnological viewpoint; they have been described completely in various technical monographs. Observers who have seen the dance in the same pueblo in successive bienniums have noted with approbation how these priests, with no guide save memory, can repeat exactly each year the numberless minute details of action and procedure, apparently without change.

Surprising as it may seem, in the case of a rite that has lately received so much attention, the first published description of the dance did not appear until 1881. Until 1900 transportation difficulties had kept away all but a few Indian officials, traders, scientists, missionaries, and army officers. The dances at some of the pueblos were seen at each performance only by a dozen or fewer non-Indians, and the outsiders admitted to the secret ceremonials could be counted on the fingers of one hand. Yet fortunately these included ethnologists, familiar with the language and customs of the Indians; they were able to gain the confidence of the chiefs, and thus have recorded in detail the ritual as it was practiced before any contamination by outside influences took place. The phrasing of the chants and the intonations of the priests were written down. Formerly cameras were permitted and, notwithstanding the difficulty of the late afternoon light, many good photographs have been published; more recently their use has been prohibited, and at present not even the taking of notes is allowed.[10]

The Hopi Snake dance is not snake worship. It is a prayer for rain and the fulfillment of adequate crops; and the snakes are used as messengers to the underworld gods of rain, as required by an elaborate and ancient snake legend. Lurid accounts have occasionally appeared in the press of priests embarrassed by premature storms, or disconsolate over the failure of rain to follow immediately upon the conclusion of the ceremony.[11] This is hardly an accurate judgment of what the dancers hope to achieve. Summer is the rainy season over the northern Arizona plateau; it is a time of scattered and sporadic afternoon thunder showers, each giving rainfall, for a brief time at least, to a limited area. The Hopi prays that an adequate number of these showers shall reach his own fields during the growing season, but he is not particularly concerned if one of these storms precedes the ceremony, or if one fails to follow immediately upon its conclusion.

An examination of the details of the ceremony, particularly the secret rites in the kivas, can leave no doubt as to the purpose of the ritual. Each part carries with it some symbolism toward the bringing of rain. All this is shown in the dramatization of the myth which the dance re-enacts, in the pantomimes, the chants and songs, the sand pictures, the fetishes. There is the thunder of the bull roarer, the lightning of the pantograph and of the sand mosaic, the clouds of ceremonial smoke, the rain of the aspergillum. The altars in the kivas are decorated with water-worn roots and stones, with sea shells, mud from riverbanks, and plants, such as the cottonwood, that seek water. And the snakes themselves are symbolic of the rain gods, as they are in other tribes as well. Apparently the connection is based on the following train of ideas: Rain—lightning—sinuous shape—snake; or: Rain—lightning—death-dealing stroke—snake. The snakes are not worshipped; they are "elder brothers of the priests"—messengers to the rain gods, who are underworld gods to whom the snakes have admission.

The dance is presumed to have had its origin in a snake myth involving the

---

[10] The mimeographed rules handed to the audience for their guidance during the past few years do not mention this prohibition. In 1933 at Walpi, my son, then a youngster, was standing near the entrance to the Snake kiva making notes on the costume that one of the priests had dropped, after the conclusion of the dance. Suddenly an Indian seized his book and threw it into the kiva, so that all the notes on the dance and the trip were lost.

[11] Example newspaper headlines: Black Clouds and Rain Answer Hopis' Snake Dance Prayers; Rain Follows Hopi Dance and Priests Smile Again; Weird Snake Dance of Hopis Opens at Dawn—Rain Due Tonight when Reptiles Freed on Desert of Arizona; Showers Follow Snake Dance Prayer for Rain; Showers Follow Rain Dance Appeal by Hopi Indians; Hopis Puzzled as Serpent Frowns on Snake Dance—No Rain Comes; Fail to Get Rain by Snake Dance.

"Spider Woman," a youth, and a maiden. After many adventures in the underworld, the youth, with the aid of the Spider Woman, won the maiden and returned with her to his village. Their first progeny were snakes, which were sent back to the underworld for biting the Hopi. Their later children were human, the ancestors of the Snake clan. After the snakes were sent back to the underworld in disgrace, there followed a drought; the corn was scorched and the springs dried up. Then the hero of the myth taught his people songs and prayers to restore the rainfall, and in this ritual the snakes were sent back to the underworld as cherished envoys rather than in disgrace as before. This legend is the basis of the songs and prayers that the Hopi repeat each August.

The literature of the Hopi Snake dance is quite extensive. In 1932 (Klauber, 1932a, p. 42) I listed some 112 items in an annotated bibliography. A few of the more important of these have been carried forward into the list of references accompanying this work. To bring the 1932 snake-dance bibliography down to date, the following new or previously unnoticed articles should be added:

Alexander (1953, p. 92), Benedict (1925, p. 460; 1934, pp. 94–95), Bogert (1933, pp. 219–21; 1941a, pp. 276–83), Bowman (1885, pp. 636–37), Colton and Baxter (1932, pp. 18–19), Corle (1941, pp. 140–45), Crowder (1946, pp. 4–6), Curtis (1926, vol. 17, pp. 195–99), Fewkes (1891, pp. 129–38; 1895b, pp. 273–82), Forrest (1929, pp. 277–330), Gianini (1928, pp. 439–49), Glenn (1933, pp. 11–12), Goddard (1931, pp. 118–22), Golder (1907, p. 75), Hall (1953, pp. 4–11), Ingersoll (1883a, p. 44), Keam (1883, pp. 14–16; 1951, pp. 144–45), Klauber (1932a, pp. 1–93; 1947, pp. 37–39), Langley (1945, pp. 5–8; 1954, pp. 4–8), Leach (1949–50, p. 1030), Lockett (1933, p. 52–69), M., J. S. (1937, p. 237), MacClary (1939b, pp. 23–24), Miller (1948, pp. 11–13), Murdock (1934, pp. 352–55), Nelson (1937, pp. 177–91), Oakden and Sturt (1927, pp. 41–44), O'Kane (1950, pp. 106–7, 193–205), Oliver (1954, pp. 170–78), Parsons (1925, pp. 101–7; 1926, p. 250; 1939, pp. 448, 654–75, 868, 1043), Polikoff (1954, pp. 3, 5), Purdie (1954, p. 22), Reagen (1907, pp. 268–72; 1914, pp. 143–50), Reid (1948, pp. 10–11), Richards (1949, p. 1), Schmedding (1951, pp. 236–50), Scott (1894, pp. 195–98), Simer (1950, p. 4), Dama M. Smith (1930, pp. 104–20); 1931, pp. 76–100); H. H. Smith (1923–32, p. 430), Mrs. W. M. Smith (1939, pp. 16–17, 38–39), Stephen (1888, pp. 109–14; 1936, pp. 577–767), Stirling (1942, pp. 551–55), Stoddard (1898, pp. 148–57), Sykes (1945, pp. 34–36; 1947, pp. 15–18), Teters (1896, pp. 564–68), Titiev (1943, pp. 44–51; 1944, pp. 149–54), Waters (1950, pp. 304–18), Whiting (1939, p. 39), and Zahn (1946, pp. 68–69).

The earliest account of the dance seems to have been that of Charles A. Taylor (1881, p. 276), and the first detailed description that of Bourke (1884). From the ethnological standpoint, the most important works, which include the details of the ceremonies, paraphernalia, and the symbolism involved, are those of Fewkes, Stephen, and Owens (1894), Fewkes (1897 and 1900), Dorsey and Voth (1902), Voth (1903), and Stephen (1936); and from the herpetological standpoint, Klauber (1932a and 1947), Bogert (1933), and Oliver (1954). Attention should also be called to additional data by Curtis contained in volume 17, pp. 195–99, of his great work *The North American Indian;* see also Titiev (1943, p. 46).

The sight of the dancing priests, who hold live, venomous snakes dangling from their mouths, is what brings the curious, from many hundreds of miles away, to see this short ceremony, lasting but a half hour or less. Inevitably an argument ensues as to why there are no serious, if not fatal, consequences. The printed accounts of the dance and the annual newspaper reports are full of an unending controversy on the subject. The following are some of the theories that have been advanced to explain this absence of casualties:

A. *Conditions Affecting the Audience*

1. The audience is suffering from some form of group hypnotism.
2. The audience is not qualified to distinguish venomous from nonvenomous snakes; no venomous snakes are used in the dance.

B. *Conditions Affecting the Snake Priests*

1. The priests have taken an internal protective medicine prior to the dance.
2. They possess a knowledge of antidotes, internal, external, or both, that quickly render rattlesnake bite innocuous and even painless.
3. Sucking, cauterizing, and tourniquets are resorted to in case of a bite.
4. The priests are so purified by the ceremonial emetic as to be immune.
5. They are smeared with a preparation so disagreeable to the snakes (as, for instance, in odor) that the latter will not bite.
6. They are covered with an invulnerable preparation, such as a thick paint.
7. They are so healthy from outdoor life that rattlesnake bite does not affect them.
8. They have an immunity resulting from a long fast prior to the dance.
9. They build up an immunity in each participant by increasing doses of venom, as is done with horses in the preparation of antivenin.
10. They have a mysterious hypnotic power over the snakes, akin to that attributed to the snake charmers of India.
11. They are fearless of snakes, which, therefore, are without power to bite them.
12. They are protected by the religious exaltation of the ritual.
13. They are actually bitten, with serious results, of which outsiders are kept in ignorance.

C. *Conditions Affecting the Rattlesnakes*

1. The snakes' fangs, venom glands, or both, have been removed.
2. Their mouths have been sewed closed.
3. They have expended their venom on harmless snakes or on other objects in the kiva.
4. They have been milked of their venom in the kiva.
5. They are tame snakes, used repeatedly in successive years.
6. They have been lately tamed by handling.
7. They are doped or hypnotized.
8. They are startled into submission.
9. They are blinded by the sacred meal, or paralyzed by the tobacco fumes from the ceremonial smokes in the kiva.
10. August is the blind season for rattlers; they cannot see to strike.
11. They are invariably held in such a way that they cannot bite.
12. The eagle-feather snake-wands prevent their biting.
13. They cannot strike because they are not permitted to coil.
14. Their facial sensory pits have been plugged, which prevents their striking.
15. Rattlers are relatively innocuous anyway.

Many of these theories are hardly worthy of serious attention. With respect to the first group, it may be said that venomous rattlesnakes are used in the dance. However, it is true that the majority are nonvenomous snakes, mostly gopher or bull snakes (*Pituophis catenifer deserticola* or *P. c. affinis*), or desert striped racers (*Masticophis taeniatus taeniatus*). McKee (1929, p. 5), at Mishongnovi in 1929, noted 35 per cent rattlers; in the same town in 1931 I observed that the dancers had 10 rattlesnakes out of 41 snakes, or 24 per cent. Bogert (1933, p. 219), in 1932 at Shongopovi (Shimopovi), observed 10 rattlers to 13 harmless snakes, or 44 per cent, and, at Hotevila, 12 rattlers to 17 harmless snakes, or 41 per cent venomous. My son, at Walpi in 1933, thought the rattlers totaled 40 per cent; his records were lost when an Indian confiscated his notes. Breese, in 1943 at Mishongnovi, observed 2 rattlers to 20 gophers and 10 racers, or only 7 per cent venomous. From several other sources, some data on the division between harmless snakes and rattlers during the past 20 years have become available. The highest proportion of rattlesnakes was observed at Hotevila in 1938 when, out of a total of 33 snakes, 17, or 51 per cent, were rattlers. The lowest proportion of rattlers, was, as already stated, 7 per cent at Mishongnovi in 1943, followed by 9 per cent at Shipaulovi in 1954. The average proportion of rattlesnakes during recent years has been 26 per cent. But the trend in the proportion of rattlers has been falling for some time.[12]

At any rate, enough persons thoroughly familiar with rattlesnakes have viewed the dance, so there can be no question as to their use in the ritual. These rattlesnakes are of two closely related kinds—the prairie rattler (*Crotalus viridis viridis*) and the Arizona prairie rattlesnake (*Crotalus viridis nuntius*[13]). The Arizona prairie rattler is a rather small snake of a reddish-brown color. *C. v. viridis* is larger and greener. Some of the snakes observed at the dance are olive green, probably intergrades between *viridis* and *nuntius*. These are the only kinds of rattlesnakes available to the Hopi in their own territory, notwithstanding reports of diamondbacks (e.g., Langley, 1945, p. 8), sidewinders, and other species which some observers at the dance claim to have seen. The prairie rattler, particularly if a large one, could produce a very serious bite—one that might well be fatal, especially to the youngsters who participate in the ceremony as neophytes.

So much for the potential danger: now how is it met? We may dismiss at once the so-called antidotes and other cures and protective conditions listed in Group B above. The Indians claim no antidote in the sense the term is used by us, for they consider their medicine a protective charm rather than a physical venom-neutralizer. The preparation they are said to use has been tested (Coleman, 1928, p. 97) and found ineffective. Whiting (1939, pp. 32, 77) says the Hopi antidote is prepared from the bladder pod (*Lesquerella intermedia*); the ceremonial emetic contains six substances (p. 39). Another reference to the Hopi protective plant is by H. H. Smith (1923–32, p. 430), who stated that *Iris versicolor* was chewed and

---

[12] If this decline in the proportion of venomous snakes should continue, it will indicate a deterioration of the dance, since there is no reason to presume that the proportion of rattlesnakes available in the wild is decreasing. According to Curtis (1922, vol. 12, p. 135) the Hopi name for the Snake dance means rattlesnake. The myth upon which the dance is based involves rattlesnakes, without which the story would have no point. A part of the symbolism is the likeness of the buzz of the rattle to the hiss of falling rain. Certainly a discontinuance of the use of rattlers would involve a fundamental change in the character of the dance as well as its hold on the audience. It would degenerate almost to the level of the dance annually held at Prescott, Arizona, where whites dance with bull snakes in their mouths. This is sponsored by the local Chamber of Commerce, ostensibly to perpetuate the Indian rites, but which Waters (1950, p. 312) calls a vulgar parody. Many of those who saw the Hopi dance before or soon after 1900 have asserted that it has degenerated in quality through white influence or commercialism, more in some pueblos than in others (e.g., Forrest, 1929, pp. 210, 330). Yet there have been contrary reports. I was told by several people who have seen the dance on a number of occasions, that the one at Shongopovi in 1954 was one of the best in recent years. There were nearly 50 participants, including about 20 young boys, which augurs well for the future continuance of the dance. There was evident no deterioration of ceremonial garb or of details of ritual.

[13] From *nuntius*, a messenger; the snake was so named because of its use in this dance.

used in the fumigation of their clothes. The reasons why various native curative preparations often gain a reputation for efficacy entirely undeserved is discussed elsewhere (pp. 712, 860). We may also dismiss all those theories based upon the supposed inability of a snake to bite without coiling. A rattler held by the neck, as the priests hold these snakes in their mouths, could certainly bite the holder's cheek; nor would it be prevented from so doing by any protective paint or odor.

Rattlesnakes are much tamer and more lethargic than is commonly supposed, particularly after they have been in captivity for a short time; so that in any case bites from them in the dance would be rather infrequent. But that there have been cases of dancers being bitten appears to be without question; elsewhere (1932a, p. 33) I have cited references to a number of such reports; some, not previously cited, are Dama M. Smith (1930, p. 118), MacClary (1939b, p. 23), and Waters (1950, p. 313). A friend of mine saw a dancer bitten in one of the ceremonies of 1939.

The Indians have always denied that the snakes have had their fangs removed or are treated in any other way to render them innocuous. Early reports by the scientists who investigated the rite seemed to bear this out. Mindeleff (1886, p. 12) tells us that Dr. H. C. Yarrow, a thoroughly competent herpetologist, examined a rattler selected at random in the kiva and found the fangs and venom glands intact. After the dance, two rattlers were chosen and sent east, where they were examined by Dr. S. Weir Mitchell, then the great authority on American venomous snakes, who reported the fangs present and the venom glands full. My son and I thought we saw the fang sheaths when the snakes opened their mouths; this would have been possible only if the fangs were intact. Various other observations have been made that seemed to weigh against any theory of defanging (Klauber, 1932a, pp. 38–39).

But E. S. Curtis (1922, vol. 12, p. 136; 1926, vol. 17, pp. 195–9; see also Benedict, 1934, p. 95, and Reid, 1948, p. 10) expressed astonishment that there had been so little skepticism. In 1922 he cited the statement of a snake priest who told him that the snakes were defanged; and this was backed up in 1926 with five sworn depositions to the same effect, taken by an official of the Bureau of Indian Affairs.[14] These, in summary, maintain that, when they are first caught, the fangs of the rattlers are broken off by being pressed against the edge of a hoe inserted in the snake's mouth. This is repeated from time to time in the kiva so that there is no chance for the reserve fangs to become operative. Also, the snakes are milked occasionally prior to the ceremony, so that when the ritual takes place even a scratch by the stump of a fang would be quite innocuous.

This procedure, if its truth be verified, would account for the fact that the Indians have rarely permitted outsiders to accompany them on their snake hunts, and in the two instances when they were followed, the intruders were not allowed to see rattlers caught. Also, even in the days when friendly ethnologists were given access to the kivas, they were not permitted to witness certain of the snake-handling ceremonies.

Finally there comes the unimpeachable evidence of Bogert (1933, p. 219), since reinforced by an additional incident (Oliver, 1954, p. 170). At Shongopovi (Shimopovi), in 1932, upon the conclusion of the dance, Bogert followed one of the

[14] The same statements contained revelations concerning debauchery following the dance which led to government threats of its discontinuance.

snake priests down from the mesa to the floor of the desert and succeeded in finding one of the rattlers shortly after its release. This was done by stealth and at considerable personal risk. Upon examination, the rattler was found to have had both functional fangs and reserve fangs cut out by some sharp instrument, such as a knife. The snake was therefore quite harmless.

In August, 1954, Dr. James A. Oliver, of the New York Zoölogical Society, received a live rattlesnake that was said to have been captured by a spectator after the dance at Walpi in August of 1951. This snake was fangless, but had survived by means of forced feeding during the intervening three years. X rays showed that the replacement fang reservoir had been removed, so that no fangs had been produced subsequent to the original operation, although the injury had healed completely (Oliver, 1954, p. 177). It is of interest to learn that the snake, although without fangs, fed readily enough when dead mice were offered it after its arrival in New York. The food was digested despite the absence of venom injection.

Thus we now know definitely that in at least two of the Hopi pueblos the rattlesnakes (or some of them) have their fangs removed. Whether this practice has always been followed, and whether at all of the pueblos, remains to be determined; I have already mentioned certain evidence contradicting such a conclusion (1932a, p. 38). I stated in 1932 (p. 41) that I considered thorough and repeated venom removal, immediately following the catching of the snakes and during the ceremonies in the kiva, to be the probable source of the Indians' immunity from serious accidents. I am more than ever convinced that, if fang removal is a comparatively recent development, say within 30 years or so, it was antedated by a system of milking, or, in some other way, of forcing the snakes to exhaust their venom. A similar opinion was expressed by Bowman as early as 1885 (p. 637). This would be the only theory squaring with Yarrow's findings, unless the Indians succeeded in deceiving him with snakes set apart especially for the purpose. But certainly all the evidence now points either to fang extraction, venom extrusion, or both, as the explanation of the Hopi's freedom from serious snake poisoning in their famous Snake dance.

SNAKE-BITE TREATMENT

The Indians devised many kinds of treatment for rattlesnake bite. Some of these were semireligious in character, involving rituals known only to special rattlesnake shamans or tribal medicine men; others were remedial measures dependent on the use of substances available to anyone. However, even when the curative materials were readily at hand, it was believed in most tribes that their effectiveness was dependent on special rites accompanying their garnering and application, as was characteristic of most Indian medical practices.

We cannot always be sure, at this late date, that all the curative schemes attributed to the Indians by the early travelers really originated with them. No doubt some were acquired from the whites, for there are several remarkable parallels with methods of treatment of viper bite used in the Old World before the days of scientific medicine. However, we may assume that some form of treatment was available in nearly every tribe, since primitive man seldom faces any crisis of disease or accident without some attempt at alleviation. Many of the cures are clearly of such ancient origin that the purpose and meaning of the steps involved have been quite forgotten.

In the following summaries of the findings of the ethnologists and others as to the Indian treatments, I have, for purposes of clarity, divided them into several groups based on whether the administration of some tangible antidote, or a magical technique, was paramount. This at best involves a highly tenuous dividing line, for even when plants or other material substances were used, the ritual of application was deemed all-important. Probably it would be better to say that I have segregated the cures that were more or less completely dependent on trained specialists—usually rattlesnake shamans—from those in which the material nature of the antidote seemed paramount, however ritualistic its application. The latter classes I shall discuss first, segregating them into the categories of plants, remedies derived from the snake culprit, suction and other surgical treatments, and miscellaneous cures. These will be followed by an outline of the shamanistic methods, in which the magical elements were definitely predominant.

How did the Indians actually fare when snake-bitten? It is difficult to tell from the meager records. They naturally did not stress the failures of their methods; only occasionally is there mention of a death. Probably they fared about as well as white men without treatment. Their failures were usually attributed to deviations from prescribed rituals or the intervention of adverse spirits.

As it was customary in many Indian tribes to treat dream bites, it may be assumed that the bites of nonvenomous snakes were also treated. That these treatments were invariably successful probably led to the confirmation of many of their curative procedures, a situation by no means restricted to Indians.

PLANT REMEDIES

By far the commonest Indian remedy for snake bite, especially among the Eastern tribes, was some plant, often a root, which generally was applied to the wound as a poultice and was taken internally as a sort of tea—that is, as an infusion or decoction. So universal was this type of remedy that it came to have wide acceptance—even among the whites, as well—although the nature of the plant differed from area to area, and from tribe to tribe. Always, however, the curative plant was available where the snakes were commonest, a providential arrangement in conformity with a fundamental belief—by no means restricted to the Indians— that, for every ill, nature provides a readily available cure, if man only has the wit to use it (see, for example, Le Page du Pratz, 1774, p. 269; Hewatt, 1779, p. 87; Weld, 1800, p. 150). Since the treatment of rattlesnake bite by whites—both colonial and recent—is discussed elsewhere (p. 879), the statement should be made here that none of the Indian vegetable remedies for snake bite has ever been shown by scientific test to be effective. As is the case with other folklore cures, their fame and reputed value stem from the uncertain conditions which affect the comparative gravity of every snake-bite case; that is, they cure the cases that would have cured themselves, a subject discussed elsewhere (pp. 712, 860). The Indians readily excused any failures by charging them to the interference of hostile spirits, or to some inaccuracy of ritualistic observance, "for the gathering of medical plants is more or less a magical process" (A. C. Parker, 1928, p. 11).

The use among the Indians of certain herbs or roots in the treatment of rattle-snake bite was widespread, and there seems no doubt that the employment of many of them had originated in pre-Columbian times. A similar use of plants for snake bite is common among primitive peoples the world around. These Indian herbal treatments gained an early and staunch adherence among the whites, which continued until the latter part of the last century, and, indeed, is by no means absent today. It should be observed that this was only one of many items of the Indian medical practice that strongly influenced American home remedies in pioneer days, especially in the rural areas, where vegetable remedies for other afflictions were common.

Among the early reports of plant treatments is that of Hernández (1615, fol. 192ʳ; 1628, p. 330), who tells of various shrubs used for rattlesnake bite by the Mexican Indians. Piso (1648, p. 41) gives information on Brazilian cures; the plant *iacape* was applied externally, and tapioca was taken internally. The earliest British publications to discuss the rattlesnake as a live creature also mentions the root of the snakeweed as a cure (Higgeson, 1630, p. 12).

In 1649, Van der Donck (1909, p. 298), writing of New Netherlands, stated: "There grows spontaneously in the country the true snakeroot, which is very highly esteemed by the Indians as an unfailing cure [for rattlesnake bite]." Liette (1947, p. 149, but written in 1702), said the Illinois had a root that would cure by the following day. Beverly (1705, book 2, p. 23; book 3, p. 50) stated that a root known to the Indians would cure rattlesnake bite in two or three hours, although without this treatment it might be fatal within a few minutes. The Indians were afraid to divulge the nature of the root to the whites for fear of incurring the anger of their deity. Lawson (1709, p. 128) said the Indians knew of at least four kinds of snakeroots, with which they had performed "several great cures." Brickell (1737, p. 143) mentions their having three vegetable remedies which they had willingly divulged, so that each planter knew of the steps to take in an emergency. Catesby (1743, p. 41) wrote that the Indians of the Carolinas used various roots and herbs in the treatment of snake bite. He expressed some doubt as to their value.

Kearsley (1766, p. 74) reported that each nation or clan favored a different herb or root. Among others he had observed the use of dittany, goldenrod, snake-root, devil's bit, and a variety of other aromatic plants. Those held in greatest esteem have a quick, warm, pungent taste, though mild and volatile on the tongue. He described the case of a girl, bitten in the stomach, and with the most serious symptoms, who was treated by an Indian woman with a plant—Kearsley thought it goldenrod—both as an infusion and a poultice. The poultice was placed on a swollen leg, not on the site of the bite. The girl recovered. Yet in spite of this and other successful cases that he witnessed, Kearsley himself seems to have favored other methods, including cauterization.

Carver (1778, pp. 483, 516; Loskiel, 1794, p. 114) believed that the rattlesnake root was most effective at the season when the snakes were most virulent. Peters (1781, p. 260) mentions the cure used by the Mohegan in Connecticut. Adair (1775, p. 234) reported that, although the Indians were often bitten, he had never heard of a fatality, for every warrior carried in his shot pouch a root or herb that was a sure cure. This was both taken internally and applied to the wound. Zeisberger, writing in 1780 (1910, p. 70), records a similar use of plants by the Seneca. His modern editors report the principal herb used to have been *Polygala senega;* other tribes employed *Liatris spicata, Asclepias tuberosa, Prenanthes alba, Fraxinus juglandifolia,* and *Alisma plantago*[15] (p. 158). Often the modern translators or editors are in disagreement as to what plants were meant by the original travelers; thus in the Kellogg translation of Charlevoix (1761; edition of 1923, vol. 1, p. 229) it is stated that the plants were the baneberry (*Actaea*) and the beggar-ticks (*Bidens frondosa*), whereas Masterson (1946, p. 184), quoting a different edition of Charlevoix, mentions *Bidens canadensis* and *Polygala canadensis*. But School-craft (1821, p. 326) thinks Charlevoix had *Podophyllum peltatum* in mind. Lacépède (1789, p. 416; Kerr, 1802, vol. 4, p. 273) says that the remedy used by the Indians was long kept secret but was determined by a Dr. Teinnint or Tennant, a Scottish physician, to be the root of the Virginian poligaly (*Polygala senega*), also called the rattlesnake root. Leach (1949–50, p. 1031) says the Seneca gave the secret to Tennant (this time spelled Tennent). J. Pope (1792, pp. 94, 97) lists various plants used as cures for rattlesnake bite, including the black poplar and *Serpentaria virginiana* [= *Aristolochia serpentaria?*]. Barton (1793, p. 114) records no less than 36 plants said to be efficacious, although not all usages were necessarily of Indian origin. He distinguishes between those for external and internal application, as well as those serving a dual purpose. He attributed the use of garden rue (*Ruta graveolens*) to the Indians of New Jersey (p. 104). As an evidence that some of the remedies may have had a Negro origin, we have the statement by Ettwein (1848, p. 38, but dated 1788) that some Indians used Robert's plantain, called Caesar's remedy, the slave Caesar having won his freedom by the discovery of its curative power (see also p. 882).

Keating (1824, vol. 1, p. 128) tells us that the Potawatomi Indians had two herbal remedies, used in poultices. According to Arfwedson (1834, vol. 1, p. 375) the Northern Indians used several plant cures. Wied-Neuwied (1843, p. 35) says the Delaware used lion's-heart (*Prenanthes rubicunda*) in the treatment of rattlesnake bite; this was boiled with milk, and two tablespoonfuls taken as a dose. Also the root was chewed. In one instance (p. 38) he reports the use of a tea made from white-ash bark. He also says (p. 391) that the Mandan had a formula but is not explicit as to its nature. Harlan (1835, p. 490) discusses several of the suggested plant remedies, but does not state which originated with the Indians. Denig (1930, p. 425), writing in 1854, tells us that the Assiniboin had roots known to be good for rattler bite. They were chewed and applied in a raw state with a bandage. The author said he could testify to their effectiveness not only for snake bite, but for gunshot wounds as well. But Pitcher (1854, p. 515) was more skeptical. He listed the six plants employed for rattlesnake bite by the Six Nations (the same ones given by the editors of Zeisberger) and concluded that, as each nation used a different plant, none could be specific, and that their repute depended

---

[15] I have made no attempt to verify, in a modern botany, any of the names listed in this outline of the plant cures and repellents favored by the Indians. If herpetology is any criterion, many of the botanical names used by the older writers are now buried in synonymy, or at least the species have been shifted to other genera. It is necessary to list the botanical names for definiteness since many of the popular names lack consistency in use. For example, a number of quite different plants were popularly called "snakeroot" or "rattlesnake root" because of their supposed curative properties.

on the fact that rattlesnake bite was seldom fatal. Harris (1855, p. 414) was among those who thought highly of the Indian plant remedies. During 40 years he had seen them often used by the Choctaw, Cherokee, and Creeks with instant relief. Kingsbury, a superintendent of missions among the Choctaw, said that he and other whites always carried the Indian remedy with them, as it must be used instantly (Hodgson, 1824, vol. 1, p. 229). Finley (1857, p. 344) tells of an Indian on the trail who, when bitten, found the required remedial plant only a few steps away. He used the root, which was taken internally as well as applied to the wound. Although the medicine made him vomit, he was able to continue his journey within an hour, for it made the snake bite as trifling as a bee sting.

When an Indian child was bitten, Marcy (1859, p. 127) saw the mother first suck the wound and then take dried plantain leaves, which she chewed and mashed for application to the wound. On top of this she used finely divided tobacco. The child recovered. But another Indian mother, upon returning from a spring and finding a rattler still coiled around her child's arm, on which several bites were evident, gave the patient brandy, thus showing, even at that early date, a change from the Indian plant cure to the standard white remedy. A Chickasaw woman near Fort Washita, Oklahoma, used an indigo poultice, as well as whiskey internally. The Osage carried rattlesnake master in their pouches as both a repellent and a cure (Hunter, 1823, pp. 351, 388).

Hobbs (1873, p. 420) tells of using a treatment that he was taught by the Comanche. He employed a running vine or weed that has a small blossom resembling a rattlesnake's eye. This weed is always available where rattlers are numerous, so he had no trouble in finding it in Sonora, Mexico, although presumably he learned the method in northeastern Wyoming. As usual, the weed was employed both internally and as a poultice. Also, the snake's liver and part of its body (split open) were applied as a poultice. Finally a little gunpowder was rubbed into the wound, but I suspect this was a Hobbs innovation. Comanche remedies are discussed further by Humfreville (1903, p. 182), Nixon (1946, p. 19), and Wallace and Hoebel (1952, p. 171). Brymer (1928, p. 306) states that echinacea, the root of the coneflower, *Echinacea* (= *Brauneria*) *angustifolia,* was used by the Comanche and Kiowa Indians.

A cure ascribed to the Delaware is the following (Anon., 1886, p. 538): Apply to the wound a poultice composed of common salt and indigo, to be renewed at half-hour intervals. Eat freely of the leaves, or drink an infusion of the arrow-leaved violet (*Viola sagittata*). If bitten on a limb, bind a circle of the leaves around it just above the swelling, moistening the leaves with cold water from time to time and changing them two or three times a day. This circlet of leaves recalls the painted ligature of the Pima and Papago that is supposed to limit the swelling.

Coues (1893, vol. 3, p. 238), in an editorial footnote, remarks that these vegetable cures are universal traditions in the West, and that everyone seems to know what plants are helpful except the botanists. He points out how the selected plant differs from place to place; and while he doubts their efficacy as antidotes, he wonders how their curative properties could have become so universally accepted without some basis of fact. He names the following as some of the plants probably used by the Indians and others: *Crotalaria* sp., *Botrych-*

ium virginianum, Goodyeara repens, Liatris scariosa or *L. squarrosa, Prenanthes serpentaria, Hieracium venosum,* and some plant of the genus *Astragalus* called "golondrina."

According to Madsen (1955, p. 131), the Nahuatl Indians of the southern part of the Valley of Mexico drank coffee and ate garlic to cure rattler bite.

The Indians of South America were also reputed to make extensive use of plant remedies for the bite of the rattlesnake and other venomous snakes (Paraguay—Dobrizhoffer, 1784, ed. 1822, p. 310, and Rengger, 1829, p. 92; Venezuela—Lacombe, 1851, p. 289; general—Mitchell, 1861, p. 302).

Beginning about 1900 more complete reports on tribal customs were made by the ethnologists, some of whom made extensive studies of the ethnobotany of various tribes. The plant identifications became more accurate. With regard to the practices of the Northeastern tribes, we are told by Speck (1917, p. 319) that the Mohegan used the common plantain (*Plantago major*), with the leaves bound over the bites to draw out the venom. Tantaquidgeon (1928, p. 266) said this tribe used the Virginia snakeroot (*Aristolochia serpentaria*) pounded into a mash and applied as a poultice. Stone (1932, p. 69) attributes the use of this plant to the Mascouten, Delaware, and Iroquois. It was both chewed and applied as a poultice. The same tribes also used *Polygala senega.* Fenton (1942, p. 521; see also Kalm, 1752–53, p. 188) lists the following plants as being employed, either as cures or repellents, by the Iroquois in colonial times: *Polygala senega, Aristolochia serpentaria, Asarum canadense,* and *Collinsonia canadensis.* The modern Seneca of Allegany, New York, maintain that the proper remedy is either *Prenanthes alba* or *P. altissima.* It is apparent that the favorite cures in the Northeast were the senega and Virginia snakeroots.

The Rappahannock use the poison-snake plant (*Asclepias tuberosa*) or the snakeroot (*Aristolochia serpentaria*) as poultices (Speck, Hassrick, and Carpenter, 1942, pp. 13, 27, 30). In the Southeast, the Catawba, according to Swanton (1918, p. 626; Speck, 1937, p. 191; 1944, p. 42; Taylor, 1940, p. 10) used the American aloe (*Agave virginica*), which was often referred to by such names as rattlesnake root, rattlesnake master, or rattlesnake masterpiece. The roots were mashed and put in water, some of which was then taken internally and some applied to the bite. Another plant used by this tribe was the milk flower (*Asclepias* sp. ?) which was rubbed on the wound (Speck, 1934, p. 61). If the bite improved, the snake would go away and die.

The neighboring Cherokee are reported by Mooney (1900, p. 295) to use the rattlesnake master (*Silene stellata*) both as a repellent and to counteract the bite. According to Mooney and Olbrechts (1932, p. 176) the Cherokee also used rattlesnake fern (*Botrychium virginianum*), poplar bark (*Liriodendron tulipifera*), or Virginia snakeroot (*Aristolochia serpentaria*) for treating a person who dreamed he had been bitten; no doubt the same remedies were employed for actual rattlesnake-bite cases.

The Creeks (Swanton, 1928b, p. 645) preferred the roots of the plant *Manfreda virginica,* which were boiled in water and the bite washed with the infusion. As an alternative they were said by Taylor (1940, pp. 45, 46) to employ the rattlesnake master or button snakeroot (*Eryngium yuccifolium*).

D. I. Bushnell (1909, p. 23; Taylor, 1940, p. 12; Stone, 1932, p. 69) says the

Choctaw used the aspen (*Populus angulata*). The stems, bark, and leaves were boiled together, and the steam was allowed to pass over the wound, a variation of the familiar poultice.

According to Speck (1941, pp. 62, 64) the Houma of Louisiana had two treatments: snake grass (*Ipomoea sagittata* [= *sagittula* ?]), which was chewed by the patient so that the juice could be swallowed, while the leaves were applied as a poultice; or moccasin grass (*Melothria pendula*), the leaves of which were pulverized, mixed with gunpowder, and applied to the wound. The Koasati used an infusion of *Tephrosia ambigua* (Taylor, 1940, p. 33).

In the upper Mississippi-Missouri Basin, according to Gilmore (1919, p. 131), the Dakota, Omaha, Pawnee, and Winnebago put their faith in the narrow-headed, purple coneflower (*Echinacea* [= *Brauneria*] *angustifolia*), a medicinal plant that served for many purposes other than treating rattlesnake bite. Stone (1932, p. 69) extends the list of plants used by these tribes to include the senega snakeroot (*Polygala senega*), yellow dock (*Rumex crispus*), common plantain (*Alisma plantago*), white ash (*Fraxinus americana*), and purple cornflower (*Ceniacea cenquistifolia*) [probably *Echinacea* (= *Brauneria*) *angustifolia*]. Grinnell (1923, vol. 2, p. 188) has stated that the plant favored by the Cheyenne was *Ratibida columnaris;* but W. R. Smith (1929, p. 71; 1930, p. 84) claims they employed the purple coneflower, as did the Pawnee. (See also Chittenden and Richardson, 1905, vol. 1, p. 210; vol. 2, p. 664.)

Densmore (1928) details the practices of the Chippewa Indians. Three kinds of plants were used in the treatment of rattlesnake bite. The first (pp. 288, 352, 353) was the rattlesnake fern (*Botrychium virginianum*), the root of which was used as a poultice. Then there was the lily (*Lilium canadense*); the root was used in a fomentation externally—also when a "snake blows on a person, causing a swelling" (pp. 291, 333, 352–3). Lastly they used the plantain (*Plantago major*), of which both the leaves and root were employed. They were chopped fine and applied to the bite externally. A case history is cited (pp. 291, 333, 352).

H. H. Smith (1923–32) has listed the plants used by the Menominee (p. 34), the Meskwaki or Fox (pp. 193, 214, 222, 233, 248), and the Ojibwa or Chippewa (pp. 365, 380, 430). One Meskwaki poultice comprised a mixture of eight plants; this may have resulted from a logical attempt to settle an uncertainty of choice between several remedies, some of which may have been recommended by neighboring tribes or even by whites. The six plants that Smith could identify, out of the eight, were *Apocynum androsaemifolium, Ptelea trifoliata, Physalis heterophylla, Polygala senega, Podophyllum peltatum,* and *Baptisia leucantha* (p. 193).

In the Pacific Northwest, plants seem not to have been so extensively favored. Among the Thompson Indians of British Columbia, Teit (1900, p. 269; 1930, p. 462) writes that *Euphorbia glyptosperma* (a spurge) was used for snake bite; it was rubbed on the wound. This plant was believed to be found only where rattlers occurred.

In California, where shamanistic treatments were paramount, such plant remedies as were employed may have resulted from an infusion of Mexican culture from the south. The Indians of Mendocino County were said to employ the rattlesnake weed *Daucus pusillus,* a favorite of the Spaniards (Chestnut, 1902, p. 372). Barrett and Gifford (1933) list several plants that were used by the Miwok. The rattlesnake weed was chewed and placed on the bite (p. 169). Of another plant with the same popular name (it was a spurge, *Euphorbia ocellata*), the leaves were mashed and rubbed into the bite; it was thought that the milky juice entered and prevented swelling. Finally, the snakeroot (*Osmorrhiza* sp.) was chewed and applied as a poultice (p. 171). However, Schenck and Gifford (1952, p. 377), in listing 37 plants used by the Karok, do not include a snake-bite cure among them. Gayton (1948, pp. 180, 182) mentions several plant remedies favored by the subtribes of the Yokuts and Western Mono. J., L. (1890, p. 518; Bard, 1894, p. 7) has reported that the Indians at San Luis Obispo (the Chumash?) favored the use of rattlesnake weed or "yerba de la víbora" (*Caucalis microcarpa*). The Tübatulabal pounded up *Euphorbia polycarpa,* taking the entire plant and applying it as a poultice (Voegelin, 1938, p. 60): this was also used by the Luiseño (Kroeber, 1925, p. 650). The Gabrielino used herbs, ashes, and fine dust from the bottoms of ants' nests (Hoffman, 1885, p. 15). The Cahuilla (Hooper, 1920, p. 352) preferred a weed called "golondrina." This was a rather broad term for any of the plant remedies derived from the Spanish-Mexican influence. Orcutt (1891, p. 192) considers the name "golondrina" to be applicable to the plants of the genus *Euphorbia* (the spurges); he says that the Californians and other Southwestern tribes used it generally for the cure of rattlesnake bite, particularly the species *albomarginata, prostrata,* and *polycarpa.* According to Eisen (1895, p. 762) the natives of the Cape Region of Baja California (Pericu Indians?) applied heated pieces of the pitahaya cactus to the wound.

Many plant remedies for snake bite have been used among the Southwestern tribes; however, it is doubtful whether they were all original with the Indians, so long had the Spanish influence been effective when the antidotes were investigated. Hrdlička (1908) made extensive studies of the medical practices among the tribes of the southwestern United States and northwestern Mexico, and found a number that used plants as snake-bite remedies. The Mescalero (Apache) chewed up a certain root and applied it to the wound; it was said to be effective even if delayed a few hours (p. 237). The precaution must be taken not to wash the bitten part with water, otherwise it would swell badly. Stone (1932, p. 69) gives the native name "kuk-bi-ze" to this root.

According to Reagan (1929, pp. 158, 160) the White Mountain Apache used the same plants and methods as the Zuñi, including the sunflower *Helianthus annuus* and *Ptiloria tenuifolia.* The various plants were ground together in metates and applied to the wound. Bourke (1894, p. 140) reported that the Indians of the Rio Grande area used the root of a plant called by the Mexicans "huaco" (or sometimes "guaco," probably the hemp weed *Mikania*) mashed in mescal; this was applied both internally and externally.

The Franciscan Fathers (1910, pp. 117, 155) state that the Navaho used plants, but it remained for Wyman and Harris (1941, p. 66; 1951, pp. 17, 23, 40, 42, 43) to supply their names. Several species having milky saps were said to be favored, including *Euphorbia, Lactuca, Sonchus asper, Frasera paniculata* (called the big-snake plant), and *Physaria newberryi.* Infusions or decoctions were taken internally, and the leaves were applied as poultices. These applications were only a part of extensive ceremonies. Elmore (1943, pp. 77, 86, 97; see also Hogg, 1931b, p. 20) mentions *Pentstemon* and *Gutierrezia sarothrae.* Vestal (1952, p. 68) lists 13 plants used by the Ramah Navaho in the treatment of snake bite, and 5 plants (pp. 17, 24, 25, 33) for the treatment of snake infection, believed by the Indians to be caused by handling snakes. Actually, rattlesnakes are the only dangerous ophidians found in the Navaho country.

Robbins, Harrington, and Freire-Marreco (1916, p. 61) state that the Tewa put their faith in the globe mallow (*Sphaeralcea lobata*); the roots were finely powdered and applied to the wound. According to M. C. Stevenson (1915, p. 53; see also Curtis, 1926, vol. 17, p. 148) the Zuñi used several plants; the roots of not less than three were chewed together and applied to the wound as a poultice, following a preliminary sucking. The plants generally employed were *Helianthus annuus* (a sunflower), *Psilostrophe tagetina*, *Amsonia brevifolia*, and *Ximenesia* [= *Verbesina*] *exaurichulata* (crownbeard). If the patient was troubled with throbbing, the wound was unbound and the priest blew tobacco smoke all over his body. Usually there was recovery by the fifth day; on this morning the patient's head was washed with yucca suds. It was claimed that only one man had died of rattlesnake bite in this tribe in 50 years; he was far from help when bitten and had to walk a long way for treatment. Another plant used by the Zuñi was *Ptiloria tenuifolia* of the chicory family. Then there was *Tripterocalyx wootonii*, a four-o'clock, used to combat the results of touching a snake (not a rattler) that exuded venom from the scales of its sides. I need hardly state that no such creature exists.

According to Fewkes (1896a, p. 16), *Physaria newberryi* is one of the ingredients of the snake charm or antidote taken by the Hopi Snake priests after the Snake dance. Hrdlička (1908, p. 228) mentions the fact that the Hopi have two such herbs. Coleman (1928, p. 97) made tests of the supposed antidote of the Snake priests and found it ineffective. Forrest (1929, p. 297) tells us the Hopi use inkweed or burroweed (*Suaeda torreyana*) and wild flax (*Linum rigidum*), neither of which is thought by botanists to have any curative properties. But Whiting (1939, pp. 32, 39, 77) names the bladder pod (*Lesquerella intermedia*) as the Hopi remedy.

According to Kelly (1939, p. 153) the Kaibab Paiute employed a plant cure, possibly *Ligusticum*, but this may have been resorted to only when no shaman was available. Another subtribe of the Paiute, near Las Vegas, Nevada, used *Pentstemon palmeri* (p. 165). Bancroft (1886, p. 521) informs us that the Mohave depended on *Euphorbia*, but Yount in Camp (1923, p. 12) says they preferred a kind of prickly pear.

Kelly (1936, p. 142), found some among the Chemehuevi who believed a tea made of the desert spurge (*Euphorbia polycarpa*) would cure rattlesnake bite, but other informants were dubious. In that tribe, the plant remedy seemed to be a recent acquisition. Among the Papago, Russell (1908, p. 264) found a poultice of *E. marginata* to be thought effective, and the same treatment was used by the Pima.

Lumholtz (1912, p. 117, see also Bancroft, 1886, p. 419) tells of an interesting cure developed by the Indians (probably Papago) in the vicinity of Altar, Sonora. They took the excrement of the leaf-eating ant (*Pogonomyrmex barbatus*) and a plant called "golondrina"—probably *Amphorbia* (= *Euphorbia*) *polycarpa*—crushed and mixed the ingredients, added alcohol, and applied as a poultice. Occasionally the leaves of a red-flowering oleander were included. The author thought the fact that the ants fed on the leaves of the antiseptic greasewood might produce a beneficial effect. Castetter and Underhill (1935, p. 65) state that the Papago chew creosote bush (*Covillea glutinosa*) and place it on snake, spider, and scorpion bites. We see here a certain relationship in these remedies as described by Lumholtz and by Castetter and Underhill. Probably the differences in the prescriptions, evident in other tribes as well, result from different interpretations of what the Indians reported.

The Opata (Hrdlička, 1908, p. 250) used a lactescent, cathartic plant called "golondrina." The principal remedy of the Tarahumare (p. 251; Stone, 1932, p. 67) was peyote, an intoxicant. They also drank an infusion of charia or fresno (ash leaves). They did not hesitate to resort to suction and cauterization as well. Lumholtz (1902, vol. 1, p. 359) said the peyote was applied externally. The Otomi (p. 253) used the plant known as "trompetia blanca" (*Manettia reclinata*); they crushed an ounce of leaves on a metate and administered it mixed with pulque. According to Beals (1945, p. 193) the contemporary Cahíta prefer a mountain plant, musúe. Naphegyi (1868, p. 251) reported that the Pinto used a decoction made from the leaves of a tree; also the juice of the maguey plant (pulque when fermented) mixed with mustard as a plaster, and chili with mescal taken internally. Roys (1931, pp. 21, 23) lists no less than 22 plants used for snake bite among the Maya. In Central America the Muskito and Sumu of Honduras and Nicaragua used several plant remedies, including guaco (huaco) weed (*Mikania* sp.), which is presumed to confer immunity on the patient (Conzemius, 1932, p. 137).

Thus we gain some idea of the many different plants thought to be effective in the cure of rattlesnake bite and the various methods of application. Locally they were often called by such names as rattlesnake weed (in Spanish, yerba de la víbora), golondrina, rattlesnake vine, rattlesnake root, rattlesnake master, snakeweed, or rattleweed. The latter is an inaccurate name, more properly applicable to plants whose dried seed pods, when vibrating in the wind, produce a rattling sound; this has nothing to do with a supposed snake-bite cure. Jepson (1925), in his work on California flowering plants, applies the name "rattlesnake weed" to *Euphorbia albomarginata* (p. 600) or to *Daucus pusillus* (p. 703), the latter being the "yerba de la víbora" of the Spanish-Californians. The rattleweeds, on the other hand, comprise the genus *Astragalus* (p. 562), also known as locoweeds. By "golondrina," some species of *Euphorbia* was usually indicated.

Although many of the Indian cures, particularly the various plant poultices and decoctions, did gain acceptance by the whites during colonial days, there were skeptics from the first. For example, John Clayton (1744, p. 153), writing in 1687, seems to have been impressed with the variability of the supposed remedy. He remarks: "Among their herbs I have had 40 several sorts, or near that number, showed me as great secrets for the Rattle-Snake-root, or that kind of snake root which is good for curing the bite of the Rattle-Snake. But I have no reason to believe that any of them are able to effect the cure."

Kearsley (1766, p. 74), although having witnessed several cures by the Indian plant remedies, recommended other methods such as cauterization and olive oil. Bingley (1803, vol. 3, p. 75) believed the Indian cures to be mostly fanciful, for it was his opinion that the real cures were effected by nature. J. Stuart (1833, vol. 2, p. 201), on the other hand, considered their herbal snake-bite treatment to be the most valuable medicinal remedy possessed by the Indians. He says he would not have believed in its power, had he not had a confirmation from the most eminent New York physicians of that day. On the other hand, Kercheval (1925, p. 273), also writing in 1833, expressed a lack of faith in the Indian remedies. Kalm (1752–53, p. 66) thought the Indian cures effective unless the snake was very angry and bit deep, or the victim was a pregnant woman. Shuler (1881, p. 293) said that the Indian remedies were all romance; when they really suffered they sought white aid.

This difference of opinion regarding the curative value of the Indian remedies has continued down to the present day. They are still well regarded in some rural areas and have become firmly imbedded in white folk-medicine. As late as 1932, Eric Stone (p. 69) seemed to ascribe real value to some of them. Often failures were attributed to a misidentification of the plants used by the Indians. In the early days the seeds of some of them were sent to Linnaeus for accurate classification (J. E. Smith, 1821, vol. 1, p. 351).

Several writers, such as Michel (1916, p. 39, but writing in 1702), Swanton (1911, p. 351), G. B. Grinnell (1923, vol. 2, p. 148), and A. C. Parker (1928, p. 11), comment on the secretiveness of the Indians with respect to the nature of some of the remedial substances employed. On the other hand, J. Clayton (1744, p. 144) writing as early as 1687, stated that in Virginia some of the priests or medicine men were quite willing to sell the snakeroot secrets. No doubt most tribes felt that divulging the nature of the plant employed was permissible, since the plant was only a part of the remedy; with regard to the accompanying rituals they were as secretive as they were about their other religious ceremonials.

There have been a few suppositions as to how the Indians may have discovered the curative properties of the plants in which they had such faith. Orcutt (1891, p. 193) quotes a newspaper article to the effect that a suicidal snake, having bitten itself and then repented, employed this remedy upon itself, and thus disclosed its value to the observant red man. This is a myth that has cropped up in a number of different areas.[16] (No snake, except possibly one kind in Africa, ever eats vegetable matter directly, although it is often contained in the stomach of its prey.) Two versions have been given by Masterson: one (1938, p. 214) from an unpublished account by Thomas Walduck, 1714, and the other (1946, p. 184) quoted from William Moraley, 1743. In the latter it is necessary for the snake to repair to the curative plant whenever it has bitten any person or animal, otherwise it will itself be poisoned and die.

One might gain the impression, from what has gone before, that these plant cures for rattlesnake bite were outstanding among the plants useful to the Indians, but this was not the fact. In each tribe many kinds of plants were used for food, clothing, building material, medicine, and the like, and in reality the snake-bite cure was not a particularly important element of the ethnobotanical

---

[16] This is akin to the rattlesnake–black-snake and tarantula–toad battle stories, well known in American folklore. In these yarns the nonvenomous participant resorts to a nearby plant each time he is bitten by his poisonous adversary. But when the plant is removed by a dastardly onlooker, the innocent victim succumbs to the next bite. (For example, see Schoolcraft, 1821, p. 327; Swanton, 1917, p. 478; Speck, 1944, p. 37.) In India the same legend tells how the mongoose cures itself after a cobra bite (Cesaresco, 1909, p. 310). Even deer and bison were said to resort to certain plants when bitten (Ingersoll, 1883a, p. 44). The myth is, in fact, as old as Pliny.

category. E. Palmer (1878), in a list of plants useful to the Indians, occupying some 20 pages, mentions only one, *Euphorbia polycarpa,* as a rattler remedy employed in the Southwest; and there are other long catalogues of plants of importance to particular tribes that do not even mention snake-bite remedies. There is little doubt that some of these plant medicines really were effective for the illnesses that they sought to cure, but this was not true of the more serious maladies, of which snake bite was one.

To summarize this survey of the plants used to cure rattlesnake bite by the Indians, attention should be called to their great variety. The ethnobotanists whom I have quoted have mentioned more than 75 different plants. Could we know the facts at this late date, we should probably find that almost every tribe had a different plant cure for rattlesnake bite, and some had several; yet all were thought by their users to be unfailing cures.[17] And this variation was not the result of availability or nonavailability, for many of the plants had wider ranges than their reputations. The fact is that these snake-bite cures should be placed in the category of magical medicine; had any one been really effective it would inevitably have supplanted the others. Most of these plants have been tested in the laboratories, yet I know of no instance in which any marked curative value has been shown to be possessed by any of them.

Maybe the Panamanian Indians, said by Tschiffely (1933, p. 216) to walk backward when bitten and to eat the leaves of the first plant they touch, have as good a plant antidote as any. Without doubt this does emphasize the magical quality the Indians attribute to their plant remedies, which the white man forgets when evaluating them.

Scattered through the ethnobotanies of the various tribes are found many duplications of the plant remedies, some in tribes far distant from each other. These similarities might be attributed to a real efficacy, separately discovered; to accidental parallelism; or to intercommunication. The first may be rejected, for the plants could only have minor secondary beneficial effects as stimulants, sedatives, emetics, or purgatives. Accidental duplication may explain some identical usages, but I am disposed to attribute most of them to the spreading of information from tribe to tribe by the wide-ranging white explorers, hunters, and settlers. No doubt many or most of the plant remedies originated with the Indians, but it remained for the whites to cause a more general adoption of some of them among a wider distribution of tribes. The fact that some of plant remedies of the Indians were congeneric with European folklore remedies for adder bite suggests that some of the Indian prescriptions actually may have originated with the whites.

REMEDIES DERIVED FROM THE SNAKE

There is a basic philosophy in primitive medicine, related to the eye-for-an-eye theory, which assumes suitable remedies always to be present in the instrument causing the injury; all that is necessary is an adequate knowledge for recognizing and using them. This autogenic idea is world-wide, and in printed form dates back at least to Pliny (1855–57, vol. 5, pp. 395, 396, 412; book xxix, chaps. 21,

---

[17] Reminding one of Pliny and the hundred or more plant remedies for snake bite scattered through the pages of his *Natural History*. Dozens of these he reported as the "best" cure. None has stood the test of time.

22, 38; Halliday, 1924, p. 133; D. McKenzie, 1927, p. 117). So, as might be expected, there were a number of Indian remedies for rattlesnake bite derived from the offending snake itself.

Piso (1648, p. 41) reported that the Brazilian natives mashed the head of the snake, mixed it with the saliva of a fasting man, and applied it to the bite as a plaster. Josselyn (1672, p. 78) recommends rattlesnake heart swallowed fresh; also the bruised liver applied to the bite. Later (1675, p. 114) he amended the prescription: the heart was to be dried and pulverized, and drunk in wine or beer. These cures are doubtfully of Indian origin; they have a strong resemblance to some of the Old World formulas. Nieuhof (1732, p. 714, but first published in 1682) said that the Brazilian natives pounded up the head of the snake and applied it as a poultice. This was repeated by Lacépède (1789, vol. 2, p. 418; Kerr, vol. 4, 1802, p. 217) and by Dobrizhoffer (1822, p. 290). Loskiel (1794, p. 114) has stated that rattler fat rubbed into the wound was beneficial, and this is also told of the Delaware and the Chippewa by Ingersoll (1883a, p. 43) and by Nelson (1894, p. 53). According to Loskiel, certain New England tribes used powered snakeskin for a cure.

In the *Rudo Ensayo* written in 1763 (1894, p. 145; Bancroft, 1886, p. 589) there is described a method employed by the Opata of Sinaloa. Catching the snake's head between two sticks, they stretched its body out by pulling the tail; the snake-bite victim then bit along the snake's body, whereupon the snake swelled up and died, and the man recovered. If the man broke every bone in the snake's body it was a sure cure. The same method was long in use in Zacatecas, Mexico, according to José Arlegui (1737, ed. 1851, p. 165; Masterson, 1946, p. 183).

We are told by De Smet (Chittenden and Richardson, 1905, vol. 2, p. 664) that among the Cheyenne, when a man, horse, or dog was bitten, they pursued the reptile, which died almost immediately.[18] It was then opened, and the blood it was believed to have swallowed in biting the victim was taken out and applied to the wound. The swelling was expected to subside at once; if it failed to do so the wound was opened further. G. B. Grinnell (1923, vol. 2, p. 138), also discussing the Cheyenne, says that one Indian treated himself by eating the offending snake.

Hobbs (1873, p. 420) learned from the Comanche of a treatment that involved the application of the snake's liver and a part of the body as a poultice. Talayesva (Simmons, 1942, p. 342) tells us of the Hopi belief that when a snake had bitten someone it was necessary to catch and open the snake quickly so as to discover the two spots of blood that it had secured from the victim, before they disappeared. This would effect a cure; and this Talayesva did when a rattler bit his dog, notwithstanding a conflicting taboo against killing a snake. Simmons, editing Talayesva's autobiography, considers this a demonstration of great force of character, so strong was the taboo (p. 403).

Hrdlička, in his studies of the medical practices of the desert tribes, reports (1908, p. 228) an alternative treatment by the Hopi that involved the application of the ventral surface of the disembowled snake to the wound. The Papago (p. 242) open the snake and take out portions that they call the "fat" or "blood" which they apply to the wound. The Pima (p. 246) use a certain fat found along

---

[18] I am not sure whether the snake was thought to die from the effects of the bite, as does a honeybee when torn from its sting, or whether it was killed by the pursuers. The author does not make this point clear.

the middle of the snake. Bennett and Zingg (1935, p. 128) state that the Tara-humare—as the *Rudo Ensayo* and Bancroft reported of the related Opata—hold the offending snake by the neck and bite it until the blood comes. If the victim can prove he has teeth as strong as the snake's he will not die. Cassidy (1951, p. 76) ascribes this also to the Pueblo. The Havasupai (Spier, 1928, p. 283) have a modi-fied procedure, along the same line: One who is bitten by a snake must catch it, and, grasping each jaw, endeavor to tear it lengthwise into two strips. If he splits it to the tail he will recover, otherwise he must die. The Navaho (Reichard, 1928, p. 145) followed the same method when a girl was bitten, although she herself was not required to tear the snake.

Stone (1932, p. 31) reported that some Northwestern tribes covered the bite with the entrails of the offending reptile; others applied pieces of the flesh to the wound. Some used powdered rattle; still others bound the fang marks, if on a limb, with the whole body of the snake. Gordon (1949, p. 11) said the colonial Indians applied sections of the culprit to the bite, as was also ascribed to Texas Indians by Holley (1836, p. 103). Lumholtz (1902, vol. 1, p. 326) says the Tarahumare use a piece of the offending rattler's liver; if the snake escapes, the patient will die. Naphegyi (1868, p. 251) reported that the Pinto Indians of Mexico applied the head of a rattler, boiled in oil, to the bite. Driver (1939, p. 421) tells us that among the Tolowa of northwestern California one remedy was to cut off the head of the guilty snake and press the stump of the neck to the wound, for raw rattler flesh is presumed to suck out venom. These are culprit-derived variations of the split-chicken remedy—a folk cure that is world-wide.

According to Kanner (1928, p. 279) the natives of Rio, Brazil, preserve fangs in cachaca, an alcoholic beverage, which is drunk in case of snake bite.

Among the Chukchansi, of the San Joaquin Valley of California, it was be-lieved that a person bitten by a rattler should kill the snake, otherwise it would continue to send poison into him (Gayton, 1948, p. 208).

Some of these Indian remedies derived from the offending snake have strong resemblances to those long current in Europe for the treatment of viper bite, cures which were subsequently brought to America by the colonists and have persisted in the folk-medicine treatment of rattlesnake bite by whites (p. 875). We shall never know which were independently derived and which were copied.

SUCTION AND SURGICAL TREATMENTS

Suction, in the treatment of snake bite, is so natural a reaction to the first sting-ing pain, that it is no surprise to find it practiced in many tribes. Stone (1932, p. 69) comments on how widespread this method was. The present section is intended to deal with the general practice, not the specialized sucking-rituals of the rattlesnake shamans, as outlined in a subsequent section of this chapter.

Nieuhof (1732, p. 714) reports the use of suction in Brazil, but says cupping glasses were employed, which, if true, would indicate a European origin of the remedy as applied in that country. Barton (1793, p. 109) says that the Creeks and other Southern tribes used a suction treatment. Dobrizhoffer (1784, ed. 1822, p. 308; Rengger, 1829, p. 92; Corlett, 1935, p. 222) said that the Paraguayan natives used suction and a ligature; and Lacombe (1851, p. 289) attributes the same treatment to the natives in Venezuela.

Bard (1894, p. 11; see also Corlett, 1935, p. 314) records suction, with incision or excision, as prevalent among the southern California Indians, auxiliary to their herbal treatments. Loeb (1932, p. 48) says the Kato of northern California first cut the bite with a flint, allowed it to bleed, and then applied an angelica poultice. Rattlesnake songs were sung.

F. Russell (1908, p. 264) says one of the remedial measures applied by the Pima was to suck the wound every morning for four days. They also ligatured the limb with horsehair, and drew a circle with charcoal to limit the swelling. Drucker (1941, pp. 160, 216) likewise mentions a painted or ceremonial ligature, used by the Pima and Papago to prevent swelling above the bite. Among the tribes using suction, at least to some extent, were the Papago, Shivwits Paiute, and Walapai (p. 160). The Apache-Yuma (= Yavapai) sucked rattlesnake bites and applied a powder, but even then some cases were fatal, according to Corbusier (1886, p. 336). The Havasupai shaman used incision, suction, and a ligature, in conjunction with a ceremony (Spier, 1928, p. 283). Hrdlička (1908, p. 246) corroborates the use of suction by the Pima. The Tarahumare (p. 251) similarly used suction, although they placed their principal dependence on the other measures mentioned elsewhere. Hrdlička (p. 234) further reports that the San Carlos Apache, when they suck a snake-bite wound, spit toward the four cardinal points and pray that the patient will not be hurt. This treatment may be applied by a friend. Corlett (1935, p. 222) reports the use of suction, together with a ligature, in the Paraguayan Chaco region.

We learn from Swanton (1928b, p. 645) that when the Creeks sucked a bite they kept tobacco in their mouths, evidently to protect the operator. Gowanloch (1943, p. 27) says that the Caddo Indians of Louisiana employ suction. According to Gladys Tantaquidgeon (1942, p. 34) the Delaware Indians applied suction, using a hollow piece of deer antler to suck through. Others describing the Indian use of this treatment are Hunter (1823, p. 388), Morton (1938, p. 214), and Wallace and Hoebel (1952, p. 171). The latter attributed it to the Comanche.

Cauterization appears to have been somewhat less usual. It is mentioned by Piso (1648, p. 41), Nieuhof (1682, ed. 1704, p. 714), Clayton (1693, p. 127), J. Long (1791, p. 150), Audubon (1827, p. 26), Lacombe (1851, p. 289), Marcy (1859, p. 129), Teit (1900, p. 369), and Bennett and Zingg (1935, p. 128). This may have been a European innovation.

Such an extreme procedure as amputation was probably seldom or never attempted by the Indians before the days of white influence, since they had great confidence in their ritualistic cures. However, Beauchamp (1922, p. 235) explains the derivation of a geographical name (Honeoye = Finger Lying) from an Iroquois tale to the effect that an Indian, bitten in the finger while picking strawberries, cut off the injured member with his tomahawk.

MISCELLANEOUS CURES

It is somewhat doubtful whether the Indians used snakestones in pre-Columbian days, although Stimpson (1946, p. 455) says they did. Clavigero (1937, p. 394, but writing in 1789) mentions one formed of a partially burned deerhorn that was tried in Baja California, but the method may have had a European origin. The *Rudo Ensayo* of 1763 (edition of 1894, p. 142) says the antlers of a deer, toasted and scraped, were used by the Opata.

Lately I heard that the Kiliwa of Baja California use the following mixture: garlic, kerosene, salt, and the gall of the rattlesnake. Certainly much of this is of non-Indian origin.

Glover (1676, p. 634) reported that the Indians of Virginia carried a powder to cure rattlesnake bites. In almost every town it had a different composition, yet was always effective, for the Indians recovered within a single day. Europeans, failing of adequate remedies, usually died. Glover himself was an "ingenious chirurgeon," but what he reported as powders may have been the Indians' customary dried snake roots.

We are told by Hrdlička (1908, p. 252) that the Cora catch a pig, cut off its snout, and apply the raw surface to the site of the snake bite. This resembles the split-chicken treatment, the use of which is still widespread among primitive as well as supposedly civilized people (see p. 876); it has now come to be used in some Indian tribes such as the Rappahannock (Speck, Hassrick, and Carpenter, 1942, p. 37) and the Catawba (Speck, 1944, p. 48). The Cora also give some of the animal's blood, diluted with warm water, as a drink. According to Purdie (1954, p. 22) certain South American Indians use the gall of the coati mundi for snake bite.

My friend E. L. Freeland tells me that in the Northwest a number of the tribes there—including the Umatilla, Nez Percé, Klickitat, and Yakima—treat rattler bite with mud poultices, a method possibly learned from observation of bitten dogs, which so often submerge themselves in mud. Driver (1939, p. 421) says the Chilula of northwestern California use mud packs, and Beals (1945, p. 193) attributes the same method to the contemporary Cahíta of Sinaloa. The mud cure, as used by Indians, is also mentioned by Gally (1880, p. 2) and Evers (1951, p. 110). White (1842, p. 38) heard, from a prisoner among the Delaware, that these Indians cured rattlesnake bites by washing the wound instantly with water. But, in British Guiana, Schomburgk (1922, vol. 2, p. 102) was told that neither the injured man, nor any of his relatives, could go near or even drink water during his convalescence, or the bite would be fatal.

Some of the Indian repellents were also cures, such as the rattler painted on one's body (Walduck, 1714, in Masterson, 1938, p. 214) and the dust of a crocodile's tooth taken in water (Dobrizhoffer, 1784, ed. 1822, p. 308).

Carver (1778, p. 516; Loskiel, 1794, pt. 1, p. 114; Anon., 1886, p. 538) said that the Indians were so sure of their snake-bite treatment they would allow themselves to be bitten for a glass of brandy. This recalls some of the standard vaudeville gags of the days when whiskey was the accepted remedy. Kane (1859, p. 265) believed that when certain Indians recommended ardent spirits as a treatment, it was only a subterfuge to obtain liquor.

Many shamanistic rites and some of the plant remedies were supposed to confer temporary or permanent immunity on their recipients. Stone (1932, p. 69) goes so far as to say that the Hopi, and other Southwestern tribes having Snake dances, permitted themselves, when neophytes, to be bitten by young snakes having weak venom, and thus immunized themselves against the greater ordeal of handling full-grown snakes later. I know of no verification of this idea.

A few tribes attempted no treatment, although this is not in accordance with the customary usages of primitive or magical medicine which provide a cure for every ill. Driver (1936, p. 197) says the Wappo of the northern California coast had none; and the Nisenan had no regular medicine except along the Miwok border (Beals, 1933, p. 393), although anyone bitten by a snake was put in a special house for 16 days. While there, many snakes visited and frightened him. Tixier (1844, ed. 1940, p. 206) thought the Osage had nothing to offer as a remedy but cries and tears. Kellogg (1917, p. 131; see also Thwaites, 1896–1901, vol. 51, p. 51) has given a translation of Father Allouez' Journey to Lake Superior, 1668, in which it is stated that the Ilimouec (Illinois) had no antidote for snake bite, and that there were many fatalities. Yet Liette (1947, p. 149) said that these Indians used a plant that was a sure cure.

RATTLESNAKE SHAMANS AND CEREMONIAL CURES

Rattlesnake shamans—medicine-priests especially trained or designated to treat rattlesnake bite—were to be found in many tribes, particularly in California and the Far West in general. The following is a list of references to tribes reported to have had specialists of this type:

Achomawi: Klimek, 1935, p. 28; Stewart, 1941, p. 414; Voegelin, 1942, p. 159.
Akwa'ala: Gifford and Lowie, 1928, p. 345; Drucker, 1941, p. 157.
Apache (Cibecue, Huachuca, Tonto, Warm Springs, White Mountain): Gifford, 1940, p. 74.
Arapaho: Kroeber, 1902–7, p. 421.
Atsugewi: Voegelin, 1942, p. 159; Garth, 1953, p. 189.
Bannock: Steward, 1943b, p. 283.
Cahuilla: Sparkman, 1908b, p. 216; Drucker, 1937b, p. 42.
Chemehuevi: Kelly, 1936, p. 137; Drucker, 1937b, p. 42.
Chilula: Driver, 1939, p. 364.
Chukchansi (Yokuts): Kroeber, 1925, p. 517; Gayton, 1948, p. 207.
Chumash: Harrington, 1942, p. 39.
Cocopa: Gifford, 1933b, p. 309.
Crow: Lowie, 1922, p. 374, and 1935, p. 63.
Cupeño: Drucker, 1937b, p. 42.
Diegueño: Spier, 1923, p. 313; Klimek, 1935, p. 28; Drucker, 1937b, p. 42.
Entimbich (Western Mono): Gayton, 1948, p. 276.
Galice: Barnett, 1937, p. 190.
Gosiute: Stewart, 1942, p. 317; Steward, 1943b, p. 283.
Havasupai: Spier, 1928, p. 283.
Hopi: Hrdlička, 1908, p. 226.
Kalekau: Essene, 1942, p. 44.
Kama: Klimek, 1935, p. 28.
Kato: Essene, 1942, p. 44.
Keres: Curtis, 1926, vol. 16, p. 144; White, 1935, p. 68; Parsons, 1939, p. 133.
Kiliwa: Meigs, 1939, p. 63.
Kiowa: LaBarre, 1947, p. 110.
Kitanemuk: Harrington, 1942, p. 39.
Klamath: Spier, 1930, pp. 30, 108 (nonspecialists); Voegelin, 1942, p. 159.
Lassik: Essene, 1942, p. 44.
Luiseño: Drucker, 1937b, p. 42.
Maidu: Dixon, 1905, p. 269; Kroeber, 1907, p. 331, and 1925, p. 427; Klimek, 1925, p. 28; Voegelin, 1942, p. 159.
Maricopa: Drucker, 1941, p. 157.
Michahai (Yokuts): Gayton, 1948, p. 230.

Miwok: Gifford, 1926c, p. 392; Klimek, 1935, p. 28; Aginsky, 1943, p. 446.

Modoc: Voegelin, 1942, p. 159.

Mohave: Hrdlička, 1908, p. 228; Klimek, 1935, p. 28; Drucker, 1941, p. 157.

Mono: Klimek, 1935, p. 28; Driver, 1937, p. 104; Aginsky, 1943, p. 446; Gayton, 1948, p. 276.

Nespelem: Ray, 1932, pp. 200, 215.

Nisenan: Kroeber, 1929, p. 273; Klimek, 1935, p. 28.

Nongatl: Klimek, 1935, p. 28.

Omaha: Fortune, 1932, p. 24.

Paiute: Kelly, 1932, p. 195, and 1939, p. 153; Park, 1938, p. 98; Steward, 1941, p. 321; Stewart, 1941, p. 414 and 1942, p. 317; Drucker (Shivwits), 1941, p. 157; Whiting, 1950, pp. 27, 31, 56.

Papago: Gifford, 1940, p. 74; Underhill, 1946, pp. 278, 294.

Paviotso: Park, 1934, p. 99 and 1938, pp. 18, 85.

Pomo: Gifford, 1926b, p. 330; Loeb, 1926, p. 375; Gifford and Kroeber, 1937, p. 157.

Sanpoil: Ray, 1932, pp. 201, 215.

Shasta: Dixon, 1907, p. 481; Kroeber, 1925, p. 303; Klimek, 1935, p. 28; Voegelin, 1942, p. 159; Holt, 1946, p. 333.

Shoshoni: Lowie, 1909a, p. 225; Steward, 1941, p. 321 and 1943b, p. 283.

Sinkaietk: Spier *et al.*, 1938, p. 162.

Sinkyone: Driver, 1939, p. 364.

Tepecano: Lumholtz, 1902, vol. 2, p. 124.

Thompson: Teit, 1900, p. 369.

Tiwa: Parsons, 1939, p. 931.

Ute: Stewart, 1942, p. 317.

Waksachi (Yokuts): Gayton, 1948, p. 230.

Walapai: Drucker, 1941, p. 157; (nonspecialists) McKennan, 1935, p. 185.

Washo: Lowie, 1939, p. 318.

Wintu (Wintun): DuBois, 1935, p. 93; Gifford and Kroeber, 1937, p. 157; Voegelin, 1942, p. 159.

Wishram: Spier and Sapir, 1930, pp. 239, 245.

Wiyot: Driver, 1939, p. 364.

Wobonuch (Western Mono): Gayton, 1948, p. 276.

Yana: Gifford and Klimek, 1936, p. 85.

Yavapai: Gifford, 1932, p. 239 and 1936, p. 310; Drucker, 1941, p. 157.

Yokuts: Kroeber, 1907, p. 331 and 1925, p. 504; Curtis, 1924, vol. 14, p. 161; Gayton, 1930, p. 380; Klimek, 1935, p. 28; Driver, 1937, p. 104; Park, 1938, p. 85; Aginsky, 1943, p. 446.

Yuki: Kroeber, 1907c, p. 331 and 1925, p. 198; Gifford and Block, 1930, p. 65; Klimek, 1935, p. 28; Essene, 1942, p. 44; Foster, 1944, p. 213.

Yuma: Forde, 1931, p. 196; Klimek, 1935, p. 28; Drucker, 1937b, p. 42.

Yurok: Driver, 1939, p. 364.

Zuñi: Stevenson, 1904, p. 396.

It should be understood that this list does not indicate the extent to which rattlesnake shamans practiced in the tribes mentioned. In some they were to be found only in limited areas, among certain subtribes; in some the office had been temporarily or permanently vacated even before white influences were manifest; and in still others the duties had come to be assumed by shamans having a broader scope of activity. But certainly it is evident from the extent of the list that most of the Southwestern tribes did have these specialists, from which it may be judged that the hazard from rattlesnake bite was sufficient to have evolved an extensive ceremonial pattern for its cure.

That certain shamans were designated as rattlesnake specialists implies the presence of other kinds of specialists, and these there were, with general practitioners as well. Kroeber (1922, p. 303) states that the most important specialists in California were the rain (weather), bear, and rattlesnake shamans.

The rattlesnake shamans constitute an interesting study, not only because of the variations in their methods of treatment, but also on account of organizational differences, such as methods of appointment and instruction, and tribal status. If any element of their treatment for rattlesnake bite could be considered standard, it was the removal of a foreign object by suction, not necessarily, and even not usually, applied at the site of the injury. Nor was this suction method restricted to snake bite or to other afflictions involving the actual introduction of foreign matter into the body; it was used in the treatment of many other diseases. Kroeber (1922, p. 304) divides shamans into two classes: singing and sucking, or diagnosing and curing (see also Gifford, 1926b, p. 330). In some tribes the sucking technique was not used, singing or other rituals being preferred. In fact, it should be understood that even the sucking procedure was rarely employed in what we would term an efficient manner designed to remove venom from the wound, for the entire shamanistic concept, regardless of method, is founded on magical effects and supernatural relationships. It was an outgrowth of the Indians' animistic concept of the universe, the attribution of life, intelligence, and supernatural power to virtually all living and lifeless things. Accompanying this theology was the belief that certain men—shamans—had the power to communicate with the supernatural world, to seek and secure the help of its denizens, and with their help to affect the course of mundane events.

The magical nature of snake bite and the equally magical manner of its cure have been commented upon by several ethnologists:

> The rattlesnake doctor, who cured or prevented the bite of the rattlesnake, was usually distinct from other medicine men. Among the Yuki his power, as that of the rattlesnake, was associated with the sun; among the Maidu with the thunder. Among the Yokuts the rattlesnake shamans annually held a public ceremony designed to prevent rattlesnake bites among the tribe (Kroeber, 1907c, p. 331).

◇

> The rattlesnake's bite was regarded as being dangerous on account of its injection into the victim's body of a material animate object, which the rattlesnake shaman must extract if death was not to ensue. Among the Yuki this object was a small snake; among the Yokuts a rodent's tooth or other object supposed to have formed part of the animals upon which the snake subsists (*Ibid.*, p. 333).

See also Clements, 1932, p. 188; Ray, 1932, p. 202; DuBois, 1935, p. 106; Park, 1938, p. 101; Foster, 1944, pp. 212, 215.

In the accounts of the shamanistic methods that follow, the nature of the presentation might lead one to infer that the ethnologists whose discussions I shall abstract had some faith, themselves, in the curative means described. Such, of course, was not the case; the ethnologists have merely repeated the statements and beliefs of the Indian informants from whom these records of tribal customs were secured.

BASIC CURES: SUCTION

As has been stated, the shamanistic pattern of treatment in the Far West was often centered on the application of suction for the removal of the foreign body that the snake had injected—so it was believed or claimed—into the victim, for it was this foreign substance that caused the swelling, discoloration, and death.[19]

---

[19] Even the most scientific adherent to modern medical theories will grant that this feeling of the presence of a foreign body in a painful swelling is so natural as to be unavoidable. The

It was usually thought to be a tooth or a tiny snake, and the suction was often applied at some point on the patient's body other than the site of the bite. The shaman, by elementary sleight of hand, would then produce from his mouth the foreign object that he claimed to have sucked out, and thus the cure was demonstrated. Almost always there were accessory rituals such as incantations, songs, and dances. In case the patient succumbed, the failure was usually blamed on some untoward event or mystic enemy, although the family of the deceased might attribute it to the evil intentions of the shaman himself.

The following list indicates the tribes having shamans that used suction, together with some details of the purpose of application: Small snakes, usually presumed to be rattlesnakes, were sucked out by the shamans among the Bannock and Shoshoni (Steward, 1943b, p. 346), the Paiute and Ute (Stewart, 1942, p. 317), the Paiute (Kelly, 1939, pp. 156, 160; Stewart, 1941, p. 414; Drucker, 1941, p. 160), the Klamath, Modoc, Shasta, Atsugewi, Wintu, and Maidu (Voegelin, 1942, p. 159), the Yuki (Gifford and Block, 1930, p. 65; Essene, 1942, p. 44; Foster, 1944, p. 216), and the Cahuilla (Sparkman, 1908b, p. 216). Among the following tribes—or at least some of their sections or subtribes—small foreign objects, such as snake fangs, or gopher teeth, were sucked out: Southern Okanagon (Spier *et al.*, 1938, p. 163), Paiute (Kelly, 1939, p. 159), Klamath, Modoc, Shasta, Atsugewi, Wintu, and Maidu (Voegelin, 1942, p. 159), Atsugewi (Garth, 1953, p. 190), Wintu (Kroeber, 1932, p. 372), Yana (Gifford and Klimek, 1936, p. 95), Yokuts (Kroeber, 1925, p. 517), and Apache (Gifford, 1940, p. 179). Tribes in which the shamans either occasionally or usually sucked the wound itself were the Thompson (Teit, 1900, p. 369), Shoshoni (Steward, 1943b, p. 285), Paviotso (Park, 1934, p. 106), Paiute (Kelly, 1932, p. 195), Ute and Paiute (Stewart, 1942, p. 317), Havasupai (Spier, 1928, p. 283), Walapai (McKennan, 1935, p. 192), Shivwits Paiute, Walapai, Papago (Drucker, 1941, p. 160), Yuma (Forde, 1931, p. 196), Chemehuevi (Kelly, 1936, p. 137), Yuki (Kroeber, 1925, p. 198; Essene, 1942, p. 44), Patwin (Kroeber, 1932, p. 292), and Maidu (Dixon, 1905, p. 269). In the following additional tribes, suction was applied, but often not at the site of the bite, or for the elimination of a physical object: Omaha (Fortune, 1932, p. 84), Kiowa (LaBarre, 1947, p. 111), Galice (Barnett, 1937, p. 190), Shasta (Dixon, 1907, p. 484; Kroeber, 1925, p. 303), Yurok and Wiyot (Driver, 1939, p. 364), Cahuilla (Hooper, 1920, p. 336), and Diegueño (Spier, 1923, p. 313).

CEREMONIAL DETAILS

Some of the more interesting or peculiar treatments administered by the rattle-snake shamans, as described to investigating ethnologists by their Indian inform-ants, were the following:

Among the Shasta the rattlesnake shamans were women. Dixon (1907, p. 484; see also Holt, 1946, p. 333) has thus described the method of treatment: She first sucked out the venom. Then she told a friend of the patient she could see her rattlesnake guardian or familiar, but that he was angry and would not look at her. The friend must then speak to the rattler, calling him by name and asking

---

Indian shamans treated many diseases by rituals of which sucking was a part. Corkill (1935, p. 253) tells how a Sudanese medicine man in Africa sucked imaginary teeth out of a snake-bite wound.

him to relent and be kind. The shaman then reported a change in the rattler's attitude by saying: "Now he lights his pipe." There was a further exchange of comments between the shaman and her mystic rattlesnake, involving payment of the fee by the friend of the patient. The shaman then dressed in her paraphernalia and danced, the rattler dancing in unison in his home far away. This completed the cure.

Among the Bear River Indians of northwestern California, the teeth of the devilfish were used to open the wound and allow the poison to escape. Then a rattlesnake rattle was burned and the ashes rubbed into the bleeding flesh of the patient. Chicken-hawk feathers were used in washing the bite to increase the efficacy of the devilfish treatment (Nomland, 1938, p. 117).

The Yaudanchi Yokuts diverged from the usual theory that the pain and swelling came either from the injection of rattlesnake fangs that remained in the wound, or from the introduction of a tiny rattlesnake. It was their belief that the offending snake injected gopher teeth, since the snake feeds on gophers, and it was these teeth that the shaman pretended to remove (Kroeber, 1925, p. 517).

Gayton (1948) has given some details of the shamanistic treatment of rattlesnake bite among the subtribes of the Yokuts and Western Mono. The Chukchansi (p. 207) send the patient away from the village with a virgin youth of the same sex. Or, the shaman may effect a cure by looking at the sun and whistling through a tube (p. 208). Among the Wobonuch and Entimbich, the rattle of a rattlesnake is one of the talismans used by the curing shamans (p. 276). One man, bitten in the course of a ritual, was treated with rabbit hair in the wound, as the hair of the rattlesnake's prey will cure the bite (p. 286).

The elaborate practices followed by the Yuki rattlesnake shamans have been described by Kroeber (1925, p. 198), Gifford and Block (1930, p. 65), Essene (1942, p. 44), and Foster (1944, p. 216). They considered the sun to be the deity of the shamans who cure rattler bite. The person bitten looked at the sun, as did the doctor as well. If it appeared milky to the latter, the patient would recover, so the doctor proceeded with the cure. First he abused the sun, and then painted symbolic rattlers on a flat stone. The wound was warmed with hot ashes, and the stone laid on for a time, after which suction was applied. This should draw out the tiny living rattler that caused the trouble in the victim's body. The little snake died just before it entered the shaman's mouth, so only a dead snake was produced to verify the cure.

DuBois (1935, p. 116) was given more information about the paraphernalia of the Wintu shaman than about the curative measures themselves. Among the objects considered sacred and helpful by shamans were rattlesnake rattles interspersed with feathers and made up into a necklace. One shaman was reputed to have a rattlesnake pet from which he occasionally removed a rattle. This indicates the power of shamanism, for the layman would rarely touch a rattler, dead or alive. The shaman's regalia was ostensibly fed with acorn meal and had smoke blown at it. According to Kroeber (1932, pp. 360, 372) the Wintu cure included dancing by the shamans, and the sucking out of the pain-objects injected by the offending rattlesnake.

We are told by Loeb (1933, p. 159) that, among the Maidu, if a person who had been bitten did not die at once, he went into seclusion for a month with an

Indian who had been bitten and recovered. The patient must observe various taboos and be fed by the helper. Rattlesnakes and lizards came to visit him in his seclusion and these visitors aided in his cure. The same method was used by the Nisenan (Kroeber, 1929, p. 274).

When a Patwin was bitten, he immediately prayed to certain deities; this pleased both the deities and the snake, and had the effect of weakening the venom. A shaman who was called in then sucked the wound and brought out blood that appeared like bundles of small rattlers. If the venom was strong it caused the priest's mouth to swell (Kroeber, 1932, pp. 286, 292).

Spier (1923, p. 313) has described the Diegueño ritual. It involved invocations and the waving of branches of sage; but most important, the shaman applied suction to the patient's back and stomach—without regard to the location of the bite—and this was presumed to extract the venom. According to Drucker (1941, p. 214) one Diegueño used the following method: he sang four times, making four circuits of the patient. All the relatives of the victim had to bathe daily for four days and fumigate themselves with chamiso brush. After this some cases recovered, but others died. Among the Cocopa (Gifford, 1933b, p. 310), the treatment comprised the singing of four songs, rubbing, and blowing smoke on the patient. The Akwa'ala treatment was also entirely spiritual (Gifford and Lowie, 1928, p. 346).

Among the Paviotso (Park, 1934, p. 106; 1938, p. 30), the shaman with power over rattlesnakes told the patient not to eat for five days; if he did he would die at once. White paint was put around the bite and blood squeezed out. The wound was sucked. At the end of five days this was repeated. The patient was then cured. The shaman received his instruction from a rattlesnake in a dream. In the case of one shaman, a necklace composed of stone beads—like rattlesnake eyes—alternating with rattlesnake fangs was an important item of the curative regalia.

The Navaho cure was characterized by one of their standard ceremonials, in this case the "Beauty Way." This included sand paintings and songs. The treatment was sometimes staged before a bite had been inflicted—but one which was known to be inevitable—and in other cases long afterward; but, regardless of these time differences, it was carried out with the utmost concentration of purpose (Wyman and Kluckhohn, 1938, p. 25; Hannum, 1945, p. 149). Pousma (1928, p. 62) reported on several actual cases among the Navaho, some of which were treated by medicine men.

According to Spier (1928, p. 283) the Havasupai shaman made short incisions all around the bite, tied a ligature above it, and sucked out blood. At night he sang songs and waved eagle feathers. A ring of sagebrush (*Artemisia ludoviciana*) was put around the bitten limb to draw out the venom; it would do this instead of drawing out blood because the snake knows this plant. The shaman cured by this means, not only the bite of the rattlesnakes found in the Havasupai area, but that of the harmless desert striped racer (*Masticophis t. taeniatus*). The latter, of course, really required no treatment.

Among the Southeastern Yavapai, the rattlesnake shaman received his curing instructions from a snake seen when he was in a trance (Gifford, 1932a, p. 239). No suction was used; tule pollen was put around the bite and the flesh pressed on all sides. Appropriate songs were sung. Sometimes the shaman called upon a snake to aid in making a cure. A rattlesnake might be taken to the shaman's camp, where it was told that the shaman didn't wish to make trouble; he knew that it had struck only because it was nearly stepped upon. The snake was then liberated.

In the method used by the Northeastern Yavapai (Gifford, 1936, p. 310), the rattlesnake shaman first sang the proper songs, either by day or by night. Then tule pollen was cast in the four cardinal directions, and some was placed on the patient—one spot on each cheek, three stripes on the chin, a cross on the chest, and another on top of the head. A snake was the spirit helper of the shaman and talked to the people. Ritualistic singing over the patient was an important part of the shamanistic treatment in a number of Arizona and adjacent tribes, such as the Shivwits Paiute, Walapai, Yavapai, and Pima (Drucker, 1941, p. 160).

A Papago woman, in an autobiography, tells how she was treated for snake bite by her son, who was a shaman. She was bitten on the wrist while picking beans. Her son chewed greasewood and put the paste on the bite. He then made a mark with a buzzard feather all around the wrist and ordered the poison not to go beyond this mark. (Such magical tourniquets are often encountered in the Southwestern treatments.) He then split the feather, tied the two pieces together, and bound this around the wrist as an additional ligature. The poison stopped here and she was well in two days (Underhill, 1936, p. 62).

The curative methods of the Keres shamans have been described by Curtis (1926, vol. 16, p. 144) and White (1935, p. 68; 1942, p. 320). According to White (p. 68), at Santo Domingo Pueblo the Snake society was an aggregation of those skilled in snake-bite treatment. The house of the society's leader was its head-quarters. When an Indian had been bitten, he was placed in this house with the snake that bit him, together with additional rattlers caught for the purpose. This was to assure his becoming acquainted with snakes so they would not bite him again. The leader of the clan was also present. After four days of this asso-ciation, a meal painting was made on the floor. Near this the patient was placed, with the snakes lying in front. After a suitable ceremony, the snakes were all taken out and liberated, and the priests dined on food furnished by the patient's family. If the rite was successful and the patient recovered, he, in turn, became a rattlesnake shaman, for the healing ceremony was his initiation.

Elsie Parsons (1932, p. 241) records the following procedure among the Tiwa at Isleta, New Mexico: Application for treatment was made direct to the snake father, or doctor, who must find the offending snake. The victim then spit into the snake's mouth, which caused the snake to cure the man, for, after the patient spit, the snake swelled until it burst and died, and the man recovered. No woman should approach the snake-bitten man, lest she instantly swell up.

Mrs. Stevenson (1904, p. 392) thus describes the method of the Galaxy frater-nity, which was famous for curing rattlesnake bite among the Zuñi Indians. (It is particularly to be observed that this was not the Rattlesnake fraternity, although there was one in the community.) The victim must remain alone in a room, for if he saw a woman nourishing a child he would surely die. Three roots, chewed by a medicine man, were applied to the wound; the patient also chewed roots. If clouds gathered after one was bitten, he was more likely to die, for then the snakes were more vigorous and the limb would swell to the heart. But when the sun was hot the snakes were lazy, and in a few days the man would recover. The plants required and details of their application are discussed by Stevenson in a later paper (1915, p. 53).

Kroeber (1902–7, pp. 421, 437, 451) has described the treatment of an Arapaho woman bitten by a rattlesnake. The shaman chopped up the rattlesnake's head, dried and powdered it, mixed it with the dried blood of the snake, a medicine root, and some pepper. This mixture was then sprinkled on a cloth. The shaman scarified the patient's wrist until it bled, tied the cloth around it, put on a piece of fat, and applied a hot stone. In preparing to treat rattlesnake bite, the shaman smoked a ceremonial pipe; also, he claimed to make two rattlesnakes visible within his body, thus proving his power to communicate with his spirit animal, which encouraged his patient.

It is evident that there was a considerable variability in the shamanistic treatment within each tribe. Sometimes this resulted from subtribal differences; in other cases no doubt it came about by reason of the inventiveness of individual shamans. For example, among the Ute and Southern Paiute some shamans sucked out poison; some, a symbolic snake; some, blood; and some applied the suction to the top of the patient's head (Stewart, 1942, p. 317).

According to Isabel Kelly (1939) the following variations in treatment were observed among the Southern Paiute: In the Kaibab area a snake shaman would touch his cane to the chest of a snake-bite victim, and, upon removing it would display a small rattler on its tip. Suction was applied to the chest and stomach—not at the site of the bite—and blood or yellow-green venom were shown to be removed (p. 153). The Shivwits shaman dreamed of a snake from which he obtained a curing song. He and his assistants pressed above the wound to keep the venom from spreading. At Saint George, Utah, the shaman pressed and removed a small snake from the wound; this was not done by sucking. He also got his curing song from a snake (p. 157). At Gunlock, the shaman could cause, as well as cure, snake bite (p. 158). At Paranigat, rattlesnake fangs were sucked from the patient in order to return them to the snake (p. 159). At Moapa, the operator sang his song and from the wound sucked a small snake that could be heard to rattle (p. 160). At Las Vegas, Nevada, there was a treatment lasting four days; it consisted of singing, dancing, and sucking. Here, as well as in some other towns, vegetable poultices were used if the shaman were not readily available (p. 165). One Northern Paiute group, according to Stewart (1941, p. 443), used rain water to cure snake bite, the shaman bringing on the rain. Drucker (1941, p. 160) says that the Mohave shaman caused rain in order to cool the patient.

Isabel Kelly (1932, p. 195) says that a real rattlesnake shaman, when they had one among the Surprise Valley, California, Paiute, did not have to cut or suck the bite. He just told it not to swell, for the rattler was his friend. He dreamed about rattlers and carried one around his neck. Sometimes he put Star brand of chewing tobacco on the bite, a modern touch. But now the last rattlesnake shaman is dead, and the present general-practitioner shamans cut around the wound, suck it, and apply the chewed roots of the corn lily (*Veratrum californicum*) as a poultice.

Some snake-bite cures of the Indians, although magical in method and executed by priests or shamans, were not the rituals of rattlesnake specialists. The Klamath (Spier, 1930, pp. 108, 123, 126, 129) had no specialized rattlesnake shaman, but there was a shamanistic cure. Curing was possible only through the intervention of certain spirits, the rattlesnake among them. In this tribe many diseases were cured by suction of some foreign object from the patient's body. In rattlesnake bite this was a snake fang that entered at the site of the bite and then traveled inward, as, for example, from a bitten finger up an arm. The arm would swell and become spotted with the pattern of the snake. The shaman sang songs and then sucked out the fang. It was usually small—so tiny it could hardly be seen in the palm of his hand, into which he had spit it. Although the rattler was the guiding spirit of many shamans, these were not necessarily able to cure rattler bite. Sometimes in this tribe a more physical cure was attempted, which involved cutting deeply into the bite, and then binding it with a fresh snakeskin.

According to McKennan (1935, p. 185) the Walapai did not have snake-bite specialists; treatment was given by an ordinary shaman. This doctor sang over the patient, using a gourd rattle, or someone else who knew the proper song would lead. The doctor cut the place with a stone knife (p. 117) and then sucked the wound. Sometimes he sucked out a small snake which he appeared to swallow, after showing it to the bystanders. The patient then recovered (p. 192).

Among the Sanpoil and Nespelem, according to Ray (1932, p. 200), a person with a specific animal power could cure himself or others injured by that creature. Thus, one with the rattlesnake as guardian could cure snake bite, although he need not be a shaman. Among the Huchnom, any poison doctor could cure snake bite (Foster, 1944, p. 229).

Some tribes east of the Rockies observed rituals having some similarity to those of the rattlesnake shamans of the Pacific Coast and the Great Basin, although they were not known to have had such specialists. G. B. Grinnell (1923, p. 149), writing of the Cheyenne, presents in detail the cure applied by a woman to Arapaho Chief (the name of an individual). One such treatment required the use of a piece of string and a horned toad. These accounts are on the border line between ritual and folklore.

We are told by Mooney (1891, p. 351; see also Rights, 1947, p. 217) that the sacred formula of the Cherokee for the treatment of rattlesnake bite followed this procedure: First (by song) say it was only a common frog that passed by and bit you; this is meant to deceive the rattler spirits that may be listening. Then rub tobacco juice on the bite, manipulating toward the left around the bite four times. Then repeat the ritual, blowing four times in a circle around the bite. A snake lying down always coils to the left, that is, counterclockwise [this is not a fact], and this motion around the bite is just the same as uncoiling the snake, which should produce a cure. Mooney says this uncoiling scheme has a parallel in European folk medicine. If an Indian dreams of being bitten, the same treatment must be followed, otherwise, maybe years afterward, the same serious consequences will ensue (see also Mooney and Olbrechts, 1932, p. 176; Gilbert, 1943, pp. 197, 293, 343).

Belden (1871, p. 67) mentions a case among the Yankton (Assiniboin) in which a young girl was treated by a medicine man who sang and rattled a gourd. La Barre (1947, p. 112) has described a Kiowa treatment. The snake medicine men are second in importance only to the buffalo shamans. When a snake bites a person the fangs are left in and must be sucked out. The center braid of the patient's hair is rolled around the left side of the neck, in the smoke of a sweet-grass fire. The patient is brushed with an eagle plume to concentrate the venom in one spot, from which the doctor removes it by sucking four times.

Corlett (1935, p. 187) has reported an instance in Central America wherein a medicine man refused to treat a friend for snake bite because the victim would buy him no rum. It seemed it would be dangerous to deal with the supernatural powers while sober.

ACQUISITION OF SHAMANISTIC POWER

Shamanistic power was acquired in a variety of ways—in some tribes by inheritance, in others through dreams or visions, or by the shaman's having been snake-bitten. I find some confusion in the accounts between the method of selection, whereby an individual became a rattlesnake shaman, and the source of the power upon which rests his ability to cure rattlesnake bite. This power has been thus described by MacCulloch, as quoted by Park (1938, p. 8): "He [the shaman] has direct intercourse with spirits and actual (bodily or spiritual) access to the spirit world. All his magical arts are done by virtue of his power over or influence with spirits."

First, as to the method by which an individual might be chosen—self-selected may be a better term—to become a rattlesnake shaman. In some tribes this was hereditary; for example, it was patrilineal among the Mono, Yokuts, and some Miwok (Driver, 1937, p. 104; Aginsky, 1943, p. 446); and alternated between the sexes, in descent from parent to child, among the Paiute (Whiting, 1950, pp. 31, 56). Among the Paviotso the power was handed down through a family, in one case from uncle to father to daughter (Park, 1934, p. 101). It was a family inheritance among the Kiowa (La Barre, 1947, p. 110).

But probably the dream or vision was the usual method of shaman designation. For example, among the Arapaho, one dreamed that he was now able to cure rattlesnake bite; he had two rattlers within him, one on each side. He dreamed, not only of being a shaman, but it was revealed to him what plant was to be used in effecting a cure, and the other details of the treatment (Kroeber, 1902–7, p. 421).

Among the Shoshoni, the special power for doing a thing was granted by a dream of doing it; of this the treatment of rattlesnake bite was an example (Steward, 1941, p. 258; 1943b, pp. 285, 346). Sometimes the dream was not of rattlesnakes, but of some animal mystically related to the rattlesnake, such as the eagle or buzzard. The Death Valley Shoshoni believed that if a man dreamed of a rattler in the fall he could cure a bite in the spring. But he might become a shaman through dreaming of an eagle, lizard, horned toad, or of killing a mountain sheep (Steward, 1941, pp. 262, 321). The Gosiute also got the call through a dream (Steward, 1943b, p. 346). The Paiute got his instructions through dreaming of a rattlesnake (Kelly, 1932, p. 195), but it was the buzzard that brought the power to the Achomawi and Atsugewi (Stewart, 1941, p. 414; Voegelin, 1942, p. 159). The Shivwits Paiute dreamed of a rattlesnake from which he obtained a curing song (Kelly, 1939, p. 156) and the same was true of the Kaibab Paiute (p. 153).

The Southeastern Yavapai received his instructions from a rattlesnake seen when he was in a trance (Gifford, 1932a, p. 239). Park (1934, p. 99) reports the effect of dreams on shamanism among the Paviotso. When one dreamed of certain animals, including rattlesnakes, he knew he was to become a shaman. A rattlesnake came to one man in a dream and told him how to cure snake bite, by the use of a string consisting of ten rattlesnake fangs and ten stone beads having the color of rattler eyes (p. 101). Eventually this knowledge was reconveyed by him to his daughter in her dream some 18 years after his death. The Washo were also notified by dreams (Lowie, 1939, p. 318). A Yuki got his start as a shaman by dreaming of creation and of his curing a rattlesnake bite (Kroeber, 1925, p. 198).

Among the Cocopa (Gifford, 1933b, p. 309), to dream of the roadrunner gave the power to cure snake bite. A roadrunner in human form took the novice up in the air to listen, and then to Feather Mountain, his home, where the neophyte was shown the cure by example. The Akwa'ala rattlesnake shaman got his power from a rattlesnake vision in a dream (Gifford and Lowie, 1928, p. 345; Gifford, 1933b, pp. 309, 312), and so did the Kiowa (La Barre, 1947, p. 111).

The source of the shaman's curative power, rather than the manner of his selection, is pointed out in many ethnological references. "Their extraordinary powers were believed by the Indians to come from supernatural beings, who at particular times, possessed the shaman and spoke through him" (Goddard, 1945, p. 117).

The most common source of the shamanistic power of the rattlesnake specialists seems to have been the snake itself, for it became a guardian, confidant, or "familiar spirit" of the medicine man. Among the tribes attributing the power to this source were the Arapaho (Kroeber, 1902–7, pp. 421, 451), Flathead (Turney-High, 1937, p. 27), Sanpoil and Nespelem (Ray, 1932, p. 215), Wishram (Spier and Sapir, 1930, pp. 236, 239, 245), Klamath (Spier, 1930, p. 123), Shasta and Wintu (Voegelin, 1942, p. 159), Shasta (Dixon, 1907, p. 481; Kroeber, 1925, p. 303), Yokuts, Mono, and Miwok (Aginsky, 1943, p. 446), Paviotso (Park, 1934, p. 101; 1938, p. 85), Akwa'ala (Gifford and Lowie, 1928, p. 345), Akwa'ala, Mohave, Maricopa, Papago, Pima, Walapai, Shivwits Paiute, and Yavapai (Drucker, 1941, p. 160), Shoshoni (Steward, 1941, p. 258; 1943b, pp. 285, 346), Gosiute (Stewart, 1941, p. 414; Voegelin, 1942, p. 159), Shivwits Paiute (Kelly, 1939, pp. 153, 156), Yavapai (Gifford, 1932a, p. 239), and Tepecano (Lumholtz, 1902, vol. 2, p. 124). Sometimes the snake imparted to its agent the most detailed formulas of protocol and ritual for treatment, and how communication might be re-established in time of need.

Birds as totems have already been mentioned in connection with nominating dreams; the eagle, buzzard, and roadrunner were the ones with this prerogative. According to the Achomawi, the power of the buzzard comes from its ability to eat rattlesnakes (Voegelin, 1942, p. 247).

The sun was associated with rattlesnakes and the curative powers of shamans in a number of California tribes, including the Yuki (Kroeber, 1925, p. 199; Gifford and Block, 1930, p. 65; Foster, 1944, p. 213), Kalekau, Kato, Lassik, and Yuki (Essene, 1942, pp. 44, 69), Yana (Gifford and Klimek, 1936, p. 85), Pomo and Wintun (Gifford and Kroeber, 1937, pp. 157, 220), and Mono and Yokuts (Driver, 1937, p. 104). In some instances, from the reaction of the sun on the patient, the shaman was able to prophesy the outcome of the treatment. Other meteorological power-sources were thunder, in the case of the Atsugewi (Voegelin, 1942, p. 159), and lightning among the Tiwa at Isleta, New Mexico (Parsons, 1939, p. 931).

In some Southwestern tribes, the experience of snake bite itself made one a shaman. This was a general organizational practice at the Keres pueblos, for those cured of snake bite automatically became members of the Snake society, to which the treatment of cases was delegated, the victim's own healing ceremony constituting the initiation of the novitiate (Curtis, 1926, vol. 16, p. 144; Parsons, 1939, pp. 893, 900, 901; White, 1930, p. 40; 1935, p. 68; 1942, p. 320). The Crow followed the same plan (Lowie, 1922, p. 374; 1935, p. 63). Among the Hupa they tell the tale of a woman who died from the bite of a rattlesnake. A handsome woman—really a rattlesnake in disguise—called upon the deceased, expressed her regret, and restored her to life, whereupon the resurrected one became a rattlesnake shaman (Driver, 1939, p. 419).

Some tribes tell of rather curious sources of shamanistic power. A small boy who refused to bathe became a snake shaman among the Chemehuevi (Kelly, 1936, p. 137) and the Paiute at Las Vegas, Nevada (1939, p. 165). Gifford (1936, p. 310) records a Northeastern Yavapai tale of a boy 15 years old, who shot a rattler with an arrow. The snake was angered and threatened the boy, asking him to pull out the arrow, but finally compromised by making a shaman of him. Among the Wintu (Cora DuBois, 1935, p. 88), the social pattern demanded no exclusive rattlesnake shaman. A shaman was self-appointed and self-trained. A woman shaman said: "I made my own . . . necklace [of rattlesnake rattles]. I killed my own rattlesnakes. A person who is a good doctor isn't afraid of rattlesnakes" (p. 93).

Among the Yuma, great and special power was needed to cure rattlesnake bite; this was secured by communion with a spirit (Forde, 1931, p. 196); but among the Northern Shoshoni, the medicine man obtained his power in a temporal manner as a chief acquires his war medicine—a bundle of objects cherished as having supernatural powers (Lowie, 1909a, p. 225).

There were various ways of maintaining the power. The Arapaho medicine man, whenever he came upon a snake of any kind, stripped off the skin and ate the snake raw (Kroeber, 1902–7, p. 421). But a Chemehuevi shaman lost his power when he treated his favorite dog, although it was thought the power might return to one of his sons (Kelly, 1936, p. 137).

TRIBAL PROTECTION FROM SNAKE BITE

Some shamanistic rituals were for the protection of the tribe, to avoid snake bite rather than for the treatment of cases after occurrence (Kroeber, 1922, p. 303). Among the Achomawi and the Upper-Sacramento Wintu, the shamans would talk to the snakes as they emerged from their holes, asking them not to molest their people (Voegelin, 1942, p. 159). The women shamans of the Shasta would go through the villages in the winter and sing songs over the children's moccasins to protect them from rattlers (Kroeber, 1925, p. 427; Voegelin, 1942, pp. 159, 247). Among the Valley Nisenan, a patient, after being cured, must be re-treated or he would be bitten again (Kroeber, 1929, p. 274). In one Miwok subtribe, special sticks are used wherewith to slap snakes; the rattlers fear these sticks and keep away from their vicinity at night (Aginsky, 1943, p. 455). The Pomo shaman conducted a ceremony involving a supposed swallowing of rattlesnakes, designed to impress the tribe (Loeb, 1926, p. 375; Kroeber, 1932, p. 404). The shaman would go out to hunt rattlesnakes for the ceremony, followed by members of the tribe. A cocoon rattle was used to deceive the snakes and cause them to come out of their dens. They would then be forced to crawl onto a ceremonial blanket, where they were fed beads and feathers, after which they were taken to the place of ceremony and fed again. Then a shaman picked up a snake and pretended to swallow it, after which he pretended to spit it out. The snakes were then liberated, for it was taboo to kill them.

According to Kroeber (1925, p. 504; see also Gayton, 1930, pp. 368, 380; 1948, p. 230; Aginsky, 1943, p. 446), the Yokuts shamans conducted an annual ceremony in the early spring before the emergence of the rattlesnakes from hibernation, in order to safeguard the people of the tribe from snake bite during the ensuing season of rattler activity. They would go to a snake den and stamp and whistle. Soon the snakes would come out, led by a lizard. They were picked up and placed in baskets filled with eagle down. In the evening a dance was held, each participating shaman carrying a rattler in a bag. From time to time the bags were placed on the heads of the spectators to find, by some appropriate sign, who would be bitten that year. On the following day, the threatened victims were cured in advance, of the snake bites they would inevitably sustain later in the season. A part of the ceremony also made it certain that in the future all rattlesnakes would give a warning rattle before striking. The Maidu conducted a somewhat similar ceremony (Kroeber, 1925, p. 427). According to Driver (1937, p. 143), among the Chukaimina subtribe of the Yokuts, the shamans called the snakes out of their dens in the rocks by means of a whistle. The snakes were then asked which ones desired to see the people. Such snakes as wished to participate in the ceremony answered by protruding their tongues and rattling.

Some Luiseño and Diegueño indulged in propitiatory dances to avoid difficulties with rattlesnakes (Drucker, 1937b, p. 42). When a Yavapai shaman met a snake in the field he explained to it that he was only looking about the country and meant the creature no harm; he then asked it not to harm his people and sprinkled it with sacred tule pollen (Gifford, 1932a, p. 240).

HANDLING RATTLESNAKES

From the close mystical association of rattlesnake shamans with the snakes, it might well be assumed that there would be a corresponding physical association, and such was indeed the case. In many tribes the shamans were reported to handle rattlers, often in public ceremonies, for this was an essential method of maintaining their standing and power in the community. Sometimes shamanism involved a reputed immunity to snake bite.

Among the tribes having shamans who handled rattlesnakes were the Galice (Barnett, 1937, p. 190), Wishram (Spier and Sapir, 1930, p. 237), Bannock (Steward, 1943b, p. 346), Shoshoni (Steward, 1941, p. 321; 1943b, p. 346), Gosiute (Stewart, 1942, p. 317; Steward, 1943b, p. 346), Ute (Stewart, 1942, p. 317), Paiute (Kelly, 1932, p. 195; Stewart, 1941, p. 414; 1942, p. 317), Paviotso (Park, 1934, p. 101; 1938, p. 31), Mono (Driver, 1937, p. 104; Aginsky, 1943, p. 446), Yokuts (Kroeber, 1925, p. 504; Harris, 1932, p. 13; Driver, 1937, p. 104; Aginsky, 1943, p. 446;

Gayton, 1948, pp. 100, 208), Tübatulabal (Voegelin, 1938, p. 65), Miwok (Gifford, 1926c, p. 392; Gifford and Kroeber, 1937, p. 157; Aginsky, 1943, p. 446), Pomo (Loeb, 1926, p. 375; Gifford and Kroeber, 1937, p. 157), Achomawi (Voegelin, 1942, p. 159), Wintu (DuBois, 1935, p. 116; Voegelin, 1942, p. 159), Nisenan (Kroeber, 1929, p. 274); Barbareño (Harrington, 1942, p. 39), Cupeño (Drucker, 1937b, p. 42), Cahuilla (Drucker, 1937b, p. 42), Luiseño (Drucker, 1937b, p. 42), Diegueño (Drucker, 1937b, p. 42), Yuma (Drucker, 1937b, p. 42), and Yavapai (Gifford, 1936, p. 310).

The handling was usually public, to impress the populace, and was often part of an annual dance or other ritual. Immunity to snake bite was attributed to at least some shamans among the Shasta, Atzugewi, Achomawi, Wintu, Maidu (Voegelin, 1942, p. 159), Yurok (Driver, 1939, p. 364), and Miwok, Mono, and Yokuts (Driver, 1937, p. 104; Aginsky, 1943, p. 446; Gayton, 1948, pp. 100, 208).

Among the Wishram, according to Spier and Sapir (1930, p. 237), a man with the rattlesnake spirit would not be bitten by one. Not only could he pick rattlers up safely, but he could kill a rattlesnake, mix the skin with his tobacco, and smoke it without ill effect. Among the Foothill Nisenan, the mere sight of a rattlesnake shaman would kill a snake (Voegelin, 1942, p. 247). The shamans of the Central Pomo could control rattlesnakes with song.[20] The informants claimed that some rattlers were swallowed and thrown up again during the progress of a dance (Gifford and Kroeber, 1937, pp. 202, 212). The Eastern Pomo shaman could collect rattlesnakes by singing to them, making them come to hand (Loeb, 1926, p. 375). The Yokuts and Mono kept rattlers in captivity in narrow-necked baskets for some of their spring ceremonies (Driver, 1937, p. 104). These were collected by the shaman's calling them with bone whistles[20] (Kroeber, 1925, p. 505; Driver, 1937, p. 104; Aginsky, 1943, p. 446). Their venom glands may have been emptied before they were handled, by causing the snakes to bite something (Harris, 1932, p. 13). The Shoshoni tell the tale of a shaman who went to a circus and bet $80 that he could handle any snake in the pit. He was bitten by a rattlesnake but rubbed spit on his wrist and suffered no injury (Steward, 1943b, p. 283). (It need hardly be stated that most circus snakes are "fixed.") A Paviotso rattlesnake shaman was accustomed to carry live rattlesnakes around his waist next to the skin (Park, 1934, p. 101).

Drucker (1941, p. 104) reports that the rattlesnake shamans among the Cocopa, Maricopa, Papago, Walapai, and Shivwits Paiute try to prevent the killing of rattlers by the tribesmen. A shaman among the Northeastern Yavapai picked up a rattlesnake, after first making a circle of dust across its body. But one priest, who was bitten by a rattler, retaliated by tearing it in half (Gifford, 1936, p. 310).

Rattlesnake doctors among the Omaha demonstrated their immunity by drinking, or appearing to drink, rattlesnake venom (Fortune, 1932, p. 30). Liette (1947, p. 150), writing in 1702, tells how the Illinois medicine men first rubbed a plant antidote on their hands and then handled rattlers. Presumably the rattler's fangs had been removed. Among the Central American Muskito and Sumu, the best snake charmers were said to eat snake heads after removing the fangs; the lesser practitioners merely cooked their food with fat extracted from the snake's head (Conzemius, 1932, p. 137).

---

[20] An impossibility, as rattlesnakes are deaf.

But, in spite of their supposed immunity, fatalities among shamans were occasionally reported. Curtis (1926, vol. 16, p. 144) records such a fatality among the Keres.

SHAMANISTIC MAGIC

Snake shamans were gifted with some magical powers not immediately connected with their primary curative functions. It was said of the Paiute that in their dreams they could turn inanimate objects into snakes (Kelly, 1939, p. 165). A Kalapuya shaman was seen to blow on a piece of cedar bark and it crawled away in the form of a buzzing rattlesnake (Gatschet *et al.*, 1945, pp. 339, 345).

The Galice rattlesnake shaman could use a snake for soothsaying or to find lost articles. A rattler, released by him in a crowd, would make its way toward either the thief or the missing object (Barnett, 1937, pp. 190, 197). At the Yokuts dance, each spring, the priests were able to predict who would be bitten that season (Gayton, 1930, p. 380; 1948, p. 286). Among the Cahuilla, Diegueño, and Yuma, the shamans knew in advance when someone would be bitten (Drucker, 1937b, p. 42). A Yuma shaman, called to treat a girl some distance away, exerted his power en route, so that when he arrived it took only an hour to complete the cure (Forde, 1931, p. 197). An Akwa'ala rattlesnake shaman could tell in advance when a distant person was on the way to receive treatment; also he knew if someone was trying to fool him with a make-believe bite (Gifford and Lowie, 1928, p. 246).

A Kiliwa shaman once made two little mounds of earth and stuck a sliver of wood between them. No Indian in the tribe could lift the sliver. The shaman flicked the stick aside and it became a rattler; he seized it and it was once more a stick (Meigs, 1939, p. 63). Steward (1933, p. 308) was told of a contest for power by two shamans, in which one conjured a rattlesnake in the path of the other as an example of his control. Among the Atsugewi, one contest for power by two shamans involved the eating of rattlesnake; the winner was the one who could eat without vomiting (Garth, 1953, p. 190).

SHAMANISTIC FEES

The matter of shamanistic fees was a delicate one. There seems no doubt that in some tribes they were exorbitant, for the patients and even their families were virtually stripped of their possessions to pay for their treatments, as, for example, among the Yuki (Kroeber, 1925, p. 198). Disputes over fees often led to accusations of poisoning and the initiation of serious intratribal feuds.

The Shasta woman shaman was not hesitant in requesting gifts (Kroeber, 1925, p. 303). Among the Klamath the fee for a cure was sometimes a horse (Spier, 1930, p. 129). Among the Clear Lake Pomo, payments amounted to the equivalent of 40 or 50 dollars in clamshell money. One-half the charge was rebated if the patient died (Gifford, 1926b, p. 330). The Yana shaman was paid in hides, beads, and similar media of exchange (Gifford and Klimek, 1936, p. 95). It was the custom of the Wintu to pile the goods the shaman was to receive before him at the start of his operations. If the cure failed, the goods were returned to the dead man's relatives (Gifford and Kroeber, 1937, p. 220). At the Yokuts spring dance, the money collected from the spectators was theoretically for the rattlesnakes, but, of course, it was the participating priests who profited (Gayton, 1930,

p. 380; Driver, 1937, p. 143). Yet in one ceremony in this tribe, it seemed to be necessary for the shamans to ransom the snakes from the laymen (Kroeber, 1925, p. 505). One Akwa'ala rattlesnake shaman was reported to have treated about a dozen snake-bitten patients; for this service he had been paid up to $15 per case (Gifford and Lowie, 1928, p. 246). The Yavapai shamans required payment only from people of property (Gifford, 1932a, p. 239). Among the Hopi, to join the Snake clan was considered the equivalent of paying the Snake chief for curing a case of snake bite (Lowie, 1929, p. 339).

SHAMANISTIC TABOOS

Shamanistic treatments by rattlesnake specialists were often surrounded by taboos similar to those affecting other Indian treatments. For example, among the Clear Lake Pomo when a tribesman was bitten, no one smoked tobacco until he had recovered (Gifford, 1926b, p. 330). Also, no one who had recently eaten meat was allowed to be present at the spring propitiatory ceremony (Loeb, 1926, p. 376). The Cahuilla required anyone suffering from snake bite to avoid proximity to a pregnant woman (Hooper, 1920, p. 350); this taboo was current in other tribes as well. Among the Wishram, no shaman could ever speak of his controlling spirit until the approach of death (Spier and Sapir, 1930, p. 241).

Among the Chemehuevi, a snake-bite victim must not eat any produce from his own garden until his neighbors' crops had been harvested; if he broke this rule his garden would dry up and his fruits be flat and tasteless (Kelly, 1936, p. 137). Similarly, when a Washo was bitten by a snake and looked at the pine nuts before they were ripe, they dried up and were rendered worthless (Lowie, 1939, p. 331). Among the Paiute at Las Vegas, Nevada, the snake-bite treatment had to be given outside of a dwelling. Passersby must not approach unless they had bathed and were clean, otherwise the patient would be adversely affected (Kelly, 1939, p. 165). It was the belief of the Shivwits Paiute, Mohave, and Walapai that drinking water must be denied a snake-bite victim and his entire family while the treatment was under way (Drucker, 1941, p. 160). This was also true of some British Guiana tribes (Schomburgk, 1922, vol. 2, p. 102). At Isleta, the Tiwa pueblo in New Mexico, no woman could approach a snake-bite patient lest she instantly swell up (Parsons, 1932, p. 241). On the other hand, among the Muskito and Sumu of Central America, the patient himself would die if he saw a pregnant woman (Banton, 1930, p. 478; Conzemius, 1932, p. 122); this is the usual direction in which this widespread taboo operates. Another restriction of these Central American Indians was that, during treatment, the patient must avoid foods of which snakes were supposed to be fond. Among the Keres, if a man died of snake bite, no one, not even his parents, was allowed to see him (White, 1942, p. 320). It is obvious that these taboos were useful to the shaman, since he could explain a failure to effect a cure as having resulted from the infraction of some taboo by the snake-bite victim or his family.

SHAMANISTIC COSTUMES

Special costumes or equipment were sometimes a part of the shamanistic ritual. The Creeks shaman wore a foxskin as a badge of office (Swanton, 1946, p. 775). The Wishram rattlesnake shaman could be identified only at the annual spirit dance, when he might be recognized by his wearing a snakeskin and imitating the sound of rattles (Spier and Sapir, 1930, p. 241). The Klamath shaman was distinguished by wearing a rattlesnake skin around the neck and a bull-snake bandoleer (Spier, 1930, p. 30). The Wintu paraphernalia was said to be neither elaborate nor uniform, but was highly sacred. One item included a rattlesnake necklace. The regalia itself, in the ritual, was ostensibly fed acorn meal and had ceremonial smoke blown at it (DuBois, 1935, pp. 116, 117).

Among the Omaha, the rattlesnake expert kept certain charms in his medicine pack or bundle; these had been taken from rattlesnakes. The bundle was a preserved reservoir of miraculous powers, given to the priest by his supernatural patron the rattlesnake (R. F. Fortune, 1932, p. 30).

Evil Shamans and Poisoners

As the shamans manifested their great powers through communion with, or control over, such dangerous creatures as rattlesnakes, it was only natural that their failures should be attributed to deliberate design. One who claims such power is sure to be accused of its misuse; and so it was that the rattlesnake shamans were not only blamed when their remedial measures failed, but were accused of causing all manner of mishaps and diseases. By no means all of these accusations were unjust, for some shamans did, upon occasion, use their power as an instrument for blackmail, failing which they endeavored to injure their victims or enemies by spells and incantations. These victims, in turn, retaliated on the shaman, by attempting to wreak vengeance for the injuries he presumably had caused.

This dual role of the shaman as a curer and destroyer has thus been summarized by Kroeber (1922, p. 302): "Central and southern California [tribes] are a unit in regarding shamanistic power as indifferently beneficent or malevolent. Whether a given shaman causes death or prevents it is merely a matter of his inclination. His power is equal in both directions. Much disease, if not the greater part, is caused by hostile or spiteful shamans. Witchcraft and the power of the doctor are therefore indissolubly bound up together. The unsuccessful shaman, particularly if repeatedly so, was thought to be giving prima facie evidence of evil intent, and earnest attempts to kill him almost invariably followed. In other cases individuals in a neighboring group were blamed. This was perhaps the most frequent cause of the feuds or so-called wars of the central and southern Californian tribes."

Some of the evil methods attributed to rattlesnake shamans among the California tribes were as follows: Among the Bear River people it was said that the rattlesnake poison with which shaman enemies were sickened or killed came from snakes caught in July, August, or September, for these are the months in which the rattlers can see; in the others they are blind. To make the witchcraft poison, the snake was hung by the head in the sun, or sometimes over a slow fire, and the grease was caught in a clam or abalone shell. To these drippings were added the powdered skins of rattlers that had been shed in the spring, together with weasel toenails. A drop of this powerful mixture was placed in an elderwood pipe and, as the operator smoked it, he spoke the name of the intended victim and blew outward on the pipe. The poison would travel to the victim, where it would settle over him; in fact, it could see its way because it was taken from rattlers during their seeing months. One drop reaching the unfortunate objective would be fatal in a year, two drops in two years, and so on. But one large drop might kill the following day. The first notice the victim had of his fatal predicament was a buzzing like that of a rattlesnake in his ears (Nomland, 1938, p. 116).

In the Round Valley area, rattlesnakes were associated with poisoners by the Kalekau, Kato, Lassik, and Yuki (Essene, 1942, p. 43). They were supposed to use either whole snakes or ground parts. The Lassik poisoner was a professional extortioner. Among the Kalekau, Kato, and Yuki, any man seen to kill a rattlesnake was suspected of being a poisoner (p. 69).

DuBois (1935, p. 111) tells of a situation of jealousy between two shamans of the Wintu. When one, a woman, visited a house and left some rattles—presumably inadvertently—she was accused by her competitor of having tried to poison the householder, so dangerous were the rattles considered.

Among the Nomlaki (Goldschmidt, 1951, p. 356), diseases often came from a magic poisoner, whose weapons were dried rattlesnake fangs and rattler venom rolled in ear wax. A person could be poisoned should the poisoner touch him or his excrement.

Freeland (1923, p. 69) and Loeb (1926, p. 330) have described at length the poisoning cult of the Pomo Indians of California. It was to be found among several adjacent tribes in somewhat similar forms. When a man was to be poisoned, a shaman was hired for the purpose. This was usually in revenge for a previous poisoning, one often supposed or imaginary, such as a natural death blamed on an enemy. With elaborate and secret rites the priest gathered suitable poisons, such as poisonous plants, rattlesnake venom, and the venoms of bees, spiders, red ants, and scorpions. These were placed in a mortar, and the blood from four rattlenakes was allowed to drip on the mixture. Finally, when the poison was ready, it was applied to the victim in a variety of ways, such as poisoning a doll in effigy, or shooting a poisoned arrow over his house. The poisoner was well paid, but part of the fee was withheld until the victim died. Rarely, if ever, was the poison applied in any but a metaphysical sense, for the whole program was one of witchcraft, a sort of hexing.

Loeb (1926, p. 332) also described a method reportedly used by the Pomo whereby an enemy might be blinded. The eyes of a rattlesnake were removed while it was blind, preparatory to shedding, and an abalone shell was coated with the substance thus obtained. Then the shell was used to flash light in the eyes of the victim, accompanied by a prayer that he would become blind. Among the Atsugewi, a doctor with rattlesnake power would shoot at his enemy a small snake, that would bite the heart of the victim (Garth, 1953, p. 189).

Gayton (1930, p. 398; 1948, p. 207) tells of a man of evil intent among the Yokuts who had the reputation of being able to cause a man to be bitten by a rattlesnake whenever he wished. These snakes were never visible to the victims. When a chief had thus been put to death, his tribal followers revenged themselves by killing the necromancer.

Among the Nisenan, a rattlesnake-poisoned arrow was said to be employed by a poisoner on his victims. No doubt the use was purely figurative, as seems to have been true of all these methods (Voegelin, 1942, p. 245). Among the Tübatulabal, witches were advised in dreams, by rattlesnakes and by other animals, how to make people sick, or to finish them off completely (Voegelin, 1938, p. 62).

A Chemehuevi shaman, when angered, could cause a snake bite by talking to himself and dreaming that a snake had bitten his victim. Such a bite was quite incurable (Kelly, 1936, p. 137).

Somewhat similar theories were held in the Pacific Northwest. Among the Sanpoil and Nespelem, certain animals, including the rattlesnake, were believed powerful and dangerous, and were likely to become the tools of malignant shamans (Ray, 1932, p. 172). According to Spier and Sapir (1930, p. 237) a Wishram rattlesnake shaman could send his snake in spirit to bite an enemy. There was a somewhat similar belief among the Kalapuya (Jacobs, 1945a, p. 59). Shamans possessed of the rattlesnake-spirit power—one of the strongest—could shoot it at any enemy with fatal results. It was a tribal theory that any rattler that struck without rattling had been sent by a shaman. If it rattled, as a normal rattlesnake should, then it was just a plain snake (p. 76). Similarly, among the Galice, a shaman could order his rattlesnake familiar to seek out and bite any designated victim (Barnett, 1937, p. 190).

A Shoshoni evil charm was prepared by the process of placing rattler heads on hot coals and cooking them with other ingredients. When this dire mixture was preserved in a buckskin bag, it was possible for the possessor to cause the death of an enemy by looking intently at him and murmuring destructive incantations (Mayhugh, 1894, p. 386; Lowie, 1909a, p. 230). Among the Paiute at Gunlock, Utah, and Las Vegas, Nevada, shamans, through their control of rattlesnakes, could cause as well as cure snake bite (Kelley, 1939, pp. 158, 165). Whiting (1950, pp. 33, 51) tells how a Paiute woman used her rattlesnake power to kill her cousin, despite the protective efforts of a shaman. Among the Papago, sorcerers (suspected shamans) might swallow the venom of a rattler, and then blow it over a victim, ostensibly as saliva to effect a cure (Underhill, 1946, p. 278).

According to Stevenson (1904, p. 396) a Zuñi witch was accused of making a compound, including rattlesnake hearts, which was directed at children, often with fatal results. Much time was spent by other shamans in an endeavor to suck out these evil—but quite mystical—missiles.

Fletcher and La Flesche (1911, p. 46) tell us that, among the Omaha, a man who harbored a grudge against another might drop into the enemy's tent the figure of a rattler cut from rawhide. Shortly thereafter the victim would be bitten by a real snake. But according to R. F. Fortune (1932, pp. 32, 138) an evil-intentioned rattlesnake shaman in this tribe used a somewhat different method. He could project venom as a physical fluid that would find lodgement in the victim's stomach. Then the doctor would be called in to suck it out, after which it was sent on to the next victim, either to produce more fees or settle a grudge.

According to Karsten (1926, p. 291) the Canelos and Wapo Indians of Ecuador believed that, when a venomous snake harmed some person or animal, it was the agent of an evil sorcerer. This included the rattler, which was called *mutúlu supia*. Some Indians, believers in reincarnation, have stated that evil men become evil animals, among these the rattlesnake (Ingersoll, 1883a, p. 44).

Within this theme of curers gone wrong, we see what a fruitful field there must have been for murder and intratribal feuds bred of ignorance and superstition—of honest but primitive doctors destroyed because of the natural failures of their crude methods; of slander, blackmail, and personal revenge.

MISCELLANEOUS INDIAN-RATTLESNAKE RELATIONSHIPS

RATTLESNAKES AS A CAUSE AND CURE OF DISEASE

Not only did the Indians have various tribal cures for rattlesnake bite, but rattlesnakes were thought both to cause and to cure certain other afflictions. Often these effects were presumed to be caused by a spiritual rather than a physical intervention of the snakes.

Take first the sinister effects. Mooney and Olbrechts (1932, p. 184) tell of a Cherokee belief that an eye disease, involving susceptibility to light, is caused by seeing a rattlesnake. According to Gilbert (1943, p. 368) the Eastern Cherokee think that if one dreams of a snake it will cause illness. Among the Creeks the rattler is thought to be the source of various diseases (Speck, 1907, pp. 122, 149), including swelling of the face and limbs (p. 132). Rattlesnakes, however, are by no means the only disease producers in this tribe; for example, the water moccasin is held to cause swelling cheeks and aching teeth and gums (p. 126).

In the Midwest, the Omaha blamed stomach disorders on the rattlesnake and treated them accordingly (Fortune, 1932, p. 26). The snake's venom was thought to be projected through the air as an influence, and lodged in the patient's stomach as a liquid. This might come about if the victim incurred the annoyance of a rattlesnake doctor, or passed too near a real snake. The rattlesnake doctor usually effected a cure by sucking the poison from the patient's stomach, the skin remaining unbroken in the process. What purported to be the venom after removal was shown to the bystanders to encourage future patients and fees, both through fear of the doctor's power of evil, and admiration for his immunity in handling the venom. Among the Kiowa, rattlesnake fangs might be used to bewitch people (La Barre, 1947, p. 111).

In the Southwest, the attribution of afflictions, other than the obvious results of snake bite, to rattlers was prevalent, as for example, among the Mohave and Yavapai (Drucker, 1941, p. 104). The Tarahumare believe (Bennett and Zingg, 1935, p. 324) that a rattlesnake eats the soul of a child, which consequently sickens. According to Opler, writing of the lore of the Chiricahua Apache, if one handles a snake it will make the skin peel (1941, p. 227). Even handling a shed skin might result in sores on the inside of the lips, on the hands, and in fact all over the body. Sometimes blisters break out; these may come at once or later. A person may be injured, not only by being bitten, but by being frightened by a snake, or by lying down where one has been (p. 228). An example is cited of the lingering illness and ultimate death of an Indian who persisted in killing rattlers and preparing their skins for sale. Among those tribes that protected rattlesnakes, serious consequences might be expected if a rattler were killed, and a tribesman might get a sore mouth for even mentioning the name of the creature.

Several tribes had beliefs respecting the unfortunate results of letting a pregnant mother look at a rattlesnake; in fact, the instances mentioned by the ethnologists come from such unrelated and widely scattered tribes that one suspects the belief must have been even more general than reported. Among the Thompson Indians of British Columbia the father of an expected child must not kill a snake of any kind or the child will resemble a dead person or ghost (Teit,

1900, p. 304). According to Ray (1932, p. 125), the Sanpoil and Nespelem of northeastern Washington believe that if either parent kills a rattler during the period of pregnancy, the child will cry and writhe like a snake. The Menominee thought that if a pregnant mother looked at a rattlesnake the child would be marked (Skinner, 1925a, p. 307). Among the Maricopa, neither the woman nor her husband should look at or touch a rattlesnake during pregnancy, lest the child be deformed and unable to walk, or even to stand, through a seeming lack of bones (Spier, 1933, p. 310). A Papago or Walapai must never kill a rattler if he has a pregnant wife or a small child, since the child would suffer serious harm (Drucker, 1941, p. 174). The Hopi believed that neither parent should look at a serpent effigy, lest the child would not be born or would swell up (Stephen, 1931, p. 288). Among the Atsugewi, a pregnant woman must avoid snakes, and must throw sand over a snake track before attempting to cross it; otherwise her child would die (Garth, 1953, p. 157).

The Franciscan Fathers (1910, p. 496) tell of the Navaho belief that the death of a snake—one of several animals in this menacing category—if seen by a pregnant woman would cause sickness eventually to overtake her offspring. This may be cured by a singing rite, in which the afflicted parts of the child are touched by an image of a rattler carved for the purpose, after which the image is deposited at a rattler's hole together with an appropriate prayer stick. Wyman and Kluckhohn (1938, p. 13) report the Navaho theory that infection from an animal may result from various kinds of contacts: by being injured by it, by hunting or trapping it, or by killing or eating it. Wyman and Harris (1941, p. 66) say the Navaho attribute kidney and bladder diseases to snake infection; these are treated by chants in which the snakes figure, and also by the use of plants (1951, pp. 40, 43). If a tribesman skins a rattler he will die a violent death (Babington, 1950, p. 205).

It is reported by Reagan (1930, p. 306) that the White Mountain and San Carlos Apache account for disasters as emanating from snakes that died in the summer and left their evil behind. They shun anything that has touched a rattlesnake. They would never use the vessel in which the author washed after he had killed a rattler. An old woman was afflicted with rheumatism from stepping in blood where a rattlesnake had been destroyed.

According to Spier (1928, p. 288) the Havasupai will kill snakes, but in the case of the rattlesnake, care must be taken not to touch the blood or let it splatter the clothing, for if "inhaled" it will cause illness. Talayesva, a Hopi, related (Simmons, 1942, p. 341) that he suffered from a severe pain in the ankle through having stepped where a pair of mating rattlers had been some time before. This poisoned him, and he had to be treated by a Hopi priest, as if it were a case of snake bite.

Among the Pima (F. Russell, 1908, p. 264), it was believed that the rattlesnake caused kidney and stomach troubles in children. As with the Navaho, a cure was effected by the singing of the rattlesnake song and by pressure on the afflicted parts with a rattler image in wood or stone. Hrdlička (1908, p. 243) gives a slightly different version: If one of the parents killed a rattler during the period of gestation, the child might be born with a swelling of the stomach.

The Papago had several rattler-disease beliefs: Rattlesnakes cause a disease—

not the result of a bite—evidenced by pain around the heart (Densmore, 1929b, p. 90); if the father of an unborn child kills a rattlesnake, the child will be subject to convulsions (Underhill, 1939, p. 156); even stepping over a rattler or its trail can cause vomiting (Underhill, 1936, p. 49; 1946, p. 294; Drucker, 1941, p. 216). This last is a Pima belief as well.

In California, the Central Pomo are of the opinion that if a rattler strikes at one's shadow, dizziness results (Gifford and Kroeber, 1937, p. 202). Among the Takelma of southwestern Oregon such an attack on one's shadow causes vomiting (Sapir, 1907b, p. 49).

In contrast to detrimental effects such as these, in other tribes rattlesnakes or their products were thought to be efficacious in the treatment of a number of afflictions. It is somewhat difficult, however, to differentiate such of these medical usages as may have originated with the Indians, from those that the colonists brought with them or devised. No doubt each group derived some practices from the other. Some of the curative methods attributed to the Indians had their parallels in Europe long before the discovery of America, vipers being used instead of rattlesnakes; and the similarity of treatment in widely separated tribes—such as rattlesnake broth for tuberculosis, used on both the east and west coasts—suggests that white hunters or traders may have been the lines of communication which spread some of these remedies, if indeed the whites did not originate them.

However, some of the medicinal applications of rattlesnakes certainly originated with the Indians, for as early as 1615, in one of the first printed descriptions of the rattlesnake, Hernández (fol. 192ᵛ; 1628, p. 330; Nieremberg, 1635, p. 269) stated that the Mexican Indians used rattlesnake fat to reduce pain, or to absorb tumors or swellings. Binding a rattler's head to the neck of the sufferer relieved throat diseases and fevers.

The early colonial accounts, and some of the more recent as well, often fail to specify just what illnesses the rattlesnake medicines were used to cure; also, they are not always definite as to whether the remedies originated with, and were used by, the Indians or the whites. Lawson (1709, p. 129; see also Brickell, 1737, p. 147; Nelson, 1740, p. 351; Carver, 1778, p. 485; and Loskiel, 1794, p. 114) said that the cast skins of rattlers were used as a physic, and the gall, made into a pill with chalk, was efficient in the treatment of fever or smallpox.

La Rochefoucault-Liancourt (1799, p. 181) found that rattlesnake skin, beaten into a powder, was used as a "cleanser of the blood." Wied-Neuwied (1843, p. 380) reported that the Mandan saved the rattles of the rattlesnake, and used them as cures for many diseases. They chewed a rattle and moistened various parts of the patient's body with the saliva.

Lawson (1709, p. 218; repeated as usual, without credit, by Brickell, 1737, p. 403) tells how a bedridden Carolina planter was cured of a mysterious and lingering ailment by an Indian using a defanged rattler. The treatment was only resorted to after the patient's family had given up hope. The rattler, a huge one, was placed around the man's waist where it squeezed "as if he had been drawn in by a Belt." Gradually the snake weakened; the next morning it was dead, whereupon the Indian said the man's "distemper" was dead also. And this proved to be the case. (See also Evers, 1951, p. 111.)[21]

---

[21] At a grotto at Bracciano, Italy, people were thought to be cured of serious maladies by large snakes that wrapped themselves around the bodies of the sick (Bourdelot, 1671, p. 3015).

Mooney (1900, p. 296) reported that rattlesnakes were generally used by the Cherokee to protect their families in the case of epidemics. A roasted rattler was hung up in the house. Each morning the father bit off a small piece, chewed it, mixed it with water, and then blew the mixture as a spray over the other members of the family. Bergen (1899, p. 70) tells of an Indian doctor in New Hampshire, who prescribed a rattler's heart, warm and whole, for fever and ague.

Many of the cures were more specific in the afflictions for which they were applied. One that seems to have been prevalent among the northerly tribes was the use of the rattle to expedite parturition in difficult cases of childbirth. This was mentioned by Lawson as early as 1709 (p. 129; see also Brickell, 1737, p. 147; Nelson, 1740, p. 351; and Daudin, 1801–4, vol. 5, p. 308). J. Long (1791, p. 149) said the Indians among whom he traveled thought a woman in labor would speed delivery by holding the tail of a rattlesnake and shaking the rattles. Keating (1824, p. 129) has recorded that the Potawatomi administered the rattle expediter internally; a similar observation was made by Bossu (1771, p. 363) to the effect the Indian women ate powdered rattle in the belief that it would facilitate a painless childbirth. David Thompson (1916, p. 525), writing in 1811, reported that the Indian women in northeastern Oregon (probably the Umatilla) took powdered rattle in water to hasten delivery, and that he knew of five cases that had been benefited. Williamson (1853, p. 252) said the Dakota mother took two or three rattle joints as a powder. Williamson also tells us the explanation given by the Dakota for the efficacy of this drug: They said the child heard the rattle, and supposing the snake was coming made haste to get out of the way (see also Ingersoll, 1883a, p. 43). The belief in the use of the rattle in childbirth was also prevalent among the Omaha (James, 1823, vol. 1, p. 215) and the Winnebago (Radin, 1925, p. 262). O. D. Wheeler (1926, vol. 1, p. 255) says that when the wife of an Indian guide of the Lewis and Clark expedition was having a difficult time with her first child, she was given the rattle of a rattlesnake mixed with water, upon which delivery took place in about ten minutes. As an extension of this method, Gibbs (1877, p. 207; also Bumpus, 1885, p. 400) says the Northwestern Indians used a powder made from the tail (rattle?) of the Pacific rattlesnake to produce abortion, as well as to expedite natural labor. Radin (1925, p. 262) found that the rattle-medicine expediter was used by Winnebago women to produce a premature delivery if an accident had injured the child within the womb. Peters (1781, p. 324) and Holm (1834, p. 53) reported that rattlesnake skins, rather than rattles, were believed to facilitate delivery. They were much sought after by pregnant women, who tied them around their bodies when their time had arrived.[22] Brinton (1896, p. 133), quoting Henry, reported that the snake's blood, as a drink, was thought to serve the same purpose. H. H. Smith (1923–32, p. 352) reported that the plains Indians used rattlesnake flesh to hasten and ease labor.

The use of rattlesnake fat or oil as a liniment or ointment is very old, as evident from its mention by Hernández in 1615. In fact, the application of snake oil for such purposes is widespread around the world among many peoples, evidently with the hope of acquiring the lithe flexibility of the serpent. The uses of rattlesnake oil and fat by the whites are treated in chapter 14.

[22] The use of snakeskins for this purpose is also an Old World practice (Lean, 1902–4, vol. 2, p. 400, quoting Lupton, 1586; and Daniels and Stevans, 1903, vol. 1, p. 4; vol. 2, p. 693).

Among the American colonial writers mentioning the curative properties of rattlesnake fat or oil, Josselyn (1672, p. 38; 1675, p. 114) thought it valuable for frozen limbs, aches, and bruises. Bossu (1771, p. 364) said the Indians used the fat to relieve rheumatic pains; it was so penetrating that it would go directly through to the bones. Loskiel (1794, pt. 1, p. 114) reported that the Indians sometimes rubbed the fat into a wound. Lacépède in 1789 (vol. 2, p. 412; Kerr, 1802, vol. 4, p. 268) mentioned its application to relieve sciatica and to reduce swellings; Dobrizhoffer (1784, ed. 1822, p. 290) records the same use in Paraguay. The Cherokee utilized rattlesnake fat or oil for the treatment of rheumatism or sore joints (Mooney, 1900, p. 296). The Miami (Kinietz, 1940, p. 387) believed the oil drawn from the fat to be effective in curing all kinds of pain. They claimed it was so penetrating that, if poured on the hand, it would go right through to the other side. H. H. Smith (1923–32, pp. 198, 352) reported that the Meskwaki (Fox) and Ojibwa (Chippewa) employed rattlesnake flesh (probably meaning the fat) as a muscle lubricant. The Keres (Curtis, vol. 16, p. 145) used rattlesnake oil for rubbing their bodies. The Tarahumare of northwestern Mexico valued the fat as an ointment in sweat baths (Bennett and Zingg, 1935, p. 128); and, according to Lumholtz (1902, vol. 1, p. 272) it was used by the same tribe to anoint a newborn child, so that light might enter its heart.

Madsen (1955, pp. 133, 138) says that the women of the Nahuatl tribe south of Mexico City stimulate hair growth by the use of rattlesnake oil. The hair will grow as long as the snake, but care must be taken lest, in a rainstorm, the hair twist like a snake and strangle the woman or her husband.

As was the case with other remedies, the method of securing the rattlesnake oil was deemed important. Thus, according to Mooney (1900, p. 296), the priest who prepared the oil must eat the rattler from which the fat was taken. Freeland (1923, pp. 60, 65) tells us that the Pomo doctors must keep themselves pure by avoiding contact with blood. They must never kill anything, so that even rattlesnake fat must be taken from snakes slit while still alive. Chamberlin (1911, p. 347) reports upon the restrictions that govern the securing of rattlesnake oil to be used by the Gosiute Indians of Utah for rheumatism. The man finding a snake addresses him thus: "My good brother you are powerful; I wish you to help me." The snake must then be killed by a single shot in the head from bow or gun. After removal of the fat, the body must be buried before it can be seen by anyone else. This performance must be repeated with each snake used or the remedy will fail.

Various tribes used rattlesnake parts in connection with headache cures. The Catawba tied rattles to their heads (Swanton, 1918, p. 627) or they may have used skins instead (Speck, 1934, pp. 57, 62; 1937, p. 189). Corbusier (1886, p. 336) says the Yavapai (referred to as Apache-Yuma) attached rattles to a lock of hair, and the Yuki of California tied the rattles to their hatbands for the same purpose (Foster, 1944, p. 174). The Sanpoil and Nespelem carried rattles under their hats (Ray, 1932, p. 215). Several of these uses of rattles are now a part of white folklore (see p. 1239). It is interesting to note that among the Micmac of Nova Scotia, to whom rattlesnakes were unavailable, an ordinary snakeskin was tied around the head or used as a hatband for headache (Wallis, 1922, p. 27).

According to Corbusier (1886, p. 336), the medicine men of the Verde Agency, Arizona, used a more spectacular treatment on the Yavapai (Apache-Mohave) seeking their help. They would hold a live rattler by the neck and tail, and apply it to the seat of pain. The snake would be caused to rattle and then, with a chant or the word "wisht," it would be swung away, evidently with the idea of carrying the pain with it. For headache the snake was put around the patient's neck, and then the same swinging procedure followed.

Among the White Mountain and San Carlos Apaches, one treatment of the sick involved pointing a wooden snake effigy—part water snake, part rattlesnake—at the seat of the affliction, while the medicine man carried on a ritual that included an imitation of the sound of a rattlesnake (Reagan, 1930, p. 323). In one such cure the wooden snake was burned after the ceremony (p. 340).

Voegelin (1942, p. 235) tells of an interesting idea-sequence of the Shasta: If a person chokes on a fishbone he will recover if he calls on the rattlesnake, for the latter swallows its food without chewing. Another peculiar association is that of the Pueblo, who believe that a child's sore navel can be cured if a man who has been bitten by a rattlesnake blows upon the child or waves ashes around its head (Parsons, 1921, p. 103; 1931, pp. 96, 422, 458, 858). Yet, if a snake-bitten man calls on a child, he must first spit or he will cause this same illness (p. 461).

Rattlesnake flesh as a cure for consumption has been noted since colonial days (Carver, 1778, p. 485; Loskiel, 1794, pt. 1, p. 114). A. C. Parker (1928, p. 12) says the Seneca gave the consumptive patient rattlesnake fat as food; and Loeb (1926, p. 328) mentions the same treatment among the Pomo of California, with the further requirement that he abstain from meat or fish for 20 to 25 *years*, for if he touches any fat except that of the rattler he will die. Hrdlička (1908, p. 242) found that the Papago of southern Arizona also used rattler flesh in the treatment of tuberculosis. The snake was killed and the meat dried and used as a powder, a small quantity being put in the food while the patient was not looking. The same remedy was applied by the Cora in northwestern Mexico but with a different ritual. In this tribe the patient himself was required to find the rattler and cut off its head and tail before the snake became angered. The body was then washed, toasted, and dried, and a piece eaten after each meal. According to Musick (1947, p. 49; 1948, p. 4), West Virginia Indians believed that tuberculosis might be cured if a live rattler were worn around the waist next to the skin. The fangs were pulled before this lively remedy was applied, which might require several weeks for completion of the cure.

Dried and powdered rattlesnake flesh was mentioned as early as 1657 by the Jesuit priests as being used by the Indians to cure fever (Parkman, 1874, p. 26; Thwaites, 1896–1901, vol. 43, p. 153, and vol. 70, p. 141; Kenton, 1927, vol. 2, p. 85; Masterson, 1946, p. 186). The Onondaga and Abnaki were two of the tribes mentioned as applying this remedy. More recently it has been prescribed for leprosy in eastern Sonora (Lumholtz, 1902, vol. 2, p. 352), for pustules by the Maya (Roys, 1931, p. 138), and for fever and ague in the Catskills of New York (Evers, 1951, p. 111).

Several Indian treatments for the teeth involved snakes, particularly rattlesnakes, the idea deriving presumably from contemplation of the strength and perfection of their fangs. A toothache cure, using the snake's rattle, was mentioned as early as 1657 (Parkman, 1874, p. 26; Thwaites, 1896–1901, vol. 43, p. 153; Kenton, 1927, vol. 2, p. 85). An Indian belief in Vermont, reported by

Bergen (1899, p. 70), is that if a child bites through a rattlesnake from head to tail it will insure sound teeth. The old Tuscarora had this custom of preserving their teeth, although the snake need not be a rattler (Beauchamp, 1892, p. 225; Kanner, 1928, p. 142). The Mohegan preferred black snakes and the Iroquois smooth green snakes (Speck, 1917, pp. 306, 319; Tantaquidgeon, 1928, p. 267). Curtis (1926, vol. 16, p. 145) found that the Keres held the rattles of a rattler against the teeth to cure headache or toothache. Parsons (1939, p. 92) reported that, among the Zuñi, it was customary for a person, who at some time had been bitten by a rattlesnake, to rub the gums of a child suffering from retarded dentition. The Maya used rattlesnake parts to ease tooth-pulling (Roys, 1931, p. 188). According to Beals (1943, p. 45), if a child among the Cahitá was backward in teething, a string of rattlesnake fangs was hung about its neck. Where headaches were caused by bad teeth, a rattlesnake liver was rubbed on the head and face; also, the head and tail of the snake were cut off, dried, powdered, and drunk as a medicine. This latter cure may be of Mexican origin (Beals, 1945, p. 195). Thwaites (1896–1901, vol. 70, p. 141; Masterson, 1946, p. 186) quotes Father Pierre Roubaud as saying that the smoke-dried gall of rattlesnakes was sometimes used to cure toothache. This was in 1757 among the Abnaki.

The smooth sharpness and the strength of the rattlesnake fangs appealed to the Indians, who used them for various surgical purposes. This was noted as early as 1615 by Hernández (fol. 192^v), who reported their use by the Mexican Indian doctors in perforating the back of the neck as a cure for headache. Dobrizhoffer (1784, ed. 1822, p. 290) attributes the same cure to Brazilian natives.

Lawson (1709, pp. 214, 224; Brickell, 1737, p. 397; C. C. Jones, 1873, p. 32; Speck, 1937, p. 185; Swanton, 1946, p. 252; Rights, 1947, p. 89) report the use of the fangs in Virginia and North Carolina as lancets for scarification preparatory to the application of medicine. They were first carefully cleaned of venom. Brickell (1737, p. 145) says the Indians secured them by letting a rattler strike and entangle its fangs in a piece of red cloth, which was then given a jerk to extract them. Keating (1824, p. 129) learned that the Potawatomi thought the fangs were a charm against rheumatism; the mode of application was to scratch the affected part until it bled. Mooney (1900, p. 296; Mooney and Olbrechts, 1932, pp. 70, 203) found among the Cherokee that the fangs were employed to scarify a patient prior to the application of various remedies. Both the securing and use of the fangs involved rather elaborate ceremonies. They were also used in toning up ball teams before a game (Albrechts, 1929, p. 276). The Seminole, using snake fangs imbedded in a bone frame, made scarifications on arms, legs, and chest, preparatory to the Green Corn dance (Greenlee, 1944, p. 326).

The Indians had various ways of mounting fangs to be used as scarifiers. Swanton (1946, p. 564) quotes Lawson to the effect that the Catawba made a sort of comb, using a row of 15 fangs. Speck (1937, p. 185) states that the Catawba no longer use fangs as scarifiers, but the Cherokee still do, employing a feather to which two fangs are attached. The Cherokee used them on ball teams by scratching deeply and noting the player's nervous endurance and ability to withstand pain. This treatment was also thought to inculcate in the players the fierceness and swiftness of the rattler's stroke.

Kanner (1928) mentions other uses for fangs among primitive people. Some

Indians believed that fever might be cured if the fangs were hung round the patient's neck; the teeth had to be pulled while the snake was alive (p. 274). The rattlesnake shamans of some of the California tribes attributed great ritualistic importance to necklaces composed of fangs together with stone beads resembling rattlesnake eyes.

With respect to most of these Indian remedies, it should be emphasized that a mere recital of the application of the substance used hardly gives a correct idea of the procedure of the treatment. In most instances ceremonies and rituals were also involved, and these the Indians considered more important and effective than the physical substance itself. Often the latter was regarded as merely a representative, symbol, or a carrier of the curative property, having little of value in its own substance. This phase of the applications was completely lost when they were adopted by the whites, and to this the Indians attributed the resulting failures.

War Uses: Arrow Poisoning

Arrows poisoned with snake venom were widely used in war, both in the Old and New Worlds. Pliny mentioned such a use among the Scythians in ancient times (1855–57, vol. 3, p. 97; book xi, chap. 115; see also Topsell, 1608, p. 299; 1658, p. 806). Other Old World references to the use of venom for poisoning arrows are: Hakluyt, 1598–1600, vol. 3, p. 507; Redi, 1670a, pp. 17, 21; Brand, 1781, p. 282; Anon., 1832a, p. 236; Livingstone, 1858, p. 189; Richards, 1885, p. 56; Simson, 1886, p. 342; Calmette, 1907, p. 76; 1908, p. 72; and Lewitus, 1935, p. 542.

Purchas (1614, p. 825) reported that the chief weapons of the Cumana Indians of South America were arrows poisoned with the blood of snakes and other mixtures. Hernández (1615, fol. 192^v) stated that the Mexican Indians used venom-tipped arrows, although the poison was not that of the rattlesnake. Waterton (1828, p. 55) said the Indians of Dutch Guiana used plants mixed with snake fangs—no doubt meaning the venom glands as well.

Since, in many areas of the United States, rattlesnakes are the only venomous snakes, it was natural that their poison should be employed for this purpose by the American Indians, and such use was mentioned at an early date (Goldsmith, 1774, vol. 7, p. 212; Lacépède, 1789, vol. 2, p. 413; Kerr, vol. 4, p. 268). From the territorial extent of the practice in North America, and the early dates of reports from some of the remoter tribes, it is certain that this application of rattlesnake venom was a pre-Columbian development. For example, Fray Estevan de Perea, writing in 1632 (1901, p. 361; Hodge, 1924, p. 118; Bloom, 1933, p. 228), observed that in New Mexico the Pueblo kept captive rattlers solely for the purpose of securing venom for arrows; and a similar report was made by Fray Alonso de Benavides in 1634 (Hodge, Hammond, and Rey, 1945, p. 73), and by Mota Padilla in 1742 (Bandelier, 1930, p. 48). The *Rudo Ensayo*, written in 1763, describes the use of rattlesnake venom, together with other ingredients, for arrow poisoning among the remote Jova and Seri (1894, pp. 187, 197). Ferris (1940, p. 214), trapping in the Rockies in 1830–35, found the custom prevalent there as a means of securing game, and as a weapon of war as well.

This use of rattlesnake venom seems to have been most extensively practiced in the West and Southwest. However, this territorial difference may be somewhat more apparent than real; the Western tribes acquired firearms later than the Eastern, and thus still retained their primitive methods of hunting and war when investigated by trained ethnologists, which was not the case with the Easterly groups. Be that as it may, the following list of references to the use of rattlesnake venom, or rattlesnake products in some form, for poisoning arrowheads, shows a preponderance of tribes of the Missouri Basin and from there westward and southward:

Achomawi: Hamilton, 1865, p. 559; Curtis, 1924, vol. 13, p. 142; Spier, 1928, p. 259; Stewart, 1941, p. 385; Voegelin, 1942, p. 72.

Apache: Coues, 1866, p. 323; S., 1878, p. 82; Hoffman, 1878, p. 466; Anon., 1878, p. 2; Bourke, 1890, p. 58; Conard, 1890, p. 141; Hoffman, 1891, p. 69; Dorsey, 1903, p. 186; Spier, 1928, p. 259.

Assiniboin: S., 1878, p. 82; Anon., 1878, p. 2.

Bannock: Conard, 1890, p. 141; Hoffman, 1891, p. 70; Spier, 1928, p. 259.

Blackfoot: S., 1878, p. 82; Anon., 1878, p. 2; Hoffman, 1891, p. 70; 1896, p. 285; Spier, 1928, p. 259.

Cahuilla: Drucker, 1937b, p. 16.

Catawba: Carpenter and Hassrick, 1947, p. 50.

Cayuga: Hoffman, 1896, p. 285.

Chemehuevi: Drucker, 1937b, p. 16.

Chickahominy: Carpenter and Hassrick, 1947, p. 51.

Chimariko: Driver, 1939, p. 327.

Chippewa: Hilger, 1951, p. 119.

Chumash: Harrington, 1942, p. 15. ,

Crow: S., 1878, p. 15; Anon., 1878, p. 2.

Dakota: S., 1878, p. 82; Anon., 1878, p. 2; Hoffman, 1896, p. 285.

Diegueño: Spier, 1923, p. 353; 1928, p. 259.

Digger (Bannock): Conard, 1890, p. 141.

Flathead: Teit, 1930a, p. 344.

Gabrielino: Harrington, 1942, p. 15.

Gosiute: Steward, 1943b, p. 314.

Hopi: Bill, 1862, p. 368; Hoffman, 1883, p. 105.

Jova: *Rudo Ensayo,* 1894, pp. 187, 198; Bancroft, 1886, p. 579.

Karok: Driver, 1939, p. 327; Schenck and Gifford, 1952, p. 384.

Kato: Driver, 1939, p. 327.

Klamath: Coville, 1897, p. 101; Curtis, 1907–30, vol. 13, p. 177; Voegelin, 1942, pp. 72, 191.

Klikitat: Ray, 1942, p. 151.

Lillooet: Teit, 1909, p. 235; Spier 1928, p. 259; Ray, 1942, p. 151.

Maidu: Dixon, 1905, p. 205; Spier, 1928, p. 259; Voegelin, 1942, p. 72.

Mattaponi: Speck, 1928, p. 350; Carpenter and Hassrick, 1947, p. 50.

Menominee: Hoffman, 1896, p. 285; Skinner, 1921, p. 327.

Miwok: Barrett and Gifford, 1933, p. 218.

Mohave: Yount in Camp, 1923, p. 12.

Mono (Wobonuch and Entimbich): Gayton, 1948, p. 261.

Navaho: Voth, 1905, p. 266; Hill, 1936, p. 10; Elmore, 1943, p. 65.

Nez Percé: Spinden, 1908, p. 227.

Nisenan: Beals, 1933, p. 341; Voegelin, 1942, pp. 72, 191.

Okanagon: Spier *et al.,* 1938, p. 54.

Paiute: Conard, 1890, p. 141; Kelly, 1932, p. 145; Stewart, 1941, pp. 385, 432; Whiting, 1950, p. 35.

Paviotso: Spier, 1928, p. 259.

Pima: Drucker, 1941, p. 118.

Pomo: Gifford and Kroeber, 1937, p. 182.

Pueblo: Hodge, 1924, p. 118; Bandelier, 1930, p. 48; Bloom, 1933, p. 228; Hodge, *et al.,* 1945, p. 73.

Rappahannock: Carpenter and Hassrick, 1947, p. 51.
Santee: Belden, 1871, p. 105.
Seminole: Carpenter and Hassrick, 1947, p. 46.
Seri: Hardy, 1829, p. 298; Bartlett, 1854, vol. 1, p. 465; Stone, 1861, p. 19; D., J. W., 1878, p. 98; Bancroft, 1886, p. 579; Hoffman, 1891, p. 69; *Rudo Ensayo*, 1894, (1763), p. 197; McGee, 1898, p. 256; Spier, 1928, p. 259.
Shasta: Voegelin, 1942, p. 72.
Shoshoni: Hoffman, 1891, p. 70; Mayhugh, 1894, p. 386; Lowie, 1909a, pp. 185, 192; 1924, p. 245; Spier, 1928, p. 259; Steward, 1941, pp. 290, 338; 1943b, pp. 314, 370.
Sinkyone: Driver, 1939, p. 327.
Snake (Northern Shoshoni): Russell, 1921, p. 145.
Takelma: Sapir, 1907a, p. 272; Spier, 1928, p. 259.
Teton: Spier, 1928, p. 259.
Thompson: Teit, 1900, p. 263; Spier, 1928, p. 259; Ray, 1942, p. 151.
Umatilla: D. Thompson, 1916, p. 525; Ray, 1942, p. 151.
Walapai: Drucker, 1941, p. 118.
Washo: Curtis, 1926, vol. 15, pp. 92, 171; Lowie, 1939, p. 328.
Wishram: Spier and Sapir, 1930, pp. 199, 231.
Yana: Gifford and Klimek, 1936, p. 98; Sapir and Spier, 1943, p. 268.
Yaqui: Drucker, 1941, p. 118.
Yavapai: Gifford, 1932a, p. 224; 1936, p. 287; Drucker, 1941, p. 118.
Yuma: Corbusier, 1886, p. 332.
Zuñi: Perea, 1632; 1901, p. 361; Hodge, 1924, p. 111; Curtis, 1926, vol. 17, p. 154; Hodge *et al.*, 1945, p. 214.

It might be expected, since there were so many related and contiguous tribes, that there would be some uniformity in the method of application of the rattle-snake venom to the arrows, and indeed a prevalent pattern of procedure was in evidence. This was to procure the liver of some animal, usually a deer, and to cause one or more rattlers to bite it, thus injecting their venom into the liver, after which it was allowed to putrefy, and the arrow points were then smeared with the product. By this means a larger quantity of poisonous preparation was available than there would have been from the venom alone, and the liver was presumed to increase its effectiveness. Belden (1871, p. 105) said one liver would poison 1,000 arrowheads.

Upon this fundamental theme several tribes introduced variations. Hardy (1829, p. 298) reported that the Seri Indians of Sonora and Tiburón Island con-fined a number of rattlesnakes, scorpions, centipedes, and tarantulas in a pit with a cow's liver. These creatures were then stirred up and infuriated until they had bitten each other and the liver. When the whole mass was in "a high state of corruption" the arrow points were dipped therein and allowed to dry (see also Stone, 1861, p. 19, and McGee, 1898, pp. 54, 78, 87, 100, 105, 256).

According to Hoffman (1883, p. 105) the Coyotero Apache mashed up the heads of rattlers with fragments of deer liver and then allowed the mixture to become putrid, when it was considered ready for use. Yount in Camp (1923, p. 12) tells us that the liver of a deceased Indian was sometimes used by the Mohave, and the mixture was enriched with the blood of a woman, this being considered extremely poisonous. The Southeastern Yavapai (Gifford, 1932a, p. 224) merely stuffed the liver with a rattler's head, as well as with spiders and tarantulas. The Chickahominy also added the snake's head to the liver-venom mixture, together with poison-ivy leaves for good measure (Carpenter and Hassrick, 1947, p. 51).

These are but a few of the variations in preparing the venom-liver combination. There is little doubt that some of the highly colored variations were the result of misinterpretations of what the Indians said, or the inaccuracies of the informers.

Seldom do the accounts explain the method of getting the rattlers to bite the liver. Some tribes kept captive rattlers for the purpose, as reported by the early New Mexican missionaries. Parsons (in Stephen, 1936, p. 577, footnote 3) thought the Pueblo snake hunts may have originated for the purpose of getting snakes for arrow poison. The Maidu (Dixon, 1905, p. 205) and the Dakota (S., 1878, p. 82; Anon., 1878, p. 2) took the deer (or antelope) livers out to snake dens in the spring, held them out to the snakes and allowed them to be struck repeatedly. Some presumed that the animal whose liver was used must be killed by the bite of a rattler (Hamilton, 1865, p. 559; Hoffman, 1891, p. 70).

A number of tribes, although using rattlesnake venom, did not employ the liver combination. The Umatilla pulled out the fangs and venom glands and dipped the arrow points in the venom, which dried on them like varnish (D. Thompson, 1916, p. 523, but writing in 1811). According to Gifford and Klimek (1936, p. 98) the Yana preferred a mixture of rattlesnake venom and deer milt. Kelly (1932, p. 145) says the Surprise Valley Paiute allowed the rattlers to bite the arrow tips directly. One somewhat doubts the accuracy of the informant in this case; it would be too difficult to get any quantity of venom distributed on the wood or stone by this means. The Washo mixed the venom with pitch and then smeared the product on the tips (Lowie, 1939, p. 328). The Shoshoni at Eureka, Nevada, mixed deer blood and rattlesnake venom for their poison preparation (Steward, 1941, p. 338).

The Shoshoni and Bannock were said to catch a live deer and cause a rattler to bite it. Then the meat was allowed to putrefy in a hole in the ground (Hoffman, 1891, p. 70). This somewhat questionable report has not been verified by subsequent investigators. The Karok (Driver, 1939, p. 390) used meat or fish that a rattler had struck. The Wishram (Spier and Sapir, 1930, pp. 199, 231) were said to secure the venom glands of a rattler and smear the arrowheads therewith directly. The Yurok also followed this scheme (Driver, 1939, p. 390). The Achomawi mixed a dried rattler head with the blood and flesh of a dog (Hamilton, 1865, p. 559). The Klamath mixed rattler venom with the roots of a poisonous water hemlock, dipped the arrowheads in the moist mixture, and then dried them over a ceremonial fire (Coville, 1897, p. 101). The Northeastern Yavapai—differing from the Southeastern section of the tribe, which employed a liver variation—used a mixture of rattler venom, spiders, centipedes, bee stings, and walnut leaves. The Western Yavapai compounded spiders with rattlesnake fangs for their prescription (Gifford, 1936, p. 287). The Navaho used three types of poison, two of which contained rattler venom (Hill, 1936, p. 10; Elmore, 1943, p. 65). Corbusier (1886, p. 332) reports that the Yuma took a rattler head, dried and powdered it, and then mixed the powder with clotted blood and red ants. The Okanagon (Spier *et al.,* 1938, p. 54) used rattlesnake heads, and so did the Klamath (Voegelin, 1942, p. 191); the latter roasted the head and smeared the resulting grease on the arrow points. The Chippewa immersed both the arrowhead and the shaft in a mixture of rattlesnake venom and water (Hilger, 1951, p. 119).

Several tribes used rattlesnake body parts or products on the theory that they were poisonous. The Karok dipped their arrows in rattlesnake brains (Schenck and Gifford, 1952, p. 384). The Achomawi and Klamath were said to use dried and pulverized rattlesnake gall (Curtis, 1924, vol. 13, p. 142). The Yana, according to Sapir and Spier (1943, p. 268), applied the grease of a whole rattler they had burned, or sometimes the gall. The Takelma availed themselves of rattler blood (Spier, 1928, p. 259). The Ruby Valley Shoshoni used rattlesnake heart (Steward, 1941, p. 338). The Hopi claimed (Voth, 1905, p. 266) that the Navaho merely suspended a rattler over a pan and dipped their arrows in the drippings mixed with venom. Hoffman (1883, p. 105) reported that the Hopi themselves irritated a rattlesnake until it bit itself, and then dipped the arrow points in its blood. The Sinkyone (Driver, 1939, p. 390) used rattlesnake blood.

The concern of these notes with rattlers should not be allowed to convey the idea that rattlesnakes and their products were the only means employed by the Indians as poison for their arrows. Putrid meat and blood were utilized without the addition of venom by some tribes. Other animal products, especially those derived from biting or stinging insects or other arthropods, such as ants, tarantulas, or scorpions, were frequently included. Among certain tribes, poisonous plants were used for the purpose. Spier (1928, p. 259) tells us that the Havasupai, Wishram, and some Yavapai employed poisonous insects and plants. The Cahuilla used poisonous herbs, mixed with ants and tarantulas (Hooper, 1920, p. 355). The Yuma availed themselves of putrefied flesh, but not that of the rattler, according to Trippel (1889, p. 576). The Maricopa had a process based on an interesting theory. According to their creation myth the cottontail was bitten by a rattler, and they used jackrabbit blood as an arrow poison for the obvious reason that it would be venomous because of the close relationship of the two rabbits (Spier, 1933, p. 135).

Some tribes restricted themselves to vegetable poisons. Bandelier (1890–92, pp. 70, 76) said this was the custom among the Opata, as the Spaniards learned as early as 1542. He doubted the use of rattlesnake venom by the Seri, although this custom seems to have been confirmed by other investigators, before and since. Among other tribes using vegetable poisons were the Gosiute (Chamberlin, 1911, pp. 368, 384) and the Cahitá (Beals, 1943, p. 26). Vegetable poisons predominated in South America and some were undoubtedly effective. Métraux (1949, p. 242) does not even mention snake venom as an important component of arrow poison in his work on the South American tribes.

Some tribes used poisoned arrows in hunting, others only in war, but most employed them for both purposes. Few tribes had any fear that the poisoned arrows would be deleterious to the meat thus secured, and they were supposed to cause the game to succumb more quickly (Ferris, 1940, p. 214; Yount in Camp, 1923, p. 12). The Chickahominy (Carpenter and Hassrick, 1947, p. 51), the Yana (Sapir and Spier, 1943, p. 268), and Maricopa (Spier, 1933, p. 135) are reported as having used poisoned arrows only in war. The plains Indians (S, 1878, p. 82; Anon., 1878, p. 2) and the Yavapai (Gifford, 1932a, p. 224) were careful to keep the more dangerous poisoned arrows either in a separate quiver, or a separate compartment, to avoid confusing them. Belden (1871, p. 106) said the Santee carried their poisoned arrows in a rattlesnake skin, so that they could be easily recognized. Corbusier (1886, p. 332) claimed that the Yuma dipped their poisoned arrows in a stinking liquid so that they could be readily distinguished. But, despite the care taken, some Indians and their domestic animals were fatally injured by their own arrows (Belden, 1871, p. 106; Conard, 1890, p. 142). Speck (1928, p. 350; Carpenter and Hassrick, 1947, p. 50) stated that the Mattaponi used arrowheads that were specially corrugated to hold venom.

The Santee were said to poison and leave on the trail any enemy arrows they might find, in the hope that the enemy would use them on game and then be killed by eating poisoned meat (Belden, 1871, p. 106). The Catawba not only used venom for arrowheads, but also poisoned the points of sharp sticks or splints that they stuck in the grass as booby traps to injure pursuing enemies. They heated the venom to increase its toxicity (James Smith, 1831, p. 30; Carpenter and Hassrick, 1947, p. 49).

Several tribes denied using poisoned arrows; among these were the Kato and Yuki (Essene, 1942, p. 50), the Kiliwa (Meigs, 1939, p. 30), the Patwin (Kroeber, 1932, p. 280), and the Sanpoil and Nespelem (Ray, 1932, p. 90). There were some discrepancies among the reports of ethnologists as to the extent of the practice, and under certain circumstances the Indians obviously attempted concealment. Major John W. Powell (Anon., 1878, p. 2) doubted whether they were ever used by the Missouri Basin tribes. Gifford (1940, p. 78) reported that various Apache groups, Ute, and Papago, previously said to have used poisoned arrows, denied they had employed them. There is no doubt that the practice did decline rapidly with the introduction of firearms among the more warlike tribes; this decline was recognized as early as 1871 (Belden, p. 104; Anon., 1878, p. 2; Kilbourn, 1881, p. 538). Some tribes reported the practice as a matter of historical interest only, e.g., the Menominee, according to Hoffman (1896, p. 285) and Skinner (1921, p. 327). Stockman (1898, p. 587) in a world-wide summary of arrow poisons, stated they were never used by the North American Indians; he must have had in mind the Aztecs and Mayans who, indeed, seem not to have tried any form of arrow poison against the European invaders, somewhat to the surprise of those who knew of the practices of the Northwesterly American tribes (D., J. W., 1878, p. 98).

The question naturally arises as to the effectiveness of these arrow poisons based on rattlesnake venom. I think we may conclude that the rattlesnake venom, as such, did not appreciably increase the peril from an arrow wound. Arrows were dangerous weapons; the threat of infection was serious and may have been increased by the nature of some of the arrow-point preparations. But the poisonous properties of snake venom are destroyed by putrefaction; and as most of the Indian methods of preparation involved a deliberate putrefying of the product, it is probable that any true venom effects were eliminated in the process. Theoretically, in the drier climates, it might have been possible to have dried pure rattlesnake venom on an arrow point, and to have protected it there until use, in which event a real venom effect might have been produced; but this must rarely have been the case (Bogert, 1948a, p. 101), and certainly not with any application of the liver process. Whether the chance of infection of a wound was increased by some of the nauseous ingredients and methods of preparation the Indians employed is a different question.

Of course, arrows were thoroughly dangerous weapons, and their swift and silent flight was greatly feared by the soldiers in the days of the Indian Wars, from the advent of the Spaniards onward (Bandelier, 1890–92, p. 70; Beals, 1932, p. 115). With what the military surgeon had to contend, we have ample accounts. Bill (1862, p. 365) reported on 76 cases of arrow wounds received from Navaho, Apache, and Ute weapons. About 38 per cent were fatal, and the fatalities from abdominal wounds were 17 out of 21 cases, or over 80 per cent. But Bill does not cite the poisoning of the arrows as a factor contributory to this high mortality; he mentions only a horse that may have been poisoned (p. 368). Although infections were not then recognized as such, it is clear that they were the usual and serious sequelae of arrow wounds. Coues (1866, p. 321) recounts his observations resulting from a year's campaign against the Apache. Their arrowheads were fragile and pieces were usually left deep in the wound when the shaft was pulled out. He attributes only one death to the presumed poisoning of an arrow; but, judging by the symptoms he describes, I think a modern physician would have diagnosed an infection in this case, for there seems little resemblance to the symptoms of rattlesnake poisoning.

Otis (1871, p. 144) gives data on the treatment of 83 arrow-wound cases sustained in the U. S. Army between 1865 and 1871. The possible effect of poison on an arrow tip is not mentioned in connection with any case. Otis states that he had a collection of arrowheads sent to the headquarters of the Surgeon General in Washington, and that many of these were believed by the senders to be poisoned. He tested them by introducing the points beneath the skins of small animals, such as frogs, birds, and mice, but they all healed readily, without signs of poisoning. David Thompson (1916, p. 523, but writing in 1811; see also Douglas, 1939, p. 136) tells of a wound received in the shoulder by one of the Oregon pioneers in an encounter with Indians, probably Umatilla or Wishram. It was stated that the arrowhead had been poisoned five years previous to the battle, and that the wound ultimately caused the man's death; but here again, although the result was blamed on arrow poison, the symptoms were more those of an infection, just as might have been expected from a dirty and contaminated arrow, especially in view of the crude treatment then available in a frontier community. Other discussions of arrow wounds are those of Parker (1883, p. 127) and Wilson (1901, p. 513). None seems to have considered poisoning—from rattlesnakes or any other source—as adding materially to the admittedly grave danger from these missles.

Psychologically the venom-poisoned arrow was undoubtedly a valuable weapon; for it was greatly feared by the soldiers who had heard wild rumors as to its potency, and it emboldened the Indians. Some of the stories told of the effectiveness of the rattler venom preparations were quite terrifying. As early as 1763 the author of the *Rudo Ensayo* reported that the Jova arrow poison would kill not only the stricken man but anyone who tried to suck the wound (1894, p. 187); and the Seri preparation would cause fresh blood to boil (1894, p. 198). The Western Yavapai claimed their preparation would kill within an hour (Gifford, 1936, p. 287). Yount was told by the Mohave that their arrows were fatal within half an hour (Camp, 1923, p. 12).

As a matter of fact, the Indians probably did not attribute any virulence they may have claimed for their poisoned arrows to the venom in the physical sense of a chemical compound having certain deleterious results, as we would view it; rather, they placed their confidence in its magical effect, for their rattlesnake relationships were largely on a mystical plane, as is evident from their other attitudes toward rattlesnakes that have been discussed. It was on a par, for example, with the theory held by various tribes that certain malevolent shamans could cause their victims to be stricken as with rattlesnake bite without the interposition of a real snake. This magical aspect of the Indians' faith in the potency of their poisoned arrows was apparent to many ethnologists. Bourke (1890, p. 58; 1891, p. 74), writing of the Apache venom-liver method, thought its efficacy more imaginary than real. He had seen many men and animals wounded and did not recall an instance of increased inflammation, beyond what would have been expected from an unpoisoned arrow. Hoffman, as early as 1891 (p. 69), thought the poison ineffective; he believed the wounds were made serious by septicemia. He later stated his opinion that the poisoning was largely a matter of mythological belief (1896, p. 285). McGee (1898, p. 257), speaking of the Seri mixture, thought its power only necromantic, although admitting it might induce an infection.

Venom-poisoned arrows, not, however, involving rattlesnake venom, were tested long ago by Redi (1670a, pp. 17, 21; Charas, 1673, p. 16), the first scientific experimenter with snake venom. He concluded that the venom was rarely effective.

So, to summarize, the widespread use of rattlesnake venom by the Indians in the poisoning of arrows must be deemed to have been more of psychological than of practical importance.

The rattlesnake may sometimes have symbolized a declaration of war between Indian tribes, for in New England a bundle of arrows covered by a rattlesnake skin was a symbol of enmity (Winslow, 1624, pp. 2, 3). Rattlesnake skins were sometimes used to reinforce bows, as reported of the Umatilla by D. Thompson in 1811 (1916, p. 525). As skins are weak, we may presume the skin to have had a ritualistic significance. J. Long (1791, p. 150) said that the Indians of some of the Northern tribes took out the rattlers' venom glands, and carried the live snakes with them when they went to war, for what purpose is unstated.

ART AND ORNAMENTATION

As might be expected of creatures so prominent in myth and legend, rattlesnakes had a place in the art, decoration, and symbolism of the American Indian tribes. Probably the earliest printed reference in English to the rattle of the rattlesnake—and therefore indirectly to the snake itself—mentions its use as a personal adornment by the Indians of Virginia: "Some on their heads weare the wing of a bird or some large feather, with a Rattel. Those Rattels are somewhat like the chape[23] of a Rapier but lesse, which they take from the taile of a snake" (from *A Map of Virginia*, by Capt. John Smith, 1612, p. 20). In another early work (E. Winslow, 1624, reprint p. 240), it is stated that in New England a bundle of arrows bound in a rattlesnake skin was an Indian message of enmity. Yet such an attribution was not universal, for Bartram (1791, p. 359) found that in the South a tribute of tobacco to a chieftain was sometimes encased in a rattlesnake's skin.

The wearing of rattlesnake skins or rattles was general in certain tribes, but

---

[23] The steel or silver tip of the scabbard. See Strachey's similar statement (Major, 1849, p. 67). Lawson said the Virginia medicine men ornamented their heads with snakeskins stuffed with moss (Swanton, 1946, p. 252).

was taboo in others (Kalm, 1752–53, p. 187; 1770–71, vol. 3, p. 10). Sometimes they were worn purely as personal adornment; in others they were thought valuable as fetishes or charms, of importance in the cure or avoidance of disease, as mentioned elsewhere (p. 1165). In some tribes, the wearing of skins and rattles constituted the badges of office of rattlesnake shamans. To secure such ornaments was fraught with difficulty in tribes that had a taboo against killing these snakes. Keating (1824, p. 128; Dorman, 1881, p. 264) tells us that when a Potawatomi brave required a rattle for an ornament, he always apologized to the snake before killing it, and left a gift of tobacco beside the body.

The Fox and Sauk used rattles on the ends of feathers as head decorations (Wied-Neuwied, 1843, p. 104), as did the Kansa (Parkman, 1872, p. 19) and the Osage (Tixier, 1940, p. 208, but written in 1840). Skinner (1923–25, p. 128), with more detail, tells us that the Sauk sometimes dyed their eagle-feather war plumes scarlet and attached to their tips bits of ermine fur and snake rattles. He also says (1926, p. 248) that the Iowa wore rattlesnake-skin belts in one of their medicine dances. The Cherokee wore rattles on their heads (Mooney, 1900, p. 296; Lowie, 1910, p. 286). In one of their dances they wore masks having rattlesnakes carved on the foreheads (Speck and Brown, 1951, pp. 21, 62). G. B. Grinnell (1923, vol. 2, p. 280) reported that the Cheyenne used rattles as decorations in one of their dances. The Teja used necklaces of bone beads, deer hoofs, and rattlesnake rattles (Harby, 1895, p. 74). Fewkes (1898, p. 740) says that some Yuman tribes wore rattles around their necks. McGee (1898, p. 172, fig. 14) has pictured a necklace of human hair to which nine rattle strings were attached; this was worn by a young Seri warrior from near Kino Bay, Sonora.

In northern California it was customary for the rattlesnake shamans to wear rattler decorations as insignia of office. According to Dixon (1907, p. 481; Kroeber, 1925, p. 303), among the Shasta, the shamans, who were women, wore rattlesnake skins around the forehead, and around the neck a collar formed of the tail feathers of a woodpecker, to which several rattles were attached. These were worn only while the shaman treated a snake-bite case. Among the adjacent Klamath, the rattlesnake shamans were men (Spier, 1930, pp. 30, 109); they wore a rattlesnake skin around the neck and that of a bull snake as a bandoleer across the chest. There was also a stuffed rattler—among many other effigies—hung under the beams of the shaman's house. Spier also tells us (pp. 129, 214) that the men of this tribe customarily wore in their hair the rattles of any snakes they might have killed; the women did not do this.

Sometimes rattlesnake figures were used as painted decorations on the Indians' bodies. This practice was mentioned as early as 1761 by Charlevoix (1923, vol. 1, p. 339). Wied-Neuwied (1843, p. 374) describes a Mandan dance in which the two participants had their backs painted with transverse black stripes to indicate that the dancers represented rattlesnakes. Teit (1909, p. 299, fig. e) shows a Lillooet shaman with a rattlesnake tattooed on the forearm. Sometimes the picture on the Indian's body was used as a snake repellent or even as a snake-bite cure (Walduck, 1714, in Masterson, 1938, p. 214).

Some of the Hopi katcinas were pictured with rattlesnakes. Thus Fewkes (1903) shows, in plate 26, two or three that are holding rattlesnakes adorned with horns and plumes, and in plate 46 one has a rattler across the forehead.

Skins were sometimes applied to the decoration of hunting equipment. Wied-Neuwied (1843, p. 175) says that the Crow Indians encased their bows with rattlesnake skins. Wyeth (1853, p. 212) mentions the same usage by Indians of the South Pass of the Snake River, probably the Bannock.

In the graphic arts, rattlesnake designs were widely exhibited. Some were realistic, others were conventionalized, or had mythical appendages such as horns, plumes, and wings.[24] They dated back to the mound builders and to pueblos long abandoned. Rattlesnake carvings on stone discs and tablets, mostly from the mounds of the Southeast, are described and figured by Squier (1851, p. 224), Holmes (1883, p. 278), Henshaw (1883, p. 147), Peet (1886, pp. 215, 221), Spinden (1913, p. 243), C. S. Brown (1926, p. 228), Shetrone (1930, pp. 389, 399), Vaillant (1939, plates 17 and 38), and Douglas and D'Harnoncourt (1941, p. 87). One of the most perfect of these discs was found in Issaquena County, Mississippi, in 1870; it is of brown sandstone eight and a half inches in diameter and one inch thick and shows two intertwined rattlers.

Among the shell gorgets or circular ornaments found so plentifully in the mounds of the Southeast there is a type of frequent occurrence having a standardized rattlesnake design. Since these discs are incised by hand, no two are exactly alike, yet all show clearly a coiled rattler with head in the center, blotches along the back, and rattles, the latter indicated by a series of V-shaped marks on the outer edge of the circle. Example rattler gorgets will be found described and illustrated in Holmes (1883, pp. 289–93), Peet (1886, pp. 217–20), Thomas (1887, p. 64), Wilson (1895, pp. 914–15), Moorehead (1906, p. 114), Hartman (1907, p. 448), and Spinden (1913, p. 242). Most of them have been taken from mound excavations in Tennessee, North Carolina, and Georgia. The timber rattlesnake (*C. h. horridus*) seems to be the snake pictured, as might be expected. In one mound in Hamilton County, Ohio, a figurine of a plumed rattler formed of mica was unearthed (Willoughby and Hooton, 1922, p. 68).

Some early travelers have testified to the presence in religious edifices of carved idols representing rattlesnakes. De Charlevoix and Pénicaut mention such a figure of wood in a Natchez temple (Swanton, 1911, pp. 159, 160; Beals, 1932, p. 208; Swanton, 1946, p. 618). Similar figures were used by the Acaxee and Aztec (Beals, 1932, p. 208). The Navaho made a small rattler image for use in the treatment of an infant, ill because of his mother's having seen—during pregnancy—the death of a snake (Franciscan Fathers, 1910, p. 496).

Various utensils were decorated with animal figures, including rattlesnakes. Squier and Davis (1848, p. 268, fig. 186; Peet, 1886, p. 214) have shown a porphyry pipe so embossed, from one of the Mississippi Valley mounds. Peet (1886, p. 216, fig. 9) illustrates an ancient stone pipe along the shank of which four rattlesnakes lie stretched; this was from near Santa Fe, New Mexico. The rattles are quite well executed. Food bowls, pots, bottles, and vases, some of relatively recent date, were similarly incised with lively rattlesnake designs. Holmes (1886, p. 401; 1903, p. 91) shows an engraved bottle from Arkansas carrying two fine figures of plumed rattlers. He has also figured the fragment of a vase from Alabama showing the

---

[24] "The serpent, especially the rattlesnake, has always taken a leading place in the mythology and the art of the more cultured American races, and crest-plumes and wings have often been considered its proper attributes." W. H. Holmes, 1886, p. 402.

tails of three rattlers (1903, p. 107, plate 57; see also p. 114), and two cylindrical cup-shaped vases from Georgia, with rattlesnake designs (1903, p. 138, plates 118–19). Schaldach (1955, p. 312) has described a small stone bowl bearing the raised figure of a rattlesnake; it was attributed to the ancient Hohokam people of southern Arizona. Pucher (1945, p. 43) has figured a vase from Samaypata, Bolivia, with a fine rattler design.

Stevenson (1894, p. 84, plate 16; Bourke in Bloom, 1933–38, vol. 11, p. 192) has pictured a rattler decorating a ceremonial vase from the Sia (Zia) Pueblo of the Keres. Fewkes (1898, p. 670, plate 129e) shows a food bowl that carries the outline of a plumed rattler, from the abandoned Hopi pueblo of Sikyatki. Spinden (1913, p. 243) illustrates a bowl from Georgia. Shetrone mentions an Alabama pot decorated with a rattler, horned and feathered as in Mexican ornamentation (1930, pp. 142, 394, fig. 83). Most of the designs are too conventionalized or embellished to be recognized as particular rattlesnake species, although Holmes (1883, p. 290) thought that the Southeastern artifacts represented the timber rattler (*horridus*) and the eastern diamondback (*adamanteus*), the two large species found in that area today. Cushing (1896, p. 376; Swanton, 1946, p. 504), exploring Key Marco off the coast of Florida, found a hairpin of bone or ivory, carved at the upper end to represent the tail of a rattler.

G. W. James (1902) has discussed the use of rattlesnake designs in the baskets of various California Indian tribes, such as the Yokuts (pp. 59, 201); Saboba, Paiute, and Shoshoni (p. 241); and the Mono (pp. 254, 257). Curtis (1924, vol. 14, p. 172) also mentions the Yokuts baskets. Some of these designs are so conventionalized—rows of diamonds for example—that their derivation can only be substantiated by explanations from the Indians themselves. The Maidu used a double series of diamonds to represent a rattlesnake (Dixon, 1902a, p. 4, plate 3), and the Wintun (p. 18, plate 23) employed another arrangement of diamonds to indicate a rattler's head. These symbolical designs are discussed, with many illustrations, by Kroeber (1905, pp. 120, 137, 143, 156, 159, 160); other authors touching on the subject are Breazeale on the Pima (1923, p. 121), Spier and Sapir on the Wishram (1930, pp. 194, 196), and Voegelin (1938, p. 33) on the Tübatulabal. Robinson (1945, pl. 68, p. 146) has pictured two rattlesnake-design baskets of the Chemehuevi. Riddle (1955, p. 96) has shown a Yokuts basket carrying the conventional rattlesnake design of rows of diamonds.

Kroeber, in discussing the Cahuilla baskets (1908, p. 48), pointed out that figures of men and animals, including snakes and lizards, were quite realistically woven in baskets currently made for sale, whereas in baskets for their own use the Indians preferred to retain their older and simpler symbolical designs. Two Cahuilla baskets, kindly loaned by the Palm Springs Museum, are shown in figures 16:4 and 16:5. These are of the modern, realistic type. I noted, as a boy in the mountains of San Diego County, that the Diegueño and Luiseño Indians, no doubt spurred by the commercial demand, offered baskets decorated with realistic and unmistakable rattlesnake figures, quite different from their conventional representations. The tourists thought these especially desirable.

Rattler designs seem never to have been so popular in blankets and bead work as in baskets. One might have expected them in the extensive Navaho output but, according to the Franciscan Fathers (1910, p. 251), such designs were taboo

Fig. 16:4. Modern Cahuilla Indian basket with rattlesnake design, showing both coiled and outstretched poses.

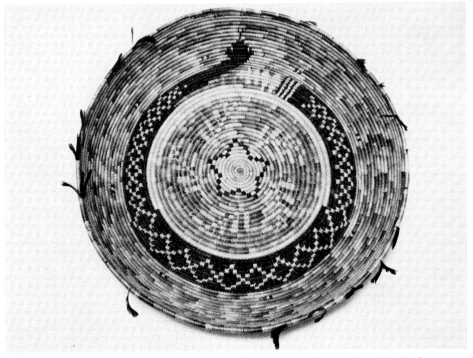

Fig. 16:5. Another modern Cahuilla design. The views are of the insides of the baskets.

(Baskets loaned by the Palm Springs Museum; photographs by R. Van Nostrand.)

on blankets, as they were in pottery as well (p. 286). The Huichol produced beautiful patterns for their blankets when inspired by putting their hands, first on a live rattlesnake, and then on their foreheads before they began to weave (Lumholtz, 1902, vol. 2, p. 234). The Seminole employed symbolic designs in their beadwork, two of which represented the diamondback and pigmy rattlers (Skinner, 1913, p. 71; Swanton, 1946, pp. 487, 624). The Klamath had a string figure or cat's cradle that was known as "A Rattlesnake and a Boy" (Jayne, 1906, p. 101).

The Indians, both ancient and recent, frequently used flat rock-surfaces as canvases for artistic expression. These designs are called pictographs if drawn or painted, and petroglyphs if carved, incised, or pecked (Renaud, 1936, p. 3). They often included animal figures, some of which were snakes, the rattler among them, as might be seen from attempted representations of rattles.

Mallery (1886, p. 225, fig. 148c) has illustrated a rather crudely executed rattler found on a sandstone rock near Morgantown, Monongalia County, West Virginia. Holmes (1890, pp. 219–20; also Mallery 1893, p. 476, plate 31) shows two far better executed figures found in a rock shelter in Harrison County, West Virginia. The rattles are indicated by short cross lines. Holmes considered these to be of comparatively recent date and probably of Algonkian origin. Brinton (1896, p. 201) describes a Chippewa petroglyph representing a god brandishing a rattlesnake as a symbol of lightning. Bartlett (1854, vol. 1, p. 172) shows a petroglyph of a rattler at Hueco Tanks near El Paso; and through the courtesy of Colonel M. L. Crimmins I have lately seen photographs of others from the same vicinity. More recent descriptions of Texas petroglyphs will be found in A. T. Jackson (1938, pp. 419, 421) and Kirkland (1939, pp. 60, 64). Renaud (1936, p. 41, plate 2, fig. 4) mentions figures, probably rattlesnakes, at Black Mesa, near Raton, New Mexico. Cosgrove (1947, p. 155) has shown a realistic rattler pictograph in Picture Cave, Hidalgo County, New Mexico. Reagan (1933, p. 551; see also Culin, 1901, p. 93) shows several petroglyphs of rattlers in Nine Mile Canyon, Utah. These are thought to be quite ancient, the work of the Basket Makers, Fremont Culture People, or the Pueblo of Pueblo II times, all Indian cultures of a time long past.

From Arizona, Mallery (1886, p. 47, fig. 18) has illustrated a rattlesnake figure among the Hopi inscriptions at Oakley Springs. Also in 1893 (p. 476, fig. 661) he described a crested serpent, having mammae and with rattles on the tail, at Canyon Segy, Arizona. This represented the god of fructification.

Farther west, petroglyphs are numerous, and serpents are often illustrated, although it is usually difficult to distinguish rattlesnakes from the other kinds. Strong and Schenck (1925, pp. 78, 80, 84) found the rattler eighth in order of frequency among animals pictured on rocks near The Dalles in Oregon. These pictographs were probably made by the Snake branch of the Shoshoni (p. 90). Cressman (1937, p. 27) figures a snake with eight rattles indicated by dots; this is at Abert Rim, east of Abert Lake, Oregon. In Washington, Cain (1950, p. 56) found that, out of 40 petroglyph sites, snakes, many of which were rattlers, were shown in 12. Steward (1929, p. 191) found snake pictures common in the Southwest, but few could be identified as rattlers. There is one at Eagle Pass (p. 83) and another at Coyote Wells, both in San Bernardino County, California, that are no doubt rattlers. Dr. Anna H. Gayton was told a story by the Yokuts to explain a rattler pictograph (p. 135) in Fresno County.

Such interior paintings as the Indians made occasionally included rattlers among the other animals depicted. Many of these were lost because of their impermanent character. Mrs. Parsons (1932, p. 210, plate 17) shows such a painting at Isleta, New Mexico. Spinden (1913, p. 246) mentions a painting of a horned rattler on a buffalo-skin lodge of the Dakota Indians.

Mosaics or ground paintings composed of brightly colored sands, carefully placed to form intricate designs, were extensively used by the Southwestern Indians in connection with various rituals. They were usually surrounded or embellished with ceremonial objects. These pictures, although perpetuated only by memory, seem to have been executed year after year virtually without change in detail.

Snakes were frequent elements of the sand designs; some were mythical or conventionalized in character, others realistic. The rattlesnake may occasionally be recognized, although often embellished with plumes or wings. One example of these sand paintings is that prepared by the Antelope Clan in preparation for the Hopi Snake dance (Dorsey and Voth, 1902, plate 92; Fewkes *et al.*, 1894, opposite p. 18; Fewkes, 1897, plates 71–73). Figure 16:1 is a reprint of Fewkes' plate 72. Although intended to picture lightning strokes, certain figures in this mosaic have unmistakable resemblances to snakes, which, we should judge from the nature of the ceremony, are rattlers. The Navaho also prepare sand paintings containing what seem to be rattlesnakes (Matthews, 1887, plate 15; 1898, p. 231). Kluckhohn and Wyman (1940, p. 133; see also Hannum, 1945, p. 149) state that, in the sand mosaics laid down by the Navaho for the ceremonial devised for the treatment of snake bite, the snake's tongues are red if the patient has been bitten by a poisonous snake, or yellow if the snake was nonvenomous. There are also differences depending on the sex of the patient.

In California the Diegueño periodically made a ground painting representing the universe, containing, as a part of the creation myth, two large rattlesnakes (Waterman, 1908, p. 41; 1910, p. 303; Dubois, 1908, pp. 92, 178; Gifford and Block, 1930, p. 55). A Luiseño mosaic symbolized a rattler by a series of diamonds end to end (Strong, 1929, p. 314). The Akwa'ala, allied to the Diegueño, used a sand mosaic in connection with their snake-bite treatment (Drucker, 1941, p. 161).

What has been said about the use of the rattlesnake in artistic expression had reference to the tribes of the United States and northern Mexico. In the higher civilizations of the Mayans, Toltecs, and Aztecs, the serpent had an even superior place in mythology and religion. One might expect that the rattlesnake would have a reduced importance in these more southerly areas, since it is no longer so predominant there—compared with other kinds of snakes—in point of either size or danger, as it is in most parts of the United States. Nevertheless, although the reptilian figures so prevalent on Mexican temple walls and in the codices are stylized and embellished to such an extent that they often retain little resemblance to a rattlesnake—or, indeed, to any snake—the rattles may still be distinguished. For example, there is the fantastically conventionalized serpent whose elements have been explained by Spinden (1913, p. 34, fig. 22; 1946, p. 90, fig. 26b). Here the flourishes of design have transported the creature beyond the realm of any reptile, living or extinct, yet the rattles are still present, although followed by a plume. Concerning the relative importance of the rattlesnake the following quotations are pertinent: "The serpent entered widely into the superstitions of the American nations and was conspicuous among their symbols. Whenever it appears, whether among the carvings of the Natchez, who, according to Charlevoix, placed it upon their altars as an object of worship, among the paintings of the Aztecs, or upon the temples of Central America, it is invariably the rattlesnake" (Peet, 1886, p. 215). "The serpent is seldom represented realistically; but we may safely infer that the rattlesnake was the prevailing model" (Spinden, 1913, p. 33). The place of the serpent—the rattlesnake in particular—in native Mexican (especially Mayan) mythology, and thus in their architecture and literature, cannot be further elaborated here. It is a subject upon which much has been and is being published, often with fine illustrations of rattlesnake designs from the façades of religious edifices or from the codices. The following are a few references in which such discussions and figures will be found: Bullock, 1825, vol. 2, p. 119; Deane, 1830, p. 267; Stephens, 1843, vol. 1, p. 302; vol. 2, p. 298; Squier, 1851, p. 145, figs. 24, 34, 49, 52–55, 61; Allen, 1881, pp. 284, 289, fig. 9, p. 316, figs. 87, 92, 93, p. 348, figs. 184g, h, m; Peet, 1886, p. 215; Jennings, 1889, p. 58; Nuttall, 1901, p. 261; Maler, 1901, pp. 62, 63, plates 18, 20; Seler, 1902–23, vol. 1, p. 187, fig. 34, p. 211, fig. 105, p. 564, fig. B; vol. 2, p. 745, fig. 32, p. 1051, fig. 1; vol. 3, p. 413, fig. 2, p. 461, fig. 3, p. 702, fig. 10; vol. 4, p. 134, fig. 100, p. 143, fig. 110, p. 680, figs. 791–95, 799, p. 681, fig. 808, p. 682, fig. 812, p. 683, fig. 815, p. 684, figs. 821–24, p. 689, fig. 835, p. 691, fig. 838, p. 692, fig. 839b, p. 694, fig. 845; Gordon, 1902, pp. 8, 17, 18, fig. 8, plate 13, a; Tozzer and Allen, 1910, p. 311, plate 9; Spinden, 1913, p. 32, figs. 22, 260; Joyce, 1914, p. 137, plate 11; Waterman, 1916, p. 345; Howey, 1928, p. 294; Beyer, 1933, p. 671, figs. 61–63, p. 673, fig. 123; Martín del Campo, 1937a, p. 495; Spinden, 1946, pp. 89, 98, 173, 175, 222, 232, fig. 26, plate 45; Proskouriakoff, 1950, p. 39.

To the Indians, rattles were important instruments for the production of music. Many kinds were constructed of deer hoofs, turtle shells, gourds, and other hollow objects. Although the rattle of the rattlesnake was a noise producer ready to hand, it never assumed any great importance, partly through taboo, but more because the sound that may be produced with it artificially—for no one can reach the vibrational speed of the rattlesnake's tail—is too faint to be effective. To some extent it was used in California, possibly more for magical reasons than as an efficient noise maker. Among the tribes using rattlesnake rattles were the Salinan (Mason, 1912, pp. 158, 177), Diegueño (Drucker, 1937b, p. 35), Sinkyone (Driver, 1939, p. 337), Achomawi, Wintu, and Maidu (Voegelin, 1942, pp. 94, 203), Yokuts and Mono (Aginsky, 1943, p. 425). For convenience in shaking, the rattles were usually attached to sticks. The Cherokee used one form of combination rattle, in which a gourd was surmounted with a long string of rattlesnake rattles (Speck and Brown, 1951, p. 22).

INDIAN FIELD KNOWLEDGE OF RATTLERS

The Indians imbued rattlesnakes with so many fanciful attributes—through myth, legend, and animism generally—that it is difficult to ascertain their relationships with the snakes on a purely materialistic plane, if, indeed, such a distinction can be made. As has been pointed out, many tribes had taboos against killing rattlers, usually through fear of retaliation. A few had no such reluctance to destroy these dangerous creatures, particularly dangerous to hunters roaming the woods without adequate protection on their legs.

Several of the early travel books or natural histories (P. Dudley, 1723, p. 292; Kalm, 1752–53, p. 316; 1758, p. 291; Lacépède, 1789, vol. 2, p. 412; Kerr, vol. 4, p. 267; Winterbotham, 1795, p. 406) have stated that the Indians would not traverse the woods during wet weather, because, through dampening, the warning rattle would be almost inaudible. It is to be doubted whether this inhibition was widespread. They were too expert woodsmen to place dependence on a rattler's always sounding off before striking; like all good hunters they must have known their best protection lay in keeping their eyes on the ground and watching their steps. Kalm (1752–53, p. 317) was told by the Indians of upper New York that rattlesnakes would not rattle while lying in wait for prey; and that they would not bite readily in midsummer (p. 54). Beals (1933, p. 394) says that, among the Nisenan of California, young hunters were advised by their elders to go around logs rather than over them, to avoid the chance of putting the foot on, or within striking distance of, a concealed rattler, which is sound advice.

Several early writers credit the Indians with a belief in the rattler's ability to capture its prey by fascination—indeed, they are said to have first brought this widespread theory to the attention of the whites (Lederer, 1672, p. 6; Mather, 1714, p. 67; Clayton, 1744, p. 149; Bossu, 1771, p. 361; Adair, 1775, p. 236; Lacépède, 1789, vol. 2, p. 409; Kerr's translation, 1802, vol. 4, p. 263). Lederer recounted an incident on March 9, 1669, when his three Indian guides told him that a rattler had only to fix its eye on a squirrel in a tree to cause it to descend and walk helplessly into the snake's waiting jaws. This question of fascination was the subject of a considerable discussion in natural history books and journals about 1800; I have treated it elsewhere (p. 1220). Whether the Indians really believed in fascination we cannot determine now; such a belief would involve a conflict between their powers of observation as woodsmen and their attribution of magical powers to the snake. Barton (1805, p. 167; see also *Gentleman's Magazine,* vol. 73, p. 253, 1803), related an Indian legend about a rattler as large as a tree, a huge snake that could charm any creature into its mouth, including Indians themselves, but he doubted that the Indians were believers in fascination. He thought it was this legend that caused the colonists to attribute to the Indians a belief in the power to secure prey by charming it.

The Pinto Indians (near Veracruz, Mexico) considered young rattlers much more dangerous than the old ones, which they deemed almost harmless (Naphegyi, 1868, p. 250). Hunter (1823, p. 179) said the Indians of the upper Missouri thought that rattlers were blind and sluggish in late summer because of the venom diffused in their systems.

I find little published on how the Indians caught rattlers alive, upon the few occasions when they wanted them. Hernández (1615, fol. 192^r; 1628, p. 329; Nieremberg, 1635, p. 269), speaking of Mexico, said some Indians caught them by the tail, holding them vertically as they squirmed and tried to reach their captors. [This can be done with safety if a snake be not so large that, in throwing the anterior part of its body sideways, when held at arm's length, it can reach the holder's body.] Brickell (1737, p. 145) states that the Indians defanged a snake by causing it to strike a red cloth, which they then jerked while the fangs were caught in it. The Meskwaki (Fox) chewed the tops of mountain mint, and placed the cud on the end of a stick that was held under the snake's mouth. The rattler, now insensible to danger, could be easily caught, or so they claimed (H. H. Smith, 1923–32, p. 226).

Much has been written of the ceremonial catching of rattlers by those tribes that used them in dances and other rituals, especially the Hopi, Yokuts, and Pomo (see, for example, Dorsey and Voth, 1902, p. 182; Kroeber, 1925, p. 504; Loeb, 1926, p. 375). The Yavapai sprinkled the prospective catch with a circle of dust (Gifford, 1936, p. 310).

According to I. Holmes (1823, p. 258), while many people think the number of rattles tells the age of the snake, some Indians believed it represented the number of the snake's victims.

Loeb (1926, p. 316) tells us that the Pomo Indians of California thought rattlesnakes sounded their rattles as a sign of good humor. The Wailaki washed themselves with a decoction of the fawn lily, which stopped rattlesnakes from having bad dreams, that is to say, reduced their irritability (Chestnut, 1902, p. 326). According to Foster (1944, p. 215), when a rattlesnake gave warning he was considered to be a good snake and was left unmolested; if he failed to rattle he was killed. Actually, if found in the open or on a rock pile, they were killed, whereas in brush it was deemed safest to pass around and ignore them. The Diegueño and Luiseño sometimes plugged rattlesnake holes to protect themselves (Drucker, 1937b, p. 42). Tome (1928, p. 35), writing of the Indians near Harrisburg, Pennsylvania, about 1800, says they protected themselves from rattlers by sleeping on pallets raised above ground and surrounded by fires.

The primitive Indians seem not to have used physical protection for their legs to so great an extent as might have been expected, preferring to depend on charms and repellents for safety. Nomland (1938, p. 107) says that the Bear River Indians of California used elkhide moccasins in their summer hunting as a protection against rattlers. Other leg coverings are mentioned by Tome (1928, p. 35), Tschiffely (1933, p. 214), Wuerttemberg (1938, p. 133, writing in 1835), and Whiting (1950, p. 27).

Some Indians may have burned brush to kill rattlesnakes; this was reported by the Karok Indians of California to Harrington (1932, p. 65). The Nisenan thought rattlesnakes were becoming more plentiful (Beals, 1933, p. 394) than they were in the old days, a rather doubtful conclusion. The Bear River thought there were none in their territory in olden times (Nomland, 1938, p. 111).

Speck (1923a, p. 273) tells us that certain northern tribes of Indians, having no knowledge of rattlers, do not ascribe venomous properties to the snakes that are found within their territories. This is of interest, since where venomous snakes are found, harmless snakes are also usually considered dangerous by primitive peoples, as, for example, the Wappo (Driver, 1936, p. 186). Of course, this is less often true in areas where rattlers are the only venomous snakes, since they are so easily identified by the rattles.

But the fear of harmless snakes is sometimes on a spiritual rather than a material plane, as is said by Speck (1946, p. 358) to be true of the Catawba. He also tells us that the Indians ordinarily classify animals by their exterior features and habits of motion (p. 356). The Indians seldom distinguished between rattlesnake species, except where there were extreme differences in size, color, or pattern, as was the case, for example, between the western diamond and the sidewinder. Stephen (1936, p. 756) tells us that the Hopi, when collecting rattlers for the dance at Shipaulovi in 1892, segregated them into four kinds by color—yellow, red, drab, and black. As a matter of fact, only one subspecies of rattler occurs naturally at the Hopi pueblos; this is the Arizona prairie rattlesnake (*Crotalus viridis nuntius*) a subspecies quite variable in color, ranging from yellowish or red, to red-brown, olive-brown, and olive-green. However, other subspecies occur in northern Arizona, including *C. v. viridis, C. v. cerberus,* and *C. v. abyssus,* and these may occasionally be brought to the Hopi pueblos by travelers, although this was probably not the case in the buckboard days of 1892.

Whether because of mystical attributes, or the actual danger from snake bite, it is probable that most Indians gave rattlesnakes a wide berth. Fanny Kelly (1872, p. 30) stated that the sudden rattling of a snake alarmed some Sioux Indians and prevented them from finding her husband, who was hiding from them.

From the above outline, it will be seen how few reports we have of the attitude of the Indians toward rattlesnakes as material creatures, or of their knowledge of rattler habits and life history; for, as was true of other wild creatures, rattlesnakes were viewed through a haze of animism and attributes of magical powers.

RATTLESNAKES AS FOOD

Although rattlesnakes were never an important part of the Indian food supply, some tribes did not hesitate to eat them, particularly if hard pressed. Hernández, as early as 1615 (fol. 193ʳ; Nieremberg, 1635, p. 269), stated that the Mexican Indians ate rattlers and preferred them to domestic fowls. Brickell (1737, p. 146), Charlevoix (1761, 1923 ed., vol. 1, pp. 229, 339), Wynne (1770, p. 244), Crèvecoeur (1782, p. 238), Pennant (1787, p. 89), La Rochefoucault Liancourt (1799, p. 181), Kerr (1802, vol. 4, p. 268, quoting Lacépède, vol. 2, p. 413, 1789), Winterbotham (1795, p. 406), and Bingley (1803, vol. 3, p. 78) are among the writers of colonial and later days who mention the eating of rattlesnakes by the Indians, mostly having reference to tribes inhabiting the eastern or central United States. But Wied-Neuwied (1843, pp. 195, 347) lists various tribes, including the Mandan and Assiniboin, that would not eat snakes of any kind, although others ate them to cure disease (p. 37). Champlain stated that the Indians would eat rattlers after they had removed the heads and tails (Biggar, 1932–36, vol. 1, p. 54).

It is to be doubted whether rattlesnakes ever comprised more than a very minor part of the diet of any Indians, since the flesh available on all but the largest snakes is quite small in quantity. Probably the colonial writers thought the idea somewhat sensational, which was their reason for mentioning it. But where food was scarce, an opportune catch of a rattler might save a life, just as it sometimes did during the westward migration of the whites. Some of the early writers said the Indians were careful to eat no rattlers that had bitten themselves.

In some instances, rattlers were eaten because of some particular virtue thought to be contained in the flesh. Josselyn (1672, p. 38; 1675, p. 114) claimed that the Indians of New England, to refresh themselves while traveling, would seize a live rattler by the neck and tail, tear off the skin with their teeth, and eat the flesh. This practice may have been related to the more widespread performance of the same rite to improve or safeguard the teeth (see p. 1166), or to the ceremonial eating of an animal to acquire some of its characteristics.

Bergen (1899, p. 70) records an Indian belief, prevalent in Vermont, that eating rattlesnakes would promote longevity. Mooney (1900, p. 296) tells of a Cherokee theory that eating the flesh of the rattler renders ball players more terrifying to their opponents, but also has the unfortunate effect of making them cross to their wives.

When the available reports on snake-eating are classified, we find tribal differences, and even many that are intratribal. Some ate no reptiles of any kind, others harmless snakes but not rattlers, while still others preferred rattlesnakes because of their relatively greater bulk. Our knowledge of the primitive customs of the Eastern Indians is not particularly accurate, as many of the early reports by travelers and colonists were highly colored. The Southern, and especially the Western groups, had been less affected by white contacts prior to the advent of trained ethnologists to record their habits. But it was not greater accuracy of reporting that makes snake-eating seem more prevalent in the Southwest; rather, it was because the country was more barren and food scarcer. Here taboos were changed to conform to necessity; the Indians could not afford to be too particular.

Tribes, other than those in the West, that ate rattlers were few. One of these was the Seminole (H. H. Smith, 1923–32, p. 198). Stone (1932, p. 31) reports that the Micmac and Penobscot ate a snake soup. The Indians of Florida (Maynard, 1884, p. 8) and the Choctaw were said to eat rattlesnakes (Swanton, 1946, p. 295), and so were the Comanche (Smith and Smith, 1927, pp. 66, 123).

The following Great Basin tribes, or some of their subdivisions, ate rattlesnakes at least occasionally: Ute (Stewart, 1942, p. 244), Paiute (Drucker, 1937b, p. 8; Stewart, 1942, p. 244), Gosiute (Stewart, 1942, p. 244; Steward, 1943b, p. 299), Shoshoni (Steward, 1941, p. 277; 1943b, p. 299), Panamint (Driver, 1937, p. 62), Mono or Owens Valley Paiute (Steward, 1933, p. 255; Driver, 1937, p. 62). The California tribes that engaged in this practice to some extent were the Shasta (Voegelin, 1942, p. 59), Maidu (Loeb, 1933, p. 174), Yokuts (Curtis, 1924, vol. 14, p. 135; Kroeber, 1925, p. 526; Driver, 1937, p. 62), Costano (Harrington, 1942, p. 7), Salinan (Mason, 1912, p. 122; Harrington, 1942, p. 7), Chumash (Harrington, 1942, p. 7), Serrano (Drucker, 1937b, p. 8), Gabrielino (Kroeber, 1925, p. 631), Luiseño (Drucker, 1937b, p. 8), Cahuilla (Hooper, 1920, p. 357), Diegueño (Drucker, 1937b, p. 8), the desert Diegueño, Cupeño, and mountain Cahuilla (Tuthill, 1951, p. 26), and Yuma (Drucker, 1937b, p. 8). In Baja California and mainland Mexico, the following were reputed to be rattlesnake eaters upon occasion: Kiliwa (Meigs, 1939, p. 25), Cahitá (Beals, 1943, p. 15), and Tarahumare (Bennett and Zingg, 1935, p. 128).

From the following tribes we have reports that snakes were not eaten: Seminole (McNight, 1951, p. 22); Cherokee (Gilbert, 1943, p. 346); Creeks, Chickasaw, Caddo, Chitimacha (Swanton, 1946, p. 295); Menominee (Hoffman, 1896, p. 287); Cree (Mandelbaum, 1940, p. 199); Laguna (Bloom, 1933–38, vol. 12, p. 275); Tewa (Henderson and Harrington, 1914, p. 47); Hopi (Simmons, 1942, pp. 11, 55); Navaho (Tschopik, letter); Walapai (Mook, 1935, p. 76); Yavapai (Gifford,

1936, p. 268); Pima (Russell, 1908, p. 83); Klikitat, Tenino, Umatilla, Wenatchi, Sanpoil, Kalispell, Shuswap, Lillooet, Lower Thompson, Kutenai, Flathead, Coeur d'Alêne (Ray, 1942, p. 130); Sinkaietk or southern Okanagon (Sapir *et al.*, 1938, p. 25); Bannock (Steward, 1943b, p. 299); Shoshoni (Curtis, 1926, vol. 15, p. 61; Shimkin, 1947, p. 278); Sanpoil, Nespelem (Ray, 1932, p. 90); Tolowa (Drucker, 1937a, p. 232); Takelma (Drucker, 1937a, p. 294); Paviotso (northern Paiute), Washo, Achomawi (Stewart, 1941, p. 419); Surprise Valley Paiutes (Kelley, 1932, p. 91); Klamath, Modoc, Atsugewi, Achomawi, Wintu, Maidu, Nisenan (Voegelin, 1942, p. 59); Maidu (Dixon, 1905, p. 184); Nisenan (Beals, 1933, p. 346); Atsugewi (Garth, 1953, p. 135); Yana (Sapir and Spier, 1943, p. 252); Tolowa, Galice, Tututni, Coos, Siuslaw, Alsea, Tillamook (Barnett, 1937, p. 194); Shasta (Dixon, 1907, p. 424); Kalekau, Kato, Lassik, Yuki (Essene, 1942, p. 54); Kato (Loeb, 1932, p. 46); Nomlaki (Goldschmidt, 1951, p. 401); Wappo (Driver, 1936, p. 186); Patwin (Kroeber, 1932, pp. 277, 294); Miwok (Curtis, 1924, vol. 14, p. 135); Tübatulabal (Voegelin, 1938, p. 12); Owens River Paiute (Mono), Kern River (Driver, 1937, p. 62); Gabrielino (Hoffman, 1885, p. 9); Diegueño (Spier, 1923, p. 313).

Some discrepancies will be found between these two lists of the Indians who did and did not eat rattlesnakes, in that some tribes will be found in both (e.g., Diegueño and Seminole). This inconsistency has resulted either from differences between intratribal divisions, or discrepancies between statements made to reporting ethnologists by their Indian informants. An example of subtribal differences has been reported among the Yokuts and Western Mono by Gayton (1948, pp. 14, 180, 224).

A few details of the customs and taboos involved in eating rattlers will be of interest. The Sanpoil and Nespelem believed that eating a snake would result in withering and death because of the poison of the reptile (Ray, 1932, p. 90). Some of the Shoshoni and Gosiute would eat rattlesnakes if hard pressed for food (Steward, 1941, p. 277; 1943b, p. 299); this was also true of the Walapai (Mook, 1935, p. 76). According to Bennett and Zingg (1935, p. 128), the Tarahumare of northern Mexico would eat them after removing the heads.

In California, the Bear River Indians refused to eat even ground squirrels because these squirrels associated with rattlers (Nomland, 1938, p. 111). Some of the Northwest Hill Maidu claimed to eat rattlers, but most of the tribe were afraid of their bites (Loeb, 1933, p. 174). The southern Miwok ate gopher and garter snakes, but rattlesnakes were used only for medicinal purposes. Among the central Miwok, the aged ate snakes, including rattlers (Barrett and Gifford, 1933, p. 137). According to Kroeber (1925, p. 526), the Chukchansi rejected gopher and garter snakes, and even frogs, but did eat rattlers. No Yana would eat a snake; they feared even the harmless species (Sapir and Spier, 1943, p. 252).

DONT TREAD ON ME

17.   Post-Columbian Knowl-edge of Rattlesnakes

INTRODUCTION

Europeans, coming to the American continent in successive waves as explorers, traders, and immigrants, gradually became familiar with the wild life of the New World. Among the novelties they found was the rattlesnake. Economically it was not important, even less so then than in later years when agricultural development made rodent control more urgent. Probably the outstanding impact of these snakes upon the colonists was that they constituted an additional hazard, one, however, that could not be considered serious, compared with the major dangers from Indians, starvation, and disease. No doubt rattlers did impose some restraint upon the timid, abetted at times by the sensationalism of those who wrote accounts of their experiences in the new land. Rattlesnakes were often a subject of some concern to people going into the woods (see p. 955). It is therefore of interest to trace the gradual accumulation of knowledge regarding them during the early colonial period.

HISTORY OF PUBLISHED DESCRIPTIONS

One might have expected that when the earliest reports of the rattlesnake reached Europe there would be a considerable interest in so strange a creature—a snake with a peculiar caudal appendage with which it could make a violent hissing sound. However, it must be remembered that those were the days when the natural history books contained apparently authentic descriptions of mermaids, seven-headed dragons, and other really noteworthy creatures. So the rattlesnake had severe competition as a novelty, and its advent into the European consciousness was slow and unimpressive, despite its being one of the distinctive oddities of New World animal life.[1]

Although I have looked through a considerable number of early travel and natural history books in search of rattlesnake references, I have no illusions as to

[1] Charles A. Lesueur, the French-American naturalist, while at the New Harmony, Indiana, co-operative community in 1825, painted a drop curtain that pictured Niagara Falls and a rattlesnake as the two natural features most characteristically American (Weiss and Ziegler, 1931, p. 168).

the completeness of my list. Its very meagerness must testify to its inadequacy; I have no doubt there is many a narrative of some voyage, with an incidental mention of rattlesnakes of which I have no record.

The early accounts of rattlers are of more than chronological interest. We may find in them the genesis of many of the queer beliefs so long current, some of which have not yet been rejected. For the old naturalists exerted a tremendous industry and erudition in the transmission of myths and old wives' tales. As they often failed to give credit to the prior writers whose material they appropriated, it is usually impossible to be sure that any story has been traced to its source.

In this historical chapter, I shall mention few works published subsequent to 1750, since rattlesnake observations contained in later works are cited under the appropriate subjects of other chapters.

It would be interesting to know in what letter or report, and by which explorer, the rattlesnake was first mentioned. Countless early communications, never yet published, are still scattered through the archives and libraries of the Old World; among these there must be many a noteworthy comment on the fauna of the New World.

The earliest publications alluding to rattlesnakes that I have found were by Spanish and Portuguese explorers, and therefore these will be mentioned first. Also, the early published statements will be segregated from the early written but unpublished statements; for the latter, although important as evidences of the knowledge of the time, were not then made available to readers, and thus did not influence the succeeding writers of that day.

The earliest printed mention of the rattlesnake that has come to my attention is contained in *La Chronica del Peru,* by Pedro de Cieça (Cieza) de Leon, published in Anvers (Antwerp) in 1554. He says (fol. 25; see Markham translation, 1864, p. 43): "There are other snakes, not so large as this one, which make a noise when they walk [move] like the sound of bells. If these snakes bite a man they kill him." There are two evidences that the author referred to rattlesnakes: first, the use of the term "cascabel" (or "caxcabel" in another printing of the same date), a term already applied to the rattle of the rattlesnake, to judge from unpublished reports of the same period; and, secondly, because De Cieça traveled to Peru along the coasts of Venezuela and Colombia, where rattlesnakes are prevalent.

The next printed record, located through a suggestion by Dr. George S. Myers of Stanford University, is to be found in Pero de Magalhães de Gandavo's *Historia da Provincia Sancta Cruz,* an account of Brazil published in Lisbon in 1576. This rare book has been reprinted in facsimile and translated from the Portuguese by John B. Stetson, Jr. (1922, 2 vols.). The remarks on the rattler (fol. 24^r, of the original; vol. 2, p. 63 of the translation) are as follows: "There are others [snakes] of another species, not so large as the former, but more poisonous. They carry at the end of their tail something like a rattle ["cascavel" in the original] and wherever they go they keep on sounding it; and whoever hears this takes care to protect himself from them."

There is a similarity evident in the Cieça and Magalhães statements, although the latter leaves no doubt of the snake intended, as the "cascavel" is carried at the end of the tail. In both accounts the idea is conveyed that the rattle sounds continuously whenever the snake moves, a common error of the early descriptions, and a further proof that Cieça alluded to the rattlesnake.

Following Magalhães, the next published work in Spanish or Portuguese that contained mention of the rattlesnake, this time with a full description, was Francisco Hernández' *Quatro Libros de la Naturaleza, y Animales que Están Recevidos en el Uso de Medicina en la Nueva España.* . . . [City of] Mexico, 1615, fol. 191ᵛ. This was reprinted in Rome in Latin under the title *Rerum Medicarum Novae Hispaniae Thesaurus seu Plantarum, Animalium, Mineralium Mexicanorum Historia.* Two of these Latin editions were published in 1628 and 1651, respectively; they differ only in the title page (see Paoli, 1940).

Some of the details given by Hernández in this first extensive description of the rattlesnake are as follows: It is called "la señora de las serpientes" as well as "teuchtlacoçauhqui."[2] It grows to a length of four feet or more. The color description is obviously that of the Central American rattler (*C. d. durissus*), but the author goes on to say that there are other species of various colors. One found near Colima, Mexico, has a retractile throat fan; evidently there has been a confusion here with some lizard. The bite is fatal if powerful remedies are not immediately available. When annoyed the snake throws itself into a defensive coil, from which it can face an enemy in any direction. The best treatment for the bite is to bury the afflicted limb in the earth until the pain ceases. This snake moves with great speed, so that the natives call it "ocozoatl," the name of a wind.[3] It has a rattle for each year of its age. It has black eyes and a pair of curved fangs like a dog's teeth. The bite causes fissures in the body of the victim, followed by death within 24 hours.

The Indians catch and hold rattlesnakes up by the tail from which they dangle helplessly in spite of their squirming and rattling. People who keep them in captivity say they can live a year without food or water. The head, if cut off, will survive 10 days or more. They are said to grow to a very large size in the province of Panico [Pánuco, Mexico], where people tame them for amusement. The venom comes out through the fangs, which are hollow. Some say they have live young but this is false [actually it is true]. When annoyed they rattle furiously, making a great noise, but they attack no one unless molested.

The Mexican (i.e., Indian) doctors use the fangs as lancets, puncturing the necks of their patients—at the back—to relieve headaches. The fat is used as an ointment to alleviate pain and reduce swellings. The Indians say the flesh is better than that of poultry. If wrapped in straw or cloth, rattlers become tame. The head of a rattlesnake, if bound to one's throat, will cure sore throat or fever. As a cure for the bite, a poultice of human excrement or of certain plants is to be recommended.

Although Hernández' account is typical of the early natural histories in its

---

[2] In the Latin editions, *teuhtlacot zauhqui.*

[3] This obvious confusion with some other snake—some racerlike creature, no doubt—found its way into many natural histories during the next 150 years, at least. It may have arisen through a misinterpretation of what the natives told Hernández. One of their supreme deities was Quetzalcoatl, the bird-serpent, alternately known as "Ehecatl," the air, and "Yolcuat," the rattlesnake (Brinton, 1896, p. 214; see also Spence, 1923, p. 118, and Spinden, 1946, p. 175). This is evidently an example of an Indian statement having reference to a being on a supernatural plane that was wrongly interpreted by the explorer as applicable to an ordinary animal. Such confusions, arising from the translation of the mysticism of the natives into European factual reports, were common.

lack of order in arrangement—the recurrence of remedies, for example—yet it contains much sound information as well as the first printed statements of several still-current myths.

Hernández not only published the first full-length account of the rattlesnake, but also the first picture, although this did not appear until the Latin edition of 1628 (p. 329). The engraving shows a rattler in its resting coil and is rather

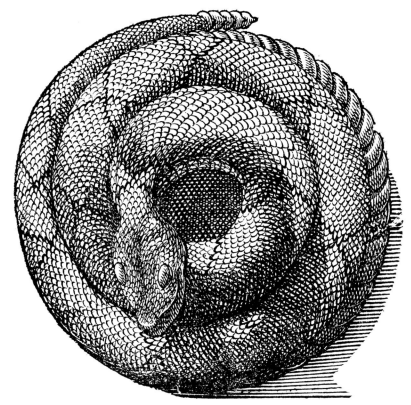

Fig. 17:1. The earliest illustration of a rattlesnake in a book. (From Francisco Hernández, *Rerum Medicarum Novae Hispaniae Thesaurus seu Plantarum Animalium Mineralium Mexicanorum Historia*, Rome, 1628, p. 329.)

well executed (fig. 17:1). For this, Goode (1901, p. 366) properly gives him credit (see also Sarton, 1944, p. 28, and Klauber, 1948, p. 334).

Hernández originally wrote in Latin; the 1615 edition was a translation into Spanish by Francisco Ximenez, under whose name references to this book are occasionally cited. To add to the bibliographic confusion, Joannes Faber's name sometimes appears in connection with the Latin editions, as well as that of Nardus Antonius Recchus, who may have been responsible for the medicinal observations.

Following Hernández, brief allusions to rattlesnakes were made by Father Estevan de Perea in 1632 (ed. 1901, p. 361; Bloom, 1933, p. 228), and by Vásquez de Espinosa (1948, p. 197) in a publication begun in 1630. The next full-length description of the rattlesnake to appear was that of Johann Nieremberg (1635, pp. 268–69). Little need be said of this since it seems to have been appropriated in its entirety from Hernández, although no credit was given to the latter. The picture (fig. 17:2) is in some details an improvement over Hernández', particularly as the tail is curved away from the body so that the rattle may be more clearly seen. However, the rattle has been rotated so that the wide side, instead of the narrow edge, is incorrectly shown as the top.

We come now to the rattlesnake descriptions of G. Piso (1648, p. 41) and G. Marcgravius (1648, p. 240) based upon researches in Brazil. Their two accounts are usually bound together, although paged separately. There is a common title page with credit given to Joannes de Laet for an appendix and illustrations, leading to some bibliographic confusion, as occasionally the entire work is attributed to De Laet. The text is in Latin. Piso says the rattler makes a sound like a bell and is very swift. It attacks with either the teeth or the rattle, the latter being the more quickly fatal. It adds a rattle a year to the string. Various antidotes are suggested, including incision, suction, and cauterization. There is a figure of a rattlesnake in a crawling position, with the usual vertical undulations of the old prints (fig. 17:3). The rattle, although quite small, is well executed. Marcgravius' section of the report contains no rattlesnake figure, although the description is quite complete. He mentions the dorsal scale protuberances so characteristic of the South American rattler. He says he received a skin from the New Netherlands (i.e., New York), where these snakes are likewise found.

In 1653 appeared the volume on serpents of J. Jonstonus' very popular natural history, a book that represented a great advance over the works of Gesner, Aldrovandus, and others who had preceded him, at least if we may judge from the snake section of his work. However, he still retained many entirely fanciful descriptions and the figures of mythical creatures. Jonstonus was essentially a compiler, and the rattlesnake material is derived from Marcgravius, Piso, and Nieremberg—and hence Hernández—who are given due credit. This occupies pp. 26–27 of the first edition (1653) and pp. 23–25 of the second (1657). Jonstonus' figure of the rattler is copied from Nieremberg, but is not so lifelike as the original. Jonstonus' work was published in Latin, as was usual in scientific treatises of the day, regardless of the country of origin. It was never translated into English in its entirety.

It is to be assumed that the Mexican edition of Hernández (1615) was not well known in Europe, but one might think that after its printing in Rome (1628), as well as Nieremberg's pirated publication in Antwerp (1635), the fame of the rattlesnake would have become fairly widespread. Yet Topsell, in the second edition of his exceedingly popular natural history in English (1658), has failed to mention it, for he continued to follow Gesner (1587), as he did in his first edition (1608). This was a loss to the British children of that day.

One of the other works of the time exclusively on snakes, Aldrovandus' *Serpentum et Draconū Historiae*, 1640, contains the interesting statement (p. 6) that the Spaniards have observed a snake which they call "cascavella" because it makes a sound like a bell. It is thought the sound is produced because the snake is armed with hard and mobile scales, and makes the noise by shaking the scales. This may be a confusion upon the part of Aldrovandus of the rattler with the

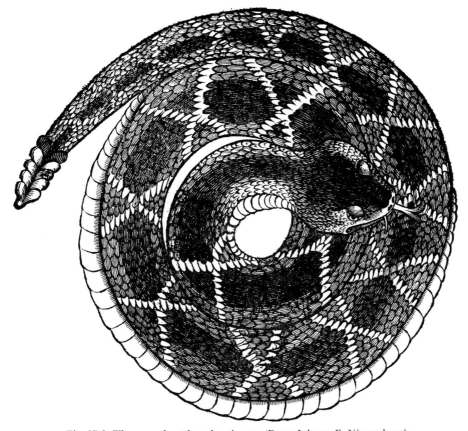

Fig. 17:2. The second rattlesnake picture. (From Johann E. Nieremberg's
Historia Naturae, Antwerp, 1635, p. 268.)

Fig. 17:3. An early crawling rattlesnake. (From Guilielmus Piso's
De Medicina Brasiliensi, Leyden, 1648, p. 41.)

saw-scaled viper, *Echis carinatus,* of Asia and Africa, which makes a noise by
rubbing two loops of the body together, the friction of the scales causing a rasp-
ing sound.

Before leaving the Spanish-Portuguese explorers for the English, I should like
to mention a few observations made by Latin American travelers, which observations remained unpublished until long after they were written. Thus these did
not influence subsequent writers of the period, but they are of interest in showing
what the explorers had learned in the field, and also what myths were then current.

One of these was by Bernal Díaz del Castillo in his *Historia Verdadera de la
Conquista de la Nueva-España.* His account of Cortez' campaign was written in

1568, but not published until 1632.[4] He wrote it, so he says, to correct the many inaccuracies contained in the history of the same campaign by Francisco López de Gomara, whose *Historia General de las Indias y Conquista de Mexico,* had appeared in 1552. Gomara made no mention of rattlers—or at least I have found none—but Díaz did, for on fol. 69ʳ (Keating translation, 1800, p. 142) he says: "In this accursed place [the zoo at Montezuma's temple of sacrifice] were many vipers, and poisonous serpents which have at their tails somewhat that sounds like castanets [*cascabeles* in the original]; these were the most dangerous of all, and were kept in vessels filled with feathers, where they reared their young, and were fed the flesh of human beings and dogs."

Among other manuscripts of the time containing mention of rattlesnakes— not published, however, until many years later—were Diego de Landa's *Relación de las Cosas de Yucatán,* written in 1566 but first published in 1864 (see Landa, 1937, 1938); Juan López de Velasco's *Geografía y Descripción Universal de las Indias . . . 1571 al de 1574,* published in 1894; and Gabriel Soares de Sousa's *Tratado Descriptivo do Brasil em 1587,* published in part in 1825, and in full in 1851 (see Soares de Sousa, 1938). Landa mentions rattlesnakes only briefly, saying that they are very large and dangerous and have rattles (*cascabeles*) on their tails (1937, p. 100; 1938, p. 233). López de Velasco refers to the snake as a "cascabel," and describes it as having small bladders on the tail that make a noise like a small bell (*cascabel*). Soares de Sousa (p. 308) says rattlers are small and venomous. The Portuguese call them "snakes of the rattle" (*cobras de cascavel*). He likens the rattle to a bird lure; he says it sounds when they move, so they are noticed and thus passersby are protected. The Indians, according to Soares de Sousa, believe the rattle to be more dangerous than the bite, an idea again mentioned by Piso some 60 years later, so this must have been a myth well grounded in native lore. And we find current as early as 1587 the imperishable myth that a rattle is added annually to the snake's string, thus showing its age. This idea must have been of native rather than European origin.

There were at least three expeditions to the Rio Grande pueblos of New Mexico in the sixteenth century, that of Friar Marcos de Niza in 1539, of Francisco Vásquez Coronado in 1540, and that of Father Augustín Rodríguez and Francisco Sánchez Chamuscado in 1581, followed by a rescue party under Antonio de Espejo in the succeeding year. Although all of these expeditions certainly encountered rattlesnakes, and Coronado was supposed to have mentioned them (Bandelier, 1930, p. 378; MacClary, 1939b, p. 23), it is only in the Gallegos and Obregón manuscript accounts of the Rodríguez-Chamuscado expedition (not published until many years later) that definite allusions to these snakes have been found.[5] These references have to do with a snake dance seen at the pueblos, in which live rattlers were held in the mouths of the participants, as in the Hopi dance (Gallegos, 1581, copy of ms. in the Newberry Library; Twitchell, 1914, vol. 1, p. 461; Mecham, 1917, p. 58; Hammond and Rey, 1927, pp. 247, 346). Again the word used for the rattle was "cascabel," showing that this term was well established by 1580 in the accounts of such widely separated places as New Mexico, Yucatán, Venezuela (or Colombia), and Brazil.

---

[4] Goode (1901, p. 369) incorrectly credits Díaz del Castillo with the first printed record of the rattlesnake.

[5] De Niza mentions (Baldwin, 1926, pp. 25, 51) calabashes decorated with rows of rattles (cascabeles), but this refers to some type of rattle other than the rattle of the rattlesnake.

Among the French explorers who wrote of rattlesnakes at an early date, but whose work was not published until later, was Champlain. In his *Brief Discours des Choses plus Remarquables que Samuel Champlain de Brouage a Reconneues aux Indes Occidentalles* written about 1602, one of the plates shows a plumed rattlesnake with a ball on the end of its tail, suggesting a child's rattle, of which he says "at the end of the tail they have a rattle [*sonnette* in the original] which makes a noise as they glide along. They are very dangerous with their teeth, and with their tail." (Biggar, 1932–36, vol. 1, p. 54, plate 46.)

The first published mention of the rattlesnake in English, as far as I know, was made by Capt. John Smith in 1612. This is contained in his *A Map of Virginia, with a Description of the Countrey, the Commodities, People, Government and Religion*. Speaking of the clothing and decorations worn by the Indians, he says (p. 20): "Some on their heads weare the wing of a bird or some large feather, with a Rattel. Those Rattels are somewhat like the chape[8] of a Rapier but lesse, which they take from the taile of a snake." The same statement is contained in Smith's *The Generall Historie of Virginia, New England and the Summer Isles*, 1624, p. 30.

The first use of the word "rattlesnake" was also made in connection with an Indian custom. Edward Winslow in 1624, in *Good Newes from New-England*, wrote: "This messenger ... leaving for him a bundle of new arrowes, lapped in a rattle Snakes skin" (p. 2); and, further, "he signified to the Governour that to send the rattle Snakes skin in that manner imported enmitie ..." (p. 3).

Of the rattlesnake as a live creature, the first English report is that of the Rev. Francis Higgeson (or Higginson) in *New-England's Plantation; or a Short and True Description of the Commodities and Discommodities of That Country*. This pamphlet of 26 pages was published in London in 1630. Says Dr. Higgeson (p. 12):

> Yea there are some Serpents called Rattle Snakes that have Rattles in their Tayles, that will not flye from a man as others will, but will flye upon him and sting him so mortally that hee will dye within a quarter of an houre after, except the partie stinged have about him some of the root of an Herbe called Snakeweed to bite on, and then he shall receive no harme: but yet seldom falles it out that any hurt is done by these. About three yeares since, an Indian was stung to death by one of them, but wee heard of none since that time.

We see in this report how early the faith in plant remedies ascribed to Indian knowledge became established among the colonists. Capt. John Smith's first use of the complete term "rattlesnake" occurs in his *Advertisements for the Unexperienced Planters of New-England, or Anywhere*, London, 1631, p. 30, where, in enumerating the complaints of the colonists, he mentions "the danger of the rattell snake."[7]

William Wood in his *New England's Prospect*, 1634, p. 47, describes the timber rattler in some detail. The teeth are as sharp as needles, and, although the neck is no thicker than a man's thumb, the snake can swallow a squirrel. The bite

---

[8] The metal protective tip of the scabbard.

[7] We often think of the early colonists as coming over entirely to secure religious and political freedom. But they came also for economic reasons, stimulated by publications that stressed the manifest blessings of the country beyond the seas. And just as some of the early accounts of New England and Virginia exaggerated the agricultural possibilities in terms of oranges, limons [*sic*], silk, etc., so also they reassured the timid by dwelling on the ease with which rattlesnake bite could be cured by the remedies of the Indians.

Fig. 17:4. Rattlesnake representations notable for their long, continuously tapering strings of rattles, a shape quite contrary to nature. (From Albertus Seba's *Locupletissimi Rerum Naturalium Thesauri . . .*, Amsterdam, 1735, vol. 2, pl. 95.)

causes death in an hour unless snakeweed is available; this is taken both internally and used as a poultice. He says it is reported that if the bitten person lives, the snake will die. Wood denies that the snake can kill with its breath, evidently a belief current at the time. He states that if a rattler swims a river it will die upon reaching the other shore.

Another early British reference is that of Thomas Morton in *New English Canaan*, 1637,[8] p. 82, who reports: "There is one creeping beast or longe creeple (as the name is in Devonshire) that hath a rattle at his tayle, that does discover his age; for so many yeares as hee hath lived, so many joynts are in that rattle, which soundeth (when it is in motion) like pease in a bladder, & this beast is called a rattlesnake."

An early mention of the rattlesnake under the name of the "snake which hath a bell in his tayle"—this by reason of the translation of "cascavel" from the Portuguese—is that by Purchas (1614, p. 842; 1625, vol. 4, p. 1304; 1905–7, vol. 16, p. 459). A marginal note indicates that the description of Brazil, in which this was originally included, was written in 1601.

Thomas Lechford (1642, p. 47) says that when a person is bitten by a rattlesnake he turns the same color as the snake "blew, white, and greene spotted." John Lederer (1672, p. 6) was one of the first of the colonial writers to attribute to the Indians a belief in the rattlesnake's reputed power of charming its prey.

John Josselyn (1672, p. 77; 1675, p. 114) has given two interesting accounts of the timber rattlesnake as found in New England. Some of his material is quoted from the earlier writers already mentioned; part is based on myths, probably of Indian origin. He dwells on the use of the rattlesnake in medicine, including the heart as a remedy for snake bite, and the fat as a liniment.

About this time, articles on rattlesnakes began to appear in the scientific journals, particularly in the *Philosophical Transactions* of the Royal Society. Some of these papers were devoted entirely to rattlesnakes (Tyson, 1683; Dudley, 1723; Hall, 1727; Ranby, 1728; Sloane, 1734); others mentioned them in connection with more general natural history observations (Glover, 1676; Clayton, 1693; Mather, 1714).

Several of these papers were physiological in nature. Edward Tyson (1683, p. 25) was the first to publish a complete and, for the time, a remarkably accurate account of the anatomy of the rattlesnake. The results of his dissection are interspersed with rattlesnake life-history notes culled from earlier works. He mentions the facial pits, and notes that European vipers lack them. Ranby (1728, p. 377) described the biting mechanism, including the venom gland and its operating muscles. Nehemiah Grew (1681, p. 50), although his results were published in book form rather than in the Society's *Philosophical Transactions*, used the Society's collection of materials in his anatomical studies. His report included the first adequate description of the construction of the rattle. He denied Piso's statement that the rattle was dangerous, and expressed doubt as to the rattle-per-year theory.

Captain Hall[9] (1727, p. 309) was probably the first to conduct extensive experiments with rattlesnake venom on live animals. Using dogs, he proved that

---

[8] There may have been an earlier edition published in 1632 or 1634.
[9] I wish someone would supply the good captain's given name or initials; even the Royal Society lacks this information.

successive bites tend to exhaust the venom supply. Sloane (1734, p. 322) discussed fascination, of which he was skeptical. Dudley (1723, p. 292), after reporting on various phases of rattlesnake life, described a specimen having 70 to 80 rattles, as well as a sprinkling of gray hairs on the body.

Glover (1676, p. 631) reported from Virginia that the rattlers grew to a length of a yard and a half, and were as thick as a man's leg. He discusses the Indian remedies for snake bite at some length (p. 634). Mather (1714, p. 64) also dwelt on remedies.

Masterson (1938, p. 213) has printed a previously unpublished paper on rattle-snakes submitted to the Royal Society by Capt. Thomas (?) Walduck in 1714. Evidently the Society deemed the paper too fanciful for publication by a scientific institution. Masterson deserves our thanks for bringing this material out of the archives, for it contains much of the folklore of the time, including an early version of the boot myth (see p. 1249).

John Ray (1693, p. 291) has given a rather full summary of the rattlesnake, as known at that date from the previous authorities. While his work was an important milestone in animal classification, it contained no new material on rattlers.

Two accounts of rattlesnakes and their habits by travelers to Virginia and North Carolina are those of John Clayton (1693) and John Lawson (1709). Some of their observations were their own, while others were evidently based on hearsay. Clayton (p. 126) says that young rattlers have no rattles for a year or so, an idea widely current for some time thereafter (and still believed by some), whereby it became customary to add two or three to the number of the segments, in fixing the age of the snake. He believes rattlesnake venom to be more virulent in summer than in spring. He discusses the various folklore remedies for rattlesnake bite employed in the Virginia of his day.

John Lawson, Surveyor General of North Carolina, wrote extensively on the natural history of that colony; he devoted several pages to the rattlesnake (1709, pp. 128–130) and also the Indians' reaction to rattlers (pp. 210, 213, 214, 219–220, 224). Lawson was one of the first to repeat a long-current fallacy that the male timber rattler could be distinguished from the female by its possession of a black velvet spot on the head (p. 128). He discusses the cures known to the Indians. He believes in the snake's power to fascinate its prey. He repeats Clayton's statement that rattler venom is more virulent in summer, an idea evidently widespread in the colonies and still heard today. He notes that snakes restore their venom supply slowly and therefore a second creature bitten is not so seriously affected as the first. He mentions a supposed enmity of the land terrapin and of the black snake toward rattlers (pp. 132, 133). He discusses snakebite remedies and the medicinal properties of certain rattlesnake products—for example, how the gall, mixed with clay, may be used in the treatment of fever and smallpox (p. 129). He tells a story, often repeated in later publications, of how an Indian cured a man of a lingering illness by causing him to sleep with a live rattler coiled around his middle. In the morning the snake was dead and the man recovered (pp. 218–220).

Lawson's account of his travels is a rather typical combination of observation and hearsay, of field notes and folklore. The natural history compilers of that day had no way of separating fact from fancy, and so it was that many of these stories became a part of the next generation's natural histories. Sometimes they misinterpreted the mysticism of their native guides; at other times they gave too much credence to the campfire tall tales, invented for their edification in accordance with an American custom quite as prevalent today.

Four other works of travel containing contemporary rattlesnake information were Robert Beverly's *The History of Virginia,* 1705 (second edition, 1722); John Brickell's *The Natural History of North-Carolina,* 1737; Mark Catesby's

Fig. 17:5. A realistic rattlesnake (timber rattler, *C. horridus*). From *The Natural History of Carolina, Florida and the Bahama Islands,* by Mark Catesby. London, 2 vols., 1731–43, vol. 2, pl. 41.)

beautifully illustrated *The Natural History of Carolina, Florida and the Bahama Islands,* 1731–43; and Jonathan Carver's *Travels through the Interior Parts of North America,* 1778. We note in their observations on rattlers a considerable similarity; this is particularly true of Brickell, whose work is largely an appropriation (without credit) from Lawson.

Beverly (1705, p. 63) makes the point that the danger from rattlers is much exaggerated in England; they are seldom encountered, and while the bite would be fatal without treatment, adequate remedies are well known. He tells of the supposed fascination of a hare by a rattler, but one may judge from his account that the hare had been bitten by the snake before Beverly came upon the scene (1722, p. 262). The snake's colors became more brilliant while in the act of charming its prey. He tells a story—admittedly secondhand—of a rattler biting a stick of green wood, which shortly thereafter split and fell apart from the effects of the venom (p. 267).

Tab. I. a.

SURINAAMSCHE RATEL~SLANG.

Fig. 17:6. A South American rattlesnake. (From Arnout Vosmaer's *Beschryving van een ...
Surinaamsche Ratelslang ...*, Amsterdam, 1768.) The pattern is quite accurate.

Brickell (p. 145) noted that some rattlers were frozen in the autumn on the way to their dens, a fact recently verified by several observers. He says they commit suicide by biting themselves when annoyed (see p. 854 for a discussion of the validity of this belief). Catesby (p. 41) draws the valid conclusion that the largest snakes are the most dangerous as they have the most venom and, by their longer fangs, effect the deepest penetration.

Carver's account (1778) is quite voluminous (pp. 43–45, 479–485). He says the colors of a rattlesnake are more beautiful when it is animated by resentment (p. 480); the victim of a bite takes on the color of the snake (p. 482); and that rattlers are charmed by music (p. 483). He lists, as do all these earlier accounts, the remedies for rattlesnake bites, and the medicinal preparations that may be made from the snakes themselves.

Fig. 17:7: A famous long rattle string, often mentioned in subsequent publications. (From *Columbian Magazine or Monthly Miscellany*, November, 1786, p. 108.) The irregularities of form indicate that this famous rattle was pieced together from the rattles of seven or eight different snakes.

Probably the most complete account of the rattlesnake that appeared during the eighteenth century was that by Peter Kalm (1752–53). It covered no less than 38 printed pages, and discussed rattlesnake habits and the cures for its bite in considerable detail. Unfortunately, only the first of the three installments in which it appeared has been republished in English (Kalm, 1758), but translations of the other two have been made available to me through the courtesy of Mrs. Mayme Swanson. In this book, I have made many references to Kalm's observations.

The first book in English devoted exclusively to snakes, after that of Topsell (1608, 1658), did not appear until the middle of the eighteenth century. This was *An Essay towards a Natural History of Serpents* by Charles Owen, 1742. The rattlesnake section was quite inadequate, showing little knowledge of recent discoveries already published; in fact, the work contained much mythical material from the books by Jonstonus and Gesner issued one or two centuries before, and was by no means representative of contemporary British knowledge.

For an adequate natural history of a popular character, the British youngster had to await the work of Oliver Goldsmith (1774, the rattlesnake in vol. 7, pp. 208–14), a great improvement over its predecessors, notwithstanding its being only a compilation, and one by an overcredulous novice in natural history.

To return to the seventeenth century—a few other works containing incidental references to rattlesnakes were those of R. Williams (1643, p. 223), Megapolensis (1644, ed. 1651, p. 43), Van der Donck (1655, ed. 1909, p. 298), Taylor (1665, pp. 43, 76), Clarke (1670, pp. 7, 41), Denton (1670, p. 10), Montanus (1671, ed. 1851, p. 79), Ashe (1682, ed. 1911, p. 145), Nieuhof (1682, ed. 1704, p. 15), Paschall (1683, p. 1), Hennepin (1683, ed. 1689, pp. 146, 221), Budd (1685, p. 35), Blome (1686, pp. 86, 161, 236), G. Thomas (1698, p. 21, final section), and H. Jones (1699, p. 438).

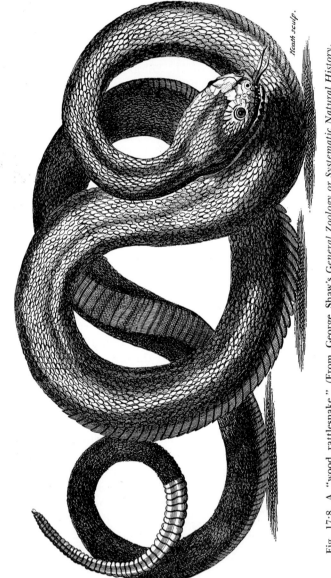

Heath sculp.

Fig. 17:8. A "wood rattlesnake." (From George Shaw's *General Zoology or Systematic Natural History*, London, 1802, vol. 3, part 2, pl. 91.)

John Evelyn says in his *Diary* under date of October 19, 1657, (1901, vol. 1, p. 318; Flower, 1925, p. 976) that he saw some live rattlesnakes lately brought to England from Virginia. Tyson (1683, p. 26) also mentions a shipment. Evidently these novel creatures attracted considerable attention in London. Scheuchzer (1732–37, vol. 8, plate 738, fig. 4) brings the rattlesnake within the scope of the Bible by considering it one of the serpents mentioned in Acts 28:3–5.

I have already mentioned early rattlesnake pictures from the works of Hernández (fig. 17:1), Nieremberg (fig. 17:2), and Piso (fig. 17:3). Other early illustrations are shown in figures 17:4–17:8. Those presented by Seba (fig. 17:4) and Shaw (fig. 17:8) are of interest in showing phenomenally long rattle strings with a continuous taper, which is quite contrary to fact, as a rattler's rattles achieve their greatest increments in the first six to eight segments, and are almost constant in size beyond the tenth or twelfth rattle. Figures 17:5 (Catesby) and 17:6 (Vosmaer) are quite realistic for the period in which they appeared. Figure 17:7 (Anon.) was probably the first faked rattle string to be illustrated; it was the source of many subsequent tales of long-lived snakes. That the string is not authentic can be seen by the discontinuities in size and shape between successive groups of rattles.

ETYMOLOGY AND SEMANTICS

As far as I have been able to determine, the first published name in a European language applied to the rattle of the rattlesnake was the Spanish "cascabel"[10] (or "caxcabel") by Cieça in 1554; and, in Portuguese, the term "cascavel" by Magalhães de Gandova, in 1576. Contemporaneous unpublished usages in Spanish were "cascabel" or "cascabeles" by Landa in 1566, Díaz del Castillo in 1568, and Gallegos in 1581, as well as the Portuguese "cascavel" by Soares de Souza in 1587. The appropriate citations have already been given. Today these terms remain unchanged as "cascabel" and "cascavel" in Spanish and Portuguese, respectively, but they have come to mean the snake as well as its rattle. Earlier the snakes had usually been referred to as "víboras," "bíboras," or "vívoras" with "cascabeles" attached. The alternative "cascavella" was employed as early as 1640 by Aldrovandus (p. 6).

The earliest Italian term applied to the rattle that I have come upon is "strepito" or "noise." This was found in an Italian translation of Cieça's *Chronicle of Peru,* published in Venetia (Venice) in 1560 (fol. 19ᵛ). Cieça's Italian translator uses "strepito" to indicate the sound made rather than the instrument that makes it, which is described as "come sonagli ò campanelli"—"like rattles or little bells." Today the Italian term for rattlesnake is "serpente a sonagli."

In Latin the term first used for the rattler (Hernández, 1628, p. 329) was "perstrepentia sonalia." Piso (1648, p. 41) referred to "tintinabuli," but Marcgravius (1648, p. 241) in the companion work, used "crepitaculum," which has been the preferred Latin term for the rattle ever since. In the same work we find the Dutch "Raetel-slange." Despite these Latin terms for the rattle, I do not find a Latin name for the snake until the use of "caudisona" by Tyson (1683, p. 25),

---

[10] In Spanish a "cascabel" was originally (and still is) a small bell attached to an animal, such as a cat, dog, cow, or falcon.

who designated the snake by the full name "vipera caudisona Americana." Until this time the Latin texts had used "cascavel" or one of the Brazilian vernacular names, such as "boicinininga" or "boiquira." Ray (1693, p. 291) added another Latin name, "crotalophorus." Both "Caudisona" and "Crotalophorus" were subsequently used as names for either or both of the two genera of rattlesnakes, although eventually replaced for technical reasons by "Crotalus" and "Sistrurus." The term "ratulis" was used by Vincent (1726, p. 4).

The earliest publication of the present generic name "Crotalus"[11] that I have found was by a student of Linnaeus (Kiernander) in 1749 (ed. 1752, p. 115). Linnaeus employed it in 1758, in the basic tenth edition of the *Systema Naturae* (p. 214). "Sistrurus," the name of the other rattlesnake genus, was first used by Garman in 1883 (pp. 110, 176). It is derived from two Greek words meaning a rattle and a tail (Stejneger, 1895, p. 410). Garman (1883, p. xxvii; 1892, p. 290) has explained the nomenclatorial rule that required the introduction of this new term at so late a date.

As to vernacular names for the snake, Hernández, 1615 (fol. 191^v) called it "la señora de la serpientes," with the alternative native name "teuchtlacoçauhqui." In Latin, in 1628, these became "domina serpentum" and "teuhtlacot zauhqui." Piso (1648, p. 41) used "boicinininga" and "tangedor"; while Marcgravius (1648, p. 240) added "boicininga,"[12] "boitininga," "boiquira," and "ayug." Do Amaral (1926, table) lists the present Brazilian vernacular names as "cascavel," "boicininga," "boiçuninga," "boicinininga," "boiçununga," "maracá," "maracaboia," and "boiquira." There is also "cobra de cascavel." Some names used today in Spanish-speaking countries are "boiquira," "cascabel," "cascabella," "víbora de cascabel," "culebra de cascabel," "víbora serrana," "hocico de puerco" (Terron, 1921 and 1931; Martín del Campo, 1937). Another is "raboseco." The larger Spanish dictionaries prefer "culebra de cascabel" or "crótalo." In northern Baja California a sidewinder is a "víbora de cascabel cuernito" or "víbora de cascabel de la arena"; a red diamond rattler (*C. r. ruber*) is a "víbora de cascabel grande."

The French "serpent à sonnettes" is said by Read (1931, p. 69) to have originated with Joutel in 1685. "Sonnette" to describe the rattle was used in manuscript by Champlain about 1602; however, his work did not appear in print until many years later (Biggar, 1932–36, vol. 1, p. 54, plate 46). Galinée (1903, p. 40) used "serpent à sonnette" in a manuscript in 1669 or 1670. An alternative French name is "crotale." Seba (1735, vol. 2, p. 46) uses the term "castagnettes" in referring to the rattles; the snake is called "vipere à queuë sonnante" p. 99). Phisalix (1922, vol. 2, p. 234) says that modern French authors prefer the terms "crepitaculum" or "crotalon" for the rattle.

The German "Klapperschlange" has long been in use for the snake, although Kalm (1752, p. 310) says the term "Rattle Schlang" was then current. Olearius used the word "klappern" in 1674 (p. 16). Megapolensis employed the Dutch "Ratel-slangen" in 1644 (1651, p. 43), and Marcgravius "Raetel-slange" in 1648 (p. 240).

---

[11] From the Latin "crotalum," a bell or castanet used by dancing girls; "crotalia," rattling ear-pendants, composed of several pearls (*A New Latin Dictionary*, Freund–Andrews, 1892, p. 484; Ingersoll, 1884b, p. 90).

[12] Native for "snake-that-makes-a-noise" (Soares de Sousa, 1938, p. 308, but writing as of 1587). "Cininga" meant "bell" (Burton, 1869, vol. 2, p. 181).

In English the use of the term "rattle" was coincident with the earliest appearance of the snake in print. Thus Capt. John Smith (1612, p. 20) is the first to mention the "Rattel."[13] The first use of the term rattlesnake, involving mention of a "rattle Snakes skin," is to be found in Winslow (1624, p. 2); and the first discussion of the snake itself, as a snake rather than a decoration, is in Higgeson, or Higginson (1630, p. 12). Capt. John Smith did not employ the term "rattlesnake" until 1631 (p. 30 of the original, p. 955 of the Arber reprint); the date of this item is sometimes given as 1630 (Craigie and Hurlbert, 1942, vol. 3, p. 1899). Another early use of the term is that of W. Wood (1634, p. 47).

The various tenses of the verb "to rattle," in describing the method of sound production of the snake, came into use at least in early colonial times. Brickell (1737) employed the phrases "by rattling their Tails" (p. 142), and "began to Rattle it's Tail" (p. 146). Catesby (1743, vol. 2, p. 41) spoke of the "rattling noise"; and the translator of Kalm (1758, p. 286) used the verb in many ways and tenses. These usages are mentioned in some detail, as Craigie and Hurlbert (1942, p. 1899) cite a quotation in 1823 as the first, or at least a relatively early, use of the verb; and Mathews (1951, p. 1624) cites none earlier than 1776.

The earliest printed use of the shortened term "rattler" is said, by Sir J. A. H. Murray in the *New English Dictionary* (1914, vol. 8, p. 173), to have been made by James Fenimore Cooper in 1827, in *The Prairie* (Cooper, vol. 1, p. 249, line 18). The quotation reads: "The snakes of the prairie are harmless, unless it be now and then an angered rattler, and he always gives you notice with his tail, afore he works his mischief with his fangs." This was the trapper speaking, and using the term as slang. I assume that "rattler" was common in vernacular usage long before its appearance in print. It has now virtually ceased to have any colloquial implication, and throughout this book I have used it on equal terms with the longer "rattlesnake."

Across the country other slang names for rattlesnakes are occasionally heard, such as "sizzle-tail," "buzz-tail," "buzz-worm," "chatter viper," and the inversion "snattle-rake." R. F. Adams (1944, p. 138) says snakes are sometimes "sand eels" while the rattles are the snake's "alarm clock" (p. 148). Small (1946, p. 88) mentions the nickname "rusty back." Mathews (1951, p. 1361) cites "rattletail snake" (in a quotation from George Washington) and "rattled snake" as rare early usages. Anon. (1858a, p. 325) says the rattler was long known in the western United States as a "musical jack," but I suspect, from some of the other facts presented in the same article, that a Britisher was being spoofed.

As discussed elsewhere (p. 1095) the names that the Indians applied to rattlesnakes, while sometimes meaning "snake with a rattle on its tail" (for example, by the Tewa Indians, Henderson and Harrington, 1914, p. 51), more often were such fanciful appellations as "grandfather" or the "admirable one" in an obvious endeavor to avoid incurring the snake's enmity. The Mayans had no such inhibitions; they called the rattler the "little shark of the woods" (Gann, 1918, p. 24).

The question naturally arises as to the suitability of the word "rattle" for the appendage described. If the word implies, in accordance with the usual definitions, a series of discrete or discontinuous sounds like those of castanets or some

---

[13] Craigie and Hurlbert, 1942, in their *Dictionary of American English*, vol. 3, p. 1899; also Mathews, 1951, p. 1361, give the date as 1624, but this was not the date of the earliest Smith work having the description of the Indian ornament using the rattle.

other clicking device, then it is inappropriate. For the successive impacts of a rattle, as vibrated by a live snake, are so closely spaced that one hears only a strident buzz or hiss, probably more like the sound of a jet of escaping steam than any other. Most people hearing the word "rattle" have in mind some of the commoner forms of children's toys, or those ascribed to the court jesters of long ago. With such a device the sound of the snake's rattle can be simulated, provided the hollow receptacle be filled with a large number of small objects such as dried peas, and the shaking be rapid. So, although the sound is more of a hiss than a rattle, I know of no English word that would better describe the instrument itself than the one originally chosen.

It is fortunate that any allusion to a bell was suppressed, for the rattle has no metallic ring such as a bell implies. Some early natural histories, particularly those containing data taken from the Spanish or Portuguese, translated "cascabel" as "bell" (e.g., Purchas, 1614, p. 842; 1625, vol. 4, p. 1304), and to some the rattlesnake became a bell snake. For a time, rattlesnakes and bell snakes were thought to be distinct kinds, with appropriately different tail appendages (e.g., Nelson, 1740, p. 367).

Various descriptive terms have long been applied to distinguish the several species and subspecies of rattlers from each other. The following list gives a sample name of each type currently used:

Name	*Criterion*
Pigmy rattlesnake (*miliarius*)	Size
Great Basin rattlesnake (*lutosus*)	Range
Prairie rattlesnake (*viridis*)	Habitat
Twin-spotted rattlesnake (*pricei*)	Pattern
Red diamond rattlesnake (*ruber*)	Color
Black-tailed rattlesnake (*molossus*)	Color of part
Small-headed rattlesnake (*intermedius*)	Shape of part
Sidewinder (*cerastes*)	Mode of progression
Willard's rattlesnake (*willardi*)	Name of discoverer
Massasauga (*catenatus*)	Name of Indian tribe

The name "diamondback" has come to be a popular generic term for most large rattlesnakes, although properly applicable only to *adamanteus,* or to *atrox* and its close relatives. In the early days (Beauvois, 1799; Kerr, 1802) the term "boiquira," a South American appellation, was applied to the timber rattler (*horridus*), but this failed to attain a general usage.

Crotalus cerastes, the horned rattler or sidewinder, was not brought to the attention of the scientific world until 1854, although it must have been long and unfavorably known to the explorers and soldiers crossing the desert before that time. The term "sidewinder"—rarely "sidewiper," "sideswiper," or "sideliner"—has been both misinterpreted and misused. It should be applied only to the horned rattlesnake (*C. cerastes*) of the Southwestern deserts, whose distinctive method of locomotion well justifies the name.[14] However, it is often applied to small or young rattlesnakes of other species far outside the range of *cerastes;* it is also used as a nickname for rattlesnakes in general. According to Gloyd (1937, p. 132) the little Arizona twin-spotted rattlesnakes (*C. p. pricei*) of the Chiricahua Mountains of southeastern Arizona are called "mountain sidewinders" by the local residents.

---

[14] The Maricopa Indians called it "the left-handed snake" (Spier, 1946, p. 115).

The term "sidewinder" has even been applied to the various mythical hillside dwellers whose legs on one side are longer than the other (H. L. Mencken, *The American Language,* supp. 1, p. 246). Sometimes the name is misinterpreted as indicating a sidewise method of striking (R. F. Adams, 1936, p. 202; 1944, p. 144) or a rattlesnake that can strike without first coiling. Yarrow (1875, p. 535) may have been the first to print the term. He quotes Lieut. George M. Wheeler's statement that certain rattlers were seen along the Colorado River in 1871 and "are called 'side-winders' by the settlers, owing to their peculiar lateral progressive motion." "Side-wiper" may be even older than "sidewinder"; it appeared in print at least as early as February 20, 1873, in the *San Diego World* (Anon., 1873b, p. 1). H. C. Hodge (1877, p. 226) was another early user of "side wiper." It is a tribute to the American capacity for vivid expression that a peculiar method of crawling was brought to popular attention by the use of the term "sidewinder." The Saharan vipers, known since ancient times, are just as adept at sidewinding, but have had no such publicity agents as had the American desert rattler.

Sometimes it is not understood that a sidewinder deserves the name "rattlesnake" as much as any other, as witness this conversation overheard at Kramer, California: "Was the boy bitten by a sidewinder?" "No, it was a rattlesnake." By this, the informant meant the Mojave rattlesnake (*C. s. scutulatus*), the other rattlesnake prevalent near Kramer. It seemed not to have occurred to him that *cerastes* was as much a rattlesnake as *scutulatus*.

As mentioned elsewhere, "rattlesnake," as an adjective, has been applied to a number of plants presumed to be beneficial, either as remedies for snake bite or as snake repellents. "Snake-weed" was mentioned in connection with rattlesnake bite as early as 1630 by Higgeson; and the term "rattlesnake root" was employed in 1682 by Ashe (1911 reprint, p. 145) and G. Thomas (1698, p. 21, final section). Since then, there have been numberless plant names with which the term "rattlesnake" has been compounded, such as bean, fern, flag, grass, herb, leaf, master, masterpiece, plantain, violet, watermelon, and weed. While most of these are so named because of their use as remedies, others, such as the rattlesnake fern and rattlesnake grass, bear resemblance to the rattle in their leaves, or, in the case of the watermelon, in its pattern. A certain shell having a likeness to a rattle is called the "rattlesnake's tail." There was formerly—and, in fact, there still is—a drink named after the snake; also a dance, the Rattlesnake Shake (Masterson, 1942, p. 14). There is a Negro tale (Adams, 1938, p. 37) of a child with a fascinating or mesmerizing eye; it was referred to as having a "rattlesnake eye." The roadrunner has been called the "rattlesnake killer," and a fish the "rattlesnake pike" (Mathews, 1951, p. 1362). Tixier (1940, p. 257, but writing in 1839) said a foamy substance noted on certain plants in Louisiana was called "rattlesnake spittle."

Other snakes, through a supposed attendance on rattlers (see chapter 18, p. 1243) have come to be known as "rattlesnake pilots." For a time the copperhead in New England was known as the "rattlesnake's mate" (Rafinesque, 1818, p. 84; Anon., 1819, p. 44) or the "rattlesnake's cousin."

The word "rattlesnake" has now come to have a figurative connotation implying a person, or creature, who is despicable, cruel, dangerous, treacherous, or, especially, vindictive. Often there is suggested a concealed or unexpected source of danger. Typical phrases of this character are: "I'd as soon handle a rattlesnake as deal with that fellow"; "It was like stepping on a rattlesnake"; "I'd have no more hesitation in killing him than a rattlesnake"; "As dangerous as a coiled rattlesnake"; "No more pity than a rattlesnake"; "Like finding a rattler in your bunk"; "He struck with the vicious speed of a rattlesnake."

INSIGNIA

An interesting human reaction to rattlesnakes is shown by their use as symbols in insignia. One example is the Mexican coat of arms, which is also incorporated in the Mexican standard, but not the merchant flag. Its derivation, according to Prescott (1843, p. 16), was as follows: "They [the Aztecs] at length halted on the southwestern borders of the principal lake [in the Valley of Mexico], in the year 1325. They there beheld, perched on the stem of a prickly pear, which shot out from the crevice of a rock that was washed by the waves, a royal eagle of extraordinary size and beauty, with a serpent in its talons, and his broad wings opened to the rising sun" (see also Lang, 1893, p. 226; Howey, 1928, p. 298). The snake, which obviously has only a subsidiary part in this allegory, is sometimes depicted as a rattlesnake, sometimes not.

Among the flags and insignia of the United States, a series bearing the representation of a rattlesnake had a brief vogue in early Revolutionary days. The rattlesnake as a colonial symbol was suggested as early as April, 1751, when an editorial appeared in Franklin's *Pennsylvania Gazette* complaining of the British practice of transporting convicts to the colonies; this was followed shortly (May 9, 1751) by another article suggesting that a cargo of rattlesnakes be exported to England in exchange (Preble, 1894, p. 213; Malleson, 1908, p. 135; Walsh, 1913, p. 719; Medden, 1929, p. 83). Three years later there appeared in the paper a cartoon showing a rattler cut into nine pieces, the head lettered to represent New England, and the other eight inscribed with the names of the remaining colonies then participating in the French and Indian War. Attached was the inscription "Join or Die," later changed, as the figure was adopted by other newspapers, to "Unite or die."[15] In the troublous times that followed, rattlesnake figures became increasingly popular on flags and other devices, particularly in the southern colonies (Hale, 1896, p. 1243). The rattler was generally accompanied by the motto "Don't Tread on Me." The New England colonies preferred a pine-tree insigne (Moss, 1941, p. 11), but in some early flags the two were combined, the rattlesnake being coiled at the base of the pine tree, as in the flag of the Massachusetts Navy (McCandless and Grosvenor, 1917, p. 399, fig. 401).

In Bradford's *Pennsylvania Journal* of December 27, 1775, there appeared an unsigned communication to the editor in which were set forth the reasons for the appropriateness of the rattlesnake device, the letter having been prompted by the sight of the "Don't Tread on Me" insigne on the drums of a regiment of Marines (Preble, 1894, p. 214; Medden, 1929, p. 84). The reasons may be summarized as follows:

1. The rattlesnake is indigenous to America.
2. Its eye exceeds that of other animals in brilliance, and, having no eyelids, is emblematic of vigilance.

[15] The snake in this device was not usually a rattlesnake (Matthews, 1910, p. 409).

3. It never begins an attack, but once in a fight never surrenders, therefore being symbolic of magnanimity and courage.

4. Its weapons (fangs) are concealed so it appears defenseless to an enemy; even when shown they seem weak, but they cause decisive and fatal wounds.

5. It always gives generous warning to an enemy.

6. The venom is fatal to an enemy but aids in digestion of the rattler's food; thus it symbolizes that which is destructive to the enemy but beneficial to one's own existence.

7. There are 13 rattles—the number of the colonies—and the rattle is the only part of the snake that can increase in numbers (the half-formed additional rattle was hopefully presumed to represent Canada).

8. Each rattle is independent yet all are firmly united.

9. One rattle alone will produce no sound; together they alarm the boldest man.

10. The rattler is solitary and associates with others only when necessary for mutual preservation.

11. In winter it joins with others to keep warm.

12. Its power of fascination suggests that those who come to America will never leave.

13. It is beautiful in youth, yet its beauty increases with age.

This presentation certainly places the rattler in a more favorable light than is deserved. The communication, often reprinted, has been attributed to Franklin—incorrectly, Preble believes.

Although rattlesnake flags of several designs were used by colonial contingents in the Revolutionary operations (McCandless and Grosvenor, figs. 365, 398, 400, 401, 402, 405), two seem to have gained a semiofficial recognition by the central authority; these were hoisted as naval flags on December 3, 1775. One was the navy jack showing a rattler outstretched diagonally across 13 alternating horizontal red and white stripes; the other, the so-called Gadsden flag, displayed a coiled rattlesnake on a yellow field, and became the standard of the naval Commander-in-Chief, Esek Hopkins. Both flags included the "Don't Tread on Me" motto.

While Commodore Byron McCandless was in command of the Naval Repair Base at San Diego, I requested his opinion on the first official use of a rattlesnake flag. He courteously replied as follows:

Christopher Gadsden, a delegate from South Carolina to the Continental Congress in 1775, and a member of the Marine Committee to outfit the first American Fleet, had a yellow flag made with a rattlesnake upon it. This was sent to Esek Hopkins, Commander-in-Chief of the Fleet, which on its way out of the Delaware had been caught in the ice below Reedy Island. Timothy Mattack, the Secretary to the Marine Committee, gave the flag to the captain of the *Providence* to take down from Philadelphia to Hopkins at Reedy Island.

Gadsden wrote Hopkins that he was about to sail for home and would take a packet boat from Lewes, Delaware. He was run aground off the Carolina Coast by a British patrol vessel. He got ashore and proceeded to Charleston, South Carolina, about February 9, 1776. Two of his colleagues had arrived overland one day in advance. At this time, Colonel Gadsden presented to the Provincial Congress an elegant standard, such as was to be used by the Commander-in-Chief of the American navy; being a yellow field, with a lively representation of a rattlesnake in the center, in the attitude of going to strike; and these words underneath: "Don't Tread on Me." It was accordingly ordered to be carefully preserved, and displayed in the Congress' room; and from that time, it was placed in the southwest corner of that room, at the left hand of the President's chair.

Esek Hopkins in his signals for the fleet indicated the use of this standard:

For Action—The standard at the main truck of the *Alfred* (his flagship) with his broad pendant halfmast high.

Cease Action—Take in the standard and two block the broad pendant.

I think that is clearly the first use of the rattlesnake flag.

The importance in those days of a naval Commander's flag is discussed by McCandless and Grosvenor (1917, p. 288) and by Quaife (1942, p. 58). The possession of this flag is said to account for the name "Rattlesnake Squadron" applied to the Continental Navy (Malleson, 1908, vol. 11, p. 135); however, it is to be noted that the rattlesnake was also a feature of the stern decorations of some of these vessels (McCandless, in letter).

Although the prototype of the present United States flag was officially adopted by Congress June 14, 1777, it seems never to have been carried on the battlefield during the Revolutionary War (McCandless and Grosvenor, 1917, p. 292). Individual state and even regimental flags served instead, and among these were several carrying the rattlesnake device (Thruston, 1926, p. 7, fig. 8). But with the end of the war they were no longer used. Probably because of the flag, South Carolina was sometimes referred to as the "Rattlesnake State."

The rattlesnake does not appear in the seal of any state except New Mexico, and here only because of the inclusion of the Mexican coat of arms (E. W. King, 1946, p. 21). It is still incorporated in the seal of the War Department, at the top with the legend "This We'll Defend," as adopted in 1778 (E. W. King, 1946, p. 32; Quaife, 1942, p. 71).

It is frequently said that Franklin advocated the rattlesnake as the national emblem in the place of the eagle (e.g., Cist, 1845, p. 18). I find no such reference in the edition of Franklin's works to which I have had access, and it is probable that this idea resulted from the mistaken attribution to him of the letter in Bradford's *Pennsylvania Journal* in 1775. Jefferson (1793, p. 413) objected to the use of a rattlesnake design in an official mace because of the disgust that snakes engender in many people. A rattlesnake design was used on some of the continental currency—that of North Carolina in 1776, for example—which consequently was sometimes called "rattlesnake money." The Columbian Society—forerunner of Tammany—issued a rattlesnake medal.

In view of the flood of new insignia required for the expanded forces and new types of services involved in World War II, and particularly because the use of individual group insignia became more general than ever before, it was natural that an occasional rattlesnake design was utilized. Among these were the shoulder-sleeve insigne of the 59th Division showing a coiled rattler (DuBois, 1944, p. 92); a coiled, winged rattler of the 50th Fighter Squadron (G. Hubbard, 1944, p. 168); a rattler coiled around a bomb for the 317th Bombardment Squadron, and another somewhat similar design of the 346th (p. 171); a coiled snake, probably a rattler, of the Marine fighters VMF-323 (p. 182); and finally a coiled rattler representing the Navy Motor Torpedo Boats Ron-20 (p. 184). There were a number of others involving snake heads that may have been intended to represent rattlesnakes.

There is an interesting discussion in the serial publication *Notes and Queries*, fifth series, vols. 10 and 11 (Malleson, 1908), concerning the use of the term "rattlesnake colonel" by an Englishwoman traveling in the colonies in 1754–55. This was during the French and Indian War, and the conclusion is drawn that the term was generally applied at the time to the colonial officers to differentiate them from the British regulars (p. 135). Commodore McCandless has called to my attention the fact that certain officers in the Continental Army (probably from Georgia) wore gorgets on which a coiled rattlesnake was engraved. If something similar was used at an earlier date, it might explain the "rattlesnake colonel" appellation; but it is much more probable that it originated as a derisive title applied to anyone who had killed a rattler. It was cited in this sense in 1744 by Dr. Alexander Hamilton, a Scottish physician traveling in the colonies. He wrote— in a diary not published until 163 years later—when he killed a harmless snake, that "had it been a rattlesnake, I should have been entitled to a colonel's commission, for it is a common saying here (in New York State) that a man has no title to that dignity until he has killed a rattlesnake" (Hamilton, 1907, p. 94; A. Matthews, 1937, p. 341; M. M. Mathews, 1951, p. 1361). There were also "rattlesnake majors" (Pencil, 1839, p. 46; Matthews, 1937, p. 344).

PLACE NAMES AND OTHER USES

One of the evidences of the impact made by rattlesnakes on the colonists, the settlers of the Midwest, and the transcontinental emigrants, was the frequency with which geographical and landscape features were named after them. When a trapper came upon a rattler as he crossed a stream, it was likely to become Rattlesnake Creek on the maps. There was a Rattlesnake Hill in Massachusetts as early as 1666 (Mathews, 1951, p. 1362).

Several post offices are said to have boasted of the name "Rattlesnake," but all except one have vanished or have been renamed at the insistence of the local chamber of commerce—only Rattlesnake, Florida, remains. But physical features, designated somewhat less formally, have more often retained the names first given them by the early settlers, and the number of Rattlesnake Creeks, Lakes, and Mountains testifies to the impression the snakes made on the pioneers. For example, in the southern half of the Sierra Nevada of California there are no less than 10 Rattlesnake Creeks, besides a Rattlesnake Hill, Lake, Meadow, and Cabin. Farther south, in southern California, there are 13 Rattlesnake Canyons, 7 Creeks, 3 Mountains, 2 Peaks, 2 Springs, 1 Valley, 1 Camp, and 1 Meadow, to say nothing of a Sidewinder Mountain, a Valley, a Well, and a Mine. And no doubt more detailed maps than those I have consulted would have shown many more. Barnes (1935, p. 356) lists a Rattlesnake Basin, Canyon, Creek, and Tank in Arizona. Even on such small scales as are used in commercial state maps, Rattlesnake Ranges may be found in Wyoming; Rattlesnake Mountains in New Hampshire, Oklahoma, and Texas; Buttes in California, Colorado, and South Dakota; a Knob in Ohio; Hills in Massachusetts,[16] New Mexico, and Washington; a Lake in Florida; a Neck in Massachusetts; Islands in New York and Ohio; a Spring in Oregon; Creeks in Virginia, Oklahoma, Kansas, Montana, Idaho, Wyoming, and Oregon; a Canyon in Utah; a Gap in Texas; a Run in Washington; a Fork in Ohio; a Key off Florida; and a Shoal off South Carolina. There are towns named Rattlesnake that do not now attain the dignity of post offices in Tennessee, Ohio, Montana, Colorado, and Nevada.

There are innumerable Rattlesnake Mines and Ranches in the West; to say nothing of Hotels, Bars, and Billiard Halls. There was hardly a stage line of

---

[16] No less than 16 according to Babcock (1925, second part, 1933, p. 4).

the old days without a Rattlesnake Pete as a driver (e.g., Root and Connelley, 1901, p. 273); and every cow outfit boasted at least one Rattlesnake Joe or Sidewinder Charlie. A California desperado became known as Rattlesnake Dick because he began his career at Rattlesnake Bar, on the American River (Jackson, 1939, p. 95). The Indians also gave the name (in their own languages) to individuals; thus a man who had been bitten in his youth was named Rattlesnake by the Menominee (Densmore, 1932, p. xix). Other Indians named Rattlesnake are mentioned by Denton (1670, p. 10) and by Coues (1897, pp. 368, 387, 399). The Indians likewise applied the name rattlesnake or snake to places. Kennebec is said to mean snake in Algonkin, and so does Antietam in an Iroquois dialect (Brinton, 1896, p. 130; Spence, 1914, p. 113). There was even H.M.S. *Rattlesnake,* which, among other exploits, engaged in a famous scientific voyage from 1846 to 1850, T. H. Huxley being one of the naturalists aboard (J. Huxley, 1936).

In Brazil there are several Cascavels, and there is a Río Cascabel in Colombia, although I presume these may have the alternative meaning of "bell"; however, there can be no question concerning the Rattlesnake River in British Guiana.

Rattlesnakes have had their place in fiction since early days. The wild-West yarns were full of them; and many a more important work—*Huckleberry Finn,* for example—has contained a rattlesnake episode or two. Probably the most famous novel having a rattlesnake theme was O. W. Holmes' *Elsie Venner,* 1861. Modern stories in which rattlesnakes are important to the plot are not infrequent. In one, a murder was solved because the rattler that was presumed to have killed the victim was of a species not indigenous to the area where the crime had been committed (Neidig, 1926, p. 18). The supposed skin-shedding blindness of rattlers in August motivates the plot of another (Beer, 1921, p. 16). In a third, a man, having been treated magnanimously by a sidewinder that could have bitten him, was likewise moved to mercy toward a bighorn (N. C. Wilson, 1945, p. 16). The rattlesnake has long been a favorite—a dependable filler—in the Sunday supplement. Rattlesnake characteristics in myths and campfire tales are discussed in chapter 18.

There is only one rattlesnake item in *Bartlett's Familiar Quotations* (1937). It is from Harry Leon Wilson's *Ruggles of Red Gap:* "She'd fight a rattlesnake and give it the first two bites." However, this was probably an old standby in Texas tall tales (Botkin, 1944, p. 182) long before it was used by Wilson.

18. Myths, Folklore, and Tall Stories

INTRODUCTION

Myths and folklore about snakes are of more than passing interest since they influence, to a considerable degree, the attitudes of people toward snakes. These attitudes, translated into action, often have important effects on economic and control measures, and on the snake-bite problem.

Some myths and legends arise out of exaggerations; others come from inaccurate field observations or interpretations. They become established through repetition. A myth to one person becomes a fact of natural history when told to another. Unfortunately, an offhand denial of the truth of some of the legends by scientists often is met with a natural, human assumption that the scientist has spent his entire life in a laboratory and hasn't the faintest idea of what goes on among living animals in the wild. One cannot prove that a thing isn't so because he himself has never witnessed it. I have no hope of eradicating completely any of the myths respecting rattlesnakes so deeply imbedded in American folklore. I shall, however, examine some of their origins, show how coincidence—the coincidence of the repeated occurrences at widely separated places of very unusual happenings (as in the boot myth, p. 1249)—strains probability to the breaking point, and how contrary some of these traditions are to various facts of nature. I expect my attitude to be judged dogmatic. In any case, I know that few of my readers will be convinced, and that some will be shocked to have their childhood memories thus questioned.

I have repeatedly been asked, when I have raised a questioning eyebrow at the tale of some rattlesnake escapade, "How can you doubt it when I saw it with my own eyes?" I can only answer that the relationship of the memory of what one has seen to the event itself is affected by time and repetition. This is no place to discuss the psychological principles involved, assuming I had the competence to do so, which I have not. Let me, however, cite an analogous problem from my own experience. Did I ever see Sothern and Marlowe in *Romeo and Juliet*? If anyone were interested enough to ask me I should probably say yes, for this was a famous team of stars in the days when the best plays were seen in the "sticks," and I was an omnivorous playgoer (gallery seats 25 cents— no programs). But as a matter of fact, I don't know whether or not I ever saw those actors in that play. True, I have a definite remembrance of various scenes and just how they were done, including the actual intonations of certain famous passages. But it is just as likely these memories are based on what was read in the theatrical reviews, or in some Sothern-Marlowe pictorial edition of the play—if there ever was one—in a movie, or even in a stage presentation by another pair of actors. Any of these explanations may have produced in my memory the effect of seeing this presentation so many years ago, or I may really have seen it. And my repeated statements in the past that I saw these players, and my descriptions to others of what I saw, have, of course, increased the certainty that I did see them. But actually I don't know whether I ever did and never will know.

I shall discuss primarily the myths attributed, in whole or in part, to rattlesnakes. Others, seldom or never applied to rattlers, such as the legends of the whip snake, hoop snake, joint snake, etc., may be found in such reliable summaries as those of Schmidt (1929a, 1929b, 1951), C. H. Pope (1937, p. 120), and others. Strecker, long a student of reptiles and of reptile superstitions, has traced the origins of various myths and legends (1925, p. 44; 1926a, p. 56; 1926b, p. 70; 1929a, p. 1; 1929b, p. 1). Gibson's *Superstitions about Animals*, London, 1904, is also of interest, including especially the following statement (p. 88): "And now we come to Snakes! And when I enter upon this part of my subject I am at an utter loss where to begin and where to end, for there is no other creature on the face of the earth of which so little is known and of which so much nonsense is spoken and written." Yet Gibson, himself, is guilty of perpetuating a myth when he speaks of the desert horned viper in the Sahara finding "supreme enjoyment in basking in the hottest places it can discover" (p. 96). A typical article, with appropriate woodcuts, illustrating how popular writers of a bygone day perpetuated and augmented rattlesnake myths and legends, is that of Thorpe (1855, p. 470).

Although I shall mention early publications of several of the better-known myths, I can give no assurance that these citations were really their first appearances in print. Natural history writers of the early days had no hesitancy in reprinting each other's stories, usually without credit; and, as many had been handed down as folklore, they had already been long in the public domain when first printed. Every such legend had been heard around the campfire and the tavern table a thousand times for each appearance in print.

Whether certain tales now told of rattlesnakes were originated with these particular snakes in mind is often difficult to determine. Only those in which the rattle itself plays a necessary part can be ascribed to rattlers with any assurance that they were not first attributed to other kinds of snakes. Many originated abroad centuries before any European had ever seen or heard of a rattlesnake. They were subsequently transplanted to America and applied to the rattlesnake, a far more spectacular creature than the European vipers to which they had previously been ascribed. This was particularly true of snake-bite remedies, medicines derived from snakes or parts of snakes, repellents to drive snakes away, and fascination and other miraculous powers attributed to snakes.

Some of the myths and legends originated with the Indians and were assigned by them to rattlesnakes before the advent of the white man. Few of these are so distinctive that they can be recognized as being non-European, or non-Old World in origin. The majority have Old World counterparts, so that we are under the necessity of determining—or, more frequently, guessing—whether they had parallel, independent American origins, or were brought to America after 1492 and later credited to Indian sources. Probably the rattlesnake folklore and legends that are most certainly of purest Indian derivation are those of the Southwestern tribes, from which trained ethnologists had some opportunity to gather information before white contamination. The myths and folklore attributed to the Indians have been discussed in chapter 16.

Some of the legends and myths were deliberately invented by hunters, guides, and cowboys to spoof the tenderfoot at the campfire. They subsequently spread like an uncontrolled campfire and came to be firmly believed by large elements of the population. Others were intentionally expanded into tall stories solely for entertainment, although even some of these were taken seriously by the credulous. Boatright (1931, p. 271), himself a compiler of tall tales, has remarked that the advent of a greenhorn or tenderfoot always stimulated the cowpunchers and guides to gild the lily.

We shall never know how much of present-day rattlesnake folklore arose from careless or mistaken observation, and how much from deliberate exaggeration. Vestal (1941, p. 146) has said that rattlers were always at the center of the folklore of the plains. Dobie (1926, p. 52) remarked that every ranch or camp conversation always got round to rattlesnakes. From Gates (1933, p. 38) we learn that a fur trader boasted of having embroidered some rattler stories that Carver (1778, pp. 43, 479) later incorporated in his frequently quoted *Travels through the Interior Parts of North-America, in the Years 1766, 1767 and 1768.* This is probably only one of many instances of misplaced confidence.

Nearly all myths and legends contain some grain of truth; many merely stretch the truth. In such cases, in this work on the habits and life histories of rattlesnakes, it has not been easy to decide whether a particular item should be allocated to the appropriate factual chapter or to this one on folklore. Inevitably some duplication has been entailed.

No discussion of herpetological folklore would be complete without a word about Pliny (Gaius Plinius Secundus, 23–79 A.D.) His encyclopedia of natural history is an almost unparalleled example of industry and credulity. As Hulme has said in his *Natural History Lore and Legend* (1895, p. 30): "Several writers of antiquity influenced the mediaeval authors, but it is scarcely necessary to detail their labours at any length, since if they lived before Pliny he borrowed from them, and if they lived afterward they borrowed from him, so that we practically in Pliny get the pith and cream of all." Pliny's *Historia Naturalis* was the funnel through which we can watch the ancient folklore pouring down into the medieval and modern worlds. So intact do some of the stories now applied to rattlers remain, that we should almost conclude that Pliny must have slipped over for a visit to America before Columbus. In my citations of Pliny, I have usually referred to the Bostock and Riley translation published in 1855–57. I trust that the use of these dates in my citations will not confuse any reader as to the time when Pliny really wrote, some 1900 years ago.

Some folklore is harmless and entertaining, some is dangerous. A hair-rope insurance against the almost negligible risk of a rattler in the blankets is relatively innocuous, and if anyone is reassured and sleeps better with a horsehair reata surrounding his desert bunk, no harm is done. But a folklore remedy for rattlesnake bite is a dangerous folly, if it delays or complicates a really necessary treatment. Also, as Boatright has pointed out (1931, p. 272), some rattlesnake horrendous incidents and tall tales related round the campfire are too often the prelude to practical jokes with live or dead rattlers, or with harmless snakes. Serious and lasting results can follow the frightening of inexperienced people in such horseplay, a practice that should be strongly discouraged (see Stillwell, 1949, p. 60).

In the references to previous accounts of tales and folklore that are here repeated, I may occasionally fail to make it clear whether the author cited believed the tale, or was merely transmitting it as a bit of folklore, just as I am doing. In such cases it should be assumed that the prior author—this is particularly true of publications appearing in the present century—was not vouching for the accuracy of the belief that he presented. Also, it is obvious that such of the references as appeared in folklore journals were presented as folklore.

MYTHS OF VENOM AND SNAKE BITE

Temporary Removal of Venom Glands

The myth that when venomous snakes drink, they temporarily remove their venom, venom glands, or fangs, is very old. Calmet (1812–24, vol. 2) and Rendell (1928, p. 12) attribute it to the *Physiologus*, a book of allegories that first appeared in the second century A.D. (see also Owen, 1742, p. 173; and Thorndike, 1923–41, vol. 2, p. 483, for other nonrattler references).

In the rattlesnake legend, the snake leaves its venom glands on a rock, as it goes to a stream or pond to drink. When it returns, if someone has stolen them in its absence, it dies in convulsions or kills itself by striking its head against the rock. Typical versions of the story have been given by Dugès (1877, p. 17), Dulog (1897, p. 202), Kincaid (1931, p. 67), King (1941, p. 24), Pound (1946, p. 175), and Randolph (1947, p. 254). I was told this tale as a belief of the Yaqui Indians in Sonora, Mexico. There are several variants. Kincaid (1931, p. 67) was informed by Mexican sheepherders that rattlers remove their fangs when courting so as not to injure each other. Le Sueur, in his voyage up the Mississippi in 1699–1700, was told by the Sioux Indians that rattlesnakes remove their venom every night and put it back again next morning (Shea, 1861, p. 99).

It is the theory that the snake removes its venom glands before drinking because otherwise it would, itself, be poisoned. This is related to other myths of the extreme contaminative power of the venom. One has to do with a man seeking revenge by putting a rattler's venom gland in a pail of water used by an enemy (Hurston, 1931, p. 416). Another is a Hopi belief in the danger from a single drop of blood from a creature that has been bitten by a rattler (MacClary, 1939, p. 24). There is a Sudanese belief that any human food or drink touched by a snake becomes poisonous (Corkill, 1935, p. 258).

Need of Water When Venom Is Used

Various myths relate to the accessibility of water to rattlesnakes when they use their venom. Witt (1768, p. 10) stated that whenever a rattlesnake bites some creature, it must have water immediately or it will die from the venom spilled in its own mouth. This has become a prairie country myth (Vestal, 1941, p. 146), and has recently been heard in Texas. Warburton (1849, vol. 1, p. 175) thought that rattlers coming out of hibernation were harmless until they had secured water; and Yarrow (1883, p. 263) reported a belief in the Southwest that rattlers were harmless if deprived of water for some time. Devoe (1951, p. 227) placed this time limit—which he considered mythical—at six days. Bergen (1899, p. 86) gave this version of the water myth: Whichever reaches water first, the snake or the creature bitten, will survive; the other will die.

EFFECT OF DEATH ON VENOM VIRULENCE

Sometimes applied to rattlers is the old myth that, when a snake dies, any victim suffering from its bite immediately recovers (Walduck, 1714, in Masterson, 1938, p. 215). It has been cited as modern folklore in Iowa (Stout, 1936, p. 190) and in Nebraska (Pound, 1946, p. 166). But, according to Robinson (1896, p. 712), in Florida the superstition is reversed; the venom becomes more virulent if the snake is killed. One of the earliest accounts of the rattlesnake in English (Wood, 1634, p. 47) gives this version of the story: If the bitten person lives, the snake will die, and vice versa.

EFFECTS OF BITING ON THE BITER

The serious result to a rattlesnake if it bites a man who has poison in his blood is a myth of some antiquity. As alcohol is an antidote for snake venom (another myth), it follows that if a man is bitten while drunk, the snake will die (Blackburn, 1853, p. 128). Fisher (1939, p. 91) and Davidson and Blake (1947, p. 271) present modern versions of this folk belief. In a tall-tale revision, Holbrook (1940, p. 268; Botkin, 1947, p. 303) tells how Ethan Allen was bitten repeatedly while drunk. The rattler became cross-eyed and inebriated. When Allen awoke he complained of mosquitoes.

In the summer of 1951, a case in Texas attained nationwide publicity. An employee at an air base was struck by a rattler. The man was uninjured but the snake died. It was explained that the man was a metal plater whose blood was charged with sodium cyanide from his having continuously handled this dangerous chemical. He was immune but the snake wasn't. Another newspaper story tells of a man who has been bitten 50 times in 20 years and is now immune. When a rattler bites him it usually dies. Steiner (1899, p. 269) mentions the Southeastern folk belief that a rattler must always seek snakeweed after biting a man, as the latter's blood is fatally poisonous to the snake.

There is a current myth to the effect that when a rattler bites, it leaves its fangs in the victim. It then either dies (Bruce, 1930, p. 93), or at least is helpless until it grows new ones (Pound, 1946, p. 172). The relation to the bee's sting is obvious.

One Western tall tale concerns the rattler that strikes a man in the hip pocket where he carries a plug of chewing tobacco, naturally with fatal results to the snake (Davidson, 1941, p. 214; Davidson and Blake, 1947, p. 269).

VENOM TRANSMITTED THROUGH MOTHER'S MILK

The effect of snake bite transmitted through mother's milk to nursing offspring has been the subject of a number of stories, some of the more recent of which deal with rattlesnakes. One of the most fanciful is that of Barstow (1807, p. 61; Williams, 1848, p. 451) of a mother who was bitten in the fourth or fifth month of pregnancy. She recovered and bore a normal child, but when she nursed the child it turned the color of a rattlesnake and died. Several small animals were fed the milk with fatal results. Maybe it was this account that suggested to Oliver Wendell Holmes (1861) the theme of the unfortunate effect on Elsie Venner of a prenatal rattlesnake bite suffered by her mother, which led to the dual (human-snake) character of the unfortunate girl in Holmes' novel.

I know of no medical case report that mentions any adverse effect on a nursing child caused by a rattlesnake bite sustained by the mother. Wyne (1937, p. 604) states that such fatalities have occurred, but this, like most of his other information, lacks verification. Jackson (1853, p. 411) has given a case report in which a mother suffered a serious copperhead bite, without adversely affecting her suckling child.

Fayrer (1872, p. 43; 1874, p. 43) records a case in India fatal to both mother and child; however, the mother was supposedly bitten at night, and the snake, if it were one, was not actually seen by anyone. Topsell (1608, p. 27) and Damiri in Jayakar (1906–8, vol. 1, p. 57) mention other nonrattlesnake cases, the latter involving a camel and her young. One of my correspondents reported hearing of a doubly fatal case of a mare and her colt.

One guess as to the source of milk-sickness, a serious scourge of the prairie states in the pioneer days, was that it was caused by rattlesnakes biting the cows (Gillmore, 1872, vol. 2, p. 154).

There are several superstitions regarding rattlesnakes and pregnant women. One is that if a patient undergoing treatment for snake bite sees a pregnant woman, he will surely die. This is an Indian belief, and was also heard by March in Honduras (1928, p. 61). There is a theory current in the Southeast that pregnant women are immune to snake bite (Anon., 1949, p. 194). On the other hand it was reported by Kalm (1752–53, p. 66) that rattlesnake bite is always fatal to pregnant women, and that even the Indian remedies, usually so effective, are of no avail.

PREFERENCES IN BITING

Rattlesnakes have some peculiar, but often praiseworthy, preferences in biting. They won't bite children, at least until they have reached the age of seven[1] (Hyatt, 1935, p. 72, Illinois folklore; Pickard and Buley, 1945, p. 78, Midwest pioneer folklore; Pound, 1946, p. 173, Nebraska folklore; Buley, 1950, vol. 1, p. 267, "old" Northwest pioneer folklore; also personal communication received on San Joaquin Valley, California, folklore). They won't strike a person from the rear, nor will they bite in water (Pound, 1946, p. 172). Also, I was advised by one of my correspondents that rattlesnakes will bite only men, not women. This chivalrous attitude they must have inherited from their distant relatives the European vipers, who have long made this distinction (Lean, 1902–4, vol. 2, p. 601). But our uncivilized rattlers seem not yet to have adopted the code of refusing to bite naked people. The ancient and contradictory myths from which this idea descended are mentioned by Calmet (1812–14, vol. 2, under Serpent), Lean (1902–4, vol.

---

[1] This is related to the well-known child-feeding-snake myth.

2, p. 601), Damiri in Jayakar (1906, vol. 1, p. 635), Rendell (1928, p. 12), and Riddell (1929, p. 222).

TRANSFER OF VENOM TO ANOTHER ANIMAL

The story that the venom of one creature, if ingested by another, makes the venom of the second doubly powerful is very ancient (Aristotle in Cresswell, 1862, p. 228, and Thompson, 1910, section 607a; Pliny, 1855–57, vol. 2, p. 98; book xi, chap. 115). It was most frequently reported as applying to vipers and scorpions. Occasionally it is heard today attributed to rattlesnakes, as mentioned by one of my correspondents: "Here in Medford [Oregon] they say that when a rattler is killed you must be sure to cut off the head and bury it, for if yellow jackets [wasps] eat the snake they will carry the venom to the next victim they sting."

STRANGE VENOM EFFECTS

Queer and unexpected effects of rattlesnake venom on man and animals have often been reported; some of these have been so fantastic as to border on the miraculous. Equally strange are some of the recorded results of venom on plants or inanimate objects, and some of these have been so often repeated as to become true folk tales.

One of the oldest is the axhead story, first told, I believe, by Cotton Mather in 1714 (p. 68; Kittredge, 1913, p. 174). In this, a rattlesnake strikes the metal bit of an ax. The metal changes color and, when the ax is used again, the discolored edge breaks off. The yarn was repeated by Wesley (1784, vol. 2, p. 37), but was questioned by Ward (1875, p. 45). It has been properly relegated to folklore by Gibson (1904, p. 112) and Botkin (1947, p. 303).

The ax tale is the only one known to me in which rattlesnake venom affects metal, but there are many stories of its effects on plants and wood. The more scientific tests of the results to plants have been mentioned elsewhere (p. 859); it remains here to present some of the more fantastic tales. Again we go to Mather for the first telling. In his story, a man kills a rattlesnake with a green branch of a tree; and is himself killed by the poison that reaches him through the branch (Mather, 1714, p. 68; Kittredge, 1913, p. 174). This is a lineal descendent of the Pliny story of the basilisk venom that traveled up a spear to kill a soldier on horseback (1855–57, vol. 2, p. 282; book viii, chap. 33). In various forms, the effect of the venom on the tree branch—not always fatal to the man—has been described by Walduck (1714, in Masterson, 1938, p. 215), Beverly (1722, p. 267), Roberts (1927, p. 203), and Botkin (1947, p. 303). Other accounts of the effects, usually fatal, of rattlesnake venom on shrubs, and even on trees, are those of Kalm (1752–53, p. 57), Breintal (1765, p. 78), Burnaby (1775, p. 78), Anon. (1858b, p. 472), Flack (1866, p. 318), Dobie (1925, p. 8; 1926, p. 52; 1947b, p. 90), and Roberts (1927, p. 203). Oswald (1879, p. 609) asks us to believe that rattlers bite the berries of the Taxus trees. Birds eat the poisoned berries and thus fall ready prey to the snakes. Rosenberg (1946, p. 105) tells of a Brazilian belief that rattlers and other snakes sharpen their fangs on the trunks of young trees.

From this point on, the legends are of the frankly tall-story type, although two of them were not always so considered. In the oldest of these yarns, a hoe handle is struck by a rattlesnake and within an hour has swelled to such an extent that it pops out of the eye of the hoe (Beadle, 1879, p. 133). In subsequent versions the hoe may be a rake or pitchfork (Gibson, 1904, p. 112; Thomas, 1931, p. 165; Halpert, Mitchell, and Dickason, 1942, p. 95; Masterson, 1942, pp. 207, 238; Brendle and Troxell, 1944, p. 187; Randolph, 1951, p. 135). In some of the stories inflation really prevails; in that of Halpert, *et al.*, the farmer gets enough lumber out of his swelled hoe handle to build 20 five-room houses, and in the Brendle and Troxell tale enough shingles to roof all his buildings.

In another yarn recorded by Halpert (1942, p. 52) a toothpick in a man's mouth is struck, with the result that there is enough lumber to build a 12-room home. Unfortunately, when the paint is applied to the new mansion, the curative property of the turpentine reduces the swelling to the original toothpick. Boatright (1931, p. 274; 1934, p. 9) recounts the tragic tale of Peg-Leg Ike, who was bitten in his wooden leg and, despite the frantic efforts of his friends armed with axes to chop away the swelling timber, was choked to death by its growth. The sorrowing survivors got enough kindling to last all winter.

Then there was the wagon tongue that was bitten. Fortunately it was possible to chop it away from the wagon in time to save the latter (Russell, 1934, p. 192; Boatright, 1934, p. 9; Botkin, 1944, p. 565). A cypress stick swelled to produce enough railroad ties to build a mile of track; the disaster that occurred when rain washed the venom out of the ties may well be imagined (Matschat, 1938, p. 110; Botkin, 1949, p. 447). In one story, a bitten sapling swelled to the size of a California sequoia (Goldsmith, 1951, p. 30). And then there was the mattress, which, when bitten, swelled into a featherbed (Fisher, 1939, p. 130).

Shippey (1948, p. 193; Botkin, 1951, p. 666) tells of a boy in an auto race around the Salton Sea. He was so unfortunate as to puncture all four tires in a cholla-cactus patch, but then ran into a bunch of rattlers that bit his tires, which swelled so that he didn't even have to slow down. Needless to say the youngster beat all the professionals. Sometimes the rattlers that bite tires are themselves blown up (Cohen and Ehrenpreis, 1947, p. 63; Dobie, 1947b, p. 90).

Related to the discoloration around a rattlesnake bite is the idea that, if a rattler strikes a piece of raw meat, the meat will almost instantly turn green (Crites, 1952, p. 65).

HOW RATTLESNAKES CATCH AND EAT THEIR PREY

Charming Prey

Another old and controversial myth relates to the supposed power of a rattlesnake to charm its prey. This idea is not restricted to rattlers and was, in fact, attributed to vipers and other snakes before rattlers had been brought to the attention of Europeans (Severinus, 1651, see Riddell, 1929, p. 222; Sprengell, 1732, p. 296; Owen, 1742, p. 136; Howey, 1928, p. 192). However, since colonial days the rattlesnake has become the principal exponent of this mysterious power, and, as a result, many of the disputes regarding the truth of the myth have centered on the rattler. Nor must it be thought that this is a belief which time has dispelled; on the contrary, credence is quite general today, as will be evidenced by some of the remarks of my correspondents.

Briefly, it is the belief that rattlesnakes have the power of so charming, fascinating, or hypnotizing prey that it makes no effort to escape, and even moves helplessly toward its doom. In its most accute form, the myth recounts how a rattler at the foot of a tree has only to fix a baleful eye on its prospective victims aloft, whereupon birds come fluttering down, or squirrels descend helplessly, and deliberately walk into the snake's open mouth.

Nonbelievers in these stories explain most of them along these lines:

1. The fluttering bird is using the broken-wing stratagem to draw the snake away from its nest or young.

2. The victim, out of curiosity, is investigating a strange and brightly colored creature.

3. The strange actions of the victim are explained by the fact that it had already been bitten, but had not succumbed, when the observer came upon the scene.

4. The victim is paralyzed by fear.

5. The victim is affected by a poisonous breath or effluvium emanating from the snake.

Modern herpetologists consider the last two explanations to be as illusory as that which they seek to explain. When all of these explanations fail, one may attribute the stories to faulty observation or inaccurate memory—inaccurate in the sense of inability to distinguish between things seen and things heard or read about, which later become imbedded in the memory as actual personal experiences.

There is some difference of opinion as to whether the Indians believed in the power of the rattlesnake to fascinate its victims. Adair (1775, p. 236) said that they had this belief. One of the earliest accounts, that of Lederer (1672, p. 6), relates that a snake, lying basking in the sun, had only to fix his eyes on a squirrel high in a tree to bring it tumbling down into its jaws. This he was told by Indians. The same story was repeated by Blome (1686, p. 161). But actually the Indians were more skeptical than the colonists, according to Barton (1805, p. 167).

Beverly (1705, p. 65; 1722, p. 262) describes the charming of a hare by a rattler; but, judged by the actions of the hare, it had been bitten before Beverly happened on the scene. Walduck's report of 1714 (Masterson, 1938, p. 214) says that squirrels and birds were charmed from a tree 50 feet high. Mather (1714, p. 67) heard the same story from the Indians. Lawson (1714, plate) pictures a rattler waiting with open mouth under a tree for a charmed squirrel to come down. This story is repeated by Dudley (1723, p. 293) and Brickell (1737, p. 144). It will be observed that the myth was quite firmly established in these early colonial days; in fact, almost every traveler who mentioned rattlers at all commented on their power of fascination (Byrd, 1929, p. 158, but written in 1728; Bonnecamps, 1929, p. 403, written in 1750; Kalm, 1752–53, p. 60; Watson, 1754, p. 284; Bossu, 1771, p. 362; Loskiel, 1794, p. 88; Winterbotham, 1795, vol. 4, p. 406).

Sloane (1734, p. 323) was one of the first to be skeptical; it was his opinion that the animals presumed to be charmed had already been bitten. Brookes (1763, vol. 3, p. 368) and Kearsley (1766, p. 73) also doubted the power of fascination.

Goldsmith (1774, vol. 7, p. 214) tells of an experiment in which a mouse was placed in a rattler's cage. The snake fixed its eyes on the little animal and opened its mouth to the widest extent, whereupon the mouse, after a mental struggle, obligingly ran in. Goldsmith does not state by whom this experiment was conducted; it was not he, although his repetition of the story increased its acceptance down through the years. Wesley (1770, p. 174; 1784, p. 35) mentions a similar experiment, possibly the same one. Later repetitions were those of Pennant (1787, p. 88), Burnaby (1798, p. 64), and T. Smith (1806–7, vol. 6, p. 86).

Barton (1799, p. 76) seems to have been the first to give serious attention to the problem of the rattler's mystic power. He read a paper on the subject before the American Philosophical Society, April 4, 1794; it was printed as a booklet in 1796. He doubts whether the idea originated with the Indians (p. 78), although he says some Indians have the theory that rattlers can charm their prey by sounding the rattle. Barton comments on Linnaeus' belief in fascination; the latter was very credulous. Lacépède also believed the story, but thought the animal might already have been poisoned by the snake's breath; but Barton denies that the breath is infectious (p. 90). His conclusion is that stories of fascination are usually told of snakes in the spring, when the creatures supposedly fascinated have eggs or young to protect, and that their curious antics are accounted for as devices for drawing snakes away from their nests.

Barton's paper started a controversy. Blumenbach (1798, p. 251), who felt that Barton had slighted some of his previously expressed opinions, replied at length. He concluded that fascination must be true because rattlers are too slow and lazy to get prey by any other means (p. 255). Barton denied this effectively (1800, p. 1). Later (1805, p. 167) he repeated an Indian legend that had led the colonists to attribute a belief in fascination to the Indians, whereas in reality they held no such belief.

Toplis (1804, p. 382) related the story of a man hypnotized by a black snake, thereby verifying the belief, already expressed by others, that man is by no means immune to the powerful eye of a snake, rattlesnakes included. It was Toplis' theory that the victims are paralyzed by fear, as had also been suggested by Stedman (1796, p. 196). Further discussions were those of Williamson (1807, p. 341), who also favored the theory of extreme fear; Foot (1807, p. 113), who suggested a kind of pleasurable mesmerism; and Darlington (1808, p. 257), who liked neither the Williamson nor Foot theories. Doddridge (1824, p. 81) adhered to the idea of an intoxicating odor; once smelled it is never to be confused with any other. He told of a laborer who placed a live rattler in a barrel. Later he leaned over the edge to look in. The eyes of the snake were fixed on him like balls of fire. He became sick at the stomach, but fortunately was pulled away by a companion before being completely overcome. Other accounts of the charming of humans are those of Garden (1817, p. 55), Howison (1822, p. 169), and Arfwedson (1834, vol. 1, p. 77). Nash (1827, p. 368) favored the poisonous-emanation and rattle theories, both of which were again disputed by Williamson (1828, p. 388). Although a more scientific attitude was now being adopted by some (Rengger, 1829, p. 92; Storer, 1839, p. 234; Linsley, 1843, p. 45; Schlegel, 1844, p. 69; Audubon and Bachman, 1854, vol. 1, p. 58; Oswald, 1879, p. 607; Brown, 1881b, p. 106; Maynard, 1884, p. 8), other popular writers continued to promulgate a belief in fascination: e.g., Hunter, 1823, p. 180; Newman, 1854, p. 14; Thorpe, 1855, p. 480; Wood, 1863, p. 102; McGee, 1879, p. 841; and Crites, 1952, p. 54. Flack (1866, p. 324) warned hunters to beware of the rattler's hypnotic eye. Even Lydekker (1896, p. 242) held to a theory of intimidation.

Several writers stress the marked dilatation of the eye of a rattler when it is charming its prey. Foot (1807, p. 119) says it projects its large eyes to an unusual size. T. (1887, p. 552) states that a rattler's eye is so dreadful that few people can look at it for more than a moment. Orcutt (1891, p. 190) mentions the strong magnetic influence of the rattler's eye (see also p. 352). Hopkins (1930, p. 87) says that, in charming a quail, the snake "exerted its mesmeric power, the eyes . . . were dilated to the size of a 10-cent piece." As a matter of fact, except for a widening of the pupil in the dark and a slight capability of angular movement, a rattlesnake has no eye control. Certainly the snake cannot control the size of its eyes, meaning the size of the exposed portion of the eyeball, since it has neither eyelids nor the power to move the scales that surround the eye. The very fact that, since a snake cannot wink, it stares unwaveringly, may have been one of the bases of the theory of fascination.

The following are some later references to fascination as folklore: Johnson (1896, p. 96), Turner (1899, p. 5), Dobie (1926, p. 52; 1947b, p. 91), Bogusch (1926, p. 115), Clark (1928, p. 143), Strecker (1929b, p. 16), Brendle and Unger (1935, p. 199), Sass (1935, p. 254), Rayburn (1941, p. 265), and Masterson (1946, p. 179).

Occasionally, carnivals or snake shows, to stimulate the apprehensive curiosity of the customers, state that attendants will be on hand to lead out anyone who may be overcome by carelessly exchanging stares with a rattlesnake.

Some reports of fascination by my own correspondents have been these:

I have seen rattlesnakes catch a blackbird out of the air while the bird was on the wing. I don't know how the snake did it, as the bird would just flutter to the snake's mouth and the snake would take it head first.

❖

Once I was in the woods in late October and on the ground was a squirrel about half grown, which seemed to stay in the same place. It was squealing and I thought it had fallen from its nest. I caught it and put it in my hunting coat. I took about two steps and heard another sound, and soon located a very large rattlesnake all coiled and rattling. His head was up and just fixing to strike. He was about two feet from the squirrel and must have had it charmed or hypnotized. I shot and killed the snake and made a pet of the squirrel.

❖

I once saw a rattlesnake charm a mouse. The mouse was about six inches from the snake's head and was perfectly still, as if frozen in one position. I stopped and watched them until the snake saw or heard me and crawled off. The mouse did not move for awhile after the snake left. So I know that rattlesnakes have the power to paralyze their prey, in spite of opinions to the contrary.

At zoos, there have been no observations on captive rattlesnakes with prey that verify any theory of fascination. Birds and small mammals placed in cages with rattlesnakes, as soon as they have become used to their new surroundings, pay no attention whatever to their reptilian cage mates. They run about, nestle against, or perch on the snakes; and, as far as rats and mice are concerned, if not supplied with food, they will frequently eat the heads, tails, or rattles of the snakes. It is true that occasionally a hungry snake will strike one of the animals and kill and eat it; but unless this occurs, the animals evince no fear. It cannot be supposed that behavior patterns in the wild could be so different that snakes, which regularly fascinate or charm their prey there, would never show the slightest ability to do so in captivity. Mitchell and Pocock (1908, p. 739) tell of the same lack of evidence of fascination in the London Zoo. Guenther (1931, p. 341) expressed the opinion that prey, when immobile, is seeking safety in procrypsis rather than being frozen by the hypnotic eye of the snake.

Field studies by the University of California have been similarly negative. Although Grinnell, Dixon, and Linsdale (1930, p. 153) saw, near a rattlesnake, a small rabbit that appeared frightened, it may have been bitten before they found it. Linsdale (1946, p. 67) and Fitch (1948, p. 555) have discussed the reactions of ground squirrels toward rattlesnakes. They have a characteristic call and tail-waving reaction that serve to alert the colony to danger, but this is quite the opposite of fascination.

As a matter of fact, rattlers require no such mysterious power to get their food. They either hunt their prey in holes or rock crevices, or, more often, lie in wait along paths and runways. An unsuspecting bird or mammal while passing is struck and released. It either dies immediately from the venom or it may run a short way before it succumbs, in which case the snake follows by scent, and, upon finding the dead animal, proceeds to eat it. Rarely a rattlesnake strikes and holds its prey; this it does more frequently with cold-blooded animals, such as lizards, upon which venom takes effect more slowly.

Rattlesnakes have a fairly good sense of sight, especially for moving objects at close range, a good sense of smell, and an additional sense in the differential-temperature receptor of the facial pit. Their venom is a means of immobilizing any prey that comes within range of a strike. Because of their low-temperature metabolism they require a much-reduced food intake, compared with birds and mammals of similar size. The conclusion with respect to fascination, whether by eye, odor, or rattle, is that they neither need nor exert it.

LICKING PREY

It is frequently stated that rattlesnakes—in common with other snakes—always lick their prey and cover it with saliva before swallowing it (Byrd, 1929, p. 158, but written in 1728; Kalm, 1752–53, p. 60; Watson, 1754, p. 287; Wesley, 1770, vol. 1, p. 173; 1784, vol. 2, p. 35; W., 1846, p. 62; Lombard, 1881, p. 88; Bealer, 1921, p. 69). As a matter of fact, such a procedure would be quite impossible with the slender tongue of a snake. The belief comes from having observed regurgitated prey that has become coated with digestive juices. This coating is applied so quickly, during the passage of the prey down the throat or in the stomach, that anyone forcing a snake to disgorge would be convinced it must have been coated prior to being swallowed. No snake, rattler or otherwise, while eating under observation in captivity, has ever been seen to coat its prey with saliva. But it is well known that they do feel or sense their prey by repeatedly touching it with their tongues, probably for olfactory reasons. This confusion of memory or observation explains such statements as the following by my correspondents: "I have watched rattlers feed on small squirrels and mice. When they eat them they cover them with a thick slime and then swallow them." Or another: "I saw a rattlesnake cover a dead coyote pup with a sort of fluid, and then start to swallow it head first."

There is a folklore belief that rattlesnakes cannot regurgitate. This is quite untrue; captured rattlers frequently throw up prey they have recently eaten.

MYTHICAL FOODS

Although it is known that rattlesnakes—like all snakes, except possibly one in South Africa (Irvine, 1953, p. 173)—eat only animal food, there is a rather widespread tradition that they eat various kinds of berries, especially chokecherries and huckleberries, as well as cactus fruits. This may have originated from the discovery, in rattlers' stomachs, of some of the items of food which had originally been eaten by the snakes' prey. One correspondent killed two large rattlers and found watermelon seeds in their bodies, from which he concluded they must have been feeding on a broken melon. It is to be assumed that the seeds were the food remains of some mammals that had been swallowed by the snakes. One visitor to the San Diego Zoo was heard to remark that rattlesnakes are fond of honey.

Another belief is that snakes can milk cows; this is an extremely ancient and widespread myth, and is told of many different kinds of snakes, occasionally including rattlers (e.g., Evers, 1951, p. 114, Catskill folklore). The idea is quite fantastic for reasons that have been sufficiently discussed by others (e.g., Schmidt and Davis, 1941, p. 7), and is mentioned here only because of the often heard myth that rattlesnakes are fond of milk and will drink from a saucer. Conceivably, a thirsty rattler might do so to secure a substitute for water, although Allen and Neill (1950d, p. 9; see also Kunzé, 1879, p. 208) found that they refused milk even when denied water. Milk is not a natural food of these reptiles, and stories of their fondness for it are imaginary. In this category we may place the tale by Byam (1849, p. 183) of the tame rattler in Central America that was so fond of milk it would climb up on its master's chair at breakfast to get its daily share. Kipling's *Jungle Book* did much to spread the idea that snakes are fond of milk. Conan Doyle's famous short story "The Adventure of the Speckled Band," in the Sherlock Holmes series, is another offender.

Bartram (1791, p. 218) tells of a rattler that went about an Indian camp picking up fragments of provisions and licking platters. Not long ago there was a press release to the effect that a rattlesnake had found, on a window sill, a macaroni salad left there to cool, and had "devoured every bit of it. The snake, unable to navigate swiftly with so heavy a load, was easily killed."

Another well-known yarn concerns the snake that crawls into a hen house, swallows a china egg, and then finds the hole by which it entered too small for escape. This is occasionally told of rattlesnakes. It is true that snakes are sometimes prevented from escaping via their means of ingress, because of the bulge produced by the prey they have swallowed. Marable (1943, p. 132) photographed a San Diegan gopher snake (*Pituophis catenifer annectens*) trying in vain to crawl through the bars of a bird cage after eating the canary.

FOLKLORE REMEDIES DERIVED FROM RATTLESNAKES

Folklore remedies that involve rattlesnakes, either in whole or in part, have been prescribed for a variety of diseases. Those attributed to the Indians, and some that were current in colonial days, have been treated in chapter 16. A section of chapter 14 has been devoted to the curative properties of rattlesnake oil and fat;

and snake-bite treatments derived from the snakes themselves have been discussed in chapter 13 on snake-bite remedies. Others, not falling in these categories, will now be described.

Remedies prepared from vipers were popular for a variety of diseases in ancient and medieval times. Particularly esteemed was a universal remedy known as theriaca, a prescription compounded of many ingredients, of which viper flesh was one. Components were added or changed from time to time, but the snake element never lost its importance. This and other ophidian remedies in the primitive European pharmacopoeia have been extensively described. The following references will be found of interest, particularly if it is desired to trace the sources of some of the folklore cures of today that include rattlesnake parts: Pliny, 1855–57, vol. 5, pp. 395–7, 403, 409, 412–5, 430–1, 435, 444, 447–9, 451, 454, 456–7, 460, 462–3, 465–6; vol. 6, pp. 35, 43–4; book xxix, chaps. 20–22, 29, 36, 38; book xxx, chaps. 8, 12, 21, 23–25, 27, 30, 32, 36, 39, 42, 43, 46, 47; book xxxii, chaps. 26, 32, 33; Topsell, 1608, pp. 33, 37–48, 302–5; 1658, 808–10; French, 1651, p. 99; Redi, 1665, p. 161; Charas, 1670b, pp. 140–220; Grew, 1681, p. 49; Mead, 1702, p. 30; 1745, p. 48; Owen, 1742, p. 36; Adams, 1844–47, vol. 3, p. 85; Furnival, 1870, p. 273; Dyer, 1884, p. 256; Jayakar (Damiri), 1906–8, vol. 1, pp. 63, 654; Leighton, 1901, p. 74; Steele (Bartholomaeus Anglicus), 1905, p. 70; Wootton, 1910, vol. 1, p. 90; vol. 2, pp. 19, 38; Budge, 1913, vol. 2, p. 409; Allbutt, 1921, p. 354; Thorndike, 1923–41, vol. 1, pp. 91, 130, 142, 159, 168, 171, 733, 756; vol. 2, pp. 210, 361, 473, 755, 795, 910; Kanner, 1928, p. 142; Gunther (Dioscorides), 1934, p. 97; and Dawson, 1935, p. 206.

Coming now to rattlesnake cures, we find some of the Indian usages in treating toothache or improving the teeth (p. 1166) still practiced by the whites. These involve such expedients as biting a live rattler along the back; using a rattler vertebra as a toothpick or hanging it around a child's neck; or putting rattler fat in a tooth cavity (Bergen, 1899, p. 70; Showers, 1900, p. 443; Puckett, 1926, p. 373; Dobie, 1926, p. 52; Blanks, 1932, p. 30; Dodson, 1932, p. 84; Relihan, 1947, p. 168; Baylor, 1947, p. 149; Reynolds, 1952, p. 66). I have heard that in Louisiana a necklace of rattlesnake bones is recommended for teething children. The smoke-dried gall was reported by Roubaud in 1757 to be a specific for toothache (Thwaites, 1896–1901, vol. 70, part 1, p. 141).

In the cure of respiratory diseases, particularly tuberculosis, the dried flesh of a rattlesnake, or a broth, has long been used (Carver, 1778, p. 485, colonial U. S.; Loskiel, 1794, p. 114; Dobrizhoffer, 1822, vol. 2, p. 290, Paraguay; Mordecai, 1860, p. 66, Virginia; Ingersoll, 1884b, p. 107, North Carolina; Surface, 1906, p. 194, Pennsylvania; Fogel, 1915, p. 273, Pennsylvania Germans; Thomas and Thomas, 1920, p. 100, Kentucky; Pound, 1946, p. 166, pneumonia in Nebraska; Musick, 1947, p. 49, West Virginia; and Evers, 1951, p. 110, Catskill Mountains). In 1950 I heard of the use of powdered dried rattlesnake, sprinkled on food, as a treatment for tuberculosis in northern Baja California, Mexico.

The following are rattler-based cures for other afflictions: The heart and liver; warm and raw, for palsy, and a backbone necklace for chills and fever (Kalm, 1752–53, p. 187); a rattler drowned in wine for leprosy (Kearsley, 1766, p. 75); rattler gall mixed with clay for fevers and smallpox (Lawson, 1709, p. 129; Carver, 1778, p. 485). In New England, rattler gall was recommended for biliousness

(Johnson, 1896, p. 77); also to promote longevity (Bergen, 1899, p. 70). In the Eastern states, rattler flesh was prescribed for epilepsy (Ingersoll, 1884b, p. 107).

Dried rattlesnake in corn whiskey for rheumatism and a necklace of rattler bones for epilepsy are favored in the Kentucky mountains (Thomas and Thomas, 1920, pp. 103, 113). Among the Pennsylvania Germans, to swallow the heart of a rattler will cure epilepsy (Fogel, 1915, p. 275). In Alabama a necklace of bones will keep you safe from all harm (Bergen, 1899, p. 13). A bracelet or anklet of bones will forestall swelling from fatigue in Louisiana (Roberts, 1927, p. 203). One may cure goiter by wrapping a rattler around the neck and then allowing it to crawl away; this is a Nebraska folk cure (Black, 1935, pp. 32, 35). Behead a rattler and put it in a jar filled with rice whiskey; then after a year, drink the whiskey for rheumatism; this is an Idaho cure said to be derived from the Chinese[2] (Fisher, 1939, p. 214). Baked and powdered rattler flesh is a cure for venereal disease in Yucatán and eastern Guatemala.

Puckett (1926, p. 249) and Hyatt (1935, p. 467) mention a rattlesnake remedy in reverse, a method of hexing: if powdered dried rattlesnake is put on the enemy's food or in his coffee, he will be filled with little snakes in four months. This is Negro folklore. Or, one may put dust under an enemy's hatband so that the dust will run down and blind him when he sweats. The dust should consist of powdered rattlesnake, or may be made from a rattler skin mixed with earth from the head of a grave (Puckett, 1926, p. 275).

There are many ancient myths of the curative power of snake skins. Some are founded on the basic idea that snakes restore their youth when they change their skins, and thus are virtually immortal (Nicander, translation of 1953, p. 37; Frazer, 1935, vol. 9, p. 302; Dyer, 1884, p. 257). Some of these myths have been attributed to rattlesnakes.

The early colonial accounts, and some of the later ones as well, often failed to specify just what diseases the skin was supposed to cure, although fever, small-pox, rheumatism, and blood cleaning were mentioned. Usually the skin was pulverized and taken internally (Lawson, 1709, p. 129; Brickell, 1737, p. 147; Nelson, 1740, p. 351; La Rochefoucault-Liancourt, 1799, p. 181; Weld, 1800, p. 410). Later a more mystical approach was evident, in that it was necessary only to carry or wear a skin to secure the curative effect. Kalm (1752–53, p. 187) reported that the skins with the rattles attached were worn against all kinds of sickness and to facilitate childbirth. This had been current as early as 1656 (Lindeström, 1925, pp. 186, 194).

In more recent times, Davenport (1898, p. 132) recorded the use of a rattler skin as a hatband to cure headache (Kansas folklore). This was also a Texas preventive in 1854 (Bell, 1932, p. 212). Bergen (1899, p. 76) reported the use of a rattler-skin belt in Kansas to prevent backache (it was essential that the rattler had not bitten itself), and in New Hampshire people wrapped the skin around an ankle to prevent cramps while swimming. The Kentucky mountaineers say that a belt will prevent rheumatism (Thomas and Thomas, 1920, p. 113); this

---

[2] In my school days in San Diego, it was rumored that our Chinese residents would pay large sums for live rattlesnakes to be used for some mysterious medicinal purpose. Rheumatism was at least one of the afflictions for which the flesh was used, but the method of preparation was secret (see also Spaulding, 1944, p. 172). I presume the rattlesnake, in America, replaced some indigenous viper that had been used at home in China.

is also a belief in the Catskills of New York (Evers, 1951, p. 110). A rattler skin worn around the wrist or ankle will ward off rheumatism in the extremities (Smiley, 1919, p. 379, Southwestern folklore; Puckett, 1926, p. 361, Southern Negroes; Roberts, 1927, p. 168, Louisiana). Worn around the throat, a rattler skin will cure sore throat; or it may be wrapped around an injured limb to alleviate aches and sprains (Walsh, 1923, p. 70). One of my correspondents told me of a case in Pennsylvania, in which a serious leg injury had reputedly been cured by binding with a rattler skin. Bell (1932, p. 212) recorded the use, by Mexicans in Texas in 1854, of rattlesnake skins on the cantle of a saddle to prevent saddle sores. In New York and Pennsylvania a poultice of rattlesnake skin was used in the treatment of felons and carbuncles (Herrick, 1953, p. 26).

Some rather more generalized effects procured from rattlesnake skins are these: The wearing of a skin will keep away disease (Dresslar, 1907, p. 49, California folklore); the skin of a newly killed rattler around the neck will prevent all illness (Bogusch, 1926, p. 115, Mexicans in Texas); a skin worn around the waist will prolong life (Bergen, 1899, p. 13, Kansas Negroes); one carried in the pocket will bring good luck (Bergen, 1899, p. 13, Kansas); but it is bad luck to touch a rattler's skin in Kentucky (Thomas and Thomas, 1920, p. 274). Finally, witches will be kept at bay if one carries or wears a piece of rattler skin (Thomas and Thomas, 1920, p. 281, Kentucky mountains; Hyatt, 1935, p. 535, western Illinois Negroes).

The many therapeutic uses to which rattlesnake venom has been put—never with any notable success—have been outlined in the last section of chapter 11.

PROTECTIVE METHODS AND DEVICES

There are a number of myths and tales concerning the ways in which people may protect themselves against rattlesnakes, especially by the use of barriers and repellents. These have little relation to the really effective steps that may be taken as described in chapter 13.

THE PROTECTIVE HAIR ROPE

The protective hair rope, once a widespread myth of the Southwest, has now lost somewhat of its vogue, presumably because fewer punchers sleep out on the ground today, and ordinary hemp ropes have largely supplanted the valued horsehair lariats of a bygone era. Briefly, the story was to the effect that a hair rope, if placed so as to encircle a bed or camp, would keep the snakes out because the hairs would scratch their bellies, causing them to turn away. At one time this legend was generally believed, and I suspect that more of these psychological fences were nightly thrown about desert beds than some of the old-timers would now be willing to admit. In fact, a few of my correspondents still swear by them.

Of course, the weakness of the scheme lies in the fact, which is easy to demonstrate by trial, that a rattler's ventral covering is so tough he would hardly feel the hairs on a reata; at any rate, they would not incommode a creature that does not hesitate to crawl through or over cactus.

The earliest published accounts I have found of the hair rope are those of Kendall (1844, vol. 1, p. 93) and Gregg (1844, vol. 2, p. 231). But Dewees (1852, p. 312) quotes a letter written from San Antonio de Bexar, Texas, on March 18, 1826, in which this use of the hair rope is mentioned. Other references are Michler (1857, p. 121), Lanham (1863, p. 230), Flack (1866, p. 337), Victor (1870, p. 215), Bailey (1876, p. 404), O'Reilly (1889, p. 19), Pollock (1911, p. 152), Randolph (1931, p. 133), Summerhayes (1939, pp. 60, 73), Vestal (1941, p. 148), Pound (1946, p. 170), Wimmer (1946, p. 8), De Lys (1948, p. 80), and Allen (1949a, p. 71). A communication from A. S. Hallidie, the inventor of the cable car, says that hair ropes were used at the mines in California in 1856. Tschiffely (1933, p. 215) mentions their use in South America, and Picado (1931, p. 25) in Costa Rica.

There have been a number of adverse comments on the value of the hair rope. Barnes (1922, p. 387; 1928, p. 48), Bogert (1927, p. 298), Bevan (1932, p. 71), and Schmidt and Davis (1941, plate 1) have reinforced denials of effectiveness with photographs of rattlers in the act of crossing hair ropes. Hogg (1928, p. 54), Peters (1937, p. 22), and Lynn (1931, p. 128) also made tests that showed ropes to be useless. Sanford (1953, p. 28) mentions an incident of a prospector who protected his bed with a grass rope and awoke to find a rattler coiled on the bedding.

One folklore report says that the rope must be striped with black and white to look like a king snake. Stimpson (1946, p. 263) and Breland (1928, p. 222) think that snakes might be repelled by the human odor of a recently handled rope. Adair (1930, p. 62), Ridings (1936, p. 371), and Blanchard (1940, p. 32), although admitting that a rattler will cross a rope when driven in a test, doubt whether it would do so in the normal course of a nocturnal ramble. But in such tests as I have seen, rattlesnakes paid no attention to the rope. Chase (1919, p. 183) tried a hair rope on a sidewinder and found that it would only cross the rope backwards, which is not surprising as this is the normal way in which a sidewinder crawls (see sidewinding, p. 338).

Strecker, in one of his interesting papers on Southwestern reptile myths and their origins (1926a, p. 69), gives this extension to the rope story: A rattlesnake has been known to squirt his venom at a victim taking refuge beyond a rope. Lanham (1863, p. 230) went so far as to report that, in one instance, a dozen rattlers were found coiled next to a hair rope in the morning, as if waiting for its removal so that they might invade the camp. Schmidt (1929, p. 4) says that in some versions of the myth a chalkline is substituted for the hair rope in the protective scheme. King (1941, p. 22) mentions a burned strip produced by lighting a ring of gunpowder as another barrier of this type.

Boatright (1934, p. 15), in one of his Texas tall stories, says some cowboys put a hair rope around their camp one night and in the morning there were 129 defunct rattlers that had tickled themselves to death trying to cross it.

The ancients used many repellents around their camps, most often chemicals or plants or leaves that the snakes were believed to fear (Adams, 1844–47, p. 157). Later it was reported that no snake would cross a ring of Irish earth (Johnson, 1896, p. 103; Daniels and Stevans, 1903, vol. 2, p. 698). The hair rope may have evolved from these ideas concerning repellents.

Finally, here are some comments from my correspondents:

It was the common practice of the cowmen in early cow days to make one's bed down and then lay a horse-hair rope around it. During years of actual range work, I do not recall an instance of a snake crossing the hair ropes to one's bed, but I have known of a number of cases where the snakes crawled upon beds not protected by a hair rope. Of course, snakes in captivity would disregard a rope as they want to get away.

⟡

I have placed hair ropes around rattlers and they pass over them as readily as they will any other obstacle. *H. Lee Morris, U. S. Fish and Wildlife Service, Tulelake, Calif.*

⟡

Rattlesnakes will crawl over a hair rope; I've tried it. *Ben Nelson, U. S. Forest Service, Mayer, Ariz.*

Stories of rattlers crawling across the bodies of sleeping persons are not infrequent. Usually this happens in the daytime with a horrified audience afraid to take any action for fear the sleeper, suddenly awakened, will make some disastrous movement. Versions of this yarn are told by Cox (1832, p. 81) and Sullivan (1852, p. 175). This story is obviously related to rattlesnakes as camp bedfellows, which I have mentioned in the section of chapter 13 on prevention of accidents. Some tall tales based on this theme are related by Boatright (1934, p. 14).

THE INFALLIBLE SHOT

Another myth, widespread throughout the West, is to the effect that it is unnecessary to aim carefully when shooting a rattler, since the snake will automatically line up his head with the barrel of the gun and the first bullet will inevitably find its mark. An even less possible variant maintains that a rattler will strike at and hit the oncoming bullet.

I think the derivation of this myth lies in the fact that one ordinarily shoots a rattler at a much closer range than almost any other object. The aim therefore is generally good, although I can testify that it is quite easy to miss a rattler even at close range, especially with a derisive audience on the sidelines.

At any rate, a simple experiment will prove that an angry rattler in his striking coil does not automatically line up with the weapon, as the following notes from my diary show:

June 7, 1945: This morning I tried the gun-barrel experiment on several rattlers with absolutely negative results. Both a 20-gauge shotgun and a .410 pistol were used. I had two large western diamonds, a Great Basin rattler, and a sidewinder. Also a red diamond, but he can't be counted as he wouldn't assume a fighting pose. It was a bright sunny day. The snakes showed, by facing a person and assuming a defensive coil, that they could see movement readily enough. They were tried with the guns close and distant (from a few inches to several feet). In no case was there any tendency of a snake's head to follow the barrel. When the gun was aimed so that it would just miss the head, the snake would not move the slight distance required to get in line, although it was looking at the gun barrel and it would have had to move its head only an inch or two, laterally, to line up with the barrel. With the breech open it was easy to watch the rattler through and along the barrel to determine just where a shot would strike.

As for a rattler's ability to move fast enough to intercept an oncoming bullet, this is unworthy of serious consideration, particularly since Van Riper's tests have shown the strike of a rattler to be much slower than is commonly supposed (see p. 449).

Among those who have recently discussed the gun myth are Bateman (1918, p. 167), Hoag (1927, p. 16), Bevan (1933, p. 59), Peters (1937, p. 86), Benton (1937, p. 210), Devoe (1945, p. 486), and Allison (1946, p. 111). Bevan shows photographs of bullets kicking up dust in front of a rattler. Yet the fact that this legend still holds sway, is shown by the following statement from one of my correspondents: "You don't have to aim at a rattler to shoot him. Just point your gun in his direction and he will line up so you can't miss." A recent newspaper report put it this way: "A Florida rattler can see a bullet speeding toward it. Instead of dodging the bullet, the rattler strikes, as it would at any other moving object. And that's the reason you hear so many reports of hunters shooting rattler's heads off. The hunters don't shoot the rattler; they shoot at it and the snake does the rest."

REPELLENTS AND AMULETS

The belief that many substances will repel snakes, keeping them out of homes and camps, and even preventing their biting people who may be traveling through the woods, is an ancient one. Nicander enumerated a number of such substances about 150 B.C. (translation of 1953, pp. 31, 33, 35; Adams, 1844–47, vol. 2, p. 156). Pliny[3] described a large number of vegetable substances, and a few of animal or mineral origin, that would repel serpents. Generally they were applied by burning them as a smudge in the home or camp, by strewing them about, or by rubbing them on the body. A few attractants were also mentioned. Lucan's *Pharsalia* likewise contains such a list (Riley, 1909, p. 375). A few other references to ancient and medieval beliefs in repellents are Topsell (1608, pp. 37, 40, 297; 1658, p. 618), Steele (1905, p. 105, lore of Bartholomaeus Anglicus about 1260 A.D.), Thorndike (1923–41, vol. 1, pp. 86, 495, 599, 614, 755), and Galen (1916, p. 85).

American repellent lore was either of European origin or derived from Indian practices. The latter have been discussed in chapter 16 (p. 1103). Although by no means all references to the repellents used in the United States specifically mention rattlesnakes, nevertheless I shall not segregate those that do from the others that refer to snakes in general, since rattlers are so much more widespread and dangerous than the few other venomous snakes found in this country that we may be sure the users of repellents had rattlesnakes primarily in mind.

One of the most popular botanical repellents was the white ash (Woodruff, 1833, p. 337; Paine, 1875, p. 133), but W. (1846, p. 63) found it useless. Another was the onion (Fogel, 1915, p. 220; and Brendle and Unger, 1935, p. 201, Pennsylvania German folklore; and Buley, 1950, vol. 1, p. 267, pioneer "old" Northwest). Ash and onions were both used for this purpose in Europe in ancient times. Other botanical repellents were mentioned by Dumont (1753, p. 109), Byrd (1929, p. 152, but written in 1728), Redfield (1937, p. 22), Botkin (1947, p. 286), and Webber (1951, p. 30).

Burning old shoes was recommended in Maryland folklore (Whitney and

---

[3] Pliny mentions about 70 substances as snake repellents. They are cited on the following pages of the 1855–57 edition: vol. 1, p. 212; vol. 2, pp. 125, 126, 282, 301, 302, 396, 548; vol. 3, pp. 136, 152, 366, 459; vol. 4, pp. 216, 218, 219, 225, 252, 253, 261, 266, 269, 270, 292, 375, 378, 385, 418, 429, 434, 467, 517; vol. 5, pp. 9, 10, 24, 25, 27, 31, 59, 60, 84, 118, 119, 124, 126, 127, 164, 246, 290, 302, 311, 317, 329, 330, 331, 395, 398; vol. 6, pp. 294, 303.

Bullock, 1925, p. 57), in that of Arkansas (Randolph, 1947, p. 68), and by the Pennsylvania Germans (Brendle and Unger, 1935, p. 200). The latter also burned snakes for the same purpose. A string of snake bones worn around the ankle will prevent snakes from biting, according to Louisiana folklore (Roberts, 1927, p. 148). Lead beads have been recommended in Tennessee (McGlasson, 1941, p. 15). As snakes will not crawl near glass—so it is believed—glass jars have been used in the Ozark country (Rayburn, 1941, p. 265).

In Texas the Mexicans throw a sombrero over a hole that a snake has been seen to enter, with the belief that this will prevent its coming out (King, 1941, p. 24). I have heard it stated that in Texas some cowpunchers greased their boots with king-snake oil to keep the rattlers from striking. It was the custom in the pioneer Northwest (upper eastern Mississippi Valley) simply to put the curse of Adam on a snake, which would crawl away and die (Buley, 1950, vol. 1, p. 267). Some other references to snake repellents are the following: Taylor, 1665, pp. 43, 76; Clayton, 1744, p. 153; Dobrizhoffer, 1822, vol. 2, p. 303; Cox, 1832, p. 82; Irving, 1836, p. 151; Flack, 1866, p. 338; Anon., 1858a, p. 327; Anon., 1883b, p. 743; Budge, 1913, vol. 2, p. 688; David Thompson, 1916, p. 525; McCulloch, 1918, p. 5; Browne, 1927, vol. 1, p. 306; de Wet, 1929, p. 1038; Dorsch, 1929, p. 3; Tschiffely, 1933, p. 215; Terhune, 1938, p. 449; Uhler, 1944, p. 2; Stimpson, 1946, p. 84; and Fawcett, 1953, p. 212.

It goes without saying that none of the innumerable botanical repellents recommended from the days of Nicander and Pliny down to the present have been effectual beyond possibly affording the user a feeling of relief from fear. Some chemicals of a caustic or volatile nature may produce some slight or brief protection; their use has been discussed elsewhere (pp. 879 and 1127).

MYTHICAL CREATURES

GIANT RATTLESNAKES

Rattlesnake lengths are usually exaggerated; in addition, some measurements are based on dried skins, which can be stretched up to half again as long as their original possessors. Thus we hear of 8- and 9-foot rattlers in Florida and Texas, where a 7-foot snake would be quite exceptional. But although a 9-foot snake is at least a possibility, as has been discussed in chapter 4, some of the stories heard about large rattlers enter the realm of the fantastic and are to be considered myths. These seem to be particularly prevalent in the Southeastern section of the country. I should say that rattlesnakes ought to be placed in the mythical category at 10 feet, thus allowing for some exaggeration.

Rattlesnakes of a truly legendary length were described at an early date. In 1714, Walduck (Masterson, 1938, p. 214) mentioned rattlers 17 feet long. Mittelberger, referring to Pennsylvania in 1750, said they grew to 18 feet (1898, p. 81); Dumont (1753, p. 109) described one of 22 feet. Wesley (1770, vol. 1, p. 173; 1784, vol. 2, p. 35) gives a range of 10 to 15 feet. Bossu (1771, p. 368) said the big ones could eat a whole roe deer. Pennant (1787, p. 87) says newspaper accounts record rattlesnakes 14 feet long. An advertisement in the London *Times*, November 9, 1796, calls attention to one on exhibition there that was between 9 and 10 feet long, reminiscent of some of the roadside snake-show signs of today. Ashe (1808, p. 143) killed one 12 feet in length that measured 15 inches around "at the shoulders." This was in Ohio and therefore a timber rattler. Spencer (1836, p. 221) tells of a fellow hunter who was chased by a rattler about a rod (16½ feet) long. Tixier, in 1844 (1940, p. 76), said that *horridus* grew to 15 to 18 feet. Mentioned by Domenech (1858, p. 48) was one that was mistaken for a dead tree. When killed it was found to measure 17 feet. Higgins (1873, p. 81) tells of an Ohio specimen that measured 12 feet 4 inches. Goode (1874b, p. 123) had heard of one weighing 117 pounds (such a snake would measure about 17 feet) with 87 rattles, killed in the previous July, and asked through the pages of *Forest and Stream,* whether anyone had any information on this snake or others phenomenally large. Robinson (1896, p. 711) mentions a mythical monster in Florida measuring 18 feet. Bailey (1905, p. 50) says he was told the rattlers in Texas grew to a length of 11 to 13 feet, but, in a thorough biological survey of the state that he made, the longest he encounterer measured 50 inches. Lloyd (1951, p. 30) reported an 11-footer blasted out by a construction crew in Oklahoma. I received from one of my correspondents a report of a Texas rattler 15 feet 3 inches long and weighing 58 pounds, minus the head. Strecker (1929b, p. 10) discusses exaggerated snake lengths as myths. McMillan (1955, no. 3, p. 30; no. 5, p. 31) showed, by offering prizes for live Texas rattlers exceeding 6 feet, how rare such creatures are. At $10 per inch for each inch over 6 feet, the largest rattler brought its finder $90.

An interesting communication lately received is this from Mrs. Alberta V. Meling, Rancho San José, Baja California, Mexico:

> For a number of years, we have been hearing stories about a very large rattlesnake said to live in some caves a few miles from our ranch. We have always listened to them with a smile and forgotten them. Last spring, a man who has worked for us a long time and whom we know to be truthful and not overexcitable, came and said he had seen the big rattlesnake. He said it was immense. He got terribly frightened and ran away. Now, three days ago, his son was gathering wild honey (the bees live in caves) when he saw the big snake. He had camped and was making a fire when he noticed his horse was excited. He looked and there, about 20 steps away, came the snake toward him. He ran to the horse and mounted and sat watching. The campfire was between him and the snake. The snake came on but when it neared the fire it raised its head 4 or 5 feet off the ground and hissed with such force it sounded like a bull. Then, it turned, went around the fire and down a draw, but kept its head up, looking back at him and hissing. The boy says it was no less than 25 feet long,[4] and he thinks it might have been 30 feet. Its rattles were as wide as his three fingers and about a foot long. The boy was terribly scared, horrified, and ran home at once. Next morning he came here to tell us. We have always told him that, if they saw the big snake at any time, we wanted to see it. So my two sons went with him. They hunted all day but could not find any trace of the snake.

There has recently been a report in circulation of a rattler 21 feet long that was killed near Poteau, Oklahoma. It was said to have bitten a woman in the foot.

Data on large rattlesnakes of the legendary or tall-story type will be found in Guild (1878, p. 52), Ericson (1941, p. 113), Vestal (1941, p. 146), Claudel (1943, p. 116), Botkin (1944, p. 182), and Randolph (1951, p. 136). I like particularly

---

[4] A rattlesnake of this length, if of the same body proportions as an ordinary rattler, would weigh 275 pounds; a 30-foot rattler would weight over 400.

Randolph's Ozark story of the snake with a head the size of a water bucket and rattles as big as coffee cups.

From the *San Diego Sun,* July 30, 1881:
One day I had my 12 daughters in a wagon, and the horse became frightened and ran to the very edge of a cliff. When I came up to see what stopped him I saw a rattlesnake had wrapped around his leg, and then had thrown a number of coils around a tree and set his teeth into the bark. I measured him and he was 12 feet long. Then I unwound him and he was only 5 feet long. You know how elastic a snake is.

Evers (1951, p. 113) has a good folk tale of the man who killed a 15-foot rattler, hoping to prove to the skeptics what he had seen, only to find that he had killed two normal snakes, one going into a patch of grass, the other coming out.

Reports of phenomenally large rattlesnakes are sometimes based on stretched or misidentified skins. I once saw in a sporting-goods store the skin of a boa constrictor, with a card claiming it to be one of the largest rattlesnakes ever killed. The magazine *Texas Game and Fish,* vol. 12, no. 11, p. 2, October, 1954, (see also no. 12, p. 31), contained a photograph of a rattlesnake skin that measured 10 feet 11 inches without the head or rattles. It is not surprising that the rattles were lost, for the skin, to judge from the pattern, was that of a python. Emerick (1951, p. 32) mentions a rattlesnake skin 10 feet 2 inches long, and Briggs (1951, p. 112) another 15 feet long, but no verifying data are supplied. McMillan (1955b, p. 8) has illustrated with photographs the inaccuracies that result from judging the lengths of rattlesnakes by measurements of skins. A western diamondback (*C. atrox*) that was 6 feet 9 inches long "in the round" stretched 3 inches when hung by the head. It was then skinned, and the skin was flattened on a board. The skin measured 8 feet 6½ inches, or 26½ per cent longer than the live snake. In circumference the live snake measured 10 inches, the flattened skin 12¼ inches—a stretch of 22½ per cent. All length measurements were exclusive of the rattle.

Not long ago one of my correspondents in Alabama wrote:
I have in my possession the skin of a rattlesnake that was killed by a train in Washington County, Alabama. The skin now measures 11 feet, but originally the snake was 14 feet 6 inches long, as measured by the train crew. The rest of it was smashed by the wheels of the train and could not be saved. This snake had 43 rattles, and it was estimated that about 10 other rattles were destroyed by the train. The snake was 13 inches across the middle of the body.

My correspondent kindly forwarded the skin to me for identification; it was found to be that of an Indian python. Should anyone have cause to doubt the identification, it may be said that the skin had 62 scale rows. No species of rattler has more than 31; furthermore, the python has smooth scales, whereas those of the rattler are keeled or ridged. No rattles accompanied the skin.

A suggestive feature of many of these stories of rattlesnakes of extraordinary length is that they have, equally extraordinarily, numerous rattles, usually from 25 up. As a matter of fact, very large rattlers, say between 6 and 7 feet in length, seldom have long strings, since they tend to break the rattles off when pulling them out from under their own heavy bodies. A 7-foot rattler will weigh upward of 15 pounds.

As an example of minimizing, Juan and Ulloa (1758, vol. 1, p. 62) state that rattlers seldom exceed 2 to 2½ feet, although one species reaches 3½ feet. This should have warranted expulsion from the explorers' union of that day.

THE HORNED RATTLESNAKE

Various mythical yarns are told of horned rattlesnakes. These are not based on the true horned rattlesnake or sidewinder (*Crotalus cerastes*), a dweller of the deserts of the Southwest, which has a short, flexible, hornlike scale over each eye. The mythical horned rattler has a single rhinoceros-like horn between the eyes. These creatures were in fact—and maybe still are—a commercial product, formed by the fastening or grafting of a rooster's spur to the top of the head of a western diamond rattler. If the skin is slit, a fair degree of adherence can be obtained. For a time there was a steady demand from snake shows for these fabricated unicorns.

Some years ago there appeared a syndicated newspaper story telling of a judge who fined a snake keeper for feeding live chickens to his charge "which devoured them whole. The snake, seldom seen in California, has a bony horn nearly two inches in length which rises between its eyes." Evidently to feed snakes in a natural manner is contrary to law, but grafting a horn on a rattler is permissible.

HAIRY RATTLESNAKES

One occasionally hears of hairy rattlers, some taken seriously by those who tell of them, others as interesting items of folklore. One of the earliest was that of Dudley (1723, p. 294). Aubry encountered hairy rattlers in Arizona in 1853 (Bieber and Bender, 1938, p. 360). Randolph (1947, p. 256; 1951, p. 140) mentions them as denizens of Ozark folklore. I am told by Carvalho that the natives in Brazil believe that very old rattlesnakes grow feathers on their bodies. Presumably these stories start from observation of rattlesnakes that were shedding their skins in patches or were studded with cactus spines. I have seen them in both conditions, and the resemblance to hair was quite apparent.

RATTLESNAKE–BULL-SNAKE HYBRIDS

A myth of wide distribution, particularly in the Missouri Basin states, is to the effect that rattlesnakes and bull snakes have crossed, producing a particularly dangerous hybrid offspring having all the venom of a rattler, but with the speed and energy of a bull snake, and, of course, without the identifying rattles. Actually, there is not the slightest ground for this idea. It probably stems from the fact that the harmless bull snake of that region (*Pituophis catenifer sayi*) has a blotched pattern somewhat resembling that of the prairie rattlesnake. Furthermore, this snake, when frightened or threatened, will sometimes become the picture of viciousness, striking and hissing, and at the same time vibrating his tail against grass or dry leaves so that it makes a good imitation of its dangerous associate. The sight of a supposedly harmless snake putting on such a show of violence is so surprising and unexpected by most people that they take it for granted miscegenation must be the explanation.

But it is well known to snake specialists that some harmless snakes are quite vicious, more so than most venomous species. The red racer (*Masticophis flagel-*

lum piceus), a common, harmless snake of the Southwest, is a case in point. To pick up one of these without being bitten several times requires the utmost dexterity, for they are quick and violent, and fearless defenders when cornered. But, as they have no venom, the bite is without ill effect, about the same as being scratched by rose thorns.

> Some people say rattlers have crossed with bull snakes in this area; I do not know with certainty whether they have. *H. B. Sanderson, Lovell, Wyo.*

◇

> I examined the snake—which had put up quite a fight—as quite a few rumors have been going the rounds on the Milk River and territory adjacent thereto, about the rattler and the bull snake crossing. Its head was not flat and broad like that of a rattlesnake, nor did it have the sharp angular shape. It had sharp teeth in its jaws, something like fish teeth, and they were certainly fixed; about ⅛ of an inch protruded out of the gum. *D. A. Fleming, Swift Current, Saskatchewan.*

◇

> The bull snake grows to a length of 8 feet, is very strong, and hisses at you and really will come after you if he thinks he cannot get away. Some of the old-timers say bull snakes cross with rattlesnakes; however, we do not believe this. It is probably just an old tradition; in fact, their mode of breeding is entirely different. *W. T. Sweet, Butte, Mont.*

A. M. Jackley gives a good description of a bull snake on the defensive:

> The bull snake really imitated a rattler to perfection. It struck repeatedly and made its tail vibrate with a rapidity equal to a rattler. Whenever it would strike it gave the usual blow or hiss and then settled back to buzzing.

While there is not the slightest evidence of bull-snake–rattlesnake crosses, it is now known that different species of rattlesnakes may occasionally interbreed, as described in chapter 4.

There is a myth or tall story current in upper New York State to the effect that black snakes are the male parents of rattlesnakes (Carmer, 1936, p. 319). Meek (1946, p. 224) mentions another fictitious hybrid, the water rattler.

Another story current in the Southwest, while not a rattlesnake myth, is worth mentioning. It is the presence of a slender, triangular-headed, grayish, venomous snake more dangerous than the biggest rattler. I have heard of this snake in California, Arizona, and New Mexico. It usually travels under the name of *pichucuate* or *pichicuate*. According to Santamaría, *Diccionario General de Americanismos*, vol. 2, p. 467, 1942, the proper spelling is *pichocuate*. The word is of Aztec origin, with the meaning "abominable venomous snake," and has reference to *Dipsas biscutata* [= *Trimorphodon biscutatus*]. This is a back-fanged snake, probably not dangerous to man, this despite the fact that Lummis (1892, p. 422) said that the *pichucuate,* which he alleged was a real asp, was invariably fatal. The species of *Trimorphodon* occurring in our Southwestern states—*T. lambda, T. vandenburghi,* and *T. vilkinsoni*—are certainly not dangerous, but in Sonora, Mexico, the term *pichicuate* is applied to a truly venomous snake, the Mexican moccasin, *Agkistrodon b. bilineatus,* which does not occur in the United States.

According to another myth, some dangerous snakes from Australia—usually reported as the venomous tiger snake—were imported into California by Hindus and have formed a colony. I know of no evidence supporting this story in any way. Bevan, in *Outdoor Life* (vol. 69, no. 6, p. 93, 1932), mentioned a similar rumor concerning a colony of cobras.

QUEER ACTIONS AND ATTRIBUTES

RATTLESNAKE ODOR

Many of the early accounts of rattlesnakes dwelt at length on their offensive odor, particularly when congregated at their dens. It was most often likened to the smell of cucumbers, and was said to be perceptible at a great distance. This idea is still widely prevalent, but, as a matter of fact, rattlesnakes are virtually odorless, even when there are a number together. We have had, at the San Diego Zoo, more than 300 in a single cage of no great size, and even with this concentration almost no odor was evident, as long as the cage was kept clean.[5] Rattlesnakes, like other snakes, have special scent glands in their tails, which they use occasionally, possibly for sex attraction, and certainly as a defense mechanism, as discussed elsewhere. But the odor from these glands is neither so strong nor so unpleasant as that of many other genera of snakes, yet the latter have no such reputations as the rattlesnakes for noxious odor. Persons having the greatest familiarity with rattlers, both in the wild and in captivity, testify that the odor, if detectable at all by the human nose, is very faint, indeed. I have repeatedly held my nose against a live rattlesnake and found the odor barely perceptible. As far as the scent glands are concerned, their secretion, although readily detectable, is seldom discharged unless a rattler is actually handled.

Mythical attributes are credited to many kinds of snakes alike, but the overpowering odor seems to have been considered particularly characteristic of rattlesnakes. Adams (1844–47, vol. 2, p. 181) mentions one account of an Old World snake supposed by the ancients to have a strong odor; and Read (1934, p. 297) records another in China. But the noxious odor of the rattlesnake was almost as often mentioned in colonial times as the rattle itself.

One early remark on the rattlesnake's odor was that of Moore (1744, p. 59). However, the strongest impetus to the myth was given by Kalm (1752–53, pp. 52, 313; 1758, p. 287). He reported that a Swede, whom he visited, killed some 60 or 70 timber rattlers at a den, when the stench—not of decomposition, be it understood—became so intolerable that he was compelled to desist. The story was repeated by Pennant (1787, p. 88), and by Doddridge (1824, p. 79). Beauvois (1799, p. 367) was one of the first to deny the truth of the odor story; he reported that he noticed no smell even when the snakes were closely confined (p. 370). At the same time Barton (1799, pp. 90–93) also denied the odor legend. He stated that, while William Bartram had advised him that horses could smell a rattler at a distance of 40 to 50 yards, he himself could detect no odor. Others had informed him that such odor as there was seemed to them unobjectionable (p. 94). He also took the opportunity to deny Lacépède's theory that the rattlesnake's supposed power of fascination really lay in its infectious or venomous breath (pp. 88, 97). Daudin (1801–4, vol. 5, p. 303) thought the rattler's reputation for odor greatly exaggerated.

---

[5] An entry in my diary, October 31, 1931: "Today I put my nose in the center cage at the Zoo. It contained 394 prairie rattlers, and had glass sides with only a few ventilating screens above. Even in this closed space, an odor was barely noticeable, and what there was no doubt came from fresh excreta."

Stories of the rattlesnake's powerful odor, usually based on Kalm's statement, continued to appear (Kerr, 1802, vol. 4, p. 246; Bosc, 1803, p. 552; T. Smith, 1806–7, p. 84; Rees, 1819, p. 1; Holmes, 1823, p. 257; Kendall, 1844, vol. 1, p. 160; Cist, 1845, p. 18; Martin, 1851, p. 271; Tome, 1854, [1928, p. 32]; Brons, 1882, p. 566; Loennberg, 1894, p. 335; Anon., 1897, p. 125; J. D. Mitchell, 1903, p. 36; Humfreville, 1903, p. 444; Surface, 1906, p. 192) although again denied by such competent authorities as S. W. Mitchell (1860, p. 5) and Stejneger (1895, p. 396). Higgins (1873, p. 86), whose book contains some outstanding inaccuracies, states that the name *Crotalus* was derived from the stupefying smell of the snake. Doddridge (1824, p. 81) says the odor is particularly noticeable after a rain; Warburton (1849, vol. 1, p. 175) believes it worse when the rattlers are coming out of hibernation. Dobie (1942c, p. 7; 1946e, p. 62) thinks it is accentuated in the dog days. J. B. Martin (1859, p. 111) thought the odor might be caused by surplus venom coming out through pores in the snake's skin.

Among the modern writers who dwell on the strong rattlesnake scent are Rollins (1922, p. 175), Scoville (1931, p. 57), Gordon (1936, p. 34), Cook (1943, p. 51), and Herrick (1953, p. 23). Rutledge, in various popular articles on rattlesnakes, repeatedly enlarges on the odor. He likens it to the smell of cucumbers (1921b, p. 217); he located a snake in a tree by its odor (1936, p. 139); he states that each venomous snake has its own distinctive odor (1935, p. 520; 1938, p. 18), and that even a man can smell a rattler 20 feet or so away, although the odor is not unpleasant. He once smelled a rattler in a woodpecker's nest in which he was about to put his hand (1951, p. 93). Kennedy (1942, p. 191) mentions the heavy, nasty smell of an angry snake; and Thatcher (1940, p. 37) finds the odor more objectionable than that of a skunk. Kalez (1954, p. 79) tells of a rattler that crawled between two sleeping men. Its odor was so strong as to awaken one of them.

Although the odor of rattlesnakes has usually been likened to that of cucumbers, some have noted a resemblance to the odors of a watermelon patch, a skunk, a goat, and garlic. A Wyoming pioneer stated that the cucumber smell was so strong that the presence of a rattler was detected in a load of hay (David, 1937, p. 266). Ariza (1948, p. 60) explains the fact that animals with a keen sense of smell—dogs, for example—are frequently bitten, despite the reputedly strong odor of rattlesnakes, by the theory that the odor is not always evident.

In sections of our Southern states it is believed that the snake's presence can be detected by the smell of its venom. We see in this a relationship with the poisonous emanation or effluvium theories of the early writers. Some of the authors who have accepted this theory of an exhalation as a means of securing prey—related to the theory of fascination—were Doddridge (1824, p. 80), Povall (1824, p. 115), Linsley (1843, p. 45), Newman (1854, p. 190), Martin (1859, p. 111), and Flack (1866, p. 332).

Charlevoix (1761, vol. 2, p. 5) reported that two small islands in Lake Erie were so infested with rattlesnakes that the air was polluted. E. A. Robinson (1895, p. 147) said that in one place in West Virginia the rattlers were reputed to be so thick they could be smelled at all times. He offered his guide a reward to find them, but not even one was forthcoming. R. G. Robinson (1896, p. 711) tells a fanciful story of a very large rattler with so strong an odor it caused a boy to faint. Other tall stories and fictional accounts will be found in Martin (1859, p. 110), Anon. (1872b, p. 642), Walsh (1913, p. 717), Thompson (1932, p. 102), and Richter (1946, p. 195).

Those who have had much experience with rattlers at their dens say that a slight odor is noticeable, especially in confined quarters. F. B. McMurry, of the U. S. Fish and Wildlife Service, told me of detecting such an odor. It is probable that any congregation of animals for a long period in a confined space would produce a similar result. Also, there is evidence of some winter mortality among the rattlers in a den, in which case an odor of decomposition would be expected. This may account for the following statement from one of my correspondents: "Rattlers give off a very strong odor; when dens are eradicated the stench is almost unbearable." Another wrote: "You can smell a den a long way off, as they have a very sickening odor."

Summarizing my own experience with rattlesnakes, including several thousand specimens of nearly all known species, I should say that they are virtually odorless when clean. Sometimes, when disturbed, they will excrete a fine liquid spray from the scent glands; the odor is pungent but not especially unpleasant—nothing to be compared with the violently disagreeable stenches emitted by such harmless snakes as the king, garter, and water snakes. It would certainly require a more sensitive nose than that of a human to detect the presence of a rattler, undisturbed in the wild, or even of a considerable aggregation of them. Whatever validity there may be to all the stories of rattlesnake odors must have come from an occasional use of the scent glands by an annoyed or injured snake.

RATTLE MYTHS

Almost the only snake myths and legends that apply solely to rattlesnakes are those pertaining to the rattle, for this is the only unique attribute of the rattlesnake. In chapter 5 I have discussed most of the superstitions and misunderstandings concerning the purpose and use of the rattle, and its formation and growth. But here are some of a different character.

There are a number of regional items of folklore regarding the use of rattles to cure or ameliorate disease. Carrying a string of rattles will prevent or cure rheumatism (Bergen, 1899, p. 13, Kansas; Woodhull, 1930, p. 66, Texas; Hyatt, 1935, p. 264, Illinois; Black, 1935, p. 20, and Pound, 1946, p. 166, Nebraska). It will prevent smallpox (Woodhull, 1930, p. 66, Mexicans in Texas; Pound, 1946, Nebraska). It will keep a person from having fits (Thomas and Thomas, 1920, p. 104, mountains of Kentucky), and is a general disease preventive, if worn around the neck (Hyatt, 1935, p. 205, western Illinois).

One of the most widespread and consistent uses of rattles is in the prevention and cure of headache or neuralgia, by wearing a rattle string in the hair or in the hatband (Anon., 1872b, p. 642; Ingersoll, 1883a, p. 43; Davis, 1888, p. 164, believed of Negro origin; Stanley, 1897, p. 34, cowboy lore; Bergen, 1899, p. 13; Dresslar, 1907, p. 49, California; Thomas and Thomas, 1920, p. 106, Kentucky; Walsh, 1923, p. 71; Smith, 1929, p. 73, 1930a, p. 82, Oklahoma; Farr, 1935, p. 326, Tennessee; Hyatt, 1935, p. 266, western Illinois; Black, 1935, p. 9, and Pound, 1946, p. 165, Nebraska; and Vestal, 1941, p. 146, high plains country). Evers (1951, p. 110) reports that rattles are worn in the Catskills, New York, to prevent sunstroke.

Rattles were used by the Indians to facilitate childbirth (p. 1164). They have also been so used by other races (Bosc, 1803, p. 555; Daudin, 1801–4, vol. 5, p. 308; Rees, 1819, p. 1, Negroes; Thomas and Thomas, 1920, p. 10, Kentucky lowlanders; Martin, 1947, p. 184, Blue Ridge mountaineers; Buley, 1950, vol. 1, p. 266, pioneer "old" Northwest).

Another widespread belief is that rattles will soothe and pacify teething children. They may be worn as a necklace, placed in a bag and hung on the neck, or the child may be allowed to chew on them (Empson, 1836, p. 40, Magdalena Valley of Colombia; Bergen, 1899, p. 13, New Orleans Negroes; Fogel, 1915, p. 313, Pennsylvania Germans; Pickett, 1926, p. 346, Southern Negroes; Woodhull, 1930, p. 69, Texas; Black, 1935, p. 22, and Pound, 1946, p. 166, Nebraska). That magical medicine is involved is indicated by some of the specifications for the use of the rattles. Thus, in one of the prescriptions in Nebraska, there must be three rattles, and the cord around the child's neck must be red (Pound). Rattles were also used to prevent fits and convulsions in the child (Shorey, 1953, p. 26, New York folklore).

Although rattles are usually considered beneficial, there is one myth to the effect that they throw off a poisonous dust that may cause blindness (Anon., 1897, p. 135; Dresslar, 1907, p. 49; Spaulding, 1944, p. 151). I am informed by two correspondents that this superstition has been heard in California and in Kentucky. It is probably widespread. Bergen (1899, p. 88) has this version from Kansas: If you cut the rattles off a snake, the juice will fly in your eyes and blind you. This must have come from someone's experience with the rattler's scent glands, although I doubt that the spray is harmful in any way.

To return to the beneficial properties of rattles—they may serve as amulets or good-luck charms (Hyatt, 1935, p. 74, western Illinois; Pound, 1946, p. 169, Nebraska). If you receive rattles from someone, you will come to no harm while that person is near (Thomas and Thomas, 1920, p. 274, Kentucky mountains). If you kill a rattler, keep the rattles for good luck (Pound). If you catch a rattler and rub the rattles on your eyes, you will always see a rattler before it sees you (Puckett, 1926, p. 322, Southern Negroes). Also, Satan himself may be summoned to aid you in black arts if you get a button (rattle ?) off a graveyard rattler, sew it up with a piece of silver in a red flannel bag, and wear it over your heart (Puckett, 1926, p. 552, Southern Negroes). To display a rattle from a dead snake will keep other rattlesnakes away; and a rattle may be worn as a charm against rattlesnake bite (Jeffrey, 1955, p. 255, Southwestern folklore).

Rattles are often put in violins—called fiddles in the areas where the rattles are so used—to improve the tone, keep out dampness, or give the owner good luck (Stanley, 1897, pp. 27, 34; Thomas and Thomas, 1920, p. 274, western Kentucky; Craddock, 1923, p. 32, Texas; Dobie, 1923, p. 89, Texas; Hyatt, 1935, p. 73, western Illinois; Pound, 1946, p. 175, Nebraska; Stimpson, 1948, p. 514; Webber, 1951, p. 30, Illinois). But Stimpson says there is one belief that the rattles will blind the fiddler. In Brazil, a rattle in a guitar will improve not only the instrument, but the singer's voice as well. There is an item of California folklore claiming that a rattle tied to a banjo head will preserve the skin. Dobie (1926, p. 52) believes the rattle-fiddle relationship to be derived from the fact that a swimming rattler elevates its rattles to keep them dry. But that it does so is also a myth.

MUSIC HATH CHARMS

The Hindu performer, with his pipe and dancing cobras, is well known. I have discussed elsewhere (p. 363) the similar reactions of rattlesnakes to music, all quite mythical, as rattlers, like other snakes, are deaf to air-borne sounds. Occasionally, in addition to the stories of colonial days that I have mentioned elsewhere, we hear modern tall tales of the effect of music on rattlers, such as the recent newspaper yarn of the berry picker who used a mouth harmonica to render the rattlers harmless while he plied his trade. Also, there is Webb's tall tale (1937, p. 325) of the Indian who trained a band of rattlesnakes to join him in song. With their rattles, they were able to carry four parts—soprano, alto, tenor, and bass. Stimpson (1948, p. 145) has presented a good discussion of some of the myths of snakes that have voices.

SOME TRADITIONAL STORIES

RATTLER ENCOUNTERS WITH OTHER CREATURES

One of the most widespread of all snake legends is the one that describes a battle between some animal and a venomous snake; each time the snake bites its adversary, the latter runs off to a nearby bush, eats a few leaves, and returns, revivified, to the fight. Then a malignant onlooker appropriates the bush, and the next time the snake's opponent is bitten, it seeks the plant in vain and dies. But its sacrifice bears fruit, for by this means the life-saving plant is disclosed to mankind.

This story has been told of many different kinds of snakes and of attacking animals, probably most frequently of the cobra and mongoose. It also provides the explanation of how the efficacy of many plant cures was discovered. It is an old legend, dating back in essence to Aristotle (Cresswell, 1862, p. 238; Thompson, 1910, sect. 612a), and to Pliny (1855–57, vol. 2, pp. 287, 426; vol. 4, pp. 253, 266, 423, 427; vol. 5, p. 115; vol. 6, p. 24; book viii, chaps. 35, 36; book ix, chap. 51; book xx, chaps. 51, 61; book xxii, chaps. 37, 45; book xxv, chap. 51; book xxxii, chap. 19).

In the United States, such stories are usually told of rattlesnake and king-snake fights (Steiner, 1899, p. 269; Swanton, 1917, p. 478; Jones, 1928, p. 9; Clark, 1928, p. 144; Meek, 1946, p. 209; Randolph, 1947, p. 255; 1951, p. 141); or of rattlesnakes and black snakes (Juvenal, 1900, pp. 24, 84; Bailey, 1919, p. 166, Brendle and Unger, 1935, p. 201; Randolph, 1951, p. 141; West, 1952, p. 6; Beck, 1952, p. 146). Beaty (1941, p. 33) tells of a wolf that sought a plant cure after an encounter with a rattler. Other reports are those of Hooper (1920, p. 352) and Swanson (1952, p. 167).

A few variations on the theme are the following: If rattlesnakes bite themselves (or get venom in their food?) they seek a certain plant as a cure (Walduck, 1714, in Masterson, 1938, p. 214). Several kinds of snakes fight rattlers, and if either contestant is bitten it goes to water, drinks, and dies (Hunter, 1823, p. 179). The Mexican cure for snake bite, the herb *huaco* (or *guaco*), was discovered by observation of the roadrunner eating some whenever it had eaten a rattler (Donnavan, 1874, p. 57; Dobie, 1937, p. 168). If a snake is killed by a rattler, the black snake rubs against it and restores it to life, hence the black snake is known as the snake doctor (Ingersoll, 1883a, p. 41, attributed to Negro folklore). When one rattler of a pair is killed, the mate searches out an herb with which it is restored to life (Dulog, 1897, p. 202, Venezuelan folklore). A California bandit agreed to let a large rattler bite him if, for so doing, he would be freed. This was done and he cured himself with the plant *Daucus pusillus,* thus disclosing this valuable cure (Kamp, 1904, p. 69). (Actually, the plant is without remedial value.) A mongoose, upon seeing a child bitten by a cobra, sought out the plant it would have used had it been bitten, and so cured the child (Cesaresco, 1909, p. 310, a legend of India).

Besides the stories of the lifesaving plant that revivifies the rattlesnake's opponent in a deadly battle, there are other myths and tall tales of some of the methods used by the snakes that seek to decimate the rattler population. According to Capt. Mayne Reid (1889, p. 233), a black snake was seen to kill a rattler by sinking its fangs *(sic)* in the opponent's rattles and whipping the rattler to death. Strecker (1926a, p. 67) says there is a Texas belief that king snakes whip rattlers to death with their tails.

Thomas (1931, p. 163) has a fairly fresh tall story about the rattler fleeing a king snake so fast the friction was setting the grass afire, but the trailing king snake was sweating so much in keeping up that it put the fire out. Their trail was a long, black streak through the grass. According to Boatright (1934, p. 11), a rattler and king snake started to swallow each other simultaneously, and naturally both disappeared. Pound (1946, p. 175) tells a Nebraska yarn of the bull snake that feints the rattler into striking. Missing the bull snake, it strikes itself and dies.

There are several tall tales in circulation concerning rattlers and various mammals. Hyatt (1935, p. 84) says it was a western Illinois belief that if a prairie dog is seen to go down his hole three times, he will go down a fourth and bring up a rattler. Virginia Duncan (1945, p. 167), as a girl in Texas, saw a rattler disappear down a prairie dog hole. Previously there had not been a prairie dog in sight, but immediately they bobbed up everywhere. They came and scratched earth into the hole, tamped it in with their snouts, thus interring their common enemy. She was told by a ranchman that he had often found rattlers buried in this way. Other versions of how prairie dogs inter rattlesnakes that seek refuge in their holes will be found in Brons, 1882, p. 565; Hopkins, 1905, p. 354; Ringle, 1924, p. 20; Pawlowsky, 1927, p. 288; and Brown, 1936, p. 24. The known methods (see p. 564) by which rattlers dispossess prairie dogs of their homes, taking over an entire town, hardly justify belief in these stories.

Kirkland (1951, p. 6), with his tongue in his cheek, ascribes a certain desert track to a desert tortoise dragging a rattler to its den. Morton (1938, p. 211) describes how, in Kentucky when he was one year old, their cat walked along the body of a huge rattler that was stretched out, from the tail to the head where it calmly sat. The cat was obviously a witch. Morton says he heard the tale narrated so often that he came to visualize it clearly, an interesting indication of how some of these tales gain positive affirmation from supposed eyewitnesses.

RATTLESNAKE PILOT

The legend of the rattlesnake pilot is subject to considerable variation. It is most prevalent in the Southeast and along the Atlantic seaboard, although occasionally heard in other sections of the country, including the Far West. The general idea is that another kind of snake known as a rattlesnake pilot warns rattlesnakes of the approach of danger and guides them to safety. Says one of my correspondents:

> We have a snake here in Louisiana called the rattlesnake pilot. This snake is said to pass by about a day ahead of a rattler. When you see one there is likely to be a rattlesnake not far behind.

The earliest reference to the pilot snake seems to be contained in a letter written by Cotton Mather dated June 4, 1723 (Mather, 1868, p. 454; Kittredge, 1916, p. 51). The pilot is described as a snake that commands and governs the rattlesnake and, if the latter fails to obey, strikes it dead with a bone in its tail. Another early account is that of Crèvecoeur (1782, p. 236; 1783, p. 99). He called the copperhead the rattlesnake pilot, because it comes out of hibernation a week earlier than the rattlers and always precedes one in crawling about.

Some later references, mostly treating the story as a myth, are Lombard (1881, p. 88), Daniels and Stevans (1903, vol. 2, p. 695), Davis (1914, p. 245), Parsons (1923, p. 101), Strecker (1925, p. 49; 1928, p. 19), Roberts (1927, p. 203), Clark (1928, p. 143), Stimpson (1946, p. 480), Moore (1949, p. 54), and Swanson (1952, p. 167).

Various kinds of snakes are credited with being rattlesnake pilots. Nowhere is there entire agreement as to which snake occupies the position. One to which this mythical relationship with the rattlesnake is frequently attributed has, for this reason, become known as the pilot black snake. It is, in fact, one of the harmless rat snakes (*Elaphe o. obsoleta*). The legend probably arose from the fact that this snake inhabits the same rocky ledges to which the timber rattler is addicted in portions of its range.

Strecker (1925, p. 49; 1928, p. 19) says that rattlesnake's pilot is the commonest vernacular name of the venomous copperhead, based on an old Texas bottomland myth to the effect that this snake leads the rattler to its prey. In Louisiana the small king or milk snake, *Lampropeltis doliata amaura*, is known by the name of rattlesnake pilot. In other sections the western pigmy rattler—itself a small rattlesnake, *Sistrurus miliarius streckeri*—is known as the pilot, for it is supposed to act as guide for its larger relative, the timber rattlesnake.

Some years ago I received from Skull Valley, Arizona, the following communication from A. N. Turner, Santa Fe Agent: "I am sending you a snake known around here as the 'rattler's pilot.' He shakes his tail like a rattlesnake." This proved to be a Pacific king snake (*Lampropeltis getulus californiae*). It is rather remarkable that this snake should become known as a rattlesnake pilot in view of the fact that it occasionally eats young rattlers.

There are differing versions as to how closely the rattlesnake follows the pilot. In some areas of the South the pilot is said to keep just ahead of its charge, so that if a pilot is seen one should stop in his tracks and look carefully about, to avoid stepping on the rattler. But in other stories, the rattler trails at some distance. As a reward for this guidance, the rattlesnake, when successful in securing prey, shares its catch with the pilot. The legend fails to state how this could be possible with creatures that swallow their prey whole. There is a Louisiana oil-field story to the effect that when rattlesnakes issue from hibernation in the spring, they are sleepy, have poor vision, and consequently are unable to strike accurately. It is the duty of the pilot to aid a rattler in determining when and in what direction to strike.

Clark (1928, p. 143) says the Mississippi folklore version is that the rattler is the male, and the pilot (which is not a rattler) is the female of the same species. In Alabama folklore, copperheads are the male rattlesnakes. In the *Dictionary of Americanisms* (Mathews, 1951, p. 1362) the copperhead is said to bear these alternative vernacular names: rattlesnake pilot, rattlesnake mate, or rattlesnake cousin. Another phase of the myth is that pilot snakes are crosses between rattlers and bull snakes.

To summarize the present views of herpetologists: there is no known relationship, either genetical or in habits, that would justify any of these reports of rattlesnake pilots.

The Vengeful Mate

That snakes travel in pairs, and wreak vengeance on anyone who may injure their mates, is a very ancient myth (Pliny, 1855–57, vol. 2, p. 286; book viii, chap. 35). It is often attributed to rattlesnakes. The basic facts of natural history involved have been discussed in chapter 10, with the conclusion that the sexes are together only during a brief mating season.

Musick (1946, p. 109) tells a tall tale about a rattler pair, related as an item of family history. A party crossing Kansas in a prairie schooner in 1853 killed a large female rattler and tied the body to the back of the wagon with the head dragging. This was early in the morning. That day they made 50 miles. The next morning a child of the party was fatally bitten as she lay rolled in her blankets. It was the supposition that the male had kept pace with the party for the entire distance.

Johnson (1953, p. 54) gives an account of Old Betsy, a Florida diamondback kept by an old hunter as a decoy. Betsy was blind and had had her fangs removed for safety, but was reported to have lured many a male rattler to his doom.

Swallowing Young for Their Protection

The most controversial of all reptile myths, the one whose denial brings out the greatest flood of indignant eyewitness protestations, is that of the snake mother that swallows her young upon any threat of danger, and then disgorges them when the menace has passed. This is an ancient and world-wide story,[6] one that is not attributed to rattlesnakes alone; it was told of vipers long before rattlesnakes had been heard of by Europeans. But it is occasionally given an original rattlesnake touch by having the mother call her offspring to her unique refuge by sounding a warning rattle.

The swallowing of young does not seem to have been a belief of the Greeks and Romans, for it is not mentioned by Pliny. But Speck (1923a, p. 299) says it was recorded by the Egyptians about 2500 b.c. Strecker (1926a, p. 66) observes

---

[6] The Thompson Motif-Index number is B751:1 (*Motif-Index of Folk Literature: A Classification of Narrative Elements in Folk-Tales, Ballads*, etc. by Stith Thompson, Helsinki, 6 volumes, 1932–36.

that in English literature it goes back at least to Spenser's *The Faërie Queene* (1590). It is to be found in Topsell (1608, p. 9; 1658, p. 597), who unfortunately, and contrary to his custom, did not cite his source; and by Grew (1681, p. 49). The earliest reference that I have found, in which it is attributed to rattlesnakes, is that of Tyson (1683, p. 33), who was not sure of the accuracy of the report.

As the story is generally told, an intruder comes upon a mother snake surrounded by her numerous progeny. Alarmed, she sounds a warning, usually by hissing, whereupon the little snakes rush to her, and one by one enter her mouth and glide quickly down her throat. When the danger has passed they emerge and resume their previous diversions.

The literature involving this story is already voluminous and I shall touch on only a few of its aspects. For general discussions, with bibliographies and some eyewitness accounts, the reader is referred to the following: Putnam, 1868; Goode, 1874a; Speck, 1921; Noble, 1921; Anon., 1938b. Other reports of interest are: Holmes (1823, p. 260), Hunter (1823, p. 178), Chateaubriand (1828, vol. 2, p. 163; 1856, pp. 112, 166). Goode (1873a, p. 418), Rivers (1874, p. 510), Brown (1881a, p. 26), Townsend (1882, p. 244), Wheatley (1886, p. 523), Hay (1887, p. 211; and 1892b, p. 536), Mays (1897, p. 225), Pike (1898, p. 38), Rolker (1903, p. 290), Metcalfe (1907, p. 124), Tome (1928, p. 114), Strecker (1929b, p. 14), Hubert (1934, p. 237), Richardson (1936, p. 44), Swanson (1941, p. 14; 1952, p. 178), Dobie (1942a, p. 16; 1942b, p. 10; 1942c, p. 7; 1946e, p. 42; 1947b, p. 93), DeLys (1948, p. 79), Devoe (1951, p. 244), Teale (1951, p. 125), and Helm (1952, p. 106). Trouslot (1887, p. 86) adds the interesting variant of seeing a mother with the head of a young rattler sticking out of a corner of her mouth like a cigar. Dury (1910, p. 69) claims that in one instance there were two mothers and two broods, and the young knew which mother to dart into for refuge. A typical early eyewitness account is that of Carver (1779, p. 485) who once saw 70 young go into a mother's mouth at his approach.

The snake-swallowing protective device has lately been mentioned as prevalent in the following regional folklore: High plains (Vestal, 1941, p. 146), Ozarks (Rayburn, 1941, p. 264), Nebraska (Pound, 1946, p. 172), and southern Illinois (Allison, 1950, p. 318).

Although probably no herpetologists have any faith in the existence of this protective habit, they naturally do not wish to be accused of dogmatism by taking the position that their theories outweigh the observations of the many people who have testified to its validity. They therefore adopt an attitude of polite skepticism, asking for some proof more weighty than the memory of something seen years before (Noble, 1921, p. 54; Ortenburger, 1930, p. 425; Schmidt, 1929, p. 13).

The question arises: How can the story be denied in the face of so many confirmatory accounts? Various explanations have been given: Unborn snakes, of species that bear living young (in contrast with those that lay eggs), are found in the body of the mother, and are assumed to have been found in the stomach; snakes are seen while eating young snakes or lizards; young snakes actually disappear in the grass or into a hole under the mother. But beyond all these explanations, the most appropriate bears upon the problem of accuracy of observation, and particularly the mental confusion existing between things seen, and those read or heard of in times past. Every telling strengthens the picture and the memory, and makes it more certainly a personal occurrence. Several investigators have commented on the fact that, in nearly every eyewitness account, a considerable time, usually from 20 to 50 years, has elapsed between the date of the supposed event and its telling. In one newspaper report, a man 105 years old described a swallowing-of-the-young episode he had witnessed at the age of 18.

Of the accounts that have appeared in print—and they are many—the greatest weight has been given by herpetologists to those of Beauvois (1799, p. 371) and Ball (1915, p. 343), for both were trained observers. Yet Beauvois was, at the time of his experience, recovering from a serious illness that had greatly weakened him; and Ball, like so many others, recounted observations made years before as a boy at school.

The fact that this protective scheme is nearly always attributed to species of snakes that give birth to living young, instead of to egg-layers, is both a favorable and unfavorable criterion: favorable because it could be only these snake species whose young would be found in the company of their mothers, even for a brief time; unfavorable in that only in the case of these mothers could unborn young be inaccurately assumed to have been found in the mother's throat or stomach, although really found in the uteri.

Reese (1942, p. 57; 1949, p. 174) believes that the existence of a habit of this kind should not be denied on purely negative evidence. The obvious reply is that if the habit is a myth, negative evidence will necessarily be the only kind available.

How stories of this kind may be unduly confirmed in the retelling is suggested by the following chain: Ellen Gallwey (1934, p. 99) says that adders in England probably swallow their young for protection, as had been previously supposed, since a similar practice upon the part of rattlesnakes had been demonstrated by "Dr. Rudolph Menger, the American herpetologist." But Miss Gallwey did not have access to Menger's original paper; she had only a second- or third-hand paraphrase. Actually, Menger (1905, p. 15; 1913, p. 154) merely recounts the observations of a friend; he makes no claim to having seen a rattler swallow its young. Incidentally, Menger asked a dealer who had handled 40,000 snakes within the previous 5 years whether he had ever seen such an occurrence, and received a negative reply.

This brings up another point, now of importance, that weighs against the protective-swallowing theory. Today there are annually born in the United States under accurate observation in laboratories and zoos, hundreds of broods of ovoviviparous snakes for every one under such observation 50 years ago. Yet, with all this multiplicity of broods, no mother has ever been seen to swallow her young for protection. Some of the mothers had been long in captivity, others but a few days when the young arrived. With all necessary allowances for the artificial effects of captivity, they would not completely nullify adherence to so ancient a custom if the story were true. In captivity, snakes may become tame and lethargic, yet they still retain many normal patterns of activity—the male combat dance, methods of courtship, and their ways of capturing and subduing food, for examples. Certainly some mother, of all the hundreds under observation, would by now have temporarily forgotten her cage and would have opened her mouth to protect her young. But none has done so.

Crouse (1902, p. 439) was told by a San Antonio dealer, who handled from 40,000 to 50,000 snakes per year, that 2,000 young had been born to his rattlers that year. The mothers paid no attention to the young. The dealer experimented and found that an adult rattler's gastric juices would kill a young snake in about 20 minutes.

Among the practical objections to the protective-swallowing tradition that have been offered are the following:

1. Young snakes, following birth, are left to shift for themselves; they remain in the vicinity of the mother for only a day or so at most. So complicated a protective scheme would not have been evolved for so short a protective period.

2. The throat opening of a snake is too restricted to permit the ready ingress and egress of young rattlers such as is described in most of the accounts. Denied the use of its teeth and the oscillating jaw action which snakes employ in engulfing prey (for these would injure the young), a snake would have great difficulty in getting the young past the throat constriction, even with their co-operation. The legendary accounts of the process picture the young as entering and leaving as they might through an open tube. Actually, the swallowing would be a slow and painful process, requiring a minute or more per youngster.

3. Another pertinent objection is that the young snakes would be injured by the digestive juices or would be suffocated, for there would be no room for their accommodation in the snake's throat. The latter point is well taken; yet the threat of suffocation is not so serious as might first be thought, for it has been shown that rattlesnakes swallowed by king snakes may be retained in the stomach for some time, possibly as much as an hour, and may then be disgorged alive and quite uninjured.

4. As snakes are deaf, there would be no purpose in the hiss or the rattle vibration—calling the baby snakes—that is usually a part of these stories.

5. Thousands of stomachs of rattlesnakes have been examined in the course of preserving specimens, especially to determine what animals constitute their natural prey. I have myself examined at least 3,000 adults. In no case have young been found hidden in the stomach. Of course, many hundreds of young have been found in their egg membranes in the uteri, some ready for birth within days, if not hours.

I have stated that the subject is controversial. For example, Starkweather (1888, p. 123) denied the truth of the story in *Forest and Stream*. His paper appeared in the September 6th issue, and within the next 3 months no less than 13 indignant eyewitness refutations were sent in to the editor (*Forest and Stream*, vol. 31, pp. 164, 185, 204, 244, 304, 363, 385). Similar controversies appeared in *The Field* in 1856 (Idle, *et al.*, pp. 164, 187, 219, 234, 266–7), in *Desert Magazine* in 1948 (Hooten *et al.*, p. 38; and again in 1953, Turner *et al.*, p. 23), and in the *Montreal Family Herald and Weekly Star* in 1950 (Shark, p. 48, etc.). In these series, the reader will find many typical eyewitness descriptions of the swallowing of young by protective mothers.

I have myself heard the story from many persons, some of whom had weight in the realms of literature, art, and finance. I must admit I have rarely had the nerve to attempt to disturb so fond a memory.

My correspondence has also contained many stories of this kind of which the following may serve as an example:

During a recent visit to the zoo I noticed a placard on a window of the reptile house to the effect that snakes do not swallow their young, as some people believe. I personally know that at least one snake did swallow 13 young many times. When I was a high-school student, about 1882, I caught a garter snake about 2 feet long and took it home. As it seemed to be unusually heavy of body, my father suggested that we keep it alive and see how many eggs it might produce. It was placed in a shallow box with a wire netting cover, and soon appeared to become quite tame. One day I happened to look into the box and saw a number of very small young snakes and noted that the size of the body of the old one was much smaller. We took it for granted that we had been mistaken in believing that snakes laid eggs, and that the young had been produced alive.[7]

Soon afterward the young ones disappeared and the body of the mother was larger again. We believed that she had eaten the young ones, but soon they appeared again as lively as ever. Although we did not see them emerge, we knew they must have been swallowed. We then pounded upon the box to frighten them, when the mother made a slight hissing noise and opened her jaws and the little ones ran down her throat.

We did this many times afterward, always with the same results. We frequently exhibited it to friends, also. When the little snakes grew larger they no longer took refuge inside their mother when disturbed. Then we examined the old snake and found she had a pouch with an opening just inside the lower jaw. Then we remembered that when she opened her mouth to take in the young, we did not see her tongue, as was always the case otherwise. The above facts are very clearly in my memory, after a lapse of 55 years.

Here are several shorter accounts:

I came upon a female rattler and watched her young scamper down her mouth. I killed her and cut her open, and found 11 little rattlers about three inches long. They all came out on the fight.

⋄

I have seen young snakes run into their mother's mouth for protection or to be carried.

⋄

At one den I saw a big yellow snake open her mouth and some little ones ran down her open mouth. We killed and opened her, and she had 22 snakes in her about five inches long.

⋄

I saw an old rattlesnake with four or five very small young rattlers around her, and when I came upon them I saw these young rattlesnakes run up to the old one. She would open her mouth and swallow each one as they came up to her; later, when the danger was over, they would come out.

⋄

I have seen 14 small rattlesnakes about the size of a worm, say four or five inches long, run into the mother's mouth and down from her mouth. We killed this rattler and shook these small rattlesnakes from her mouth. I saw this with my own eyes.

⋄

The mother rattler does swallow her young for protection. They do not go into the food channel, but into an especially prepared baby basket which is under the complete control of the mother snake. I have seen the little ones go in, and then have killed the mother and found them there.

One of the characteristics of these stories is the minimizing of the length of the young snakes, indicating that, in part at least, the lengths are based on those of immature fetuses extruded from the body of the mother. Of the commoner kinds of rattlesnakes, such as the timber, prairie, Great Basin, northern and southern Pacific, and western diamond, the young at birth are from 10 to 12 inches long. But the above statements give the lengths as 3 to 5 inches.

How the swallowing tradition may seem to be verified by a lack of knowledge of the fact that rattlesnakes do not lay eggs, but give birth to living young, is suggested by the following:

When I was attending school the boys caught a large rattlesnake at a den and put it in a fruit jar with air holes in the screw lid and left the snake in the school room overnight.

---

[7] Garter snakes give birth to live young; they are not egg-layers.

The next morning upon arriving at school we found six little snakes about six inches long in the jar. She must have swallowed these baby rattlesnakes upon being disturbed while we were catching her alive, as I understand that rattlesnakes do not give birth to young but lay eggs.

The following is a part of an account from a recent newspaper:

I heard the low buzz of a rattler and stopped the team. Right beside the front wheel of the wagon was a prairie-dog hole and in its opening was a large female rattlesnake. Her lower jaw was lying flat on the ground, and her upper jaw was raised almost straight upward. While the old snake continued the low buzz, my wife and I, and the two girls, watched five or more tiny rattlers crawl into the mouth of the old snake and disappear. The mother snake then disappeared into the prairie-dog hole, and I know not what happened to the baby snakes.

This is subject, with all due respect to the conscientious belief of the reporter, to the interpretation that the little snakes just went past the mother into the hole.

MOTHER NOURISHING YOUNG

A peculiar myth, accessory to the young-swallowing idea, is that mother rattlesnakes nourish their young in their stomachs when they swallow them. This has been seriously suggested by Rivers (1874, p. 510), Stanley (1897, p. 34), and, finally, by the great naturalist John Burroughs (1908, p. 18). There is not the slightest foundation for this story, originally proposed because of difficulty of conceiving how young rattlers could eat the same food as the adults. It is now known that, although they can and do eat young mice, they depend on lizards more than do the adults.

An ancient myth dating back to Pliny, Galen, and even to Herodotus (Rawlinson, 1942, vol. 1, p. 209), that young vipers kill their mothers at birth, has not, so far as I know, been attributed to rattlesnakes.

THE FATAL BOOT

One of the best-defined rattlesnake legends is that which may be called the story of the fatal boot. Briefly it is as follows: A man, while plowing in a field, is bitten by a rattler and succumbs. Some time later—as measured in months or years—his son, now grown to man's estate, mysteriously sickens and dies. After another interval the same sad fate overwhelms a second son; and it is only then that the family physician, seeking the cause of these successive tragedies, finds that each son had, before his death, worn a pair of boots inherited from the unfortunate parent. In the inside of one boot there is found protruding the fang of the rattler that had so foully slain the father, and which, undiscovered through the years, has lain awaiting the day when it should strike down his offspring.

In this fable there is a considerable variation in the relationships of the triads involved in the fatality, some of them being: a father and two sons; a grandfather, father, and son; or three successive husbands of the widow (serves them right).

Although this legend originated in colonial days in the East, I have heard it recently told of unfortunate families in Texas, Arizona, California, Idaho, and Washington. It was apparently first published by Crèvecoeur (1782, p. 249; 1783, p. 100), the victims being a father, son, and a neighbor. The Crèvecoeur version is given a faint color of plausibility by a deviation from later versions in that all fatalities occurred within a few weeks, and that the venom gland, as well as the fang, was found in the boot. That the story long antedated Crèvecoeur has lately been shown by Masterson (1938, p. 213), who has published the manuscript of a paper read before the Royal Society of London, January 7, 1714, but not previously printed. In this paper by one Capt. Walduck, we find the fatal boot; the fatalities occurred to three successive husbands in Virginia. The disastrous fang, after discovery, was tried on a dog with fatal results. Later it was tried on a second dog without effect; and it was then assumed that the snake itself, which once had possessed the fang, must be dead. Thus we see, in this primordial version of the myth, that the deleterious results were not entirely attributed to something physical like venom, for there is another myth to the effect that venom ceases to be dangerous when the snake that produced it is no longer alive.

Other accounts of the myth will be found scattered through the literature, some, particularly the earlier ones, repeating it seriously, whereas others merely cite it as an interesting bit of folklore. Sectionally, it has been attributed to Massachusetts (Welch, 1927, p. 372), New York (Evers, 1951, p. 112), Pennsylvania (Anon., 1858a, p. 326), Mississippi (Clark, 1928, p. 142), Texas (Boatright, 1934, p. 2; Benton, 1937, p. 210; King, 1941, p. 19; Clough, 1947, p. 155), Arkansas (Masterson, 1942, p. 39; Randolph, 1951, p. 142), Oregon (Dobie, 1947b, p. 91), California (Truit, 1896, p. 19), the Southwest (Breland, 1948, p. 221). Outside the United States it has been reported as occurring in Surinam (Schlegel, 1844, p. 68), and Honduras (Anon., 1856, p. 597; Gould and Pyle, 1897, p. 717), with a rattlesnake as the culprit; and, strangest of all, involving a cobra in India (Compton, 1893, p. 177). Some other references are Bosc (1803, p. 554), Griffith and Pidgeon (1831, p. 314), Berkeley (1861, p. 66), Mitchell (1868, p. 459), Lane (1927, p. 210, in a short story), and Stimpson (1946, p. 418). Kalm (1752–53, p. 58) antedated Crèvecoeur with a partial development of the myth. A farmer was bitten in the boot and suffered no harm. Later he scratched himself on the protruding fang and died.

One of my valued correspondents, the late E. A. McIlhenny of Avery Island, Louisiana, makes this interesting comment on the boot story:

> I am certainly very familiar with this "myth," and have done my bit to spread it. It came to me from my father more than 65 years ago. He was told it by Dr. Metcalf, a noted surgeon of New Orleans, who claimed to have direct knowledge of the incident which happened, according to him, on a sugar plantation in Plaquemines Parish, Louisiana. As my father told it to me, the rattler had struck a man, while working in the field, just above his heel, in the thick part of his boot. The fang penetrated, but the man, feeling but a slight prick, went on with his work; and when he went home some hours later, his foot was so swollen that he could hardly remove his boot, and he eventually died. His grown son, some months later, put the boot on, and, during his work in the field, felt an abrasion on the side of his heel, and thinking it was a nail in his boot paid no attention to it, until he got home at the noon hour. He then found that his foot was badly swollen, and upon examination found the fang of the rattlesnake embedded in the boot. He, too, eventually died. Thus the story goes. My father firmly believed this story, and I have believed it up until receipt of your letter.

The weakness of the story, as has been shown by Waterton (1835b, p. 5), Bogert (1948a, p. 101), and a number of others, lies in the belief that the point of a fang could contain enough dried venom to do serious damage. For the fang aperture, which conceivably might hold enough dried venom to cause at least a slight pain, lies well back of the point; and any venom on the point would be scraped off by passage through the leather of the boot. Rolker (1905, p. 201) tells how Ditmars once scratched his forefinger with the fang of a dried snake skull and almost lost an arm. But was the trouble caused by venom? I had a somewhat similar experience; I shoved my hand into a new glove into which a pin holding the price tag protruded. The result was serious indeed, but it was an ordinary infection; there was neither snake nor venom involved. S. Pope (1919, p. 51) experimented with venom on a dried fang. He discounts all stories based on a danger from this source.

Other discussions of how dangerous the venom on a single, dried fang might be are those of Kalm (1752–53, p. 58), Schoolcraft (1821, p. 325), Beltrami (1828, p. 186), Bories (1883, p. 58), and Webb (1883, p. 269). Harvey (1901, p. 157; 1924, p. 74) tells of a man who killed a rattler and left it in a field. Seven years later, while grubbing for potatoes he stuck himself with a fang and suffered severe poisoning. Another account makes the interval 18 years. In any case, assuming the accident to have happened, it was clearly an ordinary infection. No tiny quantity of a protein poison, unprotected from the elements for all those intervening years, could have produced such a result.

Besides these technical weaknesses, the widespread dispersion of the boot story brands it as typical folklore. The same singular sequence of events simply could not have happened to so many different trios of men in such widely separated parts of the country.[8]

Boatright (1931, p. 273; 1934, p. 4) gives a modern tall-story variant of the boot myth. A cowboy runs over a rattler and two successive garage men who repair the resulting puncture die from being punctured by the fang. Boatright also tells us that the original boot story is now being embroidered in Texas: After the third human death, the fang taken from the boot is buried, only to be dug up by a dog with fatal results to itself. See also Adair (1930, p. 62) concerning the rattler that punctured a tire casing.

THE ROADRUNNER'S CACTUS CORRAL

One of the most colorful, as well as widespread, rattler myths of the Southwest concerns the roadrunner (also called *paisano* or chaparral cock), a sprightly inhabitant of this arid land. According to the story, the roadrunner, upon finding a rattler asleep in the open, builds a wall about it with cactus stems or lobes. When the rattler awakes, it endeavors to escape. Prevented by the impenetrable wall and stuck by its spines, it becomes enraged, bites itself, and dies. In some versions the roadrunner eats its victim; in others, it merely gives a characteristic cry of victory and goes elsewhere to seek another customer.

As given, the story contains two essential weaknesses: First, rattlesnakes readily glide through or over cactus; for example, in southern and Baja California prickly-pear patches are favored haunts of the red diamond rattlesnake, *C. r. ruber*. Secondly, rattlesnakes are virtually immune to their own venoms, as discussed in chapter 12.

---

[8] A recent example of how a story that involves unusual incidents may be simultaneously claimed to be an actual occurrence in many sections of the country has been supplied by the *Reader's Digest*, vol. 65, no. 387, p. 90, July, 1954.

Roadrunners are omnivorous creatures that include reptiles in their bills of fare, and young rattlers are occasionally eaten (see chap. 15), but the cactus wall is just one of those stories originated for the astonishment of the Eastern visitor, which later came to be accepted as gospel by the inventors themselves.

The earliest account of this myth I have come upon is that of Heermann (1859, p. 60); he repeats it only as hearsay and not as if he had any faith in its accuracy. However, it was probably much older. Bryant (1891, p. 60), in his publication of the previously unprinted biographical notes of A. J. Grayson, includes one in which Grayson describes the roadrunner corral, although he did not vouch for the validity of the story. Since Grayson died in 1869, aged 50, he had probably written the account years before. Gregg, as early as 1844 (vol. 1, p. 195), mentioned the killing of rattlers by roadrunners.

Orcutt (1886, p. 49) and Bonelli (1888, p. 223) were among the early writers who apparently had confidence in the yarn. Van Dyke (1897, p. 38) remarked upon having seen rattlers climb over more cacti than a roadrunner could heap up in a half a day. Vorhies and Taylor (1940, p. 508) found the cholla-cactus nests built by the wood rat *Neotoma* to be no protection against snakes. Dobie (1937, p. 162; 1939, p. 79) gives several eyewitness accounts of the cactus-corral story as examples of Texan folklore. Bess Kennedy (1942, p. 117) shows that even today folklore gets the best of some of those who look for color afield. Other pertinent references are those of Wadham (1882, p. 27), Dulog (1897, p. 202), Dobie (1925, p. 162; 1947b, p. 92), Bogusch (1926, p. 115), Bevan (1932d, p. 71), Arnold (1935, p. 91), McKenna (1936, p. 225), Fenley (1940, p. 4), Pound (1946, p. 172), Breland (1948, p. 102), and Botkin (1951, p. 157).

Ramsey (1945, p. 37) has given a variation of the myth which could well have an element of truth: A roadrunner, upon finding a rattler in the open, might, by teasing and obstructing it, prevent its reaching protective shade and thus it would be killed by the heat of the sun. But cactus would have no part in the plot. Another variant is that of Humfreville (1903, p. 448; see also Dobie, 1925, p. 162, and Sibley, 1951, p. 48). In this, the roadrunner approaches the rattler with a piece of cactus in its bill. The rattler strikes the cactus and is injured by the spines, whereupon the bird picks the snake's eyes out.

I first heard the roadrunner's cactus-corral story around the campfire about 1897. It is by no means outdated today; several of my correspondents have included eyewitness accounts in the notes that they forwarded. It is current wherever roadrunners are found.

The Cabin Built on a Den

One of the early myths no longer heard is of the family of emigrants who were so unfortunate as to erect their home (presumably in winter) backed against a rock ledge. The ledge proved to be a rattlesnake den, and when the family was celebrating its housewarming with a glorious fire on the hearth, the warmed-up snakes issued forth in great numbers to the discomfort of the occupants. In an early account (Kalm, 1752–53, p. 314; 1758, p. 288) the people merely sought safety upstairs, but in later versions (Anon., 1829, p. 370; Flint, 1829, p. 115, 1832, p. 76) most of the inmates were fatally bitten, only a few escaping to the roof. Kalm's family lived in New England. Sullivan (1852, p. 174) tells of such an incident in Iowa "a few years back." According to Guild (1878, p. 53), the yarn is mentioned in the folklore of Tennessee; Benton (1937, p. 208) has recorded it from Texas; and Fisher (1939, p. 79) from Idaho. Probably this folklore is the outgrowth of the finding of a rattler or two in some settler's cabin, certainly not an unusual event.

THE RATTLER AND THE WAGON WHEEL

A snake myth current in my youth, when I drove many a mile in a fringed surrey, has now almost died out because of transportation changes. The story was to the effect that a rattler, upon being run over by the wheel of a buckboard or such-like vehicle, coiled around the felloe of the wheel and then, at the top of the travel, was thrown into the lap of one of the occupants, usually the girl of the story. This yarn had a sufficient vogue in its day, so that many a driver was glad to have the horses turn out to avoid a crossing rattler. The automobile almost ruined this story, especially since the advent of the modern fender, but it is still occasionally heard as a recent happening. A tall-story variant of the buggy yarn is given by Bailey (1947, p. 706).

THE CHILD FEEDS A RATTLESNAKE

An ancient legend, which has crossed the Atlantic to be applied to rattlesnakes, is that of the child who befriends a snake. In the usual version a child, generally a girl, repeatedly carries her lunch out into the yard to eat. Finally the curiosity of her parents is aroused; they follow her and watch her sit down to enjoy her bowl of bread and milk. At once a huge snake—often a rattlesnake, if told in the United States—issues from the grass and coils beside her, to be fed milk and bread with a spoon. The horrified parents destroy the snake, with the result that the child, pining for her playmate, goes into a decline and dies.

Some American versions of this legend will be found recorded or cited by Oliver Wendell Holmes in *Elsie Venner* (1861, vol. 1, p. 278), Flack (1866, p. 325), Johnson (1896, p. 102), Smiley (1919, p. 357), Roberts (1927, p. 203), Clark (1928, p. 144), Milling (1937, p. 50), Ericson (1941, p. 113, but dating back to 1850 or before), Richter (1946, p. 194), Meek (1946, p. 202), Masterson (1946, p. 177), Musick (1947, p. 47), Witthoft (1947, p. 136), Randolph (1947, p. 257; 1950, p. 84; 1952, p. 87), Moore (1949, p. 57), and Smith (1951, p. 1). Many, but not all, of these accounts involve rattlesnakes. They are most often heard in the Eastern and Southern sections of the country. Some foreign versions are those of Fitz-Simons (1932, p. 171), Radford and Radford (1947, p. 221), and Rose (1950, p. 248). The child-milk-snake legend is so long established and well known that it was given the number 285 in the Aarne-Thompson folk-myth catalogue, and is known as B391.1 in Thompson's *Motif-Index of Folk Literature* (1932–36).

There are many stories, some no doubt true, some legendary, about children found playing innocently with rattlesnakes. Doubtless this has often happened, since young children are usually not afraid of snakes. Although serious and sad accidents have resulted from occurrences of this kind, many have ended without harm if the rattler has not been frightened or roughly handled. From such has grown the dangerous myth that rattlesnakes will not bite children.

One of my correspondents wrote:

> I know of an incident wherein a four-year-old boy was found playing with a rattler, and had been for some time before his parents found him. They found evidence in the dust that the snake had tried to crawl away and the child had dragged it back by its rattles. The child wasn't harmed at all. *J. O. Teel, Greenville, N. C.*

A newspaper recently reported that several children had played with a rattle-snake unharmed, until one tried to force it to crawl down a hole and was bitten. In 1931 a boy of nine came to the reptile house of the San Diego Zoo, carrying a young rattler that he thought was a harmless snake. Other stories of this type are told by Leroy (1891, p. 44), Meek (1946, p. 102), and Rutledge (1947a, p. 62). Sprunt (1931, p. 13) tells a tale of a blind child found by its mother peaceably stroking a rattler. The allegation that the mother separated the playmates with "commendable calmness" at once relegates the story to the category of folklore.

THE THANKFUL RATTLESNAKES

A tall tale of early days was of the miner who kept at large in his cabin a tame rattler to which he fed the fattest mice available. Finally he was rewarded when his pet gave a warning rattle upon the entrance of an intruder who sought his cache of gold. This yarn, highly embroidered, eventually reached the lower strata of vaudeville. In this version the kindly rattler bound the burglar to a convenient bedpost with his coils and then hung his tail out of the window to rattle for the police. The story will be found in Thomas (1931, p. 180), Schmelzel in Fisher (1939, p. 116), Davidson (1941, p. 215), Botkin (1944, p. 623), and Davidson and Blake (1947, p. 268). As Shorey (1953, p. 27) tells the tale, a mother rattler held the burglar at bay while her infants rattled for the police. There was also the tale of the kindly hunter who saved the life of a big rattler, and was himself saved when he fell on a track in front of a train, whereupon the rattler pulled the hunter's red bandana out of his pocket and flagged the train.

The often-heard story that when one rattler in a den rattles, all the other inhabitants join in has now been expanded. It appears that in eastern Kansas the tocsin flashes from den to den, and when all the 200 million rattlers in that section sound off together, the inhabitants flee to their cyclone cellars (Davidson, 1943, p. 188; Davidson and Blake, 1947, p. 270).

THE DEEP FREEZE

There are a number of tall tales involving frozen rattlesnakes, such as that of the man in winter, who built a fence with 500 posts, 4 to 14 feet long, driven into the ground. But when it warmed up the posts proved to be rattlers; they crawled off dragging two miles of barbed wire (Allen, 1933, p. 29; Boatright, 1934, p. 10; Botkin, 1944, p. 625; Duncan, 1945, p. 340). Then there was the frozen rattler that was used first as a cane, and later as a poker. Every time it thawed out it was put outside to freeze (Thomas, 1931, p. 168). And the tale of the old nurse who went outside on a cold night to gather firewood; when she put the load down before the fire the sticks thawed out and crawled away (Guerra, 1941, p. 70). Another horrid tale concerns the man, who, to sleep beyond the reach of the numerous rattlers round about, built himself a hammock. Awakened by a jerking in the morning he found that what he had thought were ropes, proved to be rattlers now thawed out (Fisher, 1939, p. 130).

TRIBAL HEROES

Some tall tales apply to particular persons. Among these are rattlesnake stories attributed to Pecos Bill, the west Texas cowpuncher's Paul Bunyan, and Febold Feboldson, a man of similar stature recently arisen in the Great Plains. Pecos Bill, knowing that rattlers eat moth balls, but not chili powder, prepared some special balls with centers of mixed chili and nitroglycerine, but with exteriors of the usual naphthalene. When the coating melted off and the chili burned their insides, the rattlers struck their tails on the rocks and exploded the nitroglycerine (Boatright, 1934, p. 16). Pecos Bill also rode a mountain lion, using a 10-foot rattler as a quirt. In capturing the rattler, to be fair, he gave it the first three bites (Botkin, 1944, pp. 175, 182).

Febold Feboldson owned a 14-foot rattler named Arabella. Once, when Febold was tied up by Indians, Arabella squirted venom on the rope, disintegrating it. Again, on a stroll, Arabella rattled the snakes' national anthem, and she and Febold were immediately surrounded by a huge assemblage of her compatriots. Febold gave himself up for lost, but Arabella rattled Brahms' "Lullaby" and put her friends to sleep. To carry Arabella, Febold had a basket back of his saddle called the "rattle seat" later corrupted to "rumble seat." Febold invented the booby trap by hollowing out every fourth watermelon in his patch and putting a rattler inside. This soon caused the Indians to quit stealing the melons, but as Febold was unable to remember which melons were salted, he couldn't sell them without violating the Pure Food and Drugs Act and so had to give them away. These yarns about Febold are from Beath (1948, pp. 78, 94).

THE WONDERFUL HUNT AND OTHER YARNS

In the wonderful-hunt legend, a well-known Western story (I think there is something like it in Munchausen) the hunter fires a shot that initiates a Goldbergian chain of events, each of which causes various kinds of game to fall at his feet. It is standard practice to have the ramrod kill a huge rattler (Puckett, 1926, p. 51; Halpert, 1944, p. 111; Hartikka, 1946, p. 73).

Other stories of this type are those of the rattler, the frog, and the drink of whiskey (Thomas, 1931, p. 42; Boatright, 1934, p. 14); the pet rattler owned by the telegrapher (Botkin, 1949, p. 445); the toy made of a barrel of rattlers (Evers, 1951, p. 108); and the thankful rattler that brought his fellows to form a rope long enough to rescue the man who had befriended him from a mine shaft into which he had fallen (Davidson and Blake, 1947, p. 264). Also, there was the band of hogs that ate so many rattlesnakes they grew rattles on their tails (Reid, 1910, p. 327).

Other tales, some believed by their tellers, others deliberately bizarre or tall, will be found in Weld (1855, p. 80), Dobie (1925, p. 9), Williams (1932, p. 239), Benton (1937, p. 211), Rollins (1939, p. 31; also Botkin, 1944, p. 379), Dobie (1943, p. 1), Scudday (1944, p. 162), Dobie (1946e, p. 63), and Evers (1951, p. 113).

As is the case with most kinds of snakes, there are legends and stories about rattlers guarding treasure (e.g., Dobie, 1941, p. 529; 1947b, p. 91).

THE INFERIORITY COMPLEX

Schmidt (1945, p. 30), struck by the incredibility of the tales which the curator of a great museum is repeatedly called upon to deny, has repeated an amusing bit of folklore lately heard in Texas. In a family of nine children only the youngest daughter hadn't been bitten by a rattler. She was rapidly acquiring an inferiority complex, listening to her proud relatives boasting of their injuries, when fortunately she was bitten and became the Cinderella of the outfit (see also Dobie, 1950b, p. 1).

MISCELLANEOUS BELIEFS AND FOLKLORE

INCIPIENT MYTHS

One myth growing out of World War II is certainly destined for immortality; this is the one that tells of the soldier in training, who is advancing at a crawl under a curtain of live machine-gun fire just overhead. He meets a rattler face to face—usually a "huge sidewinder"—and raises up into the stream of bullets with disastrous results. I think I have heard this story as happening in every one of the Southwestern camps where troops were trained for desert warfare. I suppose it may have actually occurred once; this may prove an interesting item of research when the reports of the Surgeon General are finally published. It is known already that there were no snake-bite fatalities in the Southwestern camps during World War II. The myth was already going strong in early 1944 (Netting, 1944, p. 45; see also Dorson, 1947, p. 8). In another version of the myth the soldier successfully grabs the rattler by the neck and crawls with it to the end of the course. Another war-engendered myth has to do with shoals of rattlers shaken out of the ground by the treads of passing tanks or tractors.

A story that is rapidly gaining the status of folklore tells of a prospector who, while searching for fluorescent minerals with an ultraviolet lamp, almost picks up a glowing rattler by mistake. (Actually, I have found by test that rattlesnake bodies do not fluoresce in ultraviolet light, although the rattles glow slightly and the fangs strongly).

DREAMS

There are many superstitions concerning dreams about snakes. Generally they foretell the existence of an enemy; if you kill the snake, you will overcome the enemy. Few dream interpretations relate specifically to rattlesnakes; evidently identification is not important. But Showers (1900, p. 180; Puckett, 1926, p. 294) notes the Alabama belief that if you dream of a rattler a conjure man has "put something down for you." If the rattler tried to bite you and failed, you have escaped the conjure doctor's tricks. A small rattler indicates a weak doctor, a large one a strong. Bogusch (1926, p. 115) says it is a Texas superstition that to dream a rattler has bitten you presages bad luck.

Some regional folklore of dreams about snakes, but not specifically rattlers, will be found in Johnson, 1896, p. 19, New England; Dresslar, 1907, p. 124, California; Fogel, 1915, p. 79, Pennsylvania Germans; Whitney and Bullock, 1925, pp. 13, 34, Maryland; Roberts, 1927, p. 180, Louisiana; Clark, 1928, p. 141, Mississippi; Stout, 1936, p. 194, Iowa; Pound, 1946, p. 170, Nebraska; and Allison, 1950, p. 322, southeastern Illinois.

SUPERSTITIONS ABOUT MEETING RATTLERS

There are many superstitions of a world-wide character having to do with encountering snakes, such as the disaster to be expected if one sees a snake at the start of a journey or fails to kill the first snake seen in the spring. As these beliefs apply to all snakes, rattlesnakes are rarely mentioned specifically. Pound (1946, p. 169) says it is bad luck if a rattler crosses your path. This is Nebraska folklore. Neog (1951, p. 153) reports that in Madras people postpone their journeys if they see a cobra or rattlesnake. I suppose that anyone seeing a rattlesnake at large anywhere in Asia, Africa, or Europe, would be justified in taking even stronger measures.

RATTLESNAKES AND WEATHER

There are many myths, world-wide in derivation and spread, concerning the relationships of snakes to weather (Wake, 1873, p. 375). Such myths are current throughout the United States, although usually attributed to snakes in general, rather than to rattlesnakes. Often they have to do with snakes and rain; for example, how rain may be produced if you hang a snake, belly up, on a fence, tree, or bush. Regional accounts of these snake-weather correlations will be found in Dunwoody (1883, pp. 72, 80), Davis (1888, p. 164), Moore (1892, p. 231), Johnson (1896, p. 19), Dobie (1923, p. 89), Whitney and Bullock (1925, p. 25), Roberts (1927, p. 187), Clark (1928, p. 144), Smith (1930b, p. 180), Randolph (1931, p. 116; 1947, p. 14), Farr (1935, p. 334), Stout (1936, p. 162), Redfield (1937, p. 37), Pound (1946, p. 168), Baylor (1947, p. 147), and Webber (1951, p. 30).

Some specific applications of weather lore to rattlesnakes are the following: Drape a rattler on its back over a log and it will rain in three days (Dresslar, 1907, p. 49, California folklore). If rattler tracks are many and directed to high ground, rain will be abundant; or, if rattlers are unusually vicious, rain will follow (Dobie, 1923, p. 88; 1926, p. 52, Texas-Mexico border folklore). Turning a live or a dead rattler on its back will bring rain (Dobie, 1926, p. 52). Virtually the same superstitions are mentioned as being current in Texas and Oklahoma by Bogusch (1926, p. 115), Smith (1930b, p. 180), Campa (1950, p. 181), and Botkin (1951, p. 86); and in the Ozark country by Randolph (1933, p. 11; 1947, p. 14).

MISCELLLANEOUS MYTHS, LEGENDS, AND STORIES

Here are a number of myths and stories about rattlesnakes that have appeared in print, or have been heard voiced by visitors at the zoo, that do not lend themselves to classification.

A shirt spotted with rattlesnake venom cannot be cleaned (Beverly, 1722, p. 266). Michel (1916, p. 287) was told in Virginia in 1701 that people who worked new land frequently suffered from swollen legs covered with white pimples. These effects were thought to be caused by rattlesnakes having poisoned the ground. The handling of rattlesnakes can cause a troublesome swelling, as they throw off a poisonous dust (Anon., 1897, p. 125). Pound (1946, p. 173) records a Nebraska folk belief that a sidewinder will kill any living thing it touches; and Gillam (1916, p. 129) records another folktale that if the sidewinder sticks you with a horn it will be fatal. (Actually, the horns are soft and flexible.)

A man was badly poisoned by a rope burn where a rattler had bitten the rope (Barnes, 1933, p. 429). A rattler struck a boy's leggings; his dog licked the leggings and died (West Virginia folk tale reported by Musick, 1948, p. 2). A person bitten by a rattler over which birds are circling is not likely to die (Bogusch, 1926, p. 115, Texas superstition). A man, bitten by a rattler, first gave himself up as lost, but, upon consulting an almanac and finding the sign of the zodiac propitious, paid no further attention to the bite (Collot, 1924, vol. 2, p. 9, but written in 1826). Aswell (1940, p. 166) tells a tall tale of the use of rattlers to cure the bites of stinging snakes, for only bites by rattlers will do this. What a stinging snake may be remains undetermined.

Remarks made by people in front of rattlesnake cages at the zoo: All snakes shed their skins except rattlesnakes. Rattlers dislike certain colors, especially blue. Rattlesnakes won't rattle at night. The rattle is used as an anchor from which a striking snake lunges; also as a brake when sliding downhill. The reason rattlesnakes are not found in the vicinity of Puget Sound—it is true, they are not—is because the available water is so pure that rattlesnakes cannot generate venom from it and therefore starve to death. Television antennas attract rattlesnakes. (This one, at least, we may be sure did not come down from Pliny.) As animals without gall bladders are immune to rattlesnake bite (so the legend runs), a woman was heard to inquire whether her recent operation put her in that category.

Misinterpretations and Exaggerations

There are a number of ideas or beliefs respecting rattlesnake habits that, through misinterpretation or exaggeration, have come to border on the mythical. However, in essence they are based on facts. Since they have an element of actuality, they are best discussed as part of the appropriate chapters in this book, and this has been done, but to round out this chapter I shall summarize them here.

1. Rattlers always rattle before striking. As a matter of fact, sometimes they will, at others they will not. It depends upon the conditions surrounding the encounter and upon the species and individual temperament of the snake (see p. 438).

2. Rattlesnakes acquire a rattle a year, and therefore the age can be determined by the number of segments in a string. Actually, a new rattle is added each time a rattler sheds its skin, and these skin changes are more frequent than once per year, particularly when the snakes are young and growing rapidly, or in the Southern states where the active season is longer. Furthermore, rattle breakage is both usual and natural, and adults almost never have complete strings (see p. 258).

3. Rattlesnakes sting with their tongues, to judge from the remarks of zoo visitors, as they observe rattlesnakes in their cages; this confusion between the rattlesnake's delicate tongue and its fangs seems to be quite general, nor is it restricted to rattlesnakes (see p. 365).

4. Rattlesnakes are the quintessence of evil; their continuous and sole desire is to wreak vengeance on all living creatures, particularly man. As a matter of fact, unless injured, attacked, or brought to bay, they are relatively timorous and inoffensive creatures, seeking to hide unnoticed, or to escape into some secluded refuge. Unfortunately, their food-getting mechanism—fangs and venom—make them dangerous creatures out of all proportion to their size, but they are not innately vicious (see p. 437).

5. Our zoo visitors frequently express surprise that rattlesnakes will live peaceably with each other as well as with other kinds of snakes. Actually, rattlers are rather gregarious,

as has been pointed out in the description of their lives at their hibernating dens (see p. 541), to which snakes of other genera likewise repair. Unless some snake-eating species be introduced, snakes of different kinds get along quite well together in captivity.

6. There is a story with regard to reproduction to the effect that if a pair be disturbed in mating they will die. There is some truth to this idea; the male reproductive organs are so formed that a sudden forcible separation would do serious damage to both snakes.

7. There are many myths, legends, and exaggerations with respect to rattlesnake bite, its seriousness, and the great variety of remedies that have been tried or suggested for its cure. These have been mentioned with the rest of the material on snake bite in chapters 11–13.

8. Other legends, traditions, and superstitions that have been mentioned incidentally in connection with the life-history observations in other chapters are the following:

    a. The supposed happy prairie family—rattlesnakes, prairie dogs, and burrowing owls

    b. Seasonal blindness; seasonal variations in temperament and venom virulence

    c. The purpose and use of the rattle

    d. The nature of the resting and striking coils

    e. How to distinguish venomous from nonvenomous snakes

    f. The exaggerated idea of the high temperatures that snakes prefer

    g. Snake suicides; the effect of venom on the snakes themselves

Fig. 18:1. *Crotalus willardi meridionalis,* Southern Ridge-Nosed Rattlesnake. (Specimen from Durango, Mexico. Photograph by courtesy of John E. Werler, San Antonio Zoölogical Society. This snake was captured too recently to permit incorporation of the illustration in the proper sequence of the identification series.)

CONCLUSION

Of all these myths, that which has most deeply affected human impressions and attitudes toward rattlesnakes is the one that pictures these snakes as malignant, vindictive, and crafty, with an especial hatred of mankind. Recently a radio commentator called rattlesnakes the "symbol of pure evil."

But a rattlesnake is only a primitive creature with rudimentary perceptions and reactions. Dangerous it surely is, and I hold no brief for its survival except in remote areas where its capacity to destroy harmful rodents may be exercised without danger to man or his domestic animals. But that the rattlesnake bears an especial enmity toward man is mythical. It seeks only to defend itself from injury by intruders of superior size, of which man is one. It could not, through the ages, have developed any especial enmity for man, since the first human being any rattlesnake may encounter is usually the last.

Bibliography

ABBATIUS, B. A.
  1660. De Admirabili Viperae. Hagae, pp. [xxii] + 186 + [xxvi]. [1st edition, 1589; another, 1603.]
ABBOTT, C. C.
  1873. Do Rattlesnakes Climb Trees? Am. Nat., vol. 7, no. 7, p. 433.
ABERT, J. J.
  1831. Habit of Climbing of the Rattlesnake. Monthly Am. Jour. Geol. and Nat. Sci., vol. 1, no. 5, pp. 221–223.
ACKERKNECHT, E. H.
  1949. Medical Practices. In Handbook of South American Indians. Smithson. Inst., Bur. Am. Ethn., Bull. 143, vol. 5, pp. 621–643.
ACTON, H. W., and R. KNOWLES
  1914a. The Dose of Venom Given in Nature by a Cobra in a Single Bite. Indian Jour. Med. Res., vol. 1, no. 3, pp. 388–413.
  1914b. The Dose of Venom Given in Nature by the Echis carinata at a Single Bite. Indian Jour. Med. Res., vol. 1, no. 3, pp. 414–424.
  1915. Studies on the Treatment of Snake-Bite. IV. The Present Position of Antivenene Therapy. Indian Jour. Med. Res., vol. 3, no. 2, pp. 275–361.
  1921. Snakes and Snake Poisoning. In The Practice of Medicine in the Tropics, edited by W. Byam and R. G. Archibald. Oxford, 3 vols.; see vol. 1, § 5, pp. 683–762.
ADAIR, C. L.
  1930. Knowing Our Snakes. Outdoor Life, vol. 65, no. 3, pp. 32, 62.
ADAIR, C. L., and E. L. EWBANK
  1922. [Snake Lore.] Outdoor Life, vol. 49, no. 5, pp. 356–357. [See also vol. 50, no. 1, p. 74.]
ADAIR, J.
  1775. The History of the American Indians. London, pp. [vi] + 464. [Reprinted as Adair's History of the American Indians, edited by Samuel Cole Williams. Johnson City, Tenn., 1930, pp. xxxviii + 508.]
ADAMS, C. C.
  1902. Southeastern United States as a Center of Geographical Distribution of Flora and Fauna. Biol. Bull., vol. 3, pp. 115–131.
ADAMS, F. (translator)
  1844–7. The Seven Books of Paulus Aegineta. London, 3 vols., xxviii + 683; xi + 511; viii + 653.
ADAMS, G. C. S.
  1938. Rattlesnake Eye. So. Folklore Quart., vol. 2, no. 1, pp. 37–38.
ADAMS, H. C.
  1927. Traveller's Tales. New York, pp. ix + 334. [1st edition, London, 1882.]
ADAMS, R. F.
  1936. Cowboy Lingo. Boston, pp. x + 257.
  1944. Western Words. Norman, Okla., pp. xiv + 182.
ADAMSON, THELMA
  1934. Folk-Tales of the Coast Salish. Mem. Am. Folk-Lore Soc., vol. 27, pp. xv + 430.
AELIANUS, C.
  1615. De Historia Animalium. Lugduni, pp. [14] + 668 + [37]. Also 1616, Geneva, pp. [6] + 1018 + [94]. [An earlier edition, Tiguri, 1555.]
AGINSKY, B. W.
  1943. Culture Element Distributions: XXIV. Central Sierra. Univ. Calif. Anthro. Rec., vol. 8, no. 4, pp. iv, 393–468.

AHRENFELDT, R. H.
  1955. Two British Anatomical Studies on American Reptiles (1650–1750). II. Edward Tyson: Comparative Anatomy of the Timber Rattlesnake. Herpetologica, vol. 11, part 1, pp. 49–69.
AHUJA, M. L.
  1935. Specificity of Antivenomous Sera . . . Indian Jour. Med. Res., vol. 22, no. 3, pp. 478–484.
AKATSUKA, K.
  1936. Immunological Studies of Snake Venoms. Japanese Jour. Exp. Med., vol. 14, no. 2, pp. 147–183.
ALBEE, F. H., and E. MAIER
  1943. A Preliminary Report on the Use of Venom in Arthritis. Med. Rec., vol. 156, pp. 217–221, 246.
ALCOCK, A.
  1914. Snakes and Snake-Venoms. *In* Tropical Medicine and Hygiene, by C. W. Daniels and A. Alcock. New York, 2nd edition, 2 vols.; see vol. 2, chap. 18, pp. 219–269. [1st edition, New York, 1909–1912, 2 vols.]
ALCOCK, A., and L. ROGERS
  1902. On the Toxic Properties of the Saliva of Certain "Non-poisonous" Colubrines. Proc. Royal Soc. London, vol. 70, no. 465, pp. 446–454.
ALDINGTON, R.
  1949. The Strange Life of Charles Waterton, 1782–1865. London, pp. 1–200.
ALDOUS, C. M.
  1938. Deer Kills Rattlesnake. Jour. Mammal., vol. 19, p. 111.
ALDROVANDUS, U.
  1640. Serpentum et Draconū Historiae. Bononiae, pp. [iv] + 427 + [xxviii].
ALEXANDER, H. B.
  1916. The Mythology of All Races (Edited by L. H. Gray), Boston, 13 vols.; see vol. 10, North American, pp. xxiv + 325.
  1953. The World's Rim. Lincoln, Neb., pp. xx + 259.
ALEXANDER, J. B.
  1855. Remarks upon Rattlesnake Bite. St. Louis Med. and Surg. Jour., vol. 13, no. 2, pp. 116–122.
ALLBUTT, T. C.
  1921. Greek Medicine in Rome. London, pp. xiv + 633.
ALLEN, E. R.
  1937. Florida Snake Venom Experiments. Proc. Fla. Acad. Sci., vol. 2, pp. 70–76.
  1948. Save Your Dog. Field and Stream, vol. 53, no. 8, pp. 124–128. [Also published as a separate, Snake Bite First Aid for Dogs, pp. (1–6).]
  1949a. Don't Fear Snakes—Respect Them. Outdoor Life, vol. 103, no. 4, pp. 32–33, 70–72.
  1949b. Observations of the Feeding Habits of the Juvenile Cantil. Copeia, no. 3, pp. 225–226.
  1951. Here's How to Get Along with Reptiles. Fla. Wildlife, vol. 5, no. 9, pp. 6–8, 20–22.
ALLEN, E. R., and E. MAIER
  1941. The Extraction and Processing of Snake Venom. Copeia, no. 4, pp. 248–252.
ALLEN, E. R., and M. P. MERRYDAY
  1940. A Snake in the Hand. Nat. Hist., vol. 46, no. 4, pp. 234–239. [See also letter from R. V Brown and further comments by Allen in Nat. Hist., vol. 47, no. 2, pp. 65–66.]
ALLEN, E. R., and W. T. NEILL
  1950a. The Eastern Diamondback Rattlesnake. Fla. Wildlife, vol. 4, no. 2, pp. 10–11.
  1950b. The Pigmy Rattlesnake. Fla. Wildlife, vol. 5, no. 4, pp. 10–11.
  1950c. The Cane-Brake Rattlesnake. Fla. Wildlife, vol. 5, no. 6, pp. 18–19, 35.
  1950d. Keep Them Alive. Reptile Inst. Special Publ. no. 1, pp. 1–24.
  1952. The Indigo Snake. Fla. Wildlife, vol. 6, no. 3, pp. 43–47
ALLEN, E. R., and R. SLATTEN
  1945. A Herpetological Collection from the Vicinity of Key West, Florida. Herpetologica, vol. 3, no. 1, pp. 25–26.
ALLEN, E. R., and D. SWINDELL
  1948. Cottonmouth Moccasin of Florida. Herpetologica, vol. 4, supp. 1, pp. 1–16.

ALLEN, F. M.

    1938. Mechanical Treatment of Venomous Bites and Wounds. So. Med. Jour., vol. 31, no. 12, pp. 1248–1253.

    1939. Observations on Local Measures in the Treatment of Snake Bite. Am. Jour. Trop. Med., vol. 19, pp. 393–404.

    1949. Venomous Bites and Stings. Jour. Am. Med. Assn., vol. 139, no. 9, p. 616.

ALLEN, H.

    1881. An Analysis of the Life-Form in Art. Trans. Am. Philos. Soc., vol. 15 (n.s.), pp. 279–351.

ALLEN, J. A.

    1874. Notes on the Natural History of Portions of Dakota and Montana Territories. Proc. Boston Soc. Nat. Hist., vol. 17, pp. 33–85.

ALLEN, J. V.

    1933. Cowboy Lore. San Antonio, pp. xv + 165.

ALLEN, M. J.

    1932. A Survey of the Amphibians and Reptiles of Harrison County, Mississippi. Am. Mus. Nov., no. 542, pp. 1–20.

    1933. Report on a Collection of Amphibians and Reptiles from Sonora, Mexico, with the Description of a New Lizard. Occ. Papers Mus. Zoöl. Univ. Mich., no. 259, pp. 1–15.

ALLEN, W. A.

    1903. Adventures with Indians and Game. Chicago, pp. 1–302.

ALLISON, E.

    1946. Diamondback! Field and Stream, vol. 51, no. 2, pp. 46–47, 111–114.

ALLISON, LELAH

    1950. Folk Beliefs Collected in Southeastern Illinois. Jour. Am. Folklore, vol. 63, no. 249, pp. 309–327.

ALLYN, W. P.

    1937. Studies on Poisonous Snakes of Indiana. Proc. Ind. Acad. Sci., vol. 46, pp. 220–224.

    1948. Poisonous Snakes of Indiana. Outdoor Ind., vol. 15, no. 7, pp. 12–13.

ALVARO, M. E.

    1939. Snake Venom in Ophthalmology. Am. Jour. Ophth., vol. 22, no. 10, pp. 1130–1145.

AMARAL, A. DO

    1921. Contribution toward the Knowledge of Snakes in Brazil. Part II. Biology of the New Subspecies, *Lachesis insularis*. Mem. Inst. Butantan, vol. 1, pp. 83–88.

    1923a. Snake Poisoning. *In* Nelson's Loose Leaf Living Medicine. New York and Edinburgh, 8 vols.; see vol. 2, chap. 5, pp. 683–693.

    1923b. The Brazilian Contribution towards the Improvement of the Specific Snake Bite Treatment. Proc. N. Y. Path. Soc., vol. 23 (n.s.), nos. 1–5, pp. 89–98.

    1925. A General Consideration of Snake Poisoning and Observations on Neotropical Pit-Vipers. Contrib. Harv. Inst. Trop. Biol. and Med., no. 2, pp. 1–64.

    1926a. Collectanea Ophiologica. 6. Da Occorrencia de Albinismo em Cascavel, *Crotalus terrificus* (Laur.). Rev. Mus. Paul., vol. 15, pp. 53–57.

    1926b. Collectanea Ophiologica. 13. Bicephalia em Ophidios, Rev. Mus. Paul., vol. 15, pp. 93–101.

    1926c. Nomes Vulgares de Ophidios do Brasil. Bol. Mus. Nac., vol. 2, no. 2, pp. 1–11.

    1927aa. The Snake-Bite Problem in the United States and in Central America. Bull. Antivenin Inst. Am., vol. 1, no. 2, pp. 31–35.

    1927a. Notes on Nearctic Poisonous Snakes and Treatment of Their Bites. Bull. Antivenin Inst. Am., vol. 1, no. 3, pp. 61–76.

    1927b. The Anti-Snake-Bite Campaign in Texas and in the Sub-Tropical United States. Bull. Antivenin Inst. Am., vol. 1, no. 3, pp. 77–85.

    1928a. Improved Process of Venom Extraction. Bull. Antivenin Inst. Am., vol. 1, no. 4, pp. 100–102.

    1928b. Amounts of Venom Secreted by Nearctic Pit Vipers. Bull. Antivenin Inst. Am., vol. 1, no. 4, pp. 103–104.

AMARAL, A. DO (*Continued*)

1928c. Venoms and Antivenins. *In* The Newer Knowledge of Bacteriology, edited by E. O. Jordan and I. S. Falk. Chicago, pp. x + 1196; see chap. 80, pp. 1066–1077.

1929. Phylogeny of the Rattlesnakes. Bull. Antivenin Inst. Am., vol. 3, no. 1, pp. 6–8.

1930. Animaes Venenosos do Brasil. São Paulo, pp. 1–65.

1932a. Notas sobre Chromatismo de Ophidios. II. Casos de Variação de Colorido de Sertas Serpentes. Mem. Inst. Butantan, vol. 7, pp. 81–87.

1932b. Sobre um Caso de Necrophilia Heterologa na Jararaca (*Bothrops jararaca*). Mem. Inst. Butantan, vol. 7, pp. 93–94.

1934. Notas sobre Chromatismo de Ophidios. III. Um Caso de Xanthismo e um Novo de Albinismo, Observados no Brasil. Mem. Inst. Butantan, vol. 8, pp. 151–153.

1951a. Snake Venom Poisoning. *In* A Textbook of Medicine, edited by R. L. Cecil and R. F. Loeb. Philadelphia, pp. xxxi + 1627; see pp. 550–554.

1951b. Snake Venation (Ophidism). *In* Clinical Tropical Medicine, edited by R. B. H. Gradwohl, L. B. Soto, and O. Felsenfeld. St. Louis, pp. xxiii + 1647; see chap. 57, pp. 1238–1264.

AMEDEN, A. O.

1883. Serpent Venom as a Remedial Agent in Tetanus. Med. News, vol. 43, no. 13, p. 339. [See also Med. & Surg. Reporter, vol. 49, no. 23, pp. 642–643, and Albany Med. Annals, vol. 6, no. 3, pp. 91–92, 1885.]

AMERICAN GUIDE SERIES

1937. Idaho: A Guide in Word and Picture. Caldwell, Idaho, pp. 1–431.

1939. Florida: A Guide to the Southernmost State. New York, pp. xxiv + 600.

1940. Arizona: A State Guide. New York, pp. xxv + 530.

1940. Nevada: A Guide to the Silver State. Portland, Oreg., pp. xviii + 315.

1940. Oregon: End of the Trail. Portland, Oreg., pp. xxxii + 549.

1940. Texas: A Guide to the Lone Star State. New York, pp. xxxiii + 718.

AMORIM, M. DE F., and R. F. DE MELLO

1952. Nefrose do Nefron Intermediário no Envenenamento Crotálico Humano. Mem. Inst. Butantan, vol. 24, no. 2, pp. 281–316.

ANBUREY, T.

1789. Travels through the Interior Parts of America. London, 2 vols., pp. vii + [xx] + 467; 1–558. [Reprint, Boston, 1923, 2 vols., pp. xxx + 276; 1–322. See also Forest and Stream, vol. 1, no. 8, p. 125.]

ANDERSON, E. A.

1872. On the Use of Bromide of Potassium in Rattlesnake Bites (*Crotalus* [*sic*] *horridus*). Am. Jour. Med. Sci., vol. 63 (n.s.), no. 126, art. 6, pp. 366–368.

ANDERSON, J.

1895. Zoölogy of Egypt. Vol. I: Reptilia and Batrachia. London, pp. lxv + 371.

ANDERSON, J.

1951. Let Sleeping Rattlers Lie. Pa. Game News, vol. 22, no. 3, pp. 4–9.

ANDERSON, J. F.

1914. Danger in the Subcutaneous Injections of Crotalin with Report of a Fatal Case. Jour. Am. Med. Assn., vol. 62, no. 12, pp. 893–895. [See also pp. 934–935.]

ANDERSON, P.

1942. Amphibians and Reptiles of Jackson County, Missouri. Bull. Chi. Acad. Sci. vol. 6, no. 11, pp. 203–220.

1947. Observations on the Denning Habits of the Prairie Rattlesnake, *Crotalus viridis viridis* (Rafinesque). Nat. Hist. Misc., no. 9, pp. 1–2.

ANDERSON, W.

1910. The Serpent and Its Venom. Pac. Med. Jour., vol. 53, no. 12, pp. 710–721.

ANDRÉ, E.

1904. A Naturalist in the Guianas. London, pp. xiv + 310.

ANDREWS, E. H., and C. B. POLLARD

1953. Report of Snake Bites in Florida and Treatment: Venoms and Antivenoms. Jour. Fla. Med. Assn., vol. 40, no. 6, pp. 388–397.

ANON.

1750. [The Negro Caesar's Cure for Poison. From Carolina Gazette, May, 1750.] Gentleman's Mag., vol. 20, pp. 342–343.

1766. [Negro Saves His Master.] Annual Register, London, vol. 9, p. 91.

1786. A Short Description of the *Crotalus Horridus,* or Rattlesnake, with an Engraving of a Curious Rattle, Full Length, Carefully Copied from Nature. Columbian Mag. or Monthly Misc., Nov., 1786, pp. 107–108.

1804. Notes on Compton, a Township in Newport County, State of Rhode Island. Coll. Mass. Hist. Soc., ser. 1, vol. 9, pp. 199–206.

1809. [Deaths by Rattlesnake Bite.] Gentleman's Mag., vol. 79, pp. 1071, 1175.

1815. Extraordinary Snake. Niles Weekly Reg., vol. 9, no. 9, whole no. 217, p. 152.

1819. [Rattlesnake's Mate.] Niles Weekly Reg., vol. 17, no. 3, p. 44.

1829. A Den of Rattlesnakes. Mag. Nat. Hist., vol. 2, no. 9, p. 370.

1832a. Venomous Serpents. Penny Mag., vol. 1, no. 29, pp. 235–236.

1832b. History of the Delaware and Iroquois Indians. Philadelphia, pp. 1–153.

1838. Capacity of the Stomachs of Serpents. Visitor, p. 72.

1839. Rattle-Snakes and Their Use in America. Penny Mag., vol. 8, no. 439, pp. 46–47.

1856. [Tests on Efficiency of the Guaco Plant for Snake Bite.] Med. Times and Gaz., vol. 34, no. 898, p. 597.

1858a. Manners of Musical Jack. Leisure Hour, vol. 7, no. 335, pp. 325–328.

1858b. Ash Tea as a Remedy for the Bite of the Rattlesnake. Nashville Jour. Med. and Surg., vol. 15, no. 6, pp. 471–472.

1869. Death from Rattlesnake Bite. Med. and Surg. Reporter, vol. 21, no. 5, p. 93.

1872a. [Bite of Rattlesnake Head.] Med. and Surg. Reporter, vol. 27, no. 2, p. 46.

1872b. Rattlesnakes. Chambers's Jour., vol. 49 (ser. 4, vol. 9), pp. 641–644.

1873a. [Rattlesnakes in Lake George.] Forest and Stream, vol. 1, no. 8, p. 125.

1873b. Arizona Papers. V. The Gila Monster. San Diego World, vol. 2, no. 179, p. 1 (Feb. 20).

1874. A Last Resource. Lancet, vol. 1, no. 2642, p. 559.

1877. [Two-Headed Rattlesnake.] Field and Stream, vol. 9, no. 6, p. 105.

1878. Poisoned Arrows: Something about the Manners and Customs of Indians in This Regard. Rocky Mt. News (Denver), Jan. 17, p. 2.

1883a. Snakes. Edinburgh Rev., vol. 158, no. 323, art. 7, pp. 199–225. [Also in Eclectic Mag., vol. 102 (ser. 2, vol. 39), pp. 258–273.]

1883b. Snake Poisoning. [A review of Indian Snake Poisons by A. J. Wall.] Sat. Rev., vol. 55, no. 1441, pp. 742–743. [Also in Eclectic Mag., vol. 101, pp. 261–264.]

1885. Rattlesnake Tom. Caldwell Jour., June 4, p. 4.

1886. Cure for Rattlesnake Bite. Pac. Rural Press, vol. 32, no. 26, p. 538.

1887. Thrashing Rattlers. Pac. Rural Press, vol. 34, no. 8, p. 137.

1889. Rattlesnakes. Pac. Rural Press, vol. 37, no. 21, p. 518.

1891–1948. Index-Catalogue of the Library of the Surgeon-General's Office, United States Army (Army Medical Library). Washington, 57 vols. to date, in 4 series. [See under Reptiles, Serpents, and Venoms in each series.]

1894. A Few Brazilian Snakes. Chambers's Jour., ser. 5, vol. 11, no. 530, pp. 123–125.

1896. The Best Snake Story in the World. Littell's Living Age, ser. 6, vol. 12, no. 2729, pp. 251–255.

1897. Curious Rattlesnake Poison. Forest and Stream, vol. 48, no. 7, p. 125.

1898. Rattlesnake Oil. Chambers's Jour., ser. 6, vol. 1, no. 8 (= vol. 75), pp. 159–160.

1899. A Curious Case of Abnormal Development in a Rattlesnake. Sci. Am., vol. 80, no. 12, p. 185.

1901. Rattlesnakes Abundant. Pac. Rural Press, vol. 61, no. 21, p. 327.

1907. Narrative of a Voyage to Maryland, 1705–1706. Am. Hist. Rev., vol. 12, no. 2, pp. 327–340.

1908a. Bitten by a Rattler. Forest and Stream, vol. 70, no. 17, p. 679.

1908b. Died after Rattlesnake Bite. Forest and Stream, vol. 71, no. 4, p. 132.

1909. A Profit in Snakes. Harper's Weekly, vol. 53, no. 2717, p. 32.

1914. Explorations and Field-Work of the Smithsonian Institution in 1913. Smithson. Misc. Coll., vol. 63, no. 8, pp. 1–88.

ANON. (*Continued*)

1928a. The Story of Alpina Reptile Leathers. Hecht and Co., New York, pp. 1–24.

1928b. The Costa Rican Law for Protection against Ophidism. Bull. Antivenin Inst. Am., vol. 2, no. 2, pp. 50–51.

1930a. Rattler Strikes Five Feet. St. Louis Zoo, vol. 2, no. 3, p. 3.

1930b. Rattlesnakes vs. Aviator, One Mile above the Earth. Denver Post Mag. Sect., Oct. 5.

1932. Bounty on Snakes Defeated. St. Louis Zoo, vol. 4, no. 9, p. 4.

1933a. The Snakes of Missouri. Nat. Study Bull. (St. Louis Public Schools), vol. 9, no. 1, pp. 1–12.

1933b. Texas Rattlesnake Menace. Tex. Indust. Resources, vol. 10, pp. 21–22.

1936. Floridian Cans Dainty Meat of Rattlesnake. St. Louis Zoo, vol. 4, no. 12, p. 3.

1937. Bypaths of Kansas History. Kans. Hist. Quart., vol. 6, no. 2, pp. 200–210.

1938a. Bitten by Snake. Survey, vol. 19, nos. 7–8, p. 166.

1938b. Do Snakes Swallow Their Young to Protect Them? Royal Ontario Mus. Zoöl., bull. 7, pp. 10–12.

1938c. Snake Venom. Jour. Am. Med. Assn., vol. 110, no. 11, p. 834.

1940. *Crotalus* Antitoxin. Jour. Am. Med. Assn., vol. 115, no. 8, p. 684.

1943. Snakebite and Intelligence. Jour. Am. Med Assn., vol. 122, no. 5, p. 347.

1944. Snake Venoms for Rheumatism. Jour. Am. Med. Assn., vol. 124, no. 2, p. 132.

1945. American Red Cross: First Aid Textbook. Philadelphia, pp. ix + 254.

1946. Snake Bites. Physicians' Bull., vol. 11, no. 4, pp. 109–113.

1947a. Rattlesnake Round-up. Future, vol. 9, no. 8, pp. 7, 25. [See Hughes, W., 1947.]

1947b. Antivenin. Wyeth, Inc., Philadelphia, pp. 1–16.

1948a. Snakes Can Kill. Florida Game and Fresh Water Fish Comm., Tallahassee, pp. 1–7.

1948b. "There Are No Snakes in Ireland" But Millions in Other Parts of the World Provide Abundant Raw Material for Making Beautiful and Durable Reptile Leathers. Rohm & Haas Reporter, vol. 6, no. 6, pp. 4–7, 17. [Abstracted in Mech. Eng., vol. 71, no. 2, pp. 158–159.]

1949. Immunity to Snake Bite. Jour. Am. Med. Assn., vol. 139, no. 3, p. 194.

1951a. Forearmed for Snake Bite [quoted from U. S. Public Health Service]. Wyo. Wild Life, vol. 15, no. 6, pp. 31–33.

1951b. The Great Snake Hunt. Iowa Cons., vol. 10, no. 9, p. 162.

1953. Rattlesnake Hunt. St. Louis Post-Dispatch, vol. 105, no. 214 (May 3), part 2, p. 14.

1954. Ton of Snakes Taken Alive in Rattler Rodeo. Chi. Daily Tribune, April 12, pt. 3, p. 9.

ANTHONY, A. W.

1893. Birds of San Pedro Mártir, Lower California. Zoe, vol. 4, no. 3, pp. 228–247.

ANTHONY, J.

1955. Essai sur l'Évolution Anatomique de l'Appareil Venimeux des Ophidiens, Ann. Sci. Nat., Zool., ser. 11, vol. 17, pp. 7–53.

APPLEBY, L. H.

1942. The Use of Snake Venoms in Medicine. Bull. Vancouver Med. Assn., vol. 18, pp. 245–251.

ARESKINE, R.

1702. An Appendix to the Foregoing Essay. *In* A Mechanical Account of Poisons in Several Essays, by Richard Mead. London, pp. [xiv] + 176; see pp. 35–46. [In 2nd edition, London, 1708, see pp. 37–49.]

ARFWEDSON, C. D.

1834. The United States and Canada in 1832, 1833, and 1834. London, 2 vols., pp. vii + 433, vii + 418.

ARISTOTLE (For translations see under CRESWELL, R., 1862; FORSTER, E. S., 1937; LONES, T. E., 1912; OGLE, W., A. S. L. FARQUHARSON, and A. PLATT, 1912; PECK, A. L., 1937 and 1943; and THOMPSON, D. W., 1910.)

ARIZA, J. E.

1948. The Diamondback's Odor. Hunting and Fishing, vol. 25, no. 4, pp. 60–61.

ARLEGUI, J.

1851. Crónica de la Provincia . . . de Zacatecas. México, pp. xxv + 488.

ARMSTRONG, B.

1947. Grab That Rattler. Rocky Mt. Empire Mag., June 15, p. 2.

ARNOLD, O.
    1933. These White Men Do the Indian Snake Dance. Los Angeles Times Sunday Mag., June 4, pp. 4–5.
    1935. Wild Life in the Southwest. Dallas, pp. [xi] + 274.
    1938. They Found a Market for Rattlesnake Bones. Desert Mag., vol. 1, no. 6, pp. 8–9.
ARONSON, J. D.
    1929. Spontaneous Tuberculosis in Snakes. Jour. Infect. Dis., vol. 44, no. 3, pp. 215–223.
ARRINGTON, O.
    1937. Rattlesnakes in the Bag. Esquire, July, pp. 66, 134, 137.
ARTHUR, S. C.
    1937. Audubon: An Intimate Life of the American Woodsman. New Orleans, pp. 1–517.
ARTRAN, A. P.
    1940. The Venomous Reptiles of the Southwest. Snake Lore. How to Avoid Snake Bite. The First Aid Treatment of Snake Bite. [Series of unpaged articles appearing in successive monthly issues of Safety Sun, published by U. S. Engineer Office, Los Angeles.]
ASHE, T. (1)
    1682. Carolina, or a Description of the Present State of That Country. London, pp. [ii] + 40. [Reprinted in Narratives of Early Carolina, 1650–1708, edited by A. S. Salley, Jr. New York, 1911, pp. 138–159.]
ASHE, T. (2)
    1808. Travels in America Performed in 1806. London, pp. ix + 366.
ASWELL, J. R.
    1940. Snake Country. *In* God Bless the Devil: Liars Bench Tales [from Tennessee] by James R. Aswell *et. al.* Chapel Hill, N. C., pp. xi + 254; see pp. 162–171.
ATCHISON, T. A.
    1853. Bite of the Rattlesnake. Boston Med. and Surg. Jour., vol. 48, no. 10, pp. 200–201.
ATKINS, G. T.
    1948. A Texan Goes Prospecting Uranium. Mineralogist, vol. 16, no. 11, pp. 511–513.
ATKINSON, D. A., and M. G. NETTING
    1927. The Distribution and Habits of the Massasauga. Bull. Antivenin Inst. Am., vol. 1, no. 2, pp. 40–44.
ATSATT, SARAH R.
    1913. The Reptiles of the San Jacinto Area of Southern California. Univ. Calf. Publ. Zoöl., vol. 12, no. 3, pp. 31–50.
    1939. Color Changes as Controlled by Temperature and Light in the Lizards of the Desert Regions of Southern California. Publ. Univ. Calif. at Los Angeles in Biol. Sciences, vol. 1, no. 11, pp. 237–276.
ATTWATER, H. P.
    1928. Snakes. Acco Press, Houston, Tex., vol. 1, no. 1, pp. 5–6.
ATWATER, C.
    1838. A History of the State of Ohio, Natural and Civil. Cincinnati, pp. 1–407.
AUDUBON, J. J.
    1827. Notes on the Rattlesnake (*Crotalus horridus*), in a Letter Addressed to Thomas Stuart Traill, M.D. Edinburgh New Philos. Jour., vol. 3, pp. 21–30. [See also Jour. Franklin Inst. and Am. Mechanics Mag., vol. 6, no. 1, pp. 32–37; no. 2, p. 144, 1828.]
    1827–30. The Birds of America. London, 4 vols. [Also published as The Birds of America from Drawings Made in the United States and Their Territories. New York and Philadelphia, 1840–44, 7 vols.]
AUDUBON, J. J., and J. BACHMAN
    1854. The Quadrupeds of North America. New York, 3 vols., pp. viii + 383; 1–334; v + 348.
AUDUBON, J. W.
    1906. Audubon's Western Journal: 1849–1850. Cleveland, pp. 1–249.
AUDUBON, LUCY
    1869. The Life of John James Audubon, the Naturalist. New York, pp. 1–443.
AUDUBON, MARIA R.
    1917. Audubon and His Journals. New York, 2 vols., pp. xiv + 532; viii + 554.

AUGHEY, S.
1873. The Rattle of the Rattlesnake. Am. Nat., vol. 7, pp. 85–86.

AURICH, A.
1908. Der Giftapparat der Schlangen. 38 Jahres. der K. K. Staatsrealschule in Marburg, pp. 1–16.

AUSTIN, MARY
1906. The Flock. Boston and New York, pp. 1–266.

AUSTIN, MARY L.
1914. Results of the Treatment of Epilepsy with Crotalin. Ohio State Med. Jour., vol. 10, no. 5 pp. 268–270.

B., J. [probably J. BREINTNALL; also spelled BREINTAL]
1765. Remarkable and Authentic Influences of the Fascinating Power of the Rattlesnake over Man and Other Animals, with Other Curious Particulars, Communicated by Mr. Peter Collinson, from a Letter of a Correspondent at Philadelphia. Gentleman's Mag., vol. 35, pp. 511–514 [Letter signed J. B.]

BABBITT, L. H., and CORINNE H. BABBITT
1951. A Herpetological Study of Burned-Over Areas in Dade County, Florida. Copeia, no. 1, p. 79.

BABCOCK, H. L.
1925. Rattlesnakes in Massachusetts. Bull. Boston Soc. Nat. Hist., no. 35, pp. 5–10. [See also no. 68, pp. 3–4, 1933.]
1929a. Food Habits of the Timber Rattlesnake. Bull. Boston Soc. Nat. Hist., no. 51, pp. 13–14.
1929b. The Snakes of New England. Boston Soc. Nat. Hist., Nat. Hist. Guides, no. 1, pp. 1–30
1938. Tying off the Poison Ducts in Rattlesnakes. Copeia, no. 2, p. 92.

BABCOCK, S. M.
1912. Metabolic Water: Its Production and Role in Vital Phenomena. 29th Ann. Rept. Agric. Exper. Sta., Univ. Wis., Res. Bull. 22, pp. 87–181.

BABCOCK, W. W.
1944. Principles and Practice of Surgery. Philadelphia, pp. 1–1331.

BABINGTON, S. H.
1950. Navajos, Gods, and Tom-Toms. New York, pp. x + 246.

BABIS, W. A.
1949. Notes on the Food of the Indigo Snake. Copeia, no. 2, p. 147.

BACHMAN, J.
1834. Remarks in Defence of Mr. Audubon. Mag. Nat. Hist., vol. 7, no. 38, pp. 164–165.

BACKUS, W. H.
1902. Hunting Rattlesnakes with a Camera. Country Life Am., vol. 1, no. 6 (o. s. vol. 6, no. 10), pp. 212–213.
1903. The Rattlesnake and Its Venom. Out West, vol. 18, no. 6, pp. 691–696.

BAEGERT, J. J.
1952. Observations in Lower California. Translated by M. M. Brandenburg and C. L. Baumann. Berkeley and Los Angeles, pp. xx + 218. [1st edition, Mannheim, 1772, pp. [viii] + 358.]

BAILEY, C. F.
1919. A Rattler-Blacksnake Battle. Outdoor Life, vol. 44, no. 3, p. 166.

BAILEY, J. W.
1876. The Rattlesnake. Forest and Stream, vol. 5, no. 26, p. 404. [See also Pop. Sci. Monthly, vol. 9, p. 123, 1876.]

BAILEY, R. G.
1947. River of No Return. Lewiston, Idaho, pp. xxix + 754.

BAILEY, R. M.
1942. An Intergeneric Hybrid Rattlesnake. Am. Nat., vol. 76, pp. 376–385.
1949. Temperature Toleration of Garter Snakes in Hibernation. Ecology, vol. 30, no. 2, pp. 238–242.

BAILEY, V.
1905. Biological Survey of Texas. N. Am. Fauna, no. 25, pp. 1–222.
1928. Animal Life of the Carlsbad Cavern. Monog. Am. Soc. Mammal., no. 3, pp. xiii + 195.

BAILLIE, A.

1849. Bite of a Rattle-Snake. Med. Times, vol. 20, no. 518, p. 179.

1869. Cure for Snakebites. Med. Times and Gaz., vol. 1, no. 974, p. 238.

BAILLIE-GROHMAN, W. A.

1882. Camp in the Rockies. New York, pp. viii + 438.

BAIRD, E.

1946. They Shall Take Up Serpents. Woman, vol. 17, no. 2, pp. 36–39.

BAIRD, S. F.

1854. On the Serpents of New-York. 7th Ann. Rept. Regents Univ. State N.Y., appendix G, pp. 95–124. [Also published separately, Albany, pp. 1–28.]

1856. Appendix to the Report of the Secretary. 10th Ann. Rept., Smithson. Inst., pp. 36–66.

BAIRD, S. F., and C. GIRARD

1853. Catalogue of North American Reptiles in the Museum of the Smithsonian Institution. Washington, part 1—Serpents, pp. xvi + 172.

BAKER, W. H.

1878. Kerosene for Snake Bites. Pac. Rural Press, vol. 16, no. 11, p. 163.

BALDES, E. J., H. E. ESSEX, and J. MARKOWITZ

1931. The Physiologic Action of Rattlesnake Venom (Crotalin). X. Influence of Crotalin on the Viscosity of Blood. Am. Jour. Physiol., vol. 97, no. 1, pp. 26–31.

BALDWIN, E.

1937. An Introduction to Comparative Biochemistry. Cambridge, England, pp. xviii + 112.

BALDWIN, P. H., C. W. SCHWARTZ, and ELIZABETH R. SCHWARTZ

1952. Life History and Economic Status of the Mongoose in Hawaii. Jour. Mammal., vol. 33, no. 3, pp. 335–356.

BALDWIN, P. M. (translator)

1926. Fray Marcos de Niza and His Discovery of the Seven Cities of Cibola. Hist. Soc. N. Mex., Publ. Hist., no. 1, pp. 1–59.

BALL, E. D.

1915. Snakes "Swallowing" Their Young. Proc. Iowa Acad. Sci., vol. 22, pp. 343–344.

BALL, H. A.

1946. Melanosarcoma and Rhabdomyoma in Two Pine Snakes. Cancer Res., vol. 6, no. 3, pp. 134–138.

BANCROFT, H. H.

1886. Works: San Francisco, 39 vols., 1882–89; see Native Races, vol. 1, Wild Tribes, pp. xlvii + 797.

BANDELIER, A. F.

1890–2. Final Report of Investigations among the Indians of the Southwestern United States. Boston, Papers Arch. Inst. Am., American series, III, IV; part 1, pp. vii + 323; part 2, pp. vii + 591.

1930. Documentary History of the Rio Grande Pueblos, New Mexico. Part 1, 1536 to 1542 (*cont.*). N. Mex. Hist. Rev., vol. 5, no. 1, pp. 38–66. [Also part 3, 1581 to 1584. N. Mex. Hist. Rev., vol. 5, no. 4, pp. 333–385.]

BANKS, E.

1896. Rattlesnake and Horse. Forest and Stream, vol. 47, no. 8, p. 144.

BANNERMAN, W. B., and J. P. POCHA

1907. Note on the Breeding of Russell's Viper (*Vipera russelli*) in Captivity. Jour. Bombay Nat. Hist. Soc., vol. 17, no. 3, pp. 808–811.

BANTON, H. J.

1930. A Snake Doctor of the Mosquito Coast. Military Surg., vol. 67, pp. 474–478.

BARBOUR, R. W.

1950. The Reptiles of Big Black Mountain, Harlan County, Kentucky. Copeia, no. 2, pp. 100–107.

BARBOUR, T.

1920. Herpetological Notes from Florida. Copeia, no. 84, pp. 55–57.

1922. Rattlesnakes and Spitting Snakes. Copeia, no. 106, pp. 36–38.

BARBOUR, T. (*Continued*)

1926. Reptiles and Amphibians, Their Habits and Adaptations. Boston and New York, pp. xx + 125.

1934. Reptiles and Amphibians, Their Habits and Adaptations. 2nd edition, Boston and New York, pp. xx + 129.

BARCIA, A. DE

1952. Chronological History of the Continent of Florida. Translated by Anthony Kerrigan. Gainesville, Florida, pp. lx + 426. [First published in Spanish, Madrid, 1723.]

BARD, C. L.

1894. A Contribution to the History of Medicine in Southern California. Ann. Address Retiring Pres. So. Calif. Med. Soc., Los Angeles, pp. 1–34.

BARKER, E. S.

1946. When the Dogs Bark "Treed." Albuquerque, pp. xviii + 209.

BARKER, F. T.

1929. Venomous Snakes of North America and Treatment of Their Bites. Jour. Fla. Med. Assn., vol. 16, pp. 63–68.

BARNES, J. M., and J. TRUETA

1941. Absorption of Bacteria, Toxins and Snake Venoms from the Tissues. Lancet, vol. 1. pp. 623–626.

BARNES, W. C.

1922. Rattle Snakes. Am. Forestry, vol. 28, no. 343, pp. 387–393, 396.

1928. Rattlers and Horned Toads. Sat. Eve. Post., vol. 200, no. 46, p. 48.

1933. Rattlers and Their Bites. Am. Forests, vol. 39, no. 9, pp. 396–398, 429. [Reprinted in Sci. Am., vol. 151, pp. 74–76, 1934.]

1935. Arizona Place Names. Univ. Ariz. Bull., vol. 6, no. 1, pp. 1–503.

BARNETT, H. G.

1937. Culture Element Distributions: VII. Oregon Coast. Univ. Calif. Anthro. Rec., vol. 1, no. 3, pp. 155–204.

BARRETT, S. A.

1919. Myths of the Southern Sierra Miwok. Univ. Calif. Publ. Am. Arch. and Ethn., vol. 16, no. 1, pp. 1–28.

1933. Pomo Myths. Bull. Pub. Mus. Milwaukee, vol. 15, pp. 1–608.

BARRETT, S. A., and E. W. GIFFORD

1933. Miwok Material Culture. Bull. Pub. Mus. Milwaukee, vol. 2, no. 4, pp. 117–376.

BARRINGER, P. B.

1892. The Venomous Reptiles of the United States, with the Treatment of Wounds Inflicted by Them. Trans. So. Surg. and Gyn. Assn., vol. 4, pp. 283–300.

BARRIO, A., and O. VITAL BRAZIL

1951. Neuromuscular Action of the *Crotalus terrificus terrificus* (Laur.) Poison. Acta Physiologica Latinoamericana, vol. 1, no. 4, pp. 291–308.

BARROSO, R. D.

1944. Ofidismo no Brasil. Considerações em Torno de 2238 Acidentes Ofídicos Tratados com Sôro. Bol. Inst. Vital Brazil, no. 26, pp. 35–47.

BARRY, D.

1826. Experimental Researches . . . upon the Progression of Blood in the Veins. London, pp. xv + 175.

BARSTOW, S. T.

1807. Account of the Singular Effects from the Bite of a Rattle-Snake. Phila. Med. Mus., vol. 3, no. 1, pp. 61–62.

BARTLETT, J. R.

1854. Personal Narrative of Explorations and Incidents in Texas, New Mexico, California, Sonora, and Chihuahua. New York, 2 vols., pp. xxvii + 506; xvii + 624.

BARTON, A. J.

1950. Replacement Fangs in Newborn Timber Rattlesnakes. Copeia, no. 3, pp. 235–236.

BARTON, B. S.

1793. An Account of the Most Effectual Means of Preventing the Deleterious Consequences of the Bite of the *Crotalus horridus,* or Rattle-Snake. Trans. Am. Philos. Soc., vol. 3, no. 11, pp. 100–115.

1799. A Memoir concerning the Fascinating Faculty Which Has Been Ascribed to the Rattle-Snake, and Other American Serpents. Trans. Am. Philos. Soc., vol. 4, no. 11, pp. 74–113. [Appeared as a separate, Philadelphia, 1796, pp. 1–70; also in 1814. Also in Philos. Mag., vol. 15, pp. 193–202, 294–300. Reviewed in Med. Reposit., vol. 5, pp. 79–87, 1797; and in Gentleman's Mag., vol. 73, p. 253, 1803.]

1800. Supplement to a Memoir concerning the Fascinating Faculty Which Has Been Ascribed to the Rattle-Snake and Other American Serpents. Philadelphia, pp. 1–40.

1805a. [Notes on Rattlesnake Bite.] Phila. Med. and Phys. Jour., vol. 1, sect. 3, pp. 167–169.

1805b. Ophiology [notes by the editor]. Phila. Med. and Phys. Jour., vol. 2, part 1, sect. 3, pp. 165–171.

BARTRAM, J.

1744. A Letter from John Bartram, M.D., to Peter Collinson, F.R.S. Concerning a Cluster of Small Teeth Observed by Him at the Root of Each Fang or Great Tooth in the Head of a Rattle-Snake. Philos. Trans. (Royal Soc., London), vol. 41, part 1, no. 456, pp. 358–359.

BARTRAM, W.

1791. Travels through North and South Carolina, Georgia, East and West Florida, . . . Philadelphia, pp. xxxiv + 522. [Also London, 1792, pp. xxiv + 520 + [xxiv].]

BASHAW, C. A.

1946. Snakes, Ten Cents a Foot. Hunting and Fishing, vol. 23, no. 4, p. 11.

BATEMAN, G. F.

1918. Are Rattlesnakes Beneficial? Outdoor Life, vol. 42, no. 1, p. 501. [See also vol. 43, no. 3, p. 167.]

BAUMANN, F.

1929. Experimente ueber den Geruchssinn und den Beuteerwerb der Viper (*Vipera aspis* L.). Zeits. vergl. Phys., vol. 10, no. 1, pp. 36–119.

BAXTER, G., and H. RAHN

1941. Rattlesnakes of Wyoming. Wyo. Wild Life, vol. 6, no. 4, pp. [1–6].

BAYLOR, DOROTHY J.

1947. Folklore from Socorro, New Mexico. Hoosier Folklore, vol. 6, no. 3, pp. 91–100; no. 4, pp. 138–150.

BEADLE, J. H.

1873. The Undeveloped West. Philadelphia, pp. 1–823.

1879. Western Wilds. Cincinnati, pp. xvi, 17–624.

BEAL, W. J.

1872. The Music of the Rattlesnake. Am. Nat., vol. 6, p. 310.

BEALER, A. W.

1921. When Georgia's Singing Rattler Dines and is Dined Upon. Lit. Digest, vol. 68, no. 11, pp. 69–70. [Summary of article appearing in Atlanta Jour.]

BEALS, R. L.

1932. The Comparative Ethnology of Northern Mexico before 1750. Univ. Calif. Ibero-Americana, no. 2, pp. vi + 93–225.

1933. Ethnology of the Nisenan. Univ. Calif. Publ. Am. Arch. and Ethn., vol. 31, no. 6, pp. 335–414.

1943. The Aboriginal Culture of the Cáhita Indians. Univ. Calif. Ibero-Americana, no. 19, pp. x + 86.

1945. The Contemporary Culture of the Cáhita Indians. Bur. Am. Ethn., Bull. 142, pp. xii + 244.

BEASLEY, H.

1865. The Book of Prescriptions, Containing 3000 Prescriptions. Philadelphia, pp. xxiv, 25–562.

BEATH, P. R.

1948. Febold Feboldson: Tall Tales of the Great Plains. Lincoln, Nebr., pp. xii, 13–124.

BEATTIE, W. F. C.
  1873. Recovery from the Bite of a Rattlesnake. N. Y. Med. Jour., vol. 18, no. 6, pp. 619–620.

BEATY, J. Y.
  1941. Nature Is Stranger than Fiction. Philadelphia, pp. 1–286.

BEAUCHAMP, W. M.
  1892. Iroquois Notes. Jour. Am. Folk-Lore, vol. 5, no. 18, pp. 223–229.
  1922. Iroquois Folk Lore. Syracuse, pp. 247 + [3].

BEAUVOIS, P. DE
  1799. Memoir on Amphibia. Serpents. Trans. Am. Philos. Soc., vol. 4, pp. 362–381.

BECK, H. P.
  1952. Herpetological Lore from the Blue Ridge. Midwest Folklore, vol. 2, no. 3, pp. 141–150.

BECK, W. M.
  1939. The Pinellas County Snake Bounty. Fla. Nat., vol. 12, no. 4, p. 94.

BECKMAN, H.
  1952. Pharmacology in Clinical Practice. Philadelphia and London, pp. xx + 839.

BECKWITH, MARTHA W.
  1930. Mythology of the Oglala Dakota. Jour. Am. Folk-Lore, vol. 43, no. 170, pp. 339–442.
  1937. Mandan-Hidatsa Myths and Ceremonies. Mem. Am. Folk-Lore Soc., vol. 32, pp. xviii + 327.

BEDDARD, F. E.
  1904. Contributions to Our Knowledge of the Circulatory System in the Ophidia. Proc. Zoöl. Soc. London, vol. 1, no. 22, pp. 331–370.

BEDICHEK, R.
  1947. Adventures with a Texas Naturalist. Garden City, N. Y., pp. xx + 293.

BEEBE, W.
  1946. Field Notes on the Snakes of Kartabo, British Guiana, and Caripito, Venezuela. Zoologica, vol. 31, part 1, no. 4, pp. 11–52.
  1947. Snake Skins and Color. Copeia, no. 3, pp. 205–206.

BEER, T.
  1921. Addio. Sat. Eve. Post, vol. 194, no. 18, pp. 16–17, 57. [Reprinted *in* Mrs. Egg and Other Americans, New York, 1947, pp. 228–241; also *in* The Unexpected, New York, 1948, pp. 100–117.]

BEHR, H. H.
  1888. Changes in the Flora and Fauna of California. Proc. Calif. Acad. Sci., ser. 2, vol. 1, pp. 94–99.

BELDEN, G. P.
  1871. Belden, the White Chief; or Twelve Years among the Wild Indians of the Plains. Cincinnati and New York, pp. 1–513.

BELL, J. G.
  1932. A Log of the Texas-California Cattle Trail, 1854. Edited by J. Evetts Haley. Southwest. Hist. Quart., vol. 35, no. 3, pp. 208–237; no. 4, pp. 290–316.

BELL, T.
  1839. A History of British Reptiles. London, pp. xxiv + 142. [Also 2nd edition, London, 1849, pp. xxiv + 159.]

BELL, W. A.
  1869. New Tracks in North America. London, 2 vols., pp. lxiv + 236; vii + 322.

BELLAIRS, A. D'A.
  1942. Observations on Jacobson's Organ and Its Innervation in *Vipera berus*. Jour. Anat., vol. 76, part 2, pp. 167–177.

BELLAIRS, A. D'A., and G. UNDERWOOD
  1951. The Origin of Snakes. Biol. Rev., vol. 26, no. 2, pp. 193–237.

BELTRAMI, J. C.
  1828. A Pilgrimage in Europe and America. London, 2 vols., pp. lxxvi + 472; 1–545

BENDIRE, C. E.
  1881. The Rattlesnake as a Tree-Climber. Forest and Stream, vol. 16, no. 11, p. 207. [See also pp. 267, 327, 347, 368, 453, 491, 511; vol. 17, pp. 28, 46, 68.]
  1887. Tree-Climbing Rattlesnakes. Forest and Stream, vol. 29, no. 16, p. 304.

BENJAMIN, R. A., JR.
  1941. Rattlesnakes Make Good Eating. Am. Mercury, vol. 52, no. 205, pp. 53–57

BENCHLEY, BELLE J.
  1944. Potential Danger. Zoonooz, vol. 17, no. 12, pp. 1, 6.

BENEDICT, F. G.
  1932. The Physiology of Large Reptiles with Special Reference to the Heat Production of Snakes, Tortoises, Lizards, and Alligators. Carn. Inst., Publ. 425, pp. x + 539.

BENEDICT, RUTH F.
  1925. [Review of] Curtis' North American Indians, vol. 22, The Hopi. Am. Anthro., vol. 27, pp. 458–460.
  1930. Eight Stories from Acoma. Jour. Am. Folk-Lore, vol. 43, no. 167, pp. 59–87.
  1931. Tales of the Cochiti Indians. Bur. Am. Ethn., Bull. 98, pp. x + 256.
  1934. Patterns of Culture. Boston and New York, pp. xiii + 291.
  1935. Zuni Mythology. Columbia Univ. Contrib. Anthro., no. 21, 2 vols., pp. xliii + 342; vii + 345.

BENNETT, W. C., and R. M. ZINGG
  1935. The Tarahumara: An Indian Tribe of Northern Mexico. Chicago, pp. xix + 412.

BENT, A. C.
  1932. Life Histories of North American Gallinaceous Birds. U. S. Nat. Mus., Bull. 162, pp. xi + 490.
  1937. Life Histories of North American Birds of Prey: Order Falconiformes (Part 1). U. S. Nat. Mus., Bull. 167, pp. viii + 398.

BENTON, J. J.
  1945. Odd Life and Habits of Desert Creatures. Ariz. Quart., vol. 1, no. 2, pp. 77–83.

BENTON, T. H.
  1937. An Artist in America. New York, pp. xi + 276.

BERGEN, FANNY D.
  1899. Animal and Plant Lore Collected from the Oral Tradition of English Speaking Folk. Mem. Am. Folk-Lore Soc., vol. 7, pp. vii + 180

BERGMAN, H., and E. L. SABIN
  1932. When a Snake Bites a Man. Touring Topics, vol. 24, no. 1, pp. 34, 47–48.

BERKELEY, G. F.
  1861. The English Sportsman in the Western Prairies. London, pp. xi + 431.

BERNARD, J.
  1887. Retrospections of America, 1797–1811 [edited from ms. by Mrs. Bayle Bernard]. New York, pp. xiii + 380.

BERNHARD, DUKE OF SAXE-WEIMAR EISENACH
  1828. Travels through North America, during the Years 1825 and 1826. Philadelphia, 2 vols., pp. iv + 5–212; 238.

BERRIDGE, W. S.
  1926. Marvels of Reptile Life. London, pp. 1–256.
  1935. All about Reptiles and Amphibians. London, pp. 1–271.

BEVAN, W. A.
  1923. [Snake Senses.] *In* Snake Lore, Outdoor Life, vol. 52, no. 2, p. 163.
  1926. [Horned Rattlesnakes.] *In* Snake Lore, Outdoor Life, vol. 58, no. 5, p. 412. [See also vol. 59, no. 6, p. 92.]
  1927. [Maternal Instinct of Snakes.] *In* Snake Lore, Outdoor Life, vol. 60, no. 3, p. 100. [See also vol. 56, no. 1, p. 92; vol. 61, no. 1, p. 84; no. 3, p. 95; no. 6, p. 102; vol. 62, no. 2, p. 83; and vol. 63, no. 6, p. 103.]
  1929. Serum and Suction for Snake Bite. *In* Snake Lore, Outdoor Life, vol. 64, no. 2, p. 93.
  1930. Photographing Snakes. *In* Snake Lore, Outdoor Life, vol. 66, no. 1, p. 93.
  1931a. Protection against Snakes. *In* Snake Lore, Outdoor Life, vol. 67, no. 4, p. 109.
  1931b. Rattlesnake vs. Hog. *In* Snake Lore, Outdoor Life, vol. 68, no. 2, p. 78.
  1931c. Snake Bitten. Outdoor Life, vol. 68, no. 3, pp. 12–13, 47.
  1932a. The Market for Snakes. *In* Snake Lore, Outdoor Life, vol. 69, no. 1, p. 77. [See also vol.

BEVAN, W. A. (*Continued*)

60, no. 5, p. 84; no. 6, p. 84; vol. 61, no. 4, p. 108; vol. 64, no. 4, p. 93; vol. 68, no. 5, p. 76; no. 6, p. 76; and vol. 69, no. 2, p. 77.]

1932b. Lion Hunter Gets Rattlesnake Venom in Eyes. *In* Snake Lore, Outdoor Life, vol. 69, no. 4, p. 93.

1932c. Handling Rattlers. *In* Snake Lore, Outdoor Life, vol. 69, no. 5, p. 93.

1932d. The Truth about Snakes. I. The Rattler and Horse-Hair Rope or Cactus. Outdoor Life, vol. 70, no. 2, p. 71.

1933a. The Truth about Snakes. IV. Snakes That Bite Bullets and Commit Suicide. Outdoor Life, vol. 71, no. 4, p. 59. [See also vol. 68, no. 5, p. 76.]

1933b. How to Cure a Snake Hide. *In* Snake Lore, Outdoor Life, vol. 72, no. 6, p. 61. [See also vol. 49, no. 4, p. 275; vol. 64, no. 3, p. 93; vol. 67, no. 1, p. 77; no. 4, p. 109; and vol. 69, no. 3, p. 55.]

1934a. Rattlesnake Oil. *In* Snake Lore, Outdoor Life, vol. 73, no. 2, p. 61. [See also vol. 69, no. 3, p. 55.]

1934b. With the Nature Fakers. Outdoor Life, vol. 73, no. 3, p. 65.

1934c. The Truth about Snakes. V. The Danger Involved in Catching Snakes. Outdoor Life, vol. 74, no. 2, pp. 64–65. [See also vol. 49, no. 3, p. 195.]

BEVERLY, R.

1705. The History and Present State of Virginia. London, pp. [x] + 104 + 40 + 64 + 83 +16 + [iv].

1722. The History of Virginia in Four Parts. 2nd edition, London, pp. [vi] + 284 + [xxii]. [Reprinted, 1855, Richmond, Va., pp. xx + 264.]

BEVIN, G.

1875. Harmless Rattlesnakes. Forest and Stream, vol. 5, no. 1, p. 4.

BEYER, G. E.

1898. Contributions on the Life Histories of Certain Snakes. Am. Nat., vol. 32, no. 373, pp. 17–24.

1900. Louisiana Herpetology. Proc. La. Soc. Nat., session 1897–1899, pp. 25–46.

BEYER, H.

1933. A Discussion of the Gates Classification of Maya Hieroglyphs. Am. Anthro., vol. 35, no. 4, pp. 659–694.

BIEBER, R. P. (editor)

1936. Marching with the Army of the West, 1846–1848. Southwest Hist. Ser., vol. 4, Glendale Calif., pp. 1–368.

1937. Southern Trails to California in 1849. Glendale, Calif., pp. 1–386.

BIEBER, R. P., and A. B. BENDER

1938. Exploring Southwestern Trails. Southwest Hist. Ser., vol. 7, Diaries of François Xavier Aubry, 1853–1854. Glendale, Calif., pp. 351–383.

BIGELOW, J.

1817–20. American Medical Botany. Boston, 3 vols.

BIGGAR, H. P. (editor)

1932–6. The Words of Samuel de Champlain. Champlain Soc., Toronto, 6 vols. + portfolio of plates and maps.

BIGGS, H. V.

1907. The Vitality of Snakes. Jour. Bombay Nat. Hist. Soc., vol. 17, no. 4, pp. 1018–1019.

BIGLAND, J.

1844. Natural History of Birds, Fishes, Reptiles, and Insects. Philadelphia, pp. 1–179. [1st edition, Philadelphia, 1828, pp. xii + 13–179.]

BILL, J. H.

1862. Notes on Arrow Wounds. Am. Jour. Med. Sci., vol. 44 (n.s.), no. 88, art. 2, pp. 365–387.

BILLING, W. M.

1930. The Action of the Toxin of *Crotalus adamanteus* on Blood Clotting. Jour. Pharm. Exp. Ther., vol. 38, no. 2, pp. 173–196.

BINGLEY, W.

1803. Animal Biography. London, 6 vols.; see vol. 3, Amphibious Animals, Fishes, Insects, Worms, pp. 1–580.

BIRD, ISABELLA L. [MRS. I. B. BISHOP]
    1881. A Lady's Life in the Rocky Mountains. 3rd edition, New York, pp. xii + 296. [1st edition, London, 1879, pp. xii + 296.]

BISHOP, I. P.
    1892. How a Snake Sheds Its Skin. Forest and Stream, vol. 39, no. 19, p. 399.

BISHOPP, F. C., and HELEN L. TREMBLEY
    1945. Distribution and Hosts of Certain North American Ticks. Jour. Parasit., vol. 31, no. 1, pp. 1–54.

BLACK, PAULINE M.
    1935. Nebraska Folk Cures. Univ. Nebr. Stud. Lang., Lit., and Crit., no. 15, pp. 1–49.

BLACK, W. G.
    1883. Folk Medicine. London, pp. iii + 228.

BLACKBURN, J. C. C.
    1853. Bite of a Rattle-Snake—Cure. Nelson's Am. Lancet, vol. 7, no. 3, p. 128. [Also Boston Med. and Surg. Jour., vol. 48, no. 24, p. 488.]

BLACKFORD, J. L.
    1946. They Live in Heat and Drouth. Desert Mag., vol. 9, no. 11, pp. 5–10.

BLACKWOOD, W. R. D.
    1888. As to Snake-Bites. Medical Reg., vol. 3, no. 12, (whole no. 64), pp. 272–273.

BLAIN, A. W., and K. N. CAMPBELL
    1942. A Study of Digestive Phenomena in Snakes with the Aid of the Roentgen Ray. Am. Jour. Roent. and Rad. Ther., vol. 48, no. 2, pp. 229–239.

BLAIR, W. F.
    1954. Mammals of the Mesquite Plains Biotic District in Texas and Oklahoma, and Speciation in the Central Grasslands. Tex. Jour. Sci., vol. 6, no. 3, pp. 235–264.

BLAKEY, H. L.
    1937. The Wild Turkey on the Missouri Ozark Range. U. S. Biol. Surv.; Wildlife Res. and Man. Leaf., BS-97, pp. 1–32.

BLANCHARD, F. N.
    1937. Data on the Natural History of the Red-Bellied Snake, *Storeria occipito-maculata* (Storer) in Northern Michigan. Copeia, no. 3, pp. 151–162.

BLANCHARD, F. N., and FRIEDA C. BLANCHARD
    1941a. Factors Determining Time of Birth in the Garter Snake *Thamnophis sirtalis sirtalis* (Linnaeus). Papers Mich. Acad. Sci., Arts, Lett., vol. 26, pp. 161–176.
    1941b. The Inheritance of Melanism in the Garter Snake *Thamnophis sirtalis sirtalis* (Linnaeus), and Some Evidence of Effective Autumn Mating. Papers Mich. Acad. Sci., Arts, Lett., vol. 26, pp. 177–193.
    1942. Mating of the Garter Snake *Thamnophis sirtalis sirtalis* (Linnaeus). Papers Mich. Acad. Sci., Arts, Lett., vol. 27, pp. 215–234.

BLANCHARD, F. N., and ETHEL B. FINSTER
    1933. A Method of Marking Living Snakes for Future Recognition, with a Discussion of Some Problems and Results. Ecology, vol. 14, no. 4, pp. 334–347.

BLANCHARD, FRIEDA C.
    1943. A Test of Fecundity of the Garter Snake *Thamnophis sirtalis sirtalis* (Linnaeus) in the Year of Insemination. Papers Mich. Acad. Sci., Arts, Lett., vol. 28, pp. 313–316.

BLANCHARD, G.
    1940. Rattles in Thin Air. Field and Stream, vol. 44, no. 12, pp. 32–33, 82–85.

BLANE, W. N.
    1824. An Excursion through the United States and Canada. London, pp. [ii] + 511.

BLANKS, ZULA S.
    1932. Any Snakes Today, Lady? Junior League Mag., vol. 18, no. 5, pp. 30, 103.

BLOCK, M. J.
    1950. Function and Operation of the Facial Pit of the Pit Vipers. Nature, vol. 165, no. 4190. pp. 284–285.

BLOCKLEY, W. V., and C. L. TAYLOR

1949. Human Tolerance Limits for Extreme Heat. Heating, Piping and Air Conditioning, vol. 21, no. 5, pp. 111–116. [Abstracted in Mechanical Engineering, vol. 71, no. 9, p. 746.]

BLOME, R.

1686. The Present State of His Majesties Isles and Territories in America. London, pp. 262 + [44].

BLOOM, L. B.

1933. Fray Estevan de Perea's *Relación*. N. Mex. Hist. Rev., vol. 8, no. 3, pp. 211–235.

BLOOM, L. B. (editor)

1933–8. Bourke on the Southwest. N. Mex. Hist. Rev., vols. 8 to 13 incl.

BLUM, H. F., and C. R. SPEALMAN

1933. Note on the Killing of Rattlesnakes by Sunlight. Copeia, no. 3, pp. 150–151.

BLUMENBACH, J. F.

1798. On the Fascinating Power of the Rattle-Snake, with Some Remarks on Dr. Barton's Memoir on That Subject. Philos. Mag., vol. 2, pp. 251–256.

BOAG, W.

1799. On the Poison of Serpents. Asiatick Researches, vol. 6, art. 5, pp. 103–126.

BOAS, F.

1928. Keresan Texts. Publ. Am. Ethn. Soc., vol. 8, part 1, pp. xii + 300.

BOATRIGHT, M. C.

1931. The Tall Tale in Texas. So. Atl. Quart., vol. 30, no. 3, pp. 271–279.

1934. Tall Tales from Texas. Dallas, pp. xxiv + 100.

BOATRIGHT, M. C., W. M. HUDSON, and A. MAXWELL (editors)

1954. Texas Folk and Folklore. Publ. Tex. Folklore Soc., no. 26, pp. xv + 356. [Contains reprints and rearrangements of rattlesnake folklore by D. Storm, F. Woodhull, J. K. Strecker, J. F. Dobie, and R. Bedicheck.]

BOGERT, C. M.

1927. The Pacific Rattlesnake. Nature Mag., vol. 10, no. 5, pp. 297–299.

1933. Notes on the Snake Dance of the Hopi Indians. Copeia, no. 4, pp. 219–221.

1939. Reptiles under the Sun. Nat. Hist., vol. 44, no. 1, pp. 26–37.

1941a. The Hopi Snake Dance. Nat. Hist., vol. 47, no. 5, pp. 276–283.

1941b. Sensory Cues Used by Rattlesnakes in Their Recognition of Ophidian Enemies. Ann. N. Y. Acad. Sci., vol. 41, art. 5, pp. 329–343.

1942. Field Note on the Copulation of *Crotalus atrox* in California. Copeia, no. 4, p. 262.

1943. Dentitional Phenomena in Cobras and Other Elapids with Notes on Adaptive Modifications of Fangs. Bull. Am. Mus. Nat. Hist., vol. 81, art. 3, pp. 285–360.

1945. In the United States There Is Greater Danger of Being Struck by Lightning Than by a Venomous Snake. Explorers' Jour., vol. 23, no. 1, pp. 1–2.

1946. [Speed of Snakes.] Nat. Hist., vol. 55, no. 3, p. 148.

1947a. Snakes and Stuff. Nat. Hist., vol. 56, no. 2, pp. 49, 96.

1947b. Rectilinear Locomotion in Snakes. Copeia, no. 4, pp. 253–254.

1948a. Fang in Boot Story. Nat. Hist., vol. 59, no. 3, pp. 101, 142.

1948b. The Problem of Snake Control. Nat. Hist., vol. 57, no. 4, pp. 185–188.

1949. Thermoregulation in Reptiles, a Factor in Evolution. Evolution, vol. 3, no. 3, pp. 195–211.

1953. Tree-Climbing Snakes. Nat. Hist., vol. 62, no. 6, pp. 281–282.

BOGERT, C. M., and R. B. COWLES

1947. Moisture Loss in Relation to Habitat Selection in Some Floridian Reptiles. Am. Mus. Nov., no. 1358, pp. 1–34.

BOGERT, C. M., and J. A. OLIVER

1945. A Preliminary Analysis of the Herpetofauna of Sonora. Bull. Am. Mus. Nat. Hist., vol. 83, art. 6, pp. 297–426.

BOGUE, R. G.

1866. Rattlesnake Bite—Recovery. Chi. Med. Jour., vol. 23, no. 6, pp. 399–401.

BOGUSCH, E. R.

1926. Superstitions of Bexar County. Publ. Tex. Folk-Lore Soc., no. 5, pp. 112–125.

BOLTON, H. E.
1916. Spanish Exploration in the Southwest. New York, pp. xii + 487.

BONAPARTE, C. L.
1843. Analyse du Venin de Vipère et Découverte de la Vipérine. Gaz. Tosc. delle Sci. Medico Fisiche, p. 169.

BONELLI, B. F.
1888. Roadrunner and Rattlesnake. Forest and Stream, vol. 3, no. 12, p. 223.

BONI, MARGARET B. (editor)
1952. The Fireside Book of Favorite American Songs. New York, pp. 1–359.

BONNECAMPS, J. P. DE
1920. Account of the Voyage on the Beautiful River Made in 1749, under the Direction of Monsieur de Celoron. Ohio Arch. and Hist. Soc. Publ., vol. 29, pp. 397–423. [See also R. G. Thwaites (editor): Travels and Explorations of the Jesuit Missionaries in New France, vol. 69, pp. 167–169.]

BONSMANN, M. R.
1942a. Zur Frage der Wirksamkeit von Schlangengiften bei innerlicher Darreichung. Arch. f. Exper. Path. u. Pharm., vol. 200, pp. 167–175.
1942b. Ueber die Verwendbarkeit von tropischen Pflanzenauszügen gegen Schlangenbisse. Arch. f. Exper. Path. u. Pharm., vol. 200, pp. 414–418.

BOOK, A.
1945. Diseases and Infestations in Captive Snakes. Am. Biol. Teacher, vol. 8, no. 2, pp. 37–40.

BOONE, A. R.
1937. Snake Hunter Catches Rattlers for Fun. Pop. Sci. Monthly, vol. 131, no. 4, pp. 54–55, 1946.

BOOTH, [DR.]
1814. Account of a South American Remedy for the Bite of Poisonous Reptiles and Rabid Animals Denominated Algalia, Yerba del Sapo, or Contra Culebra. N. Eng. Jour. Med. and Surg., vol. 3, no. 4, pp. 322–323.

BOQUET, P.
1948. Venins de Serpents et Antivenins. Paris, pp. 1–157.

BOQUET, P., A. BUSSARD, and Y. IZARD
1952. Influence de l'Hyaluronidase sur les Propriétés Thérapeutiques du Sérum Antivenimeux. Ann. Inst. Pasteur, vol. 83, no. 5, pp. 640–652. [Summary in Trop. Dis. Bull., vol. 50, no. 3, p. 242, 1953.]

BORIES, E.
1883. Clinical Notes from the Field Hospital Service of the Northern Pacific Railroad. Polyclinic, vol. 1, no. 4, pp. 57–58.

BOSC, L. A. G.
1803. [Article on] Crotale. Nouveau Dictionnaire d'Histoire Naturelle [published in 24 vols., Paris, 1803–4, by Deterville], vol. 6, pp. 549–557. [See also vol. 8, pp. 473–480, of 36-vol. ed., 1816–19; also the article by H. Cloquet, vol. 12, pp. 35–45, of 60-vol. ed., 1816–30.]

BOSCANA, G.
1933. Chinigchinich. Revised and edited from Alfred Robinson's Translation with Annotations by John P. Harrington. Santa Ana, pp. 1–247. [English translation as early as 1846.]

BOSSU, J. F. B.
1771. Travels through That Part of North America Formerly Called Louisiana. London, 2 vols., pp. viii + 407; 1–432.
1777. Nouveaux Voyages dans l'Amerique Septentrionale. Paris, pp. xvi + 392. (1st edition, Paris, 1768.)

BOSTOCK, J., and H. T. RILEY
1855–7. Pliny's Natural History. London, 6 vols.

BOTKIN, G. A. (editor)
1944. A Treasury of American Folklore. New York, pp. xxvii + 932.
1947. A Treasury of New England Folklore. New York, pp. xxvi + 934
1949. A Treasury of Southern Folklore. New York, pp. xxiv + 776.
1951. A Treasury of Western Folklore. New York, pp. xxvi + 806.

BOULENGER, E. G.

1914. Reptiles and Amphibians. London, pp. xiv + 278.

BOULENGER, G. A.

.1893–6. Catalogue of the Snakes in the British Museum (Natural History). 3 vols., pp. xiii + 448; xi + 382; xiv + 727.

1896. Remarks on the Dentition of Snakes and on the Evolution of the Poison-Fangs. Proc. Zoöl. Soc. London, pp. 614–616.

1913. The Snakes of Europe. London, pp. xi + 269.

BOURDELOT, P. M.

1671. Recherches & Observations sur les Vipères. Philos. Trans. (Royal Soc. London) , vol. 6, no. 77, pp. 3013–3016.

BOURKE, J. G.

1884. The Snake-Dance of the Moquis of Arizona. New York, pp. xvi + 371.

1889. Notes on the Cosmogony and Theogony of the Mojave Indians of the Rio Colorado, Arizona. Jour. Am. Folk-Lore, vol. 2, no. 6, pp. 169–189.

1890. Vesper Hours of the Stone Age. Am. Anthro., vol. 3 (o. s.), no. 1, pp. 55–63.

1891. Folk-Lore concerning Arrows. Am. Anthro., vol. 4 (o. s.), no. 1, pp. 71–74.

1892. The Medicine-Men of the Apache. 9th Ann. Rept. Bur. Ethn., pp. 443–603.

1894. Popular Medicine, Customs, and Superstitions of the Rio Grande. Jour. Am. Folk-Lore, vol. 7, no. 25, pp. 119–146.

BOWMAN, J. H.

1885. [Annual Report on Moqui Pueblo Indians.] Report of the Commissioner of Indian Affairs to the Secretary of the Interior, 49th Congress, 1st Session, Exec. Doc. 1, part 5, vol. 2, pp. 636–637.

BOYLE, R.

1670. New Pneumatical Experiments upon Respiration. Philos. Trans. (Royal Soc. London), vol. 5, no. 62, pp. 2011–2033; no. 63, pp. 2035–2056.

BOZEMAN, N.

1850. A Case of Amaurosis, Resulting from a Snake Bite. N. Orleans Med. and Surg. Jour., vol. 6, part 1, art. 8, pp. 739–740.

BRACHT, V.

1931. Texas in 1848. Translation by C. F. Schmidt. San Antonio, Tex., pp. xxiv + 223. [Originally published in German, Elberfeld and Iserlohn, 1849, pp. xii + 322.]

BRADFORD, NETTIE

1946. Property Rights of Animals. Bull. Univ. Utah, vol. 37, no. 9, pp. 1–68.

BRAINARD, D.

1855. On the Nature and Cure of the Bite of Serpents and the Wounds of Poisoned Arrows. 9th Ann. Rept., Smithson. Inst., pp. 123–136.

BRAND, F. J. (translator)

1781. Select Dissertations from the Amoenitates Academicae [of Linnaeus]. London, pp. xiv + 480.

BRANSON, E. B.

1904. Snakes of Kansas. Kans. Univ. Sci. Bull., vol. 12, no. 13, pp. 353–430.

BRATTSTROM, B. H.

1953a. The Amphibians and Reptiles from Rancho La Brea. Trans. San Diego Soc. Nat. Hist., vol. 11, no. 14, pp. 365–392.

1953b. Records of Pleistocene Reptiles from California. Copeia, no. 3, pp. 174–179.

1953c. Records of Pleistocene Reptiles and Amphibians from Florida. Quart. Jour. Fla. Acad. Sci., vol. 16, no. 4, pp. 243–248.

1954a. Amphibians and Reptiles from Gypsum Cave, Nevada. Bull. So. Calif. Acad. Sci., vol. 53, part 1, pp. 8–12.

1954b. The Fossil Pit-Vipers (Reptilia: Crotalidae) of North America. Trans. San Diego Soc. Nat. Hist., vol. 12, no. 3, pp. 31–46.

1955a. Pliocene and Pleistocene Amphibians and Reptiles from Southeastern Arizona. Jour. Paleont., vol. 29, no. 1, pp. 150–154.

1955b. Records of Some Pliocene and Pleistocene Reptiles and Amphibians from Mexico. Bull So. Calif. Acad. Sci., vol. 54, part 1, pp. 1–4.

BRAZIL, V.

1911. A Defensa contra o Ophidismo. São Paulo, pp. 1–147. [Also published in French as La Défense contre L'Ophidisme. São Paulo, 1911, pp. 1–181. Also 2nd edition, 1914, pp. 1–319.]

BRAZIL, V., JR.

1934. Do Emprêgo da Peçonha em Terapêutica. Biol. Méd., vol. 1, pp. 7–21, 50–62.

BREAZEALE, J. F.

1923. The Pima and His Basket. Tucson, pp. 1–146.

BRECKENRIDGE, W. J.

1944. Reptiles and Amphibians of Minnesota. Minneapolis, pp. xiii + 202.

BREDER, C. M., JR.

1947. An Anaylsis of the Geometry of Symmetry with Especial Reference to the Squamation of Fishes. Bull. Am. Mus. Nat. Hist., vol. 88, art. 6, pp. 321–412.

BREHM, A. E.

1883. Brehms Thierleben. Zweite Auflage, Siebenter Band, Dritte Abtheilung—Kriechthiere, Lurche und Fische, pp. xiv + 673.

BREINTAL [BREINTNALL], J.

1748. A Letter . . . to Mr. Peter Collinson, F. R. S. Containing an Account of What He Felt after Being Bit by a Rattle-Snake. Philos. Trans. (Royal Soc., London), vol. 46, part 1 (for 1746), pp. 147–150 [the intermediate pages are numbered 144–145 in error].

BRELAND, O. P.

1948. Animal Facts and Fallacies. New York, pp. xvii + 268.

BRENDLE, T. R., and W. S. TROXELL

1944. Pennsylvania German Folk Tales. Proc. Pa. German Soc., vol. 50, pp. 1–238.

BRENDLE, T. R., and C. W. UNGER

1935. Folk Medicine of the Pennsylvania Germans; The Non-occult Cures. Proc. Pa. German Soc., vol. 45, part 2, pp. 1–303.

BRERETON, C. V.

1917. Squirrel Poison and Rattlesnakes. Calif. Fish and Game, vol. 3, no. 2, p. 91. [See also vol. 2, no. 4, p. 215.]

BRETON, R. S.

1944. Speed of Snakes. Country Life (London), vol. 96, no. 2490, p. 604.

BREWER, J. F.

1897. Prairie Rattlesnakes: Their Poison and Its Treatment. Kans. Med. Jour., vol. 9, no. 5, pp. 57–60.

1880. Reminiscences of John James Audubon. Harper's New Monthly Mag., vol. 61, no. 365, pp. 665–675.

BREWER, W. H.

1930. Up and Down in California in 1860–1864. New Haven, pp. xxx + 601.

BREWSTER, P. G.

1939. Folk Cures and Preventives from Southern Indiana. So. Folklore Quart., vol. 3, no. 1, pp. 33–43.

BRICKELL, J. (British)

1737. The Natural History of North Carolina. Dublin, pp. xiv + 417. [Reprint, Raleigh, N.C., 1911, same paging.]

BRICKELL, J. (American)

1805a. Miscellaneous Chemical and Medical Facts, Observations and Conjectures. Phila. Med. and Phys. Jour., vol. 2, part 1, sec. 1, pp. 101–106.

1805b. [On Two Species of *Crotalus*.] Phila. Med. and Phys. Jour., vol. 2, part 1, sec. 3, p. 164.

1805c. Effects of Alkalies on Poisons. Med. Reposit., 2nd hexade, vol. 2, no. 4, pp. 441–442.

BRIDGES, W.

1944. 46 Baby Rattlesnakes. Animal Kingdom, vol. 47, no. 5, p. 125.

BRIGGS, S.

1950. Outdoor Questions. Field and Stream, vol. 55, no. 3, p. 124.

1951. [Large Rattlesnake Skin.] Field and Stream, vol. 56, no. 4, p. 112.

BRIMLEY, C. S.

1917. Some Known Changes in the Land Vertebrate Fauna of North Carolina. Jour. Elisha Mitchell Sci. Soc., vol. 32, no. 4, pp. 176–183.

1923. North Carolina Herpetology. Copeia, no. 114, pp. 3–4.

1942. Reptiles and Amphibians of North Carolina. Carolina Tips, vol. 5, no. 5, pp. 18–19.

BRINTON, D. G.

1888. Lenâpé Conversations. Jour. Am. Folk-Lore, vol. 1, no. 1, pp. 37–43.

1896. Myths of the New World. 3rd edition, Philadelphia, pp. xii + 360. [1st edition, New York, 1868, pp. vii + 307.]

BROMAN, I.

1920. Das Organon vomero-nasale Jacobsoni—ein Wassergeruchsorgan! Anat. Hefte, vol. 58, no. 1, pp. 137–191.

BROMLEY, R. I.

1934. Rattlesnake Combat. Nat. Mag., vol. 24, no. 1, p. 45.

BRONGERSMA, L. D.

1949. On the Main Branches of the Pulmonary Artery in Some Viperidae. Bijdragen tot de Dierkunde, vol. 28, pp. 57–64.

1951. Some Remarks on the Pulmonary Artery in Snakes with Two Lungs. Zool. Verhand., no. 14, pp. 1–36.

BRONS, H. A.

1882. Notes on the Habits of Some Western Snakes. Am. Nat., vol. 16, pp. 564–567.

BROOKES, R.

1763. A New and Accurate System of Natural History. London, 6 vols; see Rattlesnakes, vol. 3, pp. 368–371.

BROOKING, W. J.

1934. Some Reptiles and Amphibians from Malheur County, in Eastern Oregon. Copeia, no. 2, pp. 93–95.

BROOKS, J. A. ("CABIA BLANCO")

1905. The Rattler and His Stroke. Forest and Stream, vol. 64, no. 17, p. 334.

BROWN, A. E.

1878. The Serpent and the Ape. Am. Nat., vol. 12, no. 4, pp. 225–228.

1881a. Habits of Snakes. Forest and Stream, vol. 15, no. 26, p. 506.

1881b. Habits of Snakes. Forest and Stream, vol. 17, no. 6, pp. 106–107.

1900. The Fear of Snakes. Forest and Stream, vol. 55, no. 24, pp. 463–464.

BROWN, B.

1908. The Conard Fissure, a Pleistocene Bone Deposit in Northern Arkansas. Mem. Am. Mus. Nat. Hist., vol. 9, part 4, pp. 155–208.

BROWN, B. C.

1950. An Annotated Check List of the Reptiles and Amphibians of Texas. Baylor Univ. Stud., pp. xii + 259.

BROWN. C. S.

1926. Archeology of Mississippi. University, Miss., pp. xii + 372.

BROWN, H.

1911. A Battle between Snakes. Forest and Stream, vol. 77, no. 6, p. 219. [See also no. 18, p. 649.]

BROWN, H. M. (translator)

1924. De Venenis of Petrus Abbonus, edition of 1498. Annals Med. Hist., vol. 6, no. 1, pp. 25–53.

BROWN, J. E.

1936. Yesteryears of Texas. San Antonio, pp. x + 157.

BROWN, O. P.

1875. The Complete Herbalist. Jersey City, pp. 1–504.

BROWN, R.

1871. [The Best Method of Destroying Poisonous Serpents.] Proc. Zoöl. Soc. London, no. 3, pp. 39–40.

BROWN, S. R.

1817. The Western Gazetteer; or Emigrant's Directory. Auburn, N. Y., pp. vi + 7–360.

Brown, T. R.

1899. On the Chemistry, Toxicology and Therapy of Snake Poisoning. Bull. Johns Hopkins Hosp., vol. 10, no. 105, pp. 221–227.

Brown, W. W.

1906. Something about Florida Snakes. Forest and Stream, vol. 66, no. 5, p. 178.

Browne, Sir Thomas

1927. Works. Edited by Charles Sayle. Edinburgh, 3 vols., pp. lv + 351; x + 400; ix + 601.

Brownell, L. W.

1934. The Rattlesnake, a Gentleman. Am. Photo., vol. 28, no. 11, pp. 694–697.

1939. Our Snakes and Their Photographs. Am. Photo., vol. 33, no. 5, pp. 368–372.

1947. Why Not Photograph Our Snakes? Am. Photo., vol. 41, no. 11, pp. 46–54.

Browning, M.

1860. Forty-four Years of the Life of a Hunter. Philadelphia, pp. xvii + 400.

Bruce, G. M.

1930. [Effect of Snake Bite on the Snake.] Outdoor Life, vol. 66, no. 2, p. 93.

Bruce, J.

1790. Travels to Discover the Source of the Nile. Edinburgh, 5 vols.

Bruff, J. G.

1944. Gold Rush. The Journals, Drawings, and Other Papers of J. Goldsborough Bruff. Edited by Georgia Willis Read and Ruth Gaines. New York, 2 vols., pp. lxxxviii + 1404.

Bruner, H. L.

1907. On the Cephalic Veins and Sinuses of Reptiles, with Description of a Mechanism for Raising the Venous Blood-Pressure in the Head. Am. Jour. Anat., vol. 7, no. 1, pp. 1–117.

Bryan, A. H.

1939. Some Notes on the Diseases of Snakes. N. Am. Vet., vol. 20, no. 5, pp. 49–54.

Bryan, T. M.

1879. Large Rattlesnakes. Am. Nat., vol. 13, no. 5, p. 322.

Bryant, H. C.

1915. Rattlesnakes on Catalina Island. Copeia, no. 23, p. 48.

1916. Habits and Food of the Roadrunner in California. Univ. Calif. Publ. Zoöl., vol. 17, no. 5, pp. 21–58.

1925. A Rattlesnake's Meal. Yosemite Nat. Notes, vol. 4, no. 12, p. 72. [See also Nature Mag., vol. 6, no. 4, p. 250.]

1929. Outdoor Heritage [from the series "California"]. Los Angeles, pp. [iv] + 464.

Bryant, W. E.

1891. Andrew Jackson Grayson. Zoe, vol. 2, no. 1, pp. 34–68.

Brymer, W. G.

1928. Treatment of Rattlesnake Bite, with Data. Med. World, vol. 46, no. 9, pp. 300–307.

Buckingham, J. S.

1842. The Slave States of America. London, 2 vols., pp. [xviii] + 487; [x] + 588.

Buckland, C. T.

1888. Something about Snakes. Longman's Mag., vol. 11, no. 66, pp. 644–652. [Also in Pop. Sci. Monthly, vol. 33, no. 4, pp. 490–497.]

Buckland, F. T.

1859. Curiosities of Natural History. 4th edition, New York, pp. xvi + 423. [1st edition, London, 1857, pp. xvi + 319.]

Buckley, Eleanor E. (editor)*

1955. [Symposium on Venoms.] Deliberations of the International Conference on Venoms Held in Berkeley, California, Dec. 26–31, 1954. [In press.]

"Buckskin Harry"

1892. Skunk and Rattlesnake. Forest and Stream, vol. 39, no. 7, p. 135.

Budd, T.

1685. Good Order Established in Pennsilvania & New-Jersey in America. London, pp. 1–40.

* Although the various participants in this symposium have been cited as appearing in "Buckley, 1955, in press," publication has been delayed until 1956, when the papers will appear under the joint editorship of Eleanor E. Buckley and Nandor Porges. Publication will be by the American Association for the Advancement of Science.

BUDGE, E. A. W.

1913. Syrian Anatomy, Pathology, and Therapeutics; or "The Book of Medicines." Oxford, 2 vols., pp. clxxviii + 612; xxv + 804.

1930. Amulets and Superstitions. Oxford, pp. xxxix + 542.

BULEY, R. C.

1950. The Old Northwest: Pioneer Period, 1815–1840. Indianapolis, 2 vols., pp. xvi + 632; x + 686.

BULGER, J. J., and A. K. NORTHROP

1951. Perforated Duodenal Ulcer following Snake Bite. Jour. Am. Med. Assn., vol. 147, no. 12, pp. 1134–1135.

BULL, W. P.

1934. From Rattlesnake Hunt to Hockey. Toronto, pp. xxvii + 564.

BULLOCK, T. H., and R. B. COWLES

1952. Physiology of an Infrared Receptor: The Facial Pit of Pit Vipers. Science, vol. 115, no. 2994, pp. 541–543.

BULLOCK, W.

1825. Six Months Residence and Travels in Mexico. 2nd edition, London, 2 vols., pp. xvi + 255; vii + 264. [1st edition, London, 1824, pp. xii + 532.]

1827. Sketch of a Journey through the Western States of North America. London, pp. xxxi + viii + 135. [Also: in Thwaites' Early American Travels, Cleveland, 32 vols., 1904–1907; see vol. 19.]

BUMPUS, H. C.

1885. Reptilia. *In* Riverside Natural History, vol. 3, pp. 345–468. [From Riverside Natural History, edited by J. S. Kingsley, Boston, 1885, 6 vols.]

BURGER, J. W.

1934. The Hibernation Habits of the Rattlesnake of the New Jersey Pine Barrens. Copeia, no. 3, p. 142.

BURGER, W. L., and P. W. SMITH

1950. The Coloration of the Tail Tip of Young Fer-de-Lances: Sexual Dimorphism Rather Than Adaptive Coloration. Science, vol. 112, no. 2911, pp. 431–433.

BURNABY, A.

1775. Travels through the Middle Settlements in North-America in the Years 1759 and 1760. Dublin, pp. xxii + 206. [3rd edition, London, 1798, pp. xix + 209.]

BURNETT, W. I.

1854a. Notes on the Rattle Snake. Proc. Boston Soc. Nat. Hist., vol. 4, pp. 311–315.

1854b. The Sedative Action of the Poison of the Rattle-Snake. Proc. Boston Soc. Nat. Hist., vol. 4, pp. 323–324

1854c. The Poison-Apparatus of the Rattlesnake. Proc. Boston Soc. Nat. Hist., vol. 5, pp. 31–34.

BURROUGHS, J.

1908. Leaf and Tendril. Boston and New York, pp. vii + 289.

BURT, OLIVE W.

1950. He Brands Snakes. Desert Mag., vol. 13, no. 12, pp. 9–12.

BURT, W. H.

1943. Territoriality and Home Range Concepts as Applied to Mammals. Jour. Mammal., vol. 24, pp. 346–352.

BURTON, R. F.

1861. The City of the Saints. London, pp. xii + 707. [Also New York, 1862, pp. xv + 574.]

1869. The Highlands of the Brazil. London, 2 vols., pp. xii + 443; viii + 478.

BURTON, R. H.

1946. Rattlesnakes. Life, vol. 21, no. 10, p. 16.

BURTSCHER, J.

1932. Mouth Rot in Snakes. Bull. Antivenin Inst. Am., vol. 5, no. 3, pp. 59–65.

BURUM, MRS. M. E.

1944. Game Hen as Mother. Game Fowl News, vol. 20, no. 4, p. 3.

Bushnell, D. I., Jr.

1909. The Choctaw of Bayou Lacomb, St. Tammany Parish, Louisiana. Bur. Am. Ethn., Bull. 48, pp. ix + 37.

1910. Myths of the Louisiana Choctaw. Am. Anthro., vol. 12, no. 4, pp. 526–535.

Butler, G. W.

1895. On the Complete or Partial Supression of the Right Lung in the Amphisbaenidae and of the Left Lung in Snakes and Snake-like Lizards and Amphibians. Proc. Zoöl. Soc. London, pp. 691–712.

Butler, P.

1940. Venomin in the Treatment of Arthritis, Arthralgia, Neuritis and Allied Affections. Jour. Intern. Coll. Surg., vol. 3, pp. 357–360. [See also Ind. Med., vol. 9, no. 6, pp. 324–327.]

Byam, G.

1849. Wild Life in the Interior of Central America. London, pp. viii + 253.

Byrd, E. E., and J. F. Denton

1938. New Trematodes of the Subfamily Reniferinae. . . . Jour. Parasit., vol. 24, no. 5, pp. 379–401.

Byrd, W., II

1921. Letters of William Byrd II, and Sir Hans Sloane Relative to Plants and Minerals of Virginia. Wm. and Mary Coll. Quart. Hist. Mag., ser. 2, vol. 1, no. 3, pp. 186–200.

[Byrd, W.]

1929. William Byrd's Histories of the Dividing Line betwixt Virginia and North Carolina. Edited by W. K. Boyd, Raleigh, N. C., pp. xxvii + 341. [Written in 1728; first published in 1733; reprinted Petersburg, Va., 1841, pp. iv + 143.]

C., C. J.

1933. They Won't Follow Rules. *In* W. A. Bevan's column Snake Lore, Outdoor Life, vol. 72, no. 3, p. 59.

"Cabia Blanco." (See under Brooks, J. A.)

Caillard, M.

1944. Speed of Snakes. Country Life (London), vol. 96, no. 2495, p. 825.

1945. A Snake Story. Country Life (London), vol. 97, no. 2508, pp. 253–254.

Cain, H. T.

1950. Petroglyphs of Central Washington. Seattle, pp. ix + 57.

Calderón de la Barca, Frances E. I.

1843. Life in Mexico. London, pp. xii + 436. [Reprint, New York, 1931, pp. xxxviii + 542.]

Caldwell, E. S.

1946. In re Some Snake Questions. Hunting and Fishing, vol. 23, no. 1, p. 22.

Callahan, N.

1952. Smoky Mountain Country. New York and Boston, pp. vii + 257.

Calmet, A.

1812–4. Great Dictionary of the Holy Bible. 4 vols., Charlestown, (Mass.?)

Calmette, A.

1894a. Sur la Toxicité du Sang de *Cobra capel*. Compt. Rend. Soc. Biol., ser. 10, vol. 1, pp. 11–12.

1894b. L'Immunisation Artificielle des Animaux Contre le Venin des Serpents, et la Thérapeutique Expérimentale des Morsures Venimeuses. Compt. Rend. Soc. Biol., vol. 46 (ser. 10, vol. 1), pp. 120–126.

1894c. Contribution a l'Étude du Venin des Serpents. Immunisation des Animaux et Traitement de l'Envenimation. Ann. Inst. Pasteur, vol. 8, no. 4, pp. 275–291.

1898. Inoculation against the Venom of Snakes and the New Treatment of Venomous Bites. Jour. Bombay Nat. Hist. Soc., vol. 11, p. 515–525.

1907. Les Venins, Les Animaux Venimeux, et al Sérothérapie Antivenimeuse. Paris, pp. xvi + 396.

1908. Venoms, Venomous Animals, and Antivenomous Serum-Therapeutics. London, pp. xvi + 403.

"Camerambler"

1900. Florida Rattlers. Forest and Stream, vol. 55, no. 20, p. 384.

CAMERON, G.
  1927. When Does a Rattlesnake Kill? Physical Culture, vol. 58, pp. 51, 70, 72–74.

CAMIN, J. H.
  1948. Mite Transmission of a Hemorrhagic Septicemia in Snakes. Jour. Parasit., vol. 34, no. 4, pp. 345–354.
  1949. An Attempt to Clarify the Status of the Species in the Genus *Ophionyssus* Mégnin (Acarina: Macronyssidae). Jour. Parasit., vol. 35, no. 6, pp. 583–589.
  1953. Observations on the Life History and Sensory Behavior of the Snake Mite, *Ophionyssus natricis* (Gervais). Chi. Acad. Sci., Spec. Publ. 10, pp. 1–75.

CAMP, C. L.
  1916. Notes on the Local Distribution and Habits of the Amphibians and Reptiles of Southeastern California in the Vicinity of the Turtle Mountains. Univ. Calif. Publ. Zoöl., vol. 12, no. 17, pp. 503–544.
  1923. The Chronicles of George C. Yount, California Pioneer of 1826. Calif. Hist. Soc. Quart., vol. 2, no. 1, pp. 3–66.

CAMPA, A. L.
  1950. Superstition and Witchcraft along the Rio Grande. Westerners (Denver) Brand Book for 1949, pp. 165–182.

CAMPANIUS HOLM, T. (See under HOLM, T. C.)

CAMPBELL, B.
  1934. Report on a Collection of Reptiles and Amphibians Made in Arizona during the Summer of 1933. Occ. Papers Mus. Zoöl. Univ. Mich., no. 289, pp. 1–10.

CAMPBELL, H.
  1950. Rattlesnakes Tangled in Wire. Herpetologica, vol. 6, part 2, p. 44.
  1953. Probable Strychnine Poisoning in a Rattlesnake. Herpetologica, vol. 8, part 4, p. 184.

CAREY, C. H.
  1923. Diary of Rev. George Gary. Oreg. Hist. Soc. Quart., vol. 24, no. 1, pp. 68–105; no. 2, pp. 153–185.

CARLANDER, K. D., and R. B. MOORMAN
  1951. How Big Are Iowa's Snakes. Iowa Cons., vol. 10, no. 2, pp. 105, 111.

CARLSTRÖM, D., and C. EDELSTAM
  1946. Methods of Marking Reptiles for Identification after Recapture. Nature, vol. 158, p. 748.

CARMER, C.
  1936. Listen for a Lonesome Drum: A York State Chronicle. New York, pp. xvii + 355.

CARMICHAEL, E. B.
  1927. Detoxification of Rattlesnake Venom by Sodium Ricinoleate. Jour. Pharm. Exp. Ther., vol. 31, no. 6, pp. 445–454.
  1934. Some Properties of Rattlesnake Venom. Ray of Gamma Sigma Epsilon, vol. 11, no. 1, pp. 17–36.

CARMICHAEL, E. B., and P. W. PETCHER
  1945. Constituents of the Blood of the Hibernating and Normal Rattlesnake, *Crotalus horridus*. Jour. Biol. Chem., vol. 161, no. 2, pp. 693–696.

CARNIE, S. K.
  1954. Food Habits of Nesting Golden Eagles in the Coast Ranges of California. Condor, vol. 56, no. 1, pp. 3–12.

CARNOCHAN, F. G., and H. C. ADAMSON
  1935. The Empire of the Snakes. London, pp. 1–356.

CARPENTER, E. S., and R. B. HASSRICK
  1947. Some Notes on Arrow Poisoning among the Tribes of the Eastern Woodlands. Proc. Delaware Co. Inst. Sci., vol. 10, no. 2, pp. 45–52.

CARR, A. F., JR.
  1940. A Contribution to the Herpetology of Florida. Univ. Fla. Publ., Biol. Sci. Ser., vol. 3, no. 1, pp. 1–118.

CARR, W. H.
  1945. Are You Afraid of Snakes? Nat. Hist., vol. 54, no. 5, pp. 232–234.
  1947. Desert Parade. New York, pp. 1–96.

CARSON, H. L.
 1945. Delayed Fertilization in the Captive Indigo Snake with Notes on Feeding and Shedding. Copeia, no. 4, pp. 222–225.

CARUTHERS, H.
 1888. Experience with Rattlesnakes. Forest and Stream, vol. 30, no. 26, pp. 511–512.

CARVER, J.
 1778. Travels through the Interior Parts of North-America, in the Years 1766, 1767, and 1768. London, pp. [x] + xvi + 543. [2nd edition, London, 1779, pp. (xxii) + 544. See also Field and Stream, vol. 54, no. 7, p. 126.]

CASSIDY, INA SIZER
 1951. Some Pueblo Ideas. West. Folklore, vol. 10, no. 1, p. 76.

CASTELLANI, A., and A. J. CHALMERS
 1913. Manual of Tropical Medicine. 3rd edition, London, pp. x + 2436. [1st edition, London, 1910, pp. xxiii + 1242.]

CASTETTER, E. F., and M. E. OPLER
 1936. The Ethnobiology of the Chiricahua and Mescalero Apache. Univ. N. Mex. Bull., Biol. Ser., vol. 4, no. 5, pp. 1–63.

CASTETTER, E. F., and RUTH M. UNDERHILL
 1935. The Ethnobiology of the Papago Indians. Univ. N. Mex. Bull., Biol. Ser., vol. 4, no. 3, pp. 1–84.

CASTIGLIONI, A.
 1942. Snake Venom in Modern Medicine. Ciba Symposia, vol. 3, no. 12, pp. 1182–1185.

CATESBY, M.
 1731–43. The Natural History of Carolina, Florida and the Bahama Islands. London, 2 vols., pp. x + 100; [6] + 100 + xliv + [6] + 20. [See also Gentleman's Mag., vol. 23, p. 609, 1753.]

CATLIN, G.
 1861. Life among the Indians. London, pp. ix + 366.
 1868. Rambles among the Indians of the Rocky Mountains and the Andes. London, pp. xx + 351.

CELSUS, A. C.
 1935–8. De Medicina; with an English Translation by W. G. Spencer. London, 3 vols.

CESARESCO, EVELYN M.
 1909. The Place of Animals in Human Thought. London, pp. 1–376.

CHABANAUD, P.
 1924. Observations sur l'Attitude Prise par les Serpents en Presence d'une Corde en Crins de Cheval. Bull. Mus. National Hist. Nat., vol. 30, no. 6, pp. 453–456.

CHADWICK, L. E., and H. RAHN
 1954. Temperature Dependence of Rattling Frequency in the Rattlesnake, *Crotalus v. viridis*. Science, vol. 119, no. 3092, pp. 442–443.

CHALMERS, T.
 1878. Snake Eat Snake. Forest and Stream, vol. 10, no. 22, p. 422.

CHAMBERLAIN, A. F.
 1901. Signification of Certain Algonquian Animal-Names. Am. Anthro., vol. 3, no. 4, pp. 669–683.

[CHAMBERLAIN, C.] (compiler)
 1850. The Indiana Gazetteer. Indianapolis, pp. viii + 9–440.

CHAMBERLIN, R. V.
 1911. The Ethno-Botany of the Gosiute Indians of Utah. Mem. Am. Anthro. Assn., vol. 2, pp. 329–405.

CHAMPLAIN (See under BIGGAR, H. P.)

CHAPIN, C. E.
 1917. A Rattler and Kingsnake Battle to the Death. Outdoor Life, vol. 40, no. 4, p. 404.

CHARAS, M.
 1669. Novvelles Experiences sur la Vipere. Paris, pp. [x] + 218 + [vi].
 1670a. Novvelles Experiences sur la Vipere. Philos. Trans. (Royal Soc. London), vol. 5, no. 54, pp. 1091–1093.

CHARAS, M. (*Continued*)

1670b. New Experiments upon Vipers. London, pp. [xii] + 223.

1672a. Novvelles Experiences sur la Vipere . . . avec une Suite des Novvelles Experiences . . . pour servir de Replique à une Lettre que Monsieur Francois Redi . . . a écrite . . . Paris, pp. [x] + 278. [2nd French edition, Paris, 1694, pp. (viii) + 367 + (xxiii).]

1672b. Suite des Nouvelles Experiences sur la Vipere. Philos. Trans. (Royal Soc. London), vol. 7, no. 83, pp. 4073–4077; no. 87, p. 5082.

1673. New Experiments upon Vipers . . . Also a Letter of Francisco Redi, concerning Some Objections Made upon His Observations about Vipers . . . Together with the Sequel of New Experiments upon Vipers, in a Reply to a Letter Written by Sign. F. Redi. London, pp. [xii] + 223 + 36. [Translation of Redi's comments] + pp. 37–112 [Charas' reply to Redi.]

CHARLEVOIX, P. DE

1761. Journal of a Voyage to North-America. London, 2 vols., pp. viii + 382; viii + 380 + [22]. [Original French edition, Paris, 1744, pp. xix, xiv, 543.]

CHASE, J. S.

1919. California Desert Trails. Boston and New York, pp. xvi + 387.

CHATEAUBRIAND, F. A. DE

1828. Travels in America and Italy. London, 2 vols., pp. [iii] + 353; 1–429.

1856. The Genius of Christianity. Translation by Charles I. White. Baltimore and New York, pp. 1–763. [1st edition, Paris, 1802.]

CHEEVERS, N.

1870. A Manual of Medical Jurisprudence for India. 3rd edition, Calcutta, pp. xix + 861.

CHENEY, A. N.

1886. Rattles and Fangs. Forest and Stream, vol. 27, no. 10, p. 185.

CHESTNUT, V. K.

1902. Plants Used by the Indians of Mendocino County, California. Contrib. U. S. Nat. Herb., vol. 7, no. 3, pp. 293–408.

CHEWNING, W. J.

1915. Crotalin in Treatment of Epilepsy. Charlotte Med. Jour., vol. 71, no. 5, pp. 261–262.

CHITTENDEN, H. M.

1902. The American Fur Trade of the Far West. New York, 3 vols., pp. xxv + 482; ix, 483–892; 893–1029. [2nd edition, New York, 1935, 2 vols., pp. xxi + 1014.]

1903. History of Early Steamboat Navigation on the Missouri River: Life and Adventures of Joseph LaBarge. New York, 2 vols., pp. xiv + 461.

CHITTENDEN, H. M., and A. T. RICHARDSON

1905. Life, Letters and Travels of Father Pierre-Jean De Smet, S.J., 1801–1873. New York, 4 vols., pp. xiii + 1624.

CHOPRA, R. N., and J. S. CHOWHAN

1932. Snake Venoms in Medicine. Indian Med. Gaz., vol. 67, no. 10, pp. 574–578.

1935. Snake Venoms in Pharmacology and Therapeutics. Indian Med. Gaz., vol. 70, no. 8, pp. 445–453.

CHOTKOWSKI, L. A.

1949. The Treatment of Snake-Bite Poisoning. A Report of Two Cases Involving the Copperhead. N. Eng. Jour. Med., vol. 241, no. 16, pp. 600–603.

CHOWAN, J. S.

1941. The Present Day Concepts of Epileptic Convulsions and Their Treatment with Snake Venoms. Antiseptic, vol. 38, no. 1, pp. 1–15.

CHURCH, B.

1716. Entertaining Passages Relating to Philip's War. Boston, pp. ii + 120.

CIEÇA DE LEON, PEDRO

1554. La Chronica del Peru. Anvers, fols. 7 + 204. [Italian translation, Venetia, 1560, fols. 7 + 215. See also under C. R. MARKHAM, 1864.]

CIESLAK, E. S.

1945. Relations between the Reproductive Cycle and Pituitary Gland in the Snake *Thamnophis radix*. Physiol. Zoöl., vol. 18, no. 3, pp. 299–329.

CIST, C.
  1845. The Cincinnati Miscellany or Antiquities of the West. Cincinnati, vol. 1, pp. 1–272.
CLARK, A. H.
  1948. Animals Alive. New York, pp. viii + 472.
CLARK, ELLA E.
  1953. Indian Legends of the Pacific Northwest. Berkeley and Los Angeles, pp. xi + 225.
CLARK, H.
  1944. The Anatomy and Embryology of the Hemipenis of *Lampropeltis, Diadophis* and *Thamnophis* and Their Value as Criteria of Relationship in the Family Colubridae. Proc. Iowa Acad. Sci., vol. 44, pp. 411–445.
CLARK, H. C.
  1942. Venomous Snakes. Some Central American Records. Incidence of Snake-bite Accidents. Am. Jour. Trop. Med., vol. 22, pp. 37–49.
CLARK, L.
  1953. The Rivers Ran East. New York, pp. xviii + 366.
CLARK, P. J., and R. F. INGER
  1942a. Scale Reduction in Snakes. Copeia, no. 3, pp. 163–170.
  1942b. Scale Reduction Studies in Certain Non-Colubrid Snakes. Copeia, no. 4, pp. 230–232.
CLARK, R. F.
  1949. Snakes of the Hill Parishes of Louisiana. Jour. Tenn. Acad. Sci., vol. 24, no. 4, pp. 244–261.
CLARK, T. D.
  1928. The Snake in Mississippi Folk-Lore. *In* Specimens of Mississippi Folk-Lore, edited by A. P. Hudson, Ann Arbor, pp. 141–144.
CLARKE, R. W.
  1838. Dreadful Effort to Cure Elephantiasis and Leprosy by Receiving the Bite of a Rattlesnake. Lancet, vol. 1, no. 798, pp. 443–445.
CLARKE, S.
  1670. A True and Faithful Account of the Four Chiefest Plantations of the English in America. London, pp. 1–85.
CLARKE, S. C.
  1877. Snake Eating Snake. Forest and Stream, vol. 8, no. 20, p. 320. [See also p. 82.]
  1881a. The Florida Rattlesnake, *Crotalus adamanteus*. Forest and Stream, vol. 16, no. 2, pp. 27–28. [See also pp. 86, 187.]
  1881b. The Swimming Powers of Serpents. Forest and Stream, vol. 16, no. 21, p. 406. [See also vol. 19, pp. 426, 485.]
CLAUDEL, C.
  1943. Tales from San Diego. Calif. Folklore Quart., vol. 2, no. 2, pp. 113–120.
CLAUSEN, H. J.
  1936. The Effect of Aggregation on the Respiratory Metabolism of the Brown Snake *Storeria dekayi*. Jour. Cell. and Comp. Physiol., vol. 8, no. 3, pp. 367–385.
CLAVIGERO, F. J.
  1787. The History of Mexico. Translation from the Italian by Charles Cullen, London, 2 vols., pp. xxv + 476; ii + 463. [First published in Italian, Cesena, 1780–1781, 4 vols.]
  1937. The History of Lower California. Translated from the Italian and Edited by Sara E. Lake and A. A. Gray. Stanford University, pp. xxvii + 413. [First published in Italian, Venezia, 1789, 2 vols., pp. 276, 212.]
[CLAYTON, J.]
  1693. A Letter from Mr. John Clayton . . . to the Royal Society, May 12, 1688, Giving an Account of Several Observables in Virginia . . . Philos. Trans. (Royal Soc., London), vol. 17, pp. 781–795, 941–948; vol. 18, pp. 121–135. [Reprinted in Tracts and Other Papers . . . Collected by Peter Force, Washington, 1844, vol. 3, no. 12, pp. 1–45.]
  1744. A Letter from the Rev'd Mr. John Clayton . . . to Dr. Grew, in Answer to Several Queries Relating to Virginia . . . A.D. 1687. Philos. Trans. (Royal Soc. London), vol. 41, part 1, pp. 143–162.
CLELAND, R. G.
  1941. The Cattle on a Thousand Hills. San Marino, Calif., pp. xiv + 327.

CLEMENTS, F. E.
　　1932. Primitive Concepts of Disease. Univ. Calif. Publ. Am. Arch. and Ethn., vol. 32, no. 2, pp. 185–252.

CLENCH, W. J.
　　1925. A Possible Manner of Snake Distribution. Copeia, no. 142, p. 40.

[CLIFTON, W. A., and P. BOWCHEY]
　　1953. Goodbye, Rattlesnake. Fla. Wildlife, vol. 7, no. 3, p. 31.

CLOUGH, B. C.
　　1947. The American Imagination at Work: Tall Tales and Folk Tales. New York, pp. xix + 707.

"COAHOMA"
　　1887. The Prejudice against Snakes. Forest and Stream, vol. 28, no. 16, p. 345.
　　1902. A Study of the Rattlesnakes. Forest and Stream, vol. 59, no. 14, pp. 263–264. [See also pp. 345–346; vol. 60, pp. 64–65.]

COCHRAN, DORIS M.
　　1929. The Striking of the Rattlesnake. Nature Mag., vol. 14, no. 2, p. 108.
　　1944. Dangerous Reptiles. Smithsonian Rept. for 1943, pp. 275–324.

COGGESHALL, A. S.
　　1942. Coons, Snakes, and Monsters. Santa Barbara Mus. Nat. Hist., Mus. Leafl., vol. 17, no. 8, pp. 87–90.

COHEN, B. B., and I. EHRENPREIS
　　1947. Tales from Indiana Students. Hoosier Folklore, vol. 6, no. 2, pp. 57–65.

COHEN, E.
　　1951. A Serological Comparison of *Sistrurus* (Pigmy Rattlesnakes) with Representatives of the Genera *Crotalus* ("True" Rattlesnakes) and *Agkistrodon* (Moccasins). Abstract. Soc. Syst. Zoöl., News Letter no. 5, p. 6.
　　1954. A Comparison of the Total Protein and Albumin Content of the Blood Sera of Some Reptiles. Science, vol. 119, no. 3081, pp. 98–99.

COKE, H. J.
　　1852. A Ride over the Rocky Mountains to Oregon and California. London, pp. x + 390.

COLE, R.
　　1926. Francesco Redi (1626–1697): Physician, Naturalist, Poet. Annals Med. Hist., vol. 8, no. 4, pp. 347–369.

COLEMAN, A.
　　1930. The Sportsmanship of the Rattler. Outdoor Life, vol. 65, no. 3, p. 108.

COLEMAN, F. W., and L. P. GRATACAP
　　1897. The Water Moccasin. Sci. Am., vol. 76, no. 20, p. 311. [See also pp. 201–202.]

COLEMAN, G. E.
　　1928. Rattlesnake Venom Antidote of the Hopi Indians. Bull. Antivenin Inst. Am., vol. 1, no. 4, pp. 97–99.

COLEMAN, R. T.
　　1872. Items of Army Experience: Snake Story. Va. Clinical Rec., vol. 2, no. 4, pp. 137–139.

COLLES, G. W.
　　1908. A Defense of Audubon. Sci. Am., vol. 98, no. 18, p. 311. [See also Brimley, H. H., *ibid.*, no. 20, p. 351.]

COLLINS, MARY T.
　　1928. Fifty Cents a Pound for Venomous Snakes. Am. Mag., vol. 106 (Sept.), pp. 65–66.

COLLINSON, P. (See under BREINTAL, J.)

COLLOT, G. H. V.
　　1924. A Journey in North America. Florence, 2 vols., pp. xxvii + 310; 297. [1st edition Paris, 1826, 2 vols., pp. viii + 416; 427 + 72.]

COLTON, H. S., and F. C. BAXTER
　　1932. Days in the Painted Desert and the San Francisco Mountains. No. Ariz. Soc. Sci. Art, Bull. no. 2, ed. 2, pp. ix + 113.

COMANCHO, E.
　　1893. A White Rattlesnake. Forest and Stream, vol. 41, no. 15, p. 316. [See also no. 17, p. 360; no. 22, pp. 469–470; no. 23, p. 492.]

COMFORT, A. I.
    1878. Case of Snake Bite. Phila. Med. Times, vol. 9, pp. 77–79.
COMPTON, H.
    1893. A King's Hussar. London, pp. vii + 360.
CONANT, R.
    1933. Three Generations of Cottonmouths, *Agkistrodon piscivorus* (Lacépède). Copeia, no. 1,
        p. 43.
    1934. Two Rattlesnakes Killed by a Cottonmouth. Science, vol. 80, no. 2078, p. 382.
    1938. The Reptiles of Ohio. Am. Midl. Nat., vol. 20, no. 1, pp. 1–200.
    1945. An Annotated Check List of the Amphibians and Reptiles of the Del-Mar-Va Peninsula.
        Wilmington, Delaware, pp. 1–8.
    1948. Regeneration of Clipped Subcaudal Scales in a Pilot Black Snake. Nat. Hist. Misc., no.
        13, pp. 1–2.
    1951. The Reptiles of Ohio. 2nd edition, Notre Dame, pp. 1–284.
CONANT, R., and W. BRIDGES
    1939. What Snake Is That? New York, pp. viii + 163.
CONANT, R. and R. M. PERKINS
    1931. This Mite Question. Bull. Antivenin Inst. Am., vol. 5, no. 2, pp. 36–39.
CONARD, H. C.
    1890. "Uncle Dick" Wootton. Chicago, pp. 1–472. [Reprinted 1950.]
CONN, H. F. (editor)
    1950. Current Therapy. Philadelphia, pp. xxxii + 736. [Later edition, 1955, Philadelphia, pp.
        xxx + 692.]
CONNIFF, J. C. G.
    1948. The Mayor of Rattlesnake Manor. Sports Afield, vol. 120, no. 1, pp. 48–49, 90–91.
CONVERSE, HARRIET M.
    1908. Myths and Legends of the New York State Iroquois. N. Y. State Mus., Bull. 125, pp. 1–195.
CONZEMIUS, E.
    1932. Ethnographical Survey of the Muskito and Sumu Indians of Honduras and Nicaragua.
        Bur. Am. Ethn., Bull. 106, pp. vii + 191.
COOK, FANNYE A.
    1943. Snakes in Mississippi. Sur. Bull., Miss. Game and Fish Comm., pp. ii + 73. [2nd edition,
        1954, pp. ii + 40.]
COOK, S. F., JR.
    1955. Rattlesnake Hybrids: *Crotalus viridis* × *Crotalus scutulatus*. Copeia, no. 2, pp. 139–141.
COOKE, G.
    1934. Deadly Snake Poison Saves Human Lives. Pop. Sci. Monthly, vol. 124, no. 5, pp. 29–30,
        118.
COOPER, J. F.
    1827. The Prairie; a Tale. Philadelphia, 2 vols., pp. xi + 12–232; 276.
COPE, E. D.
    1866. On the Reptilia and Batrachia of the Sonoran Province of the Nearctic Region. Proc.
        Acad. Nat. Sci. Phila., vol. 18, pp. 300–314.
    1871. The Method of Creation of Organic Forms. Proc. Am. Philos. Soc., vol. 12, pp. 89–123.
    1887. The Origin of the Fittest: Essays on Evolution. New York, pp. xix + 467.
    1892a. A Critical Review of the Characters and Variations of the Snakes of North America.
        Proc. U. S. Nat. Mus., vol. 14, no. 882, pp. 589–694.
    1892b. Spitting of Snakes. Forest and Stream, vol. 39, no. 6, p. 114.
    1893. Prodromus of a New System of the Non-Venomous Snakes. Am. Nat., vol. 25, pp. 477–483.
    1894a. On the Lungs of the Ophidia. Proc. Am. Philos. Soc., vol. 33, no. 145, pp. 217–224.
    1894b. The Classification of Snakes. Am. Nat., vol. 28, pp. 831–844.
    1895. The Classification of the Ophidia. Trans. Am. Philos. Soc., vol. 18, part 3, pp. 186–219.
    1900. The Crocodilians, Lizards, and Snakes of North America. Rept. U. S. Nat. Mus. for 1898,
        pp. 153–1270.
CORBUSIER, W. F.
    1886. The Apache-Yumas and Apache-Mojaves. Am. Antiq., vol. 8, no. 5, pp. 276–284; no. 6,
        pp. 325–339.

CORBYN, F.
  1839. Bite of a Rattlesnake. Lancet, vol. 2, no. 838, pp. 929–930.
CORKILL, N. L.
  1932a. An Inquiry into Snake Bite in Iraq. Indian Jour. Med. Res., vol. 20, no. 2, pp. 599–625; no. 3, pp. 679–696.
  1932b. Snakes and Snake Bite in Iraq. London, pp. ix + 51.
  1935. Snake Stories from Kordofan. Sudan Notes and Rec., vol. 18, part 2, pp. 243–258.
  1949. Malnutrition and Snake Poisoning in the Sudan. Trans. Royal Soc. Trop. Med. and Hyg., vol. 42, no. 6, pp. 613–616.
CORLE, E.
  1941. Desert Country. New York, pp. viii + 357.
CORLETT, W. T.
  1935. The Medicine-Man of the American Indian and His Cultural Background. Springfield, Ill., pp. ix + 369.
COSGROVE, C. B.
  1947. Caves of the Upper Gila and Hueco Areas in New Mexico and Texas. Papers Peabody Mus. Am. Arch. and Ethn., vol. 24, no. 2, pp. xv + 181.
COTT, H. B.
  1940. Adaptive Coloration in Animals. London, pp. xxxii + 508.
COUES, E.
  1866. Some Notes on Arrow-Wounds. Med. and Surg. Reporter, vol. 14, no. 17 (whole no. 478), pp. 321–324.
  1874. Birds of the Northwest. U. S. Geol. Surv. Terr. Misc. Publ. 3, pp. xi + 791.
  1875. Synopsis of the Reptiles and Batrachians of Arizona. Washington, One Hundredth Meridian Surveys (Wheeler Report), vol. 5, chap. 5, pp. 585–633.
  1893. History of the Expedition under the Command of Lewis and Clark. New York, 4 vols.
  1895. The Expeditions of Zebulon Montgomery Pike. New York, 3 vols.
  1897. The Manuscript Journals of Alexander Henry and of David Thompson. New York, 3 vols.
COUES, E., and H. C. YARROW
  1878. Notes on the Herpetology of Dakota and Montana. Bull. U. S. Geol. and Geog. Sur., vol. 4, no. 1, art. 11, pp. 259–291.
COURT, A.
  1949. How Hot Is Death Valley? Geog. Rev., vol. 39, no. 2, pp. 214–220.
COVILLE, F. V.
  1897. Notes on the Plants Used by the Klamath Indians of Oregon. Contrib. U. S. Nat. Herb., vol. 5, no. 2, pp. v + 87–108 + ii.
COWLES, R. B.
  1938. Unusual Defense Postures Assumed by Rattlesnakes. Copeia, no. 1, pp. 13–16.
  1940. Additional Implications of Reptilian Sensitivity to High Temperatures. Am. Nat., vol. 74, no. 755, pp. 542–561.
  1941. Observations on the Winter Activities of Desert Reptiles. Ecology, vol. 22, no. 2, pp. 125–140.
  1945a. Surface-Mass Ratio, Paleoclimate and Heat Sterility. Am. Nat., vol. 79, no. 785, pp. 561–567.
  1945b. Some of the Activities of the Sidewinder. Copeia, no. 4, pp. 220–222.
  1953. The Sidewinder: Master of Desert Travel. Pac. Discovery, vol. 6, no. 2, pp. 12–15.
COWLES, R. B., and C. M. BOGERT
  1944. A Preliminary Study of the Thermal Requirements of Desert Reptiles. Bull. Am. Mus. Nat. Hist., vol. 83, art. 5, pp. 261–296.
COX, R.
  1832. Adventures on the Columbia River. New York, pp. 1–335.
COX, W. C.
  1927. First Aid Treatment in Cases of Poisoning Due to Rattle Snake Bite. Military Surg., vol. 61, no. 1, pp. 53–55.
CRADDOCK, J. R.
  1923. The Cowboy Dance. Publ. Tex. Folk-Lore Soc., vol. 2, pp. 31–37.

CRAIGIE, SIR W. A., and J. R. HURLBERT

    1938–44. A Dictionary of American English on Historical Principles. Chicago, 4 vols.

CRANDALL, Mrs. F. W., and LOIS GANNETT

    1945. Folk Cures of New York State. N. Y. Folklore Quart., vol. 1, no. 3, pp. 178–180.

CRANSTON, C. K.

    1913. A Snake Story. Forest and Stream, vol. 80, no. 15, p. 462.

[CREBS, M. R., and R. HOLTZAPPLE]

    1951. Rattler Meets His Master. Pa. Game News, vol. 22, no. 7, p. 47.

CREED, J. M.

    1884. Australian Snakebite—Fear as a Factor in Producing Many of the Alarming Symptoms Following. Australasian Med. Gaz., vol. 3, pp. 224–229.

CREMONY, J. C.

    1868. Life among the Apaches. San Francisco, pp. 1–322.

CRESSMAN, L. S.

    1937. Petroglyphs of Oregon. Univ. Oreg. Monog., Stud. Anthro., no. 2, pp. 1–78.

CRESSWELL, R.

    1862. Aristotle's History of Animals in Ten Books. London, pp. ix + 326.

CRÈVECOEUR, M. G. J. DE [Pseudonym, J. HECTOR ST. JOHN]

    1782. Letters from an American Farmer. London, pp. [xii] + 318.

    1783. Some Account of the Snakes of North America, and of the Humming Bird. Annual Register [Dodsley's], part 2, pp. 99–103. [See also London Med. Reposit. and Rev., vol. 28, no. 167, pp. 444–446, 1827.]

CRIMMINS, M. L.

    1927a. Facts about Texas Snakes and Their Poisons. Tex. State Jour. Med., vol. 23, no. 3, pp. 198–203.

    1927b. Prevalence of Poisonous Snakes in the El Paso and San Antonio Districts in Texas. Bull. Antivenin Inst. Am., vol. 1, no. 1, pp. 23–24.

    1929. Poisonous Snakes and the Antivenin Treatment. So. Med. Jour., vol. 22, no. 7, pp. 603–605

    1930. Treatment of Shock in Rattlesnake Bites. Tex. State Jour. Med., vol. 26, pp. 449–450; also Military Surg., vol. 69, pp. 42–44, 1931.

    1931. Rattlesnakes and Their Enemies. Bull. Antivenin Inst. Am., vol. 5, no. 2, pp. 46–47.

    1934. Snake-Bites and the Saving of Human Life. Military Surg., vol. 74, no. 3, pp. 125–132.

    1946a. The Rattlesnake in the Art and Life of the American Indian. Bull. Tex. Arch. and Paleo. Soc., vol. 17, pp. 28–41.

    1946b. The Treatment of Poisonous Snake Bites in Texas. Proc. and Trans. Tex. Acad. Sci., vol. 29, pp. 54–61.

CRITES, A. S.

    1952. A Hunter's Tale of the Great Outdoors. Los Angeles, pp. xii + 229.

CROSBY, ELIZABETH C., and TRYPHENA HUMPHREY

    1939. A Comparison of the Olfactory and the Accessory Olfactory Bulbs in Certain Representative Vertebrates. Papers Mich. Acad. Sci., Arts, and Lett., vol. 24, part 2, pp. 95–104.

CROUSE, H. W.

    1902. The Venomous Snakes and Spiders of Texas. Tex. Med. News, vol. 11, no. 8, pp. 413–448.

CROWDER, F.

    1946. The Hopi Knows His Rattlesnakes. Westways, vol. 38, no. 7, pp. 4–6.

CROWE, C. E.

    1931. Treating Snake Bite in Dogs. Am. Field, vol. 116, no. 39, pp. 299–300.

CRUM, C. W. R.

    1906. Treatment of the Bites of Copperhead Snakes. Jour. Am. Med. Assn., vol. 46, no. 19, pp. 1433–1434.

CUESTA TERRON, C.

    1921. Los Crotalianos Mexicanos. Soc. Scient. "Antonio Alzate," vol. 39, pp. 173–194.

    1930-1. Los Crotalianos Mexicanos. Su Clasificación, Ecología y Distribución Geografía. Anales Inst. Biol., vol. 1, no. 3, pp. 187–199; vol. 2, no. 1, pp. 47–72.

CULIN, S.

    1901. A Summer Trip among the Western Indians. Bull. Univ. Pa. Free Mus. Sci. and Art, vol. 3, no. 2 (chap. 2), pp. 88–101.

1292   *Bibliography*

CUNNINGHAM, B.
    1937. Axial Bifurcation in Serpents. Durham, N. C., pp. vii + 117.

CUNNINGHAM, D. D.
    1897. Reports on the Results of Experiments on the Action of Various Reputed Antidotes to Snake-Venom Conducted during the Season 1895–96. Sci. Mem. Med. Officers of Army of India, Calcutta, part 10, no. 4, pp. 59–94.

CURRAN, C. H.
    1935. Rattlesnakes. Nat. Hist., vol. 36, no. 4, pp. 331–340.

CURRAN, C. H., and C. F. KAUFFELD
    1937. Snakes and Their Ways. New York, pp. xvii + 285.

CURTIN, J.
    1922. Seneca Indian Myths. New York, pp. xii + 516.

CURTIN, J., and J. N. B. HEWITT
    1918. Seneca Fiction, Legends, and Myths. 32nd Ann. Rept. Bur. Am. Ethn., pp. 37–813.

CURTIN, L. S. M.
    1930. Pioneer Medicine in New Mexico. Folk-Say, vol. 2, pp. 186–196.
    1947. Healing Herbs of the Upper Rio Grande. Santa Fe, N. Mex., pp. 1–281.

CURTIS, E. S.
    1907–30. The North American Indian. Norwood, Mass., 20 vols.

CURTIS, L.
    1949. The Snakes of Dallas County, Texas. Field and Lab., vol. 17, no. 1, pp. 5–13.

CUSHING, F. H.
    1896. Exploration of Ancient Key Dwellers' Remains on the Gulf Coast of Florida. Proc. Am. Philos. Soc., vol. 35, no. 153, pp. 329–432.
    1901. Zuni Folk Tales. New York, pp. xvii + 474.

CUSHMAN, H. B.
    1899. History of the Choctaw, Chickasaw and Natchez Indians. Greenville, Texas, pp. 1–607.

CUTTER, R. K.
    1940. Snake-Bites: A Compact Suction Kit. Calif. and West. Med., vol. 53, no. 1, pp. 32–33.

CZERMAK, J.
    1857. Ueber den Schallerzeugenden Apparat von *Crotalus*. Zeits. wiss. Zool., bd. 8, pp. 294–302.

D., J. W.
    1878. Poisoned Arrows. Pac. Rural Press, vol. 15, no. 7, p. 98. [Also Mining and Sci. Press, vol. 36, p. 99.]
    1901. Derattling a Rattler. Forest and Stream, vol. 56, no. 20, p. 385.

DABNEY, T. G.
    1916. Serpent Instinct in Man. Science, vol. 43, no. 1097, pp. 25–26.

DACK, S.
    1935. Treatment of Intractable Nasal Hemorrhage by Injections of Moccasin Snake Venom. Jour. Am. Med. Assn., vol. 105, pp. 412–413.

DALE, E. E.
    1947. Medical Practices on the Frontier. Indiana Mag. Hist., vol. 43, no. 4. pp. 307–328.

DAM, H. J. W.
    1894. Inoculation against Snake Poison: Dr. Calmette's Experiments at the Pasteur Institute. Paris. McClure's Mag., vol. 3, no. 5, pp. 460–468.

DAMIRI (AL-DAMIRI) (See under JAYAKAR, A. S. G.)

D'AMOUR, F. E., FRANCES E. BECKER, and W. VAN RIPER
    1936. The Black Widow Spider. Quart. Rev. Biol., vol. 11, no. 2, pp. 123–160.

DANIELS, CORA L., and C. M. STEVANS
    1903. Encyclopaedia of Superstitions, Folklore, and the Occult Sciences of the World. Chicago and Milwaukee, 3 vols., pp. xxiv + 1751.

DANNALDSON, J. M.
    1937. Serpent Trails. Los Angeles, pp. 1–72.
    1938. Hunting Sidewinders. Desert Mag., vol. 1, no. 11, pp. 6–7.

DARGAN, L. M., and W. H. STICKEL
    1949. An Experiment with Snake Trapping. Copeia, no. 4, pp. 264–268.

DARLINGTON, W.

    1808. Remarks on Dr. Hugh Williamson's Opinions concerning the Fascination of Serpents. Med. Reposit., hex. 2, vol. 5, no. 3, pp. 257–260.

    1828. Protest against the Admission of a Power of Fascination in Snakes. Am. Jour. Sci. and Arts., vol. 13, no. 2, pp. 388–390.

    1849. Memorials of John Bartram and Humphry Marshall. Philadelphia, xv + 585.

DARWIN, C.

    1859. On the Origin of Species by Means of Natural Selection. London, pp. ix + 502.

    1873. The Expression of the Emotions in Man and Animals. New York, pp. v + 374.

DAUDIN, F. M.

    1801–4. Histoire Naturelle, Génerale et Particulière des Reptiles. Paris, 8 vols. [Rattlesnakes, vol. 5, pp. 297–333.]

DAVENPORT, GERTRUDE C.

    1898. Folk-Cures from Kansas. Jour. Am. Folk-Lore, vol. 11, no. 41, pp. 129–132.

DAVENPORT, J. W.

    1943. Field Book of the Snakes of Bexar County, Texas, and Vicinity. San Antonio, Tex., pp. 1–132.

DAVID, R. B.

    1937. Finn Burnett, Frontiersman. Glendale, Calif., pp. 1–378.

DAVIDSON, L. J.

    1941. Rocky Mountain Folklore. So. Folklore Quart., vol. 5, no. 4, pp. 205–219.

    1943. Western Campfire Tales. Calif. Folklore Quart., vol. 2, no. 3, pp. 177–190.

DAVIDSON, L. J., and F. BLAKE

    1947. Rocky Mountain Tales. Norman, Okla., pp. xiv + 302.

DAVIS, D. D.

    1936. Courtship and Mating Behavior in Snakes. Field Mus. Nat. Hist., Zoöl. Ser., vol. 20, no. 22, pp. 257–290.

DAVIS, H. C.

    1914. Negro Folk-Lore in South Carolina. Jour. Am. Folk-Lore, vol. 27, no. 105, pp. 241–265.

DAVIS, H. E.

    1949. The American Wild Turkey. Georgetown, S. C., pp. viii + 319.

DAVIS, H. T., and C. S. BRIMLEY

    1944. Poisonous Snakes of the Eastern United States, with First Aid Guide. N. Car. State Mus., Raleigh, pp. 1–16.

DAVIS, I.

    1889. A Rattlesnake Killer. Forest and Stream, vol. 33, no. 10, pp. 182–183.

DAVIS, T. R.

    1868. A Summer on the Plains. Harper's New Monthly Mag., vol. 36, no. 213, pp. 292–307.

DAVIS, VARINA A.

    1888. Serpent Myths. N. Am. Rev., vol. 146, no. 2, pp. 161–171.

DAVIS, W. B., and H. M. SMITH

    1953. Snakes of the Mexican State of Morelos. Herpetologica, vol. 8, part 4, pp. 133–143.

DAVIS, W. T.

    1918. Bitten by a Rattlesnake. Proc. Staten Isl. Assn. Arts and Sci., vol. 7, pp. 15–18.

DAWSON, G. G.

    1935. Healing: Pagan and Christian. London, pp. ix + 322.

DAY, W. DE F.

    1876. Music from a Snake's Tail. Forest and Stream, vol. 7, no. 5, p. 68.

[DAYTON, J.]

    1949. [Snake Dance.] Wyo. Wild Life, vol. 13, no. 10, pp. 31–32.

DEANE, J. B.

    1830. The Worship of the Serpent. London, pp. xiv + 391.

DE ANGULO, J.

    1935. Pomo Creation Myth. Jour. Am. Folk-Lore, vol. 48, no. 189, pp. 203–262.

    1953. Indian Tales. New York, pp. vii + 246.

DEBO, A.
    1941. The Road to Disappearance. Norman, Okla., pp. xv + 399.
DECKER, M. H.
    1936. Tanning Snake Skins. Outdoor Life, vol. 77, no. 3, p. 72.
    1949. Tanning Rattler Skins. Outdoor Life, vol. 103, no. 5, pp. 140–141.
DEERING, T. W.
    1872. The Rattle of the Rattlesnake. Am. Nat., vol. 6, pp. 490–491.
DE HUFF, ELIZABETH W.
    1931. The Venomous Snake-Girl. Palacio, vol. 31, no. 5, pp. 73–74.
DE KAY, J. E.
    1842. Zoölogy of New-York. Albany, Part III, Reptiles and Amphibians, vol. 1, pp. vi + 98; vol. 2, plates 1–23.
DELLENBAUGH, F. S.
    1901. The North-Americans of Yesterday. New York, pp. xxvi + 487.
DELORIA, ELLA
    1932. Dakota Texts. Publ. Am. Ethn. Soc., vol. 14, pp. xvi + 279.
DE LYS, CLAUDIA
    1948. A Treasury of American Superstitions. New York, pp. xxii + 494.
DE MAYERNE, T.
    1694. A Discourse of the Viper. Philos. Trans. (Royal Soc. London), vol. 18, no. 211, pp. 162–166.
DENIG, E. T.
    1930. Indian Tribes of the Upper Missouri. 46th Ann. Rept. Bur. Am. Ethn., pp. 375–828.
DENSMORE, FRANCES
    1928. Uses of Plants by the Chippewa Indians. 44th Ann. Rept. Bur. Am. Ethn., pp. 275–397.
    1929a. Chippewa Customs. Bur. Am. Ethn., Bull. 86, pp. xii + 204.
    1929b. Papago Music. Bur. Am. Ethn., Bull. 90, pp. xx + 229.
    1929c. Pawnee Music. Bur. Am. Ethn., Bull. 93, pp. xviii + 129.
    1932. Menominee Music. Bur. Am. Ethn., Bull. 102, pp. xxii + 230.
DENTON, D.
    1670. A Brief Description of New-York: Formerly called New-Netherlands. London, pp. [ii] + 21. [Reprinted in Bull. Hist. Soc. Pa., vol. 1, pp. 1–16, 1845.]
DES LIGNERIS, M., and E. GRASSET
    1936. Clinical Experiments on the Effect of African Snake Venoms on Human Cancer Cases with or without Concomitant Deep Therapy. Am. Jour. Cancer, vol. 26, no. 3, pp. 512–520.
DESMOULINS, A.
    1824. Mémoire sur le Système Nerveux et l'Appareil Lacrymal des Serpents à Sonnettes, des Trigonocéphales, et de Quelques Autres Serpents. Jour. Phys. Expér. Path. (Magendie), vol. 4, pp. 264–284.
    1827. Note sur l'Appareil Sécréteur du Venin chez le Serpent à Sonnettes. Jour. Phys. Expér. Path. (Magendie), vol. 7, no. 1, pp. 109–112.
DESPREZ, W.
    1869. [Successful Cure for Rattlesnake Bite.] Med. Times and Gaz., vol. 1, no. 966, p. 25.
DEUTSCH, H. F., and W. H. McSHAN
    1949. Biophysical Studies of Blood Plasma Proteins. XII. Electrophoretic Studies of the Blood Serum Proteins of Some Lower Animals. Jour. Biol. Chem., vol. 180, no. 1, pp. 219–234.
DE VESEY, L.
    1858. Experiments with Bibron's Antidote to the Poison of the Rattlesnake. Am. Jour. Med. Sci., vol. 35 (n.s.), no. 70, art. 15, pp. 375–376.
DEVOE, A.
    1945. Down to Earth. Rattlesnakes: Fancies and Facts. Am. Mercury, vol. 60, no. 256, pp. 483–487.
    1951. This Fascinating Animal World. New York, pp. x + 303.
DEWEES, W. B.
    1852. Letters from an Early Settler of Texas. Louisville, Ky., pp. 1–312.
DE WET, J. C.
    1929. Snakes and Tractors on Kotapalli. Asia, vol. 27, no. 12, pp. 998–1003, 1036–1040.

DEWHURST, R. E.
> 1951. Rattlesnakes Join the Fight on Cancer. N. Mex., vol. 29, no. 4, pp. 24–25, 47, 49.

DEXTER, S. F.
> 1884. Many Rattles. Forest and Stream, vol. 22, no. 7, p. 124.

DÍAZ DEL CASTILLO, B.
> 1632. Historia Verdadera de la Conquista de la Nueva-España. Madrid, pp. [viii] + 254 fols. + [xii].
> 1800. The True History of the Conquest of Mexico . . . Written in the Year 1568. Translated by Maurice Keatinge. London, pp. viii + 515. [Also reprint, with introduction by A. D. H. Smith, New York, 1927, pp. 1–562.]

DICE, L. R.
> 1938. Some Census Methods for Mammals. Jour. Wildlife Man., vol. 2, no. 3, pp. 119–130.

DIESING, C. M.
> 1851. Systema Helminthum. Vindobonae, 2 vols., pp. xiii + 679; vi + 588 + [3].

DITMARS, R. L.
> 1905. A New Species of Rattlesnake. 9th Ann. Rept. N. Y. Zoöl. Soc., pp. 25–28.
> 1907. The Reptile Book. Garden City, N. Y., pp. xxxii + 472.
> 1912. The Feeding Habits of Serpents. Zoologica, vol. 1, no. 11, pp. 197–238.
> 1919. Our Oldest Specimens. Bull. N. Y. Zoöl. Soc., vol. 22, no. 3, pp. 60–65.
> 1921. Albinos in the Zoölogical Park and Elsewhere. Bull. N. Y. Zoöl. Soc., vol. 24, no. 6, pp. 126–132.
> 1923a. Reptiles of the Southwest. Bull. N. Y. Zoöl. Soc., vol. 26, no. 2, pp. 22–30. [See also The Sidewinder Rattlesnake, Rev. of Revs., vol. 70, no. 4, pp. 444–445.]
> 1923b. [Report of] Department of Reptiles [for 1922]. 27th Ann. Rept. N. Y. Zoöl. Soc., pp. 49–51.
> 1927. Occurrence and Habits of Our Poisonous Snakes. Bull. Antivenin Inst. Am., vol. 1, no. 1, pp. 3–5.
> 1929. Serpents of the Eastern States. Bull. N. Y. Zoöl. Soc., vol. 32, no. 3, pp. 83–120.
> 1931. Snakes of the World. New York, pp. xi + 207.
> 1935. Serpents of the Northeastern States. New edition, revised and enlarged, New York, pp 1–40.
> 1936. The Reptiles of North America. New York, pp. xvi + 476.
> 1939. Snake Bites among Domestic Animals. Jour. Am. Vet. Med. Assn., vol. 94 (n.s. 47), no. 4, pp. 383–388.
> 1940. Snakes in the Ice Box. Bull. N. Y. Zoöl. Soc., vol. 43, no. 5, pp. 144–145.

DIXON, J.
> 1926. When and How Far Can a Rattlesnake Strike? Nature Mag., vol. 7, no. 5, p. 274.
> 1928. The Ground Owl: An Interesting and Common Western Bird. Nature Mag., vol. 12, no. 5, p. 296.

DIXON, J. B.
> 1937. The Golden Eagle in San Diego County, California. Condor, vol. 39, pp. 49–56.

DIXON, R. B.
> 1902a. Basketry Designs of the Indians of Northern California. Bull. Am. Mus. Nat. Hist., vol 17, part 1, pp. 1–32.
> 1902b. Maidu Myths. Bull. Am. Mus. Nat. Hist., vol. 17, part 2, pp. 33–118.
> 1903. System and Sequence in Maidu Mythology. Jour. Am. Folk-Lore, vol. 16, no. 60, pp. 32–36.
> 1905. The Northern Maidu. Bull. Am. Mus. Nat. Hist., vol. 17, part 3, pp. 119–346.
> 1907. The Shasta. Bull. Am. Mus. Nat. Hist., vol. 17, no. 5, pp. 381–498.
> 1910. Shasta Myths. Jour. Am. Folk-Lore, vol. 23, no. 87, pp. 8–37; no. 89, pp. 364–370.

DIXON, R. M.
> 1902. The Senses of Snakes. Verhand. V. Internatl. Zool.-Cong. Berlin, pp. 990–992.

DOBIE, J. F.
> 1923. Weather Wisdom of the Texas-Mexican Border. Publ. Tex. Folk-Lore Soc., vol. 2, pp. 87–99.
> 1925. Forward Remarks by the Editor. Publ. Tex. Folk-Lore Soc., no. 4, pp. 7–9.
> 1926. Rattlesnakes. Holland's Mag. (Dallas, Tex.), vol. 45, no. 8, pp. 52, 56.

DOBIE, J. F. (*Continued*)

1937. The Roadrunner in Fact and Folk-Lore. Publ. Tex. Folk-Lore Soc., no. 15, pp. 146–174. [Reprinted in part in no. 26, pp. 289–295, 1954.]

1939. The Roadrunner in Fact and Folklore. Nat. Hist., vol. 44, no. 2, pp. 74–82.

1941a. Cache of Gold Guarded by a Rattlesnake. Frontier Times, vol. 18, no. 12, pp. 529–531.

1941b. The Longhorns. Boston, pp. xxiii + 388.

1942a. Do Rattlesnakes Swallow Their Young? Houston Post, Feb. 8, sec. 1, p. 16.

1942b. Snakes Do Swallow Young, Dobie Told. Houston Post, Mar. 1, 1942, sec. 1, p. 10.

1942c. Dobie Insists Rattlesnakes Are Not So Bad. Houston Post, Aug. 30, 1942, sec. 1, p. 7.

1943. Old Bill, Confederate Ally. Austin, Tex., pp. [1–4].

1945. A Trip to Zapata County. Austin (Tex.) Am. Statesman, April 15, 1945.

1946a. Balls of Rattlesnakes. Dallas Morning News, Sept. 16, part 2, p. 12. [Also Frontier Times, vol. 26, no. 11, pp. 240–242, 1948.]

1946b. Cat and Rattlesnake Fight. San Antonio Light, Nov. 3, p. 8c. [Also Dallas Morning News, same date.]

1946c. The Mockingbird and the Rattlesnake. San Antonio Light, Nov. 17, p. 10c.

1946d. The Eagle and the Serpent That Rattles. San Antonio Light, Dec. 1, p. 7c.

1946e. Do Rattlesnakes Swallow Their Young? Publ. Tex. Folk-Lore Soc., vol. 21, pp. 43–64.

1947a. Javelinas and Rattlesnakes. Dallas Morning News, Jan. 26, part 1, p. 6.

1947b. Tall Tales about Rattlesnakes. Life (Melbourne), Oct. 1, pp. 90–93.

1947c. Gobbler-Rattler Fight. Dallas Morning News, Dec. 14.

1949. The Voice of the Coyote. Boston, pp. xx + 386.

1950a. The Ben Lilly Legend. Boston, pp. xvii + 237.

1950b. Rattlesnake Bites Cure for Deflated Ego. Austin Am. Statesman, Dec. 10, 1950, part 3, p. 1.

1952a. A Coyote's Way with the "Wise Serpent." Austin Am. Statesman, Feb. 17, 1952, part B, p. 6.

1952b. The Mustangs. Boston, pp. xvii + 376.

DOBRIZHOFFER, M. [alternate spelling DOBRITZHOFFER]

1822. An Account of the Abipones, an Equestrian People of Paraguay. London, 3 vols. [First published in Latin and in German editions, Vienna, 1783–1784.]

DODDRIDGE, J.

1824. Notes on the Settlement and Indian Wars of the Western Parts of Virginia and Pennsylvania from the Year 1763 until the Year 1783, Inclusive. Wellsburg, Va., pp. 1–414.

DODGE, N. N.

1938. Amphibians and Reptiles of Grand Canyon National Park. Grand Canyon Nat. Hist. Assn., Bull. no. 9, pp. 1–55.

DODSON, RUTH

1932. Folk-Curing among the Mexicans. Publ. Tex. Folk-Lore Soc., vol. 10, pp. 82–98.

DOMENECH, E.

1858. Missionary Adventures in Texas and Mexico. London, pp. xv + 366. [1st edition, Paris, 1857, pp. xii + 477.]

1860. Seven Years' Residence in the Great Deserts of North America. London, 2 vols., pp. xxiv + 445; xii + 465.

DONNAVAN, C.

1847. Adventures in Mexico. Cincinnati, pp. xi, 12–112.

DORMAN, R. M.

1881. The Origin of Primitive Superstitions. Philadelphia, pp. 1–398.

"DORRIS"

1944. Recipes: Vitamins in the Rough. Tex. Game and Fish, vol. 2, no. 11, p. 16.

DORSCH, L. M.

1929. Snakes: Facts and Fancies about Snakes, Treatment for Bites and Method of Handling. Washington Bureau, pp. [1–4].

DORSEY, G. A.

1903. Indians of the Southwest. Chicago, pp. 1–223.

1904. Traditions of the Skidi Pawnee. Mem. Am. Folk-Lore Soc., vol. 8, pp. xxvi + 366.

1906. The Pawnee. Carn. Inst., Publ. 59, pp. 1–546.

DORSEY, G. A., and H. R. VOTH
    1902. The Mishongnovi Ceremonies of the Snake and Antelope Fraternities. Field Columb. Mus., Publ. No. 66, anthro. ser., vol. 3, no. 3, pp. 159–261.
DORSEY, J. O.
    1889. Omaha Folk-Lore Notes. Jour. Am. Folk-Lore, vol. 2, no. 6, p. 190.
    1890. The Cegiha Language. Contrib. N. Am. Ethn., vol. 6, pp. xviii + 794.
    1894. A Study of Siouan Cults. 11th Ann. Rept. Bur. Ethn., pp. 351–544.
DORSON, R. M.
    1947. Folklore at a Milwaukee Wedding. Hoosier Folklore, vol. 6, no. 1, pp. 1–13.
DOUGHTY, C. M.
    1888. Travels in Arabia Deserta. London, 2 vols., pp. xx + 623; xiv + 690.
DOUGHTY, J. F.
    1928. Rattlesnake Bite. Calif. and West. Med., vol. 29, no. 4, pp. 237–241.
DOUGLAS, F. H., and R. D'HARNONCOURT
    1941. Indian Art in the United States. New York, pp. 1–218.
DOUGLAS, J. S.
    1939. Matthew's Adventures on the Columbia. Oreg. Hist. Quart., vol. 40, no. 2, pp. 105–148.
DOUGLASS, E. M.
    1953. Cure for Snake Bites? Ariz. Highways, vol. 29, no. 5, p. 40.
DOUGLASS, J. H.
    1914. Crotalin Treatment of Epilepsy. Jour. Mich. State Med. Soc., vol. 13, no. 6, pp. 359–366.
DOWLING, H. G.
    1951. A Proposed Method of Expressing Scale Reductions in Snakes. Copeia, no. 2, pp. 131–134.
DRAKE, F. G.
    1921. The Fishing Habits of Snakes. Outdoor Life, vol. 48, no. 1, p. 50.
DRAKE, S. G.
    1850. Indian Captivities, or Life in the Wigwam. Auburn, pp. vi, 7–367 + [v].
DRESSLAR, F. B.
    1907. Superstition and Education. Univ. Calif. Publ. Educ., vol. 5, no. 1, pp. 1–239.
DRIVER, H. E.
    1936. Wappo Ethnography. Univ. Calif. Publ. Am. Arch. and Ethn., vol. 36, no. 3, pp. 179–220.
    1937. Cultural Element Distributions: VI. Southern Sierra Nevada. Univ. Calif. Anthro. Rec., vol. 1, no. 2, pp. 53–154.
    1939. Culture Element Distributions: X. Northwest California. Univ. Calif. Anthro. Rec., vol. 1, no. 6, pp. vi, 297–433.
DRIVER, W. F.
    1911. Our Poisonous Serpents and Treatment of Their Bites, with Report of a Fatal Case of Rattlesnake Bite. Virginia Med. Semi-monthly, vol. 15, no. 24, pp. 561–565.
DRUCKER, P.
    1937a. The Tolowa and Their Southwest Oregon Kin. Univ. Calif. Publ. Am. Arch. and Ethn., vol. 36, no. 4, pp. 221–300.
    1937b. Culture Element Distributions: V. Southern California. Univ. Calif. Anthro. Rec., vol. 1, no. 1, pp. 1–52.
    1941. Culture Element Distributions: XVII. Yuman-Piman. Univ. Calif. Anthro. Rec., vol. 6, no. 3, pp. v, 91–230.
DUBOIS, A. E.
    1944. United States Army and State Guard Insignia. Insignia and Decorations of the U. S. Armed Forces, revised edition. Washington, pp. 69–115.
DUBOIS, CONSTANCE G.
    1904. The Story of the Chaup: A Myth of the Diegueños. Jour. Am. Folk-Lore, vol. 17, no. 67, pp. 217–242.
    1906. Mythology of the Mission Indians. Jour. Am. Folk-Lore, vol. 19, no. 72, pp. 52–60.
    1908. The Religion of the Luiseño Indians of Southern California. Univ. Calif. Publ. Am. Arch. and Ethn., vol. 8, no. 3, pp. 69–186.
DUBOIS, CORA
    1935. Wintu Ethnography. Univ. Calif. Publ. Am. Arch. and Ethn., vol. 36, no. 1, pp. iv + 148.

DUDLEY, P.
　　1723. An Account of the Rattlesnake. Philos. Trans. (Royal Soc. London), vol. 32, no. 376, pp. 292–295.

DUFF, J. D. (translator)
　　1928. Lucan: The Civil War. London, pp. xv + 638.

DUGÈS, A.
　　1877. Apuntes para la Monografía de los Crotalos de México. Naturaleza, vol. 4, pp. 1–29, 33–34.

DULOG, H. G.
　　1897. The Angel of the Guard. Forest and Stream, vol. 49, no. 11, p. 202; no. 12, pp. 222–224.

DUMAREST, N.
　　1919. Notes on Cochiti, New Mexico. Edited by Elsie E. Parsons. Mem. Am. Anthro. Assn., vol. 6, pp. 135–236.

DUMÉRIL, A. H. A.
　　1854. Notice Historique sur la Ménagerie des Reptiles du Muséum d'Histoire Naturelle. Arch. Mus., vol. 7, pp. 193–320.

DUMÉRIL, A. M. C., G. BIBRON, and A. H. A. DUMÉRIL
　　1934–54. Erpétologie Générale ou Histoire Naturelle Complète des Reptiles. Paris, 9 vols. [in 10] + Atlas. [Rattlesnakes, vol. 7, part 2, pp. 1453–1485.]

DUMONT, [BUTEL-DUMONT] J. F. B.
　　1753. Memoires Historiques sur la Louisiane. Paris, 2 vols., pp. x + 261; 320.

DUNCAN, D. D.
　　1939. Farming Death for Science. Family Circle, vol. 15, no. 11, pp. 14–15, 18.

DUNCAN, VIRGINIA
　　1945. The Snake without a Friend. Southwest Rev., vol. 30, no. 2, pp. 167–172. [Reprinted in Mid Country: Writings from the Heart of America, edited by L. C. Wimberly. Lincoln, Nebr., pp. xiv + 510 (see pp. 337–342).]

DUNKLE, D. H., and H. M. SMITH
　　1937. Notes on Some Mexican Ophidians. Occ. Papers Mus. Zoöl. Univ. Mich., no. 363, pp. 1–15.

DUNLAP, K.
　　1945. Defective Color Vision and Its Remedy. Jour. Comp. Psych., vol. 38, no. 2, pp. 69–85.

DUNN, E. R.
　　1915. List of Reptiles and Amphibians from Clark County, Va. Copeia, no. 25, pp. 62–63.
　　1949. Relative Abundance of Some Panamanian Snakes. Ecology, vol. 30, no. 1, pp. 39–57.
　　1951. Venomous Reptiles of the Tropics. In Diseases of the Tropics, by G. C. Shattuck, New York, pp. xi + 803; see pp. 741–754.

DUNNING, E. C.
　　1943. A Comparative Study of Snake Venoms. Jour. Am. Inst. Homeop., vol. 36, no. 4, pp. 135–138.

DUNWOODY, H. H. C.
　　1883. Weather Proverbs. Signal Serv. Notes (Washington), no. 9, pp. 1–148.

DURAN-REYNOLDS, F.
　　1939. A Spreading Factor in Certain Snake Venoms and Its Relation to Their Mode of Action. Jour. Exper. Med., vol. 69, no. 1, pp. 69–81. [See also abstract in Jour. Am. Med. Assn., vol. 112, no. 7, p. 673.]

DURY, C.
　　1910. Young Snakes Taking Refuge in the Mother's Mouth in Time of Danger. Jour. Cincinnati Soc. Nat. Hist., vol. 21, no. 2, pp. 68–72.

DUVAL, J. C.
　　1870. The Adventures of Big-Foot Wallace, the Texas Ranger and Hunter. Macon, Ga., pp. xv + 309. [Reprinted in facsimile, Austin, Tex., 1935.]

DWIGHT, T.
　　1823. Travels in New-England and New-York. London, 4 vols.

DYCHE, L. L.
　　1909. The Poison-Glands of a Rattlesnake during the Period of Hibernation. Trans. Kans. Acad. Sci., vol. 22, pp. 312–313.

DYER, T. F. T.

1884. Folk-Lore of Shakespeare. New York, pp. viii + 559.

EARLEY, C. R.

1890. Olive Oil for Snake-Bite. Pac. Rural Press, vol. 39, pp. 383, 503.

EAST, B.

1950. Man Poisons Snake. Outdoor Life, vol. 105, no. 5, pp. 78–79.

EDGREN, R. A.

1948. Notes on a Litter of Young Timber Rattlesnakes. Copeia, no. 2, p. 132.

EDWARD, D. B.

1836. The History of Texas; or, the Emigrant's, Farmer's, and Politician's Guide to the Character, Climate, Soil and Productions of That Country. Cincinnati, pp. xii + 13–336.

EFRATI, P., and L. REIF

1953. Clinical and Pathological Observations of Sixty-five Cases of Viper Bite in Israel. Am. Jour. Trop. Med. and Hyg., vol. 2, no. 6, pp. 1085–1108.

EGAN, H. R.

1917. Pioneering the West, 1846 to 1878: Major Howard Egan's Diary. Richmond, Utah, pp. 1–302.

EHRLICH, S. P.

1928. A Case Report of Severe Snake-Bite Poisoning. Bull. Antivenin Inst. Am., vol. 2, no. 3, pp. 65–66.

EISEN, G.

1895. Explorations in the Cape Region of Baja California in 1894. Proc. Calif. Acad. Sci., ser. 2, vol. 5, pp. 733–775.

ELLIOT, R. H.

1900. An Account of Some Researches into the Nature and Action of Snake Venom. Brit. Med. Jour., vol. 1, pp. 309–310, 1146–1150; vol. 2, pp. 217–221.

1933a. Hooded Death. Blackwood's Mag., vol. 233, no. 1408, pp. 197–203.

1933b. On Immunity from Snake-Bite. Blackwood's Mag., vol. 233, no. 1409, pp. 359–365.

1933c. The Mongoose and the Cobra. Blackwood's Mag., vol. 233, no. 1411, pp. 662–673.

1933d. Snake Bite. Blackwood's Mag., vol. 234, no. 1416, pp. 542–551.

1934a. The Adder. Blackwood's Mag., vol. 235, no. 1422, pp. 502–516.

1934b. Handling Poisonous Snakes. Blackwood's Mag., vol. 236, no. 1430, pp. 793–812.

1934c. The Myth of the Mystic East. Edinburgh and London, pp. xi + 301.

1935. Snakes and Their Meals. Blackwood's Mag., vol. 237, no. 1433, pp. 325–341.

ELLIOTT, T. C.

1910. The Peter Skene Ogden Journals. Oreg. Hist. Soc. Quart., vol. 11, no. 3, pp. 355–396.

ELLSWORTH, F. B.

1918. Mounting Rattlesnake Rattles. Outdoor Life, vol. 41, no. 6, p. 433.

ELLZEY, M. G.

1884. The Venomous Snakes of the United States and the Treatment of Their Bites. Virginia Med. Monthly, vol. 11, no. 5, pp. 249–254.

1892. Does the Rattlesnake Spit? Forest and Stream, vol. 38, no. 23, p. 538. [See also pp. 562, 588, 610.]

1893. Spitting Snakes. Forest and Stream, vol. 41, no. 2, p. 25.

ELMORE, F. H.

1943. Ethnobotany of the Navajo. Univ. N. Mex. Bull., Monog. Ser., vol. 1, no. 7, pp. 1–136.

EMERICK, R. H.

1951. How to Meet a Snake. Am. Forests, vol. 57, no. 7, pp. 12–13, 32.

EMERSON, ELLEN R.

1884. Indian Myths. Boston, pp. xviii + 677.

EMPSON, C.

1836. Narratives of South America. London, pp. xvi + 322.

ENGELHARDT, G. P., J. T. NICHOLS, ROY LATHAM, and R. C. MURPHY

1915. Long Island Snakes. Copeia, no. 17, pp. [1–4].

ERICKSON, N.

1950. Strike Out. Pa. Game News, vol. 21, no. 7, p. 43.

ERICSON, E. E.

1941. Folklore and Folkway in the Tarboro (N. C.) Free Press (1824–1850). So. Folklore Quart., vol. 5, no. 2, pp. 107–125.

ERWIN, E. E.

1946. Snake-Hounds and Snake-Men. Hunting and Fishing, vol. 23, no. 4, p. 28.

ERWIN, R. P.

1925. Snakes in Idaho. Copeia, no. 138, pp. 6–7.

ESAR, E.

1946. The Animal Joker. New York, pp. vii + 289.

ESPINOSA, A. M.

1910. New-Mexican Spanish Folk-Lore. Jour. Am. Folk-Lore, vol. 23, no. 90, pp. 395–418; vol. 24, no. 94, pp. 397–444.

ESPINOSA, A. V. DE (see under VÁSQUEZ DE ESPINOSA, A.)

ESSENE, F.

1942. Culture Element Distributions: XXI. Round Valley. Univ. Calif. Anthro. Rec., vol. 8, no. 1, pp. vii + 97.

ESSEX, H. E.

1932. Studies on the Physiologic Action of Rattlesnake Venom (Crotalin): XI. The Effect of Crotalin on Swine. Am. Jour. Physiol., vol. 100, no. 2, pp. 339–341.

1945. Certain Animal Venoms and Their Physiologic Action. Physiol. Rev., vol. 25, no. 1, pp. 148–170.

ESSEX, H. E., and J. MARKOWITZ

1930. The Physiologic Action of Rattlesnake Venom (Crotalin): I. Effect on Blood Pressure. . . . Am. Jour. Physiol., vol. 92, no. 2, pp. 317–348; no. 3, pp. 695–706.

ESSEX, H. E., and J. T. PRIESTLEY

1931. Effect of Rattlesnake Venom on Flexner-Jobling's Carcinoma in the White Rat. Proc. Soc. Exp. Biol. Med., vol. 28, pp. 550–551.

ESSEX, R.

1928. Studies in Reptilian Degeneration. Proc. Zoöl. Soc. London for 1927, no. 45, pp. 879–943.

ETTWEIN, J.

1848. Remarks upon the Traditions, &., of the Indians of North America. Bull. Hist. Soc. Pa., vol. 1, no. 3, pp. 29–44. [Written in 1788.]

1901. Notes of Travel from the North Branch of the Susquehanna to the Beaver River, Pennsylvania, 1772. Pa. Mag. Hist. and Biog., vol. 25, no. 2, pp. 208–219.

EVANS, F. C., and R. HOLDENRIED

1943. A Population Study of the Beechey Ground Squirrel in Central California. Jour. Mammal., vol. 24, no. 2, pp. 231–260.

EVANS, O.

1947. What's in a Name. West. Folklore, vol. 6, no. 2, pp. 174–176.

EVANS, P. D., and H. K. GLOYD

1948. The Subspecies of the Massasauga, *Sistrurus catenatus,* in Missouri. Bull. Chi. Acad. Sci., vol. 8, no. 9, pp. 225–232.

EVELYN, J.

1901. The Diary of John Evelyn. Edited by William Bray. London, 2 vols., pp. xxvii + 380; [iii] + 366.

EVEREST, F. A.

1953. The Prior Claim. Chicago, pp. 1–192.

EVERMANN, B. W.

1915. Do Snakes Swallow Small Mammals Heads or Tails First? Copeia, no. 14, pp. [1–2].

EVERMANN, B. W., and H. W. CLARK

1914. The Snakes of the Lake Maxinkuckee Region. Proc. Indiana Acad. Sci., vol. 24, pp. 337–348.

EVERS, A.

1951. Rattlesnake Lore of the Catskills. N. Y. Folklore Quart., vol. 7, no. 2, pp. 108–115.

EWAN, J.

1932. Pacific Rattlesnake at High Altitude on San Jacinto Peak, California. Copeia, no. 1, p. 36.

EWING, C. B.

1894. The Action of Rattlesnake Venom upon the Bactericidal Power of the Blood Serum. Med. Rec., vol. 45, no. 2, pp. 663–665. [See also Lancet, vol. 1, no. 3690, pp. 1236–1238.]

EWING, H. E.

1924. A New Mite from the Lung Sac of a Rattlesnake. Proc. Ent. Soc. Wash., vol. 26, no. 6, p. 179.

FAIRLEY, N. H.

1929a. The Present Position of Snake Bite and the Snake Bitten in Australia. Med. Jour. Australia, vol. 1, no. 10, pp. 296–313. [Pp. 2–19 of separately published symposium.]

1929b. The Dentition and Biting Mechanism of Australian Snakes. Med. Jour. Australia, vol. 1, no. 10, pp. 313–327. [Pp. 19–33 of separately published symposium.]

1929c. Criteria for Determining the Efficacy of Ligature in Snake Bite. (The Subcutaneous-Intravenous Index.) Med. Jour. Australia, vol. 1, no. 12, pp. 377–394. [Pp. 69–86 of separately published symposium.]

FAIRLEY, N. H., and BERYL SPLATT

1929. Venom Yields in Australian Poisonous Snakes. Med. Jour. Australia, vol. 1, no. 11, pp. 336–348. [Also pp. 34–46 of separately published symposium.]

FALCK, E. G. J.

1940. Food of an Eastern Rock Rattlesnake in Captivity. Copeia, no. 2, p. 135.

FALK, R. M.

1939. [Inquiry about Uses of Rattlesnake Venom.] Jour. Am. Med. Assn., vol. 113, no. 11, p. 1055.

FARINI, G. A.

1886. Through the Kalahari Desert. New York, pp. xx + 475.

FARLEY, T.

1951. First Aid for Sporting Dogs. Wyo. Wild Life, vol. 15, no. 6, pp. 28–31. [Also Iowa Cons., vol. 10, no. 9, p. 165.]

FARR, T. J.

1935. Riddles and Superstitions of Middle Tennessee. Jour. Am. Folk-Lore, vol. 48, no. 189, pp. 318–336.

FAUST, E. C.

1947. Poisonous Reptiles. Oxford Medicine, Oxford, England, vol. 4, part 3, chap. 19F, pp. (664) 67–95.

FAUST, E. S.

1907. Ueber das Ophiotoxin aus dem Gifte der ostindischen Brillenschlange, Cobra di Capello (*Naja tripudians*). Arch. Exp. Path., vol. 56, pp. 236–259.

1911. Ueber das Crotalotoxin aus dem Gifte der nordamerikaneschen Klapperschlange (*Crotalus adamanteus*). Archiv. f. Exper. Path. u. Pharmak., vol. 64, nos. 3 and 4, pp. 244–273.

FAUTIN, R. W.

1946. Biotic Communities of the Northern Desert Shrub Biome in Western Utah. Ecol. Monog., vol. 16, no. 4, pp. 251–310.

FAUX, W.

1823. Memorable Days in America, Being a Journal of a Tour to the United States. London, pp. xv + 488.

FAWCETT, P. H.

1953. Lost Trails, Lost Cities. New York, pp. xvi + 332.

FAYRER, J.

1869. Experiments on the Influence of Certain Reputed Antidotes for Snake-Poisoning. Indian Med. Gaz., vol. 4, pp. 25–26, 129–132, 153–156, 177–179, 201–204. [The titles of the successive papers differ, but all are appropriate to that of the first paper as above cited.]

1872. The Thanatophidia of India. [1st edition.] London, pp. x + 156.

1874. The Thanatophidia of India. 2nd edition, London, pp. xi + 178.

1882. Destruction of Life in India by Poisonous Snakes. Nature, vol. 27, no. 687, pp. 205–208.

1892a. Snake Bites. Brit. Med. Jour., vol. 1, p. 620

1892b. On Serpent-Worship and on the Venomous Snakes of India and the Mortality Caused by Them. Jour. Trans. Victoria Inst., vol. 26, no. 102, pp. 85–122.

FENLEY, FLORENCE

1940. Snattlerakes! Lookout! Uvalde (Tex.) Leader-News, May 10, 1940, p. 4.

FENTON, W. N.

1942. Contacts between Iroquois Herbalism and Colonial Medicine. Ann. Rept. Smithson. Inst. for 1941, pp. 503–526.

1953. The Iroquois Eagle Dance: An Offshoot of the Calumet Dance. Bur. Am. Ethn., Bull. 156, pp. vi + 324.

FEOKTISTOW, A. E.

1889. Zur Physiologie der Klapper des *Crotalus durissus*. Bull. Acad. Sci. St. Pétersbourg (n.s.), vol. 1, no. 1, pp. 1–4. [Reprinted 1891, Mél. Biol. Acad. Imp. Sci. St. Pétersbourg, vol. 13, no. 1, pp. 1–4.]

1893. On the Physiology of the Rattle of *Crotalus durissus*. Ann. and Mag. Nat. Hist., ser. 6, vol. 11, pp. 54–58. [Translation of above.]

FERMIN, P.

1769. Description Générale, Historique, Géographique et Physique de la Colonie de Surinam. Amsterdam, 2 vols., pp. xxiv + 252; 352.

FERRALL [= O'FERRALL], S. A.

1832. A Ramble of Six Thousand Miles through the United States of America. London, pp. xii + 360.

FERREL, C. M., H. R. LEACH, and D. F. TILLOTSON

1953. Food Habits of the Coyote in California. Calif. Fish and Game, vol. 39, no. 3, pp. 301–341.

FERRI, R. G., and R. GUIDOLIN

1951. Fluorescence and Photoinactivation of Snake Poisons. Science, vol. 113, no. 2933, pp. 300–302.

FERRIS, W. A.

1940. Life in the Rocky Mountains, 1830–1835. Salt Lake City, pp. 1–284. [First published in Western Literary Messenger, Buffalo, N. Y., July 13, 1842, to May 4, 1844.]

FEWKES, J. W.

1890. Contribution to Passamaquoddy Folk-Lore. Jour. Am. Folk-Lore, vol. 3, no. 9, pp. 257–280.

1891. A Suggestion as to the Meaning of the Moki Snake Dance. Jour. Am. Folk-Lore, vol. 4, no. 13, pp. 129–138.

1893. A Central American Ceremony Which Suggests the Snake Dance of the Tusayan Villages. Am. Anthro., vol. 6, no. 3, pp. 285–306.

1895a. A Comparison of Sia and Tusayan Snake Ceremonials. Am. Anthro., vol. 8, no. 2, pp. 118–141.

1895b. The Oraibi Flute Altar. Jour. Am. Folk-Lore, vol. 8, no. 31, pp. 265–282.

1896a. A Contribution to Ethnobotany. Am. Anthro., vol. 9, no. 1, pp. 14–21.

1896b. The Tusayan Ritual: A Study of the Influence of Environment on Aboriginal Cults. Ann. Rept. Smithson. Inst. to July, 1895, pp. 683–700.

1897. Tusayan Snake Ceremonies. 16th Ann. Rept. Bur. Am. Ethn., pp. 267–311.

1898. Archaeological Expedition to Arizona in 1895. 17th Ann. Rept. Bur. Am. Ethn., pp. 519–744.

1900. Tusayan Flute and Snake Ceremonies. 19th Ann. Rept. Bur. Am. Ethn., part 2, pp. 957–1011.

1903. Hopi Katcinas, Drawn by Native Artists. 21st Ann. Rept. Bur. Am. Ethn., pp. 3–126.

FEWKES, J. W., A. M. STEPHEN, and J. G. OWENS

1894. The Snake Ceremonials at Walpi. Jour. Am. Ethn. and Arch., vol. 4, pp. vi + 126.

FIDLER, H. K., R. D. GLASGOW, and E. B. CARMICHAEL

1938. Pathologic Changes Produced by Subcutaneous Injection of Rattlesnake (*Crotalus*) Venom into *Macaca mulatta* Monkeys. Proc. Soc. Exper. Biol. and Med., vol. 38, pp. 892–894. [Reported more fully in Am. Jour. Path., vol. 16, no. 3, pp. 355–364, 1940.]

FIGUIER, L.

1869. Reptiles and Birds. Translated by Parker Gillmore. London, pp. xv + 648. [1st edition, Paris, 1868, pp. 1–730.]

FILLMORE, R. S.
  1941. The Early Local Treatment of Snake Bite. Tex. State Jour. Med., vol. 37, no. 4, pp. 311–313.
FINLEY, J. B.
  1857. Life among the Indians. Cincinnati, pp. 1–548.
FINNERAN, L. C.
  1948. Reptiles at Branford, Connecticut. Herpetologica, vol. 4, no. 4, pp. 123–126.
FINNEY, F., and L. L. FINNEY
  1931. Arizona Reptiles, Their Lives and Habits. Ariz. Daily Star (Tucson), pp. 1–19.
FISHER, A. K.
  1893. The Hawks and Owls of the United States in Their Relation to Agriculture. U. S. Dept. Agric., Div. Orn. and Mammal., Bull. no. 3, pp. 1–210.
FISHER, V. (director)
  1939. Idaho Lore. American Guide Series. Caldwell, pp. 1–256.
FITCH, G. A.
  1903. Bird Catching by a Snake. Sci. Am., vol. 88, no. 17, p. 315.
FITCH, H. S.
  1936. Amphibians and Reptiles of the Rogue River Basin, Oregon. Am. Midl. Nat., vol. 17, no. 3, pp. 634–652.
  1940. A Field Study of the Growth and Behavior of the Fence Lizard. Univ. Calif. Publ. Zoöl., vol. 44, no. 2, pp. 151–172.
  1947. Predation by Owls in the Sierran Foothills of California. Condor, vol. 49, no. 4, pp. 137–151.
  1948a. Ecology of the California Ground Squirrel on Grazing Lands. Am. Midl. Nat., vol. 39, no. 3, pp. 513–596.
  1948b. Habits and Economic Relationships of the Tulare Kangaroo Rat. Jour. Mammal., vol. 29, no. 1, pp. 5–35.
  1949a. Study of Snake Populations in Central California. Am. Midl. Nat., vol. 41, no. 3, pp. 513–579.
  1949b. Road Counts of Snakes in Western Louisiana. Herpetologica, vol. 5, part 4, pp. 87–90.
  1951. A Simplified Type of Funnel Trap for Reptiles. Herpetologica, vol. 7, part 2, pp. 77–80.
FITCH, H. S., and B. GLADING
  1947. A Field Study of a Rattlesnake Population. Calif. Fish and Game, vol. 33, no. 2, pp. 103–123.
FITCH, H. S., F. SWENSON, and D. F. TILLOTSON
  1946. Behavior and Food Habits of the Red-Tailed Hawk. Condor, vol. 48, no. 5, pp. 205–237.
FITCH, H. S., and H. TWINING
  1946. Feeding Habits of the Pacific Rattlesnake. Copeia, no. 2, pp. 64–71.
FITZGERALD, W. G.
  1907. Birds That Kill Snakes. Sci. Am. Supp., vol. 64, no. 1665, pp. 351–352.
FITZSIMONS, D. C.
  1934. Recent Advances in the Therapeutic Uses and Possibilities of Snake Venoms for the Treatment of Epilepsy, etc. Port Elizabeth, South Africa, pp. 1–8.
FITZSIMONS, F. W.
  1909. On the Toxic Action of the Bite of the Boomslang or South African Tree-Snake (*Dispholidus typus*). Ann. Mag. Nat. Hist., ser. 8, vol. 3, pp. 271–278.
  1912. The Snakes of South Africa. Capetown and Pretoria, pp. xvi + 547. [Another edition, Capetown, 1919, pp. xvi + 550.]
  1929. Snake Venoms: Their Therapeutic Uses and Possibilities. Port Elizabeth, South Africa, pp. 1–18.
  1932. Snakes. London, pp. xiv, 15–286.
FITZSIMONS, F. W., and V. F. M. FITZSIMONS
  1932. Snakes and the Treatment of Snake Bite. Capetown and Wynberg, pp. 1–70.
FLACK, [CAPTAIN]
  1866. A Hunter's Experiences in the Southern States of America. London, pp. [iii] + 359.

FLANAGAN, J. T.
  1952. Folklore in the Novels of Conrad Richter. Midwest Folklore, vol. 2, no. 1, pp. 5–14.
FLATTERY, M.
  1949. An Effective Way to Control Snakes. Pests and Their Control, vol. 17, no. 2, pp. 16–18.
FLEAGLE, M. M.
  1931. *Crotalus horridus* (The Poison of the Rattlesnake). Hahnemannian Monthly, vol. 66, pp. 808–811.
FLEAY, D.
  1937. Black Snakes in Combat. Proc. Royal Zoöl. Soc. New So. Wales, Aug., pp. 40–42
FLEMING, J.
  1822. The Philosophy of Zoölogy. London, 2 vols., pp. lii + 432; 1–618.
FLETCHER, ALICE C, and F. LA FLESCHE
  1911. The Omaha Tribe. 27th Ann. Rept. Bur. Am. Ethn., pp. 17–654.
FLETCHER, R.
  1883. A Study of Some Recent Experiments on Snake Venom. Am. Jour. Med. Sci., vol. 86 (n.s.), no. 171, art. 12, pp. 131–146.
FLEXNER, S., and H. NOGUCHI
  1904. Upon the Production and Properties of Anticrotalus Venin. Jour. Med. Res., vol. 11 (vol. 6, n.s.), no. 2, pp. 364–376.
FLINT, T.
  1832. The History and Geography of the Mississippi Valley. 2nd edition, Cincinnati, 2 vols., pp. 464, 276. [1st edition, Cincinnati, 1828, 2 vols.]
FLOWER, S. S.
  1925. Contributions to Our Knowledge of the Duration of Life in Vertebrate Animals. Proc. Zoöl. Soc. London, pp. 911–981.
  1937. Further Notes on the Duration of Life in Animals. III. Reptiles, Proc. Zoöl. Soc. London, ser. a, pp. 1–39.
FOBES, C. B.
  1951. Rattlesnake Mountains in Maine and New Hampshire. Appalachia, vol. 17, n.s., no. 12, pp. 530–534.
FOGEL, E. M.
  1915. Beliefs and Superstitions of the Pennsylvania Germans. Philadelphia, pp. v + 387.
FOKKER, A. D.
  1927. De Voortbeweging der Slangen. Physica, vol. 7, no. 3, pp. 65–71; no. 4, pp. 119–121.
FOLLETT, W. I.
  1927. A California Badger. Calif. Fish and Game, vol. 13, no. 3, p. 220.
FONSECA, F. DA
  1949. Animais Peçonhentos. São Paulo, pp. vii + 376.
FONTANA, F.
  1787. Treatise on the Venom of the Viper. London, 2 vols., pp. xix + 409 + xiv; ii + 395 + xiii + xxii. [First published in Italian in 1765, and in French in 1777. The first complete French edition, from which this English edition was translated by J. Skinner, was published in Paris in 1781, 2 vols., pp. xxviii + 328; xi + 373. Another French and a German edition appeared in 1787, and a second English edition in 1795.]
FOOT, M.
  1807. An Examination of Dr. Hugh Williamson's Memoir on Fascination; to Which Is Subjoined a New Theory of That Phenomenon. Med. Reposit., 2nd hexade, vol. 5, no. 2, pp. 113–122.
FORAN, W. R.
  1944. Snake vs. Horse. Country Life (London), vol. 96, no. 2492, p. 693.
FORBES, J. G.
  1821. Sketches, Historical and Topographical, of the Floridas. New York, pp. vii + 9–226.
FORD V. STANDARD LIFE INSURANCE CO.
  1947. Tennessee Court of Appeals, Eastern Division. [Reported in 12 CCH 789.]
FORDE, C. D.
  1931. Ethnography of the Yuma Indians. Univ. Calif. Publ. Am. Arch. and Ethno., vol. 28, no. 4, pp. 83–278.

FOREE, K.
> 1949. Dallas Trio Witnesses Rare Spectacle: Rattlesnake Courtship or Death Battle. Dallas Morning News, Jan. 16, sec. 2, p. 5.

FORREST, E. R.
> 1929. Missions and Pueblos of the Old Southwest. Cleveland, pp. 1–386.

FORSTER, E. S. (translator)
> 1937. Aristotle: Movement and Progression of Animals. Cambridge (Mass.) and London, pp. 435–541, 552–556.

FORSYTH, T.
> 1912. Account of the Manners and Customs of the Sauk and Fox Nations of Indian Traditions. *In:* The Indian Tribes of the Upper Mississippi Valley and Region of the Great Lakes, by Emma H. Blair. Cleveland, vol. 2, pp. 137–245. [Written in 1827.]

FORTUNE, R. F.
> 1932. Omaha Secret Societies. Columbia Univ. Contrib. Anthro., vol. 14, pp. vi + 193.

FOSTER, G. M.
> 1944. A Summary of Yuki Culture. Univ. Calif. Anthro. Rec., vol. 5, no. 3, pp. vi, 155–244.

FOUNTAIN, P.
> 1901. The Great Deserts and Forests of North America. London, pp. ix + 295.
> 1906. The Eleven Eaglets of the West. New York, pp. xi + 362.

FOWLER, H. W.
> 1906. Some Cold-Blooded Vertebrates of the Florida Keys. Proc. Acad. Nat. Sci. Phila., vol. 58, pp. 77–113.

FOX, H.
> 1913. The Venom of Heloderma. B. Structural Changes Produced in the Poison Gland by Injection of Pilocarpine. Carn. Inst., Publ. 177, pp. 29–33.

FOX, W.
> 1948. Effect of Temperature on Development of Scutulation in the Garter Snake, *Thamnophis elegans atratus.* Copeia, no. 4, pp. 252–262.
> 1954. Genetic and Environmental Variation in the Timing of the Reproductive Cycles of Male Garter Snakes. Jour. Morph., vol. 95, no. 3, pp. 415–450.

FOX, W. S.
> 1948. The Serpent in the Garden. Queen's Quart., vol. 55, no. 1, pp. 58–66.

FRACHTENBERG, L. J.
> 1915. Shasta and Athapascan Myths from Oregon, Collected by Livingston Farrand. Jour. Am. Folk-Lore, vol. 28, no. 109, pp. 207–242.

FRANCISCAN FATHERS
> 1910. An Ethnologic Dictionary of the Navaho Language. Saint Michaels, Ariz., pp. 1–536.

FRANKLIN, M. A.
> 1947. An Inexpensive Snare for Water Snakes. Copeia, no. 2, p. 143.

FRASER, A. G. L.
> 1936–7. The Snakes of Deolali. Jour. Bombay Nat. Hist. Soc., vol. 39, no. 1, pp. 58–82; no. 2, pp. 264–290; no. 3, pp. 464–501.

FRASER, T. R.
> 1895a. The Rendering of Animals Immune against the Venom of the Cobra and Other Serpents, and on the Antidotal Properties of the Blood Serum of the Immunized Animals. Brit. Med. Jour., vol. 1, pp. 1309–1312.
> 1895b. The Treatment of Snake Poisoning with Antivenin Derived from Animals Protected against Serpent's Venom. Brit. Med. Jour., vol. 2, pp. 416–419.
> 1896a. An Address on Immunisation against Serpents' Venom and the Treatment of Snake-Bite with Antivenene [abstract]. Brit. Med. Jour., vol. 1, pp. 957–960.
> 1896b. Immunisation against Serpents' Venom, and the Treatment of Snake-Bite with Antivenene. Nature, vol. 53, no. 1381, pp. 569–572; no. 1382, pp. 592–597.

FRAYNE, R.
> 1945. More Snake Advice. Hunting and Fishing, vol. 22, no. 6, p. 32.

FRAZER, SIR J. G.
> 1910. Totemism and Exogamy. London, 4 vols. [Reprinted from 1st edition, Edinburgh, 1887.]
> 1935. The Golden Bough: A Study in Magic and Religion. London, 3rd edition, 12 vols.

FREELAND, L. S.

 1923. Pomo Doctors and Poisoners. Univ. Calif. Publ. Am. Arch. and Ethn., vol. 20, pp. 57–73.

FREEMAN, MAVIS, and C. H. KELLAWAY

 1934. The Venom Yields of Common Australian Poisonous Snakes in Captivity. Med. Jour. Australia, vol. 2, pp. 373–376.

FRENCH, J.

 1651. The Art of Distillation. London, pp [xx] + 199 + [l] + [xv].

FUNKHOUSER, W. D.

 1925. Wild Life in Kentucky. Frankfort, Ky., pp. [viii] + 385.

FURNIVALL, F. J.

 1870. Andrew Boorde's Introduction and Dyetary. Early English Text Soc., no. 10, pp. 1–396.

GABB, W. A.

 1869. Exploration of Lower California. *In* J. Ross Browne's Resources of the Pacific Slope, San Francisco, 2 vols., pp. 674; 200. (See appendix, pp. 82–122.)

GADOW, H.

 1901. Amphibia and Reptiles. Cambridge Nat. Hist. (London), vol 8, pp. xiii + 668.

 1905. The Distribution of Mexican Amphibians and Reptiles. Proc. Zoöl. Soc. London, vol. 2, no. 15, pp. 191–244.

 1908. Through Southern Mexico. London, pp. xvi + 527.

 1930. Jorullo. The History of the Volcano of Jorullo and the Reclamation of the Devastated District by Animals and Plants. Cambridge, England, pp. xviii + 100.

[GALE, B.]

 1766. Extract of a Letter from Mr. Benjamin Gale, a Physician in New England . . . Con-concerning the Successful Application of Salt to the Wounds Made by the Biting of Rattle Snakes. . . . Philos. Trans. (Royal Soc. London), vol. 55, art. 27, pp. 244–245.

GALEN, C.

 1916. On the Natural Faculties. Translated by Arthur J. Brock. London and New York, pp. lv + 337.

GALINÉE, R. B. DE

 1903. Exploration of the Great Lakes, 1669–1670. Translated and edited by James H. Coyne. Ontario Hist. Soc. Papers and Rec., vol. 4, pp. xxxvii + 89.

GALLEGOS, H.

 1581. [Manuscript by the Clerk of the Rodríguez-Chamuscado Expedition to New Mexico.] Copy of manuscript in Newberry Library, Chicago.

GALLWEY, ELLEN

 1934. An Adder Family (*Vipera berus*). Naturalist, May, pp. 97–105.

GALLY, J. W.

 1880. Ancient and Modern Snakes. Argonaut, vol. 6, no. 12, pp. 1–2, Mar. 20. [Reprinted in Comstock Bonanza, edited by Duncan Emrich, New York, 1950, pp. xv + 363; see pp. 172–182.]

GAMBLE, W. H.

 1934. "Spotty," A Pacific Rattlesnake. Nature Mag., vol. 23, no. 5, pp. 229–230.

GANGULI, S. K., and L. E. NAPIER

 1946. Snakes and Snake-Bite. *In* The Principles and Practice of Tropical Medicine, by L. E. Napier. London, pp. 1–917; see pp. 836–859.

GANN, T. W. F.

 1918. The Maya Indians of Southern Yucatan and Northern British Honduras. Bur. Am. Ethn., Bull. 64, pp. 1–146.

GARB, S., A. SCRIABINE, B. B. ROY, V. VENTURI, and M. PENNA

 1955. A Protective Effect of a Carbon-Free Fraction of India Ink against Snake Venom. Jour. Lab. and Clin. Med., vol. 45, no. 4, pp. 580–582.

GARDEN, A.

 1817. [Memoir on the Fascinating Power of Serpents.] Am. Monthly Mag. and Crit. Rev., vol. 2, pp. 55–56.

GARMAN, S.

  1882. The Scream of the Young Burrowing Owl Sounds like the Warning of the Rattlesnake. Nature, vol. 27, no. 686, p. 174.

  1883. The Reptiles and Batrachians of North America. Mem. Mus. Comp. Zoöl., vol. 8, no. 3, pp. xxxi + 185.

  1887. Reptiles and Batrachians from Texas and Mexico. Bull. Essex Inst., vol. 19, pp. 1–20.

  1888. The Rattle of the Rattlesnake. Bull. Mus. Comp. Zoöl., vol. 13, no. 10, pp. 259–268.

  1889. On the Evolution of the Rattlesnake. Proc. Boston Soc. Nat. Hist., vol. 24, pp. 170–182.

  1892. The Reptilian Rattle. Science, vol. 20, no. 492, pp. 16–17.

  1893. On the Growth of the Rattle of Crotalidae. Science, vol. 21, no. 525, p. 102.

GARTH, T. R.

  1953. Atsugewi Ethnography. Univ. Calif. Anthro. Rec., vol. 14, no. 2, pp. 129–212.

GASS, P.

  1807. A Journal of the Voyages and Travels . . . under the Command of Capt. Lewis and Capt. Clarke. . . . Pittsburgh, viii + 9–262.

GATES, C. M. (editor)

  1933. Five Fur Traders of the Northwest. Minneapolis, pp. 1–298.

GATSCHET, A. S., L. J. FRACHTENBERG, and M. JACOBS

  1945. Kalapuya Texts. Univ. Wash. Publ. Anthro., vol. 11, part 3, pp. 1–394.

GAULDT, W.

  1896. A Rattlesnake's Strange End. Forest and Stream, vol. 47, no. 16, p. 303.

GAYTON, A. H.

  1930. Yokuts-Mono Chiefs and Shamans. Univ. Calif. Publ. Am. Arch. and Ethn., vol. 24, no. 8, pp. 361–420.

  1948. Yokuts and Western Mono Ethnography. I. Tulare Lake, Southern Valley, and Central Foothill Yokuts. II. Northern Foothill Yokuts and Western Mono. Univ. Calif. Anthro. Rec., vol. 10, no. 1, pp. viii + 140; no. 2, pp. viii + 143–302.

GAYTON, A. H., and S. S. NEWMAN

  1940. Yokuts and Western Mono Myths. Univ. Calif. Anthro. Rec., vol. 5, no. 1, pp. vii + 109.

GEARE, R. I.

  1903. Venomous Serpents. Sci. Am., vol. 88, pp. 118, 137, 154, 176.

GEORGE, I. D.

  1930. Notes on the Extraction of Venom at the Serpentarium of the Antivenin Institute at Tela, Honduras. Bull. Antivenin Inst. Am., vol. 4, no. 3, pp. 57–59.

GERRARD, J.

  1870. Snake-Poison and Its Alleged Antidotes. Australian Med. Gaz., vol. 2, pp. 27–28.

GERSHENFELD, L.

  1930. Snakes and Snake Protection. Pop. Sci. Talks Published by Am. Jour. Pharm., vol. 7, pp. 182–257. [First published in Am. Jour. Pharm., vol. 101, pp. 385–417; 484–527, 1929.]

GESNER, C.

  1587. Historiae Animalium, Liber V, Qui est de Serpentium Natura. Tiguri, pp. [xii] + 85 fols. + [i]. [2nd Latin edition, Francofurti, 1621, pp. xiii + 149. A German edition appeared in 1589.]

GESSNER, O.

  1940. Tierische Gifte als Heilmittel. Therapie der Gegenwart, vol. 81, pp. 343–351.

GHARPUREY, K. G.

  1935. The Snakes of India. Bombay, pp. x + 165. [A 4th edition was published in 1954, Bombay, pp. xi + 154.]

GHOSH, B. N.

  1941. Therapeutic Uses of Snake Venoms. Indian and Eastern Chemist, vol. 22, pp. 187–188, 207.

  1950. The Enzymes and Enzyme Inhibitors Contained in Snake Venoms. Immunity Bull., comm. vol., pp. 102–108.

GHOSH, B. N., and S. S. DE

  1939. Proteins of Rattlesnake Venom. Nature, vol. 143, no. 3618, pp. 380–381.

GIANINI, C. A.

  1928. The Hopi Snake Dance. Palacio, vol. 25, no. 26, pp. 439–449.

GIBBS, G.

    1877. Tribes of Western Washington and Northwestern Oregon. Contrib. North Am. Ethn., vol. 1, part 2, pp. 157–361.

GIBBS, M.

    1892. Snakes. Forest and Stream, vol. 39, no. 1, pp. 7–8; no. 2, p. 48; no. 16, p. 333; vol. 40, no. 3, p. 48.

GIBSON, F.

    1904. Superstitions about Animals. London and Newcastle, pp. 1–208.

GIBSON, G. R.

    1935. Journal of a Soldier under Kearny and Doniphan, 1846–1847. Southwest. Hist. Ser., Glendale, Calif., vol. 3, pp. 1–371.

GIBSON, T.

    1940. Sir Rattlesnake. Outdoor Life, vol. 85, no. 5, pp. 24–25, 111–113.

GIBSON, W.

    1825. The Institutes and Practice of Surgery. Philadelphia, 2 vols.

GIFFORD, E. W.

    1917. Miwok Myths. Univ. Calif. Publ. Am. Arch. and Ethn., vol. 12, no. 8, pp. 283–338.

    1923. Western Mono Myths. Jour. Am Folk-Lore, vol 36, no. 142, pp. 301–367.

    1926a. Yuma Dreams and Omens. Jour. Am. Folk-Lore, vol. 39, no. 151, pp. 58–69.

    1926b. Clear Lake Pomo Society. Univ. Calif. Publ. Am. Arch. and Ethn., vol. 18, no. 2, pp. 287–390.

    1926c. Miwok Cults. Univ. Calif. Publ. Am. Arch. and Ethn., vol. 18, no. 3, pp. 391–408.

    1932a. The Southeastern Yavapai. Univ. Calif. Publ. Am. Arch. and Ethn., vol. 29, no. 3, pp. 177–252.

    1932b. The Northfork Mono. Univ. Calif. Publ. Am. Arch. and Ethn., vol. 31, no. 2, pp. 15–65.

    1933a. Northeastern and Western Yavapai Myths. Jour. Am. Folk-Lore, vol. 46, no. 182, pp. 347–415.

    1933b. The Cocopa. Univ. Calif. Publ. Am. Arch. and Ethn., vol. 31, no. 5, pp. 257–334.

    1936. Northeastern and Western Yavapai. Univ. Calif. Publ. Am. Arch. and Ethn., vol. 34, no. 4, pp. 247–354

    1940. Culture Element Distributions: XII. Apache-Pueblo. Univ. Calif. Anthro. Rec., vol. 4, no. 1, pp. vi + 207.

GIFFORD, E. W., and GWENDOLINE H. BLOCK

    1930. Californian Indian Nights Entertainments. Glendale, Calif., pp. 1–323. [Sometimes listed under Gifford and Harris.]

GIFFORD, E. W., and S. KLIMEK

    1936. Culture Element Distributions: II. Yana. Univ. Calif. Publ. Am. Arch. and Ethn., vol. 37, no. 2, pp. 71–100.

GIFFORD, E. W., and A. L. KROEBER

    1937. Culture Element Distributions: IV. Pomo. Univ. Calif. Publ. Am. Arch. and Ethn., vol. 37, no. 4, pp. 117–254.

GIFFORD, E. W., and R. H. LOWIE

    1928. Notes on the Akwa'ala Indians of Lower California. Univ. Calif. Publ. Am. Arch. and Ethn., vol. 23, no. 7, pp. 339–352.

GILBERT, W. H., JR.

    1943. The Eastern Cherokees. Bur. Am. Ethn., Bull. 133, anth. paper no. 23, pp. 169–413.

GILES, H. A.

    1924. The "Hsi Yüan Lu" or, "Instructions to Coroners." Proc. Royal Soc. Med., vol. 17, med. hist. section, pp. 59–107.

GILLAM, A. L.

    1916. A Few Observations on Snakes in the Field. Am. Mus. Jour., vol. 16, no. 2, pp. 129–135.

GILLESPIE, T. H.

    1937. The Way of a Serpent. London, pp. 1–221.

GILLETTE, WINNIFRED

    1949. Rattler Roundup. Daily Oklahoman, Apr. 3, sec. D, p. 3.

GILLMORE, P.
   1872. Prairie Farms and Prairie Folk. London, 2 vols., pp. iv + 321; iv + 282.
GILMAN, J.
   1854. On the Venom of Serpents. St. Louis Med. and Surg. Jour., vol. 12, no. 1, pp. 25–27.
GILMORE, C. W.
   1938. Fossil Snakes of North America. Geol. Soc. Am., Spec. Paper no. 9, pp. 1–96.
GILMORE, M. R.
   1919. Uses of Plants by the Indians of the Missouri River Region. 33rd Ann. Rept. Bur. Am. Ethn., pp. 43–154.
GILMORE, R. M.
   1934. Rattlesnake and Cony. Yosemite Nat. Notes, vol. 13, no. 9, p. 70.
GITHENS, T. S.
   1931. Antivenin: Its Preparation and Standardization. Bull. Antivenin Inst. Am., vol. 4, no. 4, pp. 81–85.
   1935a. Studies on the Venoms of North American Pit Vipers. Jour. Immun., vol. 29, no. 2, pp. 165–173.
   1935b. Snake Bite in the United States. Sci. Monthly, vol. 41, no. 2, pp. 163–167.
   1936. Snake Bite and Its Treatment with Antivenin. Sharp and Dohme Abstract, July, 1936, pp. 1–12.
   1939. Moccasin Venom in the Treatment of Hemorrhagic Conditions. Clinical Med. and Surg., vol. 46, no. 4, pp. 167–169.
   1941. The Polyvalency of Crotalidic Antivenins. IV. Antinecrotic, Anticoagulant and Antiproteolytic Actions. Jour. Immun., vol. 42, no. 2, pp. 149–159.
GITHENS, T. S., and L. W. BUTZ
   1929. Venoms of North American Snakes and Their Relationships. Jour. Immun., vol. 16, no. 1, pp. 71–80. [Also Bull. Antivenin Inst. Am., vol. 2, no. 4, pp. 100–104.]
GITHENS, T. S., and I. D. GEORGE
   1931. Comparative Studies of the Venoms of Certain Rattlesnakes. Bull. Antivenin Inst. Am., vol. 5, no. 2, pp. 31–35.
GITHENS, T. S., and N. O. WOLFF
   1939. The Polyvalency of Crotalidic Antivenins. Jour. Immun., vol. 37, no. 1, pp. 33–51. [3 papers under one general title.]
GLADING, B.
   1938. Studies of the Nesting Cycle of the California Valley Quail in 1937. Calif. Fish and Game, vol. 24, no. 4, pp. 318–340.
GLADISH, D. G.
   1939. Snake Venoms in Streptococcal-Type Infections. Jour. Am. Inst. Homeop., vol. 32, no. 9, pp. 554–555.
GLASER, H. S. R.
   1948. Bactericidal Activity of *Crotalus* Venom *in Vitro*. Copeia, no. 4, pp. 245–247.
GLENN, NAN A.
   1933. Snake Dance at Moenkopi. Southwest Rev., vol. 19, Supplement pp. 11–12.
GLIDDEN, H. S.
   1936. Diseases of Reptiles. Silver Springs, Fla., pp. 1–7.
GLISSMEYER, H. R.
   1951. Symposium: A Snake Den in Tooele County, Utah. Egg Production of the Great Basin Rattlesnake. Herpetologica, vol. 7, part 1, pp. 24–27.
GLOVER, T.
   1676. An Account of Virginia. Philos. Trans. (Royal Soc. London), vol. 11, no. 126, pp. 623–636.
GLOYD, H. K.
   1928. The Amphibians and Reptiles of Franklin County, Kansas. Trans. Kans. Acad. Sci., vol. 31, pp. 115–141.
   1933a. An Unusual Feeding for the Prairie Rattlesnake. Copeia, no. 2, p. 98.
   1933b. On the Effect of Moccasin Venom upon a Rattlesnake. Science, vol. 78, no. 2010, pp. 13–14.

GLOYD, H. K. (*Continued*)

1935. Some Aberrant Color Patterns in Snakes. Papers Mich. Acad. Sci., Arts, Lett., vol. 20, pp. 661–668.

1937. A Herpetological Consideration of Faunal Areas in Southern Arizona. Bull. Chi. Acad. Sci., vol. 5, no. 5, pp. 79–136.

1938. Methods of Preserving and Labeling Amphibians and Reptiles for Scientific Study. Turtox News, vol. 16, no. 3, pp. 49–53, 66–67.

1940. The Rattlesnakes, Genera *Sistrurus* and *Crotalus*. Chi. Acad. Sci., Spec. Publ. no. 4, pp. vii + 266 + [4].

1944a. Texas Snakes. Tex. Geog. Mag., vol. 8, no. 2, pp. 1–18.

1944b. The Problem of Too Many Snakes. Chi. Nat., vol. 7, no. 4, pp. 87–97.

1946. Some Rattlesnake Dens of South Dakota. Chi. Nat., vol. 9, no. 4, pp. 87–97.

1947. Notes on the Courtship and Mating Behavior of Certain Snakes. Nat. Hist. Misc., no. 12, pp. 1–4.

1948. Another Account of the "Dance" of the Western Diamond Rattlesnake. Nat. Hist. Misc., no. 34, pp. 1–3.

1955. A Review of the Massasaugas, *Sistrurus catenatus,* of the Southwestern United States (Serpentes: Crotalidae). Bull. Chi. Acad. Sci., vol. 10, no. 6, pp. 83–98.

GLOYD, H. K., and W. A. BEVAN

1946. A Case of Intraspecific Poisoning in the Great Basin Rattlesnake. Nat. Hist. Misc., no. 3, pp. 1–3.

GODDARD, P. E.

1904. Hupa Texts. Univ. Calif. Publ. Am. Arch. and Ethn., vol. 1, no. 2, pp. 89–378.

1909. Kato Texts. Univ. Calif. Publ. Am. Arch. and Ethn., vol. 5, no. 3, pp. 65–238.

1918. Myths and Tales from the San Carlos Apache. Anthro. Papers, Am. Mus. Nat. Hist., vol. 24, part 1, pp. 1–86.

1919a. Myths and Tales from the White Mountain Apache. Anthro. Papers, Am. Mus. Nat. Hist., vol. 24, part 2, pp. 87–139.

1919b. San Carlos Apache Texts. Anthro. Papers, Am. Mus. Nat. Hist., vol. 24, part 3, pp. 141–367.

1930. White Mountain Apache Texts. Anthro. Papers, Am. Mus. Nat. Hist., vol. 24, part 4, pp. 369–533.

1931. Indians of the Southwest. Am. Mus. Nat. Hist., Handbook Ser., no. 2 (4th edition), pp. 1–205. [1st edition, New York, 1913, pp. 1–191.]

1945. Indians of the Northwest Coast. Am. Mus. Nat. Hist., Handbook Ser., no. 10 (2nd edition), pp. 1–175. [1st edition, New York, 1924, pp. 1–176.]

GOLAN, H. G.

1941. Snake Venom and Allergy. Jour. Allergy, vol. 12, pp. 11–23.

GOLDBERGER, M. A., and S. M. PECK

1937. Additional Data on the Treatment of Uterine Bleeding with Snake Venom. Am. Jour. Obstet. and Gynecol., vol. 33, no. 3, pp. 469–483.

GOLDER, F. A.

1907. Report of Meeting of Arizona Branch of American Folk-Lore Society. Jour. Am. Folk-Lore, vol. 20, no. 76, p. 75.

GOLDFRANK, ESTHER S.

1933. The Social and Ceremonial Organization of Cochiti. Mem. Am. Anthro. Assn., no. 33, pp. 1–129.

GOLDMAN, E. A.

1951. Biological Investigations in Mexico. Smithson. Misc. Coll., vol. 115, pp. xiii + 476.

GOLDSCHMIDT, J.

1901. Behandlung der Lepra mit Klapperschalangengift. Deutsche Med. Wochen., vol. 27, no. 2, p. 31. [Abstract in Jour. Am. Med. Assn., vol. 36, no. 5, p. 353.]

GOLDSCHMIDT, W.

1951. Nomlaki Ethnography. Univ. Calif. Publ. Am. Arch. and Ethn., vol. 42, no. 4, pp. viii + 303–443.

GOLDSMITH, O.
 1774. An History of the Earth and Animated Nature. London, 8 vols. Rattlesnakes, vol. 7, pp.
 208–214. [This work went through many subsequent editions.]
GOLDSMITH, S. A.
 1951. The Snake-Bit Pole. N. Mex. Folklore Rec., vol. 5, p. 30.
GOMARA, F. L. DE
 1578. The Pleasant History of the Conquest of the West India. London, pp. xii + 405. [1st edition, in Spanish, Çaragoça, 1553.]
GONÇALVES, J. M., and A. POLSON
 1947. The Electrophoretic Analysis of Snake Venoms. Arch. Biochem., vol. 13, pp. 253–259.
GONÇALVES, J. M., and LAURA G. VIEIRA
 1950. Estudos sôbre Venenos de Serpentes Brasileiras. 1. Análise Eletroforética. Anales Acad.
 Bras. de Ciencias, vol. 22, no. 1, pp. 141–150.
GOOD, P. P.
 1853. A Materia Medica Animalia. Cambridge, Mass., pp. xxiv + 24 separately paged parts and
 glossary. Part 24, *Crotalus horridus,* the Rattlesnake, pp. 1–16.
GOODE, G. B.
 1873a. Do Snakes Swallow Their Young? Am. Agric., vol. 32, no. 1, pp. 418–419. [See also pp.
 48, 165; also Forest and Stream, vol. 1, pp. 54, 86, 118, 166, 198, 214, 278.]
 1873b. Snakes Shedding Their Skins. Forest and Stream, vol. 1, no. 23, pp. 356–357.
 1874a. On the Question "Do Snakes Swallow Their Young?" Proc. Am. Assn. Adv. Sci., vol. 22,
 part 2, pp. 176–185.
 1874b. Rattlesnakes. A Query. Forest and Stream, vol. 2, no. 8, p. 123.
 1901. The Beginnings of Natural History in America. Ann. Rept. Smithson. Inst. for 1897,
 part 2, pp. 357–406. [Reprinted from Proc. Biol. Soc. Wash., vol. 3, pp. 35–105, 1886.]
GOODMAN, J. D.
 1951. Some Aspects of the Role of Parasitology in Herpetology. Herpetologica, vol. 7, part 2,
 pp. 65–67.
GOODMAN, K.
 1952. [Bullfrog Eats a Young Rattlesnake.] Fla. Wildlife, vol. 6, no. 6, p. 35.
GOODRICH, FRANCES L.
 1900. Old Ways and New in South Carolina. So. Workman, vol. 29, no. 4, pp. 207–211.
GOODRUM, P. D.
 1940. A Population Study of the Gray Squirrel, *Sciurus carolinensis carolinensis* in Eastern
 Texas. Tex. Agric. Exp. Sta., Bull. 591, pp. 1–34.
GOODWIN, G.
 1939. Myths and Tales of the White Mountain Apache. Mem. Am. Folk-Lore Soc., vol. 33, pp.
 xviii + 223.
GORDON, G.
 1936. Fangs and Rattles. Outdoor Life, vol. 77, no. 3, pp. 34–35, 95.
GORDON, G. B.
 1902. The Hieroglyphic Stairway: Ruins of Copán. Mem. Peabody Mus., vol. 1, no. 6, pp. 1–38.
GORDON, M. B.
 1949. Aesculapius Comes to the Colonies. Ventnor, N. J., pp. xiv + 560.
GORSUCH, D. M.
 1934. Life History of the Gambel Quail in Arizona. Univ. Ariz. Bull., vol. 5, no. 4, pp. 1–89.
GOSS, L. J.
 1939. Snake Parasites in a Man. Bull. N. Y. Zoöl. Soc., vol. 42, no. 6, pp. 178–179.
GOSSE, P. H.
 1850. Natural History: Reptiles. London, pp. iv + 293.
GOULD, G. M., and W. L. PYLE
 1897. Anomalies and Curiosities of Medicine. Philadelphia, pp. 1–968.
GOURLEY, R.
 1822. Statistical Account of Upper Canada. London, pp. xxi + 625.
GOWANLOCH, J. N.
 1934. Poisonous Snakes of Louisiana. La. Cons. Rev., vol. 4, no. 3, pp. 1–16.

GOWANLOCH, J. N. (*Continued*)

1940. Snakes! I Hate Them! La. Cons. Rev., vol. 9, no. 2, pp. 39–45; no. 3, pp. 37–42.

1943. Poisonous Snakes, Plants and Black Widow Spider of Louisiana. La. Dept. Cons., New Orleans, Part 1, Poisonous Snakes of Louisiana, pp. 6–62.

GRANDY, C. R.

1903. Report of a Case of Rattlesnake Bite. Virginia Med. Semi-monthly, vol. 7, no. 22, pp. 515–517.

GRANT, C.

1946. Champlain—Herpetologist. Herpetologica, vol. 3, part 3, p. 104.

1948. Reptile Sloughs in Bird Nests. Jour. Ent. and Zoöl., vol. 40, no. 2, p. 25.

GRANT, W. T.

1871. The Rattle Snake's Poison, and Its Remedies. Georgia Med. Companion, vol. 1, no. 9, pp. 457–459. [See also Med. and Surg. Reporter, vol. 25, no. 18, pp. 389–390, 1871; and Atlanta Med. and Surg. Jour., vol. 15, no. 7, pp. 393–396, 1877.]

GRANT WATSON, E. L.

1937. Mysteries of Natural History. New York, pp. x + 244.

GRASSET, E.

1932. Concentration of Polyvalent African Antivenom Serum. Trans. Royal Soc. Trop. Med. and Hyg., vol. 26, no. 3, pp. 267–272.

1933. Concentrated African Antivenom Serum: Its Preparation, Standardization and Use in the Treatment of Snake-Bite. So. African Med. Jour., vol. 7, pp. 35–39.

1936. On the Interrelation of the Antigenic Properties of Snake Venoms and Its Bearing upon the Polyvalence and the Assay of Sera. Quart. Bull. Health Org., League of Nations, vol. 5, no. 2, pp. 367–390.

1945. Anavenoms and Their Use in the Preparation of Antivenomous Sera. Trans. Royal Soc. Trop. Med. and Hyg., vol. 38, no. 6, pp. 463–488.

1946. La Vipère du Gabon. Acta Tropica, vol. 3, pp. 97–115.

GRASSET, E., and P. A. CHRISTENSEN

1947. Enzyme-Purification of Polyvalent Antivenene against Southern and Equatorial African Colubrine and Viperine Venoms. Trans. Royal Soc. Trop. Med. and Hyg., vol. 41, no. 2, pp. 207–211.

GRASSET, E., and A. W. SCHAAFSMA

1940. Studies on the Venom of the "Boomslang" (*Dispholidus typus*). So. African Med. Jour. vol. 14, pp. 236–241.

GRASSET, E., and A. ZOUTENDYK

1933. Detoxication of Snake Venoms, and the Application of the Resulting Antigens to Rapid Methods of Antivenomous Vaccination and Serum Production. Brit. Jour. Exp. Path., vol. 14, pp. 308–317.

1935. A Comparative Investigation into the Antigenic Properties of Detoxicated Indian and African Venoms and the Cross Reaction Exerted by the Respective Antivenins. Trans. Royal Soc. Trop. Med. and Hyg., vol. 28, no. 4, pp. 391–398.

1936. The Antigenic Characteristics and Relationships of Viperine Venoms Based on the Cross Neutralizing Action of Heterologous Antivenomous Sera. Trans. Royal Soc. Trop. Med. and Hyg., vol. 30, no. 3, pp. 347–354.

1938. Studies on the Gaboon Viper (*Bitis gabonica*) and the Preparation of a Specific Therapeutic Antivenene. Trans. Royal Soc. Trop. Med. and Hyg., vol. 31, no. 4, pp. 445–450.

GRASSET, E., A. ZOUTENDYK, and A. SCHAAFSMA

1935. Studies on the Toxic and Antigenic Properties of Southern African Snake Venoms with Special Reference to the Polyvalency of South African Antivenene. Trans. Royal Soc. Trop. Med. and Hyg., vol. 28, no. 6, pp. 601–612.

GRAY, A. (editor)

1843. Selections from the Scientific Correspondence of Cadwallader Colden . . . Am. Jour. Sci. and Arts, vol. 44, no. 1, art. 12, pp. 85–133.

GRAY, J.

1946. The Mechanism of Locomotion in Snakes. Jour. Exp. Biol., vol. 23, no. 2, pp. 101–119. [See also How Animals Move, Cambridge, England, 1953, pp. xii + 114, at pp. 81–88.]

GRAY, J., and H. W. LISSMANN

1950. The Kinetics of Locomotion of the Grass-Snake. Jour. Exp. Biol., vol. 26, no. 4, pp. 354–367.

GREEN, J.

1821. Some Curious Facts respecting the Bones of the Rattle Snake. Am. Jour. Sci. and Arts, vol. 3, no. 1, art. 12, pp. 85–86.

GREENFIELD, R.

1938. *Napaeozapus insignis* in Virginia. Jour. Mammal., vol. 19, no. 2, p. 254.

GREENLEE, R. F.

1944. Medicine and Curing Practices of the Modern Florida Seminoles. Am. Anthro., vol. 46, no. 3, pp. 317–328.

GREGG, J.

1845. Commerce of the Prairies or the Journal of a Santa Fe Trader. 2nd edition., New York, 2 vols., pp. x + 320; 318. [1st edition, New York, 1844. Also *in* Thwaites: Early Western Travels, Cleveland, 1904–1907, 32 vols.; see vols. 19–20.]

GRESHAM, W. A.

1905. Rattlesnake Bite. Jour. Am. Med. Assn., vol. 45, no. 23, pp. 1735–1736.

GREVAL, S. D. S

1934. Concentration of Antivenene by the Ammonium Sulphate Method. Indian Jour. Med. Res., vol. 22, no. 2, pp. 365–371.

GREVIN, J.

1568. Deux Livres des Venins. Anvers, pp. [viii] + 333 + [iv]. [Also a Latin edition, 1571. Antverpiae, pp. [xviii] + 275.]

GREW, N.

1681. Catalogue and Description of the Natural and Artificial Rarities Belonging to the Royal Society and Preserved at Gresham Colledge. London, pp. [viii] + 386 + [ii].

GRIEVE, A. L.

1908. [Snake-Bite Remedy.] Pac. Rural Press, vol. 75, no. 21, p. 327.

GRIFFIN, G.

1949. Snake-Bite Protection. Outdoor Life, vol. 104, no. 4, p. 11.

GRIFFITH, E., and E. PIDGEON

1831. The Class Reptilia Arranged by the Baron Cuvier. Vol. 9 of Cuvier's The Animal Kingdom. London, pp. 1–481.

GRINNELL, G. B.

1893. A Blackfoot Sun and Moon Myth. Jour. Am. Folk-Lore, vol. 6, no. 20, pp. 44–47.

1923. The Cheyenne Indians. New Haven, 2 vols., pp. ix + 358; vii + 430.

GRINNELL, J.

1908. The Biota of the San Bernardino Mountains. Univ. Calif. Publ. Zoöl., vol. 5, no. 1, pp. 1–170.

GRINNELL, J., J. DIXON, and J. M. LINSDALE

1930. Vertebrate Natural History of a Section of Northern California through the Lassen Peak Region. Univ. Calif. Publ. Zoöl., vol. 35, pp. v + 594.

GRINNELL, J., and HILDA W. GRINNELL

1907. Reptiles of Los Angeles County, California. Throop Inst. Bull., no. 35, pp. 1–64.

GRINNELL, J., and T. I. STORER

1924. Animal Life in the Yosemite. Berkeley and Los Angeles, pp. xviii + 752.

GRISWOLD, G.

1884. Reports on the Progress of Medicine. Snake-Poison. N. Y. Med. Jour., vol. 40, pp. 53–54.

GRIZZELL, R. A., JR.

1955. A Study of the Southern Woodchuck, *Marmota monax monax*. Am. Midl. Nat., vol. 53, no. 2, pp. 257–293.

GRONOVIUS (GRONOW), L. T.

1763. Animalia, Quadrupeda, Amphibia atque Pisces quae in Museo suo Adservat . . . Lugduni Batavorum, part 1, pp. 1–36, iv.

GRUNDMANN, I.
    1950. Die Schlangengifte, ihre Pharmakologie, Toxikologie und ihre therapeutische Verwendung. Mediz. Monats., vol. 4, no. 8, pp. 570–575.

GUDDE, E. G.
    1948. Mohave and Mojave. West. Folklore, vol. 7, no. 2, pp. 169–171.

GUDGER, E. W.
    1931. More Spider Hunters. Sci. Monthly, vol. 32, no. 5, pp. 422–433.

GUDMUNDSON, S. C.
    1921. A Rattlesnake-Bullsnake Fight. Outdoor Life, vol. 48, no. 4, p. 292.

GUENTHER, K.
    1931. A Naturalist in Brazil. Boston and New York, pp. 1–400.

GUERRA, FERMINA
    1941. Rancho Buena Vista. Tex. Folk-Lore Soc. Publ. no. 17, pp. 59–77.

GUILD, J. C.
    1878. Old Times in Tennessee. Nashville, pp. 1–503.

GUILLET, E. C.
    1933. Early Life in Upper Canada. Toronto, pp. xliii + 782.

GUNTHER, R. T. (editor)
    1934. The Greek Herbal of Dioscorides. Translated by John Goodyer, 1655. Oxford, pp. xi + 701.

GUTHRIE, J. E.
    1924. Snake Notes. Proc. Iowa Acad. Sci., vol. 31, pp. 417–418.
    1926. The Snakes of Iowa. Agric. Exp. Sta., Iowa State Coll., Bull. 239, pp. 145–192.
    1927. Rattlesnake Eggs in Iowa. Copeia, no. 162, pp. 12–14.
    1929. Snake Notes. Proc. Iowa Acad. Sci., vol. 36, pp. 349–359.

H., B. D.
    1933. Snakes Immune to Each Other's Poison. *In* W. A. Bevan's column Snake Lore, Outdoor Life, vol. 72, no. 5, p. 61.

HAAS, G.
    1952. The Head Muscles of the Genus *Causus* (Ophidia, Solenoglypha) and Some Remarks on the Origin of the Solenoglypha. Proc. Zoöl. Soc. London, vol. 122, part 3, pp. 573–592.

HAAS, MARY R.
    1941. The Choctaw Word for Rattlesnake. Am. Anthro., n.s. vol. 43, no. 1, pp. 129–132.

HABERMANN, E., and W. NEUMANN
    1955. Active Components of Snake Venom. Chem. Abst., vol. 49, no. 3, col. 1966. [Original in Naunyn-Schmiedebergs Arch. exptl. Pathol. Pharmakol., vol. 223, pp. 388–398, 1954.]

HAGAR, S.
    1896. Micmac Magic and Medicine. Jour. Am. Folk-Lore, vol. 9, no. 34, pp. 170–177.
    1897. Weather and the Seasons in Micmac Mythology. Jour. Am. Folk-Lore, vol. 10, no. 37, pp. 101–105.

HAINES, T. P.
    1940. Delayed Fertilization in *Leptodeira annulata polysticta*. Copeia, no. 2, pp. 116–118.

HAKLUYT, R.
    1598–1600. The Principal Navigations, Voiages, Traffiques and Discoueries of the English Nation. 2nd edition, London, 3 vols. [Reprinted Glasgow, 1903–1905, 20 vols. 1st edition, London, 1589.]

HALDEMAN, S. S.
    1872. Vibrations of the Tail in Snakes. Am. Nat., vol. 6, p. 304.

HALE, W.
    1896. Flags of the Revolution. Harper's Round Table, vol. 17, no. 886, pp. 1243–1244.

HALIBURTON, J. H.
    1935. Live Snakes from the Everglades. Outdoor Life, vol. 76, no. 5, pp. 36–37, 66–67.

HALL [CAPTAIN]
    1727. An Account of Some Experiments on the Effects of the Poison of the Rattle Snake. Philos. Trans. (Royal Soc. London), vol. 35, no. 399, pp. 309–315.

HALL, E. R.
1929. A "Den" of Rattlesnakes in Eastern Nevada. Bull. Antivenin Inst. Am., vol. 3, no. 3, pp. 79–80.
1946. Mammals of Nevada. Berkeley and Los Angeles, pp. xi + 710.
1951. American Weasels. Univ. Kans. Publ. Mus. Nat. Hist., vol. 4, pp. 1–466.

HALL, J.
1848. The West: Its Soil, Surface, and Productions. Cincinnati, pp. 1–260.

HALL, SHARLOT M.
1938. When the Smoki Were Young. Prescott Evening Courier, vol. 56, no. 135, June 8, pp. 1, 3

HALL, THELMA, B.
1953. Dancing the Snakes. Ariz. Highways, vol. 29, no. 7, pp. 4–11.

HALLENBECK, C.
1945. Hunting the Rattler. Hunting and Fishing, vol. 22, no. 2, pp. 8–9. [See also vol. 22, no. 5, p. 7; no. 6, p. 32; no. 7, p. 21; vol. 23, no. 1, p. 22.]

HALLIDAY, W. R.
1924. Folklore Studies. London, pp. xix + 172.

HALLOCK, C.
1905. Pacific Coast Natural History Notes. Forest and Stream, vol. 64, no. 15, p. 292. [See also vol. 73, no. 11, p. 412, 1919.]

HALLOWELL, A. I.
1926. Bear Ceremonialism in the Northern Hemisphere. Am. Anthro., vol. 28, no. 1, pp. 1–175.

HALPERT, H.
1942. Indiana Storyteller. Hoosier Folklore Bull., vol. 1, no. 2, pp. 43–61.
1944. Tales of a Mississippi Soldier. So. Folklore Quart., vol. 8, no. 2, pp. 103–114.

HALPERT, H., C. B. MITCHELL, and D. H. DICKASON
1942. Folktales from Indiana University Students. Hoosier Folklore Bull., vol. 1, no. 3, pp. 85–97.

HALSELL, H. H.
[1937]. Cowboys and Cattleland. Nashville, Tenn., pp. 1–276.

HALTER, C. R.
1915. Garter Snake Swallowed by a Pigmy Rattler. Copeia, no. 25, pp. 60–61.

HALTOM, W. L.
1931. Alabama Reptiles. Ala. Mus. Nat. Hist., Mus. Paper no. 1, pp. vi + 145.

HAM, L. S.
1861. Case of Rattlesnake Bite. Buffalo Med. and Surg. Jour., vol. 1, no. 3, pp. 82–85. [See also Med. and Surg. Reporter, vol. 7 (n.s.), nos. 18 and 19, p. 442, 1862.]

HAMBURGER, V.
1947. Monsters in Nature. Ciba Symposia, vol. 9, nos. 5, 6, pp. 666–683.

HAMILTON, A.
1907. Itinerarium, Being a Narrative of a Journey ... from May to September, 1744. St. Louis, pp. xxvii + 263.

HAMILTON, F. H.
1865. A Treatise on Military Surgery and Hygiene. New York, pp. viii, 9–648.

HAMILTON, W. H.
1938. Dakota: An Autobiography of a Cowman. S. Dak. Hist. Coll., vol. 39, pp. 475–638.

HAMILTON, WALLIS H.
1949. Snake Hunters' Big Day. Outdoor Life, vol. 104, no. 4, p. 6.

HAMILTON, W. J., JR.
1946. The Bounty System Doesn't Work. Animal Kingdom, vol. 49, no. 4, pp. 130–138.
1950. Food of the Prairie Rattlesnake. Herpetologica, vol. 6, part 2, p. 34.

HAMILTON, W. J., JR., and J. A. POLLACK
1955. The Food of Some Crotalid Snakes from Fort Benning, Georgia. Nat. Hist. Misc., no. 140, pp. 1–4.

HAMMOND, G. P., and A. REY
1927. The Rodríguez Expedition to New Mexico, 1581–1582. N. Mex. Hist. Rev., vol. 2, no. 3, pp. 239–268; no. 4, pp. 334–362. Also Hist. Soc. N. Mex. Publ. Hist., vol. 4, pp. 1–69, 1927.

HAMMOND, W. A.

1858. Experiments with Bibron's Antidote to the Poison of the Rattlesnake. Am. Jour. Med. Sci., vol. 35 (n.s.), no. 69, art. 4, pp. 94–96.

HANLEY, W.

1854. On Snake Bites. North-West. Med and Surg. Jour., vol. 11 (vol. 3, n.s.), no. 11, pp. 497–499.

HANNUM, ALBERTA

1945. Spin a Silver Dollar. New York, pp. 1–173.

HANSEN, R. M.

1954. Tolerances of Some Western Snakes to Cold. Herpetologica, vol. 10, part 3, p. 200.

HAPP, W. M.

1951. My Snake Bite Experience. Bull. San Diego Co. Med. Soc., vol. 37, no. 3, pp. 20, 22, 26.

HARBY, MRS. LEE C.

1895. The Tejas: Their Habits, Government, and Superstitions. Ann. Rept. Am. Hist. Assn. for 1894, pp. 63–82.

HARDY, R.

1945. Dermestid Beetles for Cleaning Skulls and Skeletons in Small Quantities. Turtox News, vol. 23, no. 4, pp. 69–70.

1946. Predators, Rodents and Soil. Wyo. Wild Life, vol. 10, no. 4, pp. 29–30.

1947. Animals Are a Resource Too. Utah Educ. Rev., vol. 40, no. 5, pp. 165–167.

HARDY, R. W. H.

1829. Travels in the Interior of Mexico in 1825, 1826, 1827, & 1828. London, pp. xiv + 540.

HARLAN, R.

1835. Medical and Physical Researches. Philadelphia, pp. xxxix + 653.

HARLEY, G. W.

1941. Native African Medicine. Cambridge, Mass., pp. xvi + 294.

HARMON, R. W., and C. B. POLLARD

1948. Bibliography of Animal Venoms. Gainesville, Fla., pp. xxx + 340.

HARMS, A. J.

1948. The Purification of Antitoxic Plasmas by Enzyme Treatment and Heat Denaturation. Biochem. Jour., vol. 42, no. 3, pp. 390–397.

HARRINGTON, J. P.

1908. A Yuma Account of Origins. Jour. Am. Folk-Lore, vol. 21, no. 82, pp. 324–348.

1932. Tobacco among the Karuk Indians of California. Bur. Am. Ethn., Bull. 94, pp. xxxvi + 284.

1942. Cultural Element Distributions: XIX. Central California Coast. Univ. Calif. Anthro. Rec., vol. 7, no. 1, pp. iii + 46.

HARRINGTON, J. P., and HELEN H. ROBERTS

1928. Picurís Children's Stories. 43rd Ann. Rept. Bur. Am. Ethn., pp. 289–447.

HARRINGTON, J. W.

1905. A Useful Dog on the Farm. Forest and Stream, vol. 64, no. 1, p. 9.

HARRINGTON, M. R.

1933. Gypsum Cave, Nevada. Southwest Mus. Papers, no. 8, pp. ix + 197.

HARRIS, H.

1932. California's Medical Story. San Francisco, pp. xviii + 421.

HARRIS, J. C.

1855. A Brief History of the Introduction of the *Asclepias verticellata,* for the Cure of Venomous Snake and Spider Bites. So. Med. and Surg. Jour., vol. 11, no. 7, art. 20, pp. 414–417.

HARRIS, W. T.

1821. Remarks Made during a Tour through the United States of America in the Years 1817, 1818, and 1819. London, pp. 1–196.

HARTIKKA, H. D.

1946. Tales Collected from Indiana University Students. Hoosier Folklore, vol. 5, no. 2, pp. 71–82.

HARTMAN, C. V.

1907. Two Engraved Shell Disks from Tennessee. Am. Anthro., vol. 9, no. 2, pp. 447–448.

HARTNETT, W. G.

1931. Poisonous Snake Bite: Etiology and Treatment with Case Report. Ohio State Med. Jour., vol. 27, pp. 636–639.

HARTWEG, N., and J. A. OLIVER

1940. A Contribution to the Herpetology of the Isthmus of Tehuantepec. IV. Misc. Publ. Mus. Zoöl. Univ. Mich., no. 47, pp. 1–31.

HARTWIG, G.

1873. The Tropical World. New edition, London, pp. xix + 556. [1st German edition, Wiesbaden, 1860; first English translation 1863.]

HARVEY, G. W.

1901. Bitten by a Snake Seven Years Dead. Calif. Med. Jour., vol. 22, no. 5, p. 157.

1924. [Delayed Rattlesnake Bite.] Outdoor Life, vol. 53, no. 1, p. 74. [See also vol. 55, no. 6, p. 517.]

HARWOOD, P. D.

1932. The Helminths Parasitic in the Amphibia and Reptilia of Houston, Texas, and Vicinity. Proc. U. S. Nat. Mus., vol. 81, art. 17, no. 2940, pp. 1–71.

HASTINGS, L.

1945. Speed of Snakes. Country Life (London), vol. 97, no. 2505, pp. 121–122.

HATHCOCK, B.

1937. Snake Eat Snake. Nat. Hist., vol. 39, no. 5, pp. 339–342.

HAUPT, H., JR.

1915. Hibernation of Reptiles. Copeia, no. 20, pp. 18–19.

HAWKEN, J. L.

1951. Water System Acts as Reptile and Amphibian Trap. Herpetologica, vol. 7, part 2, pp. 81–83.

HAY, O. P.

1887. The Massasauga and Its Habits. Am. Nat., vol. 21, no. 3, pp. 211–218.

1892a. On the Breeding Habits, Eggs, and Young of Certain Snakes. Proc. U. S. Nat. Mus., vol. 15, no. 909, pp. 385–397.

1892b. The Batrachians and Reptiles of the State of Indiana. 17th Ann. Rept. Ind. Dept. Geol. Nat. Res., pp. 409–624.

1902. Bibliography and Catalogue of the Fossil Vertebrata of North America. U. S. Geol. Sur., Bull. 179, pp. 1–868.

1917. Vertebrata Mostly from Stratum No. 3, at Vero, Florida, Together with Descriptions of New Species. 9th Ann. Rept. Fla. State Geol. Sur., pp. 43–68.

1920. Descriptions of Some Pleistocene Vertebrates Found in the United States. Proc. U. S. Nat. Mus., vol. 58, no. 2328, pp. 83–146.

1923. The Pleistocene of North America and Its Vertebrated Animals from the States East of the Mississippi River and from the Canadian Provinces East of Longitude 95°. Carn. Inst., Publ. no. 322, pp. viii + 499.

1924. The Pleistocene of the Middle Region of North America and Its Vertebrated Animals. Carn. Inst., Publ. 322A, pp. 1–385.

1927. The Pleistocene of the Western Region of North America and Its Vertebrated Animals. Carn. Inst., Publ. 322B, pp. 1–346.

1929. Second Bibliography and Catalogue of the Fossil Vertebrata of North America. Carn. Inst., Publ. no. 390, 2 vols., pp. viii + 916; xiv + 1074.

HAYNES, J. R.

1879. Experiments in Animal Poisons. Cincinnati Med. Advance, vol. 6, no. 10, pp. 481–487. [See also So. Practitioner, vol. 1, no. 5, p. 181.]

HAYNESWORTH, J.

1808. Some Account of the Success of the Plant Called Jestis-Weed, in Curing the Disease Induced by the Bites of the Rattle-Snake and Other Venomous Serpents. Phila. Med. and Phys. Jour., vol. 3, part 1, art. 8, pp. 57–61.

HAYWARD, E. G.

1929. Live Stock Losses from Snake-Bite. Bull. Antivenin Inst. Am., vol. 3, no. 3, pp. 87–88.

HAYWARD, J. W.

1882a. The Dose of Crotalus. Brit. Jour. Homoeop., vol. 40, no. 110, p. 113–129.

1882b. Some Symptom-Pictures of Crotalus Poisoning, and Some Diseases They Point to. Brit. Jour. Homoeop., vol. 40, no. 161, pp. 243–261.

HAYWARD, J. W. (*Continued*)

1883a. Two Cases of Malignant (Haemorrhagic) Scarlatina Treated by Crotalus. Lancet, vol. 2, pp. 54–55. [Also Brit. Jour. Homoeop., vol. 41, no. 165, pp. 246–249.]

1883b. Provings of Crotalus. Brit. Jour. Homoeop., vol. 41, no. 163, pp. 26–34.

1884. Crotalus (Rattlesnake). *In* Materia Medica: Physiological and Applied, by J. J. Drysdale *et al.*, London; see vol. 1, pp. 149–381.

HAYWOOD, C.

1950. A Bibliography of North American Folklore and Folksong. New York, pp. xxx + 1292.

HEARN, J.

1952. Beware Hitch-Hiking Rattlers. Tex. Game and Fish, vol. 10, no. 12, p. 17.

HEARST, J.

1948. Poison Pays Off for Him. Chicago Sunday Tribune Grafic, March 7, 1948, pp. 7, 17.

HECKEWELDER, J.

1819. An Account of the History, Manners, and Customs, of the Indian Nations, Who Once Inhabited Pennsylvania and the Neighboring States. Trans. Hist. Lit. Comm., Am. Philos. Soc., vol. 1, pp. iv + 347.

HEDIGER, H.

1950. Wild Animals in Captivity. Translated by G. Sircom. London, pp. ix + 207. [1st edition, in German, Basle, 1942.]

HEERMANN, A. L.

1859. Report upon Birds Collected on the Survey. Washington, Pac. R. R. Sur., vol. 10, part 4 [Williamson's Route], no. 2, pp. 29–80.

HEILBRUNN, L. V.

1954. Heat Death. Sci. Am., vol. 190, no. 4, pp. 70–75.

HEILBRUNN, L. V., D. L. HARRIS, P. G. LeFEVRE, W. L. WILSON, and A. A. WOODWARD

1946. Heat Death, Heat Injury, and Toxic Factor. Physiol. Zoöl., vol. 19, no. 4, pp. 404–429.

HELLMANN, A.

1817. Ueber den Tastsinn der Schlangen. Goettingen, pp. 1–60.

HELLMICH, W. C.

1951. On Ecotypic and Autotypic Characters, a Contribution to the Knowledge of the Evolution of the Genus *Liolaemus* (Iguanidae). Evolution, vol. 5, no. 4, pp. 359–369.

HELM, T. W., III

1952. Four Deadly Fangs. Field and Stream, vol. 56, no. 1, pp. 56–57, 104–108.

HEMMING, F. (editor)

1953. Copenhagen Decisions on Zoölogical Nomenclature. London, pp. xxix + 135.

HENDERSON, J.

1916. The Alleged Instinctive Fear of Snakes. Science, n.s., vol. 43, no. 1107, pp. 388–389.

HENDERSON, J., and J. P. HARRINGTON

1914. Ethnozoölogy of the Tewa Indians. Bur. Am. Ethn., Bull. 56, pp. x + 76.

HENDERSON, J. G.

1872. Use of the Rattles of the Rattlesnake. Am. Nat., vol. 6, no. 5, pp. 260–263.

HENDERSON, R.

1953. Just between You and Me [Editorial on Hopi and Smoki Snake Dances]. Desert Mag., vol. 16, no. 10, p. 42.

HENNEPIN, L.

1698. A New Discovery of a Vast Country in America. London, 2 vols., pp. xx + 243; xxx + 228. [Thwaites' reprint, Chicago, 1903, 2 vols., pp. lxiv + 353; 354–711. 1st French edition, 1683.]

HENRY, A.

1809. Travels and Adventures in Canada and the Indian Territories between the Years 1760 and 1776. New York, pp. vi + 330.

HENSHAW, H. W.

1883. Animal Carvings from Mounds of Mississippi Valley. 2nd Ann. Rept. Bur. Ethn., pp. 117–166.

HERING, C.

1844. Some Cases Cured by Lachesis. Brit. Jour. Homoeop., vol. 2, no. 8, pp. 369–378. [First appeared in 1837, in German.]

1884. Condensed Materia Medica. 3rd edition, revised by E. A. Farrington. Philadelphia, pp. xvi + 968. [1st edition, Philadelphia, 1877, pp. xv + 870.]

HERMANN, J. A.

1950. Mammals of the Stockton Plateau of Northeastern Terrell County, Texas. Tex. Jour. Sci., vol. 2, no. 3, pp. 368–393.

HERNÁNDEZ, F.

1615. Quatro Libros de la Naturaleza, y Virtudes de la Plantas, y Animales que Estan Recevidos en el Uso de Medicina en la Nueva España. . . . México, pp. [viii] + 201 fols. + [12 pp.].

1628. Rerum Medicarum Novae Hispaniae Thesaurus seu Plantarum Animalium Mineralium Mexicanorum Historia. Romae, pp. [ii] + 950 + [34] + 90 + [vi].

1651. Rerum Medicarum Novae Hispaniae Thesaurus seu Plantarum Animalium Mineralium Mexicanorum Historia. Romae, pp. [xxxiv] + 950 + 90 + [vi].

HERNE, P.

1858. Perils and Pleasures of a Hunter's Life; or the Romance of Hunting. New York, pp. x, 14–336.

HERODOTUS (See under RAWLINSON, G.)

HERRICK, F. H.

1917. Audubon the Naturalist. New York, 2 vols., pp. xl + 451; 1–494.

HERRICK, J. P.

1953. New York Only One of Nation's Oil Producing States in Which Fields Were Free of Rattlers. Olean (N. Y.) Times Herald, June 18, vol. 93, no. 143, sec. 2, p. 23.

HETT, MARY, L.

1924. On the Family Linguatulidae. Proc. Zoöl. Soc. London, vol. 1, pp. 107–159.

[HEWATT, A.]

1779. An Historical Account of the Rise and Progress of the Colonies of South Carolina and Georgia. London, 2 vols., pp. xiv + 347; ix + 329.

HEYREND, F. LaM., and A. CALL

1951. Symposium: A Snake Den in Tooele County, Utah. Growth and Age in Western Striped Racer and Great Basin Rattlesnake. Herpetologica, vol. 7, part 1, pp. 28–40.

HIBBARD, C. W.

1936. The Amphibians and Reptiles of Mammoth Cave National Park Proposed. Trans. Kans. Acad. Sci., vol. 39, pp. 277–281.

HIGGESON (or HIGGINSON), F.

1630. New-England's Plantation; or, a Short and True Description of the Commodities and Discommodities of that Country. London, 26 pp. [Reprint in Coll. Mass. Hist. Soc., for 1792, vol. 1, pp. 117–124. Boston, 1806. Also reprinted in Peter Force's Tracts, Washington, 4 vols., 1836–1846; see vol. 1, no. 12, pp. 1–14, 1836.]

HIGGINS, S. B.

1873. Ophidians, Zoölogical Arrangement of the Different Genera . . . New York and Philadelphia, pp. 1–239.

HIGHTOWER, J.

1945. Death Wears Diamonds. Elks Mag., Nov., pp. 8–9, 42–44.

HILDIGO, J.

1899. Practical Snake Lore. Modern Treatment of Snake Bites. Forest and Stream, vol. 53, no. 2, pp. 26–27.

HILGER, M. INEZ

1951. Chippewa Child Life and Its Cultural Background. Bur. Am. Ethn., Bull. 146, pp. xiv + 204.

HILL, H. R.

1935. New Host Records of the Linguatulid, *Kiricephalus coarctatus* (Diesing) in the United States. Bull. So. Calif. Acad. Sci., vol. 34, part 3, pp. 226–267.

1948. Annotated Bibliography of the Linguatulida. Bull. So. Calif. Acad. Sci., vol. 47, part 2 pp. 56–73.

HILL, J.

1752. An History of Animals. London, pp. [iv] + 584 + [iv].

HILL, T.
    1890. A Journey on Horseback from New Brunswick, New Jersey, to Lycoming County, Pennsylvania, in 1799. Pa. Mag., vol. 14, pp. 189–198.

HILL, W. W.
    1936. Navaho Warfare. Yale Univ. Publ. Anthro., no. 5, pp. 1–19.

HILLCOURT, W.
    1950. Field Book of Nature Activities. New York, pp. 1–320.

HILTON, J. W.
    1947. Sonora Sketch Book. New York, pp. [viii] + 333.

HINMAN, K. C.
    1951. Killer vs. Killer. Pa. Games News, vol. 22, no. 7, p. 46.

HINSHAW, W. R., and ETHEL McNEIL
    1944. Gopher Snakes as Carriers of Salmonellosis and Paracolon Infections. Cornell Vet., vol. 34, no. 3, pp. 248–254.
    1945. Salmonella Types Isolated from Snakes. Am. Jour. Vet. Res., vol. 6, no. 21, pp. 264–266.
    1946. Paracolon Type 10 from Captive Rattlesnakes. Jour. Bacter., vol. 51, no. 3, pp. 397–398.

HINTON, R. J.
    1878. A Handbook to Arizona: Its Resources, History, Towns, Mines, Rivers and Scenery. San Francisco, pp. 431 + ci.

HIRST, S.
    1915. On a Blood-Sucking Mite (*Ichoronyssus serpentium*, sp. n.?), Parasitic on Couper's Snake. Proc. Zoöl. Soc. London, pp. 383–386.

HOAG, J. E.
    1927. Adventures in Herpetology. Touring Topics, vol. 19, no. 4, pp. 14–17, 36–37.

HOBACK, W. W., and T. W. GREEN
    1953. Treatment of Snake Venom Poisoning with Cortisone and Corticotropin. Jour. Am. Med. Assn., vol. 152, no. 3, pp. 236–237.

HOBBS, J.
    1873. Wild Life in the Far West. Hartford, Conn., pp. 1–488.

HOCKLEY, R.
    1903–4. Selected Letters from the Letter-Book of Richard Hockley of Philadelphia, 1739–1743. Pa. Mag. Hist. and Biog., vol. 27, no. 3, pp. 305–328; no. 4, pp. 421–435; vol. 28, no. 1, pp. 26–43.

HODGE, F. W.
    1896. Pueblo Snake Ceremonials. Am. Anthro., vol. 9, no. 4, pp. 133–136.
    1924. Snake-Pens at Hawikuh, New Mexico. Indian Notes, Mus. Am. Indian, Heye Found., New York, vol. 1, no. 3, pp. 111–119.
    1937. History of Hawikuh, New Mexico. Los Angeles, pp. xviii + 155.

HODGE, F. W., G. P. HAMMOND, and A. REY
    1945. Fray Alonso de Benavides' Revised Memorial of 1634. Albuquerque, Coronado Cuarto Centennial Publ., 1540–1940, vol. 4, pp. xvi + 368.

HODGE, H. C.
    1877. Arizona As It Is. New York, pp. xii + 14–273.

HODGSON, A.
    1824. Letters from North America. London, 2 vols., pp. xv + 405; iv + 473.

HOFFMAN, W. J.
    1878. Miscellaneous Ethnographic Observations on Indians Inhabiting Nevada, California, and Arizona. 10th Ann. Rept. U. S. Geol. and Geog. Sur., pp. 459–478.
    1883. Poisoned Arrows. Med. and Surg. Reporter, vol. 49, no. 4 (whole no. 1378), p. 105.
    1885. Hugo Ried's Account of the Indians of Los Angeles County, California. Bull. Essex Inst., vol. 17, nos. 1–3, pp. 1–36.
    1891. Poisoned Arrows. Am. Anthro., vol. 4 (o. s.), no. 1, pp. 67–71.
    1894. Beliefs Concerning Rattlesnake Bite. Am. Anthro., vol. 7, no. 1, p. 128.
    1896. The Menomini Indians. 14th Ann. Rept. Bur. Ethn., part 1, pp. 3–328.

HOFFMANN, C. K.
    1894. Reptilien. *In* Dr. H. G. Bronn's Klassen und Ordnungen des Thier-Reichs, Leipzig, Bd. 6, Abt. 3; 3 vols., pp. 1–1399.

Hogan, E. M.
  1950. Rattlesnake Steak—It Really Makes Good Eating. Bradford (Pa.). Era, June 7, p. 9.
Hoge, A. R.
  1952. Farbenaberrationem bei Brasilianischen Schlangen. Mem. Inst. Butantan, vol. 24, no. 2, pp. 269–270.
Hoge, A. R., and P. S. Santos
  1953. Submicroscopic Structure of "Stratum Corneum" of Snakes. Science, vol. 118, no. 3067, pp. 410–411.
Hogg, J. E.
  1928. Dangerous Snakes—How to Avoid Them. Outdoor Life, vol. 62, no. 1, pp. 15–17, 52–55.
  1931a. With Rod and Reel on Desert Sands. Nature Mag., vol. 18, no. 3, pp. 169–172, 194.
  1931b. Big Medicine. Touring Topics, vol. 23, no 8., pp. 18–21, 37–38.
Hogner, Dorothy G.
  1938. Westward, High, Low, and Dry. New York, pp. 1–310.
Hoit, M.
  1844. Snake Bites. Boston Med. and Surg. Jour., vol. 30, no. 12, p. 243.
Holbrook, J. E.
  1836–40. North American Herpetology; or a Description of the Reptiles Inhabiting the United States. Philadelphia, 4 vols., pp. 120, 125 + [1], 122, 126.
  1842. North American Herpetology. [2nd edition], Philadelphia, 5 vols., pp. 152, 142, 128, 138, 118.
Holbrook, S. H.
  1940. Ethan Allen. New York, pp. ix + 283.
Holcombe, W. H.
  1853. Epidemic Yellow-Fever, and Its Homoeopathic Treatment. N. Am. Jour. of Homoeop., vol. 3, pp. 465–503.
Holder, C. F.
  1892. Hunting the Antelope. Californian, vol. 1, no. 3, pp. 209–214.
Holland, P.
  1601. The Historie of the World, Commonly Called the Naturall Historie of C. Plinius Secundus. London, 2 vols., pp. [viii] + [xlviii] + 614 + [xlii]; [x] + 632 + [lxxxvi]. Also 1635, pp. [lvi] + 614 + [xl]; x + 632 + [lxxxiv] + [i].
Holland, R. P.
  1953. Snakes Make Folks Funny. Field and Stream, vol. 58, no. 6, pp. 38–39, 98–101.
Hollender, F.
  1948. Close Call for Baker. Field and Stream, vol. 53, no. 8, pp. 129–130.
Holley, Mary Austin
  1836. Texas. Lexington, Ky., pp. viii + 410. [Also facsimile reprint, Austin, Tex., 1935.]
Holm, T. C.
  1834. A Short Description of the Province of New Sweden. Translated by P. S. du Ponceau. Mem. Hist. Soc. Pa., vol. 3, pp. xi + 166. [First published in Stockholm, 1702.]
Holmes, I.
  1823. An Account of the United States of America. London, pp. viii, 9–476
Holmes, O. W.
  1861. Elsie Venner. Boston, 2 vols., pp. xii, 13–288; 312.
Holmes, W. H.
  1883. Art in Shell of the Ancient Americans. 2nd Ann. Rept. Bur. Ethn., pp. 179–305.
  1886. Ancient Pottery of the Mississippi Valley. 4th Ann. Rept. Bur. Ethn., pp. 361–436.
  1890. A West Virginia Rock-Shelter. Am. Anthro., vol. 3 (o.s), no. 3, pp. 217–225.
  1903. Aboriginal Pottery of the Eastern United States. 20th Ann. Rept. Bur. Am. Ethn., pp. 1–201.
Holt, Catharine
  1946. Shasta Ethnography. Univ. Calif. Anthro. Rec., vol. 3, no. 4, pp. iii, 299–349.
Holt, R.
  1950. Treatment of Snake Bites. Southwest. Med., vol. 31, no. 1, pp. 13–15. [Also no. 2, p. 44.]

H[OLT], W. B.
  1939. Sidewinders. Santa Barbara Mus. Nat. Hist. Mus. Leafl., vol. 14, no. 4, pp. 43–46.
HOME, E.
  1804. Some Remarks on the Structure of Those Orifices [in Certain Poisonous Snakes]. Philos. Trans. (Royal Soc. London), vol. 94, part 1, art. 6, pp. 72–75. [See also Russell, pp. 70–72, 1804.]
  1809. The Case of a Man, Who Died in Consequence of the Bite of a Rattle-Snake. Philos. Trans. (Royal Soc. London), vol. 100, part 1, art. 3, pp. 75–88.
  1812. Observations Intended to Show That the Progressive Motion of Snakes Is Partly Performed by Means of the Ribs. Philos. Trans. (Royal Soc. London), vol. 102, part 1, pp. 163–168.
HOOKER, J. D.
  1903. A Case of Snakebite Treated with Adrenalin Chloride. Texas Med. Jour., vol. 19, no. 3, pp. 87–88.
HOOPER, LUCILE
  1920. The Cahuilla Indians. Univ. Calif. Publ. Am. Arch. and Ethn., vol. 16, no. 6, pp. 315–380.
HOOTEN, T., et al.
  1948. Big Mouthful of Snakes. Desert Mag., vol. 11, no. 4, p. 38.
HOPKINS, A. A.
  1930. How a Rattlesnake Charms a Quail. Outdoor Life, vol. 66, no. 1, p. 87.
HOPKINS, L.
  1906. Romancing. Forest and Stream, vol. 66, no. 5, p. 171.
HOPKINS, M., JR.
  1905. The Rattlesnake's Strike. Forest and Stream, vol. 64, no. 18, p. 354.
HOPKINS, W. K.
  1853. Alcohol as a Remedy for the Poison of the Rattlesnake. North-West. Med. and Surg. Jour., vol. 9 (vol. 1, n.s.), no. 9, pp. 389–391.
HOPLEY, CATHERINE C.
  1882. Snakes: Curiosities and Wonders of Serpent Life. London, pp. viii + 614.
  1887. The Rattle. Forest and Stream, vol. 28, no. 24, pp. 512–513. [See also figure correction, vol. 29, no. 10, p. 183.]
HORN, E. E., and H. S. FITCH
  1942. Interrelations of Rodents and Other Wildlife of the Range [San Joaquin Experimental Range]. Univ. Calif. Agric. Exp. Sta., Bull. 663, pp. 96–129.
HORNADAY, W. T.
  1904. The American Natural History. New York, pp. xxv + 449.
  1908. Camp-Fires on Desert and Lava. New York, pp. xix + 366.
HORNER, W. E.
  1831. Post-mortem Examination of a Patient Who Died from the Bite of a Rattlesnake (*Crotalus horridus*). Am. Jour. Med. Sci., vol. 8, no. 16, art. 12, pp. 397–400.
HORTON, C. W.
  1951. The Near Ultraviolet Absorption Spectrum of *Crotalus* Venom. Herpetologica, vol. 7, part 4, pp. 173–174.
HOUSSAY, B. A.
  1923. Quantités de Venin Fournies par les Serpents Venimeux de l'Argentine. Comp. Rend. Soc. Biol., vol. 89, pp. 449–451.
  1930. Classification des Actions des Venins de Serpents sur l'Organisme Animal. Compt. Rend. Soc. Biol., vol. 105, pp. 308–310.
HOUTTUYN, M.
  1761–72. Natuurlyke Historie. Amsterdam, 17 vols. [Rattlesnakes in vol. 6, pp. 289–315, 1764.]
HOWARD, W. E.
  1953. Rodent Control on California Ranges. Jour. Range Man., vol. 6, no. 6, pp. 423–434.
HOWDEN, H.
  1943. Control of Diseases and Parasites of Snakes. Bull. Nat. Hist. Soc. Maryland, vol. 13, no. 3, pp. 41–44.

Howe, H.
  1847. Historical Collections of Ohio. Cincinnati, pp. 581 + [1].
Howey, M. O.
  1928. The Encircled Serpent: A Study of Serpent Symbolism in All Countries and Ages. London, pp. xi + 411.
Howison, J.
  1822. Sketches of Upper Canada. 2nd edition, Edinburgh, pp. 1–353. [1st edition, Edinburgh, 1821, pp. xvi + 339.]
Howitt, E.
  1820. Selections from Letters Written during a Tour of the United States in the Summer and Autumn of 1819. Nottingham, pp. xxii + 230.
Hoy, P. R.
  1865. Journal of an Exploration of Western Missouri in 1854. Ann. Rept. Smithson. Inst. for 1865, pp. 432–438.
Hrdlička, A.
  1908. Physiological and Medical Observations among the Indians of Southwestern United States and Northern Mexico. Bur. Am. Ethn., Bull. 34, pp. ix + 460.
Hubbard, D. H.
  1941. The Vertebrate Animals of Friant Reservoir Basin with Special Reference to the Possible Effects upon Them of the Friant Dam. Calif. Fish and Game, vol. 27, no. 4, pp. 198–215.
Hubbard, G.
  1944. Aircraft Insignia, Spirit of Youth. Insignia and Decorations of the U. S. Armed Forces, revised edition. Washington, Natl. Geog. Soc., pp. 165–184, 203–206.
Hubbard, W. E.
  1939. *Entonyssus ewingi* n. sp., an Ophidian Lung Mite. Am. Midl. Nat., vol. 21, no. 3, pp. 657–662.
Hubbard, W. P.
  1948. Revenge in the Meadow. Nature Mag., vol. 41, no. 5, pp. 232–236.
Hubble, J.
  1825. Observations on the *Prenanthes altissima*. N. Y. Med. and Phys. Jour., vol. 4, no. 4, pp. 484–486. [See also N. Am. Med. and Surg. Jour., vol. 1, no. 2, p. 447, 1826.]
Hubert, E. E.
  1934. A Desert Secret. Frontier and Midland, vol. 14, no. 3, pp. 237–238.
Hudgens, M. W.
  1953. I Wake Up Screaming. Fla. Wildlife, vol. 6, no. 9, p. 48.
Hudson, G. E.
  1942. The Amphibians and Reptiles of Nebraska. Nebr. Cons. Bull., no. 24, pp. 1–146.
Hudson, R. G.
  1947. An Unusual Method of Shedding. Herpetologica, vol. 4, part 2, p. 69.
Hudson, W. H.
  1893a. The Serpent's Tongue. Fort. Rev., vol. 54 (n.s.), no. 320, pp. 198–206.
  1893b. The Bruised Serpent. Macmillan's Mag., vol. 67, no. 402, pp. 451–457.
  1894. The Serpent's Strangeness. Fort. Rev., vol. 55 (n.s.), no. 328, pp. 528–537.
  1903. The Naturalist in La Plata. New edition, New York, pp. ix + 394. [1st edition, London, 1892.]
  1910. A Shepherd's Life. New York, pp. xi + 361.
  1919. The Book of a Naturalist. New York, pp. viii + 360.
Huey, L. M.
  1942. A Vertebrate Faunal Survey of the Organ Pipe Cactus National Monument, Arizona. Trans. San Diego Soc. Nat. Hist., vol. 9, no. 32, pp. 353–376.
Hughes, F. N.
  1938. Snakes, Venoms and Medicine. Canadian Pharm. Jour., vol. 71, pp. 689–690.
Hughes, R. C., J. R. Baker, and C. B. Dawson
  1941. The Trematodes of Reptiles, Part II, Host Catalogue. Proc. Okla. Acad. Sci., vol. 21, pp. 37–43.

HUGHES, R. C., J. W. HIGGINBOTHAM, and J. W. CLARY
    1942. The Trematodes of Reptiles, Part I, Systematic Section. Am. Midl. Nat., vol. 27, no. 1, pp. 109–134.
HUGHES, W.
    1947. Rattlesnake Roundup. Okla. Game and Fish News, vol. 3, no. 5, pp. 4–5, 16.
HUIDEKOPER, A.
    1850. Incidents in the Early History of Crawford County, Pennsylvania. Mem. Hist. Soc. Pa., vol. 4, part 2, pp. 113–163.
HULME, F. E.
    1895. Natural History Lore and Legend. London, pp. viii + 350.
HUMBOLDT, F. H. A. VON
    1811. Sur un Ver Intestin Trouvé dans les Poumons du Serpent à Sonnettes, de Cumana. Rec. Obs. Zool. et Anat. Comp., vol. 1, pp. 298–304.
HUMFREVILLE, J. L.
    1903. Twenty Years among Our Hostile Indians. New York, pp. xiii + 480. [1st edition, New York, 1899, pp. xi, xxxvi, 45–479.]
HUMPHREY, R. R.
    1936. Notes on Altitudinal Distribution of Rattlesnakes. Ecology, vol. 17, no. 2, pp. 328–329.
HUMPHREYS, E. C.
    1951. The Benefits of Snake Venom. Tex. Game and Fish, vol. 9, no. 3, pp. 12–13.
HUNT, ANN
    1934. Sunlight Is Fatal to the Pacific Rattlesnake. Yosemite Nat. Notes, vol. 13, no. 2, p. 16.
HUNTER, G. R.
    1951. An Unseasonable Rattler. Outdoor Life, vol. 107, no. 5, p. 18.
HUNTER, J. D.
    1823. Manners and Customs of Several Indian Tribes. Philadelphia, pp. viii, 9–402.
HURSTON, ZORA
    1931. Hoodoo in America. Jour. Am. Folk-Lore, vol. 44, no. 174, pp. 317–417.
HURTER, J.
    1893. Catalogue of Reptiles and Batrachians Found in the Vicinity of St. Louis, Mo. Trans. Acad. Sci. St. Louis, vol. 6, no. 11, pp. 251–261.
    1911. Herpetology of Missouri. Trans. Acad. Sci. St. Louis, vol. 20, no. 5, pp. 59–274.
HUTCHINS, R. E.
    1941. Debunking the Snake. Hunting and Fishing, vol. 18, no. 7, pp. 10–11, 20–21.
HUTCHINSON, H. F.
    1879. About Snakes. Nature, vol. 20, no. 518, pp. 528–530.
HUTCHISON, R. H.
    1929. On the Incidence of Snake-Bite Poisoning in the United States and the Results of the Newer Methods of Treatment. Bull. Antivenin Inst. Am., vol. 3, no. 2, pp. 43–57
    1930. Further Notes on the Incidence of Snake-Bite Poisoning in the United States. Bull. Antivenin Inst. Am., vol. 4, no. 2, pp. 40–43.
HUTCHISON, T., and A. D. McCAIN
    1950. Rattlesnake Recipes. Barstow, Calif., pp. 1–16.
HUTT, W. N.
    1908. Audubon the Original "Nature Faker." Sci. Am., vol. 98, no. 4, p. 59.
HUXLEY, J. S.
    1936. T. H. Huxley's Diary of the Voyage of H.M.S. Rattlesnake. New York, pp. xiv + 301.
    1938. Animal Language. London, pp. xi + 62.
    1939. "Animal Language." Nature, vol. 143, no. 3626, p. 725.
HYATT, H. M.
    1935. Folk-Lore from Adams County, Illinois. New York, pp. xvi + 723.
HYDE, B. T. B.
    1923. When Snakes Share Food, What Is the Sequel? Nat. Hist., vol. 23, no. 5, pp. 448–449.
    1925. Two-Headed Snakes: A Not Uncommon Phenomenon of the Reptile World. Nat. Hist., vol. 25, no. 2, pp. 184–187.

HYLANDER, C. J.
 1951. Adventures with Reptiles: The Story of Ross Allen. New York, pp. xii + 174.
I., G. A.
 1908. Encounters with Rattlesnakes. Forest and Stream, vol. 70, no. 25, pp. 971–972.
IDLE, C., *et al.*
 1856. Adder's or Viper's Bite. Field, vol. 8, pp. 164, 187, 219, 234, 266–267.
IMLER, R. H.
 1945. Bullsnakes and Their Control on a Nebraska Wildlife Refuge. Jour. Wildlife Man., vol.
  9, no. 4, pp. 265–273.
INGERSOLL, E.
 1883a. The Rattlesnake. Manhattan, vol. 2, pp. 35–45.
 1883b. Knocking round the Rockies. New York, pp. vii + 220.
 1884a. The Crotalus. Gentleman's Mag., vol. 256 (n.s. vol. 32), no. 1840, pp. 400–404.
 1884b. Country Cousins. New York, pp. 1–252.
INGLES, L. G.
 1929. The Seasonal and Associational Distribution of the Fauna of the Upper Santa Ana River
  Wash. Jour. Ent. and Zoöl. (Pomona College), vol. 21, nos. 1 and 2, pp. 1–48, 57–96.
 1946. California Wild Life. Pac. Pathways, vol. 1, no. 8, pp. 29–31, 45.
INMAN, H. (compiler)
 1899. Buffalo Jones' Forty Years of Adventure. Topeka, pp. xii + 469.
IPSEN, J.
 1938. Progress Report on the Possibility of Standardizing Anti-Snake-Venom Sera. Bull. World
  Health Org., League of Nations, vol. 7, pp. 785–806.
IRONMONGER, C. J.
 1889. Antidote for Snake-Bites. Pac. Rural Press, vol. 38, no. 4, p. 67.
IRVIN, S. M., and W. HAMILTON
 1853. Iowa and Sac Tribes. *In* H. R. Schoolcraft, Information respecting the History, Conditions and Prospects of the Indian Tribes of the United States. Philadelphia, 1851–1857, 6
  vols. [See vol. 3, part 3, pp. 259–276.]
IRVINE, F. R.
 1953. Herbivorous Snakes. Brit. Jour. Herpet., vol. 1, no. 9, p. 173; Copeia, no. 2 of 1954, p. 168.
  [See also comments by J. A. Oliver, Brit. Jour. Herpet., vol. 1, no. 10, p. 192.]
IRVING, W.
 1836. Astoria. Philadelphia, 2 vols., pp. xii + 13–285; viii + 9–279.
IRWIN, B. J. D.
 1861. Notes on "Euphorbia Prostrata" as an Antidote to the Poison of the Rattlesnake. Am.
  Jour. Med. Sci., vol. 41 (n.s.), no. 81, art. 4, pp. 89–91.
ISELY, B.
 1951. Oklahoma Rattlesnake Market Will Re-open with 30,000 Attending. Wall St. Jour. (N.
  Y. edition), vol. 137, no. 73, p. 1.
J., L.
 1890. *Caucalis microcarpa* or Rattlesnake Weed. Pac. Rural Press, vol. 39, no. 25, p. 518.
JACKLEY, A. M.
 1933. Method for Wiping Out Rattlers. Outdoor Life, vol. 72, no. 3, p. 58.
 1938. Badgers Feed on Rattlesnakes. Jour. Mammal., vol. 19, no. 3, pp. 374–375.
 1939. Rattlesnake Control and Conservation. S. Dak. Cons. Digest, vol. 6, no. 12, p. 11.
 1943. New Snake Trap and Some of Its Strange Catches. S. Dak. Cons. Digest, vol. 10, no. 6,
  pp. 1, 7.
 1944. Badger—Rattlesnake Enemy. S. Dak. Cons. Digest, vol. 11, no. 1, pp. 2–3, 16.
 1946a. Traits and Characteristics of Rattlesnakes. Radio Talk over KGFX, March 14, 1946.
  Published by S. Dak. Dept. Agric., Pierre, 2 pp.
 1946b. Annual Report of the Department of Agriculture, South Dakota, Reptile Control Division, Pierre, pp. 16–17.
 1947. How to Locate and Trap Dens of Rattlesnakes. Mont. Farmer, vol. 34, no. 12, pp. 1, 3–5.
JACKSON, A. T.
 1938. Picture-Writing of Texas Indians. Univ. Tex. Publ. no. 3809, Anthro. Papers, vol. 2,
  Study no. 27, pp. xxv + 490.

JACKSON, D.

1926. Treatment of Snake Bite. *In* W. A. Bevan's column, Snake Lore, Outdoor Life, vol. 58, no. 2, pp. 172–173.

1927. First Aid Treatment for Snake Bite. Tex. State Jour. Med., vol. 23, no. 3, pp. 203–209. [Also published as a pamphlet, Fort Worth, pp. 1–20.]

1929. Treatment of Snake Bite. So. Med. Jour., vol. 22, no. 7, pp. 605–608. [Also published as a pamphlet, Birmingham, Ala., pp. 1–6.]

1936. The Management of Snake-Bite. Am. Rifleman, May, 1936, pp. 24–26.

JACKSON, D., and T. S. GITHENS

1931. Treatment of *Crotalus atrox* Venom Poisoning in Dogs. Bull. Antivenin Inst. Am., vol. 5, no. 1, pp. 1–6.

JACKSON, D., and W. T. HARRISON

1928. Mechanical Treatment of Experimental Rattlesnake Venom Poisoning. Jour. Am. Med. Assn., vol. 90, no. 24, pp. 1928–1929. [Also published as a pamphlet, Chicago, pp. 1–5.]

JACKSON, E.

1940. Slightly Cuckoo. Natl. Park Serv., Region III Quart., vol. 2, no. 4, pp. 4–12.

1942. Handle with Care. Ariz. Highways, vol. 18, no. 2, pp. 8–9, 41–42.

1943. Salute Your Compatriot. Ariz. Highways, vol. 19, nos. 9–10, pp. 14, 50.

JACKSON, J. H.

1939. Tintypes in Gold. New York, pp. 1–191.

JACKSON, M. H.

1879. Rattlensake Bites. So. Practitioner, vol. 1, no. 8, pp. 259–260; no. 9, pp. 295–296 [comments by W. R. D. Blackwood]; no. 11, pp. 360–362 [rejoinder by Jackson].

JACKSON, S.

1853. Account of Two Cases of Bites from Venomous Serpents. Trans. Coll. Phys. Phila., vol. 1 (n.s.), no. 9, pp. 409–411.

JACOBS, M.

1934. Northwest Sahaptin Texts. Columbia Univ. Contrib. Anthro., vol. 19, part 1, pp. xi + 291.

1945a. Santiam Kalapuya Ethnologic Texts. Univ. Wash. Publ. Anthro., vol. 11, part 1, pp. 3–81.

1945b. Santiam Kalapuya Myth Texts. Univ. Wash. Publ. Anthro., vol. 11, part 2, pp. 83–142.

JACOBSEN, W. C.

1945. The Bounty System and Predator Control. Calif. Fish and Game, vol. 31, no. 2, pp. 53–63.

JAEGER, E. C.

1927. Birds of the Charleston Mountains of Nevada. Occ. Papers Riverside Jr. Coll., vol. 2, no. 1, pp. 1–8.

JAMES, E.

1823. Account of an Expedition from Pittsburgh to the Rocky Mountains Performed in the Years 1819, 1820 . . . under the Command of Major S. H. Long. London, 1823, 3 vols., pp. vii + 344; 356; 347. [Reprinted in Thwaites: Early Western Travels, 32 vols., Cleveland, 1904–1907; see vols. 14–17.]

JAMES, G. W.

1902. Indian Basketry. 2nd edition, New York, pp. 1–274. [1st edition, Pasadena, 1901, pp. 1–238.]

1906? The Rattlesnake Bite and How to Cure It. Pasadena, pp. 1–12.

JAQUES, E. P.

1908. Rattlesnakes, Skunks and Robins. Forest and Stream, vol. 70, no. 3, p. 91.

JAROS, D. B.

1940. Occlusion of the Venom Duct of Crotalidae by Electrocoagulation: an Innovation in Operative Technique. Zoologica, vol. 25, part 1, no. 4, pp. 49–51.

JAYAKAR, A. S. G. (translator)

1906–8. Damiri's Zoölogical Lexicon. London and Bombay, 2 vols., pp. xxx + 875; 604.

JAYNE, CAROLINE F.

1906. String Figures: A Study of Cat's-Cradle in Many Lands. New York, pp. xxiii + 407.

JAYNE, W. A.

1925. The Healing Gods of Ancient Civilizations. New Haven, pp. xxxix + 569.

JEFFERSON, T.

1793. [Letter to Henry Lee, Governor of Virginia, June 28, 1793.] The Works of Thomas Jefferson, Federal edition, New York, vol. 7, p. 413.

JEFFERYS, T.

1760. The Natural and Civil History of the French Dominions in North and South America. London, part 1, pp. [vi] + 168; part 2, pp. [ii] + 246.

JEFFREY, L. N.

1955. Snake Yarns of the West and Southwest. Western Folklore, vol. 14, no. 4, pp. 246–258.

JENKINS, C. L., and A. S. PENDLETON

1914. Crotalin in Epilepsy. Jour. Am. Med. Assn., vol. 63, no. 20, pp. 1749–1750.

JENKINS, G. F.

1870. Rattlesnake Bite Treated by Hypodermic Injection of Ammonia. Med. and Surg. Reporter, vol. 22, no. 22, pp. 458–459.

JENKINS, G. W.

1878. Observations on the Pathology and Treatment of the Bite of the Rattlesnake. Trans. Wis. State Med. Soc., vol. 12, pp. 63–65.

[JENNINGS, H.]

1889. Ophiolatreia or Serpent Worship. Pp. viii + 103. [Another undated edition is paged viii + 131.]

JENSEN, J. K.

1926. Red-Tailed Hawk Killing Snakes. Auk, vol. 43, no. 3, pp. 368–369.

JEPSON, W. L.

1925. A Manual of the Flowering Plants of California. Berkeley and Los Angeles, pp. 1–1238.

JETER, A. F.

1854. Poisoned Wounds: Their Distinctive Features, Classification. . . . Report of Committee to the Medical Assn. of Missouri. Quincy, Mo., pp. 1–32.

JEWETT, S. G.

1939. A Rattlesnake Kills a California Quail. Condor, vol. 41, no. 1, p. 30.

JOHNSON, CHARLES

1953. Decoy. Fla. Wildlife, vol. 6, no. 9, p. 54.

JOHNSON, CLIFTON

1896. What They Say in New England. Boston, pp. 1–263.

1932. Historic Hampshire in the Connecticut Valley. Springfield, Mass., pp. [iv] + 406.

JOHNSON, C. M.

1938. A New Method for Stripping Venomous Snakes. Am. Jour. Trop. Med., vol. 18, no. 4, pp. 385–386.

JOHNSON, D. H., M. D. BRYANT, and A. H. MILLER

1948. Vertebrate Animals of the Providence Mountains Area of California. Univ. Calif. Publ. Zoöl., vol. 48, no. 5, pp. 221–376.

JOHNSON, R. H.

1902. Axial Bifurcation in Snakes. Trans. Wis. Acad. Sci., Arts and Lett., vol. 13, pp. 523–538.

JOHNSTON, I. H.

1929. Road-Runner vs. Rattler. Bull. Nat. Club So. Calif., vol. 7, no. 4, p. 3.

JONES, ALA A.

1947. Hunting Rattlesnakes for Fun. N. Mex. Mag., vol. 25, no. 12, pp. 22–23, 48–50.

JONES, C. C.

1873. Antiquities of the Southern Indians, Particularly of the Georgia Tribes. New York, pp. xvi + 532.

JONES, H.

1699. Part of a Letter from the Reverend Mr. Hugh Jones to the Reverend Dr. Benjamin Woodroofe, F.R.S. Concerning Several Observables in Maryland. Philos. Trans. (Royal Soc. London), vol. 21, pp. 436–442.

1724. The Present State of Virginia. London, pp. viii + 151.

JONES, J. M. (editor)

1950. Physician's Desk Reference to Pharmaceutical Specialties and Biologicals. Rutherford, N. J., pp. viii + 100–180; 200–240; 300–380; 400–544; 600–632.

JONES, J. P.
  1928. A Few Facts Regarding Some Tennessee Snakes. Jour. Tenn. Acad. Sci., vol. 3, no. 2, pp. [1–13].

JONES, J. T.
  1857. Rattle Snake Bite. So. Jour. Med. and Phys. Sci., vol. 6, no. 5, pp. 376–377.

JONES, R. W.
  1892. The Rattlesnake of the Bottom-Lands of Mississippi. Science, vol. 20, no. 510, p. 277.

JONES, T. P.
  1828. The Romance of the Rattlesnake. Franklin Jour., n.s., vol. 6, p. 144.

JONES, W.
  1911. Notes on the Fox Indians. Jour. Am. Folk-Lore, vol. 24, no. 92, pp. 209–237.

JONES, W. R.
  1896. Rattlesnake Bite—with Report of a Case. Bi-monthly Bull., Univ. Coll. Med., Richmond, Va., vol. 1, no. 6, pp. 143–146.

JONSTONUS, J.
  1653. Historiae Naturalis de Serpentibus, Libri II. Francofurti, pp. 1–40 + [3]. [Another edition, 1657, Amstelodami, pp. 1–38.]

JORDAN, D. S.
  1900. Old Rattler and the King Snake. Appletons' Pop. Sci. Monthly, vol. 56, no. 3, pp. 371–374.

JOSSELYN, J.
  1672. New-Englands Rarities Discovered: in Birds, Beasts, Fishes, Serpents, and Plants of That Country. London, pp. 1–114. [Reprint, Boston, 1865, pp. viii + 169.]
  1675. An Account of Two Voyages to New-England. 2nd edition, London, pp. 1–279. [1st edition, London, 1674. Reprinted in Mass. Hist. Soc. Coll., ser. 3, vol. 3, pp. 211–396, 1833.]

JOUGHLIN, ROBERTA, and SALVADORA G. VALENZUELA
  1953. Cupeño Genesis. Museo, vol. 1, no. 4, pp. 16–23.

JOUTEL, H.
  1714. A Journal of the Last Voyage Perform'd by Monsr. de la Sale to the Gulph of Mexico. London, pp. xxi + [9] + 205 + [5]. [Styles Reprint, Albany, 1906, pp. 1–258.]

JOYCE, A. S.
  1913. Rattlesnake Venom May Cure Epilepsy. Tech. World Mag., vol. 18, no. 5, pp. 535–537.

JOYCE, T. A.
  1914. Mexican Archaeology. New York, pp. xvi + 384.

JUAN, G., and A. DE ULLOA
  1758. A Voyage to South-America. London, 2 vols., pp. xvi + [viii] + 509; [iii] + 420 + [xviii]. [First published in Madrid in 1748.]

JUDSON, KATHARINE B.
  1912. Myths and Legends of California and the Old Southwest. Chicago, pp. 1–193.

JULIAN, G.
  1951. Symposium: A Snake Den in Tooele County, Utah. Sex Ratios of the Winter Populations. Herpetologica, vol. 7, part 1, pp. 20–24.

JUSSIEU, B. DE
  1747. Sur les Effets de l'Eau de Luce contre la Morsure des Vipères. Mém. Acad. Roy. Sci., p. 54.

"JUVENAL"
  1900. Some Snake Stories. Forest and Stream, vol. 55, no. 2, p. 24. [See also p. 84.]

K., A. [ALLEN KELLY]
  1905. The Rattlesnake's Strike. Forest and Steam, vol. 64, no. 18, p. 354. [See also vol. 73, no. 2, p. 51, 1909.]

KAHMANN, H.
  1932. Sinnesphysiologische Studien an Reptilien. I. Experimentelle Untersuchungen ueber das Jacobson'sche Organ der Eidechsen und Schlangen. Zool. Jahrb. (Allg. Zool. und Physiol.), vol. 51, no. 2, pp. 173–238.
  1934. Zur Chemorezeption der Schlangen (ein Nachtrag). Zool. Anz., vol. 107, nos. 9–10, pp. 249–263.

KAHN, F. K.
  1942. The Problem of Snake-Bite. Jour. Indian Med. Assn., vol. 11, no. 9, pp. 288–289.

KALEZ, J.
  1954. Call Me Mr. Rattler. Field and Stream, vol. 59, no. 2, pp. 50–51, 76–79.

KALM, P.
  1752–3. Berattelse om Skaller-ormen . . . Kongl. Vetens. Acad. Stockholm, vol. 13, pp. 308–319;
    vol. 14, pp. 52–67, 185–194.
  1758. An Account of the Rattle-Snake and the Cure of Its Bite, as Used in North America.
    Med., Chir. Anat. Cases and Experiments. London, pp. 282–293. [Translated from original
    paper in Swedish, 1752–3, part 1.]
  1770–1. Travels into North America. Translation by J. R. Forster. London, 3 vols., pp. xvi +
    [viii] + 400; 352; viii + 310 + [xvi]. [1st edition, in Swedish, Stockholm, 1753–61, 3 vols.]
  1937. Peter Kalm's Travels in North America. Revised and edited by Adolph B. Benson. New
    York, 2 vols., pp. xviii + 380; 381–797.

KAMP, A.
  1904. A Rattlesnake Weed Story. Pac. Rural Press, vol. 68, no. 4, p. 62. [See also no. 1, p. 2.]

KANE, P.
  1859. Wanderings of an Artist among the Indians of North America. London, pp. xviii + 455 +
    [vii].

KANNER, L.
  1928. Folklore of the Teeth. New York, pp. xiii + 316.

KANTHACK, A. A.
  1892. The Nature of Cobra Poison. Jour. Physiol., vol. 13, nos. 3 and 4, pp. 272–299.
  1897. Report on Snake Venom in Its Prophylactic Relation with Poisons of the Same and Other
    Sorts. Report of Medical Officers of Local Govt. Board for 1895–6, London, pp. 235–266.

KARLSTROM, E. L., and S. F. COOK
  1955. Notes on Snake Anesthesia. Copeia, no. 1, pp. 57–58.

KARSTEN, R.
  1926. The Civilization of the South American Indians with Special Reference to Magic and
    Religion. New York, pp. xxxii + 540.

KARTZMARK, W. M.
  1926. [Snake Dens.] *In* W. A. Bevan's column, Snake Lore, Outdoor Life, vol. 58, no. 4, p. 331.

KATHARINER, L.
  1897. Ueber Bildung und Ersatz der Giftzähne bei Giftschlangen. Zool. Jahrb. Anat. Ont., vol.
    10, no. 1, pp. 55–92.
  1900. Die Mechanik des Bisses der solenoglyphen Giftschlangen. Biologisches Centralblatt, vol.
    20, no. 1, pp. 45–53.

KAUFFELD, C. F.
  1939. If You Like Danger—There Are Snakes. Outdoor Life, vol. 83, no. 2, pp. 32–33, 67–68.
  1940. Snake Country and the Sportsman. Outdoor Life, vol. 86, no. 1, pp. 44–45, 54, 92.
  1942. Don't Tread on Me. Fauna, vol. 4, no. 3, pp. 79–90.
  1943a. Field Notes on Some Arizona Reptiles and Amphibians. Am. Midl. Nat., vol. 29, no. 2,
    pp. 342–358.
  1943b. Growth and Feeding of New-Born Price's and Green Rock Rattlesnakes. Am. Midl. Nat.,
    vol. 29, no. 3, pp. 607–614.
  1953a. Methods of Feeding Captive Snakes. Herpetologica, vol. 9, part 3, pp. 129–131.
  1953b. Newer Treatment of Mouthrot in Snakes. Herpetologica, vol. 9, part 3, p. 132.
  1955. Off with Their Skins. In Animaland, vol. 12, no. 5, pp. [1–4].

KAUFMANN, M.
  1891. Du Venin de la Vipère. Mém. Acad. Méd., vol. 36, no. 1, pp. 1–56.
  1893. Les Vipères de France. Paris, pp. vi + 180.

KEAM, T. V.
  1883. An Indian Snake Dance. Chambers Jour., Jan. 6, pp. 14–16. [Reprinted in Hobbies, vol.
    55, no. 11, pp. 144–145, Jan., 1951.]

KEARSLEY, J.
  1766. Extract of a Letter from Dr. Kearsley to Mr. P. Collinson; dated Philadelphia, Nov. 18,
    1735. Gentleman's Mag., vol. 36, pp. 72–76.

KEATING, W. H.
    1824. Narrative of An Expedition to the Source of St. Peter's River, Lake Winnepeek, Lake of
        the Woods ... [Major Long's Second Expedition]. Philadelphia, 2 vols., pp. xii + 439; vi + 459.
KEEGAN, H. L.
    1944. Indigo Snakes Feeding upon Poisonous Snakes. Copeia, no. 1, p. 59.
KEEGAN, H. L., and T. F. ANDREWS
    1942. Effects of Crotalid Venom on North American Snakes. Copeia, no. 4, pp. 251–254.
KEELEY, J. L.
    1937. The Treatment of Snake Venom Poisoning. Wis. Med. Jour., vol. 36, no. 7, pp. 534–540.
[KEEP, O. H.]
    1882. Feathers from a Rattlesnake. Forest and Stream, vol. 18, no. 2, p. 27.
KEIM, DE B. R.
    1870. Sheridan's Troopers on the Borders. Philadelphia, pp. 1–308.
KEITH, W.
    1873. Inhalation of Ammonia as an Antidote to Snake Poison. Kansas City Med. Jour., vol. 3,
        no. 6, pp. 337–340.
KELLAWAY, C. H.
    1929a. The Venom of *Notechis scutatus*. Med. Jour. Australia, vol. 1, no. 11, pp. 348–358. [Pp.
        46–56 of separately published symposium.]
    1929b. A Preliminary Note on the Venom of the Australian Copper-head (*Denisonia superba*).
        Med. Jour. Australia, vol. 1, no. 11, pp. 358–365. [Pp. 56–63 of separately published sym-
        posium.]
    1929c. A Preliminary Note on the Venom of *Pseudechis guttatus*. Med. Jour. Australia, vol. 1,
        no. 11, pp. 372–377. [Pp. 64–69 of separately published symposium.]
    1929d. Observations on the Certainly Lethal Dose of the Venom of the Death Adder (*Ancan-
        thophis antarcticus*) for the Common Laboratory Animals. Med. Jour. Australia, vol. 1, pp.
        764–772. [Pp. 87–95 of separately published symposium.]
    1929e. The Action of the Venoms of the Copper-head (*Denisonia superba*) and of the Death
        Adder (*Ancanthophis antarcticus*) on the Coagulation of the Blood. Med. Jour. Australia,
        vol. 1, pp. 772–781. [Pp. 95–104 of separately published symposium.]
    1937. Snake Venoms. I. Their Constitution and Therapeutic Applications. II. Their Peripheral
        Action. III. Immunity. Bull. Johns Hopkins Hosp., vol. 60, no. 1, p. 1–39; no. 3, pp. 159–177.
    1939. Animal Poisons. Ann. Rev. Biochem., vol. 8, pp. 541–556.
KELLOGG, LOUISE P.
    1917. Early Narratives of the Northwest: 1634–1699. New York, pp. xiv + 382.
KELLY, A. (See also under K., A.)
    1909a. Rattlesnakes Striking. Forest and Stream, vol. 73, no. 2, p. 51.
    1909b. A Yuma Rattler. Forest and Stream, vol. 73, no. 18, p. 691.
KELLY, C. F., T. E. BOND, and H. HEITMAN, JR.
    1954. The Role of Thermal Radiation in Animal Ecology. Ecology, vol. 35, no. 4, pp. 563–569.
KELLY, FANNY
    1872. Narrative of My Captivity among the Sioux Indians. Philadelphia, pp. 1–285.
KELLY, H. A.
    1899. The Recognition of the Poisonous Serpents of North America. Bull. Johns Hopkins Hosp.,
        vol. 10, no. 105, pp. 217–221.
    1926. Snakes and Snake Bite. Hygeia, vol. 4, no. 1, pp. 32–38.
KELLY, H. A., AUDREY W. DAVIS, and H. C. ROBERTSON
    1936. Snakes of Maryland. Nat. Hist. Soc. Md., Baltimore, pp. 1–103.
KELLY, ISABEL T.
    1932. Ethnography of the Surprise Valley Paiute. Univ. Calif. Publ. Am. Arch. and Ethn., vol.
        31, no. 3, pp. 67–210.
    1936. Chemehuevi Shamanism. *In* Essays in Anthropology, Presented to A. L. Kroeber. Berke-
        ley, pp. xxiii + 433; see pp. 129–142.
    1938. Northern Paiute Tales. Jour. Am. Folk-Lore, vol. 51, no. 202, pp. 363–438.
    1939. Southern Paiute Shamanism. Univ. Calif. Anthro. Rec., vol. 2, no. 4, pp. 151–167.

KELSEY, ANNA MARIETTA
1952. Through the Years: Reminiscences of Pioneer Days on the Texas Border. San Antonio, pp. xii + 179.

KEMBLE, FRANCES A.
1863. Journal of a Residence on a Georgia Plantation in 1838–1839. New York, pp. 1–337.

KEMSLEY, W. M.
1928. Snake Skins and Oil. Outdoor Life, vol. 62, no. 6, pp. 55–56. [See also vol. 68, no. 6, p. 76; vol. 67, no. 4, p. 109; vol. 67, no. 1, p. 77.]

KENDALL, G. W.
1844. Narrative of the Texan Santa Fé Expedition. New York, 2 vols., pp. xii + 405; xii + 406.

KENDALL, S. D.
1892. Rattlesnakes and Their Ways. Forest and Stream, vol. 38, no. 25, p. 588.

KENNEDY, BESS
1942. The Lady and the Lions. New York, pp. 1–221.

KENNEDY, G.
1905. Another Snake Story. Forest and Stream, vol. 65, no. 23, p. 451. [See also p. 489.]

KENNEDY, W.
1841. Texas: The Rise, Progress, and Prospects of the Republic of Texas. London, 2 vols., pp. liii + 378; vii + 548.

KENNEDY, W. L.
1879. Medicinal Plants. Pac. Rural Press, vol. 17, no. 20, p. 328.

KENTON, EDNA (editor)
1927. The Indians of North America. New York, 2 vols., pp. xvii + 597; xv + 579.

KER, H.
1816. Travels through the Western Interior of the United States. Elizabethtown. N. J., pp. viii + 9–376.

KERCHEVAL, S.
1833. A History of the Valley of Virginia. Winchester, Va., pp. xlvi + 47–486.

KERMAN, K.
1942. Rattlesnake Religion. *In* Eve's Stepchildren: A Collection of Folk Americana, edited by Lealon N. Jones. Caldwell, Idaho, pp. 1–310; see pp. 93–102.

KERR, R. (translator)
1802. The Natural History of Oviparous Quadrupeds and Serpents. [A translation of Lacépède's Histoire Naturelle des Quadrupedes Ovipares et des Serpens. Paris, 2 vols., 1788–1789.] Edinburgh, 4 vols., 1802. [Rattlesnakes in vol. 4, pp. 245–284.]

KERRISON, R. F.
1945. Chased by a Mamba. Country Life (London), vol. 97, no. 2505, p. 122.

KEY, E.
1950. He Should Have Been Hibernating. Desert Mag., vol. 13, no. 5, p. 30.

KEYSOR, C. W.
1948. It Could Happen to You. Field and Stream, vol. 52, no. 12, pp. 58–59, 146–148.

KIERNANDER, J.
1749. Radix Senega. Holmiae, pp. 1–32 [not seen]. Reprinted in Amoen. Acad. (Linné), vol. 2, no. 22, pp. 112–136, Amstelaedami, 1752.

KILBOURNE, H. S.
1881. Arrow Wounds. Buffalo Med. and Surg. Jour., vol. 20, no. 12, pp. 538–544.

KIMBERLY, JANE
1954. Neighbors: Lore of Worcester, Mass. N. Y. Folklore Quart., vol. 10, no. 1, pp. 57–67.

KINCAID, E. B.
1931. The New Mexican *Pastor*. Publ. Tex. Folk-lore Soc., vol. 9, pp. 63–68.

[KING, C.]
1932. Snake-Bite Victim Saved by Officers. U. S. Army Recruiting News, vol. 14, no. 18, p. 7.

KING, E. P.
1848. Bite of a "Copper Head" Successfully Treated by Indigo. Annalist, vol. 2, no. 12, p. 229. [Also Buffalo Med. Jour., vol. 4, no. 2, pp. 115–116.]

KING, ELIZABETH W.

1946. Seals of Our Nation, States, and Territories. Natl. Geog. Mag., vol. 90, no. 1, pp. 1–42.

KING, J. A.

1955. Social Behavior, Social Organization, and Population Dynamics in a Black-Tailed Prairie-dog Town in the Black Hills of South Dakota. Contrib. Lab. Vert. Biol., Univ. Mich., no. 67, pp. 1–123.

KING, W.

1939. A Survey of the Herpetology of Great Smoky Mountains National Park. Am. Midl. Nat., vol. 21, no. 3, pp. 531–582.

KING, W. A., JR.

1941. The Reptile Reporter. Brownsville, Tex., pp. vi + 65.

KINGHORN, J. R., and C. H. KELLAWAY

1943. The Dangerous Snakes of the Southwest Pacific Area. Melbourne, pp. 1–43.

KINGMAN, D. C.

1894. The Suicide of a Serpent. Forest and Stream, vol. 42, no. 23, p. 488. [See also p. 532, and vol. 43, p. 28.]

KINIETZ, W. V.

1940. The Indians of the Western Great Lakes, 1615–1760. Occ. Contrib. Mus. Anthro. Univ Mich., no. 10, pp. xiv + 427.

KIPLING, R.

1928. Poison of Asps. Liberty, March 3, 1928, pp. 17–18.

KIRKLAND, E. S.

1951. Did He Make the Tracks? Calico Print, vol. 7, no. 3, p. 6.

KIRKLAND, F.

1939. Indian Pictures in the Dry Shelters of Val Verde County, Texas. Bull. Tex. Arch. and Paleo. Soc., vol. 11, pp. 47–76.

KIRTLAND, J. P.

1838. Report on the Zoölogy of Ohio. 2nd Ann. Rept. Geol. Sur. Ohio, pp. 157–200.

KITTREDGE, G. L.

1913. Letters of Samuel Lee and Samuel Sewall Relating to New England and the Indians. Publ. Col. Soc. Mass., vol. 14, pp. 142–186.

1916. Cotton Mather's Scientific Communications to the Royal Society. Proc. Am. Antiq. Soc., vol. 26 (n.s.), pp. 18–57.

KLAPWYK, M.

1944. The Speed of Snakes. Country Life (London), vol. 96, no. 2488, p. 516.

KLAUBER, L. M.

1924. Notes on the Distribution of Snakes in San Diego County, California. Bull. Zoöl. Soc. San Diego, no. 1, pp. 1–23.

1927. Some Observations on the Rattlesnakes of the Extreme Southwest. Bull. Antivenin Inst. Am., vol. 1, no. 1, pp. 7–21.

1928. The Collection of Rattlesnake Venom. Bull. Antivenin Inst. Am., vol. 2, no. 1, pp. 11–18.

1930a. New and Renamed Subspecies of *Crotalus confluentus* Say, with Remarks on Related Species. Trans. San Diego Soc. Nat. Hist., vol. 6, no. 3, pp. 95–144.

1930b. Differential Characteristics of Southwestern Rattlesnakes Allied to *Crotalus atrox*. Bull. Zoöl. Soc. San Diego, no. 6, pp. 1–70.

1931a. *Crotalus tigris* and *Crotalus enyo*, Two Little Known Rattlesnakes of the Southwest. Trans. San Diego Soc. Nat. Hist., vol. 6, no. 24, pp. 353–370.

1931b. A Statistical Survey of the Snakes of the Southern Border of California. Bull. Zoöl. Soc. San Diego, no. 8, pp. 1–93.

1932a. A Herpetological Review of the Hopi Snake Dance. Bull. Zoöl. Soc. San Diego, no. 9, pp. 1–93.

1932b. Amphibians and Reptiles Observed Enroute to Hoover Dam. Copeia, no. 3, pp. 118–128.

1934. Annotated List of the Amphibians and Reptiles of the Southern Border of California. Bull. Zoöl. Soc. San Diego, no. 11, p. 1–28.

1935a. A New Subspecies of *Crotalus confluentus*, the Prairie Rattlesnake. Trans. San Diego Soc. Nat. Hist., vol. 8, no. 13, pp. 75–90.

1935b. Notes on Herpetological Field Collecting. San Diego Soc. Nat. Hist., Coll. Leafl. no. 1, pp. 1–10.

1936a. *Crotalus mitchellii,* the Speckled Rattlesnake. Trans. San Diego Soc. Nat. Hist., vol. 8, no. 19, pp. 149–184.

1936b. A Statistical Study of the Rattlesnakes: I. Introduction; II. Sex Ratio; III. Birth Rate. Occ. Papers San Diego Soc. Nat. Hist., no. 1, pp. 1–24.

1936c. Key to the Rattlesnakes with Summary of Characteristics. Trans. San Diego Soc. Nat. Hist., vol. 8, no. 20, pp. 185–276.

1936d. The California King Snake, a Case of Pattern Dimorphism. Herpetologica, vol. 1, no. 1, pp. 18–27.

1937. A Statistical Study of the Rattlesnakes. IV. The Growth of the Rattlesnake. Occ. Papers San Diego Soc. Nat. Hist., no. 3, pp. 1–56.

1938. A Statistical Study of the Rattlesnakes. V. Head Dimensions. Occ. Papers San Diego Soc. Nat. Hist., no. 4, pp. 1–53.

1939a. Studies of Reptile Life in the Arid Southwest. Part I, Night Collecting on the Desert with Ecological Statistics; Part II, Speculations on Protective Coloration and Protective Reflectivity; Part III, Notes on Some Lizards of the Southwestern United States. Bull. Zoöl. Soc. San Diego, no. 14, pp. 1–100.

1939b. A Statistical Study of the Rattlesnakes. VI. Fangs. Occ. Papers San Diego Soc. Nat. Hist., no. 5, pp. 1–61.

1939c. A Further Study of Pattern Dimorphism in the California King Snake. Bull. Zoöl. Soc. San Diego, no. 15, pp. 1–23.

1940a. The Lyre Snakes (Genus *Trimorphodon*) of the United States. Trans. San Diego Soc. Nat. Hist., vol. 9, no. 19, pp. 163–194.

1940b. A Statistical Study of the Rattlesnakes. VII. The Rattle, Part I. Occ. Papers San Diego Soc. Nat. Hist., no. 6, pp. 1–62.

1941a. A New Species of Rattlesnake from Venezuela. Trans. San Diego Soc. Nat. Hist., vol. 9, no. 30, pp. 333–336.

1941b. Four Papers on the Application of Statistical Methods to Herpetological Problems. Bull. Zoöl. Soc. San Diego, no. 17, pp. 1–95.

1943a. Tail-Length Differences in Snakes with Notes on Sexual Dimorphism and the Coefficient of Divergence. Bull. Zoöl. Soc. San Diego, no. 18, pp. 1–60.

1943b. A Graphic Method of Showing Relationships. Bull. Zoöl. Soc. San Diego, no. 18, pp. 61–76.

1943c. The Correlation of Variability within and between Rattlesnake Populations. Copeia, no. 2, pp. 115–118.

1944. The Sidewinder, *Crotalus cerastes,* with Description of a New Subspecies. Trans. San Diego Soc. Nat. Hist., vol. 10, no. 8, pp. 91–126.

1945. Herpetological Correlations. I. Correlations in Homogeneous Populations. Bull. Zoöl. Soc. San Diego, no. 21, pp. 1–101.

1947. How the Hopi Handle Rattlesnakes. Plateau, vol. 19, no. 3, pp. 37–39.

1948a. Earliest Printed Illustration of Rattlesnakes. Isis, vol. 39, no. 118, part 4, pp. 334–335

1948b. The Truth about the Speckled Band. Baker Street Jour., vol. 3, no. 2, pp. 149–157.

1949a. The Relationship of *Crotalus ruber* and *Crotalus lucasensis.* Trans. San Diego Soc. Nat. Hist., vol. 11, no. 5, pp. 57–60.

1949b. Some New and Revived Subspecies of Rattlesnakes. Trans. San Diego Soc. Nat. Hist., vol. 11, no. 6, pp. 61–116.

1949c. The Subspecies of the Ridge-Nosed Rattlesnake, *Crotalus willardi.* Trans. San Diego Soc. Nat. Hist., vol. 11, no. 8, pp. 121–140.

1952. Taxonomic Studies of the Rattlesnakes of Mainland Mexico. Bull Zoöl. Soc. San Diego, no. 26, pp. 1–143.

KLIMEK, S.
1935. Culture Element Distributions: I. The Structure of California Indian Culture. Univ. Calif. Publ. Am. Arch. and Ethn., vol. 37, no. 1, pp. 1–70.

KLUCKHOHN, C.
1944. Navaho Witchcraft. Papers Peabody Mus. Am. Arch. and Ethn., vol. 22, no. 2, pp. x + 149.

KLUCKHOHN, C., and L. C. WYMAN

1940. An Introduction to Navaho Chant Practice. Mem. Am. Anthro. Assn., no. 53, pp. 1–204.

KNOTT, J. J.

1877. A Case of Rattlesnake Bite Successfully Treated by Injections of Carbonate of Ammonia into Veins. Med. and Surg. Reporter, vol. 37, no. 3, pp. 46–48; no. 4, pp. 79–80. [See also T. A. Elder, no. 6, pp. 118–119.]

KNOX, R.

1826. On the Mode of Growth, Reproduction, and Structure of the Poison-Fangs in Serpents. Mem. Werner Nat. Hist. Soc., vol. 5, no. 24, pp. 411–423.

KOCH, F. J.

1925. Rattlesnake Venom for Use of the Druggist: Unique Methods for Obtaining This One of the Homeopath's Most Treasured Drugs. Am. Drug., vol. 73, no. 6, pp. 16–17.

KOENIG, C.

1906. Die Rassel der Klapperschlange. Naturwiss. Wochensch., vol. 21, no. 4, pp. 49–55.

KOLB, D. W.

1946. Snake Story. Okla. Game and Fish News, vol. 2, no. 10, p. 22.

KOLLER, J.

1946. Rattlesnake Harvests Pay in Preventing Livestock Losses. Westerner (Denver), vol. 9, no. 2, pp. 13, 43–47.

KOPSTEIN, F.

1914. *Vipera macrops* Méhély in Freiheit und im Aquarium. Blat. Aquar. Terr., vol. 25, pp. 589–596.

1938. Ein Beitrag zur Eierkunde Fortpflanzung der Malaüschen Reptilien. Bull. Raffles Mus., vol. 14, pp. 81–167.

KOSCICKY, ———

1878. Antidote to Snake Bites. Pac. Rural Press, vol. 15, no. 16, p. 247.

KOSTER, H.

1817. Travels in Brazil. 2nd edition, London, 2 vols., pp. xii + 406; iv + 380. [1st edition, London, 1816.]

KRAPPE, A. H.

1930. The Science of Folk-Lore. London, pp. xxi + 344.

KRAUS, R.

1923. Sôbre a Sorotherapia de Mordeduras de Cobras no Brazil. Brazil-Medico, vol. 37, pp. 326–328. [Abstract in Jour. Am. Med. Assn., vol. 81, no. 17, p. 1477.]

1924. Ueber biologische Schlangenforschung. Med. Klinik, vol. 20, no. 23, pp. 771–775.

KRAUS, R., and F. WERNER

1931. Giftschlangen und die Serumbehandlung der Schlangenbisse. Jena, pp. vi + 220.

KROEBER, A. L.

1902–7. The Arapaho. Bull. Am. Mus. Nat. Hist., vol. 18, pp. 1–229; 279–454.

1905. Basket Designs of the Indians of Northwestern California. Univ. Calif. Publ. Am. Arch. and Ethn., vol. 2, no. 4, pp. 105–164.

1906. Two Myths of the Mission Indians of California. Jour. Am. Folk-Lore, vol. 19, no. 75, pp. 309–321.

1907a. The Yokuts Language of South Central California. Univ. Calif. Publ. Am. Arch. and Ethn., vol. 2, no. 5, pp. 165–377.

1907b. Indian Myths of South Central California. Univ. Calif. Publ. Am. Arch. and Ethn., vol. 4, no. 4, pp. 167–250.

1907c. The Religion of the Indians of California. Univ. Calif. Publ. Am. Arch. and Ethn., vol. 4, no. 6, pp. 319–356.

1908. Ethnography of the Cahuilla Indians. Univ. Calif. Publ. Am. Arch. and Ethn., vol. 8, no. 2, pp. 29–68.

1916. Inheritance by Magic. Am. Anthro., vol. 18, no. 1, pp. 19–40.

1922. Elements of Culture in Native California. Univ. Calif. Publ. Am. Arch. and Ethn., vol. 13, no. 8, pp. 259–328.

1925. Handbook of the Indians of California. Bur. Am. Ethn., Bull. 78, pp. xxviii + 995.

1929. The Valley Nisenan. Univ. Calf. Publ. Am. Arch. and Ethn., vol. 24, no. 4, pp. 253–290.

1931. The Seri. Southwest Mus. Papers, no 6, pp. 1–60.

1932. The Patwin and Their Neighbors. Univ. Calif. Publ. Am. Arch. and Ethn., vol. 29, no. 4, pp. 253–423.

1948. Seven Mohave Myths. Univ. Calif. Anthro. Rec., vol. 11, no. 1, pp. vii + 70.

KROEBER, A. L., and E. W. GIFFORD

1949. World Renewal: A Cult System of Native Northwest California. Univ. Calif. Anthro. Rec., vol. 13, no. 1, pp. iv + 155.

KROEBER, HENRIETTE R.

1912. Traditions of the Papago Indians. Jour. Am. Folk-Lore, vol. 25, no. 96, pp. 95–105.

KRUMM-HELLER, A.

1910. Die Feinde der Klapperschlange. Kosmos, vol. 7, no. 11, pp. 418–419.

KUNKLER, G. A.

1855. On the Bite of a Copper Snake. Weekly Med. Gaz. (Columbus), vol. 1, no. 31, pp. 481–483.

KUNZÉ, R. E.

1879. A Rattlesnake. Sci. News, vol. 1, no. 20, pp. 308–312; no. 21, 332–333.

KYES, P., L. MARKIN, and O. J. GRAHAM

1940. Abrupt Increase in Resistance to *Crotalus* Venom. Jour. Infect. Dis., vol. 67, no. 2, pp. 81–83.

LaBARRE, W.

1947. Kiowa Folk Sciences. Jour. Am. Folk-Lore, vol. 60, no. 236, pp. 105–114.

1948. The Aymara Indians of the Lake Titicaca Plateau, Bolivia. Am. Anthro., vol. 50, no. 1, part 2, pp. 1–250.

LABAT, J. B.

1722. Nouveau Voyage aux Isles de l'Amérique. Paris, 6 vols.

LACÉPÈDE, B. G. E.

1788–9. Histoire Naturelle des Quadrupèdes Ovipares et des Serpens. Paris, 2 vols., pp. 18 + 651; 144 + 527. [Many later editions *in* Histoire Naturelle par Buffon.]

LACERDA, J. B. DE

1881. O Permanganato de Potassa como Antidoto da Peçonha das Cobras. União Medica, vol. 1, pp. 514–519, 561–568. [Also Compt. Rend. Acad. Sci., vol. 93, pp. 466–468.]

1884. Leçons sur le Venin des Serpents du Brésil et sur la Méthode de Traitement des Morsures Venimeuses par le Permanganate de Potasse. Rio de Janeiro, pp. xvii + 194.

LACOMBE, A.

1851. Bites of Rattle and Other Poisonous Snakes Treated in Venezuela. Boston Med. and Surg. Jour., vol. 44, no. 15, pp. 289–292. [See also pp. 119–120.]

LaFLESCHE, F.

1921. The Osage Tribe: Rite of the Chiefs; Sayings of the Ancient Men. 36th Ann. Rept. Bur. Am. Ethn., pp. 37–597.

1930. The Osage Tribe: Rite of the Wa-xo-be. 45th Ann. Rept. Bur. Am. Ethn., pp. 523–833.

LAHONTAN, L-A. DE

1703. New Voyages to North-America. London, 2 vols., pp. [xxii] + 280; 302 + [xiii]. [First published Paris, 1703.]

LAMB, G.

1903. Specificity of Antivenomous Sera. Sci. Mem. by Officers of Med. San. Depts. of India, Calcutta, no. 5, pp. 1–14. [Also 2nd communication, 1904, no. 10, pp. 1–25.]

1904. On the Serum Therapeutics of Cases of Snake-Bite. Lancet, vol. 2, no. 4236, pp. 1273–1277.

LAMB, G., and W. HANNA

1902. Standardization of Calmette's Anti-Venomous Serum with Pure Cobra Venom. Sci. Mem. Govt. India, n. s., no. 1, pp. 1–19.

LANDA, DIEGO DE

1937. Yucatan before and after the Conquest. Translated with notes by William Gates. 2nd edition, Baltimore, pp. xvi + 162. [First published in Paris, 1864, as Relation des Choses de Yucatan, pp. [4] + cxii + 516.]

1938. Relación de las Cosas de Yucatán. 7th edition. Introducción y Notas por H. P. Martínez. México, pp. 1–411.

LANE, F. W.

    1944. The Speed of Snakes. Country Life (London), vol. 96, no. 2489, p. 557.

    1951. Animal Wonder World. New York, pp. 1–310.

[LANE, R. L.]

    1946. Deep Fork Rattler. Okla. Game and Fish News, vol. 2, no. 10, p. 20.

LANE, ROSE WILDER

    1927. Yarbwoman. Harper's Mag., vol. 155, pp. 210–221.

LANG, A.

    1893. The True Story Book. London, pp. xiv + 337.

LANGFORD, J. O., and F. GIPSON

    1952. Big Bend: A Homesteader's Story. Austin, Tex., pp. viii + 159.

LANGLEY, DAMA MARGARET (MRS. WHITE MOUNTAIN SMITH)

    1945. "I Was a Snake Priest." Desert Mag., vol. 8, no. 11, pp. 5–8.

    1954. Revolt against Ancient Gods. Desert Mag., vol. 17, no. 8, pp. 4–8.

LANGMANN, G.

    1900. Poisonous Snakes and Snake Poison. Med. Rec., vol. 58, no. 11, pp. 401–409. [See also vol. 57, no. 22, pp. 968–969. Condensed in Sci. Am. Supp., vol. 50, no. 1296, p. 20777; no. 1297, pp. 20785–20786.]

LANMAN, C.

    1863. Adventures in the Wilds of North America. The Travellers Library, London, vol. 12, pp. vi + 300.

LANSZWEERT, L.

    1871. Arseniate of Strychnia: New Antidote to the Poison of Snakes. Pac. Med. and Surg. Jour., vol. 5, no. 51, pp. 108–115.

LA POINTE, J.

    1953. Case Report of a Bite from the Massasauga, *Sistrurus catenatus catenatus.* Copeia, no. 2, pp. 128–129.

LaRIVERS, I.

    1942. Some New Amphibian and Reptile Records for Nevada. Jour. Ent. and Zoöl. (Pomona College), vol. 34, no. 3, pp. 53–68.

    1944. Observations on the Nesting Mortality of the Brewer Blackbird, *Euphagus cyanocephalus.* Am. Midl. Nat., vol. 32, no. 2, pp. 417–437.

LaROCHEFOUCAULT* LIANCOURT, F. A. F. DUC DE

    1799. Travels through the United States of North America. London, 2 vols., pp. xxiii + 642 + [12]; 686 + [9]. [1st edition, Paris, 8 vols., 1799.]

LASLEY, MARY

    1902. Sac and Fox Tales. Jour. Am. Folk-Lore, vol. 15, no. 58, pp. 170–178.

LATHAM, R. M.

    1950. The Food of Predaceous Animals in Northeastern United States. Pa. Game Comm., Harrisburg, pp. 1–69.

    1951. The Ecology and Economics of Predator Management. Pa. Game Comm., Harrisburg, pp. 1–96.

LATROBE, C. J.

    1836. The Rambler in North America: 1832–1833. 2nd edition, London, 2 vols., pp. xi + 321; viii + 336. [1st edition, 1835, New York and London, same pagination.]

LATTA, F. F.

    1936. California Indian Folklore. Shafter, Calif., pp. [iv] + 209.

LAVERAN, A.

    1902. Sur quelques Hemogregarines des Ophidiens. Comp. Rend. Acad. Sci., vol. 135, pp. 1036–1040.

LAWRENCE, A. B.

    1840. Texas in 1840, or the Emigrant's Guide to the New Republic. New York, pp. 1–275.

LAWSON, J.

    1709. A New Voyage to Carolina. London, pp. [iii] + 258. [Reprinted 1714 as History of North Carolina, London, pp. 1–258; also 1937, Richmond, Va., pp. xxix + 259.]

---

* More properly Rochefoucauld, but in citations I have used the spelling of the English edition.

LAY, D. W.
 1940. Bob-White Populations as Affected by Woodland Management in Eastern Texas. Tex. Agric. Exp. Sta., Bull. 592, pp. 1–37.

LEACH, MARIA (editor)
 1949–50. Dictionary of Folklore, Mythology, and Legend. New York, 2 vols., pp. xii + 531; 532–1196.

LEAN, V. S.
 1902–4. Lean's Collectanea. Bristol, 4 vols.

LEBEAU, C.
 1738. Avantures du Sr. C. LeBeau, Avocat en Parlement ou Voyage Curieux et Nouveau, Parmi les Sauvages de l'Amérique Septentrionale. Amsterdam, 2 vols., pp. [xii] + 370 + [vi]; 1–430 + [vi].

LECHFORD, T.
 1642. Plain Dealing: or, Newes from New-England. London, pp. 1–80.

LECONTE, J.
 1853. Observations on the So-Called *Crotalus durissus* and *C. adamanteus* cf Modern Authors. Proc. Acad. Nat. Sci. Phila., vol. 6, pp. 415–420.
 1858. On the Venomous Serpents of Georgia. So. Med. and Surg. Jour., vol. 9, no. 11, part 1, pp. 645–667.

LEDERER, G.
 1936. Beobachtungen und Klapperschlangen. Zool. Garten, vol. 8, pp. 132–136.

[LEDERER, J.]
 1672. The Discoveries of John Lederer in Three Several Marches from Virginia to the West of Carolina . . . Translated out of the Latine . . . by Sir William Talbot. London, pp. [iv] + 1–27. [Reprint Rochester, N. Y., 1902, pp. 1–30.]

LEECH, P. N.
 1940a. Report of the Council. Snake Venom Solution (Moccasin) Not Acceptable for N. N. R. Jour. Am. Med. Assn., vol. 114, no. 22, pp. 2218–2219.
 1940b. Cobra Venom Solution (Secretion of *Naja*). Jour. Am. Med. Assn., vol. 115, pp. 1196–1197.

LEIDY, J.
 1884. *Pentastomum proboscideum.* Proc. Acad. Sci. Phila., vol. 36, p. 140.

LEIGHTON, G. R.
 1901. The Life-History of British Serpents. Edinburgh and London, pp. xvi + 383.

LEIGHTON, M. W.
 1892. Something about Snakes. St. Nicholas, vol. 19, no. 10, pp. 730–736.

LELAND, C. G.
 1884. The Algonquin Legends of New England. Boston and New York, pp. xvii + 379.

LEOPOLD, A. S.
 1950. Vegetation Zones of Mexico. Ecology, vol. 31, no. 4, pp. 507–518.

LEPAGE DU PRATZ, M.
 1774. The History of Louisiana. London, pp. xxxvi + 387. [First published Paris, 1758, 3 vols. 1st English edition, London, 1763, 2 vols.]

LERAY, W. J.
 1930. The Rattlesnake (*Sistrurus catenatus*) in Ontario. Can. Field Nat., vol. 44, no. 9, pp. 201–203.

"LEROY"
 1891. Good-Natured Rattlesnakes. Forest and Stream, vol. 37, no. 3, p. 44.

LESSER, M. A.
 1938. Therapeutic Venoms. Drug and Cosmetic Ind., vol. 43, no. 3, pp. 286–289, 294–295.

LESTER, H. M.
 1955. How We Photographed a Rattlesnake's Strike. PSA [Photo. Soc. Am.] Jour., vol. 21, no. 8, pp. 22–26. [See also Animal Kingdom, vol. 58, no. 4, pp. 116–123.]

LEUTSCHER, A.
 1950. The Mechanics of Snakes. Discovery, vol. 11, no. 12, p. 390–395. [Reprinted in Ann. Rept. Smithson. Inst., 1951, pp. 303–312.]

LEVERING, N.
    1878. The Two Headed Snake. Pac. Rural Press, vol. 15, no. 13, p. 194. [Also in Mining and Sci. Press, vol. 36, no. 13, p. 194.]

LEWIS, E.
    1874. Concerning Serpents. Pop. Sci. Monthly, vol. 6, pp. 257–275.

LEWIS, MARGARET L.
    1892. The Valley Manuscript. So. Hist. Mag., vol. 1, no. 5, pp. 227–240.

LEWIS, T. H.
    1949. Dark Coloration in the Reptiles of the Tularosa Malpais, New Mexico. Copeia, no. 3, pp. 181–184.

LEWIS, W. A.
    1906. Death from Rattlesnake Bite. Jour. Am. Med. Assn., vol. 47, no. 24, p. 2012.

LEWITUS, V.
    1935. Venomous Snakes. Am. Jour. Nursing, vol. 35, no. 6, pp. 542–547.

LEYDIG, F.
    1868. Ueber Organe eines sechsten Sinnes. Verhand. Kaiser Leopold-Carol. deutschen Akad. der Naturforscher, vol. 34, no. 5, pp. 1–108.

    1872. Zur Kenntniss der Sinnesorgane der Schlangen. Archiv. Mikrosk. Anat., vol. 8, pp. 317–357.

LIETTE, P. DE
    1947. Memoir of Pierre de Liette. Edited by Milo M. Quaife. The Western Country in the 17th Century. Chicago, pp. xxx + 181; see pp. 87–171. [Written in 1702.]

LINDESTRÖM, P.
    1925. Geographia Americae with an Account of the Delaware Indians. Based on Survey and Notes Made in 1654–1656. Translated by Amandus Johnson. Philadelphia, pp. xliv + 418. [Earliest edition, Stockholm, 1923, pp. 200.]

LINDSLY, H.
    1852. Alcohol as a Remedy for the Poison of the Rattlesnake. Steth. and Va. Med. Gaz., vol. 2, no. 10, pp. 540–541. [Reprinted in North-west. Med. and Surg. Jour., vol. 1 (n.s.), no. 7, pp. 317–318.]

LINNAEUS, C. [C. LINNÉ]
    1746. Museum Adolpho-Fridericianum, quod . . . Subpraesidio . . . C. Linnaei . . . submittit L. Balk . . . Holmiae, pp. 1–48. [Reprinted as Museum Principis in Amoenitates Academicae, Holmiae et Lipsae, 1749, vol. 1, no. 11, pp. 277–326.]

    1758. Systema Naturae per Regna Tria Naturae. 10th edition, Holmiae, vol. 1, Animalia, pp [iv] + 823 + [1].

LINSDALE, J. M.
    1927. Amphibians and Reptiles of Doniphan County, Kansas. Copeia, no. 164, pp. 75–81.

    1932. Amphibians and Reptiles from Lower California. Univ. Calif. Publ. Zoöl., vol. 38, no. 6, pp. 345–386.

    1940. Amphibians and Reptiles in Nevada. Proc. Am. Acad. Arts and Sci., vol. 73, no. 8, pp. 197–257.

    1946. The California Ground Squirrel. Berkeley and Los Angeles, pp. xi + 475.

LINSDALE, J. M., and L. P. TEVIS, JR.
    1951. The Dusky-Footed Wood Rat. Berkeley and Los Angeles, pp. x + 664.

LINSLEY, J. H.
    1843. A Catalogue of the Reptiles of Connecticut. Am. Jour. Sci. and Arts, vol. 46, no. 1, pp. 37–51.

LISSMANN, H. W.
    1950. Rectilinear Locomotion in a Snake (*Boa occidentalis*). Jour. Exp. Biol., vol. 26, no. 4, pp. 368–379.

LIVINGSTONE, D.
    1858. Missionary Travels and Researches in South Africa. New York, pp. xxiv + 732.

LLOYD, A.
    1951. Oklahoma's Big Snake. Desert Mag., vol. 14, no. 3, p. 30.

    1954. The Immune Indian. Desert Mag., vol. 17, no. 4, p. 28.

LLOYD, D. J., A. F. R. COTTON, H. W. PARKER, D. PRAIN, and J. R. FURLONG

1933. The Collection of Reptile Skins for Commercial Purposes with Reference to the Possibilities in Empire Countries. Report by the Advisory Committee on Hides and Skins. Imperial Institute, London, pp. 1–33.

LLOYD, F.

1925. Mr. Rattlesnake, a Gentleman. Touring Topics, vol. 24, pp. 18–19, 32.

"LOCH LADDIE"

1908. Missouri Rattlesnakes. Forest and Stream, vol. 71, no. 25, p. 979.

LOCKETT, HATTIE G.

1933. The Unwritten Literature of the Hopi. Univ. Ariz. Bull., vol. 4, no. 4 (Soc. Sci. Bull. no. 2), pp. 1–101.

LOEB, E. M.

1926. Pomo Folkways. Univ. Calif. Publ. Am. Arch. and Ethn., vol. 19, no. 2, pp. 149–405.

1932. The Western Kuksu Cult. Univ. Calif Publ. Am. Arch. and Ethn., vol. 33, no. 1, pp. 1–137.

1933. The Eastern Kuksu Cult. Univ. Calif. Publ. Am. Arch. and Ethn., vol. 33, no. 2, pp. 139–232.

LOENNBERG, E.

1894. Notes on Reptiles and Batrachians Collected in Florida in 1892 and 1893. Proc. U. S. Nat. Mus., vol. 17, no. 1003, pp. 317–339.

LOEWEN, S. L.

1940. On Some Reptilian Cestodes of the Genus *Oochoristica* (Anoplocephalidae). Trans. Am. Micro. Soc., vol. 59, no. 4, pp. 511–518.

1947. Notes on a Rattlesnake in Captivity. Turtox News, vol. 25, no. 2, pp. 53–54.

LOGAN, J. H.

1859. A History of the Upper Country of South Carolina, vol. 1 [all published]. Charleston, S. C., pp. xi + 521.

LOGIER, E. B. S.

1941. The Amphibians and Reptiles of Prince Edward County, Ontario. Univ. Toronto Stud., Biol. Ser., no. 48, pp. 93–106.

LOMBARD, H. I.

1881. The Rattlesnake and the Copperhead. Forest and Stream, vol. 17, no. 5, p. 88.

LONES, T. E.

1912. Aristotle's Researches in Natural Science. London, pp. viii + 274.

LONG, J.

1791. Voyages and Travels of an Indian Interpreter and Trader. London, pp. x + 295. [Also in Thwaites: Early Western Travels, 32 vols., Cleveland, 1904–1907; see vol. 2.]

LONG, W. S.

1935. Rattlesnakes. Zion-Bryce Nat. Notes, vol. 7, no. 4, pp. 32–34.

LOOMIS, C. G.

1949. Indications of Miners' Medicine. West. Folklore, vol. 8, no. 2, pp. 117–122.

LOOMIS, R. B.

1948. Notes on the Herpetology of Adams County, Iowa. Herpetologica, vol. 4, no. 4, pp. 121–122.

1951. Increased Rate of Ecdysis in *Crotalus* Caused by Chiggers Damaging a Facial Pit. Herpetologica, vol. 7, part 2, pp. 83–84.

LÓPEZ DE GOMARA, F. (See under GOMARA, F. L. DE)

LÓPEZ DE VELASCO, J.

1894. Geographía y Descripción Universal de las Indias ... 1571 al 1574 ... con Adiciones por Don Justo Zaragoza. Bol. Soc. Geog., Madrid, pp. xvi + 808.

LOSKIEL, G. H.

1794. History of the Mission of the United Brethren among the Indians in North America. London, 3 parts, pp. xii + 159, 234, 233 + [21].

LOUNSBERRY, C. R.

1934. Rattlesnake Anaphylaxis Associated with a Generalized Dermatitis. Arch. Dermat. and Syph., vol. 29, pp. 658–667.

Lovejoy, T. P.
    1881. Rattlesnakes Climbing Trees. Forest and Stream, vol. 16, no. 18, p. 347.
Lovell, R.
    1661. Panzoologicomineralogia or a Compleat History of Animals and Minerals. Oxford, pp.
    [iii] + [90] + 519 + 105-152 + 103.
Lowe, C. H. Jr.
    1942. Notes on the Mating of Desert Rattlesnakes. Copeia, no. 4, pp. 261-262.
    1943. An Improved Method of Snake Feeding. Copeia, no. 1, p. 58.
    1948. Territorial Behavior in Snakes and the So-Called Courtship Dance. Herpetologica, vol.
    4, no. 4, pp. 129-135.
Lowe, C. H., Jr., and K. S. Norris
    1950. Aggressive Behavior in Male Sidewinders, *Crotalus cerastes*, with a Discussion of Aggres-
    sive Behavior and Territoriality in Snakes. Nat. Hist. Misc., no. 66, pp. 1-13.
    1954. Analysis of the Herpetofauna of Baja California, Mexico. Trans. San Diego Soc. Nat. Hist.,
    vol. 12, no. 4, pp. 47-64.
Lowe, W. P.
    1944. The Speed of Snakes. Country Life (London), vol. 96, no. 2488, p. 516.
Lowie, R. H.
    1909a. The Northern Shoshone. Anthro. Papers Am. Mus. Nat. Hist., vol. 2, part 2, pp. 165-
    372.
    1909b. The Assiniboine. Anthro. Papers, Am. Mus. Nat. Hist., vol. 4, part 1, pp. 1-270.
    1910. Notes concerning New Collections. Anthro. Papers, Am. Mus. Nat. Hist., vol. 4, part 2,
    pp. 271-329.
    1922. The Religion of the Crow Indians. Anthro. Papers, Am. Mus. Nat. Hist., vol. 25, part 2,
    pp. 309-444.
    1924. Notes on Shoshonean Ethnography. Anthro. Papers, Am. Mus. Nat. Hist., vol. 20, part 3,
    pp. 185-312.
    1929. Notes on Hopi Clans. Anthro. Papers, Am. Mus. Nat. Hist., vol. 30, part 6, pp. 303-360.
    1935. The Crow Indians. New York, pp. xxii + 350.
    1939. Ethnographic Notes on the Washo. Univ. Calif. Publ. Am. Arch. and Ethn., vol. 36, no. 5,
    pp. 301-352.
    1942. Studies in Plains Indian Folklore. Univ. Calif. Publ. Am. Arch. and Ethn., vol. 40, no. 1,
    pp. 1-28.
Lucan [Lucanus, Marcus Annaeus] (See under Duff, J. D., and under Riley, H. T.)
Luck, J. M., and L. Keeler
    1929. The Blood Chemistry of Two Species of Rattlesnakes, *Crotalus atrox* and *Crotalus
    oregonus*. Jour. Biol. Chem., vol. 82, pp. 703-707.
Ludrick, J. N.
    1948. Rattlesnake Roundup. Ford Times, vol. 40, no. 3, pp. 11-14.
Ludwick, Kathleen
    1930. When Rattlers Bite. West. Story Mag., vol. 99, no. 1, pp. 120-122.
Ludwig, M., and H. Rahn
    1943. Sperm Storage and Copulatory Adjustment in the Prairie Rattlesnake. Copeia, no. 1
    pp. 15-18.
Ludy, J. M.
    1926. Allergy from Animal Emanations. Weekly Roster and Med. Digest, vol. 22, no. 7, p. 28.
Lueth, F. X.
    1941a. Effects of Temperature on Snakes. Copeia, no. 3, pp. 125-132.
    1941b. Manual of Illinois Snakes. Illinois Department of Conservation, Springfield, Ill., pp.
    1-48.
Lugger, O.
    1883. Rattlesnakes. Forest and Stream, vol. 20, no. 14, pp. 266-267.
Lumholtz, C.
    1900. Symbolism of the Huichol Indians. Mem. Am. Mus. Nat. Hist., vol. 3, no. 1, pp. 1-228.
    1902. Unknown Mexico. New York, 2 vols., pp. xxxii + 530; xv + 496.
    1912. New Trails in Mexico. New York, pp. xxv + 411.

LUMMIS, C. F.
   1892. Strange Corners of Our Country. III. The Snake Dance of the Moquis. St. Nicholas, vol. 19, no. 6, pp. 421–428.

"LUTRON"
   1878. Snake Fascination. Forest and Stream, vol. 10, no. 8, p. 135. [See also p. 256.]

LYDEKKER, R. (editor)
   1896. The Royal Natural History. London, 1893–1896, 6 vols.; see vol. 5, part 1, Reptiles, pp. 1–256.

LYMAN, H. S.
   1900. Reminiscences of Hugh Cosgrove. Oreg. Hist. Soc. Quart., vol. 1, no. 3, pp. 253–269.

LYMAN, V. A.
   1939. Electric Shocker Extracts Venom from Snakes. Pop. Sci., vol. 134, no. 4, pp. 104–106.

LYNN, W. G.
   1931. The Structure and Function of the Facial Pit of the Pit Vipers. Am. Jour. Anat., vol. 49, no. 1, pp. 97–139.

LYON, M. W., and C. A. BISHOP
   1936. Bite of the Prairie Rattlesnake, *Sistrurus catenatus* Raf. Proc. Ind. Acad. Sci., vol. 45, pp. 253–256.

LYON, W. C.
   1910. Venomous Snakes of the United States, Their Bites and Treatment. Military Surg., vol. 27, no. 4, pp. 383–385.

LYONS, J. J.
   1860. A Case of Snake Bite. N. Orleans Med. and Surg. Jour., vol. 17, pp. 526–527.

McCALLION, J.
   1945. Notes on Texas Reptiles. Herpetologica, vol. 2, nos. 7–8, pp. 197–198.

MacCALLUM, G. A.
   1921. Epidemic Pneumonia in Reptiles. Science, n.s., vol. 54, no. 1395, pp. 279–281.

McCANDLESS, A. D.
   1907. Views on Rattlesnakes. Forest and Stream, vol. 69, no. 26, p. 1012. [See also vol. 70, no. 2, p. 91; no. 6, p. 213.]

McCANDLESS, B., and G. GROSVENOR
   1917. Flags of the World. Natl. Geog. Mag., vol. 32, no. 4, pp. 281–420.

McCANN, C.
   1935. Male Rat-Snakes (*Zamenis mucosus* Boulenger) Fighting. Jour. Bombay Nat. Hist. Soc., vol. 38, no. 2, p. 400.

McCARTY, M. T.
   1914. Asthma, Sciatica and Hysteroepilepsy Treated by a New Method. Am. Med., vol. 20 (vol. 9, n.s.), no. 10, pp. 658–660.

McCAULEY, R. H., JR.
   1941. A Distributional Study of the Reptiles of Maryland and the District of Columbia. Abstract Theses, Cornell Univ., 1940, pp. 267–269.
   1945. The Reptiles of Maryland and the District of Columbia. Hagerstown, Md., pp. [ii] + 194.

MacCLARY, J. S.
   1939a. Fanged Foes of Life in the Open. Rocky Mountain Sportsman (Denver), vol. 3, no. 5, pp. 12–14.
   1939b. Rattlesnakes Are Used. Rocky Mountain Sportsman (Denver), vol. 3, no. 6, pp. 23–24, 30–31, 35.

McCLELLAN, W. H.
   1916. The Alleged Fear of Snakes. Science, vol. 43, no. 1107, pp. 387–388. [See also no. 1117, pp. 744–745.]

McCLURE, D.
   1899. Diary of David McClure, Doctor of Divinity, 1748–1820. New York, pp. vi + 219.

MacCOY, C. V.
   1932. Herpetological Notes from Tucson, Arizona. Occ. Papers Boston Soc. Nat. Hist., vol. 8, pp. 11–24.

McCULLOCH, C. C.
   1918. Ophidismus or Snake Poisoning. N. Y. Med. Jour., vol. 107, no. 1, pp. 1–5.
McDANIELD, H. F., and N. A. TAYLOR
   1877. The Coming Empire; or, Two Thousand Miles in Texas on Horseback. New York, pp.
      1–389.
MacDONALD, C. H.
   1939. Hit by a Rattler. Field and Stream, vol. 44, no. 8, pp. 34–35, 77; also Field and Stream
      Reader, Garden City, N. Y., pp. 133–140 (1946).
McDONNELL, B.
   1950. Can Music Charm Snakes? [with reply by C. M. Bogert]. Nat. Hist., vol. 59, no. 7, pp.
      330–332.
McFARLAND, J.
   1901. Immunization of Animals to Rattlesnake Venom, and Some Studies of Antivenine. Sci-
      ence, vol. 13 (n.s.), no. 322, pp. 325–326. [See also Jour. Am. Med. Assn., vol. 37, pp. 1597–1601.]
   1902. The Progress of Knowledge concerning Venom and Antivenine. A Synoptical Review
      of the Literature of the Past Fifteen Years. Phila. Med. Jour., vol. 9, no. 7, pp. 329–332;
      no. 8, pp. 369–372; no. 9, pp. 403–407; no. 10, pp. 450–457; no. 11, pp. 492–499.
McGEE, W. J.
   1879. Serpent-Charm. Pop. Sci. Monthly, vol. 15, no. 46, pp. 841–842.
   1897. The Siouan Indians. 15th Ann. Rept. Bur. Am. Ethn., pp. 153–244.
   1898. The Seri Indians. 17th Ann. Rept. Bur. Am. Ethn., pp. 1–344.
McGLASSON, CLEO
   1941. Superstitions and Folk Beliefs of Overton County. Tenn. Folklore Soc. Bull., vol. 7,
      no. 2, pp. 13–27.
McGUIRE, W. M.
   1930. Habits of Rattlers. *In* W. A. Bevan's column, Snake Lore. Outdoor Life, vol. 65, no. 2,
      p. 93.
McHUGH, T.
   1952. All Snakes Are Yellow. Mechanix Illustrated, Sept., pp. 92–95.
McKEE, E. D.
   1929. Snakes as Mediators. Grand Canyon Nat. Notes, vol. 4, no. 1, p. 5.
McKENNA, J. A.
   1936. Black Range Tales. New York, pp. xiv + 300.
McKENNAN, R.
   1935. Walapai Ethnography: Medicine: Shamanism. Mem. Am. Anthro. Assn., no. 42, pp.
      117–121; 185–194.
McKENNEY, T. L.
   1846. Memoirs, Official and Personal with Sketches of Travels among the Northern and
      Southern Indians. New York, 2 vols., pp. viii + 17–340; vi + 9–136.
McKENZIE, D.
   1927. The Infancy of Medicine. London, pp. xiii + 421.
McKNIGHT, BLANCHE
   1951. Invincible Seminoles. Fla. Wildlife, vol. 5, no. 6, pp. 4–5, 22–25.
McLANE, J. N.
   1943. Retinal Hemorrhage in a Case of Rattlesnake Bite. Jour. Fla. Med. Assn., vol. 30, no. 1,
      pp. 22–25.
McLEAN, D. D.
   1926. Rattlesnake Swallows a Golden-Manteled Ground Squirrel. Yosemite Nat. Notes, vol. 5,
      no. 8, p. 62.
McMILLAN, W. G.
   1955a. Rattlers [Offer of Payment for Texas Rattlers Exceeding Six Feet in Length]. Tex. Game
      and Fish, vol. 13, no. 3, p. 30; also no. 5, p. 31.
   1955b. Some Truths about the Western Diamondback Rattlesnake in Texas. Tex. Game and
      Fish, vol. 13, no. 8, pp. 8–9, 30.
McNELLIS, R.
   1949. Rattlesnake Bite [in Horses]. Jour. Am. Vet. Med. Assn., vol. 114, no. 864, pp. 145–146.

MacQuarrie, G.
  1941. King of the Snake Country. Outdoor Life, vol. 88, no. 1, pp. 22–23, 82–83.
McReynolds, R.
  1906. Thirty Years on the Frontier. Colorado Springs, pp. iv + 256.
M., J. S.
  1937. Snake Dance Secret Bared. Sci. Am., vol. 156, no. 4, p. 237.
Macbride, T. H.
  1928. In Cabins and Sod-Houses. Iowa City, pp. xv + 368.
Machado, O.
  1945. Estudo Comparativo das Crotalideas do Brasil. Bol. Inst. Vital Brazil, vol. 5, no. 2, pp. 47–66.
Macht, D. I.
  1933. Effects of Snake Venoms on Plants. Proc. Soc. Exp. Biol. and Med., vol. 30, no. 7, pp. 988–990.
  1935. The Effect of Ultraviolet Rays on Snake Venoms. Am. Jour. Med. Sci., vol. 189, pp. 520–533.
  1936a. Experimental and Clinical Study of Cobra Venom as an Analgesic. Proc. Natl. Acad. Sci., vol. 22, no. 1, pp. 61–71.
  1936b. Therapeutic Uses of Snake Venom. Med. Rec., vol. 144, no. 12, pp. 537–539. [See also Jour. Am. Pharm. Assn., vol. 26, pp. 161–162.]
  1937. Comparative Toxicity of Sixteen Specimens of *Crotalus* Venom. Proc. Soc. Exper. Biol. and Med., vol. 36, no. 4, pp. 499–501.
  1938. A Drug or Poison? Sci. Monthly, vol. 47, no. 1, pp. 34–40
  1944. A Pharmacological Note on Proverbs XXIII.32 and Isaiah LIX.5. Bull. Hist. Med., vol. 15, no. 4, pp. 359–374.
  1954. Serpents' Sense of Hearing. Jour. Am. Med. Assn., vol. 154, no. 1, p. 81.
Macht, D. I., and Dorothy B. Kehoe
  1943. The Toxicity of Snake Venoms after Administration by Stomach. Federation Proc., vol. 2, no. 1, p. 31.
Mackie, T. T., G. W. Hunter, III, and C. B. Worth
  1945. A Manual of Tropical Medicine: Prepared under the Auspices of the Division of Medical Sciences of the National Research Council. Philadelphia, pp. xix + 727. [Snakes, pp. 497–502.]
Macleod, N. C.
  1944a. Seven Miles an Hour. Country Life (London), vol. 96, no. 2488, p. 516.
  1944b. The Speed of Snakes. Country Life (London), vol. 96, no. 2492, p. 693.
Maddox, W. A.
  1940. Historical Carvings in Leather: A Lost Art Reclaimed. San Antonio, Tex. pp. xv + 325.
Madsen, W.
  1955. Hot and Cold in the Universe of San Francisco Tecospa, Valley of Mexico. Jour. Am. Folklore, vol. 68, no. 268, pp. 123–139.
Magalhães de Gandavo, Pero de
  1576. Historia da Provincia Sancta Cruz. Lisboa, 48 fols.
  1922. The Histories of Brazil. Translated and Annotated by John B. Stetson, Jr., New York, Cortes Soc., Publ. no. 5, 2 vols., pp. 1–60 + 48 fols.; 1–266.
Magee, J. A.
  1943. Poisonous Snakes of Southern California. Military Surg., vol. 93, pp. 85–90.
Magnin, A.
  1869. The Desert World. London, pp. 1–624.
Maier, E.
  1939. Therapeutic Effects of Snake Venoms. Med. World, vol. 57, no. 3, pp. 181–185.
  1940. Recent Developments in the Pharmacognosy of Snake Venoms. Jour. Int. Coll. Surg., vol. 3, no. 4, pp. 352–356.
Maier, H. K.
  1951. Benadryl Hydrochloride in Treatment of Snake Bite in Dogs. Vet. Med., vol. 46, no. 11, p. 463.

MAIER, N. R. F., and T. C. SCHNEIRLA

    1935. Principles of Animal Psychology. New York, pp. xiii + 529.

MAINZER, F. S.

    1935. Snakebite (*Crotalus horridus*). Med. World, vol. 53, pp. 376–377; also Med. Record, vol. 148, pp. 329–330.

MAITRA, G. C., and M. L. AHUJA

    1931. Potency of Time-Expired Antivenomous Sera Stocked under Ordinary Conditions of Storage at the Central Research Institute, Kasauli. Indian Jour. Med. Res., vol. 19, no. 1, pp. 155–158.

MAJOR, R. H. (editor)

    1849. The Historie of Travaile into Virginia Britannia by William Strachey. London, pp. xxxvi + 203.

MAJORS, A.

    1893. Seventy Years on the Frontier. Chicago, pp. 1–325.

MALER, T.

    1901. Researches in the Central Portion of the Usumatsintla Valley. Mem. Peabody Mus., vol. 2, no. 1, pp. 1–75.

MALLERY, G.

    1886. Pictographs of the North American Indians. 4th Ann. Rept. Bur. Ethn., pp. 3–256.

    1893. Picture-Writing of the American Indians. 10th Ann. Rept. Bur. Ethn., pp. 3–807.

MALLESON, W. T.

    1908. Rattlesnake Colonel. Notes and Queries, ser. 10, vol. 10, p. 189; vol. 11, pp. 17, 135, 191–192, 213.

MALLICK, S. M. K., and G. C. MAITRA

    1932. On the Distribution of Protective Principle in Different Protein Fractions of Horse Serum Immunized against Snake Venom. Indian Jour. Med. Res., vol. 19, no. 3, pp. 951–955.

MALONEY, J.

    1945. Another Man's Poison. Liberty, vol. 22, no. 31, pp. 30–31, 80

MANDELBAUM, D. G.

    1940. The Plains Cree. Anthro. Papers, Am. Mus. Nat. Hist., vol. 37, part 2, pp. 155–316.

MANNING, F. B.

    1923. Hearing in Rattlesnakes. Jour. Comp. Psych., vol. 3, no. 4, pp. 241–247.

MANNIX, D. P.

    1948. True Witnesses a Fatal Cobra Strike. True, vol. 23, no. 138, pp. 28–31, 59–64.

MANU, J. M.

    1947. Rattlers Can Be Treed. Hunting and Fishing, vol. 24, no. 3, p. 53.

"MANZANITA"

    1906. Racer and Rattler. Forest and Stream, vol. 67, no. 19, p. 734.

MANZINI, N. B. L.

    1858. Histoire de l'Inoculation Préservative de la Fièvre Jaune. Paris, pp. xii + 243.

MARABLE, F. W.

    1943. Wages of Sin. Life, vol. 15, no. 16, p. 132.

MARCGRAVIUS, G.

    1648. Historiae Rerum Naturalium Brasiliae. [With an appendix by Joannes de Laet.] Lugduni Batavorum et Amstelodami, pp. vi + 293 + [vii].

MARCH, D. D. H.

    1928. Field Notes on the Neotropical Rattlesnake (*Crotalus terrificus*). Bull. Antivenin Inst. Am., vol. 2, no. 3, pp. 55–61.

    1933. Snakes. Facts about Poisonous Reptiles Gleaned from a Lifelong Association with Them. Field and Stream, vol. 37, no. 9, pp. 36–38, 65, 72.

MARCOS DE NIZA, FRAY (See under BALDWIN, P. M.)

MARCY, D.

    1945. Birth of a Brood of *Crotalus basiliscus*. Copeia, no. 3, pp. 169–170.

MARCY, R. B.

    1850. Report of . . . Route from Fort Smith to Santa Fe. Reports of the Secretary of War, Sen. Doc. 64, pp. 169–227.

1859. The Prairie Traveler: A Hand-Book for Overland Expeditions. New York, pp. xiii + 14–340.

MARKHAM, C. R. (translator and editor)

1864. The Travels of Pedro de Cieza de Leon, A.D. 1532–50. London, pp. lvii + 438.

MARKOWITZ, J., H. E. ESSEX, and F. C. MANN

1931a. The Physiologic Action of Rattlesnake Venom (*Crotalin*). IX. Activity of Protein Fractions of Crotalin. Am., Jour. Physiol., vol. 97, no. 1, pp. 22–25.

1931b. Studies on Immunity to Rattlesnake Venom (Crotalin). Am. Jour. Physiol., vol. 97, no. 1, pp. 180–199. [See also Bull. Antivenin Inst. Am., vol. 5, no. 1, pp. 28–29.]

MARR, J. C.

1944. Notes on Amphibians and Reptiles from the Central United States. Am. Midl. Nat., vol. 32, no. 2, pp. 478–490.

MARRYAT, F. S.

1855. Mountains and Molehills. New York, pp. x + 393.

MARTIN, C. J.

1897. Curative Value of Calmette's Antivenomous Serum in the Treatment of Inoculations with the Poisons of Australian Snakes. Intercolonial Med. Jour. Australasia, vol. 2, no. 8, pp. 527–536. [Also vol. 3, pp. 713–720.]

1930. Thermal Adjustment of Man and Animals to External Conditions. Lancet, vol. 219, no. 5585, pp. 561–567; no. 5586, pp. 617–620; no. 5587, pp. 673–678.

MARTIN, C. J., and G. LAMB

1907. Snake-Poison and Snake-Bite. *In* A System of Medicine, edited by T. C. Allbutt and H. D. Rolleston, London, 1905–1911, 11 vols.; see vol. 2, part 2, pp. 783–821. [1st edition, London, 1896–1899, 8 vols.]

MARTIN, F.-X.

1882. The History of Louisiana from the Earliest Period. New edition, New Orleans, pp. xxxviii + 469 + xvi. [1st edition, New Orleans, 1827–1829, 2 vols.]

MARTIN, H. N.

1946. Folktales of the Alabama-Coushatta Indians. Publ. Tex. Folklore Soc., vol. 21, pp. 65–80.

MARTIN, J. B.

1859. A Remarkable Case of Snake Poison. St. Louis Med. and Surg. Jour., vol. 17, no. 2, pp. 110–116.

MARTIN, MABELLE E. (editor)

1926. From Texas to California in 1849: Diary of C. C. Cox. Southwest. Hist. Quart., vol. 29, no. 3, pp. 201–223.

MARTIN, P. J.

1930. Snake Hunt Nets Large Catch. Bull. Antivenin Inst. Am., vol. 4, no. 3, pp. 77–78.

MARTIN, ROXIE

1947. Old Remedies Collected in the Blue Ridge Mountains. Jour. Am. Folklore, vol. 60, no. 236, pp. 184–185.

MARTIN, W. C. L.

(1851?) A Popular History of Reptiles. London, pp. xii + 328.

MARTÍN DEL CAMPO, R.

1937a. Los Batracios y Reptiles según los Codices y Relatos de los Antiguos Mexicanos. Anales Inst. Biol., vol. 7, no. 4, pp. 489–512.

1937b. Reptiles Ponzoñosos de México: Las Víboras de Cascabel. Foll. Div. Cient., Inst. Biol., no. 27, pp. 1–18.

MASLIN, T. P.

1952. Morphological Criteria of Phyletic Relationships. Syst. Zoöl., vol. 1, no. 2, pp. 49–70.

MASON, J. A.

1912. The Ethnology of the Salinan Indians. Univ. Calif. Publ. Am. Arch. and Ethn., vol. 10, no. 4, pp. 97–240.

MASTERSON, J. R.

1938. Colonial Rattlesnake Lore, 1714. Zoologica, vol. 23, no. 9, pp. 213–216.

1939. The Tale of the Living Fang. Am. Literature, vol. 11, no. 1, pp. 66–73.

MASTERSON, J. R. (*Continued*)

    1942. Tall Tales from Arkansaw. Boston, pp. xi + 443.
    1946. Travelers' Tales of Colonial Natural History. Jour. Am. Folklore, vol. 59, no. 231, pp. 51–67; no. 232, pp. 174–188.

[MATHER, C.]

    1714. An Extract from Several Letters from Cotton Mather, D.D. to John Woodward, M.D. and Richard Waller, Esq.; S. R. Secr. Philos. Trans. (Royal Soc. London), vol. 29, no. 339, pp. 62–71.
    1868. The Mather Papers. Coll. Mass. Hist. Soc., ser. 4, vol. 8, pp. xvi + 736. [See also KITTREDGE, G. L., 1916.]

MATHER, F.

    1873. Do Snakes Hiss? Forest and Stream, vol. 1, no. 18, p. 278. [See also pp. 310, 327, 357; and vol. 14, 1880, pp. 389, 449, 508.]

MATHEWS, M. M.

    1951. A Dictionary of Americanisms on Historical Principles. Chicago, 2 vols., pp. xvi + 976; 977–1946.

MATHEWSON, R.

    1942. Questions Everybody Asks about Snakes. Animal Kingdom, vol. 45, no. 3, pp. 71–75; no. 4, pp. 95–98.

MATSCHAT, CECILE H.

    1938. Suwannee River: Strange Green Land. New York, pp. x + 296.

MATSON, D. S.

    1953. Papago Recordings. Ariz. Quart., vol. 9, no. 1, pp. 45–54.

MATTESON, S. W.

    1899. Daring the Rattler in His Den. Cosmopolitan, vol. 26, no. 6, pp. 665–672.

MATTHEWS, A.

    1910. The Snake Devices, 1754–1776, and the Constitutional Courant, 1765. Publ. Col. Soc. Mass., vol. 11, pp. 409–453.
    1937. "Rattlesnake Colonel." N. Eng. Quart., vol. 10, no. 2, pp. 341–345.

MATTHEWS, W.

    1887. The Mountain Chant: A Navajo Ceremony. 5th Ann. Rept. Bur. Ethn., pp. 379–467.
    1898. Serpent Worship among the Navajos. Land of Sunshine, vol. 9, no. 5, pp. 228–235.

MAUDE, J.

    1826. Visit to the Falls of Niagara in 1800. London, pp. v + 313 + xxvi.

MAUDUYT, R. J. E.

    1774. Sur Quelques Objets du Regne Animal, Apportés de la Louisiane. Observations sur la Physique, vol. 4, pp. 384–397.

MAYHUGH, J. S.

    1894. Western Shoshone Agency. Report Indians Taxed and Not Taxed, 11th Census, pp. 382–395.

[MAYNARD, C. J.]

    1884. Rattlesnakes. Naturalist in Florida, vol. 1, no. 2, p. 8.

MAYRANT, W.

    1823. On the Use of Alcohol in the Disease Produced by the Bite of the Rattlesnake. Am. Med. Rec., vol. 6, no. 4, art. 8, pp. 619–621.

MAYS, M.

    1897. The Ways of Snakes. Forest and Stream, vol. 49, no. 12, p. 225.

MAYS, T. J.

    1909. The Therapeutic Action of Rattlesnake Venom in Pulmonary Consumption, in Acute and Chronic Bronchitis, Asthma, etc., and in Some Well-Recognized Neuroses. Boston Med. and Surg. Jour., vol. 160, no. 15, pp. 481–485.
    1910. Crotalin, an Improved Method for Its Administration. Boston Med. and Surg. Jour., vol. 162, no. 2, pp. 46–47.
    1913a. The Action and Administration of Crotalin in Pulmonary Consumption and in Epilepsy. Med. Rec., vol. 83, no. 13, pp. 561–564.

1913b. The Rattlesnake-Venom Treatment of Epilepsy. Jour. Am. Med. Assn., vol. 60, no. 23, pp. 1811–1812. [See also no. 13, p. 1001.]

1914. The Therapeutic Value of Crotalin in the Treatment of Epilepsy. Med. Rec., vol. 85, no. 3, pp. 105–108.

MEAD, R.

1702. A Mechanical Account of Poisons in Several Essays. London, pp. [xiv] + 175; 2nd edition, 1708, London, pp. [x] + 191.

1745. A Mechanical Account of Poisons in Several Essays. 3rd edition, London, xlviii + 320; 4th edition, 1747, same.

MEADE, G. P.

1940. Observations on Louisiana Captive Snakes. Copeia, no. 3, pp. 165–168.

MEASE, J.

1807. A Geological Account of the United States comprehending a Short Description of Their Animal, Vegetable and Mineral Productions, Antiquities and Curiosities. Philadelphia, pp. 496 + xiv.

1808. On Snake Stones and Other Remedies for the Cure of Diseases Produced by the Bites of Snakes and Mad Dogs. Phila. Med. Mus., vol. 5, no. 1, pp. 1–15.

MECHAM, J. L.

1917. The Rodríguez Expedition into New Mexico, 1581–1582. Unpublished M.A. Thesis, University of California, Berkeley.

MEDDEN, RHEUA V.

1929–31. Tales of the Rattlesnake: From the Works of Early Travelers in America. Bull. Antivenin Inst. Am., vol. 3, no. 3, pp. 82–87; no. 4, pp. 103–112; vol. 4, no. 1, pp. 17–23; no. 2, pp. 43–50; no. 3, pp. 71–75; no. 4, pp. 106–109; vol. 5, no. 1, pp. 24–27; no. 2, pp. 42–46.

MEEK, G.

1946. Creatures of Mystery. Macon, Ga., pp. xii + 274.

MEEK, S. E.

1905. An Annotated List of a Collection of Reptiles from Southern California and Northern Lower California. Field Columb. Mus., Zoöl. Ser., vol. 7, no. 1, pp. 1–19.

MEGAPOLENSIS, J., JR.

1651. Kort ontwerp Vande Mahakuase Indianen in Nieuw-Nederlandt. . . . *In* Joost Hartgers' "Beschrijvinghe van Virginia, Nieuw Nederlandt, . . . ," pp. 42–49.

1857. A Short Account of the Mohawk Indians. Coll. N. Y. Hist. Soc., ser. 2, vol. 3, part 2, pp. 137–160. [First published in Amsterdam in 1651; also in Narratives of New Netherland, 1609–1664, edited by J. Franklin Jameson, New York, 1909, pp. 168–180.]

MEIGS, P., III

1939. The Kiliwa Indians of Lower California. Univ. Calif. Ibero-Americana, no. 15, pp. [iii] + 88.

MELINE, J. F.

1873. Two Thousand Miles on Horseback. New York, pp. x + 317.

MENDES, E.

1952. Snake Venom Allergy. Jour. Am. Med. Assn., vol. 150, no. 13, p. 1328.

MENGER, R.

1903. The Rational Treatment of Snake-Bite and Others with Adrenalin Chloride. Tex. Med. Jour., vol. 18, no. 11, pp. 445–449. [See also vol. 20, no. 7, pp. 263–266, 1905.]

1905. Original Observations, with Photographic Illustrations, on Reptiles and Insects of Texas. Bull. Sci. Soc. San Antonio, vol. 1, no. 1, pp. 11–31.

1913. Texas Nature Observations and Reminiscences. San Antonio, pp. 1–323.

MERCHANTE, F. P.

1936. Composición y Acción de las Proteínas de las Ponzoñas de Serpiente. Rev. Soc. Argentina Biol., vol. 12, no. 1, p. 23–35.

MERRIAM, C. H.

1893. [Field Notes on Rattlesnakes.] *In* STEJNEGER, L. S., 1893.

1910. The Dawn of the World. Myths and Weird Tales Told by the Mewan Indians of California. Cleveland, pp. 1–273.

MERRILL, E., and P. MERRILL

    1817. Gazetteer of State of New-Hampshire. Exeter, pp. 218 + [13].

MERRILL, E. D.

    1943. Figments of the Imagination. Science, vol. 97, no. 2506, pp. 41–42.

MERTENS, R.

    1930. Bemerkungen ueber die von Herrn Dr. K. Lafrentz in Mexiko Gesammelten Amphibien und Reptilien. Abhand. und Berichte Natur. Ver. in Magdeburg, vol. 6, no. 2, pp. 153–161.

    1934. Die Insel-Reptilien, ihre Ausbreitung, Variation und Artbildung. Zoologica (Stuttgart), vol. 84, no. 32, pp. 1–209.

    1953. Die Wüstenottern und ihre Anpassungen an ihren Lebensraum. Natur und Volk, vol. 83, no. 5, pp. 148–156.

MESSELING, E.

    1953. Rattlesnakes in Southwestern Wisconsin. Wis. Cons. Bull., vol. 18, no. 10, pp. 21–23.

METCALFE, F.

    1907. Some Popular Fallacies concerning Rattlesnakes. Outing, vol. 51, no. 1, pp. 122–125.

MÉTRAUX, A.

    1949. Weapons. *In* Handbook of South American Indians, Bur. Am. Ethn., Bull. 143, vol. 5, pp. 229–263.

MICHAUX, F. A.

    1805. Travels to the West of the Alleghany Mountains. London, pp. x + 294. [1st edition Paris, 1804, pp. [iv] + 6 + 312; also *in* Thwaites: Early Western Travels, 32 vols., Cleveland, 1904–1907, vol. 3.]

MICHEEL, F.

    1941. Schlangengifte und ihre Heilsera. Die Umschau, vol. 45, no. 11, pp. 170–173.

MICHEL, F. L.

    1916. Report of the Journey of Francis Louis Michel, from Berne, Switzerland, to Virginia, October 2, 1701–December 1, 1702. Translated and edited by Prof. Wm. J. Hinke. Va. Mag. Hist. and Biog., vol. 24, pp. 1–43; 113–141; 275–303.

MICHENER, H. D.

    1935. Reptiles and Amphibians of the Yosemite Creek Research Reserve. Yosemite Nat. Notes, vol. 14, no. 6, pp. 49–52.

MICHLER, N.

    1857. Report. *In* United States and Mexican Boundary Survey (Emory). Washington, 3 vols.; see vol. 1, pp. 101–125.

MILES, A. H.

    1895. Natural History in Anecdote. New York, pp. xii + 385.

MILI, G.

    1946. How a Rattlesnake Strikes. Life, vol. 21, no. 7, pp. 57–58.

MILLER, A. M.

    1916. Serpent Dread in the Primate Family. Science, vol. 43, no. 1117, pp. 744–745.

MILLER, D.

    1937. Killers of the Desert. Outdoor Life, vol. 8, no. 4, pp. 40–41, 57.

MILLER, H. E.

    1938. Three Dangerous Serpents of Pennsylvania. Pa. Farmer, vol. 119, no. 5, pp. 5, 17–18.

MILLER, J.

    1799. On the Effects of Oil in Cases of the Bite of Serpents. Med. Reposit., vol. 2, no. 2, pp. 253–254.

MILLER, JOSEPH

    1952. The Arizona Story. New York, pp. xvii + 345.

MILLER, L. H.

    1912. Contributions to Avian Paleontology from the Pacific Coast of North America. Univ. Calif. Publ. Geol., vol. 7, no. 5, pp. 61–115.

    1932. Notes on the Desert Tortoise (*Testudo agassizii*). Trans. San Diego Soc. Nat. Hist., vol. 7, no. 18, pp. 187–208.

MILLER, R. J.

    1948. Warning Rattles for Snake Dance Visitors. Desert Mag., vol. 11, no. 10, pp. 11–13.

MILLING, C. J.
1937. Is the Serpent Tale an Indian Survival? So. Folklore Quart., vol. 1, no. 1, pp. 43–55.

MILLS, C. A.
1949. Temperature Dominance over Human Life. Science, vol. 110, no. 2855, pp. 267–271.

MILNE, L. J., and MARGERY J. MILNE
1948. Arizona Is the Horned Toad State. Ariz. Highways, vol. 24, no. 10, pp. 24–27.
1950. Notes on the Behavior of Horned Toads. Am. Midl. Nat., vol. 44, no. 3, pp. 720–741.
1952. The Biotic World and Man. New York, pp. xiv + 588.
1954. The Mating Instinct. Boston, pp. 1–243.

MILSTEAD, W. W., J. S. MECHAM, and H. McCLINTOCK
1950. The Amphibians and Reptiles of the Stockton Plateau in Northern Terrell County, Texas. Tex. Jour. Sci., vol. 2, no. 4, pp. 543–562.

MINDELEFF, C.
1886. An Indian Snake Dance. Science, vol. 8, no. 178, pp. 12–13.

MINICI, ANNA L.
1955. Mockingbird Sounds Alarm. Desert Mag., vol. 18, no. 1, p. 21.

MINTON, S. A., JR.
1944. Introduction to the Study of the Reptiles of Indiana. Am. Midl. Nat., vol. 32, no. 2, pp. 438–477.
1950. Injuries by Venomous Animals in Indiana. Proc. Ind. Acad. Sci., vol. 60, pp. 315–323.
1953. Variation in Venom Samples from Copperheads (*Agkistrodon contortrix mokeson*) and Timber Rattlesnakes (*Crotalus horridus horridus*). Copeia, no. 4, pp. 212–215.
1954. Polyvalent Antivenin in the Treatment of Experimental Snake Poisoning. Am. Jour. Trop. Med. and Hyg., vol. 3, no. 6, pp. 1077–1082.

MITCHELL, A.
1874. Bite of the Diamond Rattlesnake (*Crotalus adamanteus*). Boston Med. and Surg. Jour., vol. 89, no. 14, pp. 331–333.

MITCHELL, J. D.
1903. The Poisonous Snakes of Texas, with Notes on Their Habits. Trans. Tex. Acad. Sci., vol. 5, part 1, no. 2, pp. 21–48.

MITCHELL, P. C.
1922. Monkeys and the Fear of Snakes. Proc. Zoöl. Soc. London for 1922, part 2, pp. 347–348.

MITCHELL, P. C., and R. I. POCOCK
1908. On the Feeding of Reptiles in Captivity. With Observations on the Fear of Snakes by Other Vertebrates. Proc. Zoöl. Soc. London for 1907, pp. 785–794.

MITCHELL, S. W.
1860. Researches upon the Venom of the Rattlesnake. Smithson. Contrib. Knowl., vol. 12, art. 6, pp. viii + 145.
1861. On the Treatment of Rattlesnake Bites, with Experimental Criticisms upon the Various Remedies Now in Use. N. Amer. Medico-Chirurgical Rev., vol. 5, pp. 269–311. [Also briefed in Med. and Surg. Reporter, vol. 6 (n.s.), no. 21, p. 472, 1861.]
1868a. The Poison of the Rattlesnake. Atlantic Monthly, vol. 21, pp. 452–461.
1868b. Experimental Contributions to the Toxicology of Rattlesnake Venom. N. Y. Med. Jour., vol. 6, no. 4, pp. 289–322.
1869. The Venom of Serpents. Med. Times and Gaz., vol. 1, no. 971, pp. 137–138.
1870. Observations on Poisoning with Rattlesnake Venom. With Microscopical Notes by Jos. G. Richardson, M. D. Am. Jour. Med. Sci., vol. 59 (n.s.), no. 2, pp. 317–323.
1889. The Poison of Serpents. Century Ill. Mag., vol. 38, no. 4, pp. 503–514.

MITCHELL, S. W., and E. T. REICHERT
1886. Researches upon the Venoms of Poisonous Serpents. Smithson. Contrib. Knowl., vol. 26, art. 1, pp. ix + 186.

MITCHELL, S. W., and A. H. STEWART
1898. A Contribution to the Study of the Effect of the Venom of *Crotalus adamanteus* upon the Blood of Man and Animals. Mem. Natl. Acad. Sci., vol. 8, no. 2, pp. 1–14.

MITTELBERGER, G.
  1898. Journey to Pennsylvania in the Year 1750 and Return to Germany in the Year 1754. Translation by C. T. Eben. Philadelphia, pp. 1–129. [Original edition Stuttgart, 1756.]

MIVART, ST. G.
  1871. On the Genesis of Species. London, pp. xv + 296.
  1888. Rattlesnake. Encyc. Brit., 9th edition, London, vol. 20, p. 293.

MOHR, C. (committee chairman)
  1901. The Homoeopathic Pharmacopeia of the United States. 2nd edition. Boston, pp. 1–674.

MOHR, C. O.
  1947. Table of Equivalent Populations of North American Small Mammals. Am. Midl. Nat., vol. 37, no. 1, pp. 223–249.

MOLE, R. R.
  1895. On the Formation and Disintegration of Segments of Caudal Appendage in *C. horridus.* Jour. Field Nat. Club (Trinidad), vol. 2, pp. 189–191.

MONAELLESSER, A., and C. TAGUET
  1933. Traitement des Algies et des Tumeurs par le Venin de Cobra. Bull. Acad. Méd., Ser. 3, vol. 109, pp. 371–377.

MONROE, J.
  1824. The American Botanist and Family Physician. Danville, Vt., pp. i–viii, 9–203.

MONTANUS, A.
  1851. Description of New Netherland, 1671. Documentary History of the State of New York, vol. 4, no. 5, pp. 73–83. [Originally published, Amsterdam, 1671, pp. [iv] + 585 + [27], as De Nieuwe en Onbekende Weereld.]

MONTULE, E.
  1821. A Voyage to North America and the West Indies. London, pp. 1–102. [Also edition of 1951, Bloomington, Ind., pp. 1–197.]

MOODY, C. S.
  1907. The Snake's Rattles. Forest and Stream, vol. 69, no. 14, p. 533. [See also pp. 411, 492, 573, 773, 1012; vol. 70, pp. 91, 213.]

MOOK, M. A.
  1935. Walapai Ethnography: Animal Foods. Mem. Am. Anthro. Assn., no. 42, pp. 70–76.

MOONEY, J.
  1891. The Sacred Formulas of the Cherokees. 7th Ann. Rept. Bur. Ethn., pp. 301–397.
  1896. The Ghost-Dance Religion and the Sioux Outbreak of 1890. 14th Ann. Rept. Bur. Ethn., vol. 2, pp. 641–1110.
  1900. Myths of the Cherokee. 19th Ann. Rept. Bur. Am. Ethn., pp. 3–548.

MOONEY, J., and F. M. OLBRECHTS
  1932. The Swimmer Manuscript: Cherokee Sacred Formulas and Medicinal Prescriptions. Bur. Am. Ethn., Bull. 99, pp. xvii + 319.

MOORE, C. B.
  1949. America's Mythical Snakes. Sci. Monthly, vol. 68, no. 1, pp. 52–58.

MOORE, F.
  1744. A Voyage to Georgia, Begun in the Year 1735. London, pp. 1–108 + ii.

MOORE, I.
  1828. Cases Showing the Efficacy of the Volatile Alkali in the Bites of Venomous Snakes. Am. Jour. Med. Sci., vol. 1, no. 2, art. 12, pp. 341–344.

MOORE, J. B.
  1930. Snakes Met—In Passing. *In* W. A. Bevan's column Snake Lore. Outdoor Life, vol. 66, no. 5, p. 92.

MOORE, J. P.
  1951. Rattlesnake. Encyclopedia Americana, New York, Chicago, and Washington, 23 vols.; see vol. 23, pp. 229–230.

MOORE, RUBY A.
  1892. Superstitions in Georgia. Jour. Am. Folk-Lore, vol. 5, no. 18, pp. 230–231.

MOOREHEAD, W. K.
  1906. A Narrative of Explorations in New Mexico, Arizona, Indiana, etc. Phillips Acad., Dept. Arch., Bull. 3, pp. 1–179.

MOORMAN, M. B.

1948. The Journal of Madison Berryman Moorman, 1850–51. Edited by Irene D. Paden. Calif. Hist. Soc. Spec. Publ. no. 23, pp. ix + 145.

MORAGNE, N. H.

1853. Bite of a Copperhead . . . Treated with Whiskey. So. Med. and Surg. Jour., vol. 9, no. 2, pp. 81–82.

MORAN, G. H.

1876. When Do Snakes Shed Their Skins? Forest and Stream, vol. 7, no. 6, p. 84.

1878. Habits of the Rattlesnake. Forest and Stream, vol. 10, no. 14, p. 262; no. 25, p. 483; vol. 11, no. 17, p. 341.

MORDECAI, S.

1860. Virginia, Especially Richmond, in By-gone Days. 2nd edition, Richmond, pp. 1–362. [1st edition, Richmond, 1856, pp. xii + 13–321.]

"MORE ANON"

1905. The Snake Stone or Mad Stone. Forest and Stream, vol. 64, no. 23, p. 453.

MORGAN, ANN H.

1939. Field Book of Animals in Winter. New York, pp. xv + 572.

MORGAN, B. B.

1943. The Physaloptera (Nematoda) of Reptiles. Naturaliste Can., vol. 70, pp. 179–185.

MORGAN, C. L.

1889. Snakes. Murray's Mag., vol. 5, no. 26, pp. 226–237. [Also in Littell's Living Age, ser. 5, vol. 65 (whole no. vol. 180), no. 2332, pp. 635–640.]

MORGAN, W.

1931. Navaho Treatment of Sickness: Diagnosticians. Am. Anthro., vol. 33, no. 3, pp. 390–402.

MORRIS, G. R.

1897. The Ways of Snakes. Forest and Stream, vol. 49, no. 11, pp. 203–204.

MORSE, E. F.

1927. The Story of a Gold Miner. Calif. Hist. Soc. Quart., vol. 6, no. 3, pp. 205–237; no. 4, pp. 332–359.

MORSE, J.

1822. A Report to the Secretary of War of the United States, on Indian Affairs. New Haven, pp. 1–400.

MORSE, M.

1904. Batrachians and Reptiles of Ohio. Proc. Ohio State Acad. Sci., vol. 4, part 3, spec. paper no. 9, pp. 93–144.

MORTIMER, C.

1736. A Narration of the Experiments . . . on a Man, Who Suffer'd Himself to Be Bit by a Viper . . . Philos. Trans. (Royal Soc. London), vol. 39, no. 443, art. 6, pp. 313–320. [See also vol. 40, no. 445, pp. 26–27 (1737).]

MORTON, M. B.

1938. Kentuckians Are Different. Louisville, pp. [iii] + 337.

MORTON, T.

1637. New English Canaan; or, New Canaan, Containing an Abstract of New England. London, pp. 188 + iii. [An earlier edition may have been issued in 1632 or 1634; also published in Amsterdam in 1637.]

MOSAUER, W.

1930. A Note on the Sidewinding Locomotion of Snakes. Am. Nat., vol. 64, pp. 179–183.

1931. The Psychology of Snakes. N. Y. Times Mag., April 26, sec. 5, p. 16.

1932a. Adaptive Convergence in the Sand Reptiles of the Sahara and of California: A Study in Structure and Behavior. Copeia, no. 2, pp. 72–78.

1932b. Über die Ortsbewegung der Schlangen. Zool. Jahrb. (Physiol.), band 52, heft. 2, pp. 179–215.

1932c. On the Locomotion of Snakes. Science, vol. 76, no. 1982, pp. 583–585.

1932d. The Amphibians and Reptiles of the Guadalupe Mountains of New Mexico and Texas. Occ. Papers Mus. Zoöl. Univ. Mich., no. 246, pp. 1–19.

Mosauer, W. (*Continued*)

1933. Locomotion and Diurnal Range of *Sonora occipitalis, Crotalus cerastes,* and *Crotalus atrox* as Seen from Their Tracks. Copeia, no. 1, pp. 14–16.

1934. The Reptiles and Amphibians of Tunisia. Publ. Univ. Calif. at Los Angeles in Biol. Sci., vol. 1, no. 3, pp. 49–64.

1935a. How Fast Can Snakes Travel? Copeia, no. 1, pp. 6–9.

1935b. The Reptiles of a Sand Dune Area and Its Surroundings in the Colorado Desert, California: A Study in Habitat Preference. Ecology, vol. 16, no. 1, pp. 13–27.

1935c. Sense and Nonsense about the Sidewinder. Westways, vol. 27, no. 3, pp. 22, 33.

1936a. The Toleration of Solar Heat in Desert Reptiles. Ecology, vol. 17, no. 1, pp. 55–66.

1936b. The Reptilian Fauna of Sand Dune Areas of the Vizcaino Desert and of Northwestern Lower California. Occ. Papers Mus. Zoöl. Univ. Mich., no. 329, pp. 1–21.

Mosauer, W., and E. L. Lazier

1933. Death from Insolation in Desert Snakes. Copeia, no. 3, p. 149.

Mosauer, W., and K. Wallis

1928. Beiträge zur Kenntnis der Reptilienfauna von Tunesien. 1. Über die Sandspuren einiger Kleintiere der Sahara und ihre Deutung aus dem Bewegungsmechanismus. Zool. Anz., vol. 79, no. 5/6, pp. 195–207.

Mosby, H. S., and C. O. Handley

1943. The Wild Turkey in Virginia. Richmond, Va., pp. xx + 281.

Moseley, B.

1792. A Treatise on Tropical Diseases. 3rd edition, London, pp. xv + 568. [1st edition, 1787.]

Mosimann, J. E., and G. B. Rabb

1952. The Herpetology of Tiber Reservoir Area, Montana. Copeia, no. 1, pp. 23–27.

Moss, J. A.

1941. The Flag of the United States: Its History and Symbolism. Washington, pp. xii + 272.

Mosse, A. H.

1911. Immunity of Animals to Snake-Bite. Jour. Bombay Nat. Hist. Soc., vol. 21, no. 1, pp. 295–298.

Mote, W. D.

1952. Rattlesnake Round-Up. Field and Stream, vol. 56, no. 11, pp. 42–44, 118–120.

Motl, G.

[1936]. Hunting Rattle Snakes in West Texas. San Angelo, Tex., pp. 1–9.

Mueller, A.

1888. On the Action of Snake Poison and the Use of Strychnine as an Antidote. Australia Med. Jour., vol. 10, pp. 196–210.

1893. On Snake-Poison. Its Action and its Antidote. Sydney, pp. vi + 85.

Munro, D. F.

1947. Effect of a Bite by *Sistrurus* on *Crotalus.* Herpetologica, vol. 4, part 2, p. 57.

Murdock, G. P.

1934. Our Primitive Contemporaries. New York, pp. xxii + 614.

Murphree, A.

1948. Can Snakes Live High Up? Denver Post, Apr. 16, p. 17.

Murphy, R. C.

1917. Natural History Observations from the Mexican Portion of the Colorado Desert. Proc. Linn. Soc. N. Y. for 1916, nos. 28–29, pp. 43–101.

Murray, C. A.

1839. Travels in North America during the Years 1834, 1835, & 1836. New York, 2 vols., pp. 324, 247.

Murray, H.

1829. Historical Account of Discovery and Travels in North America. London, 2 vols., pp. xi + 530; ix + 556.

Murray, K. F.

1955. Herpetological Collections from Baja California. Herpetologica, vol. 11, part 1, pp. 33–48.

MURRAY, L. T.
1939. Annotated List of Amphibians and Reptiles from the Chisos Mountains. Contrib., Baylor Univ. Mus., no. 24, pp. 4–16.

MURRAY, SIR J. A. H. (editor)
1888–1933. The New English Dictionary on Historical Principles. Oxford, 10 vols. + 1 vol. supplement.

MURRAY-AYNSLEY, HARRIETT G. M.
1900. Symbolism of the East and West. London, pp. xxiv + 212.

MURRILL, W. A.
1932. Rattlesnakes. West. Story Mag., vol. 111, no. 2, pp. 128–131.

MUSICK, RUTH A.
1946. Iowa Student Tales. Hoosier Folklore, vol. 5, no. 3, pp. 103–110.
1947. Folklore from West Virginia. Hoosier Folklore, vol. 6, no. 2, pp. 41–49.
1948. West Virginia Folklore. Hoosier Folklore, vol. 7, no. 1, pp. 1–14.

NABERS, R. V.
1953. Road Runner a Predator? Tex. Game and Fish, vol. 11, no. 11, p. 2.

NACHMANSOHN, D., and I. B. WILSON
1951. The Enzymic Hydrolysis and Synthesis of Acetylcholine. Advances in Enzymology, vol. 12, pp. 259–339.

NAGGIAR, M. H.
1954. Swampland Coon. Fla. Wildlife, vol. 7, no. 11, pp. 20–21, 45.

NAKAMURA, K.
1938. Studies on Some Specimens of Double Monsters of Snakes and Tortoises. Mem. Coll. Sci. Kyoto Imp. Univ., ser. B, vol. 14, no. 2, art. 7, pp. 171–191.

NAPHEGYI, G.
1868. Treatment of Rattlesnake Bites by the Pinto Indians of Mexico. Med. and Surg. Reporter, vol. 18, no. 12, pp. 249–252.

NASH, A.
1827. The Fascination of Snakes. Am. Jour. Sci. and Arts, vol. 12, pp. 368–370. [See also London Med. Reposit. and Rev., vol. 28, no. 167, pp. 444–445.]

NASH, L. J.
1944. Black Mamba's Speed. Country Life (London), vol. 96, no. 2496, p. 868.

NAUMAN, E. D.
1929. Birds and Snakes. Bird-Lore, vol. 31, no. 5, pp. 330–331.

NEAL, D.
1720. The History of New England. London, 2 vols., pp. vi + x + 330; 331–712 + xv.

NECKER, W. L.
1939. Poisonous Snakes of Illinois. Chi. Nat., vol. 2, no. 2, pp. 35–47.

NEFF, MARY L.
1912. Pima and Papago Legends. Jour. Am. Folk-Lore, vol. 25, no. 95, pp. 51–65.

NEHER, E. M.
1935. The Origin of the Brille in *Crotalus confluentus lutosus* (Great Basin Rattlesnake). Trans. Am. Ophthal. Soc., vol. 33, pp. 533–545.

NEIDHARD, C.
1860. On the Efficacy of *Crotalus horridus* in Yellow Fever. New York, pp. 1–82. [Also 2nd edition, New York, 1868, pp. xvi, 9–87.]

NEIDIG, W. J.
1926. Rattlesnake. Sat. Eve. Post, vol. 198, no. 36, pp. 18–19, 162–170.

NEILL, W. T.
1948. Hibernation of Amphibians and Reptiles in Richmond County, Georgia. Herpetologica, vol. 4, part 3, pp. 107–114.
1949. Increased Rate of Ecdysis in Injured Snakes. Herpetologica, vol. 5, part 6, pp. 115–116.
1952. The Pigmy Rattlesnake, *Sistrurus miliarius barbouri,* in Southwestern Florida. Copeia, no. 1, p. 48.

NELSON, D. J.
1950. A Treatment for Helminthiasis in Ophidia. Herpetologica, vol. 8, part 3, pp. 57–59.

NELSON, G.

1740. The Wonders of Nature throughout the World Displayed. London, pp. [vi] + 475 + [xii].

NELSON, J. L.

1937. Rhythm for Rain. Boston, pp. xi + 272.

NELSON, W.

1894. The Indians of New Jeresy. Paterson, pp. 1–168.

NEOG, M.

1951. Serpent-Lore and Serpent-Worship in Assam. Eastern Anthropologist, vol. 4, nos. 3 and 4, pp. 150–159.

"NESSMUK" [GEORGE W. SEARS]

1888. Snakes Swallowing Young. Forest and Stream, vol. 31, no. 9, p. 164.

NETTING, M. G.

1927. Amphibians and Reptiles in Relation to Birds. Cardinal, vol. 2, no. 2, pp. 1–6.

1929. The Venom of *Sistrurus catenatus*. Bull. Antivenin Inst. Am., vol. 2, no. 4, pp. 108–109.

1930. The Poisonous Snakes of Pennsylvania and the Treatment of Snake Bites. Ann. Carn. Mus., vol. 19, no. 3, pp. 175–184.

1932. The Poisonous Snakes of Pennsylvania. Carn. Mus., Vert. Zoöl. Pamphlet 1, pp. 1–16.

1944. Poisonous Snakes—A Minor Hazard to Soldiers. Biologist, vol. 25, nos. 3 and 4, pp. 44–47.

NEUMANN, R.

1953. New Treatment for Snake Bite. Field and Stream, vol. 58, no. 7, pp. 43, 115–117; also vol. 58, no. 10, p. 8.

NEWMAN, J. B.

1854. Fascination or the Philosophy of Charming. New York, pp. x, 11–176.

NICANDER [OF COLOPHON]

1953. The Poems and Poetical Fragments. Edited with a translation and notes by A. S. F. Gow and A. F. Scholfield. Cambridge, England, pp. xii + 247.

NICHOL, A. A., V. DOUGLAS, and L. PECK

1933. On the Immunity of Rattlesnakes to Their Venom. Copeia, no. 4, pp. 211–213.

NICHOLLS, F.

1745. An Appendix Containing an Anatomical Description of those Parts in a Viper, and in a Rattlesnake, Which Are Concerned in Their Poison. *In* A Mechanical Account of Poisons in Several Essays, by Richard Mead, 3d edition, London, pp. xlviii + 320; see pp. 56–84.

NICHOLSON, E.

1874. Indian Snakes. An Elementary Treatise on Ophiology. 2nd edition, Madras, pp. [vii] + 188. [1st edition, Madras, 1870, pp. 118.]

NICHOLSON, H.

1877. Rattle-snakes in Wet Weather. Nature, vol. 16, no. 405, p. 266.

NIEMANN, F.

1892. Beitraege zur Morphologie und Physiologie der Oberlippendruesen einiger Ophidier. Doctoral Thesis, Berlin, pp. 1–29. [Also published in Archiv. Naturg., vol. 58, no. 1, part 3, pp. 262–286.]

NIEREMBERG, J. E.

1635. Historia Naturae. Antverpiae, pp. [vi] + 502 + [cii].

NIEUHOF, J.

1704. Voyages and Travels into Brasil, and the East Indies. Churchill's Collection of Voyages and Travels, London, vol. 2, pp. [ii] + 369. [Original appeared in Dutch in 1682. Another English edition in Pinkerton's Voyages and Travels, 1813, vol. 14, pp. 697–881.]

NIXON, P. I.

1946. The Medical Story of Early Texas. San Antonio, Tex., pp. xv + 507.

NOBLE, G. K.

1921a. Snakes That Inflate. Nat. Hist., vol. 21, no. 2, pp. 166–171.

1921b. Do Snakes Swallow Their Young for Protection? Copeia, no. 98, pp. 54–57. [Also no. 105 (1922), p. 30.]

1934. The Structure of the Facial Pit of the Pit Vipers and Its Probable Function. Anat. Rec., vol. 58, supp. p. 4.

1937. The Sense Organs Involved in the Courtship of *Storeria, Thamnophis* and Other Snakes. Bull. Am. Mus. Nat. Hist., vol. 73, art. 7, pp. 673–725.

NOBLE, G. K., and H. J. CLAUSEN

1936. The Aggregation Behavior of *Storeria dekayi* and Other Snakes with Especial Reference to the Sense Organs Involved. Ecol. Monog., vol. 6, pp. 269–316.

NOBLE, G. K., and K. F. KUMPF

1936. The Function of Jacobson's Organ in Lizards. Jour. Genetic Psych., vol. 48, pp. 371–382.

NOBLE, G. K., and A. SCHMIDT

1937. The Structure and Function of the Facial and Labial Pits of Snakes. Proc. Am. Philos. Soc., vol. 77, no. 3, pp. 263–288.

NOBLE, J. W.

1954. The Lake That Time Forgot. Collier's, vol. 134, no. 5, pp. 40–43.

NOBLE, RUTH C.

1945. The Nature of the Beast. Garden City, N. Y., pp. xi + 224.

NOGUCHI, H.

1904. The Action of Snake Venom upon Cold-Blooded Animals. Carn. Inst., Publ. 12, pp. 1–16.

1909. Snake Venoms: An Investigation of Venomous Snakes with Special Reference to the Phenomena of Their Venoms. Carn. Inst., Publ. no. 111, pp. xvii + 315.

NOMLAND, GLADYS A.

1938. Bear River Ethnography. Univ. Calif. Anthro. Rec., vol. 2, no. 2, pp. 91–126.

NORTON, A. H.

1929. The Rattlesnake in Maine. Maine Nat., vol. 9, no. 1, pp. 25–28.

NOTESTEIN, F. N.

1905. The Ophidia of Michigan with an Analytical Key. Mich. Acad. Sci., 7th Rept., pp. 111–125.

NUTTALL, ZELIA

1895. A Note on Ancient Mexican Folk-Lore. Jour. Am. Folk-Lore, vol. 8, no. 29, pp. 117–129.

1901. The Fundamental Principles of Old and New World Civilizations. Arch. and Ethn Papers, Peabody Mus., vol. 2, pp. 1–602.

OAKDEN, E. C., and MARY STURT

1927. The Snake Dance of the Hopi Indians. Scot. Geog. Mag., vol. 43, no. 1, pp. 41–44.

OBERHOLSER, H. C.

1906. The North American Eagles and Their Economic Relations. U. S. Biol. Sur. Bull. no. 27, pp. 1–31.

O'DELL, RUTH W.

1944. Signs and Superstitions. Tenn. Folklore Soc. Bull., vol. 10, no. 4, pp. 1–6.

OERTEL, T. E.

1929. Our Poisonous Serpents. Jour. Med. Assn. Ga., vol. 18, pp. 312–317.

1930. A Talk about Snakes. Field and Stream, vol. 34, pp. 20–21, 87–89.

OGLE, W., A. S. L. FARQUHARSON, and A. PLATT (translators)

1912. The Works of Aristotle. V. De Partibus Animalium, Oxford, pp. viii + sections 639–697 + [xviii]; De Incessu Animalium and De Motu Animalium, pp. viii + sections 698–714 + [xii]; De Generatione Animalium, pp. viii + sections 715–789 + [xviii].

O'KANE, W. C.

1950. Sun in the Sky. Norman, Okla., pp. xvii + 261.

1953. The Hopis: Portrait of a Desert People. Norman, Okla., pp. xii + 267.

OLBRECHTS, F. M.

1929. Some Notes on Cherokee Treatment of Disease. Janus, vol. 33, no. 19, pp. 271–280.

OLDMIXON, J.

1708. The British Empire in America. London, 2 vols., pp. xxxviii + [ii] + 412; 382 + [xxxiv].

1741. The British Empire in America. 2nd edition. London, 2 vols., pp. xxxiv + 567; 478.

OLDS, F. A.

1910. Big Rattlers. Forest and Stream, vol. 75, no. 8, p. 292.

OLEARIUS, A.

1674. Gottorffische Kunst-Kammer worinnen Allerhand ungemeine Sachen. Schlesswig, pp. x + 80.

OLIVER, J. A.

  1944. Snakes and Snake Poisoning. *In* Clinical and Tropical Medicine, by Z. T. Bercovitz, New York, pp. xvii + 957; see chap. 66, pp. 855–880.

  1946. What Do You Think? [Answer to question on snakes climbing trees asked by W. B. Gray.] Nat. Hist., vol. 55, no. 6, pp. 295–296.

  1947. The Seasonal Incidence of Snakes. Am. Mus. Nov., no. 1363, pp. 1–14.

  1952. The Prevention and Treatment of Snakebite. Animal Kingdom, vol. 55, no. 3, pp. 66–83. [Also as a separate, New York, pp. (1–32).]

  1954. This Hopi Messenger Went Astray. Animal Kingdom, vol. 57, no. 6, pp. 170–178.

  1955a. Is the Mongoose a Snake Killer? Nat. Hist., vol. 64, no. 8, pp. 426–429.

  1955b. The Natural History of North American Amphibians and Reptiles. Princeton, N. J., pp. xi + 359.

OLIVER, J. A., and L. J. GOSS

  1952. Antivenin Available for the Treatment of Snakebite. Copeia, no. 4, pp. 270–272.

OLIVER, J. D.

  1951. When Cat Meets Rattler. Desert Mag., vol. 14, no. 4, pp. 38–39.

OLIVERAS, E. J.

  1858. Whiskey as a Neutralizing Agent to the Poison of the Rattlesnake. Oglethorpe Med. and Surg. Jour., vol. 1, no. 4, pp. 224–228.

OPLER, M. E.

  1938. Myths and Tales of the Jicarilla Apache Indians. Mem. Am. Folk-Lore Soc., vol. 31, pp. xxiii + 406.

  1940. Myths and Legends of the Lipan Apache Indians. Mem. Am. Folk-Lore Soc., vol. 36, pp. x + 296.

  1941. An Apache Life-Way: The Economic, Social, and Religious Institutions of the Chiricahua Indians. Chicago, pp. xvii + 500.

  1945. Japanese Folk Belief concerning the Snake. Southwest. Jour. Anthro., vol. 1, no. 2, pp. 249–259.

OPPIAN (OF CILICIA)

  1928. Cynegetica, or The Chase; Halieutica, or Fishing. Translation by A. W. Mair. London and New York, pp. lxxx + 531.

ORCUTT, C. R.

  1886. Roadrunners Corralling Rattlesnakes. West Am. Sci., vol. 2, no. 16, p. 49.

  1891. The Golondrina Plant. West Am. Sci., vol. 7, no. 61, pp. 190–195.

ORD, G.

  1815. North American Zoölogy. *In* William Guthrie's New Geographical Historical and Commercial Grammar. . . . 2nd edition, Philadelphia, vol. 2, pp. 290–361. [Rhoads' Reprint, Haddonfield, N. J., 1894, pp. x + 290–361 + 90.]

O'REILLY, G. R.

  1891a. Characteristic Poses of Snakes. Sci. Am., vol. 65, no. 6, p. 87. [Also editorial p. 81.]

  1891b. Color of Snakes as Affected by Climatic Influences. Sci. Am., vol. 65, no. 8, p. 121.

  1894. The Cobra and Other Serpents. Pop. Sci. Monthly, vol. 46, no. 1, pp. 67–78.

  1899. How to Recognize Deadly Snakes. Outing, vol. 33, no. 4, pp. 375–378.

O'REILLY, J.

  1889. Fifty Years on the Trail [Life of John Y. Nelson]. New York, pp. xvi + 381.

ORFILA, M. P.

  1818. Traité des Poisons. Paris, 2nd edition, 2 vols., pp. xxxii + 658; xvi + 703. [1st edition, Paris, 1814–1815, 2 vols.]

  1820. Directions for the Treatment of Persons Who Have Taken Poison . . . Translated by R. H. Black. London, pp. xxi + 248. [Much abridged.]

  1821. A General System of Toxicology. Translated by J. A. Waller. 2nd edition. London, 2 vols. and appendix, pp. xxxi + 517; xvi + 568 + 27.

ORTEL, J. F.

  1932. Watch Your Step. Atlantic Sportsman, vol. 1, no. 11, pp. 200, 202.

ORTENBURGER, A. I.

  1922. Some Cases of Albinism in Snakes. Copeia, no. 113, p. 90.

1923. A Method of Preparing Reptile Penes. Copeia, no. 119, pp. 71–73.

1928. The Whip Snakes and Racers, Genera *Masticophis* and *Coluber*. Mem. Univ. Mich. Mus., vol. 1, pp. xviii + 247.

1930. Some Common Snake Stories. School Sci. and Math., vol. 30, no. 4, pp. 420–428.

ORTENBURGER, A. I., and RUTH D. ORTENBURGER

1926. Field Observations on Some Amphibians and Reptiles of Pima County, Arizona. Proc. Okla. Acad. Sci., vol. 6, no. 17, pp. 101–121.

OSBORN, B., and P. F. ALLAN

1949. Vegetation of an Abandoned Prairie-Dog Town in Tall Grass Prairie. Ecology, vol. 30, no. 3, pp. 322–332.

OSOL, A., and G. E. FARRAR

1947. The Dispensatory of the United States of America. 24th edition. Philadelphia, pp. 1928; see Snake Venom, p. 1587.

OSWALD, F. L.

1879. Serpent-Charm. Pop. Sci. Monthly, vol. 15, no. 37, pp. 606–612.

OTIS, G. A.

1871. Arrow Wounds. *In* A Report of Surgical Cases Treated in the Army of the United States from 1865 to 1871. Washington, U. S. Army Circular no. 3, pp. 1–296; see pp. 144–163.

OTKEN, C. H.

1942. Snake Bites. Med. World, vol. 60, pp. 185–186.

OTT, I.

1882. The Vibration of the Rattlesnake's Tail. Jour. Nerv. and Ment. Disease, vol. 9, no. 3, pp. 514–516.

OVER, W. H.

1923. Amphibians and Reptiles of South Dakota. S. Dak. Geol. Nat. Hist. Sur., Bull. 12, pp. 1–34.

1928. A Personal Experience with Rattlesnake Bite. Bull. Antivenin Inst. Am., vol. 2, no. 1, pp. 8–10.

OWEN, C.

1742. An Essay towards a Natural History of Serpents. London, pp. xiii + 240 + [12].

OWEN, R.

1866. On the Anatomy of Vertebrates. London, 3 vols. Vol. 1, Fishes and Reptiles, pp. xlii + 650.

OZMER, R. R.

1930. False Security. Field and Stream, vol. 35, no. 7, pp. 32–33, 68–69, 79.

PACK, H. J.

1930. Snakes of Utah. Utah Agric. Exp. Sta., Bull. 221, pp. 1–32.

PACKARD, A. S.

1886. The Rattlesnake in New England. Am. Nat., vol. 20, no. 8, pp. 736–737.

PAINE, A. S.

1875. On Rattlesnake Poison, Rabies Canina, etc. So. Med. Rec., vol. 5, no. 3, pp. 129–145.

PALFREY, J. G.

1892. History of New England during the Stuart Dynasty. Boston, 3 vols., pp. xxxi + 636; xx + 640; xxii + 659.

PALMER, E.

1878. Plants Used by the Indians of the United States. Am. Nat., vol. 12, nos. 9–10, pp. 593–606, 646–655.

PALMER, J. E.

1915. A True Samaritan among Reptiles. Out West, vol. 41, no. 6, pp. 240–244.

PALMER, N.

1887. Rattlesnakes in Trees. Forest and Stream, vol. 29, no. 18, p. 343.

PALMER, R. S.

1946. The Rattlesnake in Maine. Nat. Hist. Misc., Chi. Acad. Sci., vol. 2, pp. 1–3.

PAOLI, H. J.

1940. Vicisitudes de las Obras de Francisco Hernández (1514–1578). Archeion, vol. 22, no. 2, pp. 154–170.

PARK, W. Z.

1934. Paviotso Shamanism. Am. Anthro., vol. 36 (n.s.), no. 1, pp. 98–113.

1938. Shamanism in Western North America. Northwest. Univ. Stud. Soc. Sci., no. 2, pp. viii + 166.

PARKER, A. C.

1923. Seneca Myths and Folk Tales. Buffalo Hist. Soc. Publ., vol. 27, pp. xxviii + 465.

1928. Indian Medicine and Medicine Men. 36th Ann. Arch. Rept. (Appendix to Rept. of Minister of Education of Ontario), pp. 9–17.

PARKER, G. H.

1948. Animal Colour Changes and Their Neurohumours. Cambridge, England, pp. x + 377.

PARKER, H. W.

1932. Scientific Results of the Cambridge Expedition to the East African Lakes, 1930–1. 5. Reptiles and Amphibians. Jour. Linn. Soc., Zoöl., vol. 38, no. 258, pp. 213–229.

PARKER, S.

1840. Journal of an Exploring Tour beyond the Rocky Mountains. 2nd edition, Ithaca, N. Y., pp. xvi + 400. [1st edition, Ithaca, N. Y., 1838, pp. 1–371.]

PARKER, W. T.

1883. Concerning Arrow Wounds. Phila. Med. Times, vol. 14, pp. 127–129

PARKMAN, F.

1870. The Conspiracy of Pontiac and the Indian War after the Conquest of Canada. Boston, 1902, 2 vols., pp. xxi + 381; x + 484. [1st edition, Boston, 1851, pp. xxiv + 630.]

1872. The Oregon Trail. 4th edition, Boston, pp. xviii + 479. [1st edition, New York, 1849, pp. 1–448.]

1874. The Old Régime in Canada. Boston, pp. xvi + 448.

PARSONS, ELSIE C.

1921. Hopi Mothers and Children. Man, vol. 21, no. 7, pp. 98–104.

1923. Folk-Lore of the Sea Islands, South Carolina. Mem. Am. Folk-Lore Soc., vol. 16, pp. xxx + 217.

1925. A Pueblo Indian Journal, 1920–1921. Mem. Am. Anthro. Soc., no. 32, pp. 1–123.

1926. Tewa Tales. Mem. Am. Folk-Lore Soc., vol. 19, pp. vi + 301.

1932. Isleta, New Mexico. 47th Ann. Rept. Bur. Am. Ethn., pp. 193–466.

1933. Hopi and Zuñi Ceremonialism. Mem. Am. Anthro. Soc., no. 39, pp. 1–108.

1939. Pueblo Indian Religion. Chicago, 2 vols., pp. xviii + 1275.

PASCHALL, T.

1683. Letter . . . Describing Pennsilvania. London, p. [2]. [Reprinted in Narratives of Early Pennsylvania, West New Jersey, and Delaware, 1630–1707, edited by A. C. Myers. New York, 1912, pp. xiv + 476; see pp. 250–254.]

[PAULDING, J. K.]

1817. Letters from the South. New York, 2 vols., pp. 254, 260.

PAULUS AEGINETA (See under ADAMS, F.)

PAUSANIAS

1918–35. Description of Greece. Translation by W. H. S. Jones. London and Cambridge, Mass., 5 vols.

PAWLOWSKY, E. N.

1927. Gifttiere und ihre Giftigkeit. Jena, pp. xvi + 516.

PAYNE, A.

1945. The Sense of Smell in Snakes. Jour. Bombay Nat. Hist. Soc., vol. 45, no. 4, pp. 507–515.

PAYNE, E. A.

1938. The Resistance of the Rattlesnake to Carbon Monoxide Poisoning. Yosemite Nat. Notes, vol. 17, no. 5, pp. 65–66.

PAYNE, R. L.

1872. The Bites of Venomous Snakes. Med. and Surg. Reporter, vol. 26, no. 10, p. 223.

PEACOCK, J. C.

1928. Antivenin (Nearctic Crotalidae). Jour. Am. Pharm. Assn., vol. 17, no. 8, pp. 750–760.

PEAKE, H., *et al.*

1860–1. Tobacco an Antidote for the Poison of the Rattle Snake. New Orleans Med. and Surg. Jour., vol. 17, pp. 50–51; pp. 289–290 (S. C. Young); pp. 375–377 (H. Peake); pp. 487–488 (W. D. Johnson); pp. 526–527 (J. J. Lyons); vol. 18, pp. 187–188 (A. V. Warr). [See also Med. and Surg. Reporter, vol. 4 (n.s.), no. 16, p. 338, 1860; vol. 5 (n.s.), no. 23, p. 632, 1861.]

PECK, A. L. (translator)

1937. Aristotle: Parts of Animals. Cambridge, Mass., and London, pp. 1–433, 543–551.

1943. Aristotle: Generation of Animals. Cambridge, Mass., and London, pp. lxxviii + 608.

PECK, S. M.

1932. Attempts at Treatment of Hemorrhagic Diathesis by Injections of Snake Venom. Proc. Soc. Exper. Biol. and Med., vol. 29, pp. 579–581.

1933. Sensitization and Desensitization in Man with Snake Venom (*Ancistrodon piscivorus*). Arch. Dermat. and Syph., vol. 27, pp. 312–315.

PECK, S. M., M. L. CRIMMINS, and L. A. ERF

1935. Coagulating Power of *Bothrops atrox* Venom on Hemophiliac Blood. Proc. Soc. Exper. Biol. and Med., vol. 32, pp. 1525–1527.

PECK, S. M., and N. ROSENTHAL

1935. Effect of Moccasin Snake Venom (*Ancistrodon piscivorus*) in Hemorrhagic Conditions. Jour. Am. Med. Assn., vol. 104, pp. 1066–1070. [Also reprint with additions, Chicago, pp. 1–15.]

PEDERSEN, W.

1949. In Bed with a Rattler. Outdoor Life, vol. 104, no. 5, p. 16.

PEET, S. D.

1886. The Serpent Symbol in America. Am. Antiq., vol. 8, no. 4, pp. 197–221.

PELLEGRIN, J.

1902a. Un Cas de Jeûne de 2 ans 1/2 chez un Python. Bull. Soc. Zool. France, vol. 27, pp. 164–166.

1902b. The Long Fasts of Snakes. Public Opinion, vol. 33, no. 8, p. 244.

PENCIL, MARK (pseudonym)

1839. The White Sulphur Papers, or Life at the Springs of Western Virginia. New York, pp. 1–166.

PENN, G. H.

1942. The Life History of *Porocephalus crotali*, a Parasite of the Louisiana Muskrat. Jour. Parasit., vol. 28, no. 4, pp. 277–283.

PENNANT, T.

1787. Supplement to the Arctic Zoölogy. London, pp. viii + 163.

PENNOCK, C. W.

1828. Observations and Experiments on the Efficacy and Modus Operandi of Cupping Glasses in Preventing and Arresting the Effects of Poisoned Wounds. Am. Jour. Med. Sci., vol. 2, no. 3, pp. 9–26.

PEPPER, G. H., and G. L. WILSON

1908. An Hidatsa Shrine and the Beliefs respecting It. Mem. Am. Anthro. Soc., vol. 2, no. 4, pp. 275–328.

PEQUEGNAT, W. E.

1915. A Report upon the Biota of the Santa Ana Mountains. Jour. Ent. and Zoöl. (Pomona College), vol. 37, no. 1, pp. 1–7; no. 2, pp. 25–41; no. 3, pp. 69–74; no. 4, pp. 85–96; vol. 39, no. 1, pp. 1–13.

1951. The Biota of the Santa Ana Mountains. Jour. Ent. and Zoöl. (Pomona College), vol. 42, nos. 3 and 4, pp. 1–84.

PEREA, FRAY ESTEVAN DE

1632. Verdadera Relación de la Gran Conversión que ha Avido en el Nuevo México. Sevilla, pp. [1–4]. [Also Secunda Relación, Sevilla, 1633, pp. [1–4].]

1901. Truthful Report of the Magnificent Conversion Which Has Been Had in New Mexico. Land of Sunshine, vol. 15, no. 5, pp. 357–362; no. 6, pp. 465–469.

PERKINS, C. B.

  1942a. Something about Rattlesnakes. Zoonooz, vol. 15, no. 11, pp. 4–5.

  1942b. More about Rattlesnakes. Zoonooz, vol. 15, no. 12, pp. 5–6

  1943. Notes on Captive-Bred Snakes. Copeia, no. 2, pp. 108–112.

  1948. Longevity of Snakes in Captivity in the United States. Copeia, no. 3, p. 217.

  1949a. The Snakes of San Diego County with Descriptions and Key. 2nd edition. Bull. Zoöl. Soc. San Diego, no. 23, pp. 1–77.

  1949b. Longevity of Snakes in Captivity in the United States. Copeia, no. 3, p. 223.

  1950a. Frequency of Shedding in Injured Snakes. Herpetologica, vol. 6, part 2, pp. 35–36.

  1950b. Longevity of Snakes in Captivity in the United States. Copeia, no. 3, p. 238.

  1951a. Longevity of Snakes in Captivity in the United States. Copeia, no. 2, p. 182.

  1951b. Hybrid Rattlesnakes. Herpetologica, vol. 7, part 3, p. 146.

  1952. Longevity of Snakes in Captivity in the United States. Copeia, no. 4, pp. 280–281.

  1953. Longevity of Snakes in Captivity in the United States as of January 1, 1953. Copeia, no. 4, p. 243.

  1954. Longevity of Snakes in Captivity in the United States as of January 1, 1954. Copeia, no. 3, pp. 229–230.

  1955. Longevity of Snakes in Captivity in the United States as of January 1, 1955. Copeia, no. 3, p. 262.

PERKINS, F. R.

  1944. The Speed of Snakes. Country Life (London), vol. 96, no. 2483, p. 296.

PERRINE, F. S. (editor)

  1928. Hugh Evan's Journal. Miss. Valley Hist. Rev., vol. 14, no. 2, pp. 192–214.

PERRY, A.

  1920. *Crotalus horridus* Rattles for Half Hour. Copeia, no. 86, pp. 85–86.

PERRY, G. S.

  1942. Texas: A World in Itself. New York, pp. xi + 293.

PETCH, T.

  1919. Garcia da Orta's Mongoose Plants. Ceylon Antiquary and Literary Register, vol. 4, part 3, pp. 143–149.

PETERS, S.

  1781. A General History of Connecticut. London, pp. x + 436.

PETERS, W. H.

  1937. Snakes Want to Be Left Alone. Outdoor Life, vol. 79, no. 2, pp. 22–23, 86.

PETRUS DE ABANO (PETRUS ABBANUS). (See under BROWN, H. M.)

PETTER-ROUSSEAUX, A.

  1953. Recherches sur la Croissance et le Cycle d'Activite Testiculaire de *Natrix natrix helvetica* (Lacépède). Terre et Vie, no. 4, pp. 175–223.

"PHIL. HARMONICUS"

  1741. On Music. Gentleman's Mag., vol. 11, pp. 199–201.

PHILIPS, H. B.

  1831. Case of Poison by Rattlesnake. Am. Jour. Med. Sci., vol. 8, no. 16, p. 540.

PHILLIPS, A. R.

  1948. Survival of Birds at High Temperatures. Am. Nat., vol. 82, no. 807, pp. 331–334.

PHILPOT, V. B., JR., and R. G. SMITH

  1950. Neutralization of Pit Viper Venom by King Snake Serum. Proc. Soc. Exp. Biol. and Med., vol. 74, pp. 521–523. [See also Time, vol. 56, no. 8, p. 71, Apr. 21, 1950.]

PHILPOTT, C. H.

  1929. Effect of Toxins and Venoms upon Protozoa. Proc. Soc. Exp. Biol. and Med., vol. 26, no. 6, pp. 522–523.

  1930. Effect of Toxins and Venoms on Protozoa. Jour. Exp. Zoöl., vol. 56, no. 2, pp. 167–183.

  1931. Relative Resistance of Fourteen Species of Protozoa to the Action of *Crotalus atrox* and Cobra Venoms. Biol. Bull., vol. 60, no. 1, pp. 64–66. [Abstracted in Bull. Antivenin Inst. Am., vol. 5, no. 1, p. 28.]

PHILYSS, H. B.

  1831. Case of Poison by Rattlesnake. Am. Jour. Med. Sci., vol. 8, no. 16, p. 540.

PHINNEY, A.

 1934. Nez Percé Texts. Columbia Univ. Contrib. Anthro., vol. 25, pp. xii + 497.

PHISALIX, C., and G. BERTRAND

 1893. Toxicité du Sang de la Vipère (*Vipera aspis* L.). Compt. Rend. Acad. Sci., vol. 117, pp. 1099–1102.

 1894a. Atténuation du Venin de Vipère par la Chaleur et Vaccination du Cobaye contre ce Venin. Compt. Rend. Acad. Sci., vol. 118, pp. 288–291.

 1894b. Sur la Propriété Antitoxique du Sang des Animaux Vaccinés contre le Venin de Vipère. Compt. Rend. Acad. Sci., vol. 118, pp. 356–358. [Also Compt. Rend. Soc. Biol., vol. 46 (ser. 10, vol. 1), pp. 111–113.]

 1894c. Sur les Effets de l'Ablation des Glandes à Venin chez la Vipère (*Vipera aspis* Linn.). Compt. Rend. Acad. Sci., vol. 119, pp. 919–921. [Also Compt. Rend. Soc. Biol., ser. 10, vol. 1, pp. 747–749.]

 1895. Recherches sur l'Immunité du Hérisson contre le Venin de Vipère. Compt. Rend. Soc Biol., ser. 10, vol. 2, pp. 639–641.

PHISALIX, MARIE

 1914. Sur une Hémogrégarine Nouvelle, Parasite de *Sistrurus catenatus* Garman. Bull. Mus. Paris, pp. 167–168.

 1922. Animaux Venimeux et Venins. Paris, 2 vols., pp. xxv + 656; xii + 864.

PHISALIX, MARIE, and R. P. F. CAIUS

 1916. Propriétés Venimeuses de la Parotidienne chez des Colubridés Aglyphes. Bull. Mus. Hist. Nat., vol. 22, pp. 213–218. [See also vol. 23, pp. 343–350; 415–418.]

 1917. Sur les Propriétés Venimeuses de la Sécrétion Parotidienne des Espèces de Serpents Appartenant aux Boidés et aux Uropeltidés. Compt. Rend. Acad. Sci., Paris, vol. 165, pp. 35–37.

 1918. L'Extension de la Fonction Venimeuse dans l'Ordre entier des Ophidiens. Jour. Physiol. Path. (Paris), vol. 17, pp. 923–964.

PICADO T., C.

 1931. Serpientes Venenosas de Costa Rica. Sus Venenos Seroterapia Anti-Ofidica. San José, Costa Rica, pp. 1–219.

PICKARD, MADGE E., and R. C. BULEY

 1945. The Midwest Pioneer: His Ills, Cures, and Doctors. Crawfordsville, Ind., pp. 1–339.

PIERCE, W. M.

 1933. Rattlesnake and Plumed Quail. Calif. Fish and Game, vol. 19, no. 1, p. 62.

PIFFARD, H. G.

 1875. Periodical Vesicular Eruption following the Bite of a Rattlesnake. Med. Rec., vol. 10, pp. 62–63.

PIHOREL, M.

 1827. Observations sur la Morsure d'un Serpent à Sonnettes. Jour. Physiol. Expér. et Path. (Magendie), vol. 7, no. 1, pp. 97–108.

PIKE, N.

 1898. Common Errors about Snakes. Sci. Am., vol. 78, no. 3, p. 38.

PINKERTON, R. E.

 1949. Man to Man Answers [column]. True, vol. 24, no. 143, pp. 19–22.

PISO, G.

 1648. De Medicina Brasiliensi. Lugduni Batavorum et Amstelodami, pp. [viii] + 122 + [ii].

PISTORIUS, T.

 1763. Korte en Zakelyke Beschryvinge van de Colonie van Zuriname. Amsterdam, pp. [viii] + 160.

PITCHER, Z.

 1854. Medicine; Or Some Account of the Remedies Used by the American Indians in the Cure of Diseases . . . *In* Schoolcraft, Information . . . of the Indian Tribes of the United States, Philadelphia, 6 vols., 1851–1857; see part iv, pp. 502–518.

PITMAN, C. R. S.

 1938. A Guide to the Snakes of Uganda. Kampala, Uganda, pp. xvii + 362.

PLATT, T.
   1672. An Extract of a Letter Written . . . Concerning Some Experiments . . . upon Vipers. Philos. Trans. (Royal Soc. London), vol. 7, no. 87, pp. 5060–5066. [Abridged ed., vol. 2, pp. 814–816.]

PLINY, C. [S.] See under HOLLAND, P., 1601 and 1635; also under BOSTOCK, J., and H. T. RILEY, 1855–57.

PODOLSKY, E.
   1934. Medicine Marches On. New York, pp. xvi + 343.

POLASKI, MARY, and C. POLASKI
   1952. Rattlesnake Queen. Cactus and Succulent Jour., vol. 24, no. 5, pp. 138–140.

POLIKOFF, BARBARA
   1954. Hopis Risk Venom of Snakes in Ritual to End Drought. Chi. Nat. Hist. Mus. Bull., vol. 25, no. 8, pp. 3, 5.

POLLARD, C. B.
   1954. Developments in the Field of Venoms, Antivenoms and Snakebite Treatment. Am. Jour Med. Tech., vol. 20, no. 4, pp. 239–243.

POLLARD, C. B., and J. McLAUGHLIN, JR.
   1950. Some Physical and Chemical Properties of Certain Snake Oils. Jour. Am. Oil Chem. Soc., vol. 27, no. 10, pp. 393–394.

POLLARD, C. B., A. F. NOVAK, R. W. HARMON, and W. H. RUNZLER
   1952. A Study of the Toxicity and Stability of Dried Moccasin (*Agkistrodon piscivorus*) Venom. Quart. Jour. Fla. Acad. Sci., vol. 15, no. 3, pp. 161–164.

POLLARD, C. B., and D. C. YOUNG, JR.
   1952. Some Physical and Chemical Properties of Certain Snake Oils. Quart. Jour. Fla. Acad. Sci., vol. 15, no. 3, pp. 133–136.

POLLOCK, J. M.
   1911. The Unvarnished West. London, pp. [vi] + 253.

POPE, C. G.
   1938. Disaggregation of Proteins by Enzymes. Brit. Jour. Exp. Path., vol. 19, pp. 245–251.
   1939. The Action of Proteolytic Enzymes on the Antitoxins and Proteins in Immune Sera. I. True Digestion of the Proteins. Brit. Jour. Exp. Path., vol. 20, no. 2, pp. 132–149. II. Heat Denaturation after Partial Enzyme Action, vol. 20, no. 3, pp. 201–212.

POPE, C. H.
   1937. Snakes Alive and How They Live. New York, pp. xii + 238.
   1944a. The Poisonous Snakes of the New World. New York, pp. viii + 47. [Reprinted in Animal Kingdom, vol. 47, no. 4, pp. 82–90; no. 5, pp. 111–120; no. 6, pp. 143–152; vol. 48, no. 1, pp. 17–23; no. 2, pp. 44–47.]
   1944b. Amphibians and Reptiles of the Chicago Area. Chi. Nat. Hist. Mus., pp. 1–275.
   1946. Snakes of the Northeastern United States. New York, pp. 1–52.
   1950. The Snake-Bite Problem. Chi. Nat. Hist. Mus. Bull., vol. 21, no. 6, pp. 6–7.
   1952. What Would a Rattlesnake Do to You—Bite or Stab? Chi. Nat. Hist. Mus. Bull., vol. 23, no. 3, pp. 3–4.
   1955. The Reptile World. New York, pp. xxv + 325 + xiii.

POPE, C. H., and R. M. PERKINS
   1944. Differences in the Patterns of Bites of Venomous and of Harmless Snakes. Arch. Surg., vol. 49, pp. 331–336.

POPE, C. H., and L. W. PETERSON
   1946. Treatment of Poisoning with Rattlesnake Venom: Experiments with Negative Pressure, Tourniquet and Bulb Suction. Arch. Surg., vol. 53, pp. 564–569.

POPE, J.
   1792. A Tour through the Southern and Western Territories of the United States of North-America; the Spanish Dominions on the River Mississippi, and the Floridas. Richmond, Va., pp. 104 + iv. [Reprint, New York, 1888, pp. 104 + 4.]

POPE, S.
   1919. Rattlesnakes. Their Venom and Antidotes. Calif. State Jour. Med., vol. 17, no. 2, pp. 49–52.

POPE, T. E. B.

　1925a. Hunting Wisconsin Rattlesnakes. Yearbook Pub. Mus. City Milwaukee for 1923, pp. 13–26.

　1925b. Facts and Fallacies concerning Rattlesnakes. Yearbook Pub. Mus. City Milwaukee for 1923, pp. 130–141.

　1929. The Diamond-Back Rattlesnake in Wisconsin. Yearbook Pub. Mus. City Milwaukee for 1928, pp. 167–177.

　1930. Wisconsin Herpetological Notes. Trans. Wis. Acad. Sci., Arts and Lett., vol. 25, pp. 273–284.

　1931. Wisconsin Herpetological Notes. Trans. Wis. Acad. Sci., Arts and Lett., vol. 26, pp. 321–329.

PORGES, N.

　1953. Snake Venoms, Their Biochemistry and Mode of Action. Science, vol. 117, no. 3029, pp. 47–51.

POST, W. B.

　1878. Cure for Rattlesnake Bite. Pac. Rural Press, vol. 16, no. 23, p. 360.

　1879. Rattlesnake Weed. Pac. Rural Press, vol. 18, no. 4, p. 56.

POTTER, E. S.

　1937. Serpents in Symbolism, Art and Medicine: The Babylonian Caduceus and Aesculapian Club. Santa Barbara, pp. xv + 85.

POTTER, O. F.

　1870. Organic Poisoning: A Case of Snake Bite with Some Observations on the Same. Buffalo Med. and Surg. Jour., vol. 9, no. 7, pp. 287 [= 247]–251.

POUND, LOUISE

　1946. Nebraska Snake Lore. So. Folklore Quart., vol. 10, no. 3, pp. 163–176.

POUSMA, R. H.

　1928. Report of Four Cases of Rattlesnake Bite. Bull. Antivenin Inst. Am., vol. 2, no. 3, pp. 61–63.

POVALL, R.

　1824. An Attempt to Account for the Origin of the Belief in the "Uncommon Subtlety," and "Fascinating Faculty," Generally Ascribed to the Serpent. Phila. Jour. Med. and Phys. Sci., vol. 8, no. 15, art. 9, pp. 113–117.

POWELL, A. M.

　1918. Heat for Snakebite. Outdoor Life, vol. 42, no. 5, p. 329.

POWERS, S.

　1877. Tribes of California. Contrib. N. Am. Ethn., vol. 3, pp. 1–635.

PRADHAN, S. N.

　1952. Antihistaminics in Ophidiasis. Indian Jour. Med. Res., vol. 40, no. 1, pp. 63–66.

PRADO, A., and F. P. DE BARROS

　1940. Duas Cascaveis Albinas do Brasil. Mem. Inst. Butantan, vol. 14, pp. 31–33. [See also Ciencia, vol. 1, no. 6, p. 255.]

PRATER, S. H.

　1924. The Snakes of Bombay Island and Salsette. Jour. Bombay Nat. Hist. Soc., vol. 30, no. 1, pp. 151–176.

　1933. The Social Life of Snakes. Jour. Bombay Nat. Hist. Soc., vol. 36, no. 2, pp. 469–476.

PRATT, HELEN

　1942. Rattlesnake Skins Are My Hobby. Desert Mag., vol. 5, no. 9, pp. 24–26.

PREBLE, G. H.

　1894. History of the Flag of the United States of America. 4th edition, Boston and New York, pp. xxi + 808. [First published as Our Flag. . . . , Albany, N. Y., 1872, pp. x, 11–535.]

PRESCOTT, W. H.

　1843. History of the Conquest of Mexico. New York, 3 vols., pp. xxxiv + 488; xviii + 480; xvii + 524.

PREVOST, A. F., *et al.*

　1746–89. Histoire Générale des Voïages. Quarto ed., 23 vols. Livre 6: Suite des Voïages, des Découvertes, & des Etablissemens en Amérique. Chapitre 8, sec. 3, Perou et Contrées Voisines (in vol. 14) .

PRIEST, J.

1882. A True Narrative of the Capture of David Ogden among the Indians in the Time of the Revolution. New York, pp. 1–32. [First published, 1840, Lansingburgh, N. Y.]

PRIOR, H. T. J.

1933. The Dance of the Adders: A Remarkable Example of Reptilian Rivalry. Country-side (n.s.) vol. 9, no. 11, pp. 492–493.

PRITCHARD, C. W.

1940. Black Widow Spider and Snake Venom in Small Animals. Jour. Am. Vet. Med. Assn., vol. 96, pp. 356–358.

PROSKOURIAKOFF, TATIANA

1950. A Study of Classic Maya Sculpture. Carn. Inst., Publ. 593, pp. xi + 209.

PUCHER, L.

1945. Ensayo sobre el Arte Pre-Historico de Samaypata. IV. El Templo Animístico y Tome-místico de Samaypata. Rev. Mus. Arque. Univ. San Francisco Xavier, Sucre, Bolivia, pp. 17–61.

PUCKETT, N. N.

1926. Folk Beliefs of the Southern Negro. Chapel Hill, pp. xiv + 644.

PURCHAS, S.

1614. Purchas His Pilgrimage. London, pp. [xxii] + 918 + [xxxvi]. [1st edition, London, 1613, pp. 14 + 752 + 2.]

1625. Hakluytus Posthumus or Purchas His Pilgrimes. London, 5 vols. [Also reprint, Glasgow, 1905–1907, 20 vols.]

PURDIE, E. R.

1954. Rx: Three Drops of Gall. Desert Mag., vol. 17, no. 3, p. 22. [See also vol. 17, no. 4, p. 28; no. 5, p. 28; no. 7, p. 27.]

PURRY, J. P., J. RICHARD, A. MEURON, and H. RAYMOND

1732. A Description of the Province of South Carolina. Gentleman's Mag., vol. 2, no. 20, pp. 894–896; no. 21, pp. 969–970; no. 22, pp. 1017–1018. [Reprinted in Peter Force's Tracts and Other Papers . . . of the Colonies of North America, vol. 2, no. 11, pp. 1–15, 1838. See also Historical Collections of South Carolina, New York, 1836, vol. 2, pp. 120–140.]

PUTNAM, F. W.

1868. Do Snakes Swallow Their Young? Am. Nat., vol. 2, no. 3, pp. 133–143.

1872. The Rattle of the Rattlesnake. Am. Nat., vol. 6, no. 11, pp. 693–694.

QUAIFE, M. M.

1942. The Flag of the United States. New York, pp. xiv + 210.

QUELCH, J. J.

1891. The Rattlesnake—Growth of the Rattle. Timehri, vol. 5 (n.s.), part 1, pp. 1–11. [See also pp. 170–171.]

R., E. P.

1951. Scared Snakes. Field and Stream, vol. 55, no. 11, p. 12.

RADFORD, E., and MONA A. RADFORD

1947. Encyclopaedia of Superstitions. London, pp. x + 11–269.

RADIN, P.

1909. Winnebago Tales. Jour. Am. Folk-Lore, vol. 22, no. 85, pp. 288–313.

1924. Wappo Texts: First Series. Univ. Calif. Publ. Am. Arch. and Ethn., vol. 19, no. 1, pp. 1–147.

1925. The Winnebago Tribe. 37th Ann. Rept. Bur. Am. Ethn., pp. 35–550.

RAFINESQUE, C. S.

1818. Natural History of *Scytalus cupreus,* or the Copper-head Snake. Am. Jour. Sci. (Silliman), vol. 1, no. 1, pp. 84–86.

RAHN, H.

1940. Sperm Viability in the Uterus of the Garter Snake, *Thamnophis.* Copeia, no. 2, pp. 109–115.

1941. The Pituitary Regulation of Melanophores in the Rattlesnake. Biol. Bull., vol. 80, no. 2, pp. 228–237. [Summary in Anat. Rec., vol. 78, pp. 138–139, 1940.]

1942a. Effect of Temperature on Color Change in the Rattlesnake. Copeia, no. 3, p. 178.

1942b. The Reproductive Cycle of the Prairie Rattler. Copeia, no. 4, pp. 233–240.

RAMON, G.

1924. Des Anatoxins. Compt. Rend. Acad. Sci., vol. 178, no. 17, pp. 1436–1439.

RAMSAY, J. D.

1944. The Speed of Snakes. Country Life (London), vol. 96, no. 2494, p. 780.

RAMSEY, F.

1945. New Mexico Rattlesnakes. N. Mex. Mag., vol. 23, no. 5, pp. 23, 37–40.

RANBY, J.

1728. The Anatomy of the Poisonous Apparatus of a Rattle-Snake. Philos. Trans. (Royal Soc. London), vol. 35, no. 401, pp. 377–381.

RANDALL, W. C., D. E. STULLKEN, and W. A. HIESTAND

1944. Respiration of Reptiles as Influenced by the Composition of the Inspired Air. Copeia, no. 3, pp. 136–144.

RANDOLPH, V.

1931. The Ozarks: An American Survival of Primitive Society. New York, pp. ix + 310.

1933. Ozark Superstitions. Jour. Am. Folk-Lore, vol. 46, no. 179, pp. 1–21.

1947. Ozark Superstitions. New York, pp. ix + 367.

1950. Tales from South Missouri. So. Folklore Quart., vol. 14, no. 2, pp. 79–86.

1951. We Always Lie to Strangers: Tall Tales from the Ozarks. New York, pp. viii + 309.

1952. Who Blowed Up the Church House? New York, pp. xix + 232.

"RANSACKER"

1899. A Snake and a Man with a Hoe. Forest and Stream, vol. 53, no. 14, p. 264. [See also no. 18, p. 344.]

RAWLINGS, MARJORIE K.

1950. The Yearling. New York, pp. viii + 400. [1st edition, New York, 1938, pp. [iii] + 428.]

RAWLINSON, G. (translator)

1942. Herodotus: The Persian Wars. The Greek Historians, edited by Francis R. B. Godolphin. New York, 2 vols., pp. xxxviii + 1001; 964; see vol. 1, pp. 1–563.

RAY, J.

1693. Synopsis Methodica Animalium Quadrupedum et Serpentini Generis. London, pp. [xiv] + 336 + [viii].

RAY, V. F.

1932. The Sanpoil and Nespelem: Salishan Peoples of Northeastern Washington. Univ. Wash., Publ. Anthro., vol. 5, pp. 1–232.

1942. Culture Element Distributions: XXII. Plateau. Univ. Calif. Anthro. Rec., vol. 8, no. 2, pp. iii, 99–258.

RAYBURN, O. E.

1941. Ozark Country. New York, pp. ix + 352.

READ, B. E.

1934. Chinese Materia Medica. Part 7, Dragon and Snake Drugs. Peking Nat. Hist. Bull., vol. 8, part 4, pp. 297–362. [Also published separately, Peking, pp. 1–66.]

READ, W. A.

1931. Louisiana-French. La. State Univ. Stud., no. 5, pp. xxiv + 253.

REAGAN, A. B.

1907. Dances of the Jemez Pueblo Indians. Trans. Kans. Acad. Sci., vol. 20, part 2, pp. 241–272.

1914. Don Diego or the Pueblo Indian Uprising of 1680. New York, pp. x + 352.

1929. Plants Used by the White Mountain Apache Indians of Arizona. Wis. Arch., vol. 8 (n.s.), no. 4, pp. 143–161.

1930. Notes on the Indians of the Fort Apache Region. Anthro. Papers, Am. Mus. Nat. Hist., vol. 31, part 5, pp. 283–345.

1933. Some Notes on the Snake Pictographs of Nine Mile Canyon, Utah. Am. Anthro., vol. 35, no. 3, pp. 550–551.

REDFIELD, W. A.

1937. Superstitions and Folk Beliefs. Tenn. Folklore Soc. Bull., vol. 3, no. 2, pp. 11–43.

REDI, F.

  1664. Osservazioni Intorno alle Vipere. Firenze, pp. 91 + [iv].

  1665. Some Observations of Vipers. Philos. Trans. (Royal Soc. London), vol. 1, no. 9, pp. 160–162.

  1670a. Lettera . . . sopra alcune Opposizioni fatte alle sue Osservazioni Intorno alle Vipere. Firenze, pp. 1–47.

  1670b. Lettera di Francesco Redi sopra alcune Opposizioni fatte alle sue Observationi Intorno alle Vipere, (Firenze, 1670). Philos. Trans. (Royal Soc. London) vol. 5, no. 66, pp. 2036–2038.

  1673. Concerning Some Objections Made upon His Observations about Vipers. *In* M. Charas' New Experiments upon Vipers. London, 2nd edition, suppl., pp. 1–36.

"RED WING"

  1884. Coachwhip and Rattler. Forest and Stream, vol. 22, no. 11, p. 203.

REED, A. C.

  1953. Arizona's Venom Man. Ariz. Highways, vol. 29, no. 2, pp. 28–34.

REED, L. J., and H. MUENCH

  1938. A Simple Method of Estimating Fifty Per Cent Endpoints. Am. Jour. Hyg., vol. 27, no. 3, pp. 493–497.

REES, A.

  1819. Crotalus. Rees' Cyclopaedia, London, vol. 10, 3 pp.

REES, R. K.

  1945. Catching Snakes Alive. Hunting and Fishing, vol. 22, no. 7, pp. 21–22.

REESE, A. M.

  1910. The Home of the Alligator. Pop. Sci. Monthly, vol. 77, no. 4, pp. 365–372.

  1926. The Venom of New-Born Copperheads. Science, vol. 63, no. 1631, p. 357.

  1932. Potassium Permanganate as an Antidote for Snake Venom. Science, vol. 76, no. 1967, pp. 234–235. [Also pamphlet published in 1934, pp. 1–20.]

  1934. The Treatment of Snake Poisoning. Am. Med., vol. 40, pp. 103–110.

  1935. The Destruction of "Vermin." Science, vol. 82, no. 2138, pp. 593–594.

  1937. The Destruction of "Vermin." Sci. Monthly, vol. 45, no. 4, pp. 349–353.

  1942. Do Snakes Swallow Their Young? Proc. W. Va. Acad. Sci., vol. 15, pp. 57–58.

  1949. Old Snake Stories: Do Snakes Swallow Their Young? Turtox News, vol. 27, no. 8, pp. 174–175.

REICHARD, GLADYS A.

  1928. Social Life of the Navajo Indians. Columbia Univ. Contrib. Anthro., vol. 7, pp. vii + 239.

  1947. An Analysis of Coeur D'Alene Indian Myths. Mem. Am. Folklore Soc., vol. 41, pp. x + 218.

REICHERT, E.

  1930. Einiges aus meinem Zoo. I. *Crotalus adamanteus* var. *atrox*. Bl. f. Aquar. u. Terr. Kunde., vol. 41, pp. 262–264.

REID, F. A.

  1948 Hopi Snake Poison. Masterkey, vol. 22, no. 1, pp. 10–11.

REID, M.

  1889. The Desert Home. New York, pp. 1–411. [1st edition, London, 1852, pp. v + 456.]

REID, W. M.

  1910. Lake George and Lake Champlain. New York, pp. xviii + 368.

RELIHAN, CATHERINE M. (compiler)

  1947. Farm Lore: Folk Remedies. N. Y. Folklore Quart., vol. 3, no. 1, pp. 81–84; no. 2, pp. 166–169.

RENAUD, E. B.

  1936. The Archaeological Survey of the High Western Plains. 8th Report. Pictographs and Petroglyphs of the High Western Plains. Univ. of Denver, Denver, pp. 1–47.

RENAULT, L., and G. SCHREIBER

  1949. Consideraçoẽs sôbre Albinismo em Cascavel. Folia Clinica et Biologica, vol. 16, pp. 91–92.

RENDELL, A. E. (translator)

  1928. Physiologus. A Metrical Bestiary of Twelve Chapters by Bishop Theobald, Printed in Cologne, 1492. London, pp. xxvii + [34] + 100.

RENGGER, J. R.

   1829. Ueber die Wirkung des Bisses der südamerkanischen Giftschlangen. Archiv. für Anat. u. Physiol. (Meckel), Jahr. 1829, pp. 271–298. [Abstract translation, Lancet, vol. 2 of 1829–1830, pp. 90–92, under name "Renzger."]

RENSHAW, S.

   1944. The Speed of Snakes. Country Life (London), vol. 96, no. 2501, p. 1090.

REUSS, F. A. T.

   1951. Humming Snakes of North America. Herpetologica, vol. 7, part 3, p. 144.

REUSS, T.

   1926. Balzkaempfe der Kreuzottern. Koralle, vol. 1 (March), pp. 42–49.

   1931. Does Venom Affect Plants? Bull. Antivenin Inst. Am., vol. 4, no. 4, p. 109.

REYNOLDS, A. H.

   1952. Tourniquet for Snake Bite. Jour. Am. Med. Assn., vol. 150, no. 12, p. 1268.

REYNOLDS, N. B.

   1952. The Counties: Lore from Schenectady County. N. Y. Folklore Quart., vol. 8, no. 1, pp. 65–72.

RHONE, E.

   1928. Is the Rattlesnake a Gentleman? *In* W. A. Bevan's column, Snake Lore. Outdoor Life, vol. 62, no. 5, p. 87.

RICE, A. F.

   1895. Vermont Rattlesnakes. Forest and Stream, vol. 44, no. 20, p. 389. [See also pp. 281, 346.]

RICHARDS, J. M.

   1949. The Hopi Snake Dance. Winslow, Ariz., pp. 1–28.

RICHARDS, R. W.

   1951. Allergy and the Antihistamines. Discovery, vol. 12, no. 6, pp. 189–192.

RICHARDS, V.

   1885. The Land-Marks of Snake-Poison Literature. Calcutta, pp. xi + 176 + v. [Also 2nd edition, Calcutta, 1886, pp. viii + 191.]

RICHARDSON, C. H.

   1915. Reptiles of Northwestern Nevada and Adjacent Territory. Proc. U. S. Nat. Mus., vol. 48, no. 2078, pp. 403–435.

RICHARDSON, F. H.

   1949. Snake Bite. Sports Afield, vol. 122, no. 3, pp. 36–37, 86–87.

RICHARDSON, J. F.

   1879. Rattlesnake Poison. Phila. Med. Times, vol. 9, no. 13, p. 306.

RICHARDSON, J. M.

   1899. The Rattlesnake's Bite. Forest and Stream, vol. 53, no. 8, pp. 144–145.

RICHARDSON, S. C.

   1936. Making Friends with Rattlers. Travel, vol. 68, no. 2, pp. 44–45, 59–60.

RICHTER, C.

   1946. The Fields. New York, pp. 1–288.

RICKETTS, B. M.

   1898. Serpents and Their Venom. Cincinnati Lancet-Clinic, vol. 80 (vol. 41, n. s.), pp. 219–224.

RIDDELL, F. A.

   1955. Notes on Yokuts Weather Shamanism and the Rattlesnake Ceremony. Masterkey, vol. 29, no. 3, pp. 94–98.

RIDDELL, W. R.

   1929. Lying about the Simple Viper. Med. Jour. and Rec., vol. 130, no. 4, pp. 222–223.

RIDDLE, O.

   1909. The Rate of Digestion in Cold-Blooded Vertebrates.—The Influence of Season and Temperature. Am. Jour. Physiol., vol. 24, no. 5, pp. 447–458.

RIDINGS, S. P.

   1936. The Chisholm Trail. Guthrie, Okla., pp. [vi] + 591.

RIGHTMIRE, W. F.

   1900. Treatment for Snake Bite. Forest and Stream, vol. 55, no. 16, p. 306.

RIGHTS, D. L.
  1947. The American Indian in North Carolina. Durham, pp. xx + 296.
RILEY, H. T. (translator)
  1909. The Pharsalia of Lucan. London, pp. xi + 427.
[RIMKUS, J.]
  1947. Double Trouble. Pa. Game News., vol. 18, no. 8, p. 23. [See also Hunting and Fishing, vol. 25, no. 5, p. 7.]
RINGLE, H. A.
  1924. Prairie Dogs and Rattlers. Hunter-Trader-Trapper, vol. 48, pp. 19–20.
RISTER, C. C.
  1938. Southern Plainsmen. Norman, Okla., pp. xviii + 289.
RITCHIE, J. W.
  1948. Biology and Human Affairs. New edition, Yonkers, N. Y., pp. xiv + 818. [1st edition, Yonkers, N. Y., 1941, pp. xiv + 1026.]
RITTER, W. E.
  1921. The Rattling of Rattle Snakes. Copeia, no. 94, pp. 29–31.
RIVERS, G. M.
  1874. The Rattlesnake—Its Poison and Antidote. So. Med. Rec., vol. 4, no. 9, pp. 505–517.
ROBBINS, W. W., J. P. HARRINGTON, and BARBARA FREIRE-MARRECO
  1916. Ethnobotany of the Tewa Indians. Bur. Am. Ethn., Bull. 55, pp. xii + 118.
ROBERTS, A. R., and J. QUARTERS
  1947. *Sistrurus* in Michigan. Herpetologica, vol. 4, part 1, p. 6.
ROBERTS, HELEN H.
  1932. The Reason for the Departure of the Pecos Indians for Jemez Pueblo. Am. Anthro., n.s., vol. 34, no. 2, pp. 359–360.
ROBERTS, HILDA
  1927. Louisiana Superstitions. Jour. Am. Folk-Lore, vol. 40, no. 156, pp. 144–208.
ROBERTS, J. C.
  1888. Snake Bite: Recovery. So. Practitioner, vol. 10, no. 9, pp. 374–376.
ROBERTS, M.
  1930. The Serpent's Fang: Essays in Biological Criticism. London, pp. 1–263.
ROBIN, P. A.
  1932. Animal Lore in English Literature. London, pp. ix + 196.
ROBINSON, B.
  1954. The Basket Weavers of Arizona. Albuquerque, pp. xii + 164.
ROBINSON, E. A.
  1895. An Angler's Snake Notes. Forest and Stream, vol. 44, no. 8, p. 147.
ROBINSON, LUCY
  1901. An Undesirable Immigrant. Land of Sunshine, vol. 14, no. 1, pp. 22–26.
ROBINSON, R. G.
  1896. Florida Snakes. Lippincott's Mag., vol. 48, pp. 710–713.
RODBARD, S.
  1948. Body Temperature, Blood Pressure, and Hypothalamus. Science, vol. 108, no. 2807, pp. 413–415.
  1953. Warm-Bloodedness. Sci. Monthly, vol. 77, no. 3, pp. 137–142.
RODGERS, T. L., and W. L. JELLISON
  1942. A Collection of Amphibians and Reptiles from Western Montana. Copeia, no. 1, pp. 10–13.
ROGERS, L.
  1905. The Physiological Action and Antidotes of Colubrine and Viperine Snake Venoms. Philos. Trans. (Royal Soc. London), ser. B, vol. 197, art. 6, pp. 123–191.
ROGET, P. M.
  1870. Animal and Vegetable Physiology. 4th edition, London, 2 vols., pp. xvi + 466; viii + 534. [1st edition, London, 1834, 2 vols.]

ROLKER, A. W.
    1903. The Story of the Snake. McClure's Mag., vol. 21, no. 3, pp. 280–290.
    1905. The Truth about Rattlesnakes. Pearson's Mag. (Am. ed.) , vol. 13, pp. 200–208.
ROLLINS, P. A.
    1922. The Cowboy. New York, pp. xiv + 353.
    1939. Gone Haywire. New York, pp. ix + 269.
ROLLINSON, J. K.
    1944. Pony Trails in Wyoming. Caldwell, Idaho, pp. 1–425.
    1948. Wyoming Cattle Trails. Caldwell, Idaho, pp. 1–366.
ROMER, A. S.
    1945. Vertebrate Zoölogy. 2nd edition. Chicago, pp. viii + 687.
ROOSEVELT, T.
    1913. The Hopi Snake Dance. Outlook, vol. 105, no. 7, pp. 365–373.
ROOT, F. A., and W. E. CONNELLEY
    1901. The Overland Stage to California. Topeka, pp. xvii + 630.
ROS, MARGARETE
    1935. Die Lippengruben der Pythonen als Temperaturorgane. Jenaisch. Zeit. für Naturwiss,
        vol. 70, pp. 1–32.
ROSE, W.
    1929. Veld & Vlei. Wynberg and Capetown, pp. xxiii + 240.
    1950. The Reptiles and Amphibians of Southern Africa. Cape Town, pp. xxv + 378.
ROSENBERG, T.
    1946. La Serpiente en la Medicina y en el Folklore. Buenos Aires, pp. 1–107.
ROSENFELD, S., and S. GLASS
    1940. The Inhibiting Effect of Snake Bloods upon the Hemorrhagic Action of Viper Venoms
        on Mice. Am. Jour. Med. Sci., vol. 199 (n.s.), no. 4, pp. 482–486.
ROSENFELD, S., and S. E. LENKE
    1935. Tiger-Snake Venom in the Treatment of Accessible Hemorrhage. Am. Jour. Med. Sci.,
        vol. 190, no. 6, pp. 779–791.
ROUDABUSH, R. L., and G. R. COATNEY
    1937. On Some Blood Protozoa of Reptiles and Amphibians. Trans. Am. Micro. Soc., vol. 56,
        no. 3, pp. 291–297.
ROURKE, CONSTANCE
    1936. Audubon. New York, pp. 1–342.
ROYS, R.
    1931. The Ethno-Botany of the Maya. Tulane Univ., Mid. Am. Res. Ser., Publ. no. 2, pp.
        xxiv + 359.
"RUDO ENSAYO"
    1894. Sonora. Translation of Document [Rough Essay] Dated 1763; translation by Eusebio
        Guitéras, edited by Laurence F. Flick. Rec. Am. Cath. Hist. Soc. Phila., vol. 5, no. 1, pp.
        109–264.
RUIS, J. M.
    1952. Sobre a Distinção Genérica dos Crotalidae (Ophidia: Crotaloidea) Baseada em Alguns
        Characteres Osteológicos (Nota preliminar). Mem. Inst. Butantan, vol. 23, pp. 109–114.
RUSHTON, W. J.
    1944. Speed of the Black Mamba. Country Life (London), vol. 96, no. 2496, p. 956.
RUSKIN, J.
    1869. Queen of the Air. London, pp. viii + 199.
    1875. Deucalion: Collected Studies of the Lapse of Waves, and Life of Stones. New York, pp.
        1–234. [1st edition, Orpington, Kent, 1875, pp. vi + 290.]
RUSLING, J. F.
    1875. Across America: or the Great West and the Pacific Coast. New York, pp. xx + 503.
RUSS, D.
    1950. Rattlesnake Hunter. Pa. Game News, vol. 21, no. 6, p. 47.
RUSSELL, C. M.
    1934. Trails Plowed Under. New York, pp. xx + 210.

RUSSELL, C. P.

1926. How a Rattlesnake Feeds. Yosemite Nat. Notes, vol. 5, no. 1, p. 3. [See also Margaret Byrkit, *ibid.,* vol. 7, no. 12, pp. 107–108.]

RUSSELL, F.

1908. The Pima Indians. 26th Ann. Rept. Bur. Am. Ethn., pp. 3–389.

RUSSELL, H.

1929. King Snake Eats a Rattlesnake. Zion-Bryce Nat. Notes, vol. 1, no. 1, p. 3.

RUSSELL, M. A.

1946. In Re Some Snake Questions. Hunting and Fishing, vol. 23, no. 1, p. 22.

RUSSELL, O.

1921. Journal of a Trapper, 1834–1843. Boise, pp. xviii + 149.

RUSSELL, P.

1796–1801. An Account of Indian Serpents, London, pp. viii + 91. A Continuation of an Account of Indian Serpents, London, pp. v + 38.

1804. Observations on the Orifices Found in Certain Poisonous Snakes Situated between the Nostril and Eye. Philos. Trans. (Royal Soc. London), vol. 94, part 1, art. 6, pp. 70–72 [See also E. Home, 1804.]

RUTHERFORD, R. N.

1939. The Use of Cobra Venom in the Relief of Intractable Pain. N. Eng. Jour. Med., vol. 221, no. 11, pp. 408–413.

RUTHLING, P. D. R.

1916. Observing the Feeding Habits of the Pacific Rattlesnake. Lorquinia, vol. 1, no. 4, pp. 26–29.

RUTHVEN, A. G.

1907. A Collection of Reptiles and Amphibians from Southern New Mexico and Arizona. Bull. Am. Mus. Nat. Hist., vol. 23, art. 23, pp. 483–604.

1908. Variations and Genetic Relationships of the Garter-Snakes. Bull. U. S. Nat. Mus., no. 61, pp. xii + 201.

1911. A Biological Survey of the Sand Dune Region on the South Shore of Saginaw Bay, Michigan. Amphibians and Reptiles. Mich. Geol. and Biol. Surv., Publ. 4, Biol. Ser. 2, pp. 257–272.

RUTHVEN, A. G., CRYSTAL THOMPSON, and HELEN THOMPSON

1912. The Herpetology of Michigan. Mich. Geol. and Biol. Surv., Publ. 10, Biol. Ser. 3, pp. 1–190.

RUTHVEN, A. G., CRYSTAL THOMPSON, and HELEN T. GAIGE

1928. The Herpetology of Michigan. Mich. Handbook Series, Ann Arbor, no. 3, pp. ix + 229.

RUTLEDGE, A.

1921a. Serpents of the Trail. Outlook, vol. 129, no. 1, pp. 23–25.

1921b. Venomous Snakes of North America. How to Tell Them When You See Them and What to Do With Them. Outing, vol. 78, no. 5, pp. 217–219, 236–237.

1931. Radio of the Wild. Am. Forests, vol. 36, no. 11, pp. 643–646.

1932. Radio of the Wild. Outdoor Life, vol. 69, no. 1, pp. 13–14, 52–53.

1935. The Great King. Va. Quart. Rev., vol. 11, no. 4, pp. 518–528.

1936. Birds and Serpents. Nature Mag., vol. 27, no. 3, pp. 137–139.

1938. Snakes against the World. Outdoor Life, vol. 82, no. 6, pp. 18–19, 79.

1946. Milstead Ropes One. *In* Field and Stream Reader. Garden City, N. Y., pp. 224–238.

1947a. Mysteries of Nature. Sports Afield, vol. 117, no. 1, pp. 30–31, 62–65.

1947b. God's Children. New York, pp. 1–159.

1949. Who Knows Nature Best? Sports Afield, vol. 122, no. 2, pp. 38–41, 80–83

1951. Eight of My Lives. Outdoor Life, vol. 108, no. 4, pp. 42–44, 90–93.

1953. Combats in the Wild. Pa. Game News, vol. 24, no. 1, pp. 27–30, 35.

RUXTON, G. F.

1848. Adventures in Mexico and the Rocky Mountains. New York, pp. 1–312.

1849. Life in the Far West. New York, pp. xii + 235. [Reprint, 1951, L. R. Hafen, editor, Norman, Okla., pp. xviii + 252.]

S.

1787. Poisoned Arrows. Pac. Rural Press, vol. 15, no. 6, p. 82. [See also Mining and Sci. Press, vol. 36, p. 162.]

S., E.

1883. Reptiles and Their Habits. Forest and Stream, vol. 20, no. 1, p. 7.

SABIN, J.

1868–1936. Bibliotheca Americana: A Dictionary of Books Relating to America. New York, 29 vols.

ST. JOHN, J. H. (Pseudonym. See under CRÈVECOEUR, M. G. J. DE)

SALISBURY, J. H.

1852. Influence of the Poison of the Northern Rattlesnake (*Crotalus durissus*) on Plants. Proc. Am. Assn. Adv. Sci., vol. 6, pp. 336–337. [See also N. Y. Jour. Med., vol. 13 (n.s.), no 3, pp. 337–339, 1854.]

SALMON, T.

1744–6. Modern History. 3rd edition, London, 3 vols., pp. xii + 777 + [xii]; [iv] + 832 + [xiv]; ii + 628 + [x]. [1st edition, London, 1725–1739, 32 vols.; vols. 28–31 on America.]

SAMBON, L. W.

1922. A Synopsis of the Family Linguatulidae. Jour. Trop. Med. and Hyg., vol. 25, pp. 188–206, 391–428.

SAMPSON, A. W.

1952. Range Management: Principles and Practices. New York, pp. xiv + 570.

SANDERS, R. T.

1951. Symposium: A Snake Den in Tooele County, Utah. Effect of Venom Injections in Rattlesnakes. Herpetologica, vol. 7, part 1, pp. 47–52.

SANFORD, M. M.

1953. The Grass Rope Myth. Desert Mag., vol. 16, no. 6, p. 28.

SANGER, D. B.

1931. An Adventure with Snakes. Bull. Antivenin Inst. Am., vol. 5, no. 2, pp. 34–35.

SANTLEBEN, A.

1910. A Texas Pioneer: Early Staging and Overland Freighting Days on the Frontiers of Texas and Mexico. New York and Washington, pp. 1–321.

SAPIR, E.

1907a. Notes on the Takelma Indians of Southwestern Oregon. Am. Anthro., vol. 9 (n.s.), no. 2, pp. 251–275.

1907b. Religious Ideas of the Takelma Indians of Southwestern Oregon. Jour. Am. Folk-Lore, vol. 20, no. 76, pp. 33–49.

1908. Luck-Stones among the Yana. Jour. Am. Folk-Lore, vol. 21, no. 80, p. 42.

1909. Wishram Texts: Wasco Tales and Myths. Publ. Am. Ethn. Soc., vol. 2, pp. xv + 314.

1910a. Yana Texts. Univ. Calif. Publ. Am. Arch. and Ethn., vol. 9, no. 1, pp. 1–235.

1910b. Song Recitative in Paiute Mythology. Jour. Am. Folk-Lore, vol. 23, no. 90, pp. 455–472.

1930. Texts of the Kaibab Paiutes and Uintah Utes. Proc. Am. Acad. Arts and Sci., vol. 65, no. 2, pp. 297–535.

SAPIR, E., and L. SPIER

1943. Notes on the Culture of the Yana. Univ. Calif. Anthro. Rec., vol. 3, no. 3, pp. vi + 239–297

SARKAR, S. C.

1923. A Comparative Study of the Buccal Glands and Teeth of the Opisthoglypha, and a Discussion on the Evolution of the Order from Aglypha. Proc. Zoöl. Soc. London, part 2, pp. 295–322.

SARTON, G.

1927–48. Introduction to the History of Science. Carn. Inst., Publ. no. 376. Washington, 3 vols. [5 parts].

1944. Earliest Illustration of Rattlesnake. Isis, vol. 35, part 1, pp. 28–29.

SASS, H. R.

1935a. The Great Horned Serpent. Atlantic Monthly, vol. 155, no. 5, pp. 619–628.

1935b. Adventures in Green Places. New York, pp. xiii + 297.

SAVAGE, F.
    1893. [Albino Rattlesnake.] Forest and Stream, vol. 41, no. 23, p. 492.
SAVAGE, J.
    1877. On the Bite of the Rattlesnake. Trans. Kans. Acad. Sci., vol. 6, pp. 36–38.
SAVAGE, J. M., and F. S. CLIFF
    1953. A New Subspecies of Sidewinder, *Crotalus cerastes,* from Arizona. Nat. Hist. Misc., no. 119, pp. 1–7.
SAWYER, H. W.
    1933. Rattlesnake Bite in the Dog and Cat. Vet. Med., vol. 28, no. 1, pp. 21–25.
SAY, T.
    1819. Notes on Herpetology. Am. Jour. Sci. (Silliman's Jour.) , vol. 1, no. 3, art. 10, pp. 256–265.
SCARBROUGH, MARTHA N.
    1941. Snakes and Whiskey. Junior Historian, vol. 2, no. 3, p. 10.
SCHAEFER, W. H.
    1933. Hypophysectomy and Thyroidectomy of Snakes. Proc. Soc. Exper. Biol. and Med., vol. 30, pp. 1363–1365.
    1934. Diagnosis of Sex in Snakes. Copeia, no. 4, p. 181.
SCHALDACH, W. J.
    1955. Want to Collect Indian Relics? Nat. Hist., vol. 64, no. 6, pp. 312–318.
SCHENCK, SARA M., and E. W. GIFFORD
    1952. Karok Ethnobotany. Univ. Calif. Anthro. Rec., vol. 13, no. 6, pp. iv + 377–392.
SCHEUCHZER, J. J.
    1732–7. Physique Sacrée ou Histoire-Naturelle de la Bible. Amsterdam, 8 vols.
SCHLEGEL, H.
    1837. Essai sur la Physionomie des Serpens. Leide, 2 vols. + atlas, pp. xxviii + 251 + xvi; 1–605.
    1843. Essay on the Physiognomy of Serpents. Translated by Thos. S. Traill. Edinburgh, pp. v + 254.
    1844. Fables and Prejudices regarding Serpents. Edinburgh New Philos. Jour., vol. 36, no. 71, pp. 63–71.
SCHLENKER, MRS. J.
    1942. [Letter re Cats and Copperhead.] Nat. Hist., vol. 49, no. 1, p. 60.
SCHLOSSBERGER, H.
    1936. Die Geschichte der Schlangengift-Forschung. Behringwerke-Mitteilungen, vol. 7, pp. 1–32.
SCHMEDDING, J.
    1951. Cowboy and Indian Trader. Caldwell, Idaho, pp. 1–364.
SCHMIDT, K. P.
    1929a. The Truth about Snake Stories. Field Mus. Nat. Hist., Zoöl. Leafl. no. 10, pp. 1–19. [2nd edition, 1951, pp. 1–23.]
    1929b. The Truth about Snake Stories. Sci. Amer., vol. 141, no. 2, pp. 134–136.
    1930. Reptiles of Marshall Field North Arabian Desert Expedition, 1927–1928. Field Mus. Nat. Hist., Zoöl. Ser., vol. 17, no. 6, pp. 223–230.
    1945. The Girl Who Had Never Been Bitten by a Rattlesnake: A Texas Folktale. Chi. Nat., vol. 8, no. 2, pp. 30–31.
    1950. Modes of Evolution Discernible in the Taxonomy of Snakes. Evolution, vol. 4, no. 1, pp. 79–86.
    1954. J. E. Johnson, Jr.—An Appreciation. Copeia, no. 3, pp. 247–248.
SCHMIDT, K. P., and D. D. DAVIS
    1941. Field Book of Snakes of the United States and Canada. New York, pp. xiii + 365.
SCHMIDT, K. P., and T. F. SMITH
    1944. Amphibians and Reptiles of the Big Bend Region of Texas. Field Mus. Nat. Hist., Zoöl. Ser., vol. 29, no. 5, pp. 75–96.
SCHMIDT-NIELSEN, BODIL, and K. SCHMIDT-NIELSEN
    1949. The Water Economy of Desert Mammals. Sci. Monthly, vol. 69, no. 3, pp. 180–185. [Also Sci. Am., vol. 189, no. 1, pp. 73–78, 1953.]

1950. Evaporative Water Loss in Desert Rodents in Their Natural Habitat. Ecology, vol. 31, no. 1, pp. 75–85.

SCHNECK, J.
1878. Is the Bite of the Heterodon, or Spreading Adder, Venomous? Chi. Med. Jour., vol. 37, no. 6, pp. 585–587.

SCHOETTLER, W. H. A.
1950. Copula zwischen *Bothrops* und *Crotalus*. Deutsche Aquar. Terrar. Zeits., vol. 3, no. 1, p. 14.
1951a. Toxicity of the Principal Snake Venoms of Brazil. Am. Jour. Trop. Med., vol. 31, no. 4, pp. 489–499.
1951b. Antigen-Antibody Relations in the Present Antivenin Production in Brazil. Am. Jour. Trop. Med., vol. 31, no. 4, pp. 500–509.
1951c. On the Stability of Desiccated Snake Venoms. Jour. Immun., vol. 67, no. 4, pp. 299–304.
1951d. Para-specific Action of Bothropic and Crotalic Antivenins. Am. Jour. Trop. Med., vol. 31, no. 6, pp. 836–841.
1952a. Problems of Antivenin Standardization. Bull. World Health Org., League of Nations, vol. 5, pp. 293–320.
1952b. Experimental Study on the Importance of Early Antivenin Treatment in Snake Bite. Am. Jour. Trop. Med. and Hyg., vol. 1, no. 6, pp. 1038–1042.
1954a. Antihistamine, ACTH, Cortisone, Hydrocortisone and Anesthetics in Snake Bite. Am. Jour. Trop. Med. and Hyg., vol. 3, no. 6, pp. 1083–1091.
1954b. Lista Suplementar de Bibliographia sôbre Venenos Animais Publicada nos Anos de 1863 até 1946. Mem. Inst. Butantan, vol. 26, pp. 7–73.
1954c. Aspectos Methodológicos da Titulação de Soros Antipeçonhentos. Mem. Inst. Butantan, vol. 26, pp. 249–256.
1955. Serological Analysis of Venoms and Antivenins. Bull. World Health Organization, vol. 12, pp. 877–903.

SCHOMBURGK, M. R.
1922. Travels in British Guiana, 1840–44. [Translated from the original German edition, 3 vols., Leipzig, 1847–48, by Walter E. Roth.] Georgetown, British Guiana, 2 vols., pp. xxxviii + [viii] + 402; [viii] + 443.

SCHOOLCRAFT, H. R.
1821. Narrative Journal of Travels . . . through the Great Chain of American Lakes, to the Sources of the Mississippi River. Albany, pp. xiv + 419.
1851-7. Historical and Statistical Information, respecting the History, Condition and Prospects of the Indian Tribes of the United States. Philadelphia, 6 vols.

SCHOOLEY, J. W.
1895. Experience with a Rattler. Forest and Stream, vol. 45, no. 17, p. 356.

SCHRENKEISEN, R.
1930. Further Notes on the Diamond-back Rattler. Field and Stream, vol. 34 (Jan.), pp. 68, 70.

SCHROEDER, C. R.
1934. The Snake Mite (*Ophionyssus serpentium* Hirst). Jour. Econ. Ent., vol. 27, no. 5, pp. 1004–1014.

SCHWAB, P. J.
1927. Rattlers and Tarantulas. Outdoor Life, vol. 60, no. 5, pp. 18–19.

SCORTECCI, G.
1939. Gli Ofidi Velenosi dell'Africa Italiana. Milan, pp. xv + 292.

SCOTT, J.
1894. Report on the Moqui Pueblos of Arizona. Rept. on Indians Taxed and Not Taxed, Washington, 11th Census (1890), pp. 186–198.

SCOVILLE, S., JR.
1929. The Diamondback: The Lurking Menace of the Swamp. Nature Mag., vol. 14, no. 3, pp. 143–145.
1931. Bad Actor. Am. Legion Monthly, vol. 11, no. 6, pp. 16–17, 56–57.

SCUDDAY, R.
1944. Musical Snake. Tex. Folk-Lore Soc. Publ., no. 19, pp. 162–164.

SEARS, G. W. (See under "NESSMUK.")

SEBA, A.

1734–65. Locupletissimi Rerum Naturalium Thesauri Accurata Descriptio.... Amstelaedami, 4 vols., pp. [xxix] + 178 (1734); [xxx] + 154 (1735); [xxi] + 212 (1758); viii, 9–226 (1765).

SEDLON, CONSTANCE

1946. [Swimming Rattlesnake.] Nat. Hist., vol. 55, no. 2, p. 96.

SEEMANN, B. C.

1853. Narrative of the Voyage of H. M. S. Herald during the Years 1845–51. London, 2 vols., pp. xvi + 322; 1–302.

SEIBERT, H. C., and C. W. HAGEN, JR.

1947. Studies on a Population of Snakes in Illinois. Copeia, no. 1, pp. 6–22.

SEITZ, A.

1933. Begegnungen mit Schlangen. Natur und Museum, vol. 63, no. 3, pp. 95–102. [See also Folgen des Schlangenbisses, vol. 63, no. 5, pp. 156–162.]

SELER, E.

1902–23. Gesammelte Abhandlungen zur amerikanischen Sprach- und Alterthumskunde. Berlin, 5 vols., pp. xxviii + 862; xxxvi + 1107; xxx + 729; viii + 758; 585 + 79.

SELF, J. T., and F. B. McMURRY

1948. *Porocephalus crotali* Humboldt (Pentastomida) in Oklahoma. Jour. Parasit., vol. 34, no. 1, pp. 21–23.

SELF, L. E.

1908. Snake Bite for Epilepsy. Med. World, vol. 26, no. 7, pp. 305–306.

SETON, E. T.

1929. Lives of Game Animals. Garden City, N. Y., 4 vols., pp. xxxix + 640; xvii + 746; xix + 780; xxii + 949.

1940. Trail of an Artist-Naturalist. New York, pp. xii + 412.

SETON, W.

1903. The Rattlesnake. Catholic World, vol. 77, no. 460, pp. 436–444.

SEVERINUS, M. A.

1651. Vipera Phythia. Patavii, pp. [xiii] + 522 + [xxiv].

SEWALL, H.

1887. Experiments on the Preventive Inoculation of Rattlesnake Venom. Jour. Physiol., vol. 8, pp. 203–210.

SHALER, N. S.

1872. The Rattlesnake and Natural Selection. Am. Nat., vol. 6, no. 1, pp. 32–37.

SHANNON, F. A.

1953. Comments on the Treatment of Reptile Poisoning in the Southwest. Southwest. Med., vol. 34, no. 10, pp. 367–373. [See also pp. 634–635, *in* Current Therapy, H. F. Conn, editor, Philadelphia, 1955, pp. xxx + 692.]

SHAPLEIGH, E. B.

1868. Death from Rattlesnake Bite. Trans. College of Physicians Phila., vol. 4 (n.s.), no. 4, pp. 263–264. [Also Am. Jour. Med. Sci., vol. 57, p. 392, 1869.]

SHARK, G.

1950. Motherhood by the Yard. Family Herald and Weekly Star (Montreal), vol. 81, no. 27, p. 48. [See also no. 31, p. 2; no. 41, p. 2; no. 46, p. 2; vol. 82, no. 46, p. 2; no. 47, p. 2; no. 48, p. 2; and vol. 83, no. 1, p. 2.]

SHARPE, ELIZABETH

1937. An Eight-Hundred Year Old Book of Indian Medicine and Formulas [by Waghji Muni]. London, pp. 1–135.

SHAW, C. E.

1948. The Male Combat "Dance" of Some Crotalid Snakes. Herpetologica, vol. 4, no. 4, pp. 137–145.

1951. Male Combat in American Colubrid Snakes with Remarks on Combat in Other Colubrid and Elapid Snakes. Herpetologica, vol. 7, part 4, pp. 149–168.

SHAW, G.

1802. General Zoölogy or Systematic Natural History. London, vol. 3, Amphibia, parts 1 and 2, pp. viii + 312; vi + 313–615.

SHEA, J. M.
    1861. Early Voyages Up and Down the Mississippi. Albany, pp. xiv + 15–188.
SHETRONE, H. C.
    1930. The Mound Builders. New York, pp. xx + 508.
SHIMKIN, D. B.
    1947. Wind River Shoshone Ethnogeography. Univ. Calif. Anthro. Rec., vol. 5, no. 4, pp. v +
        245–288.
SHIPPEY, L.
    1948. It's an Old California Custom. New York, pp. [iv] + 292.
SHIRAS, G., III
    1921. The Wild Life of Lake Superior. Natl. Geog. Mag., vol. 40, no. 2, pp. 113–204.
SHOREY, A. T.
    1953. Yes—We Have Rattlesnakes. N. Y. State Conservationist, vol. 7, no. 4, pp. 25–27.
SHORT, R. T.
    1869. [Treatment of Rattlesnake Bite with Opium.] Med. Archives, vol. 3, no. 9, pp. 564–565.
        [Also Boston Med. and Surg. Jour., vol. 4 (n.s.), no. 9, p. 159, 1869.]
SHORTT, H. E. and S. M. K. MALLICK
    1935. Detoxication of Snake Venom by the Photodynamic Action of Methylene Blue. Jour.
        Ind. Med. Res., vol. 22, no. 3, pp. 529–536.
SHOWERS, SUSAN
    1900. Alabama Folk-Lore. So. Workman, vol. 29, no. 3, pp. 178–180; no. 7, pp. 443–444.
SHULER, W. M.
    1881. Snake Bites. Med. Gaz., vol. 8, pp. 292–293.
SIBLEY, H.
    1951. Snakes Are Scared of You! Field and Stream, vol. 55, no. 9, pp. 46–48.
SILLIMAN, B.
    1820. Sketches of a Tour in the Counties of New-Haven and Litchfield in Connecticut. Am.
        Jour. Sci. and Arts, vol. 2, no. 2, pp. 201–235.
SIMCOE, MRS. JOHN GRAVES
    1911. Diary of, with Notes and a Biography by J. Ross Robertson. Toronto, pp. xxix + 440.
SIMER, MYRTLE M.
    1950. When the Hopis Dance for Rain. Desert Mag., vol. 13, no. 10, pp. 4–8.
SIMMONS, L. W. (editor)
    1942. Sun Chief: The Autobiography of a Hopi Indian [Don C. Talayesva]. New Haven, pp.
        xi + 460.
SIMMS, S. C.
    1906. Myths of the Bungees or Swampy Indians of Lake Winnipeg. Jour. Am. Folk-Lore, vol.
        19, no. 75, pp. 334–340.
SIMPICH, F.
    1928. So Big Texas. Natl. Geog. Mag., vol. 53, no. 6, pp. 635–693.
SIMPSON, F.
    1915. Points about Rattlers. Outing, vol. 67, no. 3, pp. 279–281.
SIMSON, F. B.
    1886. Letters on Sport in Eastern Bengal. London, pp. xviii + 255.
SINCLAIR, W. J.
    1904. The Exploration of the Potter Creek Cave. Univ. Calif. Publ. Am. Arch. and Ethn., vol.
        2, no. 1, pp. 1–27.
SIPE, C. H.
    1927. The Indian Chiefs of Pennsylvania. Butler, Pa., pp. 1–569.
SIPLE, P. A.
    1944. Intra-Clothing Climate. Amer. Geophysical Union, Trans. of 1944, part 3, pp. 412–417.
        [See also Keeping Comfortable with Clothing, G. E. Science Forum Broadcast over Station
        WGY, Schenectady, N. Y., July 10, 1946, reprint, pp. 1–6.]
SKINNER, A.
    1913. Notes on the Florida Seminole. Am. Anthro., vol. 15, no. 1, pp. 63–77.
    1921. Material Culture of the Menomini. Indian Notes and Monog., Mus. Am. Indian, Heye
        Found., pp. 1–478.

SKINNER, A. (*Continued*)

1923–5. Observations on the Ethnology of the Sauk Indians. Bull. Pub. Mus. City Milwaukee, vol. 5, no. 1, pp. 1–57; no. 2, pp. 59–95; no. 3, pp. 119–180.

1925a. Songs of the Menomini Medicine Ceremony. Am. Anthro., vol. 27, no. 2, pp. 290–314.

1925b. Traditions of the Iowa Indians. Jour. Am. Folk-Lore, vol. 38, no. 150, pp. 425–506.

1926. Ethnology of the Ioway Indians. Bull. Pub. Mus. City Milwaukee, vol. 5, no. 4, pp. 181–354.

SLEVIN, J. R.

1927. The Making of a Scientific Collection of Reptiles and Amphibians. Proc. Calif. Acad. Sci., ser. 4, vol. 16, no. 9, pp. 231–259.

SLOANE, H.

1734. Conjectures on the Charming or Fascinating Power Attributed to the Rattle-Snake. Philos. Trans. (Royal Soc. London), vol. 38, no. 433, pp. 321–331.

SLOTTA, K. H.

1938. A Crotoxina Primeira Substancia Pura dos Venenos Ofidicos. Ann. Acad. Brasil. Sciencias, vol. 10, no. 3, pp. 195–209 .

1953. Zur Chemie der Schlangengifte. Experientia, vol. 9, no. 3, pp. 81–88.

SLOTTA, K. H., and H. FRAENKEL-CONRAT

1937. Estudos Chimicos sôbre os Venenos Ophidicos: 2. Sôbre a Forma de Ligação do Enxofre. Mem. Inst., Butantan, vol. 11, pp. 121–132.

1938. Two Active Proteins from Rattlesnake Venom. Nature, vol. 142, no. 3587, p. 213.

1939. Crotoxin. Nature, vol. 144, no. 3641, pp. 290–291.

SLOTTA, K. H., and J. PRIMOSIGH

1951. Amino-Acid Composition of Crotoxin. Nature, vol. 168, no. 4277, pp. 696–697.

1952. Estudos Químicos sôbre os Venenos Ofídicos. 6. Composição da Crotoxina. Mem. Inst. Butantan, vol. 23, pp. 51–62.

SLOTTA, K. H., G. SZYSZKA, H. L. FRAENKEL-CONRAT, and W. FORSTER

1937–9. Estudos Chimicos sôbre os Venenos Ophidicos (5 papers). Mem. Inst. Butantan, vol 11, pp. 109–147; vol. 12, pp. 505–521. [See also Ber. Deuts. Chem. Gesell, vol. 71b, pp. 258–271, 1076–1088; Chem. Abs., vol. 32, cols. 3435, 7946; Biol. Abs., vol. 12, p. 1585.]

SMALL, J. A.

1946. They Don't Always Buzz. Sports Afield, vol. 116, no. 2, pp. 32, 87–89.

SMART, E. W.

1951. Symposium: A Snake Den in Tooele County, Utah. Color Analysis in the Great Basin Rattlesnake. Herpetologica, vol. 7, part 1, pp. 41–46.

SMILEY, PORTIA

1919. Folk-Lore from Virginia, South Carolina, Georgia, Alabama, and Florida. Jour. Am. Folk-Lore, vol. 32, no. 125, pp. 357–383.

SMITH, C. L., and J. D. SMITH

1927. The Boy Captives. Bandera, Tex., pp. 1–219. [Written by J. M. Hunter.]

SMITH, DAMA MARGARET [MRS. WHITE MOUNTAIN SMITH]

1930. I Married a Ranger. Stanford University, pp. ix + 179.

1931. Hopi Girl. Stanford University, pp. ix + 273.

SMITH, E.

1933. King Snake *vs.* Rattler. Field and Stream, Aug., p. 55.

SMITH, H. H.

1923–32. Ethnobotany of the Menomini Indians. Bull. Pub. Mus. City Milwaukee, vol. 4, no. 1, pp. 1–174. Meskwaki Indians, vol. 4, no. 2, pp. 175–326. Ojibway Indians, vol. 4, no. 3, pp. 327–525.

SMITH, H. M.

1940. An Analysis of the Biotic Provinces of Mexico, as Indicated by the Distribution of the Lizards of the Genus *Sceloporus*. Anales Escuela Nacional Ciencias Biologicas, vol. 2, no. 1, pp. 95–110.

1946a. Snake Detection. Chi. Nat., vol. 9, no. 3, pp. 63–67.

1946b. Preliminary Notes and Speculations on the *Triseriatus* Group of Rattlesnakes in Mexico. Bull. Univ. Kans., vol. 31, pt. 1, no. 3, pp. 75–101.

1949. Herpetogeny in Mexico and Guatemala. Ann. Assn. Am. Geog., vol. 39, no. 3, pp. 219–238.

1950. Handbook of Amphibians and Reptiles of Kansas. Univ. Kans. Mus. Nat. Hist., Misc. Publ. no. 2, pp. 1–336.

1952. A Revised Arrangement of Maxillary Fangs of Snakes. Turtox News, vol. 30, no. 12, pp. 214–218.

SMITH, H. M., and E. H. TAYLOR

1945. An Annotated Checklist and Key to the Snakes of Mexico. U. S. Nat. Mus., Bull. 187, pp. 1–239.

SMITH, IDA

1951. Old Yellowcoat. Calico Print, vol. 7, no. 11, p. 1.

SMITH, J.

1831. An Account of the Remarkable Occurrences in the Life and Travels of Colonel James Smith . . . in the Years 1755, '56, '57, '58 and '59. Philadelphia, pp. xi + 162. [First published in Lexington, Ky., in 1799.]

SMITH, CAPT. J.

1612. A Map of Virginia, with a Description of the Countrey, the Commodities, People, Government and Religion. Oxford, pp. 1–39. [Birmingham, 1884, reprint, pp. 41–84.]

1624. The Generall Historie of Virginia, New England and the Summer Isles. London, pp. 1–248.

1631. Advertisements for the Unexperienced Planters of New-England, or Anywhere. London, pp. 1–40. [Reprinted *in* Arber, Travels and Works of Captain John Smith, 2 vols., Edinburgh, 1910, pp. cxxxvi + 382; 383–984; see pp. 917–966.]

SMITH, J. E.

1821. A Selection of the Correspondence of Linnaeus and Other Naturalists. London, 2 vols., pp. xiv + 605; iv + 580 + [26].

SMITH, M. A.

1943. The Fauna of British India, Ceylon and Burma, including the Whole of the Indo-Chinese Sub-region. Reptilia and Amphibia. Vol. III.—Serpentes. London, pp. xii + 583.

1944. The Speed of Snakes. Country Life (London), vol. 96, no. 2486, p. 428.

1955. Deaths from Snake-Bite. Country Life (London), vol. 117, no. 3029, pp. 324–325.

SMITH, M. A., and A. D'A. BELLAIRS

1947. The Head Glands of Snakes, with Remarks on the Evolution of the Parotid Gland and Teeth of the Opisthoglypha. Jour. Linn. Soc., Zoöl., vol. 41, no. 279, pp. 351–368.

SMITH, M. A., A. D'A. BELLAIRS, and A. E. W. MILES

1953. Observations on the Premaxillary Dentition of Snakes with Special Reference to the Egg-tooth. Jour. Linn. Soc. Zoöl., vol. 42, no. 285, pp. 260–268.

SMITH, P. W., and J. C. LIST

1955. Notes on Mississippi Amphibians and Reptiles. Am. Midl. Nat., vol. 53, no. 1, pp. 115–125.

SMITH, S.

1765. The History of the Colony of Nova-Caesaria, or New Jersey. Burlington, N. J., pp. xiv + 602.

SMITH, T.

1806–7. The Naturalist's Cabinet: Containing Interesting Sketches of the Animal History; Illustrative of the Natures, Dispositions, Manners and Habits of All the Most Remarkable Quadrupeds, Birds, Fishes, Amphibia, Reptiles, etc., in the Known World. London, 6 vols. [Rattlesnakes in vol. 6, pp. 83–95.]

1818. On the Structure of the Poisonous Fangs of Serpents. Philos. Trans. (Royal Soc. London), vol. 108, pt. 2, no. 24, pp. 471–476.

SMITH, W. H.

1882. Report on the Reptiles and Amphibians of Ohio. Geol. Sur. Ohio, vol. 4, pt. 1, pp. 631–734.

SMITH, W. R.

1929. Animals and Plants in Oklahoma Folk Cures. Folk-Say, vol. 1, pp. 69–78.

1930a. Northwestern Oklahoma Folk Cures. Publ. Tex. Folk-Lore Soc., vol. 8, pp. 74–85.

1930b. "You Can't Tell about the Weather." Folk-Say, vol. 2, pp. 173–185.

SMITH, MRS. WHITE MOUNTAIN [DAMA MARGARET SMITH]

1939. Brotherhood of Snakes. Ariz. Highways, vol. 15, no. 7, pp. 16–17, 38–39.

SMYTH, F. J. D.
    1784. A Tour in the United States of America. London, 2 vols., pp. [xiv] + 400; [viii] + 455.
SMYTH, T.
    1949. Notes on the Timber Rattlesnake at Mountain Lake, Virginia. Copeia, no. 1, p. 78.
SNYDER, B.
    1949. Diamondbacks and Dollar Bills. Fla. Wildlife, vol. 3, no. 4, pp. 3–5, 16, 19.
SNYDER, R. C.
    1945. Notes on the Snakes of Southeastern Alabama. Copeia, no. 3, pp. 173–174.
SOARES DE SOUSA, G.
    1938. Tratado Descriptivo do Brasil em 1587. Brasiliana, vol. 117, pp. liii + 493. [3rd edition;
        the first complete edition, Rio de Janeiro, 1851. There was an anonymous partial publica-
        tion in 1825.]
SPALDING, A. M.
    1884. Rattlesnake Bite. N. Y. Med. Jour., vol. 40, pp. 66–67.
SPANGLER, R. H.
    1910. The Treatment of Epilepsy with Hypodermic Injections of Rattlesnake Venom (Cro-
        talin). Preliminary Report. N. Y. Med. Jour., vol. 92, no. 10, pp. 462–466.
    1911. Crotalin Treatment of Epilepsy. N. Y. Med. Jour., vol. 94, no. 11, pp. 517–520.
    1912. The Crotalin Treatment of Epilepsy. N. Y. Med. Jour., vol. 96, no. 11, pp. 520–523.
    1913. The Treatment of Epilepsy with Hypodermic Injections of Crotalin. N. Y. Med. Jour.,
        vol. 97, no. 14, pp. 699–702.
    1918. The Intramuscular Injection of a Foreign Protein, Crotalin, in 300 Cases of Epilepsy.
        N. Y. Med. Jour., vol. 107, no. 16, pp. 727–733.
    1924. Therapy of the Nonspecific Protein Reactions: Observations Based on the Intramuscular
        Injection of Venom Protein (Crotalin) Solution in Six Hundred Cases. Med. Jour. and
        Rec., vol. 120, no. 8, pp. 387–389; no. 9, pp. 440–441; no. 10, pp. 495–496. [See also Atlantic
        Med. Jour., vol. 28, no. 3, pp. 138–144.]
    1925. Nonspecific Desensitization. Therapy in Allergic Asthma. Arch. Int. Med., vol. 36, no. 6,
        pp. 779–787.
    1943. Allergic Findings in Epileptic Patients and Ancestors. Annals Allergy, vol. 1, no. 2, pp.
        91–114.
SPARKMAN, P. S.
    1908a. Notes on California Folk-Lore: A Luiseño Tale. Jour. Am. Folk-Lore, vol. 21, no. 80,
        pp. 35–36.
    1908b. The Culture of the Luiseño Indians. Univ. Calif. Publ. Am. Arch. and Ethn., vol. 8, no.
        4, pp. 187–234.
SPAULDING, E. S.
    1944. Wild Oats and Chaparral. Santa Barbara, pp. 1–180.
SPECK, F. G.
    1907. The Creek Indians of Taskigi Town. Mem. Am. Anthro. Assn., vol. 2, no. 2, pp. 99–164.
    1917. Medicine Practices of the Northeastern Algonquians. Proc. 19th Int. Cong. Americanists,
        pp. 303–321.
    1921. The Origin of the Belief That Snakes Swallow Their Young for Protection. Copeia, no.
        98, pp. 51–54.
    1923a. Reptile Lore of the Northern Indians. Jour. Am. Folk-Lore, vol. 36, no. 141, pp. 273–280.
    1923b. Snake Folk-Lore: The Snake Who Swallows Her Young. Jour. Am. Folk-Lore, vol. 36,
        no. 141, pp. 298–300.
    1928. Chapters on the Ethnology of the Powhatan Tribes of Virginia. Indian Notes and
        Monog., Mus. Am. Indian, Heye Foundation, vol. 1, no. 5, pp. 225–455.
    1934. Catawba Texts. Columbia Univ. Contrib. Anthro., vol. 24, pp. xviii + 91.
    1935. Penobscot Tales and Religious Beliefs. Jour. Am. Folk-Lore, vol. 48, no. 187, pp. 1–107.
    1937. Catawba Medicines and Curative Practices. 25th Ann. Stud., Phila. Anthro. Soc., pp.
        179–197.
    1941. A List of Plant Curatives Obtained from the Houma Indians of Louisiana. Primitive
        Man, vol. 14, no. 4, pp. 49–73.
    1944. Catawba Herbals and Curative Practices. Jour. Am. Folklore, vol. 57, no. 223, pp. 37–50.

1946. Ethnoherpetology of the Catawba and Cherokee Indians. Jour. Wash. Acad. Sci., vol. 36, no. 10, pp. 355–360.

SPECK, F. G., and L. BROWN

1951. Cherokee Dance and Drama. Berkeley and Los Angeles, pp. xxv + 106.

SPECK, F. G., and E. S. DODGE

1945. Amphibian and Reptile Lore of the Six Nations Cayuga. Jour. Am. Folklore, vol. 58, no. 23, pp. 306–309.

SPECK, F. G., R. B. HASSRICK, and E. S. CARPENTER

1942. Rappahannock Herbals, Folk-Lore and Science of Cures. Proc. Delaware Co. Inst. Sci., vol. 10, no. 1, pp. 7–47.

SPEER, F.

1941. Treatment of Rattlesnake Bite. Military Surg., vol. 88, no. 6, pp. 640–641.

SPENCE, L.

1913. The Myths of Mexico and Peru. New York, pp. xiii + 366.

1914. The Myths of the North American Indians. London, pp. xii + 393.

1923. The Gods of Mexico. London, pp. xvi + 388.

SPENCER, D. L.

1908. Notes on the Maidu Indians of Butte County. Jour. Am. Folk-Lore, vol. 21, nos. 81–82, pp. 242–245.

SPENCER, O. M.

1836. Narrative of O. M. Spencer. London, pp. xxxvii + 247. [Reprint edited by M. M. Quaife, Chicago, 1917, pp. xxv + 188.]

SPERRY, C. C.

1941. Food Habits of the Coyote. Wildlife Res. Bull. 4, pp. 1–70.

SPHAR, R. H.

1953. Snake Outsmarts Mink. Pa. Game News, vol. 24, no. 9, p. 37.

SPIELMAN, J. G.

1950. 36 Rattles and a Button. Desert Mag., vol. 13, no. 12, p. 29.

SPIER, L.

1923. Southern Diegueño Customs. Univ. Calif. Publ. Am. Arch. and Ethn., vol. 20, no. 16, pp. 295–358.

1928. Havasupai Ethnography. Anthro. Papers, Am. Mus. Nat. Hist., vol. 29, part 3, pp. 81–392.

1930. Klamath Ethnography. Univ. Calif. Publ. Am. Arch and Ethn., vol. 30, pp. x + 338.

1933. Yuman Tribes of the Gila River. Chicago, pp. xviii + 433.

1936. Cultural Relations of the Gila River and Lower Colorado Tribes. Yale Univ. Publ. Anthro., no. 3, pp. 1–22.

1946. Comparative Vocabularies and Parallel Texts in Two Yuman Languages of Arizona. Univ. N. Mex. Publ. Anthro., no. 2, pp. 1–150.

SPIER, L., W. CLINE, RACHEL S. COMMONS, MAY MANDELBAUM, R. H. POST, and L. V. W. WALTERS

1938. The Sinkaietk or Southern Okanagon of Washington. Yale General Series in Anthropology, no. 6, pp. 1–262.

SPIER, L., and E. SAPIR

1930. Wishram Ethnography. Univ. Wash. Publ. Anthro., vol. 3, no. 3, pp. 151–300.

SPINDEN, H. J.

1908. The Nez Percé Indians. Mem. Am. Anthro. Assn., vol. 2, no. 3, pp. 165–274.

1913. A Study of Maya Art. Mem. Peabody Mus., vol. 6, pp. xxiii + 285.

1946. Ancient Civilizations of Mexico and Central America. Am. Mus. Nat. Hist., Handbook Ser., no. 3 (3rd edition), pp. 1–270. [1st edition, New York, 1917, pp. 1–238.]

SPOTT, R., and A. L. KROEBER

1942. Yurok Narratives. Univ. Calif. Publ. Am. Arch. and Ethn., vol. 35, no. 9, pp. 143–256.

SPRENGELL, C. J.

1732. Some Observations upon Vipers. Philos. Trans. (Royal Soc. London), vol. 32, no. 376, pp. 296–297.

SPRUNT, A., JR.

1931. Suffering Snakes. Am. Legion Monthly, vol. 10, no. 6, pp. 12–13, 45–47.

1933. Ever See a Horn Snake? Am. Legion Monthly, vol. 14, no. 3, pp. 24–25, 60–62.

SQUIER, E. G.
1851. The Serpent Symbol, and the Worship of the Reciprocal Principles of Nature in America. New York, Am. Arch. Researches, no. 1, pp. xvi, 11–254.

SQUIER, E. G. and E. H. DAVIS
1848. Ancient Monuments of the Mississippi Valley. Smithson. Contrib. Knowl., pp. xxxix + 306.

STABLER, R. M.
1939. Frequency of Skin Shedding in Snakes. Copeia, no. 4, pp. 227–229.
1948. Prairie Rattlesnake Eats Spadefoot Toad. Herpetologica, vol. 4, part 5, p. 168.

STADELMAN, R. E.
1928. The Poisoning Power of the New-Born Copperhead with Case Report. Bull. Antivenin Inst. Am., vol. 2, no. 3, pp. 67–69. [Also vol. 3, no. 3, p. 81.]
1929. Some Venom Extraction Records. Bull. Antivenin Inst. Am., vol. 3, no. 1, p. 29.

STAHNKE, H. L.
1949. Scorpions. Tempe, Ariz., pp. 1–23.
1950. The Arizona Scorpion Problem. Ariz. Med., vol. 7, no. 3, pp. 23–29.
1953a. The L-C Treatment of Venomous Bites and Stings. Amer. Jour. Trop. Med. and Hyg., vol. 2, no. 1, pp. 142–143. [See also Ariz. Highways, vol. 29, no. 2, p. 35; La. Cons., vol. 5, no. 10, pp. 10–11; and San Diego County Farm Bur. News, vol. 40, no. 1, p. 8.]
1953b. The L-C Treatment of Venomous Bites or Stings. Tempe, Ariz., pp. [1–4].
1954. The L-C Method of Treating Venomous Bites and Stings. Tempe, Ariz., pp. 1–15.

STALEY, F. H.
1939. The Present Rationale in the Treatment of Poisonous Snake Bites. Weekly Bull. St. Louis Med. Soc., vol. 33, no. 41, pp. 548–552.

STANLEY, C.
1897. The Life and Adventures of the American Cow-Boy. [Providence], pp. 39 + [11].

STANLEY, D. S.
1917. Personal Memoirs. Cambridge, Mass., pp. 1–271.

STANLEY, E.
1854. Bite of a Rattlesnake Treated and Recorded. Buffalo Med. Jour., vol. 9, no. 8, pp. 464–465. [See also Boston Med. and Surg. Jour., vol. 49, no. 25, pp. 506–507.]

STANLEY, E. J.
1916. Life of Rev. L. B. Stateler. Revised edition, Nashville, Tenn., pp. xxi + 356. [First published in 1907.]

STANLEY, R.
1947. The Smoki Tribe. Westways, vol. 37, no. 7, pp. 8–9.

STAPLES, G. M.
1865. Case of Poisoning by a Rattlesnake Bite—Treated with Bi-sulphite of Soda. Med. and Surg. Reporter, vol. 8, no. 18, pp. 279–280.

STARKWEATHER, N.
1888. Of Serpents. Forest and Stream, vol. 31, no. 7, pp. 122–123; no. 8, pp. 142–143.

STAUFFER, C.
1952. Too Scared to Pray. Fla. Wildlife, vol. 6, no. 6, pp. 16–17.

STEARNS, R. E. C.
1877. A Black Rattlesnake. Am. Nat., vol. 11, no. 10, p. 623.

STEBBINS, R. C.
1943. Diurnal Activity of *Crotalus cerastes*. Copeia, no. 2, pp. 128–129.
1954. Amphibians and Reptiles of Western North America. New York, pp. xxii + 528.

STEDMAN, J. G.
1796. Narrative of a Five Years Expedition against the Revolted Negroes of Surinam, in Guiana, on the Wild Coast of South America from the Year 1772 to 1777. London, 2 vols., pp. xviii + 407 + [5]; 404 + [7].

STEELE, R. R.
1905. Mediaeval Lore from Bartholomaeus Anglicus. London, pp. xv + 195.

STEGGERDA, M.
1941. Maya Indians of Yucatán. Carn. Inst., Publ. no. 531, pp. xx + 280.

STEINER, R.

  1899. Superstitions and Beliefs from Central Georgia. Jour. Am. Folk-Lore, vol. 12, no. 47, pp. 261–271.

STEJNEGER, L. S.

  1893. Annotated List of the Reptiles and Batrachians Collected by the Death Valley Expedition in 1891, with Descriptions of New Species. N. Am. Fauna, no. 7, pp. 159–228.

  1895. The Poisonous Snakes of North America. Rept. U. S. Nat. Mus. for 1893, pp. 337–487.

STEJNEGER, L. S., and T. BARBOUR

  1940. The Generic Concept. Copeia, no. 4, pp. 217–218.

STEPHEN, A. M.

  1888. Legend of the Snake Order of the Moquis. Jour. Am. Folk-Lore, vol. 1, no. 2, pp. 109–114.

  1929. Hopi Tales. Jour. Am. Folk-Lore, vol. 42, no. 163, pp. 1–72.

  1936. Hopi Journal. Edited by Elsie Clews Parsons. New York, 2 vols., pp. lii + 1417.

STEPHENS, J. L.

  1843. Incidents of Travel in Yucatán. New York, 2 vols., pp. xii + 459; xvi + 478.

STEPHENS, T. W. W., and W. MEYERS

  1898. Test-Tube Reactions between Cobra Poison and Its Antitoxin. Brit. Med. Jour., vol. 1, no. 1940, pp. 620–621.

STERN, R.

  1871. The Antidote for Rattlesnake Venom. Med. and Surg. Reporter, vol. 25, no. 25, p. 557.

STERNBERG, G. M.

  1869. Does the Prairie-Dog Require Any Water? Am. Nat., vol. 3, no. 3, pp. 156–157.

STETSON, J. B., JR. (See under MAGALHÃES DE GANDAVO, PERO DE.)

STEVENSON, MATILDA C.

  1894. The Sia. 11th Ann. Rept. Bur. Ethn., pp. 3–157.

  1904. The Zuñi Indians. Their Mythology, Esoteric Fraternities, and Ceremonies. 23rd Ann. Rept. Bur. Am. Ethn., pp. 3–608.

  1915. Ethnobotany of the Zuñi Indians. 30th Ann. Rept. Bur. Am. Ethn., pp. 31–102.

STEWARD, J. H.

  1929. Petroglyphs of California and Adjoining States. Univ. Calif. Publ. Am. Arch. and Ethn., vol. 24, no. 2, pp. 47–238.

  1933. Ethnography of the Owens Valley Paiute. Univ. Calif. Publ. Am. Arch. and Ethn., vol. 33, no. 3, pp. 233–350.

  1936. Myths of the Owens Valley Paiute. Univ. Calif. Publ. Am. Arch. and Ethn., vol. 34, no. 5, pp. 355–440.

  1938. Panatubiji, an Owens Valley Paiute. Bur. Am. Ethn., Bull. 119, Anthro. Papers, no. 6, pp. 183–195.

  1941. Culture Element Distributions: XIII. Nevada Shoshone. Univ. Calif. Anthro. Rec., vol. 4, no. 2, pp. v, 209–359.

  1943a. Some Western Shoshoni Myths. Bur. Am. Ethn., Bull. 136, pp. 249–299.

  1943b. Culture Element Distributions: XXIII. Northern and Gosiute Shoshoni. Univ. Calif. Anthro. Rec., vol. 8, no. 3, pp. iii, 263–392.

STEWART, C. D.

  1933. The Acrobatic Snake. Atlantic Monthly, vol. 152, no. 4, pp. 462–470.

STEWART, O. C.

  1941. Culture Element Distributions: XIV. Northern Paiute. Univ. Calif. Anthro. Rec., vol. 4, no. 3, pp. iv, 361–446.

  1942. Culture Element Distributions: XVIII. Ute-Southern Paiute. Univ. Calif. Anthro. Rec., vol. 6, no. 4, pp. iii, 231–356.

STICKEL, W. H.

  1943. The Mexican Snakes of the Genera *Sonora* and *Chionactis* with Notes on the Status of Other Colubrid Genera. Proc. Biol. Soc. Wash., vol. 56, pp. 109–128.

  1952. Venomous Snakes of the United States and Treatment of Their Bites. U. S. Fish and Wildlife Serv., Wildlife Leafl. no. 339, pp. 1–29.

STICKEL, W. H., and J. B. COPE

  1947. The Home Ranges and Wanderings of Snakes. Copeia, no. 2, pp. 127–136.

STILLWELL, H. [STILWELL, H.]

    1939. Snakes in the Grass. Elks Mag., vol. 17, no. 10, pp. 14–17, 49–50.

    1949. Fanged-Death Horseplay. Field and Stream, vol. 54, no. 7, pp. 60, 110–113.

STIMPSON, G.

    1946. A Book about a Thousand Things. New York, pp. x + 552.

    1948. Information Roundup. New York, pp. x + 587.

STIRLING, M. W.

    1942. Snake Bites and the Hopi Snake Dance. Smithson. Rept. for 1941, pp. 551–555.

STOCK, C.

    1918. The Pleistocene Fauna of Hawver Cave. Univ. Calif. Publ. Geol., vol. 10, no. 24, pp. 461–515.

STOCKBRIDGE, W.

    1843. Snakes and Snake-Bites at the South West. Boston Med. and Surg. Jour., vol. 29, no. 1, pp. 40–43.

STOCKMAN, R.

    1898. Arrow Poisons: Their History, Sources, and Constituents. Pharm. Jour., vol. 61 (ser. 4, vol. 7), pp. 548–550; 585–587.

STODDARD, H. L.

    1942. The Bobwhite Quail: Its Habits, Preservation and Increase. New York, pp. xxix + 559.

STODDARD, J. L.

    1898. John L. Stoddard's Lectures. New York, 10 vols.; see vol. 10, pp. 148–157.

STONE, C. P.

    1861. Notes on the State of Sonora. Washington, pp. 1–28.

STONE, E.

    1932. Medicine among the American Indians. Clio Medica, vol. 7, pp. xi + 139.

STONE, L.

    1881. The Stroke of the Rattlesnake. Forest and Stream, vol. 16, no. 24, p. 473.

STONE, W.

    1911. On Some Collections of Reptiles and Batrachians from the Western United States. Proc. Acad. Nat. Sci. Phila., vol. 63, pp. 222–232.

STONHAM, T. G.

    1906. Snake Venoms: Showing How Recent Discoveries with Regard to Them Emphasize the Parallelism between Their Pathological and Therapeutic Action. Monthly Homoeop. Rev., vol. 50, no. 8, pp. 453–477.

STORER, D. H.

    1839. Reports on the Ichthyology and Herpetology of Massachusetts. Comm. Zoöl. and Bot. Sur. Mass., Boston, pp. 201–253.

STORER, T. I., F. P. CRONEMILLER, E. E. HORN, and B. GLADING

    1942. Studies on Valley Quail. [The San Joaquin Experimental Range.] Univ. Calif. Agric. Exp. Sta., Bull. 663, pp. 130–135.

STORER, T. I., and BERYL M. WILSON

    1932. Feeding Habits and Molt of *Crotalus confluentus oreganus* in Captivity. Copeia, no. 4, pp. 169–173.

STOUT, E. J.

    1936. Folklore from Iowa. Mem. Am. Folk-Lore Soc., vol. 29, pp. x + 228.

STRACHEY, W. (See under MAJOR, R. H.)

STRADLING, A.

    1881. Keeping Reptiles. Field, vol. 58, no. 1481, pp. 148–149.

    1882. Notes about Snakes. Nature, vol. 25, no. 642, pp. 377–388.

    1883. The Extermination of Venomous Serpents. Sci. Am., vol. 48 (n.s.), no. 15, p. 225.

STRASSER, F. D.

    1931. An Encounter between a Collared Lizard and a Rattlesnake. Bull. Antivenin Inst. Am., vol. 5, no. 2, p. 41.

STRECKER, J. K.

    1908. The Reptiles and Batrachians of McLennan County, Texas. Proc. Biol. Soc. Wash., vol. 21, pp. 69–84.

1910. Notes on the Fauna of Northwestern Texas. Baylor Univ. Bull., vol. 13, nos. 4 and 5, pp. 1–31.

1925. Reptile Myths in Northwestern Louisiana. Publ. Tex. Folk-Lore Soc., no. 4, pp. 44–52.

1926a. Reptiles of the South and Southwest in Folk-Lore. Publ. Tex. Folk-Lore Soc., no. 5, pp. 56–69.

1926b. On the Origins of Reptile Myths. Publ. Tex. Folk-Lore Soc., no. 5, pp. 70–77.

1926c. On the Use by Birds of Snake's Sloughs as Nesting Material. Auk, vol. 43, no. 4, pp. 501–507.

1927a. Observations on the Food Habits of Texas Amphibians and Reptiles. Copeia, no. 162, pp. 6–9.

1927b. Birds and Snake Skins. Contrib. Baylor Univ. Mus., no. 11, pp. 1–12.

1928. Common English and Folk Names for Texas Amphibians and Reptiles. Contrib. Baylor Univ. Mus., no. 16, pp. 1–21.

1929a. Further Studies in the Folk-Lore of Reptiles. Baylor Univ. Contrib. Folk-Lore, no. 1, pp. 1–16.

1929b. Dragons and Other Reptiles, Real and Imaginary. Baylor Univ. Contrib. Folk-Lore, no. 3, pp. 1–19.

1935. Notes on the Pit-Vipers in McLennan County, Texas. Baylor Bull., vol. 38, no. 3, pp. 26–28.

STRONG, R. A.
1928. Newer Knowledge of Venomous Snakes. Int. Med. Digest, vol. 12, pp. 233–252.

STRONG, W. D.
1929. Aboriginal Society in Southern California. Univ. Calif. Publ. Am. Arch. and Ethn., vol. 26, pp. x + 358.

STRONG, W. D., and W. E. SCHENCK
1925. Petroglyphs near the Dalles of the Columbia River. Am. Anthro., vol. 27 (n.s.), no. 1, pp. 76–90.

STUART, J.
1833. Three Years in North America. Edinburgh, 2 vols., pp. ix + 496; vi + 580.

STUART, L. C.
1954. A Description of a Subhumid Corridor across Northern Central America, with Comments on Its Herpetofaunal Indicators. Contrib. Lab. Vert. Biol. Univ. Mich., no. 65, pp. 1–40.

SULLIVAN, E.
1852. Rambles and Scrambles in North and South America. London, pp. 1–424.

SUMMERHAYES, MARTHA
1939. Vanished Arizona: Recollections of My Army Life. Chicago, pp. xix + 337.

SURFACE, H. A.
1906. The Serpents of Pennsylvania. Pa. State Dept. Agric., Monthly Bull. Div. Zoöl., vol. 4, nos. 4–5, pp. 114–208.

SUTCLIFFE, R.
1952. Notes Made by Dr. Edward Hallowell. Copeia, no. 2, pp. 113–114.

SUTTON, G. M.
1946. Great Blue Heron Swallows a Large Snake. Auk, vol. 63, no. 1, p. 97.

SWALM, T., and N. SWALM
1947. Pinellas St. Patrick. Fla. Wildlife, vol. 1, no. 7, pp. 4–5, 13.

SWANSON, P. L.
1930. Notes on the Massasauga. Bull. Antivenin Inst. Am., vol. 4, no. 3, pp. 70–71.

1933a. Pennsylvania's Poisonous Snakes. Wyoming Valley Motorist, vol. 1, no. 11, pp. 6, 16–18.

1933b. The Size of *Sistrurus catenatus catenatus* at Birth. Copeia, no. 1, p. 37.

1941. Do Snakes Swallow Their Young? Pa. Angler, vol. 10, no. 4, pp. 14–15.

1945. Herpetological Notes from Panama. Copeia, no. 4, pp. 210–216.

1946a. X. Nat. Hist., vol. 55, no. 10, pp. 457–459.

1946b. Effects of Snake Venoms on Snakes. Copeia, no. 4, pp. 242–249.

1952. The Reptiles of Venango County, Pennsylvania. Am. Midl. Nat., vol. 42, no. 1, pp. 161–182.

SWANTON, J. R.
    1907. Mythology of the Indians of Louisiana and the Texas Coast. Jour. Am. Folk-Lore, vol. 20, no. 79, pp. 285–289.
    1911. Indian Tribes of the Lower Mississippi Valley and the Adjacent Gulf Coast of the Gulf of Mexico. Bur. Am. Ethn., Bull. 43, pp. vii + 387.
    1917. Some Chitimacha Myths and Beliefs. Jour. Am. Folk-Lore, vol. 30, no. 118, pp. 474–478.
    1918. Catawba Notes. Jour. Wash. Acad. Sci., vol. 8, no. 19, pp. 623–629.
    1928a. Social Organization and Social Usages of the Indians of the Creek Confederacy. 42nd Ann. Rept. Bur. Am. Ethn., pp. 23–472.
    1928b. Religious Beliefs and Medical Practices of the Creek Indians. 42nd Ann. Rept. Bur. Am. Ethn., pp. 473–672.
    1928c. Social and Religious Beliefs and Usages of the Chickasaw Indians. 44th Ann. Rept. Bur. Am. Ethn., pp. 169–273.
    1929. Myths and Tales of the Southeastern Indians. Bur. Am. Ethn., Bull. 88, pp. x + 275.
    1931. Source Material for the Social and Ceremonial Life of the Choctaw Indians. Bur. Am. Ethn., Bull. 103, pp. vii + 282.
    1946. The Indians of the Southeastern United States. Bur. Am. Ethn., Bull. 137, pp. xiii + 943.
    1953. The Indian Tribes of North America. Bur. Am. Eth., Bull. 145, pp. vi + 726.

SWAROOP, S., and B. GRAB
    1954. Snakebite Mortality in the World. Bull. World Health Org., League of Nations, vol. 10, no. 1, pp. 35–76.

SWARTZWELDER, J. C.
    1950. Snake-Bite Accidents in Louisiana: with Data on 306 Cases. Am. Jour. Trop. Med., vol. 30, no. 4, pp. 575–589.

SWEENEY, DR.
    1860. Singular Effects of Snake Poison. Cincinnati Lancet and Observer, vol. 5, no. 5, p. 318.

SWEET, W. T.
    1954. I've Killed 5000 Rattlers. Outdoor Life, vol. 113, no. 2, pp. 54–55, 110–112.

SWIFT, L. W.
    1933. Death of a Rattlesnake from Continued Exposure to Direct Sunlight. Copeia, no. 3, p. 150.

SYKES, G.
    1945. Hopi Snake-Washing: 1893. Ariz. Quart., vol. 1, no. 4, pp. 34–36.
    1947. In the Kiva of the Snake Clan. Desert Mag., vol. 10, no. 10, pp. 15–18.

T., N. A.
    1882. The Rattlesnake. Forest and Stream, vol. 19, no. 1, pp. 6–7.
    1887. Snake Fascination. Forest and Stream, vol. 28, no. 26, pp. 551–552.

TAIT, J.
    1938. Surgical Removal of the Poison Glands of the Rattlesnakes. Copeia, no. 1, pp. 10–13.

TALAYESVA, D. C. (See under SIMMONS, L. W.)

TALBOT, M. W., J. W. NELSON, and R. E. STORIE
    1942. The Experimental Area [San Joaquin Experimental Range]. Univ. Calif. Agric. Exp. Sta. Bull. 663, pp. 7–12.

TALKOV, R. H., and W. BAUER
    1943. The Failure of Cobra Venom to Relieve Pain in Rheumatoid Arthritis. N. Eng. Jour. Med., vol. 228, p. 152.

TANNER, J.
    1830. A Narrative of the Captivity and Adventures of John Tanner. Edited by Edwin James. London, pp. 1–426.

TANNER, J. C., JR., and J. K. SCHELLACK
    1950. Management of Snakebite in Southeastern States. Bull. Crawford W. Long Mem. Hosp., vol. 2, no. 4, pp. 61–67.

TANNER, W. W.
    1940. Notes on the Herpetological Specimens Added to the Brigham Young University Vertebrate Collection during 1939. Great Basin Nat., vol. 1, nos. 3 & 4, pp. 138–146.

TANTAQUIDGEON, GLADYS

1928. Mohegan Medicinal Practices, Weather Lore and Superstition. 43rd Ann. Rept. Bur. Am. Ethn., pp. 264–276.

1942. A Study of Delaware Indian Medicine Practice and Folk Beliefs. Pa. Hist. Commission, Harrisburg, pp. xi + 91.

TAUBE, H. N., and H. E. ESSEX

1937. Pathologic Changes in the Tissues of the Dog following Injections of Rattlesnake Venom. Arch. Path., vol. 24, no. 1. pp. 43–51.

TAYLOR, E. H.

1936. Notes on the Herpetological Fauna of the Mexican State of Sonora. Bull. Univ. Kans., vol. 37, no. 14, pp. 475–503.

TAYLOR, J.

1940. Observations Relative to the Standardization of Cobra Antivenene. Indian Med. Jour., vol. 28, no. 1, pp. 279–290.

TAYLOR, LYDA A.

1940. Plants Used as Curatives by Certain Southeastern Tribes. Bot. Mus. Harvard Univ., Cambridge, pp. xi + 88.

TAYLOR, R. C.

1835. On the Geology and Natural History of the North-Eastern Extremity of the Alleghany Mountain Range, in Pennsylvania, United States. Mag. Nat. Hist., vol. 8, no. 54, pp. 529–541.

TAYLOR, S.

1665. A Way of Killing Rattlesnakes. Philos. Trans. (Royal Soc. London), vol. 1, no. 3, p. 43; no. 4, p. 76. [Abridged edition, vol. 2, p. 814.]

TAYLOR, W. E.

1892a. Catalogue of the Snakes of Nebraska with Notes on Their Habits and Distribution. Am. Nat., vol. 26, no. 309, pp. 742–752.

1892b. The Ophidia of Nebraska. Ann. Rept. Nebr. State Board Agric. for 1891, pp. 310–357.

1895. Preliminary Notes on the Osteology of the North American Crotalidae. Am. Nat., vol. 29, no. 339, pp. 281–285.

TAYLOR, W. P.

1912. Field Notes on Amphibians, Reptiles and Birds of Northern Humboldt County, Nevada. Univ. Calif. Publ. Zoöl., vol. 7, no. 10, pp. 319–436.

1935. Notes on *Crotalus atrox* near Tucson, Arizona, with Special Reference to Its Breeding Habits. Copeia, no. 3, pp. 154–155.

1954. Food Habits and Notes on Life History of the Ring-Tailed Cat in Texas. Jour. Mammal., vol. 35, no. 1, pp. 55–63.

TEALE, E. W.

1945. The Lost Woods: Adventures of a Naturalist. New York, pp. xiii + 326.

1951. North with the Spring. New York, pp. xviii + 366.

TEIT, J. A.

1900. The Thompson Indians of British Columbia. Mem. Am. Mus. Nat. Hist., vol. 2, part 4, pp. 163–392.

1909. The Lilloet Indians. Mem. Am. Mus. Nat. Hist., vol. 4, part 5, pp. 193–300.

1916. European Tales from the Upper Thompson Indians. Jour. Am. Folk-Lore, vol. 29, no. 113, pp. 301–329.

1930a. The Salishan Tribes of the Western Plateaus. 45th Ann. Rept. Bur. Am. Ethn., pp. 23–296.

1930b. Ethnobotany of the Thompson Indians of British Columbia. 45th Ann. Rept. Bur. Am. Ethn., pp. 441–522.

TELFORD, S. R.

1952. A Herpetological Survey in the Vicinity of Lake Shipp, Polk County, Florida. Quart. Jour. Fla. Acad. Sci., vol. 15, no. 3, pp. 175–185.

TENNENT, J. E.

1860. Ceylon: An Account of the Island. London, 2 vols., pp. xxxix + 643; xvi + 669.

TERHUNE, R. W.

1938. Pioneer Folklore Relative to Snakes. Indiana Mag. Hist., vol. 34, no. 4, pp. 443–450.

TETERS, LUE ELLEN
    1896. The Moqui Snake Dance. Godey's Mag., vol. 137, no. 792, pp. 564–568.
TEVIS, L., JR.
    1943. Field Notes on a Red Rattlesnake in Lower California. Copeia, no. 4, pp. 242–245.
THATCHER, J.
    1823. [Rattlesnake-Bite Treatment.] Boston Med. Intelligencer, vol. 1, no. 16, p. 62.
THATCHER, T. O.
    1940. Rattlesnakes. Nat'l Park Serv., Region III Quart., vol. 2, no. 1, pp. 34–40.
THEISS, L. E.
    1925. Do Snakes Climb Trees? Amer. Forests and Forest Life, vol. 31, no. 374, p. 109.
THOM, D. A.
    1914. The Present Status of Crotalin in the Treatment of Epilepsy. Boston Med. and Surg.
        Jour., vol. 171, no. 25, pp. 933–935.
THOMAS, CRAIG
    1934. Feeding Rattlesnakes. Yosemite Nat. Notes, vol. 13, no. 4, p. 32.
THOMAS, CYRUS
    1887. Burial Mounds of the Northern Sections of the United States. 5th Ann. Rept. Bur. Ethn.,
        pp. 3–119.
THOMAS, D.
    1819. Travels through the Western Country in the Summer of 1816. Auburn, N. Y., pp. [ii] +
        320.
THOMAS, D. L., and LUCY B. THOMAS
    1920. Kentucky Superstitions. Princeton, pp. viii + 334.
THOMAS, G.
    1698. An Historical Description of the Province and Country of West-New-Jersey in America.
        London, pp. 8 + 55 + 11 + 34. [Also facsimile edition, New York, 1848; and in Narratives of
        Early Pennsylvania, West New Jersey, and Delaware, 1630–1707, New York, pp. 313–352,
        1912.]
THOMAS, J. R.
    1855. Snake Bites—Treated by Brandy. North-West. Med. and Surg. Jour., vol. 12 [vol. 4, n.s.],
        no. 7, art. 4, pp. 305–306.
THOMAS, J. T.
    1890. Deaths from Snake Bite. Med. Rec., vol. 37, no. 5 (whole no. 1004), p. 123. [See also H. H.
        Hopkins, vol. 36, no. 16 (whole no. 989), p. 431, 1889.]
THOMAS, JEAN
    1942. Blue Ridge Country. New York, pp. x + 338.
THOMAS, L.
    1931. Tall Stories. New York and London, pp. xi + 245.
THOMAS, W. S.
    1954. Folklore Figures of Rochester, N. Y. N .Y. Folklore Quart., vol. 10, no. 1, pp. 9–17.
THOMPSON, C. J. S.
    1932. The Hand of Destiny: The Folk-Lore and Superstitions of Everyday Life. London, pp.
        1–303.
[THOMPSON, D.]
    1916. David Thompson's Narrative of His Explorations in Western North America, 1784–1812.
        Edited by J. B. Tyrrell. Toronto, Champlain Soc., Publ. no. 12, pp. xcviii + 582.
THOMPSON, D. W. (translator)
    1910. The Works of Aristotle. IV. Historia Animalium. Oxford, pp. xv + sections 486–633 +
        [xxx].
THOMPSON, E. H.
    1932. People of the Serpent: Life and Adventure among the Mayas. Boston, pp. xv + 301.
THOMPSON, J. A.
    1924. Science, Old and New. New York, pp. ix + 440.
THOMPSON, J. C.
    1913. Contributions to the Anatomy of the Ophidia. Proc. Zoöl. Soc. London, pp. 414–425.

THOMPSON, J. E.
1933. Mexico before Cortez. New York, pp. x + 298.

THORNDIKE, L.
1923–41. A History of Magic and Experimental Science. New York, 6 vols.

[THORPE, T. B.]
1855. The Rattlesnake and Its Congeners. Harper's New Monthly Mag., vol. 10, pp. 470–483.

THRUSTON, R. C. B.
1926. The Origin and Evolution of the United States Flag. Washington, pp. 1–26.

THURSTON, E.
1912. Omens and Superstitions of Southern India. London, pp. 1–320.

THWAITES, R. G. (editor)
1896–1901. Travels and Explorations of the Jesuit Missionaries in New France, 1610–1791. Cleveland, 73 vols.

1904–7. Early Western Travels, 1748–1846. Cleveland, 32 vols.

TIMBERLAKE, H.
1765. The Memoirs of Lieut. Henry Timberlake. London, pp. viii + 160. [Reprint, with an introduction by S. C. Williams, Johnson City, Tenn., 1927, pp. 1–197.]

TITIEV, M.
1943. Hopi Snake Handling. Sci. Monthly, vol. 57, no. 1, pp. 44–51.

1944. Old Oraibi. Papers Peabody Mus. Am. Arch. and Ethn., vol. 22, no. 1, pp. xi + 277.

TIXIER, V.
1940. Tixier's Travels on the Osage Prairies. Edited by John F. McDermott and translated by Albert J. Salvan. Norman, Okla., pp. xv + 309. [1st edition, Clermont-Ferrand, 1844.]

To, S.
1940. Statistical Studies on Victims of Poisonous Snake Bites in Formosa. Japanese Jour. Med. Sci., part 4, Pharmacology, vol. 12, pp. 130–133. [See also Jour. Med. Assn. Formosa, vol. 60, nos. 8–9, pp. 1477–1524, 1941.]

TODD, C. B.
1899. Two Ways of Killing Rattlesnakes. Forest and Stream, vol. 52, no. 8, pp. 145–146.

TOME, P.
1928. Pioneer Life: or, Thirty Years a Hunter. Harrisburg, Pa., pp. ix + 173. [Reprint, with appendix by A. M. Aurand, Jr., of original edition of 1854.]

TOMES, C. S.
1877. On the Development and Succession of the Poison-Fangs of Snakes. Philos. Trans. (Royal Soc. London), vol. 166, no. 14, pp. 377–385.

TOPLIS, J.
1804. On the Fascinating Power of Snakes. Philos. Mag., vol. 19, no. 76, pp. 379–384.

TOPSELL, E.
1608. The Historie of Serpents. Or, The Second Book of Living Creatures. London, pp. [viii] + 315 + [viii]. [2nd edition, London, 1658, the serpent section being pp. 587–824.]

TOWNE, C. W., and E. N. WENTWORTH
1946. Shepherd's Empire. Norman, Okla., pp. xii + 364.

TOWNSEND, C. H.
1882. Character of Our Native Snakes. Forest and Stream, vol. 19, no. 13, pp. 244–245.

TOWNSEND, J. K.
1839. Narrative of a Journey across the Rocky Mountains to the Columbia River. Philadelphia, pp. viii + 352. [Reprinted in Thwaites: Early Western Travels, 32 vols. Cleveland, 1904–7; see vol. 21, pp. 107–369.]

TOZZER, A. M.
1908. A Note on Star-Lore among the Navajos. Jour. Am. Folk-Lore, vol. 21, no. 80, pp. 28–32.

TOZZER, A. M., and G. M. ALLEN
1910. Animal Figures in the Maya Codices. Papers Peabody Mus., vol. 4, no. 3, pp. 273–372.

TRACY, J. G.
1828. On the *Uvularia grandiflora*, as a Remedy for the Bite of the Rattlesnake, N. Y. Med. and Phys. Jour., vol. 7, no. 1, pp. 65–68.

1388   *Bibliography*

TRAPIDO, H.

1939. Parturition in the Timber Rattlesnake, *Crotalus horridus horridus* Linné. Copeia, no. 4, p. 230.

1940. Mating Time and Sperm Viability in *Storeria*. Copeia, no. 2, pp. 107–109.

1941. The Timber Rattlesnake in Vermont. N. Eng. Nat., no. 10, pp. 26–27.

TRASK, J. L. R.

1892. Petition of Palmer Goulding, 1741, Who Claimed Skill in Curing Rattlesnake's Bites. N.-Eng. Hist. and Geneal. Reg., vol. 46, pp. 215–216.

TRETHEWIE, E. R., and A. J. DAY

1948. New Therapy of Ophidiasis. Australian Jour. Exp. Biol. and Med. Sci., vol. 26, part 2, pp. 153–161.

TREVAN, J. W.

1927. The Error of Determination of Toxicity. Proc. Royal Soc. London, Ser. B (Biol.), vol. 101, No. B 712, pp. 483–514.

TRIPLEHORN, C. A.

1955. Notes on the Young of Some North American Reptiles. Copeia, no. 3, pp. 248–249.

TRIPPEL, E. J.

1889. The Yuma Indians. Overland Monthly, vol. 13 (2nd ser.), no. 78, pp. 561–581; vol. 14, no. 79, pp. 1–11.

TROUSLOT, R. B.

1887. Rattlesnakes in Hendricks County. Hoosier Nat., vol. 2, no. 6, pp. 86–87.

TROWBRIDGE, J.

1848. On the Treatment of Poisoning by the Bite of a Rattlesnake. Buffalo Med. Jour., vol. 4, no. 4, pp. 203–206.

TRUITT, R. K., *et al.*

1896. The Snake That Truitt Saw and Some Others of the California Kind, San Francisco Call, May 31, p. 19; Further Studies of the California Snake by Those Who Have Met Him. June 7, p. 19.

TSCHIFFELY, A. F.

1933. Tschiffely's Ride. New York, pp. xxiii + 328.

TUCKER, H.

1912. A Review of the Dangerously Poisonous Snakes of the United States. Therapeutic Gaz., vol. 36 (n.s., 28), no. 5, pp. 313–323.

TUMARKIN, A.

1955. On the Evolution of the Auditory Conducting Apparatus: A New Theory Based on Functional Considerations. Evolution, vol. 9, no. 3, pp. 221–243.

TURK, F. A.

1947. Studies of Acari. IV. A Review of the Lung Mites of Snakes. Parasit., vol. 38, nos. 1 and 2, pp. 17–26.

TURNER, L.

1953. A Rattlesnake's Buttons. Desert Mag., vol. 16, no. 9, p. 22. [See also vol. 16, no. 11, p. 23; vol. 17, no. 1, p. 27; no. 3, p. 22; no. 4, p. 28; no. 5, p. 28.]

[TURNER, W. E.]

1899. Why Mr. Rattler Rattles. Denver Evening Post, Dec. 25, p. 5.

TURNEY-HIGH, H. H.

1937. The Flathead Indians of Montana. Mem. Am. Anthro. Assn., no. 48, pp. 1–161.

TUTEN, J. G.

1897. The Successful Treatment of Snake Bite. Jour. Am. Med. Assn., vol. 29, no. 18, pp. 896–897.

TUTHILL, C.

1951. Indian Hunting Customs in San Diego County. Museo, n.s., vol. 1, no. 1, pp. 2–4, 23–30.

TWITCHELL, R. E.

1914. The Spanish Archives of New Mexico. Cedar Rapids, 2 vols., pp. xxiii + 525; vi + 683.

TYLER, A.

1946. On Natural Auto-Antibodies as Evidenced by Antivenin in Serum and Liver Extract of the Gila Monster. Proc. Natl. Acad. Sci., vol. 32, no. 7, pp. 195–201.

Tyson, E.
  1683. Vipera Caudi-sona Americana, Or the Anatomy of a Rattle-Snake Dissected at the Repository of the Royal Society in January 1682/3. Philos. Trans. (Royal Soc. London), vol. 12, no. 144, pp. 25–58.

Ueda, E., T. Sasaki, and M-T. Peng
  1951. A Chemical Study on Formosan Cobra Venom. Mem. Fac. Med., National Taiwan Univ., vol. 1, no. 4, pp. 194–199.

[Uhler, F. M.]
  1943. Poisonous Snakes of the United States. U. S. Dept. Interior, Fish and Wildlife Serv., Wildlife Leafl. 233, pp. 1–17.
  1944. Facts about Snakes. U. S. Dept. Interior, Fish and Wildlife Serv., Wildlife Leafl. 257, pp. 1–10.

Uhler, F. M., C. Cottam, and T. E. Clarke
  1939. Food of Snakes of the George Washington National Forest, Virginia. Trans. 4th N. A. Wildlife Conference, Washington, pp. 605–622.

Underhill, Ruth M.
  1936. The Autobiography of a Papago Woman. Mem. Am. Anthro. Assn., no. 46, pp. 1–67.
  1939. Social Organization of the Papago Indians. Columbia Univ. Contrib. Anthro., vol. 30, pp. xiv + 280.
  1946. Papago Indian Religion. Columbia Univ. Contrib. Anthro., no. 33, pp. viii + 359.

Unonius, G.
  1950. A Pioneer in Northwest America, 1841–1858. Minneapolis, vol. 1, pp. xii + 419.

Urich, F. W., and R. R. Mole
  1894. Notes on a South American Diamond Rattlesnake. Jour. Trinidad Field Nat. Club, vol. 1, no. 12, pp. 293–297.

V., C. A.
  1913. The Whirr of the Rattler. Forest and Stream, vol. 81, no. 16, pp. 498–499.

Vaillant, G. C.
  1939. Indian Arts in North America. New York, pp. xiii + 63.

Valentine, D.
  1947. One Man's Poison, Another Man's Milk. Future, Sept., p. 5.

Van Denburgh, J.
  1922. The Reptiles of Western North America. Occas. Papers Calif. Acad. Sci., no. 10, 2 vols., pp. 1–1028.

Van Denburgh, J., and J. R. Slevin
  1913. A List of the Amphibians and Reptiles of Arizona, with Notes on the Species in the Collection of the Academy. Proc. Calif. Acad. Sci., ser. 4, vol. 3, pp. 391–454.
  1914. Reptiles and Amphibians of the Islands of the West Coast of North America. Proc. Calif. Acad. Sci., ser. 4, vol. 4, no. 5, pp. 129–152.

Vandercook, J. W.
  1925. White Magic and Black. Harper's Mag., vol. 151, no. 905, pp. 548–554.

Van der Donck, A., et al.
  1909. The Representation of New Netherland. Narratives of New Netherland, 1609–1664, edited by J. Franklin Jameson, New York, pp. 293–354. [Written in 1649; first published in Dutch, Graven-Hage, 1650; also in Coll. N. Y. Hist. Soc., ser. 2, vol. 1, pp. 125–242; see also ser. 2, vol. 2, pp. 251–329, 1849.]

Van Duyn, G.
  1943. Can Snakes Disgorge Partially Swallowed Prey? Yosemite Nat. Notes, vol. 13, no. 8, pp. 63–64.

Van Dyke, T. S.
  1897. The Road Runner and Snake. The Avifauna (Santa Barbara), pp. 36–38.

Van Frank, R., and M. K. Hecht
  1954. Fossil Rattlesnakes of the Genus *Crotalus* from Northern Massachusetts. Copeia, no. 2, pp. 158–159.

Van Riper, W.
  1950. How a Rattlesnake Strikes. Nat. Hist., vol. 59, no. 3, pp. 128–129.

VAN RIPER, W. (*Continued*)

1953. How a Rattlesnake Strikes. Sci. Am., vol. 189, no. 4, pp. 100–102.

1954. Measuring the Speed of a Rattlesnake's Strike. Animal Kingdom, vol. 57, no. 2, pp. 50–53.

1955a. How a Rattlesnake Strikes. Nat. Hist., vol. 64, no. 6, pp. 308–311.

1955b. Unwinding the Sidewinder. Nat. Hist., vol. 64, no. 9, pp. 489–491.

VAN RIPER, W., R. J. NIEDRACH, and A. M. BAILEY

1952. Nature Photography with the High-Speed Flash. Denver Mus. Nat. Hist., Mus. Pict., no. 5, pp. 1–64.

VANZOLINI, P. E.

1947. Notas sôbre um Deródimo de *Crotalus durissus terrificus* (Laur.). Papéis Avulsos, Dept. de Zool., vol. 8, no. 24, pp. 273–283.

VARDE, M. R.

1951. The Morphology and Histology of the Lung in Snakes. Jour. Univ. Bombay, vol. 19 (n.s.), part 5, no. 29, pp. 79–89.

VASU, V. M.

1946. Do Snakes Drink Milk? Jour. Bombay Nat. Hist. Soc., vol. 46, no. 2, p. 404.

VAUGHN, D. L.

1947. Don't Commit Suicide! Fla. Wildlife, vol. 1, no. 7, pp. 8–9.

VAZ, E.

1951. Instituto Butantan. São Paulo, pp. 1–61.

VÁZQUEZ DE ESPINOSA, A.

1942. Compendium and Description of the West Indies. Translated by Charles Upson Clark. Smithson. Misc. Coll., vol. 102, pp. xii + 862.

1948. Compendio y Descripción de las Indias Occidentales. Manuscript transcribed by C. U. Clark. Smithson. Misc. Coll., vol. 108, pp. xii + 801. [Written in 1628.]

VEATCH, J. A.

1869. Cerros or Cedros Island. *In* J. Ross Browne's Resources of the Pacific Slope, San Francisco, 2 vols., pp. 674; 200; see appendix, pp. 143–154.

VELIKANJE, S. M.

1950. Rattler Meets His Match. Outdoor Life, vol. 105, no. 4, pp. 14–15.

VELLARD, J.

1928. Importance des Charactères Fournis par l'Hémipénis pour la Classification des Ophidiens. Bull. Soc. Zool. France, vol. 53, pp. 406–418. [See also Bol. Inst. Vital Brazil, no. 6, pp. 1–19.]

1929. Acções Phylacticas não Especificas em Relação aos Venenos Ophidicos. Mem. Inst. Oswaldo Cruz, no. 9, pp. 156–167.

1938. Variaciones Geográficas del Veneno de *Crotalus terrificus*. Rev. Soc. Argentina Biol., vol. 14, no. 7, pp. 409–421.

1939. Variations Géographiques du Venin de *Crotalus terrificus*. Compt. Rend. Soc. Biol., vol. 130, no. 5, pp. 463–464.

1943. Diferenciación Biológica de la Cascabel Sudamericana. Acta Zool. Lilloana, vol. 1, no. 1, pp. 55–88.

1945. Resistencia de los "Didelphis" (Zarigueya) a los Venenos Ofidicos. Rev. Brasil Biol., vol. 5, no. 4, pp. 463–467.

1949a. Investigaciones sobre Inmunidad Natural contra los Venenos de Serpientes. Publ. Mus. Hist. Nat. "Javier Prado," Ser. A, Zool., vol. 1, no. 2, pp. 1–63.

1949b. Résistance de Quelques Espèces Animales au Venin de Serpent. Compt. Rend. Soc. Biol., vol. 143, p. 5–6.

1950a. Investigaciones sobre Inmunidad Natural contra los Venenos de Serpientes. Mem. 2. El Zorrino de la Sierra Central del Peru. Publ. Mus. Hist. Nat. "Javier Prado," Ser. A, no. 4, pp. 1–16.

1950b. Résistance Naturelle et Immunité contre le Venin de Serpent chez la Mouffette des Andes. Compt. Rend. Acad. Sci. Paris, vol. 230, no. 4, pp. 418–419.

VERNATTI, P.

1665. Of the Nature of a Certain Stone, Found in the Indies, in the Head of a Serpent. Philos. Trans. (Royal Soc. London), vol. 1, no. 6, pp. 102–103.

VERRILL, A. H.
   1937. Strange Reptiles and Their Stories. Boston, pp. xiv + 195.
   1946. Strange Customs, Manners and Beliefs. Boston, pp. xiii + 302.

VESSELS, J.
   1954. Drouth Toughens Rattlers. Tex. Game and Fish, vol. 12, no. 5, p. 28.

VESTAL, P. A.
   1952. Ethnobotany of the Ramah Navaho. Peabody Mus. Am. Arch. Ethn., vol. 40, no. 4, pp. ix + 94.

VESTAL, S.
   1941. Short Grass Country. New York, pp. x + 304.

VETAS, B.
   1951. Symposium: A Snake Den in Tooele County, Utah. Temperatures of Entrance and Emergence. Herpetologica, vol. 7, part 1, pp. 15–19.

VICTOR, FRANCES F.
   1870. The River of the West: Life and Adventure in the Rocky Mountains and Oregon. Hartford, pp. xxii, 23–602.

VIGNE, G. T.
   1832. Six Months in America. London, 2 vols., pp. 1–283; 1–276.

VINCENT, L.
   1726. Catalogus et Descriptio Animalium, Volatilium, Reptilium, et Aquatilium. La Haye, pp. viii + 72.

VINSON, C.
   1946. Wild "Rooshians" of Tennessee. Nature Mag., vol. 39, no. 8, pp. 405–406.

VIOSCA, P., JR.
   1926. The Venom of New Born Pit Vipers. Science, vol. 64, no. 1657, p. 328.

VIQUEZ, C.
   1933. Animales Venenosos de Costa Rica. San José, Costa Rica, pp. iv + 313. [2nd edition, San José, Costa Rica, 1940, pp. 1–312.]

VOEGELIN, ERMINIE W.
   1938. Tübatulabal Ethnography. Univ. Calif. Anthro. Rec., vol. 2, no. 1, pp. iv + 90.
   1942. Culture Element Distributions: XX. Northeast California. Univ. Calif. Anthro. Rec., vol. 7, no. 2, pp. v, 47–251.

VOELGYI, J. R.
   1926. A Texasi Csoergoekigyokrol. Termeszettud. Koez., vol. 58, pp. 140–141.

VOGE, MARIETTA
   1953. New Host Records for *Mesocestoides* (Cestoda: Cyclophyllidea) in California. Am. Midl. Nat., vol. 49, no. 1, pp. 249–251.

VOLSØE, H.
   1944. Structure and Seasonal Variation of the Male Reproductive Organs in *Vipera berus* (L.). Spolia Zool. Mus. Hauniensis V. Reprint, Copenhagen, pp. 1–172.

VON BLOEKER, J. C., JR.
   1942. Amphibians and Reptiles of the Dunes. Bull. So. Calif. Acad. Sci., vol. 41, part 1, pp. 29–38.

[VON CAUB, J. W.]
   1517. Ortus Sanitas. Argentorati [Strassburg], 782 fols.

VORHIES, C. T.
   1917. Poisonous Animals of the Desert. Univ. Ariz. Agric. Exp. Sta., Bull. 83, pp. 356–392.
   1928. *Heloderma suspectum*, Automobile Tourists and Animal Distribution. Science, vol. 68, no. 1756, pp. 182–183.
   1932. A Sad Case of Indigestion. Nature Mag., vol. 19, no. 6, pp. 372–373.
   1936a. The Pacific Rattlesnake. Weekly Bull., Calif. State Dept. Pub. Health, vol. 15, no. 21, pp. 81–83; no. 22, pp. 86–87.
   1936b. Arizona and Its Heritage: Important Reptiles. Univ. Ariz. Bull., Gen. Bull. no. 3, pp. 97–109.
   1945. Water Requirements of Desert Animals in the Southwest. Univ. Ariz. Coll. Agric., Tech. Bull. 107, pp. 485–525.
   1948. Food Items of Rattlesnakes. Copeia, no. 4, pp. 302–303.

VORHIES, C. T., and W. P. TAYLOR

1940. Life History and Ecology of the White-Throated Wood Rat, *Neotoma albigula albigula*, in Relation to Grazing in Arizona. Univ. Ariz. Coll. Agric., Tech. Bull. no. 86, pp. 453–529.

VOTH, H. R.

1903. The Oraibi Summer Snake Ceremony. Field Columbian Mus., Publ. 83, Anthro. Ser., vol. 3, no. 4, pp. 263–358.

1905. The Traditions of the Hopi. Field Columbian Mus., Publ. 96, Anthro. Ser., vol. 8, pp. vi + 319.

W.

1846. The Rattle-Snake (*Crotalus horridus*). Lit. Rec. and Jour. Linn. Assoc. Pa. College, vol. 2, no. 3, pp. 62–65.

1892. Rattlesnakes and Their Ways. Forest and Stream, vol. 38, no. 25, p. 588.

1894. Mild and Touchy Rattlers. Field and Stream, vol. 42, no. 23, p. 488.

W., H.

1890. Snake Bite. Forest and Stream, vol. 35, no. 9, p. 167.

W., R.

1891. Experience with Rattlesnakes. Forest and Stream, vol. 36, no. 7, p. 124.

WADDELL, L. A.

1889. Are Venomous Snakes Auto-toxic?—An Inquiry into the Effect of Serpent-Venom upon the Serpents Themselves. Sci. Mem. Med. Officers of Army of India, Calcutta, part 4, no. 4, pp. 47–72.

WADE, D. E.

1945. Pilot Black Snake Attacks Man. Copeia, no. 3, pp. 172–173.

WADE, W.

1900. Urban Rattlesnakes. Forest and Stream, vol. 54, no. 26, p. 505.

WADHAM, J. E.

1882. The Road-Runner. Forest and Stream, vol. 18, no. 2, p. 27.

WAGNER, G.

1931. Yuchi Tales. Publ. Am. Ethn. Soc., vol. 13, pp. x + 357.

WAGNON, K. A., H. R. GUILBERT, and G. H. HART

1942. Experimental Herd Management. [The San Joaquin Experimental Range.] Univ. Calif. Agric. Exp. Sta., Bull. 663, pp. 50–82.

1945. Death Losses in the San Joaquin Experimental Range Herd. Calif. Cattleman, Sept., pp. 18, 22.

1946. Cutting Death Losses Ads [*sic*] to Profits. Pac. Stockman, vol. 12, no. 3, pp. 13, 27.

WAKE, C. S.

1873. The Origin of Serpent-Worship. Jour. Anthro. Inst., vol. 2, no. 3, pp. 373–390.

WAKEFIELD, PRISCILLA

1819. Excursions in North America. 3rd edition. London, pp. xi + 371 + [iv]. [1st edition, London, 1810.]

WALKER, C. F.

1931. Notes on Reptiles in the Collection of the Ohio State Museum. Copeia, no. 1, pp. 9–13.

WALKER, C. W.

1945. Notes on Adder-Bite (England and Wales). Brit. Med. Jour., vol. 2, pp. 13–14.

WALKER, E. P.

1939. Eyes That Shine at Night. Smithson. Inst. Rept., 1938, pp. 349–360.

WALKER, L. W.

1945. The Hawaiian Mongoose—Friend or Foe? Nat. Hist., vol. 54, no. 9, pp. 396–400.

1952. Underground with Burrowing Owls. Nat. Hist., vol. 61, no. 2, pp. 78–81, 95.

WALL, A. J.

1883. Indian Snake Poisons, Their Nature and Effects. London, pp. xi + 171.

WALL, F.

1906. The Snake and Its Natural Foes. Jour. Bombay Nat. Hist. Soc., vol. 17, no. 2, pp. 375–395.

1921. Ophidia Taprobanica or the Snakes of Ceylon. Colombo, pp. xxii + 581.

1928. The Poisonous Terrestrial Snakes of Our British Indian Dominions (Including Ceylon) and How to Recognize Them, with Symptoms of Snake Poisoning and Treatment. 4th edition. Bombay, pp. xiv + 173. [1st edition, Bombay, 1908.]

WALLACE, A. R.
 1890. Darwinism. 2nd edition. London, pp. xvi + 494. [1st edition, London, 1889.]
WALLACE, E., and E. A. HOEBEL
 1952. The Comanches: Lords of the South Plains. Norman, Okla., pp. xvii + 381.
WALLACE, J.
 1950. Old Swamp Demon. Coronet, vol. 27, no. 3, pp. 116–119.
WALLACE, J. W.
 1827. Rattlesnake Poison. *In* The American Dispensatory, by J. R. Coxe. 7th edition, Philadelphia, pp. iv + 780; see pp. 663–664. [1st edition, Philadelphia, 1806, pp. xvi + 787.]
WALLACE, W. J.
 1947. The Dream in Mohave Life. Jour. Am. Folklore, vol. 60, no. 237, pp. 252–258.
WALLER, R. P.
 1944. The Speed of Snakes. Country Life (London), vol. 96, no. 2486, p. 428.
WALLIS, W. D.
 1922. Medicines Used by Micmac Indians. Am. Anthro., vol. 24, no. 1, pp. 24–30.
WALLS, G. L.
 1931. The Occurrence of Colored Lenses in the Eyes of Snakes and Squirrels, and Their Probable Significance. Copeia, no. 3, pp. 125–127.
 1932a. Visual Purple in Snakes. Science, vol. 75, no. 1948, pp. 467–468.
 1932b. Pupil Shapes in Reptilian Eyes. Bull. Antivenin Inst. Am., vol. 5, no. 3, pp. 68–70.
 1934a. The Reptilian Retina. Am. Jour. Ophthal., vol. 17, no. 10, pp. 892–915.
 1934b. The Significance of the Reptilian "Spectacle." Am. Jour. Ophthal., vol. 17, no. 11, pp.
  1045–1047.
 1938. It's Done with Mirrors. Chi. Nat., vol. 1, no. 4, pp. 103–109.
 1940. Ophthalmological Implications for the Early History of the Snakes. Copeia, no. 1, pp. 1–8.
 1942a. The Vertebrate Eye and Its Adaptive Radiation. Cranbrook Inst. Sci., Bull. no. 19, pp.
  xiv + 785.
 1942b. The Visual Cells and Their History. Biol. Symposia, vol. 7, pp. 203–251.
WALLS, G. L., and H. D. JUDD
 1933. The Intra-Ocular Colour-Filters of Vertebrates. Brit. Jour. Ophthal., vol. 17, pp. 641–
  675; 705–725.
WALSH, J. J.
 1923. Cures: The Story of the Cures That Fail. New York, pp. xi + 291.
WALSH, W. S.
 1913. A Handy Book of Curious Information. Philadelphia, pp. iv + 942.
W[ARBURTON], G. [D.]
 1849. The Conquest of Canada. London, 2 vols., pp. xxxi + 432; 508.
WARD, C. A.
 1875. Rattlesnake. Notes and Queries, 5th ser., vol. 3, p. 45.
WARD, L.
 1941. Shooting a Rattler as He Strikes. Pop. Photo., Feb., p. 72.
WARDEN, D. B.
 1816. A Chorographical and Statistical Description of the District of Columbia. Paris, pp.
  vii +212 + [ii].
WARDLE, R. A., and J. A. McLEOD
 1952. The Zoölogy of Tapeworms. Minneapolis, pp. xxiv + 780.
WASHBURN, C.
 1869. Reminiscences of the Indians. Richmond, Va., pp. viii + 236.
WATERMAN, T. T.
 1908. Diegueño Identification of Color with the Cardinal Points. Jour. Am. Folk-Lore, vol.
  21, no. 80, pp. 40–42.
 1910. The Religious Practices of the Diegueño Indians. Univ. Calif. Publ. Am. Arch. and
  Ethn., vol. 8, no. 6, pp. 271–358.
 1916. The Delineation of the Day-Signs in the Aztec Manuscripts. Univ. Calif. Publ. Am.
  Arch. and Ethn., vol. 11, no. 6, pp. 297–398.

WATERS, F.
    1950. Masked Gods: Navaho and Pueblo Ceremonialism. Albuquerque, pp. 1–438.
WATERTON, C.
    1828. Wanderings in South America. 2nd edition. London, pp. vii + 341. [1st edition, London, 1825, pp. vii + 326.]
    1834. [Comment on] Mr. Audubon, Junior. Mag. Nat. Hist., vol. 7, no. 37, pp. 67–68.
    1835a. On Snakes, Their Fangs, and Their Mode of Procuring Food. Mag. Nat. Hist., vol. 8, no 56, pp. 663–667.
    1835b. A Letter to James Jameson, Esq., Regius Professor of Natural History in the University of Edinburgh. Wakefield, pp. 1–14. [See also Mag. Nat. Hist., vol. 8, no. 47, pp. 190–192.]
    1851. Essays on Natural History. 1st ser., 8th edition. London, pp. lxxxiii + 334. [1st edition, London, 1838, pp. lxxxiii + 312.]
WATSON, F.
    1754. The Animal World Display'd. London, pp. xvi + 302 + [6].
WATT, H. F., and C. B. POLLARD
    1954. Case of Serious Florida Diamondback Rattlesnake (*Crotalus adamanteus*) Bite. Jour. Fla. Med. Assn., vol. 41, pp. 367–370.
WAVRIN, R. DE
    1939. Les Bêtes Sauvages de l'Amazonie. Paris, pp. 1–301.
WEBB, C. H.
    1888. Diamond-Backs in Paradise. St. Nicholas, vol. 15, no. 4, pp. 263–271.
WEBB, W. P.
    1937. The Singing Snakes of the Karankawas. Southwest Review, vol. 22, pp. 325–337. [Also *in* Southwesterners Write, edited by T. M. Pearce and A. P. Thomason, Albuquerque, 1946, pp. ix + 365; see pp. 227–240.]
WEBBER, J. P.
    1951. Snake Facts and Fiction. Tex. Game and Fish, vol. 9, no. 6, pp. 12–13, 30.
WEISS, H. B., and GRACE M. ZIEGLER
    1931. Thomas Say, Early American Naturalist. Springfield, Ill., pp. xiv + 260.
WELCH, H.
    1930. The Detoxification of Snake Venoms by Ultra-Violet Light. Bull. Antivenin Inst. Am., vol. 4, no. 2, pp. 35–40.
WELCH, J. H., JR.
    1927. Rattlesnakes. Stone and Webster Jour., vol. 41, no. 3, pp. 367–373.
WELCH, W. H., and C. B. EWING
    1895. The Action of Rattlesnake Venom upon the Bactericidal Properties of the Blood. Trans. First Pan-Am. Med. Cong., part 1, pp. 354–355.
WELD, C. W.
    1855. A Vacation Tour in the United States and Canada. London, pp. xi + 394.
WELD, I.
    1800. Travels through the States of North America and the Provinces of Upper and Lower Canada, during the Years 1795, 1796, and 1797. 4th edition. London, pp. 1–552. [1st edition, London, 1799, pp. xxiv + 464.]
WELKER, W. H., and J. MARSHALL
    1915. The Toxicity of Rattlesnake Serum and Bile with a Note on the Effect of Bile on the Toxicity of Venom. Jour. Pharm. and Exp. Therap., vol. 6, no. 5, pp. 563–568.
WELTFISH, G.
    1937. Caddoan Texts. Publ. Am. Ethn. Soc., vol. 17, pp. x + 251.
WENTWORTH, E. N.
    1948. America's Sheep Trails. Ames, Iowa, pp. xxii + 667.
WERLER, J. E.
    1950. The Poisonous Snakes of Texas and the First Aid Treatment of Their Bites. Tex. Game and Fish, vol. 8, no. 3, pp. 25–41. [Also published as a pamphlet, pp. 1–16. Revised as Tex. Game and Fish Comm. Bull. 31, pp. 1–40, 1953.]

WESLEY, J.

1770. A Survey of the Wisdom of God in the Creation. 2nd edition. Bristol, 2 vols., pp. vi, 7–286; 256 + [xxx]. [1st edition, London, 3 vols., 1763.]

1784. A Survey of the Wisdom of God in the Creation. 4th edition. London, 5 vols. Of Reptiles, vol. 2, chap. iv, pp. 29–55.

WEST, G. S.

1895. On the Buccal Glands and Teeth of Certain Poisonous Snakes. Proc. Zoöl. Soc. London, no. 51, pp. 812–826.

1898. On the Histology of the Salivary, Buccal, and Harderian Glands of the Colubridae with Notes on Their Tooth-Succession and the Relationships of the Poison-Duct. Jour. Linn. Soc. (Zoöl), vol. 26, no. 171, pp. 517–526.

1900. On the Sensory Pit of the Crotalinae. Quart. Jour. Micro. Sci., vol. 43 (n.s.), no. 169, pp. 49–59.

WEST, R. A.

1952. Snake Stories. W. Va. Folklore, vol. 2, no. 4, pp. 2–7.

WEST, R. E.

1929. Bass—and a Rattler. Outdoor Life, vol. 63, no. 4, pp. 34–35, 62–63.

WESTON, R.

1836. A Visit to the United States and Canada in 1833. Edinburgh, pp. ii + 312.

WETMORE, A.

1837. Gazetteer of the State of Missouri. St. Louis, pp. 1–382.

WHEATLEY, C. M.

1871. Notice of the Discovery of a Cave in Eastern Pennsylvania Containing Remains of Post-Pliocene Fossils, including Those of Mastodon, Tapir, Megalonyx, Mylodon, etc. Am. Jour. Sci. and Arts, ser. 3, vol. 1, no. 4, pp. 235–237.

WHEATLEY, R.

1886. Rattlesnakes. Harper's Weekly, vol. 30, no. 1547, p. 523.

WHEELER, O. D.

1926. The Trail of Lewis and Clark: 1804–1904. New York, 2 vols., pp. xxix + 377; xv + 419.

WHISENHUNT, M. H., JR.

1949. An Account of Copulation of the Western Diamond Rattlesnake. Nat. Hist. Misc., no. 49, pp. 1–2.

WHITBY, W.

1920. Bull Snakes. Outdoor Life, vol. 46, no. 3, pp. 188–189.

WHITE, J.

1842. Signification of Hockhocking and Wheeling. Am. Pioneer, vol. 1, no. 1, p. 38.

WHITE, L. A.

1930a. The Pueblo of San Felipe. Mem. Am. Anthro. Assn, no. 38, pp. 1–69.

1930b. A Comparative Study of Keresan Medicine Societies. Proc. 23rd Int. Cong. Americanists, pp. 604–619.

1935. The Pueblo of Santo Domingo, New Mexico. Mem. Am. Anthro. Assn., vol. 43, pp. 1–201.

1942. The Pueblo of Santa Ana, New Mexico. Am. Anthro., vol. 44 (n.s.), no. 4, part 2, pp. 1–360 [= Mem. Am. Anthrop. Assn., no. 60.]

1947. Notes on the Ethnozoölogy of the Keresan Pueblo Indians. Papers Mich. Acad. Sci., Arts, and Lett., vol. 31 (1945), pp. 223–243.

WHITEHEAD, D.

1940. Handling Rattlesnakes to Demonstrate One's Faith. Syndicated by Associated Press in September.

WHITEMAN, L. J., and R. HENDERSON

1947. Public Enemy No. 1. Desert Mag., vol. 10, no. 12, p. 27.

WHITING, A. F.

1939. Ethnobotany of the Hopi. Mus. N. Ariz., Bull. 15, pp. viii + 120.

WHITING, BEATRICE B.

1950. Paiute Sorcery. New York, Viking Fund Publ. Anthro., no. 15, pp. 1–110.

WHITING, L. E.

1854. Bite of a Rattlesnake—Recovery. Boston Med. and Surg. Jour., vol. 50, no. 13, p. 258.

WHITLAW, C.

   1824. On a Reputed Cure for the Bite of the Rattle-Snake, and for Hydrophobia. Technical Reposit., vol. 6, pp. 254–259.

WHITMAN, W.

   1937. The Oto. Columbia Univ. Contrib. Anthro., vol. 28, pp. xvi + 132.

WHITMIRE, J. S.

   1849. Iodine an Antidote to the Venom of the Rattlesnake. North-West. Med. and Surg. Jour., vol. 1, no. 5, pp. 396–398. [Also Buffalo Med. Jour. and Monthly Rev., vol. 4, no. 9, pp. 575–576, 1849. See also North-West Med. and Surg. Jour., vol. 3, no. 5, p. 403, 1851 (J. Langworthy); vol. 11 (vol. 3, n.s.), no. 4, pp. 187–188, 1854 (E. Harwood); vol. 13 (vol. 5, n.s.), no. 2, pp. 61–62, 1856 (B. Woodward); and Western Lancet, vol. 11, no. 5, pp. 284–285, 1850 (J. R. Smith).]

   1860. Iodine: An Antidote to the Venom of the Rattlesnake. Chi. Med. Jour., vol. 17 (vol. 3, n.s.) no. 5, pp. 267–270.

WHITNEY, ANNIE W., and CAROLINE C. BULLOCK

   1925. Folk-Lore from Maryland. Mem. Am. Folk-Lore Soc., vol. 18, pp. 1–239.

WIED-NEUWEID, M. A. P. (Prince zu)

   1843. Travels in the Interior of America. Translated by H. Evans Lloyd. London, pp. 1–520. [1st edition, Coblenz, 1838, 2 vols.; also in Thwaites: Early Western Travels, 32 vols., Cleveland, 1904–7; see vols. 22–24.]

WIEDEMANN, E.

   1932. Zur Ortsbewegung der Schlangen und Schliechen. Zool. Jahr. (allg. Zool), vol. 50, no. 4, pp. 557–596.

WIFFEN, E. T.

   1913. The Massasauga in New York State. Bull. Zoöl. Soc. N. Y., vol. 16, no. 55, pp. 949–950.

WILCOX, U. V.

   1928. Rattlesnake Farming. Sci. Am., vol. 138, no. 5, pp. 438–439.

WILDE, W. S.

   1938. The Role of Jacobson's Organ in the Feeding Reaction of the Common Garter Snake, *Thamnophis sirtalis sirtalis* (Linn.). Jour. Exp. Zoöl., vol. 77, no. 3, pp. 445–464.

WILDWOOD, W.

   1862. Thrilling Adventures among the Early Settlers. Philadelphia, pp. 1–384.

WILEY, GRACE O.

   1929. Notes on the Texas Rattlesnake in Captivity with Special Reference to the Birth of a Litter of Young. Bull. Antivenin Inst. Am., vol. 3, no. 1, pp. 8–14

   1930. Notes on the Neotropical Rattlesnake (*Crotalus terrificus basiliscus*) in Captivity. Bull. Antivenin Inst. Am., vol. 3, no. 4, pp. 100–103.

WILHELM, T.

   1873. History of the Eighth U. S. Infantry. 2nd edition. Washington, 2 vols., pp. xiv + 430; xiv + 431 + vii.

WILLIAMS, C. B.

   1918. The Food of the Mongoose in Trinidad. Bull. Dept. Agric., Trinidad and Tobago, vol. 17, part 4, pp. 167–186.

WILLIAMS, E. D.

   1947. The Rattlesnake Murder. *In* Los Angeles Murders, edited by Craig Rice. New York, pp. [iv] + 249; see pp. 179–198.

WILLIAMS, H.

   1932. Legends of the Great Southwest. San Antonio, pp. [viii] + 269.

WILLIAMS, I. B.

   1892. Water Rattlesnake in Captivity. Science, vol. 20, no. 515, p. 345.

WILLIAMS, J.

   1792. On the Cure of Persons Bitten by Snakes. *In* Dissertations and Miscellaneous Pieces Relating to the History and Antiquities ... of Asia, by Sir William Jones *et al.* London, 2 vols. pp. [viii] + 420; [iv] + 411. [See vol. 2, chap. 16, pp. 222–231. See also Pac. Med. and Surg. Jour., vol. 1, pp. 96–100, 1858.]

WILLIAMS, J. L.
  1827. A View of West Florida. Philadelphia, pp. iv + 5–178.
  1837. The Territory of Florida. New York, pp. 1–304.
  1891. Experiments in Snake Locomotion. Science, vol. 18, no. 447, pp. 123–124.
WILLIAMS, MABEL C.
  1920. Vibration Rate of the Tail of a Rattlesnake. Science, vol. 51, no. 1305, pp. 15–16.
WILLIAMS, R.
  1643. A Key to the Language of America. London, pp. [xiv] + 197 [= 205] + iii.
WILLIAMS, S. W.
  1834. On the Medical Uses of the *Viola ovata*. Am. Jour. Med. Sci., vol. 13, no. 26, art. 1, pp. 310–312.
  1848. Rattlesnakes—*Crotalus horridus*. Boston Med. and Surg. Jour., vol. 37, no. 23, pp. 449–453.
WILLIAMSON, F.
  1869. Poisoning by the Bite of a Rattlesnake. Boston Med. and Surg. Jour., vol. 4 (n.s.), no. 26, p. 398. [See also p. 404.]
WILLIAMSON, H.
  1807. Of the Fascination of Serpents. Med. Repository, 2nd hexade, vol. 4, no. 4, pp. 341–348.
WILLIAMSON, T. S.
  1853. Dacotas of the Mississippi. *In* Schoolcraft's Historical and Statistical Information respecting the . . . Indian Tribes of the United States. Philadelphia, 6 vols.; see part 1, pp. 247–256.
WILLISTON, S. W.
  1878. The Prairie Dog, Owl and Rattlesnake. Am. Nat., vol. 12, no. 4, pp. 203–208.
WILLOUGHBY, C. C., and E. A. HOOTON
  1922. The Turner Group of Earthworks, Hamilton County, Ohio. Papers Peabody Mus., vol. 8, no. 3, pp. viii + 132.
WILLSON, P.
  1908. Snake Poisoning in the United States: A Study Based on an Analysis of 740 Cases. Arch. Int. Med., vol. 1, no. 5, pp. 516–570.
WILSON, N. C.
  1945. Partners. Sat. Eve. Post, vol. 218, no. 27, pp. 16, 68–70.
WILSON, S. C.
  1954. Snake Fight. Tex. Game and Fish, vol. 12, no. 5, pp. 16–17.
WILSON, T.
  1895. The Swastika. Rept. U. S. Nat. Mus. for 1894, pp. 763–983.
  1901. Arrow Wounds. Am. Anthro., vol. 3, no. 3, pp. 513–531.
WIMMER, B.
  1946. Hair Ropes and Rattlesnakes. Desert Mag., vol. 9, no. 10, p. 8.
WINSLOW, E.
  1624. Good Newes from New England; or a True Relation of Things Very Remarkable at the Plantation of Plimouth in N. England: Together with a Relation of Customes among the Indians. London, pp. viii + 67. [Reprinted, abbreviated from Purchas, 1625, in Collections of Mass. Hist. Soc., vol. 8, pp. 239–276, 1802.]
WINTERBOTHAM, W.
  1795. Reptiles of America. *In* An Historical, Geographical, Commercial and Philosophical View of the American United States. . . . London, 4 vols; see vol. 4, pp. 403–409.
WINTON, W. M.
  1916. The Significance of Venoms. Sci. Monthly, vol. 2, pp. 475–478.
WISDOM, C.
  1952. The Supernatural World and Curing. *In* The Heritage of Conquest, by Sol Tax *et al.*, Chicago, pp. 1–312; see pp. 119–141.
WISSLER, C.
  1941. North American Indians of the Plains. Am. Mus. Nat. Hist., Handbook Ser., no. 1 (3rd edition), pp. 1–172. [1st edition, New York, 1912, pp. 1–147.]

Witebsky, E., S. Peck, and E. Neter

    1935. Demonstration of Hemorrhagins in Snake Venom by Means of the Chicken Embryo. Proc. Soc. Exp. Biol. and Med., vol. 32, no. 5, pp. 722–725.

Witt, C.

    1768. Part of a Letter from the Late Dr. Witt, of German Town, in Pennsylvania, to Peter Collinson, Esq. Gentleman's Mag., vol. 38, p. 10.

Wittek, A.

    1943. Rattler Lessons. Westways, vol. 35, no. 9, p. 9.

Witthoft, J.

    1947. A Snake Tale from Northern New York. N. Y. Folklore Quart., vol. 3, no. 2, pp. 134–137.

Wolfe, F. E.

    1905. The Rattlesnake's Bite. Forest and Stream, vol. 65, no. 18, p. 351.

Wolfe, Linnie M.

    1938. John of the Mountains: The Unpublished Journals of John Muir. Boston, pp. xxii + 459.

Wolfenbarger, K.

    1953. Systematic and Biological Studies on North American Chiggers of the Genus *Trombicula*, Subgenus *Eutrombicula*. Ann. Ent. Soc. Am., vol. 45, no. 4, pp. 645–677.

Wolfenden, R. N.

    1886. On the Nature and Action of the Venom of Poisonous Snakes. I. The Venom of the Indian Cobra (*Naja tripudians*). II. A Note upon the Venom of the Indian Viper (*Daboia russellii*). Jour. Physiol., vol. 7, pp. 326–364.

Wolff, N. O., and T. S. Githens

    1939a. Record Venom Extraction from Water Moccasin. Copeia, no. 1, p. 52.

    1939b. Yield and Toxicity of Venom from Snakes Extracted over a Period of Two Years. Copeia, no. 4, p. 234.

Wolman, L. D.

    1937. Milking Time for Rattlers. Desert Mag., vol. 1, no. 2, pp. 12, 21.

Wood, C. A.

    1931. An Introduction to the Literature of Vertebrate Zoölogy. London, pp. xix + 643.

Wood, Florence D.

    1933. Mating of the Prairie Rattlesnake, *Crotalus confluentus confluentus*. Copeia, no. 2, pp. 84–87.

Wood, J. G.

    1855. The Illustrated Natural History. New edition. London, pp. xx + 444. [1st edition, London, 1851.]

    1863. The Illustrated Natural History. London, 3 vols; vol. 3, Reptiles, Fishes, Molluscs, pp. 1–810.

Wood, J. T.

    1954. A Survey of 200 Cases of Snake-Bite in Virginia. Am. Jour. Trop. Med. and Hyg., vol. 3, no. 5, pp. 936–943.

Wood, J. T., W. W. Hoback, and T. W. Green

    1955. Treatment of Snake Venom Poisoning with ACTH and Cortisone. Va. Med. Monthly, vol. 82, no. 3, pp. 130–135.

Wood, S. F., and F. D. Wood

    1936. Occurrence of Haematozoa in Some California Cold-Blooded Vertebrates. Jour. Parasit., vol. 22, no. 5, pp. 518–520.

Wood, W.

    1634. New Englands Prospect. London, pp. viii + 98 + [v]. [Boston reprint, pp. (vi) + 103 + (vi), 1898.]

Woodbury, A. M.

    1931. A Descriptive Catalog of the Reptiles of Utah. Bull. Univ. Utah, vol. 21, no. 5, pp. x + 129.

    1933. Rattlesnakes Eat Birds. Zion-Bryce Nature Notes, vol. 5, no. 4, p. 8.

    1945. My Rattlesnake Bite. Proc. Utah Acad. Sci., Arts and Lett., vols. 19–20, pp. 179–184.

    1948. Marking Reptiles with an Electric Tattooing Outfit. Copeia, no. 2, pp. 127–128.

    1951. Symposium: A Snake Den in Tooele County, Utah. Introduction—A Ten Year Study. Herpetologica, vol. 7, part 1, pp. 1–14.

WOODBURY, A. M., and MRS. J. D. ANDERSON

 1945. Report of Rattlesnake Bite of J. Dwain Anderson. Proc. Utah Acad. Sci., Arts and Lett., vols. 19–20, pp. 185–188.

WOODBURY, A. M., and R. M. HANSEN

 1950. A Snake Den in Tintic Mountains, Utah. Herpetologica, vol. 6, part 3, pp. 66–70.

WOODBURY, A. M., and R. HARDY

 1948. Studies of the Desert Tortoise *Gopherus agassizii*. Ecol. Monog., vol. 18, pp. 145–200.

WOODBURY, A. M., and E. W. SMART

 1950. Unusual Snake Records from Utah and Nevada. Herpetologica, vol. 6, part 2, pp. 45–46.

WOODBURY, A. M., and D. M. WOODBURY

 1944. Notes on Mexican Snakes from Oaxaca. Jour. Wash. Acad. Sci., vol. 34, no. 11, pp. 360–373.

WOODHOUSE, S. W.

 1854. Medical Report. *In* Report of an Expedition down the Zuni and Colorado Rivers, by Capt. L. Sitgreaves. Washington, pp. 1–198; see pp. 181–185. [See also Edward Hallowell in Trans. College of Physicians Phila., vol. 1 (n.s.), pp. 394–401, 1853.]

WOODHULL, F.

 1930. Ranch Remedios. Publ. Tex. Folk-Lore Soc., no. 8, pp. 9–73.

WOODIN, W. H., III

 1953. Notes on Some Reptiles from the Huachuca Area of Southeastern Arizona. Bull. Chi. Acad. Sci., vol. 9, no. 15, pp. 285–296.

WOODRUFF, J. B.

 1913. Crotalin in the Treatment of Epilepsy and Nerve Disorders. N. Y. Med. Jour., vol. 97, no. 2, pp. 71–74.

WOODRUFF, S.

 1833. The Rattle Snake (*Crotalus horridus,* L.) Disarmed by the Leaves of the White Ash (*Fraxinus americana,* Mich. f.). Am. Jour. Sci. and Arts, vol. 23, no. 2, art. 16, pp. 337–339. [See also vol. 30, p. 208, confirmation by W. R. Morris.]

WOODWARD, S. F.

 1933. A Few Notes on the Persistence of Active Spermatozoa in the African Night Adder, *Causus rhombeatus.* Proc. Zoöl. Soc., London, pp. 189–190.

WOOSTER, L. D.

 1933. Rattlesnake Poisoning by Self-Inflicted Bites. Science, vol. 78, no. 2030, p. 479.

WOOTTON, A. C.

 1910. Chronicles of Pharmacy. London, 2 vols., pp. xii + 428; 1–332.

WORRELL, E.

 [1952]. Dangerous Snakes of Australia. Sydney, pp. 1–64.

WOTTON, E.

 1552. De Differentiis Animalium. Vascosanus, Lutetiae Parisiorum, fols. [11] + 220 + [12].

WRIGHT, A. H.

 1950. Common Names of the Snakes of the United States. Herpetologica, vol. 6, part 6, pp. 141–186.

WRIGHT, A. H., and S. C. BISHOP

 1915. A Biological Reconnaissance of the Okefinokee Swamp in Georgia: II. Snakes. Proc. Acad. Nat. Sci. Phila., vol. 67, pp. 139–192.

WRIGHT, B. A.

 1940. Cephalic Deformities in Embryos of the Massasauga Rattlesnake (*Sistrurus c. catenatus,* Raf.). Trans. Ill. State Acad. Sci., vol. 33, no. 2, pp. 221–222.

 1941. Habit and Habitat Studies of the Massasauga Rattlesnake (*Sistrurus catenatus catenatus* Raf.) in Northeastern Illinois. Am. Midl. Nat., vol. 25, no. 3, pp. 659–672.

WRIGHT, J. E., and DORIS S. CORBETT

 1940. Pioneer Life in Western Pennsylvania. Pittsburgh, pp. [iv] + 251.

WRIGHT, R.

 1939. Grandfather Was Queer. Philadelphia, pp. 1–358.

WRIGHT, W. A.

 1900. The Erratic Rattler. Land of Sunshine, vol. 13, no. 4, pp. 254–257.

WUERTTEMBERG, PAUL WILHELM, DUKE OF

   1938. First Journey to North America in the Years 1822 to 1824. Translated by Dr. Wm. G. Bek. S. Dak. Hist. Coll., vol. 19, pp. 7–474. [First published in Stuttgart in 1835.]

WULSIN, F. R.

   1953. Hot Weather and High Achievement. Fla. Anthro., vol. 6, no. 4, pp. 103–120.

WYETH, N. J.

   1853. Indian Tribes of the South Pass of the Rocky Mountains. *In* Schoolcraft's Information . . . of the Indian Tribes of the United States, Philadelphia, 6 vols; see vol. 1, pp. 204–228.

WYMAN, G. H.

   1892. Rattlesnakes and Their Ways. Forest and Stream, vol. 38, no. 25, p. 588.

WYMAN, J.

   1861. [The Poison Apparatus of the Rattlesnake.] Proc. Boston Soc. Nat. Hist., vol. 7, pp. 293–294.

   1862. [On the Mode of Formation of the Rattle of the Rattlesnake.] Proc. Boston Soc. Nat. Hist., vol. 8, p. 121.

WYMAN, L. C.

   1951. Notes on Obsolete Navaho Ceremonies. Plateau, vol. 23, no. 3, pp. 44–48.

WYMAN, L. C., and S. K. HARRIS

   1941. Navajo Indian Medical Ethnobotany. Univ. N. Mex. Bull., Anthro. Ser., vol. 3, no. 5, pp. 1–76.

   1951. The Ethnobotany of the Kayenta Navaho. Univ. N. Mex. Publ. Biol., no. 5, pp. 1–66.

WYMAN, L. C., and C. KLUCKHOHN

   1938. Navaho Classification of Their Song Ceremonials. Mem. Am. Anthro. Assn., no. 50, pp. 1–38.

WYNE, P. S.

   1937. Homeopathicity of Toxins of Snake Venoms. Jour. Am. Inst. Homeop., vol. 30, no. 10, pp. 604–607.

WYNNE, J. H.

   1770. A General History of the British Empire in America. London, 2 vols., pp. viii + vi + 520; iv + 546.

YARROW, H. C.

   1875. Reports upon the Zoölogical Collections Obtained from Portions of Nevada, Utah, California, Colorado, New Mexico, and Arizona, during the years 1871, 1872, 1873, and 1874. One Hundredth Meridian Surveys (Wheeler Report), Washington, vol. 5, chap. 4, pp. 509–584.

   1883a. Notes about Reptiles. Forest and Stream, vol. 21, no. 14, pp. 263–264, 283–284.

   1883b. Check List of North American Reptilia and Batrachia, with Catalogue of Specimens in U. S. National Museum. Bull. U. S. Nat. Mus., no. 24, pp. 1–249.

   1884. Case of Poisoning from the Bite of a Copperhead (*Ancistrodon contortrix* Linn.). Am. Jour. Med. Sci., vol. 87 (n.s.), no. 174, art. 10, pp. 422–435.

   1887. Recurrence of Symptoms of Poisoning after Snake-Bite. Med. News, vol. 50, no. 23, pp. 623–624.

   1888. Snake Bite and Its Antidote. Forest and Stream, vol. 30, pp. 307, 327–328, 349–350, 369–370, 386–388, 412–413, 431–432. [See also pp. 449–450.]

   1928. Recurrence of Symptoms after Snake Bite. Military Surg., vol. 62, no. 1, pp. 73–76.

YARROW, H. C., and H. W. HENSHAW

   1878. Report upon the Reptiles and Batrachians Collected during the Years of 1875, 1876, and 1877, in California, Arizona, and Nevada. Ann. Rept. Chief of Engineers to the Secretary of War for 1878, Washington, part 3, pp. 1628–1648.

YAWGER, N. S.

   1914. Experience with Crotalin at the Oakbourne Epileptic Colony. Jour. Am. Med. Assn., vol. 62, no. 20, pp. 1533–1535.

YORRIS, X.

   1881. Snakes—Fact and Fable. Forest and Stream, vol. 16, no. 7, p. 126.

YOUNG, E. R.

    1903. Algonquin Indian Tales. New York, pp. 1–258.

[YOUNG, L. D.]

    1946. Diary of Lorenzo Dow Young, Written in 1846–8. Utah Hist. Quart., vol. 14, pp. 133–170.

YOUNG, NETTIE

    1940. Snakebite: Treatment and Nursing Care. Am. Jour. Nursing, vol. 40, no. 6, pp. 657–660.

ZAHN, C.

    1946. The Dance That Hid the Sun. Holiday, vol. 1, no. 6, pp. 68–69.

ZEISBERGER, D.

    1910. A History of the Indians. [Written in 1779–80.] Edited by A. B. Hulbert and W. N. Schwarze. Ohio Arch. Hist. Quart., vol. 19, nos. 1 and 2, pp. 1–189.

ZELLER, E. A.

    1948. Enzymes of Snake Venoms and Their Biological Significance. Advances in Enzymology, vol. 8, pp. 459–495.

ZIMMERMANN, A. A., and C. H. POPE

    1948. Development and Growth of the Rattle of Rattlesnakes. Fieldiana: Zoöl., vol. 32, no. 6, pp. 357–413.

ZIPPERER, E. W.

    1947. Dead Snakes Keep Moving. Fishing and Hunting, vol. 24, no. 3, p. 30.

ZOZAYA, J., and R. E. STADELMAN

    1930. Hypersensitiveness to Snake Venom Proteins. A Case Report. Bull. Antivenin Inst. Am., vol. 3, no. 4, pp. 93–95.

ZWEIFEL, R. G.

    1952. Notes on the Lizards of the Coronados Islands, Baja California, Mexico. Herpetologica, vol. 8, part 2, pp. 9–11.

Index

These introductory remarks on the index are inserted in the hope that its usefulness may be increased.

The reader seeking the facts on any particular rattlesnake will find them under the technical name of the snake, entered alphabetically under the subspecific name, or under the specific name if the species has not been divided into subspecies. Example: *morulus, Crotalus lepidus.* If he knows the common name, but not the technical name of the rattler in which he is interested, he will find a cross reference under the common name. If there is some doubt concerning appropriate names, he should consult the cross-index list on p. 88. The maps and the geographical tables (tables 2:1–2:6) may also prove helpful.

Books of a monographic character often list in their indexes every page upon which each species or subspecies is mentioned. This method has appeared undesirable here, since the page references under most of the species would have been so numerous as to become quite useless. Instead, under each species or subspecies of rattlesnake only those page references are given—and these with appropriate subentries—wherein the reader will find data on certain pertinent characters, habits, or distributions, as, for example, disposition and temperament, food, habitat and ecology, length, and so on.

An attempt has been made to use as entries the key words that are most likely to occur to the reader seeking some fact of rattlesnake life. Where two or more such words might be taken equally well to characterize some fact or habit, entries have been duplicated under each key word, or suitable cross references have been made.

To a considerable extent, major subjects have been subdivided into numbers of subentries, to facilitate finding the required page. If the reader knows the main category of his search he can often find the appropriate subentry by running his eye down the subsidiary list.

The following list, supplied for the reader's convenience, contains the categories that include 30 or more subentries:

Antivenin
Art and ornamentation, Indian
Authors quoted
Bite of the rattlesnake
Color
Communications, authors of
Den(s)
Enemies
Fang(s)
Indian attitudes, beliefs, and reactions toward rattlesnakes
Indian tribes

Juvenile(s)
Myths and folklore, legendary actions, attributes, and creatures
Parasites
Prey
Rattle(s)
Reproduction
Shamans or medicine priests, Indian
Size
Squamation
Symptoms and aftereffects of rattlesnake bite
Temperature
Therapeutic uses of rattlesnakes
Treatment of rattlesnake bite
Treatment of rattlesnake bite, Indian
Venom

Since this is a book on rattlesnakes it has been deemed unnecessary to repeat the word in most index phrases. Where there is ambiguity the word is to be inferred.

The most important page citations have been set in boldface type. *Passim* after a set of page entries indicates that the subject has been mentioned incidentally on all or almost all the pages included, but that it is not the principal subject treated on those pages, nor is its discussion uninterrupted. The letter "n" after a page entry signifies a footnote.

This index has been expanded somewhat beyond what was contemplated when the introduction to the book was written. Among the additions are lists of Indian tribes and of authors whose communications have been quoted.

A

C

Cabin built on a den, a legend, 1252

Cactus corral made by roadrunners, 1053, 1055, **1251–1252**

Caduceus, 672

Caesar's remedy, **882–883,** 1129

Cage, recommended size, 643–644

Calamospiza, 600. *See also* Bunting

Calcium cyanide for control, 983

California
altitudes attained by rattlers, 478, 482–484
boa, 194, 653, 1077. See also *Lichanura*
mortality statistics, 808–809
number of bites in 1928, 814
rattlers found in, table 2:3
striped racer (fig. 15:4), 1073

caliginis, Crotalus viridis (fig. 2:49)
climbing proclivity, 458
food, 588, 601
habitat and ecology, 513
length, 144, 304
range, 46
  map, 55
squamation, table 2:7, 171, 180, 181, 182
synonymy, 45–46

Callisaurus, 590, 596. *See also* Lizard, gridiron-tailed; Lizard, zebra-tailed

Camp precautions, 929–937 *passim,* **938**

Campaigns for eradication, 475, 528, 551, **973–991**

Campfire tales, 192, 956, 1199, 1214, 1215

Canada, key to rattlers, 99

Canadian rattlesnakes, by provinces, 121

Canebrake rattlesnake. See *atricaudatus, Crotalus horridus*

Cannibalism, **585–586,** 610, 611, 644, 1077

Captive rattlesnakes, **643–652**
attacks by rodents, 646, 1046–1048, 1223
care, 650
eggs for food, 646, 651
feeding, 643–652
frequency of feeding, 646–647
parasites and diseases, 1079–1083
rattle-growth, distortion in, 246–247, 274, 280
reproductive cycle, 689, 692

Capture and release, effect on growth, 292, 302–303

Caracara, 1052

Carbon bisulphide, 565, 983

Carbon dioxide, 163

Carbon monoxide, 984

Carbon tetrachloride, 984

Carnivals, 1014–1016

Carolina pigmy rattlesnake. See *miliarius, Sistrurus miliarius*

Carrion as food, 585–586, 590, 610, 627

Cascabel (cascavel), 218, 238, 1189, 1192, 1194, **1203–1204**

cascavella, Crotalus, 32 n, 33, 85

Case reports, symptomatic, 830–839

Cases, duration of snake-bite, 903–907

Cat. *See also* Enemies, cat
as rattlesnake destroyer, 228, 1032, **1045–1046**
reactions to rattlers, 228, 958
susceptibility to venom, 850

Cat, ring-tailed (*Bassariscus*), 1048

catalinensis, Crotalus
range, 30
  map, 52
squamation, table 2:7
synonymy, 30

Catbird, 600

Catches of rattlers at dens, 978–981, 995–997

Catching prey in holes, 415, **613–615**

Catching rattlers, 995–1008

catenatus, Sistrurus catenatus (fig. 2:57)
bite symptoms, 839
disposition and temperament, 422
food, 581, 585, 586, 610
habitat and ecology, 521
length, 144
range, 49
map, 58
squamation, table 2:7, 177, 180, 181
swimming ability, 466, **470**
synonymy, 49
teeth, 125
venom yield and quality, 763–770 *passim,* 773, 777, 790

Caterpillar, 587, 591

Caterpillar progression. See Rectilinear progression

catesbaei, Crotalus, 36, 85

catesbyanum, (Crotalus), 36 n

Cattle, **957–970** *passim*
destroyers of rattlers, 1037–1038
effect of grazing on rattler population, 533. *See also* Agriculture, effect on range and population
effect of rattle sound on, 228–229
fear of rattlers, 969
losses and damage from rattler bite, 958–970 *passim*
reactions to rattlers, 957–958, **969**
susceptibility to venom, 850, 959–963 *passim,* **964–965,** 966–970 *passim*
treatment for bite, 907–909. *See also* Veterinary treatments

Caudals, table 2:7, 93, 99

Caudisona, 29, 30, 34, 37, 38, 40, 42, 46, 49, 50, 85, 1204

caudisona, Crotalus, 86

Causus, 133, 741

Caves, 129

Cedar waxwing, 593

Cedros Island diamond rattlesnake. See *exsul, Crotalus*

Cells, temperature tolerance, 380 n

Centers of distribution, 474

Centipede, 587, 598, 611, 806, 809

Central American rattlesnake. See *durissus, Crotalus durissus*

Central-plateau dusky rattlesnake. See *triseriatus, Crotalus triseriatus*

use of lungs, 159–160
use of venom properties, 135, 762–763
Claws of prey, digestibility, 640
Clearing forests, effect on rattlers, 532–535. *See also* Cultivation, effect on range and population
Cleopatra, 846
Clethrionomys, 593. *See also* Mouse, red-backed
Climate. *See also* Temperature
  changes affecting distribution, 474
  correlation with gestation, 692–695
  effect on size, 416
  effect on squamation, 177, 182
Climbing ability, **454–463**, 937
  controversial opinions, 461–463
  myths, 460, 463
Clines, character, 137
Clostridium, 842. *See also* Gangrene; Tetanus
Clothing, protective, 711, 732, 804, 805, 817, 929, 937, **948–952**, 975, 997, 1184
Cnemidophorus, 590, 591, 595, 596, 597, 598, 603, 605, 607, 623, 638. *See also* Lizard, whiptail; Race runner
Coachwhip snake, 567, 1074
Cobra, 17, 231, 669, 672, 706, 714, 724, 744, 746, 758, 773, 784, 785, 805, 822, 846, 847, 849, 851, 852, 868, 872, 898, 922, 955, 1241
  bounties, 987
  dancing to music, 360, 364, 846, 1241
  king. *See* King cobra
  spitting, 231, 738, 843–844
  therapeutic uses of venom, 790, 791, 795, 796
Cobra-mongoose fight, 851, 1031, 1241
Co-denizens of dens, 540, **564–569**
Coefficient of
  correlation, rattle width and body size, 275
  sexual dimorphism in squamation, 167
  sexual divergence, 657
Coefficient of variation of
  adult size, 296
  blotches, 187
  dry residue of venom, 755
  fang length, 733
  fringes of hemipenes, 663
  head sizes, 153
  lengths of young in a brood, 703
  lethal dose of venom, 772–773
  rattle speed, 243–244
  rattle width, 275–276
  scale series, 168–169
  size, 294–296
  size of young-of-the-year, 704
  solid residue in venom, 755
  speed of strike, 449
Coil
  resting (pancake) (fig. 7:1), 378, 444–449, 452, 1150
  striking or S-shaped (figs. 7:2, 7:3, 7:5), 227, 432, 437–454 *passim*
  two-story, 446
Cold
  effect on swimming, 577
  experiments on effects, 387–391

lethargy from, 387, 390–391. *See also* Temperature, immobilization by cold
  sudden onset, 387, 389, **400–401**, 556, 561
  survival, 388–389, 401
Coleonyx, 590, 954. *See also* Gecko
Coleoptera, 609. *See also* Beetle
Collared lizard, 1078, 1102. See also *Crotaphytus*
Collecting, **997–1102**. *See also* Preserved collections of snakes
  by brush burning, 999
  by rapping on rocks, 503, 1001
  methods, 997–1002
  road, 404, 412, 414, 415, 536, 998
  tools and equipment, 997, **1002–1005**
  tracking. *See* Tracks and tracking of rattlesnakes
Collective instinct in denning, 376, 569–571
collilineatus, Crotalus terrificus, 33, 86
collirhombeatus, Crotalus terrificus, 33, 86
Colonel, rattlesnake, 1210–1211
Colonial activities, 1195–1203
  bounties, 987
  control measures, 977–978
  extermination, 991–992
  shipments, 1014, 1203
Colonization
  by escaped rattlers, 578–579
  rumored colonies of dangerous foreign snakes, 19, 1236
  temporary, 575–577
Color, **183–193**
  aberrations, 199–207
  albinism, 199–202
  altitudinal effects, 137, 188–190, 520
  anomalies, 204–207
  application of, 184–185
  blue repels rattlers, 951 n, 1258
  change, mythical, 191–192, 443–444, 1199
  change, physiological, 191–192
  change, power to, 184, 191–192, 411
  concealing. *See* Procrypsis
  deficiency, 204–205
  ecological effects, 137, 188–190, 520
  effect of pituitary gland, 191, 411
  effect of rainfall, 137, 190
  effect of temperature, 191
  identification by, 185–189 *passim*
  intrasubspecific variations, 188
  melanism, 202–204
  occurring in rattlers, 184–185
  ontogenetic differences in, 187–189 *passim*, **192–193**, 201, 202, 411
  plasticity of, 186–189
  power to change, 184, 191–192, 411
  prey, effect of color of, 359, 648
  range of color among rattlers, 184–185
  rattle, 270, 290
  reaction to, 1258
  sexual dichromatism, 193, **656–657**, 1198
  shed skin, retention of pattern, 320, 322
  territorial variations, 137, 188
  variability, intraspecific, 106 n, 186, 188–189
  venom hue, 753

C

E

Fertility, **686–697,** 699–702

Fertilization, 688. *See also* Sperm retention or storage

Fetal capsules or membranes, 696–697

Fiction, rattlers in, 948, 1212

Field advice and precautions, **929–946**

Fights
  mythical, between rattlesnakes and other creatures, 671, 1070, 1136, 1241–1242
  staged, 1016

Figurative connotations of word "rattlesnake," 1207–1208

Finding rattlesnakes, **997–1002**
  by animal reactions, 1001
  by burning brush or grass, 999
  by causing snakes to rattle, 1001
  by driving on desert roads at night, 404, 412, 415, 536, 998
  by locating dens, 556–558, 976
  by tapping rocks, 1001
  by use of dogs, 1000–1001

First aid
  example cases, 901–903
  instructions for treatment of bite, 901–903, **924–926**
  kits, 863–864, 925–926, **928–929**

Fire(s), 578, **992–994**
  attraction to, 358–359, 386–387
  brush, 578, 992–993, 1184
  effect on dispersal, 578, 992–994
  forest, 535, 992–993
  grass, 992–993
  use in collecting, 999

Fishes
  as enemies, 1079
  as food, 586, 594, 610
  susceptibility to venom, 858

"Fixed" (defanged) rattlesnakes, 944–945, 1013–1015, 1155

Flags, rattlesnake, 1188, 1208–1210

Flattening of body, 440, **443**

Flesh, rattlesnake, **1022–1025,** 1185–1187, 1190
  canned, 1024
  food value, 1022
  Indian use, 1153, 1156, **1185–1187,** 1190
  palatability, 1023–1024
  rattleburgers, 1025
  recipes for cooking, 1023–1024
  taste, 1023
  therapeutic value. *See* Therapeutic uses of rattlesnakes, parts or products used, flesh
  venom, effect on edibility, 1024

Flexibility of jaw, **622–625,** 634, 636, 646

Flexure of vertebral column, 333–334, 349–350

Flies (insects), 587, 605

Flight from danger, 430–433

Floods, 404, 460, 469, 471, 503, 519, 522, 524, **575–578,** 994
  effect on dispersal, 575–578, 994

Florida
  Keys (islands), 489
  mortality statistics, 808, 809
  rattlesnakes, of, 121

Fluctuations in abundance, 403, **531–532,** 594

Fluorescence, 193, 1256

Folklore, **1213–1259.** *See also* Legends; Myth and folklore; Tales; Tall stories

Folklore remedies derived from rattlesnakes. *See* Therapeutic uses of rattlesnakes, parts or products used

Folklore treatment of rattlesnake bite, 860–862, 875–890 *passim,* 893–895, 900, 902, 907–910, 926. *See also* Treatment of rattlesnake bite, folklore cures; Treatment of rattlesnake bite, Indian
  animal sources, 875–879, 889
  plant sources, 879–889

Fontana, Felice, venom tests, 713

Food, **580–652.** *See also* Feeding; Food, kinds; Food requirements and supply; Prey
  carrion, 585–586, 590, 610, 627
  competitors for, 537
  dead food, 585–586, 590, 595, 596, 610, 620, **627,** 644, 647, 651
  disgorging, 601, **626–627,** 644, 1224
  effect on venom restoration, 787
  fatal meals, 590, **627–628**
  metabolism, 379, 392, 632, 640, 642, 648, 984
  multiple meals, 636
  mythical foods and feeding, 638, 1194, **1225**
  ontogenetic changes in, 584, 631, 634–635
  oxidation of, 642
  proportions of kinds, 581, 584, 589, 592, 594, 602, 605, 607–608
  quantity per meal, 634
  relation of weight of rattler to prey, 636, 647
  shortages for juveniles, 634–635
  species preferences, 588–611
  survival without, 532, 634, 649–650

Food, kinds of, **580–588,** 588–652 *passim. See also* the several common names of animals eaten as listed below:
  amphibians, 586. *See also* Frog; Newt; Salamander; Spadefoot toad; Toad
  arthropods, **586–587.** *See also* Ant; Beetle; Caterpillar; Centipede; Cicada; Crawfish; Cricket; Flies; Grasshopper; Insects; Mealworm; Scorpion; Spider
  birds, 582–584. *See also* Blackbird; Bluebird; Bobwhite; Bunting; Catbird; Cedar waxwing; Chicken; Cuckoo; Dove; Goldfinch; Grouse; Jay; Lark; Mockingbird; Ovenbird; Owl; Pheasant; Poultry; Quail; Rail, king; Raven; Roadrunner; Robin; Sparrow; Thrasher; Thrush; Towhee; Turkey; Warbler; Woodpecker; Wren
  eggs, **582–584.** *See also* Egg(s) of birds or poultry
  fishes, 586, 594, 610. *See also* Minnow; Trout
  mammals, 580–582. *See also* Bat; Chipmunk; Cony; Cottontail rabbit; Gopher; Guinea pig; Hamster; Hare; Jackrabbit; Lagomorph; Lemming; Marmot; Mink; Mole; Mouse; Muskrat; Opossum; Pika; Porcupine; Praia; Prairie dog; Rabbit; Rat;

H

Homoiotherms, 380. *See also* Endotherms
Homology
  of skin with rattle, 250, 270
  of venom gland with parotid, 742, 745–746
Homonyms, secondary, 28
Homosexuality, 680
Hook-nosed snake. See *Gyalopion*
Hoop snake, 1214
Hopi Snake dance (figs. 16:2, 16:3), 579, 1016–
    1017, 1092, **1113–1126,** 1185, 1194
  accessories, 1115–1116, 1118, 1120
  dates, 1114
  defanging of rattlers, 1125–1126
  hunting snakes for ceremony, 1114, 1125
  legend, 1121–1122
  literature, 1122
  number of priests, 1117
  proportion of rattlers, 1123–1124
  purpose, 1092, 1121
  sand mosaic (fig. 16:1), 1115, 1117, 1181
  symbolism, 1115, 1121
  theories of immunity from accident, 1122–
    1124
Horizontal undulatory progression, **331–335,**
    617
Horn snake. *See* Myths and folklore, horn snake
Horned owl, 1053
Horned rattlesnake (mythical or manufactured),
    1015, 1086, **1235**
Horned rattlesnake (sidewinder). See *cerastes;*
    cercobombus; laterorepens (subspecies of
    Crotalus cerastes)
Horned toad, 584, 590, 591, 595, 601, 628, 638,
    652, 879, 1102, 1150, 1151. See also
    Phrynosoma
  fatalities from eating, 590, 628
Horned viper, 386, 448. See also *Aspis*
Horns of sidewinder (figs. 2:84, 2:85), 172, 174,
    1258
horridus, Crotalus horridus (fig. 2:24)
  altitude attained, 479
  bite, symptoms of, 837–838
  climbing proclivity, 456, 461–463
  denning habits, 541, 545–547, 551–552, 556,
    562, 564, 567, 572
  disposition and temperament, 419, 424
  food, 581–587 *passim,* **591–594**
  fossils, 131–132
  habitat and ecology, 479, **499–500**
  length, 143, **149,** 304
  maximum size, 149
  nocturnal activity, 408
  range, 35
    map, 55
  squamation, table 2:7, 175, 180
  swimming ability, 466, 467, 471
  synonymy, 35
  teeth, 125
  venom yield and quality, 752, 753, 757, 763,
    766, 767, 770–776 *passim,* 782, 784, 788,
    790, 792, 795
Horror of rattlers, human. *See* Fear of snakes,
  human

Horse(s), 228, 229, 435, 561, 850, 907, 913, 917,
    957–970 *passim,* 1032, 1037, 1237
  destruction of rattlers by, 1032, 1037
  detection of rattlers by, 1237
  effect of rattlesnake bite, 959–964 *passim,*
    965, 967–970 *passim*
  fatalities, 960–968 *passim*
  how bites occur, 959–962, **963–964,** 965
  immunization for antivenin preparation, 789,
    913–918 *passim*
  losses from rattlesnake bite, 959–964 *passim,*
    965, 967–970 *passim*
  permanent effects of bite, 959, **966**
  rattle noise, effect on, 228, 229, **957**
  reactions to rattlers, 957, 969
  susceptibility to venom, 850–851, 911, 913,
    918, 957–964 *passim,* **965,** 966–970 *passim*
  treatment of snake bite in, 907–908, 960, 963
Horse-serum allergy, 898, 917, 920–922. *See also*
    Antivenin, serum sickness, shock, or re-
    action
"Hot" rattlesnakes, 1013–1015
Huamantlan rattlesnake. See *salvini, Crotalus*
    scutulatus
Huckleberry Finn, 1212
Human attitudes toward rattlesnakes, **946–956**
Human farming activities, effect on rattlesnake
    population, 474–475, 487–488, 500, **532–**
    535, 991–992
Human recreational activities, effect of rattle-
    snakes on, 2, 955–956
Human sacrifice, 1086
Humidity, effects of, 403, **404–406,** 504, 642
  subterranean, 403
Humorous *nomina nuda. See nocturnus, Cro-*
    talus; visaversus, Crotalus cerastes
Hunger, effect on disposition, 425, 426
Hunting prey in holes, 415, **613–615.** *See also*
    Prey
Hunting rattlesnakes, methods used, 995–1002
  brush burning, 999
  locating dens, 556–558, 976
  night driving, 404, 412, 414, 415, 536, 998
  tapping on rocks, 503, 1001
  tracking, 337, 339–340, 350, 495, 684, **998–999**
Hyaluronidase, 863, 865, 919. *See also* Spreading
    factor in venom
Hybrids, hybridization, 14 n, 20, **207–216,** 328,
    477, 540, 659, 667, 682, 686, 692, 694,
    1235–1236
  adamanteus × atricaudatus, 208–209
  bull-snake × rattler, 20, 207, 686, **1235–1236**
  catenatus × horridus, **208,** 686
  Crotalus × Sistrurus, **208,** 686
  helleri × ruber, 210–212
  intergeneric, 208, 686
  intermediacy of characters, 207–208
  mythical, 20, 207, 686, **1235–1236**
  oreganus × scutulatus, 215–216
  scutulatus × unicolor, 212–215
  second generation, 213–214
  squamation, 208–216 *passim*
Hyla, 610

N

Preservatives, 1006–1007
  alcohol, 312 n, 1006
  formaldehyde, formalin, 1006
  rattle, effect on, 273
  shrinkage of specimens in, 151
Preserved collections of snakes, 1005–1007
  preparation methods, 140, 312 n, 1006–1007
  purpose and use, 1005
  record data, 1007
Prevention of rattlesnake bite, 929–936, **937–938,**
    939–946. *See also* Accidents, causes of;
    Fear of snakes.
Preventive immunization, 849–850
Prey, **580–642,** 643–652 *passim. See also* Food;
    Food, kinds of; Food requirements; Food
    supply
  activities related to those of rattlers, 415, 630–
    631
  ambushing, 430, 581, **611–613,** 616, 621, 1224
  artificially colored, 359, 648
  breathing while swallowing, 160–161, 625
  charming. *See* Myth(s), fascination, power of
  color, effect of, 359, 648
  curiosity evidenced, 615, 629–630
  disgorging, 601, 612, **626–627,** 644, 646, 1224
  effect of kind of prey on actions of rattler,
    618–620
  fascination. *See* Myth and folklore, fascina-
    tion, power of
  fatal to rattler, 590, **627–628**
  finding after striking, 367, 611, 616–621 *passim*
  frightened toward rattler by an intruder, 614,
    615
  head hold on, 624, 625
  holding to prevent escape, after striking, 606,
    610, 614, 618, 619, 651, 802, 852
  hunted in holes, 415, **613–615**
  injury to rattler by rodents, 620, 646
  kinds. *See* Food, kinds
  licking, 365, **625–626,** 1224
  maximum size, 582, 622–624, 634
  myths of catching and eating, 624–625, 1220–
    1225
  pursuit, **616–617,** 618–621 *passim*
  reactions to rattlers, **628–631,** 649, 1223–1224
  relation to weight of snake, 634, 636, 647
  searching for, 367, 611–621 *passim*
  securing, **611–631,** 1224
  senses used in finding, 367, 368, 611–618 *pas-
    sim,* **620–621**
  stalking, 345, 367, 616, 620–621
  startled toward rattler, 614, **615**
  striking, 611–612, 617, 620
  survival, in spite of strike, 617, 618
  swallowing, 462, **622–625**
    breathing during, 160–161, 625
    distention of jaws, **622–625,** 634, 636, 646
    method of, 622
    tail first, 462, 625
    time required, 624–625
    use of fangs, 623–624, 716, 725
  trailing, 367, 616, 620–621
  uneaten, 617, **618**

use of pit in securing, 351, 369–373 *passim,*
    581, 611, 614, **620–621,** 633. *See also* Facial
    pit
use of tongue in finding, 367, 368, 611, 613–
    615, 620–621
variability in effect of bite, **617–618,** 972
venom, rapidity of action on, 611, 617–618
pricei, Crotalus pricei (fig. 2:36)
  altitude attained, 506–507
  food, 581, 584, 587, 597
  habitat and ecology, 506–507
  length, 142, 143, 304
  nocturnal activity, 409
  range, 40
    map, 57
  squamation, table 2:7, 174–180 *passim*
  swimming ability, 466
  synonymy, 40
  venom yield and quality, 766, 777
Prices for live rattlers, 1011–1013
Priests, Indian. *See* Shamans or medicine priests,
    Indian
Primates, reactions of, to rattlers, 953–955, 957
Primitive ranges, 475
Process of venom extraction. *See* Venom, ex-
    traction (milking)
Procrypsis, 183, 189, 191, 229, 416, **428–430,** 439,
    440, 473, 613, 937, 995
Products, markets for rattlesnake, 1008–1028
    passim
Products, skin. *See* Skin of rattlesnake, products
    and novelties made from
Prognosis of rattlesnake bite, 710
Progression, **330–350.** *See also* Concertina pro-
    gression; Horizontal undulatory progres-
    sion; Rectilinear progression; Sidewind-
    ing
  speed, 342, **346–349,** 1190
  prowling, 337, 342
Pronghorn, 1035–1036
Proportion
  of fatalities to bites. *See* Mortality from rat-
    tlesnake bite
  of kinds of food. *See* Food, proportions of
    kinds
  of rattlesnakes to other snakes, 535–537
Protection
  of children, 982
  of harmless snakes, 953, 973, 974, **984–985**
  of legs and feet, 711, 805, 817, 929, **948–952,**
    975, 997
  of playgrounds, 982
  of young rattlers by mothers, 693, **704–706.**
    See also Juveniles swallowed by mother
    for protection
Protection afforded by clothing, 711, 804, 805,
    817, 837, 929, **948–952,** 975, 997
  Indian, 1184
Protective coloration. *See* Procrypsis
Protective cover. *See* Refuge(s)
Protective devices and methods, folklore, 1228–
    1232

on human beings, 228, 231, 234, 956

on other rattlesnakes, 218, **220–222**, 562, 1254

sounding before striking, 217, 218, 233, **437–440,** 1258

sounds simulated, 218, **238–240,** 1194, 1197

species differences, 283–290

speed of vibration. *See* Rattle(s), vibration, vibrating speed

string length, 250–260, 1201, 1203. *See also* Rattle(s), myths, long strings

stroboscopic tests, 240–241

structure, formation, 245–271

stunted races, 277, 285–286, 290

tail tilt (fig. 6:5), 240, 261–262

taper, 251–252, 284 n

taxonomic use, 113, 272, 283–290

teething children, use for, 1166, 1167, 1240

temperature, effect on sound and speed, 235, **241–244,** 388, 390

terminology (figs. 2:74, 2:75, 5:1–5:5, 5:12–5:14), 97, 236–238, 272. *See also* Rattle(s), semantics

therapeutic uses, 1106–1107, 1139, 1163–1167 *passim,* 1239, 1240

translucence, 290

uniformity of segments, 274–276

use, **219–244,** 437–440

at birth, 424

feeding, 224–225

imitation of insects, 224

stimulation of curiosity, 224

uninterrupted, 231, 233–234

warning to threatening enemies, **225–231,** 437–440

variations of sound, 225, 235, 241–244, 388, 390

ventriloquistic effect, 235

vibration, vibrating speed, 220, 232, **240–244,** 271

amplitude, 241, 243

coefficient of variation in speed, 243–244

direction, 240, 241

effect of anger on, 235, 244

equation relating frequency to temperature, 244

juvenile rate, 244

nature, 243

muscles producing, 271

warning, use as a, 221, **225–231,** 437–440

weapon, use as a, 217–218, 220, 1107, 1194, 1197, 1240, 1257

wear and breakage, 240, 250–260 *passim. See also* Rattle(s), estimating lost segments

width, 272–290 *passim*

wild, seldom heard in, 220, 223

Rattlesnake (For data on particular species see the technical name of that species. For cross references between common and technical names see page 88. For rattlesnake bite *see* Bite of the rattlesnake.)

colonel, 1210–1211

definition of word, 11–13

farm, 789, 1009, 1011

first use of word, 1195

medal, 1210

money, 1210

oil. *See* Oil, rattlesnake

pilot, 21, 1207, **1243–1244**

state (South Carolina), 1210

worship, 1085–1103 *passim*

Rattleless rattlesnakes (fig. 5:15), 13, 247, 317. *See also* Juvenile(s), rattleless young

Rattus, 592. *See also* Rat

Raven, 600, 1058

ravus, Sistrurus (fig. 2:62)

altitude attained, 522

food, 581, 611

habitat and ecology, 522

length, 144

range, 51

map, 58

squamation, table 2:7, 177

synonymy, 51

teeth, 125

Reactions of animals to rattlesnakes, 2. (For particular animals *see* Enemies. Prey animals are listed as primary entries. For example, *see* Ground squirrel)

domestic animals, 957–958

enemies and predators, 225–233, **1032–1079**

man, 946, 953–956

prey, **628–631,** 649, 1223–1224

Reata as a barrier, 941, 948, 1215, **1228–1230**

Recapture. *See* Marking rattlesnakes for release and recapture

Recipes for cooking rattlers, 1023–1204

Recipes for tanning skins, 1025–1027

Recognition of attendant by captives, 376, 645

Recognition of species, 90–120

Recommended treatment for rattlesnake bite, 923–928

in the field, 924–926

in the hospital, 926–928

Recovery from bite, time required, 903–907

Rectilinear progression, 166, 315, 331, **335–338,** 616–617

function of ventrals, 166

rib-walking, 333, 335–336

Recurvature of fangs. *See* Fangs, reverse curvature in

Red diamond rattlesnake. See *ruber, Crotalus ruber*

Red racer, 21, 1070–1073 *passim,* 1235

Red-tailed hawk, 1049–1053

Redi–Charas controversy, 742, 744

Redwood forest, 519

References (published) for snake-bite treatment, 923, 928

Reflectivity, 191, 385, 386, 411

Reflex movements, 314–317

Refuge(s), 411–412, 415, 425, 431, 474, 477, 504, 515, 518, **541–575,** 979, 987, 998, 1002. *See also* Den(s)

artificial, 979

caves, mine tunnels, 1002

stephensi, Crotalus mitchelli (fig. 2:32)
  altitude attained, 505
  climbing proclivity, 457
  denning habits, 552
  disposition and temperament, 419–420
  food, 596
  habitat and ecology, 503–505
  hemipenes (figs. 10:2c, 10:2d)
  length, 143
  nocturnal activity, 407, 409
  range, 39
    map, 56
  squamation, table 2:7, 166, 173–176 *passim,*
    181
  swimming ability, 469–470
  synonymy, 39
  venom yield and quality, 766, 767, 776, 778
Stereoscopic vision. *See* Vision, stereoscopic
Stimulus inducing denning. *See* Denning,
    stimuli toward
Sting, myth that tongue is a, 365, 744, 1258
Stock, domestic
  damage, 958–970, 974–975. *See also* Domestic
    animals; Losses of stock and domestic
    animals
  enmity toward rattlers, 1036–1040
  treatment for bites, 907–910. *See also* Vet-
    erinary treatment
Storage of fat. *See* Fat, reserve nutriment storage
Storeria, 376, 442, 570, 585, 681
Stories
  fiction, rattlers in, 948, 1212
  Indian, 1097–1099
  miscellaneous, 1256–1259
Story plots containing rattlesnakes, 948, 1212
Strata of skin. *See* Skin of rattlesnake, strata of
streckeri, Sistrurus miliarius (fig. 2:61)
  climbing proclivity, 459
  disposition and temperament, 422
  food, 581, 585, 586, 587, 611
  habitat and ecology, 521–522
  length, 144
  range, 51
    map, 58
  squamation, table 2:7, 177, 179
  swimming ability, **470**
  synonymy, 51
Strength of king snake, 1069
strepitans, Crotalus, 33, 88
Streptosaurus, 596.
Strike(s), striking, **449–454,** 797–803. *See also*
    Bite of the rattlesnake
  accuracy, 798
  action of mouth, 799–802
  actions following, 802–803
  coil, striking, 227, 432, 437–454 *passim. See*
    also Warning behavior and devices of
    rattlesnakes
  comparison with bite, 797–802
  definition, 438, 452–454
  depth of penetration, 802–803
  distance reached, 450–452

  effect of composition and shape of object
    struck, 798–799
  factors affecting, 710–712
  force, 450, 949
  height attainable vertically, 358, 450–452, 803
  inaccuracy, 617, 620, 798
  low temperature, effect of, 390, 449–450
  mouth action, 799–802
  myths and folklore, 449, 451, 454
  nature, 798–799
  pattern made by teeth, 799–802
  penetration experiments, 949
  photographs, 800–801
  prey, effect on, 611–612
  range, 450–452
  retention of prey after, 606, 610, 614, 618, 651,
    802, 852
  speed, 449–450, 1230–1231
    effect of temperature, 390, 449–450
  targets, artificial, 798–799, 949
  under water, 467, 803
  upward, 358, 450–452, 803
Striped racer (fig. 15:4), 567, 1073–1074
Striped rattlesnakes (figs. 2:17–2:19, 4:7), 205–
    207
Stroboscope, 240, 242, 449
Strychnine for control, 984
Stunted rattlesnakes. *See* Dwarfed forms
Style. *See* Shaker (of rattle)
Subcaudal scales. *See* Squamation, subcaudals
Subspecies of rattlesnakes, 14
  list, 15–16
  island, 122, 523–527 *passim*
Substratal vibrations, sensitivity to, 222, 315,
    359–364 *passim,* **374–376,** 562, 939
Successive bites, 782–788 *passim*
Sucking a bite, danger involved, 865–867
Suction devices, 863–864, 925–926, 928–929
Suicide, committing with rattlesnakes, 947–948
Suicides by rattlers, myth of, 854–856, 1136, 1201
Sulfa drugs, 841, 897
Sulfur content of venom, 757–758
Summer
  activity duration in, 399–400
  aggregations, 552
  dispersal or migration, 402–404, 555, 571–575
  estivation, 402–404, 477 n
  range, 571–575
    traveling to, 555–556
Superiority of rattlers among snakes, Indian be-
    lief in, 1087
Superstitions, 1213–1260. *See also* Myth and
    folklore
  Indian, 1085–1103
  effect of meeting a rattler, 1257
  miscellaneous, 1256–1259
Suppression of rattlesnakes, 973–994. *See also*
    Control, methods and agencies of rattle-
    snake control
  part played by predators, 984, 985, 1032–1079
    passim
Supralabial scales. *See* Squamation, supralabials

cytolysins, 761
deficiencies for therapeutic uses, 794, 796
dehydration, **750–751,** 754–756, 759
demand for, 790, 796, 1017–1018
desiccation. *See* Venom, dehydration
destruction by digestion, 866, 867
deterioration in storage, 759–760
detoxication, 758–760, 910, 913, **914–915**
differences between Nearctic and Neotropical
rattlesnake venoms, 762, 764, 840–841
differences in quality within a species, 764–773
digestion aided by, 612, 713, **745–746,** 761
digestion of venom if swallowed, 865–867
discharge, control of, by the snake, 617, 711,
741, 742
diseases treated with, **790–796,** 911, 1106
distillate, nonpoisonous quality of, 755
dogs, susceptibility of, 850–851, 914, 957–964
passim, 967, **970–972**
domestic animals, susceptibility of, 850–851,
959–970
dregs left after purification, 750–752
drinking of venom by Indian shamans, 1155
drop, quantitative value, 753
drying. *See* Venom, dehydration
duct, venom, 727, **739–741**
ectotherms compared to endotherms in susceptibility, 773, **845,** 852, 858
effect on edibility of rattlesnake flesh, 1024
elapid, 714, 761, 763, 898
electrophoresis, 758
enzymes, presence and effects, 757, **758,** 761,
762
epilepsy treated with, 792–795, 1227
experiments, historical, 713, 1197–1198
extraction (milking), 743, **746–750,** 944
anesthetizing or refrigerating the snakes,
750
electric stimulation, 750
intervals between extractions, 783, 786–787
time required per snake, 750
extrusion, muscles controlling, 711, 741, 742
ferments in, 761
fish, susceptibility of, 858
fluorescence, 193
food, effect on replenishment of venom, 787
formaldehyde, detoxication by, 915
freezing, preservation by, 751, 754, 759–760
generation (formation), 743
gland (fig. 11:16), 739, **741–743,** 744–750 *passim*
evolution, 715, 746, 758
homology, 715, 742, 745–746
muscles controlling, discharge, 711, 741, 742
myth of temporary removal, 1101, 1216
position (fig. 11:16), 742
globulin content, 757
glycerine for preservation, 759
heat, effect on, 759, 762, 910, 914
hemolysins, 760–764 *passim*
hemorrhagins, 761, 762. *See also* Symptoms
and aftereffects of rattlesnake bite, hemorrhagic

histamine content, 763, 898
hogs, susceptibility of, **850,** 959, 963, 966, **968,**
970, **1038–1040**
homeopathic names for venoms, 791
homeopathic use of venoms, 791–793
homology of venom with saliva, 715, 742, 745,
746, 758
horses, susceptibility of, 850–851, 911, 913,
918, 957–964 *passim,* **965,** 966–970 *passim*
hyaluronidase. *See* Venom, spreading factor
immunity, 845–859. *See also* Immunity
injections repeated to secure, 848–850
of rattlesnakes to their own, 707, **852–858,**
1251
injection, effect of type on gravity of result,
765–771 *passim,* 919
insects, susceptibility of, 858
internally, effect of taking venom, 865–867
juvenile(s), 711, 752, 755, 772, 774, 779–782
quantity produced by, 780–781
kidneys, effect on, 762, 763, 843, 844, 850, 914,
928
kinases, 761
liver, effect on, 763, 844, 850, 914
lyophilization for preservation, 751
magical use, 1158–1160
man, susceptibility of, 768, 846–847
market for, 790, 1017
maximum yields by species, 775, 778
milking or extraction method, 743, **746–750,**
944
minimum lethal dose (m.l.d.), 764–773 *passim*
calculation, 769–771
definition, 765
for man, 768
miscellaneous animals, immunity of, 850–859
moccasin venom, utilization, 790–791, 796
molecular weight, 757–758
mortality, constituents causing, 763
myths, 744, 760, 787, **1216–1220.** *See also*
Myths and folklore, venom
necrotic factor, 763. *See also* Symptoms and
aftereffects of rattlesnake bite, necrosis
neurotoxins, 761, 762, 763. *See also* Symptoms
and aftereffects of rattlesnake bite, neurotoxic effects
new-born young, venom of, 706–707
nursing offspring, effect on, when mother is
bitten, 960, 1217
odor, 753–754, 1238
old snakes, yield from, 780
ontogenetic differences in yield, 779–783
ophiotoxin, 757
oxidation, 751
pain, source of, in venom, 762
Paramecium, effect on, 858–859
phosphatidases in, 762
physical properties, 751–754
physiological effect as a basis of classification,
760–764
pilocarpine to facilitate extraction, 750
plants, effect on, **859,** 1199, 1219–1220

W

cum folijs suis & radicib; q̃fcqns
oſtulcam anctaing; ſecum pꝛtauit:
ab omnib; ſerpentib; tutus erit.